Teacher's Guide
for
THE ANNOTATED EDITION OF
BIOLOGY
THE STUDY OF LIFE

William D. Schraer
Chairperson
Science Department
Middletown High School
Middletown, New York

Herbert J. Stoltze
Professor of Biology
Northeastern Illinois University
Chicago, Illinois

Cebco Standard Publishing
9 Kulick Road, Fairfield, New Jersey 07006

a Standex company

Technical Consultants

Donald Deters
University of Texas
(Respiration)

Gary B. Ellis
University of Texas
(Vertebrates)

Kenneth R. Miller
Brown University
(Photosynthesis)

M.V. Parthasarathy
Cornell University
(Plant structure and function)

Irwin Rubenstein
University of Minnesota
(The cell)

Charles F. Stevens
Yale University
(Nervous and endocrine systems)

Daryl Sweeney
University of Illinois
(Invertebrates)

Marjorie B. Zucker
New York University School of Medicine
(Circulatory systems)

ACKNOWLEDGMENTS

The authors are indebted to many individuals whose comments, suggestions, and criticisms during the writing of the manuscript helped to create a better textbook. The authors especially acknowledge the assistance of Dr. Eugene McArdle, Betty Mishkin, Dr. Herbert Lamp, Gerri Leffner, William Conrad, and Ray Smith.

We wish to express our appreciation of the thorough review of sections of the manuscript given by the technical consultants. It must be stressed, however, that the authors bear the sole responsibility for the accuracy of the content of the final product.

The authors also wish to give special thanks to the following teachers who reviewed a trial section of the text during its development, answered a questionnaire, and offered many useful comments and suggestions: Carole Brenkacz, West Seneca East Senior High School, West Seneca, New York; Brenda L. Dorsey, York Community High School, Elmhurst, Illinois; Karen L. Fout, Fenwick High School, Middletown, Ohio; Richard L. Gaume, Plain Local Schools, Canton, Ohio; Norm Grimes, Columbian High School, Tiffin, Ohio; Emiel Hamberlin, Du Sable High School, Chicago, Illinois; Sister M. Francis Hopcus, Pomona Catholic High School, Pomona, California; Mic Jaeger, East Union High School, Manteca, California; Harold Pratt, Jefferson County Schools, Lakewood, Colorado; Helen Louise Shafer, Science and Technology Magnet School, Dallas, Texas; Russell H. Stanhope, Worcester Public Schools, Worcester, Massachusetts; Harlow B. Swartout, Woodstock High School, Woodstock, Illinois; Robert C. Wallace, Reavis High School, Burbank, Illinois; Melanie Wojtulewicz, Whitney M. Young Magnet High School, Chicago, Illinois.

The authors are grateful for the help and guidance given to them by their editors Deena Cloud and Bertram Coren.

Finally, but surely not least in importance, is our gratitude to our wives, Beverley Schraer and Golda Stoltze, and our children, Lynann Schraer and Jonathan, Barry, and Sarah Stoltze, for their patience and encouragement.

William D. Schraer
Herbert J. Stoltze

Design and Illustration
ASSOCIATED DESIGNERS
George A. Bakacs, *Art Director*

Supplementary features developed by
EDUCATIONAL CHALLENGES, INC.
Alexandria, Virginia

ISBN: 0-88320-715-X

1 3 5 7 9 10 8 6 4 2

Contents of Teacher's Guide

Introduction

That science plays a significant role in modern life is an obvious fact. For both the needs of society and the needs of the individual, scientific literacy is essential. For many students, the high school course in biology will be the last science course they take. It is therefore especially important that their study of biology be a positive experience that expands their horizons and broadens their understanding of the nature of science.

Many people regard science as the mere collection of facts. True, science deals with facts, but facts alone do not constitute a science. The philosophy behind *Biology: The Study of Life* is that the facts of biology should serve two purposes: (1) to lead the student to understand the process, that is, the logic and methodology, of science; (2) to provide a foundation for understanding the fundamental characteristics and functions of living things.

Throughout the textbook, examples of the processes of science are developed so that students see biology as inquiry and not as just a giant reservoir of facts. Many of the classical experiments that led to important discoveries are analyzed and discussed. This enables the student to begin to understand how scientists learn about the world.

An examination of current textbooks in biology will show that there is no general agreement as to how the subject matter should be organized. The sequence of topics in *Biology: The Study of Life* is one that the authors have found to work well in the classroom because it is logical and interesting. Essentially, it develops an understanding of the fundamental processes of life that apply to all organisms. Once these basic principles are understood, the study of life forms in all their diversity becomes a fascinating comparison of functioning systems rather than a tedious catalog of structures.

In keeping with this overall plan, the first unit begins with a discussion of the nature of life and of biology as a method of inquiry into life. Certain essential concepts of chemistry and biochemistry are presented next, followed by a study of the cell as the basic unit of living things. The unit concludes with a brief introduction to the need for and method of classifying organisms.

The processes of animal maintenance, beginning with cellular respiration, are treated in Unit 2. Plant maintenance, including photosynthesis, is covered in Unit 3. The general principles of reproduction and the transmission of genetic information are developed in Units 4 and 5.

Unit 6 treats the evidences of change in kinds of organisms, followed by discussion of the theories of evolution to account for the variety of life forms found living today.

These six units lay the groundwork for a detailed study of the various groups of living organisms in Unit 7 and the relationships between living things and their environment in Unit 8.

This comprehensive text is designed to give students a broad background in all the major areas of biology. At the same time it makes biology relevant to the students' lives through discussion of topics of current interest.

Each chapter presents information simply, clearly, and logically. Learning is facilitated by taking students from the simple to the complex, from the concrete to the abstract, and from the familiar to the unfamiliar. Wherever possible, analogies and examples are used.

It is hoped that this text will enable students to achieve a greater appreciation of science and a greater understanding of the living world.

Features of *Biology: The Study of Life*

High school biology courses cover a wide range of material and include many difficult concepts. Like all modern sciences, the science of biology has a large and specialized vocabulary that students must master. Because the scope of the course is so wide and the vocabulary so extensive, it is necessary for students to be able to recognize and concentrate on important facts and concepts. Otherwise the amount of material in the course can be overwhelming. The design of the text is meant to make clear to students what they have to know.

At the beginning of each main section there are learning goals (behavioral objectives) that stress the major concepts and vocabulary terms to be learned. Within the text, the important vocabulary terms are in boldface type where they are defined, and most have a phonetic pronunciation. These terms are listed at the end of the chapter and are defined in the glossary at the end of the book. New scientific terms that are necessary for the discussion, but which the students will probably not be expected to recall, appear in the text in italics. These terms also have a phonetic pronunciation where needed.

At the end of each chapter there is a summary that reviews the major concepts of the chapter. The section-by-section questions under *Test Your Learning* provide, in effect, a sequential review of all the important points in the chapter. The student having difficulty recalling the answer to any given question knows precisely which section of text to read again. Under *Test Your Understanding* there are two types of questions. Some require the student to apply facts or concepts from the chapter to a new situation or problem. Others require an overview or summarizing of information from the chapter.

The general vocabulary of the text, excluding the science terms, has been kept to a level easily managed by high school students. Vocabulary usage was checked with *The Living Word Vocabulary*, by Edgar Dale, Ph.D., and Joseph O'Rourke, Ph.D. (Field Enterprises Educational Corporation, 1976). Sentence length and structure have also been controlled so that the material reads easily. However, the text has not been broken up into artificially short sentences that disrupt the continuity of ideas.

The book contains approximately 700 photographs, illustrations, tables, and graphs that supplement the text. In many instances there is both a labeled diagram and a photograph, an arrangement that conveys the maximum amount of information for the student.

At intervals throughout the book there are marginal and full-page features that cover areas not dealt with in the text ("sidelights"); recent developments and controversial topics ("frontiers of biology"); careers for people with an interest in biology ("careers"); and descriptions of research of historical importance ("historical notes").

Additional Information in the Annotated Teacher's Edition

Beginning on Page 8 of this Teacher's Guide section, you will find a detailed Program Guide for using the text. It includes a suggested teaching schedule, related activities in the accompanying laboratory manual, and related activities in the workbook *A Learning Program for Biology,* by Schraer and Noelle.

In the teaching schedule, the content of the text has been divided into core concepts and extended areas. The extended areas may be considered optional topics to be omitted to fit your course objectives and time limitations.

The remainder of the Teacher's Guide provides chapter rationales, lists of some of the available audiovisual materials, and answers to all end-of-chapter questions.

The student pages of this Teacher's Edition contain annotations printed in blue ink. These annotations provide additional information to aid the teacher in presenting the topic.

Suppliers of Audiovisual Materials

BFA Educational Media
2211 Michigan Avenue
Santa Monica, California 90404

Carolina Biological Supply Company
Burlington, North Carolina 27215

Churchill Films
662 North Robertson Blvd.
Los Angeles, California 90069

Coronet Films
65 East South Water Street
Chicago, Illinois 60601

CRM Films
1011 Camino Del Mar
Del Mar, California 92014

Educational Audio Visual, Inc.
Pleasantville, New York 10570

Encyclopedia Britannica Educational Corp.
425 North Michigan Avenue
Chicago, Illinois 60611

Fisher Scientific Company
711 Forbes Avenue
Pittsburgh, Pennsylvania 15219

Indiana University
Audio-Visual Center
Bloomington, Indiana 47405

International Film Bureau
332 Michigan Avenue
Chicago, Illinois 60604

Macmillan Films, Inc.
866 Third Avenue
New York, New York 10022

McGraw-Hill Book Company
1221 Avenue of the Americas
New York, New York 10020

Modern Learning Aids—See Ward's

Prentice-Hall Media
ServCode WC
150 White Plains Road
Tarrytown, New York 10591

Time-Life Films
43 West 16th Street
New York, New York 10011

University of California
Visual Institute
2272 Union Street
Berkeley, California 94720

University of Illinois
Visual Aids Service
Champaign, Illinois 61820

Ward's Natural Science Establishment, Inc.
P.O. Box 1712
Rochester, New York 14603

General References for the Teacher

Animal Physiology

Eckert, Roger, *Animal Physiology*. W.H. Freeman, San Francisco, 1978.
Guyton, Arthur G., *Textbook of Medical Physiology*. Saunders, Philadelphia, 1981.
Prosser, C. Ladd, *Comparative Animal Physiology*. Holt, Rinehart & Winston, New York, 1973.

Biology

Storer, Tracy I., et al. *General Zoology*. McGraw-Hill, New York, 1979.
Villee, Claude A., *Biology*. Holt, Rinehart & Winston, New York, 1977.
Weisz, Paul B., & Keogh, Richard N., *Elements of Biology*. McGraw-Hill, New York, 1977.

Botany

Cronquist, Arthur, *Basic Botany*. Harper & Row, New York, 1973.
Esau, Katherine, *Anatomy of Seed Plants*. Wiley, New York, 1977.
Laetsch, Watson M., *Plants: Basic Concepts in Botany*. Little, Brown, Boston, 1979.
Wilson, Carl, et al. *Botany*. Holt, Rinehart & Winston, 1971.

Chemistry

Parry, Robert W., et al. *Chemistry: Experimental Foundations*. Prentice-Hall, Englewood Cliffs, N.J., 1982.
Sienko, Michell J., and Plane, Robert A. *Chemistry*. McGraw-Hill, New York, 1976.
Stryer, Lubert, *Biochemistry*. W.H. Freeman, San Francisco, 1975.

Cytology & Histology

Bloom, William, & Fawcett, Don W., *A Textbook of Histology*. Saunders, Philadelphia, 1975
Copenhaver, et al. *Bailey's Textbook of Histology*. Williams & Wilkins, Baltimore, 1978.
Dyson, Robert D., *Cell Biology: A Molecular Approach*. Allyn & Bacon, Boston, 1978.

Ecology

Odum, Eugene P., *Fundamentals of Ecology*. Holt, Rinehart & Winston, New York, 1971.
Smith, Robert L., *Ecology and Field Biology*. Harper & Row, New York, 1980.

Embryology

Oppenheimer, *Introduction to Embryonic Development*. Allyn & Bacon, Boston, 1980.
Patten, Bradley, & Carlson, Bruce M., *Foundations of Embryology*. McGraw-Hill, New York, 1974.

Endocrinology

Barrington, E.J., *An Introduction to General and Comparative Endocrinology*. Oxford University Press, New York, 1975.
Turner, C. Donnell, & Bagnara, Joseph T., *General Endocrinology*. Holt, Rinehart & Winston, New York, 1976.

Evolution

Blum, Harold F., *Time's Arrow and Evolution*. Princeton University Press, Princeton, N.J., 1968.
Dobzhansky, Theodosius, et al. *Evolution*. W.H. Freeman, San Francisco, 1977.
Ehrlich, Paul R., and Holm, R.W., *Evolution*. McGraw-Hill, New York, 1974.
Gould, Stephen J., *Ever Since Darwin: Reflections in Natural History*. Norton, New York, 1979.
Grant, Verne, *Organic Evolution*. W.H. Freeman, San Francisco, 1977.

Genetics

Gardner, Eldon J., & Snustad, D. Peter, *Principles of Genetics*. Wiley, New York, 1980.
Novitski, Edward, *Human Genetics*. Macmillan, New York, 1977.
Stent, Gunther S., and Calendar, Richard, *Molecular Genetics: An Introductory Narrative*. W.H. Freeman, San Francisco, 1978.
Watson, J.D., *Molecular Biology of the Gene*. Addison-Wesley, Reading, Mass., 1976.
Winchester, A.M., *Genetics: A Survey of the Principles of Heredity*. Houghton Mifflin, Boston, 1977.

Program Guide

	Chapter	Suggested Teaching Schedule: Class Periods	Core Concepts	Extended Areas	Suggested Laboratory Activities[1]	Related Activities in *A Learning Program for Biology*[2]
Unit 1: 4 weeks	1	1	1-1—1-11			1-1
	2	2	2-1—2-13		Using the Microscope Microscopic Measurement	1-3
	3	5	3-1—3-24			2-1
	4	5	4-1—4-7, 4-10, 4-11, 4-14—4-17	4-8, 4-9, 4-12, 4-13, 4-18	Organic Molecules and Simple Reactions	2-2, 3-3
	5	5	5-1—5-26		Cork Cells and Onion Cells How Plant and Animal Cells Differ Diffusion Through a Membrane Osmosis, Plasmolysis, and Turgor	1-2, 6-1
	6	2	6-1—6-13		Learning About Animal Classification	4-1
Unit 2: 10 weeks	7	6	7-1—7-4, 7-7	7-5, 7-6, 7-8—7-16	Yeast Respiration Measuring Carbon Dioxide Production	3-1, 3-2
	8	6	8-1—8-14		Nutrition in Paramecia Nutrient Tests Digestion of Sucrose by Yeast Digestion of Protein and Starch	5-1, 5-2, 5-3
	9	6	9-1—9-7	9-8—9-12	Capillary Circulation Measuring Heart Rate in Daphnia Investigating Pulse Rate	6-2, 6-3, 6-4

[1] *A Laboratory Program for Biology*, by Bjork, Horn, Schraer, and Stoltze, Cebco Standard Publishing.
[2] *A Learning Program for Biology*, by Schraer and Noelle, Cebco Standard Publishing.

	10	5	10-1—10-5, 10-8	10-6, 10-7, 10-9—10-15	Looking at Blood Cells Blood Typing and Clotting	6-5, 6-6
	11	4	11-1—11-10	11-11, 11-12	Water Temperature and Fish Respiration Lung Capacity	7-1, 7-2
	12	4	12-1—12-10			8-1, 8-2
	13	4	13-1—13-11		Muscle, Bone, and Cartilage	11-1, 11-2, 11-3
	14	4	14-1—14-5, 14-8—14-14	14-6, 14-7		9-1, 9-2
	15	4	15-1—15-6 15-12, 15-13	15-7—15-11, 15-14—15-18	Sight, Touch, and Taste Human Reflexes and Reaction Time	9-3, 9-4
	16	7	16-1—16-5	16-6—16-16		10-1, 10-2
Unit 3: 4 weeks	17	6	17-1, 17-10, 17-11	17-2—17-9, 17-12, 17-13	Analysis of Plant Pigments	12-1, 12-2, 12-3
	18	9	18-1—18-14		Stem Anatomy Root Anatomy Leaf Anatomy	13-1, 13-2, 13-3, 13-4
	19	5	19-1—19-10			14-1, 14-2, 14-3
Unit 4: 4 weeks	20	5	20-1—20-13		Mitosis in Animal Cells Mitosis in Plant Cells Mushroom Spores Regeneration and Metabolic Activities in Hydra	15-1, 15-2, 15-3
	21	5	21-1—21-12			16-1, 16-2
	22	4	22-1, 22-2, 22-6—22-8	22-3—22-5	Development of Chick Embryos	16-3
	23	4		23-1—23-10		16-4
	24	3	24-6—24-11	24-1—24-5, 24-12, 24-13	Seeds: Anatomy and Development Classification of Fruits Growth of Seedlings	17-1, 17-2

Suggested Teaching Schedule

	Chapter	Class Periods	Core Concepts	Extended Areas	Suggested Laboratory Activities[1]	Related Activities in *A Learning Program for Biology*[2]
Unit 5: 4 weeks	25	7	25-1—25-15		Probability and Mendelian Genetics Finding Genotypes and Phenotypes for One Trait	18-1
	26	7	26-1—26-11, 26-16	26-12—26-15	Human Inheritance Sex-Linked or not Sex-Linked Karyotypes	18-2
	27	8	27-1—27-7, 27-14, 27-16—27-18	27-8—27-13, 27-15	DNA Models Protein Synthesis	19-1, 19-2, 19-3
Unit 6: 2 weeks	28	6	28-1—28-16			20-1, 20-2
	29	6	29-1, 29-2, 29-8—29-21	29-3—29-7	Investigating Spontaneous Generation Natural Selection in Populations Adaptation	20-3, 20-4
Unit 7: 4 weeks	30	3		30-1—30-14	Monerans: Blue-Green Algae More Monerans: Bacteria Looking at Simple Algae Looking at Amebas Life in Hay Infusions	4-2
	31	3		31-1—31-19	Looking at Bread Mold	4-2, 4-3
	32	3		32-1—32-17	Looking at Hydra Clam Anatomy	4-4
	33	3		33-1—33-18	Crayfish Anatomy Comparison of Crustacean and Insect Starfish Anatomy	4-4
	34	3		34-1—34-17	Frog Anatomy	4-5
	35	5		35-1—35-7		4-5

Unit 8: 3 weeks	36	5	36-1—36-8, 36-10, 36-11, 36-13—36-15, 36-18, 36-19	36-9, 36-12, 36-16, 36-17	Population Densities and Food Relationships Nutritional Relationships Population Growth	21-1, 21-2, 21-3, 21-4
	37	5		37-1—37-11	Field Study of a Terrestrial Community Life in a Soil Community Looking at Pond Water	21-5
	38	5	38-1—38-16		Water Pollution Air Pollution	21-6, 21-7

Total time = 36 weeks

Chapter-By-Chapter: Rationales Audiovisual Materials Answers to Questions

Chapter 1

Rationale

Chapter 1 introduces the characteristics that distinguish living things from nonliving things. Brief descriptions of the life processes are included. This chapter also introduces the idea that although living things show great diversity in appearance, etc., they have many characteristics in common. An appropriate movie and/or film strip should stimulate thought and discussion.

Audiovisual Materials

"Life in a Vacant Lot," (10 min., color) EBE.
"Life in the Forest," (11 min., color) EBE.
"Life in the Ocean," (16 min., color) BFA.
"Life in a Pond," rev. (10 min., color) Coronet.
"The Sea," (27 min., color) EBE.

Answers to Test Your Learning

1. An *organism* is an individual living thing.

2. Living things: are highly organized and contain complex chemical substances; are made up of one or more cells; use energy; have a definite form and a limited size; have a limited life span; grow; respond to environmental change; reproduce.

3. Answers will vary: Viruses are nonliving—they show no characteristics of life outside of living cells, and even within cells, they only appear to reproduce; Or, viruses are living—they can reproduce in the proper environment within a cell. It can be argued that seeds are living even when the life processes are greatly slowed down (dormant) because under suitable conditions they sprout, and show the characteristics of living things; Or, like viruses, they show none of the characteristics of living things except under certain conditions.

4. *Nutrition* is the process by which organisms take materials from the environment and change them to forms that can be used for energy, growth, or repair. *Nutrients* are substances that organisms can use for energy, growth, or repair. *Ingestion* is the process by which an organism takes food from the environment into its body. *Digestion* is the breaking down of complex food materials into forms that can be used by the organism.

5. *Transport* is the process by which usable materials are taken into an organism (absorption) and distributed throughout its body (circulation).

6. Organisms obtain the energy they need by the process of *cellular respiration*, in which the chemical energy in nutrients is released.

7. Aerobic respiration requires the presence of free oxygen. Anaerobic respiration does not require oxygen.

8. *Synthesis* is the process in which simple substances are combined chemically to form more complex substances. *Assimilation* is the incorporation of materials into the body of the organism.

9. In many-celled organisms, growth occurs through an increase in the number of cells.

10. Metabolic wastes are removed from an organism by the process of *excretion*.

11. *Homeostasis* is the maintenance of a stable internal environment.

12. The nervous system consists of a network of specialized cells that carry impulses throughout the organism. The endocrine system consists of glands that secrete chemicals that are carried throughout the organism. Both systems can bring about changes in the organism in response to changes in the environment.

13. In asexual reproduction there is only one parent, and all offspring are identical to that parent. In sexual reproduction there are two parents, and the offspring are not identical to either parent.

14. *Metabolism* includes all the chemical reactions of the life processes of an organism.

Answers to Test Your Understanding

1. Answers will vary.

2. *Breathing* involves the exchange of gases in the lungs. *Respiration* is the release of chemical energy stored in nutrients.

3. nutrition—including ingestion and digestion; transport—including absorption and circulation; synthesis; assimilation.

Chapter 2

Rationale

This chapter will give students some insights into the methods of biological research. The scientific method is explained clearly and simply, and some of the basic instruments and techniques used in biological research are described.

A guest speaker who is involved in research would be enlightening and thought-provoking for students. A bulletin board with magazine and newspaper articles related to biology would focus attention both on current research and on the importance of a basic knowledge of biology in understanding events and issues that affect our lives.

Audiovisual Materials

"Microscopic Life," (16 min., b&w) EBE.
"Electron Microscopy," (14 min., color) Wards.
"Micro 70," (23 min., color) Bausch and Lomb Optical Co.
"Using the Scientific Method," (11 min., color) Coronet.

Answers to Test Your Learning

1. The first task is to define the problem. Next, an experiment must be designed to test some aspect of the problem. All aspects of the experiment, including design and materials used, must be recorded. All observations or measurements made during the experiment must also be recorded. The results of the experiment are then analyzed. Any patterns or regularities are noted so that hypotheses and theories can be formulated. All material pertaining to the experiment must be arranged and presented in a logical manner so that the experiment can be evaluated and tried by other scientists.

2. A *hypothesis* is a possible explanation of an observed set of facts. A *theory* is an explanation that applies to a broad range of phenomena.

3. In the metric system, the unit of length is the *meter*, the unit of mass is the *gram*, the unit of volume is the *liter*, and the unit of temperature is the *Celsius degree*, or *kelvin*.

4. Instruments increase the range and accuracy of the human senses.

5. A *microscope* is any device that enables us to see small details of an object by apparently enlarging it.

6. An optical microscope uses light to produce an enlarged image. Light rays change direction when they pass from one transparent medium to another. Optical microscopes contain lenses, which are pieces of glass with curved surfaces. The lenses cause light rays from an object to bend in such a way as to produce an enlarged image.

7. The common name for a simple microscope is *magnifying glass*.

8. A simple microscope has a single lens.

9. A compound microscope has two lenses.

10. The two lenses of the optical system are the *objective* and the *ocular*. In most microscopes, the objective and ocular each consist of several lenses combined to give the desired optical qualities. The first set of lenses produces an enlarged image that is further magnified by the second.

11. The mechanical system consists of the structural parts of the microscope that hold the specimen and lenses and permit focusing of the image.

12. Two adjustment knobs are used to focus the compound microscope—the coarse adjustment knob and the fine adjustment knob.

13. The coarse adjustment is used for rough focusing of the low-power objective. The fine adjustment knob is used for fine focusing of the low-power objective and for all focusing of the high-power objective. The specimen is in focus when the image is sharpest for the observer.

14. The light system in student microscopes generally consists of a *mirror* and a *diaphragm*. The mirror directs light up through the specimen into the objective, and the diaphragm regulates the amount of light reaching the objective. Some microscopes have a *substage illuminator*, which is an electric light that is directed up through the specimen, and some have *condensers*, which are lenses that concentrate the light on the specimen.

15. *Magnification* is the amount that the image is enlarged.

16. The total magnification is calculated by multiplying the magnifying power of the objective lens by the magnifying power of the ocular lens.

17. *Resolution* is the capacity of a microscope to show as separate images two points that are close together.

18. The specimen must be cut into small pieces, soaked in a fixative, embedded in wax or plastic, and sliced into very thin sections through which light can pass. Colored stains are often applied to the thin sections to bring out details that cannot otherwise be seen.

19. A binocular microscope has an ocular and objective for each eye. It provides a three-dimensional image of the specimen and is used for studying the external structure of small organisms and for dissections.

20. As light waves pass through different structures in a specimen they become out of phase. The optical system of a phase-contrast microscope enables the viewer to detect the differences in the phases of light waves passing through the various structures in the specimen. (Note that the light source for a phase-contrast microscope is polarized light, where the light waves are in phase before entering the specimen. In ordinary light, the light waves are not in phase.)

21. In the ordinary compound microscope, the cells of the specimen have been killed by fixing and staining. With the phase-contrast microscope, the structures in living cells are visible without stains.

22. An electron microscope uses an electron beam in place of light waves, and electromagnetic lenses instead of glass lenses.

23. The electron microscope can obtain magnifications of more than 250,000 times with good resolution. This is much greater than can possibly be obtained with a light microscope.

24. *Ultracentrifugation* involves spinning a liquid material at very high speeds, which separates its constituents according to their densities. It is used to separate the different parts of cells. *Microdissection* is the use of very small instruments to perform various operations on living cells or tissues. *Tissue culture* is a technique for maintaining living cells or tissues in a medium outside the body. *Chromatography* is a process used for separating and analyzing mixtures of substances on the basis of how tightly they adhere to a particular material. *Electrophoresis* is a technique for separating and analyzing mixtures of substances whose particles have an electrical charge.

Answers to Test Your Understanding

1. A control provides a valid basis for comparison of the effects of a single test factor. The control allows the scientist to state that the factor being tested has a definite, particular role or effect. Without the control, there would be no basis for comparison.

2. A hypothesis is an educated guess based on a pattern or regularity observed in data collected during an investigation. It is an idea about why the observed pattern occurs. The hypothesis is important because it is an explanation that can be tested by further research. If disproven, the hypothesis can be modified or discarded.

3. *Resolution* is most often neglected in a sales pitch. Magnification alone is useless if the lenses are of poor quality and do not offer a reasonable sharpness of image.

4. Set up a ratio between the low- and high-power objectives (10×/40×). Cancel like terms. The high-power field will be 1/4 of the low-power field, or 0.5mm (1/4 × 2.0 mm = 0.5mm). Since 1 millimeter equals 1,000 microns, 0.5mm = 500 microns.

Chapter 3

Rationale

The present state of biological science requires that students have an understanding of basic chemical concepts. This chapter presents the concepts students will need to understand material presented in later chapters. The chapter includes basic information on atoms, elements, and compounds, chemical bonding, and chemical reactions. Elementary chemical terms, including *symbol, formula, equation, acid, base,* and *salt,* are defined and illustrated. Mixtures, solutions, suspensions, and colloids are discussed in a way appropriate to biology.

Audiovisual Materials

"A is for Atom," (15 min., color) General Electric Co.
"Acid-Base Indicators," (18 min., color) Modern Learning Aids.
"Chemical Bonding," (16 min., color) Modern Learning Aids.
"Chemical Families," (22 min., color) Modern Learning Aids.
"Hydrogen Atom," (13 min., color) Modern Learning Aids.
"Shapes and Polarities of Molecules," (18 min., color) Modern Learning Aids.

Answers to Test Your Learning

1. An element is a substance composed of one kind of atom.

2. A compound is a substance composed of two or more kinds of atoms combined in definite proportions. Compounds can be separated by chemical means into their constituent elements. Elements cannot be broken down by ordinary chemical means.

3. An atom consists of protons and neutrons, which are found in the nucleus, and electrons, which are found in the space around the nucleus.

4. The atomic number indicates the number of protons in the nucleus of an atom. Since an atom has the same number of electrons as protons, the atomic number also indicates the number of electrons.

5. Different isotopes of the same element differ from one another in the number of neutrons in their nuclei.

6. The atomic mass of an atom is equal to the sum of the masses of its protons and neutrons.

7. The symbols for the isotopes of oxygen are ^{16}O, ^{17}O, and ^{18}O.

8. When a radioactive isotope disintegrates, the atom emits charged particles and radiation, and the number of protons and/or neutrons changes. In the process, the isotope usually changes to an isotope of a different element.

9. Radioisotopes can be detected and measured by instruments or films sensitive to the radiation they emit. They can be used to follow materials in the body and to detect abnormalities in the size, shape, or function of organs; they can also be used to study biochemical reactions in living organisms. Nonradioactive tracer isotopes can be measured with a mass spectrometer.

10. Electrons are arranged in energy levels, or shells, at different distances from the nucleus of the atom. The first, or innermost, shell can hold a maximum of two electrons. The outermost shell of an atom with more than two electrons can hold a maximum of eight electrons.

11. In an atom with more than two electrons, a filled outer shell will contain eight electrons.

12. A *chemical bond* is the force of attraction that holds two atoms together.

13. A *covalent bond* is a bond formed by the sharing of electrons by two atoms.

14. An *ion* is an atom (or atoms) that has an electrical charge.

15. An *ionic bond* is an attractive force between two ions. Such bonds are formed by the transfer of electrons from one atom to another.

16. A *diatomic molecule* is one composed of two atoms of the same element bonded together by a covalent bond.

17. An *empirical formula* shows the simplest proportion of atoms in a compound. A *molecular formula* shows the actual composition (the numbers and types of atoms) in a molecule of a compound.

18. A *structural formula* shows the numbers and types of atoms in a molecule and how they are bonded to one another.

19. A balanced equation has the same number of each kind of atom on both sides of the equation.

20. A *mixture* contains substances that are physically mingled but not chemically bonded together. A *homogeneous mixture* is one in which the ingredients are spread uniformly throughout.

21. A *solution* is actually just a homogeneous mixture, but the term is usually applied to liquids. The *solvent* makes up most of the liquid. *Solutes* are substances present in lesser amounts that are dissolved in the solvent.

22. When a molecular substance dissolves in a liquid, its molecules separate and spread throughout the solvent.

23. When an ionic compound dissolves in a liquid, the compound breaks up into its individual ions.

24. A *suspension* is a mixture whose components separate on standing.

25. In a suspension the particles are large enough to be affected by the force of gravity, which causes them to settle out. In a *colloidal dispersion,* the particles are larger than ions or molecules but are still too small to settle out.

26. An *acid* is a substance that produces hydrogen ions when dissolved in water.

27. A *base* is a substance that produces hydroxyl ions when dissolved in water.

28. In a neutralization reaction, the hydrogen ions from an acid combine with the hydroxyl ions of a base to form water. A neutral solution is produced.

29. The products of a neutralization reaction are water and a salt that is formed from the positive ions of the base and the negative ions of the acid.

30. Water molecules dissociate into hydrogen and hydroxyl ions.

31. Water is neutral. When water molecules dissociate, they form equal numbers of hydrogen and hydroxyl ions: $H_2O \rightarrow H^+ + OH^-$.

32. The *pH scale* is a method of stating the concentration of hydrogen ions in a solution.

33. An *indicator* is a substance that changes color when the pH goes above or below a certain value.

Answers to Test Your Understanding

1. A. neutrons
B. 3 protons and 3 electrons
C. 1 electron
D. no
E. $2Li + Cl_2 \rightarrow 2LiCl$
F. ionic bonds

2. In a *mixture,* the substances are physically mingled, but not necessarily distributed in a uniform manner. A *solution* is a homogeneous mixture, generally a liquid, that does not separate on standing. A *suspension* is a mixture that separates on standing. The solute particles in a suspension are heavy and settle to the bottom. A *colloidal dispersion* contains particles that are larger than molecules or ions but are too small to settle out.

3. A. electrons
B. protons
C. neutrons

Chapter 4

Rationale

Living organisms are composed of organic compounds and the chemical reactions of metabolism involve organic compounds. This chapter covers the basic characteristics of the different types of organic compounds—carbohydrates, lipids, proteins, and nucleic acids. The chemical reactions of dehydration synthesis and hydrolysis are simply explained. A brief description of the functions of enzymes concludes the chapter.

Audiovisual Materials

"Biochemistry and Molecular Structure," (22 min., color) Modern Learning Aids.

"Mechanism of Organic Reaction," (10 min., color) Modern Learning Aids.

"Enzymes—Nature's Magic," (13 min., color) Sterling Educational Films.

Answers to Test Your Learning

1. Organic compounds always contain carbon and usually hydrogen. They may also contain oxygen, nitrogen, phosphorus, and sulfur.

2. A carbon atom can form 4 covalent bonds.

3. Carbohydrates generally have a ratio of 2 atoms of hydrogen to 1 atom of oxygen.

4. CH_2O

5. Sugars are biologically important because they provide much of the energy for living things.

6. In dehydration synthesis, two molecules are bonded together to form a more complex molecule. The bond occurs where an OH group is located in each molecule. One OH combines with the H from the other OH, forming a molecule of water. The two molecules become bonded through the remaining O.

7. A disaccharide is formed.

8. A polysaccharide is a type of carbohydrate made up of a long chain of repeating sugar units.

9. Starch and cellulose are polysaccharides found in plants; glycogen and chitin are polysaccharides found in animals.

10. In hydrolysis, a water molecule is returned to the place where it was removed in dehydration synthesis. The bond between the two monosaccharide molecules is broken leaving each molecule with its original OH group.

11. A fat is made up of fatty acids and glycerol.

12. A *lipid* is a type of compound made up of carbon, hydrogen, and oxygen, but containing less oxygen than a carbohydrate. Fats, oils, and waxes are lipids. An *oil* is a fat that is liquid at room temperature. A *wax* is a lipid formed by the combination of fatty acids with an alcohol other than glycerol. A *fatty acid* is a weak organic acid that contains a carboxyl group and a chain of carbon atoms with attached hydrogens. *Glycerol* is an alcohol with three OH groups.

13. In a saturated fatty acid all carbon-to-carbon bonds are single bonds, while in an unsaturated fatty acid there are one or more double or triple bonds between carbon atoms.

14. *Hydrogenation* is the process in which hydrogen atoms are added to unsaturated fats converting them to saturated fats.

15. Saturated fats may contribute to the formation of cholesterol in the body. Deposits of cholesterol cause narrowing of arteries, which leads to heart attacks and strokes.

16. Lipids are components of cell structures, such as cell membranes. They are also used as a form of stored food, and they also cushion the body and insulate it against heat loss.

17. Proteins form structural parts of cells and tissues, pigments, hormones, contractile fibers, antibodies, and enzymes.

18.

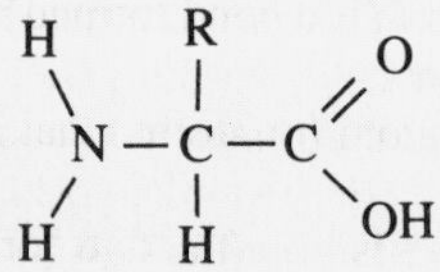

19. twenty

20. A *peptide bond* forms between the amino group of one amino acid and the carboxyl group of another amino acid by dehydration synthesis.

21. A *dipeptide* is a molecule made up of two amino acids bonded together. A *polypeptide* is made up of a chain of amino acids bonded together.

22. The tremendous variety found among protein molecules results from the fact that: the twenty amino acid molecules found in proteins can be arranged in any sequence; the chains of amino acids can vary greatly in length; and the three-dimensional structure of the molecules can also vary.

23. DNA and RNA

24. DNA is the hereditary material that is transferred from one generation to the next. DNA and RNA together control the development and activities of the cells of an organism.

25. DNA consists of two parallel chains of repeating units made up of the sugar deoxyribose, phosphate groups, and one of four bases. The bases of the two chains are bonded together, and the chains are twisted to form a double helix. The RNA molecule consists of a single strand made up of repeating units of the sugar ribose, phosphate groups, and one of four bases. The bases found in DNA are adenine, guanine, cytosine, and thymine. In RNA, uracil replaces thymine.

26. Enzymes are proteins that function as catalysts, allowing the chemical reactions necessary for life to take place at the relatively low temperatures found in living cells.

27. The name of an enzyme is usually derived from the substrate on which it acts. The name usually ends with the suffix *-ase*.

28. According to the lock-and-key model of enzyme action, the enzyme molecule has an active site with a highly specific shape. Only a specific type of substrate molecule fits the active site. When the substrate molecule comes in contact with the active site, it forms a temporary union with the enzyme, resulting in an enzyme-substrate complex. When the reaction is completed, the enzyme and reaction product separate.

29. Enzymes usually have a narrow range of temperature and pH at which they work best. Outside that range, the efficiency of the enzyme is reduced. A low concentration of the enzyme limits the number of substrate molecules it can act on. Increasing the enzyme concentration above this level will increase the reaction rate. But once all substrate molecules are being acted on, further increases in enzyme concentration will have no effect. The same effects are true of substrate concentration.

30. A coenzyme is an organic substance that helps an enzyme perform its catalytic function.

Answers to Test Your Understanding

1. Organic compounds have larger and more complex molecules than inorganic compounds because the carbon atoms of organic compounds can form four covalent bonds. Carbon atoms can form bonds with other carbon atoms, producing long, highly branched chains.

2. In most plants, cellulose, a polysaccharide, is the main constituent of cell walls. Plants store food in the form of starch, which is also a polysaccharide. Animals store food in the form of glycogen, a polysaccharide, and in arthropods, the exoskeleton is composed of chitin, a polysaccharide.

3. Many medical authorities believe that a diet high in saturated fats contributes to diseases of the heart and circulatory system.

4. The four bases found in DNA are adenine, cytosine, guanine, and thymine. The sequence of the bases determines what proteins are synthesized in the cell.

5. Enzymes control all the metabolic reactions of living things. Without enzymes, which acts as catalysts, many of these reactions would not occur at all.

Chapter 5

Rationale

This chapter is an introduction to the cell. The chapter opens with the historical development of the cell theory. This is followed by a simple explanation of cell structure and function. The passage of materials through the cell membrane is described, with an emphasis on the semipermeable nature of the cell membrane. Active and passive transport are included, stressing the necessary link between the living cell and its environment. The organization of cells into more complex colonial and multicellular organisms is also discussed.

Audiovisual Materials

"The Worlds of Dr. Vishniac," (19 min., color) Educational Testing Service.

"Life and Death of a Cell," (21 min., color) University of California.

"The Cell," (15 min., b&w) Association-Sterling Films.

"Diffusion and Osmosis," 2nd ed. (14 min., color) EBE.

"The Cell: A Functioning Structure," Part I (29 min., color) McGraw-Hill.

Answers to Test Your Learning

1. *Robert Hooke* examined sections of cork and other plant tissues with a microscope and discovered that they were composed of boxlike structures, which he called "cells." *Van Leeuwenhoek* constructed simple microscopes through which he saw many types of one-celled organisms. *Robert Brown* realized that all cells contain a small, round, dense structure, which he called the "nucleus." *Matthias Schleidin* theorized that all plants were made up of cells. *Theodor Schwann* proposed that all animals were made up of cells. *Rudolph Virchow* stated that all new cells arise from existing cells.

2. The cell theory states that all organisms are made up of one or more cells and the products of those cells; that all cells carry on their own life activities; and that new cells arise only from other living cells by the process of cell division or reproduction.

3. All cells are surrounded by a cell, or plasma, membrane.

4. Cytoplasm, a fluid material, fills the space inside the cell.

5. The cell wall of plants is composed of cellulose.

6. The cell wall provides protection and gives the cell its shape.

7. The cell membrane separates the interior of the cell from the environment, and by controlling the passage of materials into and out of the cell, it makes it possible for the cell contents to be chemically different from the environment.

8. A semipermeable membrane is permeable to some materials but not to others—that is some substances can pass through it, but others cannot.

9. The cell membrane is a two-layered structure composed of lipids and proteins. The lipids are arranged in two layers, with an area between them that consists of the "tail ends" of the lipid molecules. Proteins may be embedded in either side of the membrane, and in some cases are thought to extend through the membrane.

10. In *pinocytosis,* there is an inpocketing of the cell membrane, which eventually pinches off producing a vacuole in the cell. In *phagocytosis,* extensions of the cell called pseudopods surround particles or small organisms, which are engulfed into the cell. As in pinocytosis, they are separated from the other cell contents, enclosed in a vacuole.

11. The *nucleus* is the control center for cell metabolism and reproduction.

12. The nucleus is a round, dense body surrounded by a semipermeable, double membrane. It contains one or more nucleoli.

13. The nuclear membrane has pores, while the cell membrane does not.

14. *Nucleoli* are dense, granular bodies composed of RNA and protein. A particular type of RNA is synthesized in the nucleolus.

15. The *cytoplasm* is a watery material in which many of the substances involved in cell metabolism are dissolved. Many metabolic reactions take place in the cytoplasm. Specialized structures called *organelles* are found in the cytoplasm.

16. The *endoplasmic reticulum* is a system of fluid-filled canals enclosed by membranes. The canals serve in the transport of materials throughout the cell, and many reactions occur on the membranes of the system. Rough endoplasmic reticulum is lined with ribosomes. Proteins produced by the ribosomes are transported by the endoplasmic reticulum out of the cell. Smooth endoplasmic reticulum contains no ribosomes on its membranes.

17. *Ribosomes* are the sites of protein synthesis in the cell. They are found free in the cytoplasm as well as on the membranes of the endoplasmic reticulum.

18. *Golgi bodies* consist of both flattened and rounded membrane-enclosed sacs. Products to be secreted from the cell are enclosed in a sac in the Golgi body and then released from the cell.

19. *Lysosomes* are small, membrane-enclosed sacs that contain digestive enzymes. In unicellular organisms, lysosomes fuse with food vacuoles, providing the enzymes for digestion. In multicellular organisms, lysosomes break down worn-out organelles.

20. A *mitochondrion* is a round or slipper-shaped organelle surrounded by a double membrane. The inner membrane forms deep folds that extend into the mitochondrion. Reactions of cellular respiration occur in the mitochondrion and on the surfaces of the folded membranes.

21. Mitochondria are thought to be capable of self-duplication.

22. *Microtubules* serve as a skeleton for the cell, giving it shape.

23. Microtubules are long, hollow, cylindrical organelles. They are composed of a helix-type protein called *tubulin*.

24. *Microfilaments* are long, solid, threadlike organelles found in some types of cells. They are generally composed of the protein actin and are usually associated with cell movement.

25. A *centriole* is made up of a ring of nine groups of three microtubules.

26. Centrioles are found in animal cells and in some algae and fungi; they are usually missing in plant cells. Centrioles are involved in cell division in animal cells.

27. *Cilia* and *flagella* are both composed of a ring of nine pairs of microtubules with another pair in the center. Cilia and flagella arise from a structure called a *basal body*. Flagella are much longer than cilia. A cell might have one or two flagella, but ciliated cells or tissues are often covered with cilia.

28. Both cilia and flagella are involved in locomotion in unicellular organisms. In multicellular organisms, cilia move substances over the surface of the cells.

29. A *vacuole* is a fluid-filled organelle enclosed by a membrane. In plant cells some vacuoles are filled with fluid cell sap, some contain stored food, and some contain cell wastes. In microorganisms and some simple animals, food is digested in food vacuoles. In some simple organisms, excess water collects in contractile vacuoles and is then expelled from the cell. Vacuoles also serve as storage sites for cell products.

30. *Plastids* are membrane-enclosed organelles found in the cells of most plants and some protists. *Leucoplasts* are colorless plastids in which glucose is converted to starch and starch and other nutrients are stored. *Chromoplasts* contain the pigments that color fruits, flowers, and leaves. The pigments are synthesized within the chromoplasts. *Chloroplasts* are a type of chromoplast that contain the green photosynthetic pigment chlorophyll. They are the site of photosynthesis.

31. A chloroplast contains a system of double membranes called *lamellae*. Stacks of lamellae form structures called *grana*. The photosynthetic pigments are found in the membranes of the grana. The rest of the chloroplast is filled with a protein-containing material that is called the *stroma*.

32. Small molecules, such as water, glucose, amino acids, carbon dioxide, and oxygen pass easily through cell membranes. Electrically neutral molecules pass through the membrane more easily than ions. Lipid molecules and substances that dissolve in lipids pass more readily through cell membranes than water-soluble substances.

33. *Diffusion* is the movement of molecules or particles from a region of greater concentration to a region of lesser concentration. A *concentration gradient* is the difference in concentration between the region of greater concentration and the region of lesser concentration. An *equilibrium* is a situation in which there are as many molecules moving into an area as there are leaving the same area.

34. Many substances move into and out of cells by diffusion. These are substances to which the cell membrane is permeable.

35. *Facilitated diffusion* is a process in which various substances pass through the cell membrane at rates faster than can be explained by diffusion alone. It is thought that facilitated diffusion may involve the temporary opening of certain channels in the cell membrane.

36. *Osmosis* is the diffusion of water across a semipermeable membrane from a region of greater concentration of water to a region of lesser concentration of water.

37. When water moves through a semipermeable membrane in the direction of the concentration gradient, the weight of water on that side of the membrane increases. The weight causes increased pressure—*osmotic pressure*—on that side of the membrane.

38. In hypotonic solutions, animal cells swell and burst; plant cells fill with excess water that collects in the large vacuole, causing increased turgor pressure. In hypertonic solutions, animal cells shrink; in plant cells, the cytoplasm contracts into a ball, a process called plasmolysis. In isotonic solutions, cells neither gain nor lose water.

39. In passive transport, no cellular energy is needed to move materials into or out of the cell. In active transport, cellular energy must be expended to move the materials.

40. Active transport makes it possible for cells to maintain internal conditions that are chemically different from the surrounding medium.

41. A unicellular organism consists of a single cell that exists independently. Examples are ameba, paramecium, euglena. In a simple colonial organism, a number of cells are attached together, but each carries on its own life processes, and all the cells are structurally alike. In more complex colonies, some cells may be specialized to perform a specific function, such as reproduction. Colonial organisms include volvox and Portuguese man-of-war.

42. In a complex, multicellular animal, there are tissues composed of similar, specialized cells; organs composed of groups of tissues that together perform specific functions; and organ systems, which are groups of organs that work together to perform specific functions.

Answers to Test Your Understanding

1. The primary structure that controls the biochemical composition of the cell contents is the cell membrane. Within the cell, the membranes of the endoplasmic reticulum partition the cell into chemically distinct areas. The canals of the endoplasmic reticulum and the Golgi body transport certain substances, separating them from the rest of the cell contents. Digestive enzymes are localized in lysosomes, while the enzymes for cellular respiration are localized within mitochondria. Diffusion, osmosis, facilitated diffusion, and active transport are processes that are involved in the movement of materials into and out of the cell and within the cell. Cyclosis is also involved in the movement of materials within the cell.

2. In diffusion, osmosis, and facilitated diffusion, the movement of substances is in the direction of the concentration gradient—from the area of greater concentration to the area of lesser concentration. In active transport, substances may be moved against the concentration gradient—from an area of lesser concentration to an area of greater concentration. Active transport requires the expenditure of cell energy, while passive transport does not.

3. The nucleus, mitochondria, and chloroplasts have the ability to duplicate themselves.

4. In colonial organisms, each cell carries on its own life processes, and the cells tend to be structurally alike. In multicellular organisms there are many different kinds of cells that may function together to form tissues, organs, and organ systems.

Chapter 6

Rationale

In this chapter, students are introduced to taxonomy and given an overview of the diversity of life. More detailed descriptions of each of the kingdoms and their major phyla are given in Unit 7.

The chapter begins with a section on the functions of classification systems and introduces the classification schemes of Aristotle, Theophrastus, John Ray, and Carolus Linnaeus. The classification categories and the binomial system of nomenclature are discussed, as are the five-kingdom system of classification, the species concept, and the use of taxonomic keys.

Audiovisual Materials

"Animal Classification," (11 min., color) UC.
"Characteristics of Plants and Animals," (10 min., color) IU.
"Classifying Plants and Animals," (11 min., color) Coronet.
"Great Names in Biology: Carolus Linnaeus," EBE.

Answers to Test Your Learning

1. The branch of biology that deals with the classification and naming of organisms is *taxonomy*.

2. A classification system enables biologists to identify an organism without having to check every organism in a large group.

3. Aristotle grouped animals according to the kind of environment in which they lived—air-dwellers, land-dwellers, and water-dwellers. *Theophrastus* grouped plants according to stem structure. Herbs were soft-stemmed plants, shrubs were plants with several woody stems, and trees were plants with a single woody stem. *John Ray* classified living organisms on the basis of structural similarities. *Linnaeus,* like Ray, used structural similarities as the basis for his classification system.

4. John Ray

5. species, genus, family, order, class, phylum, and kingdom

6. In binomial nomenclature, each organism is identified by a two-word Latin name—its genus name and a descriptive species name.

7. A taxonomic key consists of a series of paired statements, each describing a certain characteristic. By choosing from this series of paired characteristics, an unknown organism can be placed in successively smaller groups until, through a process of elimination, it is identified.

8. Modern taxonomists use similarities in biochemical makeup and patterns of embryonic development, as well as fossil evidence and structural similarities, in determining relationships between organisms.

9. A species is a group of organisms that can interbreed in nature.

10. Modern taxonomists have added new kingdoms to their classification systems to accommodate organisms that are not distinctly plants or animals.

11. The cells of Monera do not have an organized nucleus surrounded by a nuclear membrane. They also lack most of the other types of organelles found in the cells of other groups. The kingdom Monera includes the bacteria and blue-green algae.

12. The kingdom Protista includes unicellular and very simple multicellular organisms. Their cells contain a membrane-bounded nucleus and other types of organelles. The group includes the protozoa, some types of algae, and the euglena-like organisms.

13. Fungi are unicellular or multicellular organisms that cannot synthesize their own food. They are not capable of movement. Their cells contain a distinct nucleus and many types of organelles, and they are surrounded by a cell wall.

14. The plants have a tissue and organ level of organization, they generally carry on photosynthesis, and they are not capable of movement.

15. Animals must obtain food from the environment. They are complex multicellular organisms that can usually move about from place to place during at least some part of their life cycle.

Answers to Test Your Understanding

1.

	honeybee	sugar maple
Kingdom:	Animalia	Plantae
phylum:	Arthropoda	Tracheophyta
Class:	Insecta	Angiospermae
Order:	Hymenoptera	Sapindales
Family:	Apidae	Aceraceae
Genus:	*Apis*	*Acer*
Species:	*mellifera*	*saccharum*

2. Possible answers include pineapple, jellyfish, sea cucumber, sea horse, guinea pig, sow bug, and water flea.

3. All dogs are considered members of one species because they form a population of similar, interbreeding organisms.

4. The use of two Latin name enables biologists all over the world to know that they are referring to the same kind of organism.

Chapter 7

Rationale

This chapter deals with the release and transfer of energy in the cell. The pathways of anaerobic and aerobic respiration are simply and clearly presented. The chapter also discusses the efficiency of cellular respiration, the role of coenzymes, and catabolism and anabolism.

Audiovisual Materials

''Biochemistry and Molecular Structure,'' (22 min., color) Modern Learning Aids.

''Energy Cycles in the Cell,'' (16 min., color) McGraw-Hill.

''Pattern of Energy Transfer,'' (11 min., color or b&w) MGraw-Hill.

''The Chemical System of the Cell,'' (16 min., color) McGraw-Hill.

Answers to Test Your Learning

1. The burning of fuel is a chemical process in which carbon and hydrogen in the fuel combine with oxygen from the air to form carbon dioxide and water. Heat and light are given off. In burning, solid and liquid fuels are partially or completely converted to gases.

2. In living organisms the release of energy must take place in small steps because the release of heat would kill the cell, and even in small quantities, the cell cannot use heat for its energy needs.

3. *Cellular respiration* is the process by which the chemical energy in food is released and transferred and stored in particular compounds within the cell.

4. The part of the ATP molecule that is important in energy storage is the phosphate groups bonded to adenine and ribose. Two of the three phosphate groups have high-energy bonds, and it is the last phosphate group with its high-energy bond that is particularly important.

5. ATP has three phosphate groups, while ADP has only two.

6. A *phosphorylation reaction* is one in which there is a transfer of a phosphate group from one compound to another.

7. The energy released by cellular respiration is used to form ATP by the phosphorylation of ADP.

8. The amount of energy in a molecule of ATP is about the amount needed for the average chemical reaction in the cell.

9. *Oxidation* refers to any reaction where an atom or molecule loses electrons. *Reduction* refers to any reaction where an atom or molecule gains electrons.

10. In an oxidation-reduction reaction, one substance is oxidized, giving up electrons, and another substance is reduced, gaining electrons. There is also a transfer of energy, with the oxidized substance losing energy and the reduced substance gaining energy.

11. NAD and FAD

12. In anaerobic respiration, which occurs in the absence of oxygen, glucose is only partially broken down and relatively little energy is released. In aerobic respiration, which occurs in the presence of free oxygen, glucose is completely oxidized to carbon dioxide and water, and a maximum amount of energy is released.

13. In glycolysis, glucose is broken down into two molecules of PGAL, which are then converted to two molecules of pyruvic acid.

14. The initial reactions of glycolysis require the expenditure of two molecules of ATP. Four ATP are produced by the reactions of glycolysis, so there is a net gain of two ATP.

15. In fermentation, the pyruvic acid molecules produced by glycolysis are converted to some other end product with no further release of energy.

16. Oxygen serves as the final hydrogen acceptor in the reactions of cellular respiration. Its presence makes possible the complete oxidation of glucose with the release of its energy.

17. The reactions of the Krebs cycle occur in the mitochondria.

18. In the Krebs cycle pyruvic acid is broken down to carbon dioxide and hydrogen. The carbon dioxide goes off as waste gas and the hydrogen is picked up by the coenzymes NAD and FAD.

19. The electron transport chain involves a series of oxidation-reduction reactions.

20. In the electron transport chain, the electrons from the hydrogen atoms are passed from one compound to another. At three places along the chain, the electrons give up some energy and molecules of ATP are formed.

21. A total of 36ATP can be produced from one molecule of glucose.

22. Oxygen is the final hydrogen acceptor.

23. $C_6H_{12}O_6 + 6O_2 \rightarrow 6CO_2 + 6H_2O + 36ATP$

24. Anaerobic respiration produces a net gain of 2ATP, while aerobic respiration produces 36. Aerobic respiration is approximately 18 times more efficient.

25. Muscle cells can function for a short time without adequate oxygen. They release a smaller amount of energy and produce lactic acid.

26. *Oxygen debt* is the amount of oxygen needed to dispose of the lactic acid accumulated in the muscle cells.

27. Glycerol, fructose, and simple compounds produced from amino acids and fatty acids can enter the respiratory pathway.

28. *Catabolism* is the breakdown of complex substances in the body. *Anabolism* is the synthesis of materials needed in the organism.

Answers to Test Your Understanding

1. Fermentation results in a net gain of only 2ATP, while aerobic respiration results in a net gain of 36ATP. In fermentation, much of the energy of the original glucose molecule is still present in the molecules of the end product. In aerobic respiration, glucose is completely broken down.

2. Oxygen is the final hydrogen acceptor in aerobic respiration. If oxygen is not present, the reaction sequence cannot proceed to completion, and intermediate products accumulate.

3. In cellular respiration, energy released by the breakdown of food is used in the phosphorylation of ADP, producing ATP. The ATP is then used in the many reactions within the cell that require energy. In these reactions, the high-energy bond of the last phosphate group is broken, releasing energy and producing ADP. A phosphate group is again attached to the ADP by the reactions of cellular respiration, and the cycle continues.

4. NAD and FAD are coenzymes that serve as hydrogen acceptors in cellular respiration. When they pick up the hydrogen atoms, they are reduced, and also gain energy. NAD and FAD give up the hydrogen atoms and energy to the enzymes of the electron transport chain. Without these coenzymes, the reactions of cellular respiration could not proceed to completion.

5. During prolonged exercise, the muscles of the body do not receive adequate oxygen to fill their needs. Without oxygen, which is the final hydrogen acceptor in the electron transport chain, aerobic cellular respiration cannot occur. Instead, the pyruvic acid molecules produced by glycolysis act as hydrogen acceptors and are converted to lactic acid, which accumulates in the muscle cells, causing muscle fatigue. After physical activity ceases and oxygen again reaches the cells, lactic acid is broken down to carbon dioxide and water in the aerobic pathways.

Chapter 8

Rationale

In this chapter students learn about nutrients, the energy content of food, the differences between autotrophs and heterotrophs, and about digestion and why it is necessary.

A section on adaptations for nutrition compares the digestive processes in protozoa, hydra, the earthworm, and the grasshopper. The chapter concludes with a detailed discussion of the human digestive system.

Audiovisual Materials

"Digestion, (Part I) Mechanical," (17 min., b&w) UW.
"Digestion, (Part II) Chemical," (19 min., b&w) UW.
"Digestive System," (17 min., color) EBE.
"Digestive System," (12 min., color) FI.
"Digestive Systems of Animals," (15 min., color) IU.
"Food and Nutrition," (11 min., b&w) EBE.
"How the Body Uses Energy," (15 min., color) McGraw-Hill.
"Human Body: The Chemistry of Digestion," (15 min., color) Coronet.
"I Am Joe's Stomach," (26 min., color) Pyramid.
"William Beaumont," (23 min., color) UC.
"You're Too Fat," (52 min., color) FI.

Answers to Test Your Learning

1. *Nutrition* is the process by which organisms obtain food, change it into forms they can use to carry on their life processes, and transform it into living tissue. *Nutrients* are substances that can be used in metabolism.

2. The six types of necessary nutrients are proteins, carbohydrates, fats, vitamins, minerals, and water.

3. A *calorie* is the amount of heat needed to raise the temperature of 1 gram of water 1°C. A *kilocalorie* is 1,000 calories and is the amount of heat needed to raise the temperature of 1 kilogram of water 1°C.

4. The energy content of food is determined with a calorimeter. A food sample is burned in the calorimeter, and the amount of heat given off is measured.

5. One gram of fat releases 9 kilocalories of heat, while an equal amount of protein or carbohydrate liberates about 4 kilocalories.

6. *Autotrophs* are organisms that can synthesize the organic nutrients they need from simple inorganic substances. Most autotrophs are photosynthetic. *Chemotrophs* are autotrophs that do not use light as a source of energy, but instead obtain energy from certain chemical reactions. *Heterotrophs* are organisms that must obtain ready-made nutrients from other organisms.

7. Digestion is the process by which large food molecules are broken down into smaller molecules that can be used by the cells. Digestion is necessary because most food molecules are too large and complex to be used by the cells.

8. Mechanical breakdown increases the surface area of the food particles, which increases the area on which digestive enzymes can work.

9. In protozoa, digestion is intracellular. The ameba engulfs its food with pseudopods, and the food particle is incorporated into the cell in a food vacuole. The food vacuole fuses with a lysosome, and the digestive enzymes from the lysosome break down the food into usable forms. The products of digestion diffuse out of the food vacuole into the cytoplasm, where they are used. The indigestible contents of the food vacuole are expelled from the cell when the food vacuole fuses with the cell membrane.

In the paramecium, the movement of cilia sweeps food particles down the oral groove into the gullet, where they are incorporated into a food vacuole. The food vacuole fuses with a lysosome. Digestion takes place in the vacuole, and usable products of digestion diffuse into the cytoplasm. The indigestible material in the food vacuole is discharged from the cell through the anal pore.

10. The hydra uses its tentacles with their nematocysts to capture food and stuff it down the mouth into the gastrovascular cavity. Digestion is both extracellular and intracellular. Some cells in the endoderm secrete digestive enzymes into the gastrovascular cavity, where they partially break down food. Small food particles are then engulfed into endodermal cells where they are enclosed in food vacuoles. Digestion is completed by enzymes secreted into the food vacuoles. The end products of digestion diffuse out of the food vacuoles and into the cells of both the endoderm and ectoderm. Wastes from the endoderm cells diffuse back into the gastrovascular cavity and are carried out through the mouth by water currents. Wastes from the ectoderm cells diffuse directly into the surrounding water.

11. In the earthworm, food is pulled into the mouth by the sucking action of the muscular pharynx. From the pharynx, food passes through the esophagus into the crop, which functions as a storage chamber. Food is gradually released from the crop into the gizzard, a thick-walled structure that grinds the food. From the gizzard, the pastelike food passes into the intestine, where chemical digestion and absorption occur. The typhlosole increases the surface area of the intestine. Undigested materials, including soil, pass out of the worm through the anus.

12. mouth (and salivary glands), esophagus, crop, gizzard, stomach, intestine, rectum, and anus.

13. The human digestive system includes the mouth, pharynx (or throat), esophagus, stomach, small intestine, large intestine, rectum, and anus. Accessory digestive glands include the salivary glands, the liver, and the pancreas.

14. Mucus acts as a lubricant for the food so that it slides more easily through the digestive tube. It also protects the walls of the digestive tube from the action of acid, digestive enzymes, and abrasive substances in food.

15. Saliva wets the food and acts as a lubricant. It helps form the food particles into a mass. Ptyalin, or salivary amylase, is an enzyme that breaks down starch to maltose.

16. When food is sufficiently chewed, it is pushed by the tongue to the back of the throat. The swallowing reflex is initiated, and food passes from the throat into the esophagus. During swallowing, the larynx move up and is covered by the epiglottis. This blocks the trachea temporarily and keeps food from entering it. In breathing, air passes from the throat through the larynx, which is uncovered, and down the trachea to the lungs.

17. the esophagus

18. Food is moved down the digestive tube by *peristalsis,* the alternate waves of contraction and relaxation of muscles in the walls of the alimentary canal. The muscles in front of the food mass relax, while those behind it contract and push the food forward.

19. Glands of the stomach lining are *pyloric glands* and *gastric glands*. Pyloric glands secrete mucus and gastric glands secrete gastric juice, which contains hydrochloric acid and pepsin.

20. In the stomach, pepsin breaks down large protein molecules into shorter polypeptides. Ptyalin from the mouth works in the stomach for a short time (until it is inactivated by the acid), breaking down starch.

21. The flow of gastric juice is stimulated in several ways. The thought, smell, or taste of food stimulates the brain to send messages to the gastric glands to secrete gastric juice. Food touching the lining of the stomach stimulates secretion of gastric juice. The stomach lining is stimulated to secrete the hormone gastrin by the stretching of the stomach walls when food enters the stomach or by the presence of proteins, caffeine, alcohol, and other substances. Gastrin stimulates the gastric glands to secrete gastric juice.

22. The *cardiac sphincter* controls the passage of food from the esophagus into the stomach. The *pyloric sphincter* controls the passage of food from the stomach into the small intestine.

23. Bile, pancreatic juice, and intestinal juice mix with the food in the small intestine.

24. In the small intestine, peristalsis (1) squeezes chyme through the intestine, (2) mixes chyme with digestive enzymes, (3) breaks down food particles mechanically, and (4) speeds up the absorption of digestive end products by bringing them in contact with the intestinal wall.

25. Proteins are broken down into amino acids; carbohydrates are broken down into simple sugars; and fats are broken down into fatty acids and glycerol.

26. They are enzymes. Amylase breaks down starch to maltose; proteases break down proteins into amino acids; and lipases break down fats into fatty acids and glycerol.

27. Bile is secreted by the liver, stored in the gallbladder, and carried to the small intestine in the bile duct. In the small intestine, bile aids in the digestion of fats and oils by breaking them down into tiny droplets, a process called *emulsification*. Emulsification increases the surface area for enzyme action. Bile also aids in neutralizing the acid chyme from the stomach.

28. The end products of digestion are amino acids, simple sugars, fatty acids, and glycerol.

29. The small intestine is very long. Its lining has many folds and is covered with millions of microscopic, fingerlike projections called villi. The epithelial cells that make up the intestinal lining have tiny projections called microvilli that further increase the surface area.

30. Simple sugars, amino acids, vitamins, and minerals enter the capillaries of the villi. Fatty acids and glycerol are absorbed into the lacteals.

31. The large intestine is the site of reabsorption of water, absorption of vitamins produced by intestinal bacteria, and elimination of undigested and indigestible material from the digestive tract.

Answers to Test Your Understanding

1. Chewing increases the surface area on which digestive enzymes can act. If food is not properly chewed, digestion will be slower because there is less surface area for enzyme action.

2. In the mouth, ptyalin begins the breakdown of starch into maltose. Ptyalin is inactivated by the low pH of the stomach, and digestion of starch stops. In the small intestine, amylase in pancreatic juice breaks down the remaining starch. Enzymes secreted by the intestinal glands complete the digestion of carbohydrates by converting disaccharides, such as maltose, to monosaccharides.

3. If nutrients are not absorbed in the small intestine, they pass out of the body with the digestive wastes and never reach the cells of the body. If the body cells do not receive the nutrients they need, they die.

4. Although these glands are not part of the digestive tube—food does not pass through them—they secrete substances that do enter the digestive tube and play an important role in digestion.

5. Because most digestion and all absorption occur in the small intestine, removal of part or all of the stomach does not produce drastic effects. However, the amount of food the person could eat at one time would be limited.

Chapter 9

Rationale

Students are interested in the circulatory system and are eager to learn about it. Chapter 9 will stimulate discussion about heart attacks, arteriosclerosis, high blood pressure, strokes, and other cardiovascular diseases. Take advantage of the questions and examples the students bring up in class and discuss timely news articles. Teaching aids, such as models, overhead transparencies, films, and filmloops will be helpful.

This chapter begins with a discussion of transport in protists and hydra. Next, the closed circulatory system of the earthworm is compared with the open circulatory system of the grasshopper. The fact that in a large organism the circulatory system links the internal environment with the external environment is stressed.

The bulk of the chapter concerns the human circulatory system. The structure and function of the blood vessels and heart, the heartbeat cycle, control of the heartbeat, the flow of blood in the blood vessels, and blood pressure are explained. Next, the pulmonary and systemic circulations are discussed, with special attention given to the coronary, hepatic-portal, and renal circulations. The chapter concludes with a detailed section on the structure and function of the lymphatic system.

Audiovisual Materials

"Arteriosclerosis," (14 min., b&w) American Heart Association.

"Circulation," (16 min., color) UW.

"Heart and Circulation," (10 min., b&w) EBE.

"Heart and Circulatory System," (16 min., color) FI.

"The Heart: Attack," (27 min., color) CRM, McGraw-Hill.

"The Heart: Counterattack," (30 min., color) CRM, McGraw-Hill.

"The Human Body: Circulatory System," (16 min., color) Coronet.

"William Harvey and the Circulation of the Blood," (36 min., color) A.M.A.

"Work of the Heart," (19 min., color) EBE.

Answers to Test Your Learning

1. *Transport* refers to the processes by which substances pass into or out of cells and move within the organism. The two processes involved in transport are absorption and circulation.

2. The function of the circulatory system is to move materials from one part of the organism to another. It links the cells of the organism to the environment.

3. The basic parts of a circulatory system are a fluid, in which transported materials are dissolved, a network of tubes or spaces through which the fluid flows, and a pump, generally called a *heart*.

4. Diffusion, active transport, and cyclosis are involved in the circulation of materials in ameba and paramecium.

5. The cells of hydra obtain oxygen and get rid of wastes by diffusion. Nutrients pass into the cells by active transport and diffusion.

6. A *closed circulatory system* is one in which the blood is confined in vessels throughout the system.

7. In the earthworm, the heartlike aortic arches pump the blood from the dorsal blood vessel to the ventral blood vessel. The ventral blood vessel divides into smaller and smaller vessels that go to all parts of the body, eventually becoming capillaries. The capillaries join to form increasingly large vessels that carry the blood back to the dorsal blood vessel. The dorsal vessel contracts rhythmically, forcing the blood back into the aortic arches.

8. An *open circulatory system* is one in which the blood is not always enclosed in blood vessels. It flows into open spaces and bathes the tissues directly.

9. In the grasshopper, a tubular heart and a single blood vessel, the aorta, are located along the dorsal surface. Contraction of the heart forces the blood forward through the aorta toward the head. The blood flows out of the aorta and trickles through the body spaces (sinuses) and over the body tissues. Blood is kept moving through the sinuses by breathing movements and other body movements. The blood returns to the heart through valvelike openings.

10. *Arteries* carry blood away from the heart. The thick, elastic walls of arteries contain layers of connective tissue, muscle, and epithelial tissue. *Veins* return blood from the body tissues to the heart. The walls of veins are thin and only slightly elastic. Flaplike valves in the veins keep the blood flowing in only one direction—toward the heart. *Capillaries* connect the smallest arteries, the *arterioles,* with the smallest veins, the *venules*. The walls of capillaries consist of a single layer of epithelial cells. In the capillaries, dissolved nutrients, wastes, oxygen, and other substances are exchanged between the blood and the body cells.

11. The four chambers of the human heart are the right atrium, left atrium, right ventricle, and left ventricle. The right atrium receives deoxygenated blood from the body tissues and the left atrium receives oxygenated blood from the lungs. The right ventricle receives the deoxygenated blood from the right atrium and pumps it to the lungs, while the left ventricle receives the oxygenated blood from the left atrium and pumps it to the rest of the body.

12. The right atrioventricular valve, or tricuspid valve, is located between the right atrium and the right ventricle. The left atrioventricular valve, which is also known as the bicuspid or mitral valve, is located between the left atrium and the left ventricle. Both the right and left atrioventricular valves allow blood to flow from the atria into the ventricles, but prevent the flow of blood from the ventricles back into the atria. Each ventricle also contains a semilunar valve. The right semilunar valve allows blood to flow from the right ventricle into the pulmonary arteries, but blocks backflow into the heart. The left semilunar valve allows blood to flow from the left ventricle into the aorta, but prevents backflow from the aorta into the heart.

13. Blood from the body tissues enters the right atrium of the heart. From there it passes into the right ventricle. Contraction of the right ventricle sends the blood through the pulmonary arteries to the lungs, where it is oxygenated. Blood from the lungs is returned to the left atrium through the pulmonary veins. From the left atrium, blood enters the left ventricle, and is then pumped out through the aorta to all the tissues of the body.

14. The relaxation phase of the heartbeat cycle is *diastole*. During diastole the atrioventricular valves open, and blood flows from the atria into the ventricles. *Systole,* the period of contraction, begins with contraction of the atria, which forces more blood into the ventricles and then causes the ventricles to contract. The pressure of the contraction causes the A-V valves to close and the semilunar valves to open. Blood flows out of the right ventricle into the pulmonary arteries and out of the left ventricle into the aorta.

15. Heart muscle has an innate ability to contract. The sinoatrial node, or pacemaker, in the wall of the right atrium initiates an electrical signal that causes the atria to contract first, then the ventricles. The rate of the heartbeat is regulated by certain nerves that enter the pacemaker. Impulses from the vagus nerves slow down the pacemaker, while impulses from the cardioaccelerator nerves speed up the pacemaker. The innate rhythm of the heartbeat is also affected by changes in body temperature and by certain chemicals circulating in the blood.

16. The *pulse* is the alternate expansion (high pressure) and contraction (lower pressure) that can be felt in an artery each time the left ventricle contracts.

17. The *precapillary sphincters* control the blood flow through the capillaries.

18. Blood pressure is highest in the arteries and lowest in the veins.

19. The contraction of the ventricles forces the blood through the arteries. Between heartbeats, the elasticity of the artery walls helps to maintain the pressure and keep the blood flowing through the arteries.

The valves in the veins permit the blood to flow only in one direction—toward the heart. The blood is forced through the veins by contraction of skeletal muscles that press on the veins. Breathing movements also help to move the blood through the veins.

20. Blood from the right ventricle is carried by the pulmonary arteries to the lungs. In the lungs the arteries branch into capillaries, and the capillaries merge into pulmonary veins, which return the blood to the left atrium of the heart.

21. The *pulmonary circulation* carries blood that is low in oxygen and high in carbon dioxide from the right ventricle to the lungs, where it gains oxygen and gets rid of carbon dioxide; the oxygenated blood is then returned to the heart to be pumped out to the rest of the body.

22. The *systemic circulation* serves all parts of the body.

23. The *coronary circulation* supplies blood to the heart muscle. The *hepatic-portal circulation* carries blood from the digestive tract to the liver and helps to maintain the blood glucose concentration at a constant level. The *renal circulation* carries blood to and from the kidneys so that wastes can be removed.

24. The *intercellular fluid* is the colorless, watery fluid that bathes all the cells of the body. It is formed from the blood plasma that passes out of the capillaries.

25. The lymphatic system consists of a system of lymphatic vessels and lymph nodes. The smallest lymphatic vessels are the lymphatic capillaries, which arise in the body tissues. These capillaries merge to form larger and larger lymph vessels. Eventually, two large lymph vessels empty into large veins in the neck. At various places along the lymphatic vessels are lymph nodes.

26. The lymphatic system returns the intercellular fluid to the blood. The lymph nodes filter foreign substances from the lymph before they get into the bloodstream. They also produce lymphocytes, which can destroy bacteria and other foreign substances.

Answers to Test Your Understanding

1. In a closed system, the blood is under pressure and moves rapidly to all parts of the animal to provide the tissues with oxygen and nutrients and get rid of cellular wastes. In an open system, the blood is under much less pressure and moves more slowly. This type of system is only efficient enough to meet the needs of small animals, such as insects.

2. Humans have a closed circulatory system consisting of arteries, veins, and capillaries and a four-chambered heart. The grasshopper, on the other hand, has an open circulatory system consisting of a single blood vessel, the aorta, and a tubular heart. In this system, blood pumped by the heart flows through the aorta and then out into body spaces to bathe the tissues. In humans, the blood remains within the vessels.

3. When the walls of the arteries lose their elasticity, the blood pressure increases. This puts a strain on both the heart and blood vessels and, if untreated, can lead to heart attacks and strokes.

4. In the capillaries, some of the liquid part of the blood diffuses out of the capillaries and becomes the intercellular fluid. The constant loss of fluid would drain the circulatory system and flood the body tissues if the fluid were not returned to the circulatory system. The lymphatic system returns excess intercellular fluid to the blood, keeping the blood volume constant.

5. Blood flows from the capillaries in the right big toe into venules and then into larger and larger veins until it reaches the inferior vena cava. From the inferior vena cava, the blood travels through the right atrium, into the right ventricle, and then through the pulmonary arteries into the lungs and into the pulmonary capillaries. From the pulmonary capillaries, the blood travels through the pulmonary veins to the left atrium of the heart. From the left atrium, the blood passes into the left ventricle and is pumped out of the heart through the aorta. The blood travels through smaller and smaller arteries and then flows through arterioles into the capillaries of the right big toe.

Chapter 10

Rationale

Students are generally interested in the blood, as well as the rest of the circulatory system. Chapter 10 will stimulate discussion about such topics as anemia, leukemia, hemophilia, blood clots, immunity, arthritis, allergies, cancer, transplants, transfusions, and Rh factors. Recent developments in these fields are often covered in newspapers, news magazines, and science magazines. Such articles can be used to stimulate both general student interest and interest in further research on a particular topic.

The chapter begins with sections on the composition of blood, and includes detailed discussions of the plasma, red cells, white cells, and platelets. Following sections deal with blood clotting and clotting problems.

In the sections on immunity, the student will learn about Edward Jenner's contribution to disease control, about how immunity works, and about different types of immunity. The material on the immune system and transplants is of particular interest to students. The closing sections of the chapter concern the human blood groups, with discussion of the ABO blood groups and transfusions and the Rh factors and their associated problems.

Audiovisual Materials

''Infectious Diseases and Natural Body Defenses,'' (11 min., color) Coronet.
''Pulse of Life,'' (24 min., color) American Red Cross.
''Secret of the White Cell,'' (30 min., b&w) UC, IU.
''The Blood,'' (16 min., color) EBE.
''Work of the Blood,'' (14 min., color) EBE.

Answers to Test Your Learning

1. Blood transports respiratory gases, nutrients, regulatory substances, and cellular wastes to and from all parts of the body. It helps to regulate all body functions by maintaining and regulating the chemical state, pH, and water content of cells and body fluids. Blood is involved in the regulation of body temperature, and it also protects the body from disease-causing microorganisms.

2. The liquid portion of the blood, the plasma, consists mainly of water, and contains dissolved proteins, salts, glucose, amino acids, fatty acids, vitamins, hormones, and cellular wastes.

3. The *red blood cells,* or *erythrocytes,* are disk-shaped cells that are thinner in the center than around the rim. They do not contain a nucleus when mature. Red blood cells transport oxygen from the lungs to the body tissues and carbon dioxide from the body tissues to the lungs.

4. *Hemoglobin* is a red, iron-containing pigment that is found in red blood cells and that increases the oxygen-carrying capacity of the blood.

5. *White blood cells,* or *leukocytes,* are larger than red cells and contain one or more nuclei. They can leave the blood and move through the body tissues by ameboid motion. White cells protect the body against infection.

6. A *phagocyte* is a white blood cell that engulfs microorganisms and other foreign materials in the same way as an ameba engulfs food.

7. *Platelets* are small, round or oval fragments of a type of blood cell. They consist of bits of cytoplasm surrounded by a membrane; a platelet does not contain a nucleus. Platelets help to trigger the blood-clotting process and to fill the wound.

8. Clotting is initiated by the release of a substance (thromboplastin) by the injured tissues. Platelets coming in contact with the injured blood vessel walls stick to them. The platelets secrete a substance that makes other platelets sticky, and a solid plug begins to form in the wound. A series of reactions converts the plasma protein prothrombin to thrombin, an enzyme that in turn converts the plasma protein fibrinogen to insoluble strands of fibrin. The fibrin strands along with the platelets and trapped red cells fill the wound. The mass is the clot, and when water evaporates, it forms a scab.

9. The smoothness of the inner walls of blood vessels and the presence of anticoagulants in the blood (e.g., heparin and antithrombin) prevent clots from forming in the circulating blood.

10. Hemophilia is a hereditary disease in which the blood does not clot properly because it is missing certain necessary factors.

11. The body's defenses against disease include: (1) the skin, which keeps microorganisms out of the body, and stomach acid, which kills organisms in food; (2) phagocytes, which engulf and destroy microorganisms that enter the body tissues; and (3) immunity, which is the ability of the body to resist infection by a particular microorganism.

12. The basis of immunity lies in the body's ability to distinguish between its own cells and molecules and foreign cells and molecules.

13. An *antigen* is any substance that can cause an immune response.

14. When B lymphocytes are activated by an antigen, they divide to produce plasma cells and memory cells. The plasma cells secrete antibodies that react with the antigens and inactivate them. The memory cells remain in the lymphoid tissue and provide immunity against future infection. When T lymphocytes are stimulated by an antigen, they undergo cell division, forming more lymphocytes sensitive to that antigen. Some of these sensitized T lymphocytes remain as memory cells; most, however, pass into the circulatory system and migrate throughout the body tissues. When these T lymphocytes come in contact with the antigen to which they are sensitive, they combine with it and destroy it.

15. *Inborn immunity* is present at birth. *Acquired immunity* is immunity that develops over a lifetime.

16. *Active acquired immunity* is the result of having a disease or having received a vaccine against that disease. The body produces its own antibodies and/or sensitized lymphocytes to attack a particular antigen.

17. In *passive acquired immunity,* a person is given antibodies obtained from the blood of either another person or an animal. Thus, passive immunity is ''borrowed'' immunity.

18. *Autoimmune diseases* are diseases that occur when a person's immune system breaks down, and antibodies and sensitized lymphocytes develop in response to the body's own tissue antigens.

19. An *allergy* is an immune response caused by the production of antibodies against antigens that do not bother most people.

20. Rejection of transplanted organs occurs when the recipient's immune system recognizes the organ as ''foreign'' and produces antibodies and sensitized lymphocytes against it. The transplanted organ is then destroyed by the recipient's immune response.

21. Agglutination occurs when the wrong blood types are mixed. Antibodies in the blood plasma react with antigens on the transfused cells, causing the cells to clump together.

22. Blood type A has A antigens on the red cells and anti-B antibodies in the plasma. Blood type B has B antigens on the red cells and anti-A antibodies in the plasma. Blood type AB has both A and B antigens on the red cells and no antibodies in the plasma. Blood type O has no antigens on the red cells and both anti-A and anti-B antibodies in the plasma.

23. Type A blood can receive types A and O. Type B blood can receive types B and O. Type AB can receive types A, B, AB, and O. Type O blood can receive type O.

24. An Rh+ blood type is one in which the red blood cells contain one or more of the Rh factors that can cause a transfusion reaction.

25. The Rh factor is a problem during pregnancy when the mother is Rh− but the child has inherited Rh+ blood from the father. There is no problem with the first pregnancy, but in later pregnancies with an Rh+ baby, antibodies from the mother's blood may enter the baby's blood and destroy the baby's red blood cells.

Answers to Test Your Understanding

1. By injecting the allergy-causing antigen in gradually increasing amounts, the person becomes desensitized to the antigen. The body develops a tolerance to the antigen.

2. The chances of a clot forming within the circulatory system are increased just after surgery because the walls of some of the injured blood vessels may release substances that initiate the clotting process.

3. Transplants between identical twins are generally successful because their tissue proteins are almost identical so that no immune response is initiated by the body of the recipient.

4. The blood of an Rh− person does not originally contain anti-Rh antibodies. The first time Rh+ blood enters the circulation of an Rh− person, it stimulates production of anti-Rh antibodies, but there is no transfusion reaction. However, the second time Rh+ blood is given, the anti-Rh antibodies are present in the blood, and an antigen-antibody reaction occurs.

5. A vaccine consists of dead or weakened bacteria or viruses or modified bacterial toxins. It stimulates the immune system to produce antibodies or activated lymphocytes against the disease-causing organism or toxin, but it is not strong enough to cause disease symptoms in the recipient.

Chapter 11

Rationale

Chapter 11 begins with a general discussion of respiration and the characteristics of a respiratory surface. Adaptations for respiration in the protozoa, hydra, earthworm, grasshopper, and animals with gills are presented. The problems of respiration in large multicellular animals and the importance of respiratory pigments are also discussed in some detail.

Next the focus shifts to the human respiratory system. The pathway of air is discussed, with an emphasis on the structure and function of the parts of the system. The four phases of human respiration are covered. You may wish to review aspects of the circulatory system that are important in respiration. The ways in which oxygen and carbon dioxide are transported in the blood are also studied.

The chapter ends with a discussion of diseases of the respiratory system. This affords the teacher an opportunity to discuss and emphasize the harmful effects of cigarette smoking on health. Some teachers may also wish to discuss certain aspects of air pollution here, where the direct effects on the respiratory system can be stressed.

Audiovisual Materials

"Mechanics of Life Series: Breathing and Respiration," (8 min., color) BFA.
"Respiration in Man," (25 min., color) EBE.
"Smoking/Emphysema: A Fight for Breath," (12 min., color) McGraw-Hill.
"The Human Body: Respiratory System," (12 min., color) Coronet.
"The Lungs and Respiratory System," (17 min., color) EBE.
"The Nose (Structure and Function)," (11 min., color) EBE.

Answers to Test Your Learning

1. Respiration is the exchange of oxygen and carbon dioxide between a living organism and the environment.

2. The respiratory surface is the surface through which gas exchange takes place. It must be thin-walled, moist, and in contact with an environmental source of oxygen; in large organisms, it must be in close contact with the transport system.

3. The direction of movement of gases across the respiratory surface is determined by the concentration gradient across the surface.

4. The respiratory surface in protozoa is the cell membrane. Oxygen dissolved in the water diffuses through the cell membrane into the cytoplasm. Carbon dioxide diffuses out of the cytoplasm through the cell membrane into the surrounding water.

5. In hydra, gas exchange takes place by direct diffusion between the body cells and the environment.

6. Aquatic animals must move large volumes of water over their respiratory surfaces because the concentration of dissolved oxygen in water is much lower than the concentration of oxygen in air and because diffusion is much slower in water than in air.

7. Hemoglobin transports oxygen and carbon dioxide between the respiratory surface and the body cells. It increases the capacity of the blood to carry oxygen and carbon dioxide.

8. The respiratory surface of the earthworm is the moist skin. Oxygen from the air in the soil diffuses through the moist skin into the blood of the skin capillaries. It is transported by the hemoglobin-containing blood to the cells of the body. At the body cells, the oxygen diffuses out of the blood, while carbon dioxide from the cells diffuses into the blood. In the capillaries of the skin, the carbon dioxide diffuses out of the blood, through the skin, and into the environment.

9. The respiratory system of the grasshopper consists of a system of branching air tubes called *tracheae*, or *tracheal tubes*. Air enters and leaves the system through ten pairs of openings called *spiracles*. Air enters the body through the first four pairs of spiracles. From each spiracle, the tracheae branch repeatedly into smaller and smaller tubes. The fluid-filled ends of these microscopic air tubes are in direct contact with the body cells and are the actual respiratory surface. In the ends of these tubes, oxygen diffuses from the tracheae into the body cells, and carbon dioxide diffuses from the body cells into the tracheae. The air is squeezed out of the tracheae through the six posterior pairs of spiracles. Air is pumped into and out of the tracheal system by the contraction of the grasshopper's muscles.

10. Gills are the respiratory organs of many aquatic animals, including fish, clams, and lobsters. They are thin filaments of skin that are richly supplied with blood vessels. As water passes over the gills, dissolved oxygen diffuses from the water across the thin gill surface, and into the blood, which transports it to all parts of the body. Carbon dioxide from the body cells diffuses out of the blood in the gills and into the water.

11. The lungs occupy a large portion of the chest cavity. They are separated from the abdominal cavity by the diaphragm, which forms the floor of the chest cavity.

12. Large foreign particles are blocked by the hairs at the openings of the nostrils; mucus on the walls of the nasal passages traps bacteria, dust, and other small particles in the air and also moistens the air; and the blood in the capillaries of the nasal passages warms the inhaled air.

13. The larynx, or voice box, is located in the neck and connects the pharynx with the trachea.

14. Air travels from the nasal passages through the pharynx, larynx, trachea, bronchi, bronchial tubes, and bronchioles into the alveoli.

15. The walls of the alveoli are the respiratory surface of the lungs.

16. Smoking paralyzes the cilia of the respiratory tract and increases the production of mucus, resulting in a smoker's cough. The particles in the smoke can eventually break down the walls of the air sacs and cause the formation of inelastic, scarlike tissue, which greatly reduces the functional area of the respiratory system.

17. The four phases of respiration in humans are *breathing, external respiration, circulation,* and *internal respiration*.

18. During inhalation, the ribs are pulled up and out, the diaphragm is pulled downward, and the chest cavity is enlarged. Because the pressure within the chest cavity is reduced, external air rushes down the air passages into the air sacs, forcing the lungs to expand. During exhalation, the diaphragm relaxes and pushes upward and the rib muscles relax, causing the ribs to drop. This decreases the size of the chest cavity and increases the pressure on the lungs, causing the air to be squeezed out of the lungs.

19. Breathing moves air into and out of the lungs.

20. The rate of breathing is mainly determined by the concentration of carbon dioxide in the blood. The acidity of the blood also affects the breathing rate. Breathing is controlled by the respiratory center of the brain.

21. External respiration is the exchange of respiratory gases between the air and the blood in the lungs. Internal respiration is the exchange of respiratory gases between the blood and the body cells.

22. In the lungs, where the oxygen concentration is high, hemoglobin combines with oxygen to form oxyhemoglobin. When the blood reaches the capillaries of the body, where the oxygen concentration of the tissues is low, the oxyhemoglobin breaks down into oxygen and hemoglobin. The oxygen diffuses out of the blood and into the body cells.

23. In the capillaries, carbon dioxide from the body cells diffuses into the blood. About 70 percent of the carbon dioxide in the blood is in the form of bicarbonate ions that are dissolved in the plasma; about 20 percent is in the form of carboxyhemoglobin in the red cells, and about 10 percent is in solution in the plasma. In the lungs, the carbon dioxide diffuses out of the blood and into the lungs and is exhaled from the body.

24. *Asthma* is a severe allergic reaction in which contraction of the bronchioles makes breathing difficult. *Bronchitis* is an inflammation of the linings of the bronchial tubes. The condition is generally marked by severe coughing and difficulty in breathing. *Emphysema* is a condition in which the lungs lose their elasticity. It is characterized by shortness of breath and extreme difficulty in breathing. *Pneumonia* is a condition in which the alveoli become filled with fluid, preventing the exchange of gases in the lungs. *Lung cancer* is a disease in which tumors form in the lungs as a result of irregular and uncontrolled cell growth.

Answers to Test Your Understanding

1. The respiratory surface in land-dwelling animals is located within the body to keep it moist and protect it from drying out. An internal respiratory surface would not be suitable for a fish because large quantities of water must pass over the respiratory surface of aquatic animals to provide adequate oxygen. If the respiratory surface were internal, these large quantities of water would have to pass through the body of the fish.

2. *Cellular respiration* is the process by which nutrient molecules are broken down for the release of energy. *Breathing* is the movement of respiratory gases into and out of the lungs. *Internal respiration* is the exchange of respiratory gases between the blood in the capillaries and the body cells. *External respiration* is the exchange of respiratory gases between the air and the blood in the lungs.

3. Oxygen enters the body through the nostrils and passes through the nasal passages, the pharynx, larynx, trachea, bronchus, and bronchial tube into an alveolus. It diffuses through the wall of the alveolus and into a capillary, through the blood plasma and into a red blood cell, where it is bound to a hemoglobin molecule, forming oxyhemoglobin. The red cell travels from the capillary into a pulmonary vein, which carries it to the left atrium of the heart. From the left atrium it passes into the left ventricle and then into the aorta. It then passes through smaller and smaller arteries, through an arteriole, and into a capillary near a body cell. The oxyhemoglobin releases the oxygen molecule. It passes out of the red cell, into the blood plasma, through the capillary wall, into the intercellular fluid, and through the cell membrane into a body cell.

4. If you hold your breath, the oxygen concentration in the blood drops and the carbon dioxide concentration rises. If you breathe deeply and rapidly, the oxygen level in the blood rises and the carbon dioxide level drops.

Chapter 12

Rationale

Chapter 12 discusses the role of excretory structures in the maintenance of homeostasis. The chapter begins with a definition of excretion and a description of the major metabolic wastes. Next, adaptations for excretion in protozoa, hydra, the earthworm, and the grasshopper are covered.

The focus then shifts to excretion in humans. The excretory role of the liver in detoxification, bile formation, and deamination and urea formation is examined. The anatomy of the urinary system and the structure and function of the kidneys are presented. Students usually have difficulty understanding the mechanism of urine formation. Stress the importance of the kidneys in maintaining the composition of the blood and other body fluids. The excretory role of the lungs is examined briefly, and the chapter ends with a detailed discussion of the structure and functions of the skin.

Audiovisual Materials

"Kidneys," (11 min., color) FI.

"Regulating Body Temperature," (22 min., color) EBE.

"The Human Body: Excretory System," (13 min., color) Coronet.

"The Work of the Kidneys," (20 min., color) EBE.

Answers to Test Your Learning

1. *Excretion* is the process by which the wastes of cellular metabolism are removed from an organism.

2. The major metabolic wastes are carbon dioxide, water, nitrogenous wastes, and mineral salts. Carbon dioxide and water are produced by cellular respiration. Water is produced by reactions involving dehydration synthesis. Nitrogenous wastes (ammonia, urea, and uric acid) are produced by the breakdown of amino acids. Mineral salts accumulate from various metabolic processes.

3. The metabolic wastes of protozoa include carbon dioxide, mineral salts, and ammonia. These wastes diffuse through the cell membrane into the surrounding watery environment.

4. In freshwater protozoans, water balance is maintained by contractile vacuoles. Excess water collects in the contractile vacuoles and is periodically ejected from the cell, a process involving active transport.

5. The body of the hydra is only two cell layers thick. Wastes diffuse through the cell membranes directly into the surrounding water.

6. The excretory organs of the earthworm are the *nephridia*. Some of the cellular wastes diffuse directly into the fluid in the body cavity. The fluid enters the funnel-like openings of the nephridia and is moved through them by the beating of cilia. As the fluid passes through the tubules of the nephridia, useful substances are reabsorbed into the blood. At the same time, wastes from the bloodstream pass out of the capillaries into the nephridia. The wastes in the nephridia are discharged through the *nephridiopores* as a dilute urine. The excreted wastes include water, mineral salts, ammonia, and urea. Carbon dioxide is excreted through the moist skin.

7. The excretory organs of the grasshopper are the *Malpighian tubules*. These slender tubules are bathed by the blood in the body spaces. Wastes from the blood enter the tubules by diffusion and active transport and then pass into the intestine. Useful substances are reabsorbed both in the tubules and in the digestive tract, and are returned to the body fluids. The dry nitrogenous waste, uric acid, is eliminated with the feces through the anus. Carbon dioxide diffuses from the body tissues into the tracheal tubes and leaves the body through the spiracles.

8. Although toxic to cells, ammonia is highly soluble in water. In aquatic organisms, ammonia is quickly diluted so that it does not reach toxic levels. Uric acid, on the other hand, requires almost no water. Thus it helps to conserve water in land animals whose water supply is limited.

9. The liver carries out detoxification, the removal of toxic substances from the blood. The cells of the liver synthesize bile, which contains part of the hemoglobin molecule from broken-down red blood cells. And finally, the liver breaks down excess amino acids. The amino groups are converted to ammonia, which is quickly converted to urea.

10. *Deamination* is the process by which amino groups are removed from amino acids and converted to ammonia.

11. Excess amino acids are not stored, but are broken down. The amino group is converted to ammonia and then urea, while the rest of the molecule is converted to pyruvic acid or glycogen.

12. The kidneys remove the wastes of cellular metabolism from the blood and regulate the composition of body fluids.

13. The functional units of the kidneys are the *nephrons*.

14. In filtration, substances such as water, salts, urea, glucose, and amino acids, pass from the glomerulus into the Bowman's capsule of the nephron.

15. In reabsorption, useful substances pass out of the nephron and back into the blood in the surrounding capillaries. Reabsorption is an energy-requiring process.

16. The fluid remaining after reabsorption is called *urine*. Urine consists of water, urea, and salts.

17. Urine passes out of the kidneys through the ureters to the bladder and is discharged from the bladder through the urethra.

18. The lungs serve to excrete carbon dioxide and water (in the form of water vapor) from the body.

19. The outer layer of the skin is the *epidermis* and the inner layer is the *dermis*.

20. The sebaceous glands produce an oily secretion that keeps the skin and hair soft and pliable and provides a protective coating. The sweat glands produce perspiration. The evaporation of perspiration helps to lower the body temperature.

21. The four functions of the skin are protection, excretion, regulation of body temperature, and detection of pain, touch, pressure, and temperature.

Answers to Test Your Understanding

1. The liver, kidneys, lungs, and skin regulate the chemical makeup of the blood and other body fluids by removing metabolic wastes and excess substances. The liver purifies the blood, synthesizes and excretes bile, and deaminates amino acids. The kidneys filter metabolic wastes and various other substances from the blood. The lungs excrete carbon dioxide and water vapor. The skin excretes small amounts of urea and salt in perspiration and regulates body temperature.

2. As blood flows through the glomerulus within the Bowman's capsule, water containing many substances is forced out of the glomerulus and into the capsule. As this filtrate passes through the long tubule of the nephron most of the water, all the glucose and amino acids, and many of the salt ions are reabsorbed. They are returned to the blood in the capillary network that surrounds the tubule. The wastes and some of the water that remains in the tubule pass into the collecting duct and form the urine.

3. Excess heat is lost when the blood vessels of the skin dilate, increasing the blood supply and causing a flushed appearance. Heat from the blood is radiated into the air. There is also an increase in sweating, and the evaporation of sweat produces a cooling effect.

4. To conserve heat, the blood vessels of the skin constrict, reducing the blood supply to the surface of the skin and retaining the heat within the body. Sweating is reduced. Shivering and muscle tension increase heat production by the muscles, which warms the body.

Chapter 13

Rationale

This chapter looks at the problems of support and locomotion. It begins with a discussion of the advantages of locomotion and a comparison of exoskeletons and endoskeletons. Next, adaptations for locomotion in protists, hydra, the earthworm, and the grasshopper are presented.

The remainder of the chapter deals with the human musculoskeletal system. The functions of bones are discussed, followed by a description of their structure. The parts of the human skeleton are described with an emphasis on the major bones that make up the axial and appendicular skeletons; this is followed by a description of the types of joints in the skeleton. The chapter ends with a discussion of the structure and function of skeletal muscle, including the sliding-filament theory of muscle contraction, and how movement is accomplished in humans.

Audiovisual Materials

"Muscle: A Study of Integration," (25 min., color) CRM.

"Muscle: Chemistry of Contraction," (15 min., color) EBE.

"Muscle: Dynamics of Contraction," (22 min., color) EBE.

"Muscle: Electrical Activity of Contraction," (9 min., color) EBE.

"The Human Body: Muscular System," (11 min., color) Coronet.

"The Human Body: Skeletal System," (12 min., color) Coronet.

"The Skeleton," (17 min., color) EBE.

Answers to Test Your Learning

1. *Locomotion* is the ability of an organism to move around on its own from one place to another. Locomotion increases the opportunities for organisms to obtain food, find suitable places to live, escape enemies, and find mates.

2. Exoskeletons provide good protection for the soft inner parts of the body and they function in locomotion. But because they cannot grow, they must be periodically molted and replaced by a new exoskeleton. Just after molting and until the new skeleton hardens, the animal is in a very vulnerable condition. Although endoskeletons do not protect the entire animal as well as exoskeletons, they do grow without the problem of molting and they function well in locomotion.

3. The ameba moves by means of pseudopods, which are extensions of the cell surface. The flowing of the cytoplasm from the rear end of the cell into the pseudopod results in locomotion.

4. In ciliated protists, the rhythmic, oarlike beating of the many short cilia propels the organism through the water. In flagellates, the whiplike movements of long, hairlike flagella pull the organism through the water.

5. The hydra can move by: gliding along on its base; somersaulting its base completely over its tentacles; attaching its tentacles to an object and then pulling its base over; producing an air bubble on its base and floating in the water.

6. In locomotion in the earthworm, setae in the rear of the worm hook into the ground and the circular muscles of the body contract, lengthening the body and extending the worm forward. Then the setae near the front of the worm anchor into the ground, and the setae in the rear relax. The longitudinal muscles contract, shortening the body and pulling the hind end of the worm forward. The fluid-filled body cavity acts as a fluid skeleton, stiffening the body and allowing the muscles to push the worm through the soil.

7. In the grasshopper, the short and comparatively delicate first two pairs of legs are used in walking. The third pair of legs is much longer and more powerful and is used in jumping. The hard, outer pair of wings protect the delicate inner pair of wings, which is used in flying.

8. Bones serve as sites of attachment for skeletal muscles and as levers that produce movement of body parts when muscles contract. Bones give the body its general shape and support body structures. They protect delicate body parts and serve as storage sites for minerals.

9. *Osteoblasts* are bone cells that secrete collagen and various polysaccharides. The polysaccharides bind the collagen fibers together, and bone is formed when calcium phosphate crystals precipitate in the mass of collagen.

10. *Osteocytes* are osteoblasts that are trapped in small cavities in the bone material.

11. The *periosteum* is a tough membrane that covers the outside of bones except at the ends where bones connect. It functions in the production of new bone for growth and repair. It also serves as the point of attachment for muscles to bones.

12. Red marrow produces red blood cells, platelets, and some types of white blood cells. In adults, it is found in the spongy bone of the vertebrae, ribs, sternum, cranium, and long bones.

13. *Ossification* is the process by which cartilage is converted to bone by the gradual deposition of minerals.

14. The axial skeleton includes the skull, vertebrae, ribs, and sternum. The appendicular skeleton includes the arms, legs, pectoral girdle (shoulder blades and collar bones), and the pelvic girdle (pelvic bones).

15. A *joint* is a point in the skeleton where bones meet.

16. The five types of joints are: *immovable* (cranium); *hinge joint* (elbow, knee); *ball-and-socket joint* (shoulder, hip); *pivot joint* (between skull and spine); and *gliding joint* (between vertebrae).

17. Bones are held together at movable joints by tough, fibrous bands of connective tissue called *ligaments*.

18. Striated muscle is involved in locomotion and all other voluntary movements.

19. Striated muscle is made up of bundles of muscle fibers bound together by connective tissue. Muscle fibers are made up of smaller fibers that, in turn, are made up of two types of protein filaments. There is a relatively thick type of filament composed of myosin and a thin type of filament composed of actin. The ends of the two types of filaments overlap in such a way as to produce the characteristic striped appearance of striated muscle.

20. During muscle contraction, the actin and myosin filaments slide over one another, increasing the amount of overlap between them and shortening the fiber. Cross bridges between filaments allow the fiber to exert a pull.

21. The source of energy for muscle contraction is ATP.

22. Skeletal muscles are connected to bones by strong fibers of connective tissue called *tendons*.

23. Muscles work in antagonistic pairs because a muscle can exert pull when it contracts, but it cannot push when it relaxes. Thus, contraction of one muscle can move a part of the body in one direction, but another muscle must be involved to move that part in the opposite direction.

24. A *flexor* is a muscle that bends, or flexes, a joint. An *extensor* is a muscle that straightens a joint.

25. *Muscle tone* is the state of partial contraction in which muscles are normally kept.

26. Smooth muscle is made up of distinct, elongated cells that overlap to form sheets of muscle.

Answers to Test Your Understanding

1. In grasshoppers, the muscles of the legs are attached to the inside of the exoskeleton. The muscles of the joints function in antagonistic pairs, one bending the joint and the other extending it. In humans, the skeletal muscles are attached to the bones of the endoskeleton. At movable joints, the muscles function in antagonistic pairs, one bending the joint and the other extending it. Thus, in both grasshoppers and humans the principles involved in moving parts, such as the legs, are the same.

2. Striated muscle is striped because of the repeating, overlapping arrangement of the thick and thin (myosin and actin) filaments that make it up. When the muscle fiber contracts, the bands move closer together as the overlap between filaments increases.

3. When a bone is broken, the osteocytes become active, producing new bone tissue.

4. The bones of children contain more cartilage than the bones of older people and this makes them more flexible and less easily broken. Also, in older people the bones may become more brittle through loss of calcium.

Chapter 14

Rationale

Chapter 14 begins with an introduction to the functions of nervous regulation and the roles of sense organs, nerve cells, and effectors. Next, the structure of neurons and types of neurons and nerves are covered. The nerve impulse is given expanded treatment. Use the drawings in the chapter to assist students in understanding the electrochemical state of the resting neuron and the changes associated with the transmission of impulses. Emphasize the identical nature of all nerve impulses and that stimuli of different strengths affect the frequency of impulses and the number of neurons that fire. Stress that it is the brain that analyzes and interprets the impulses it receives.

Transmission at the synapse is also given expanded treatment. Students will be particularly interested in learning how various drugs affect synaptic transmission.

The chapter ends with a discussion of the adaptations for nervous regulation in the protozoa, hydra, earthworm, and grasshopper. Compare the nervous systems of the earthworm and grasshopper.

Audiovisual Materials

"Drugs and the Nervous System," (18 min.) Churchill.
"Fundamentals of the Nervous System," (17 min., color) EBE.
"Nervous Systems in Animals," (17 min., color) IU.
"The Nerve Impulse," (22 min., color) EBE.
"The Nervous System—Coelenterates to Vertebrates," (28 min., color) McGraw-Hill.

Answers to Test Your Learning

1. The nervous system and endocrine system are involved in the regulation and coordination of responses.

2. *Irritability* is the capacity of a cell to respond to change.

3. A true nervous system includes *sense organs, nerve cells,* and *effectors*.

4. A *receptor,* or *sense organ,* is a specialized structure that is sensitive to certain changes, physical forces, or chemicals in the internal or external environment. Stimulation of a particular receptor causes impulses to be transmitted over a particular nerve pathway. Examples of receptors are the eyes, ears, taste buds, and pressure, touch, pain, and temperature receptors in the skin.

5. The two types of effectors are muscles and glands. In response to stimuli, muscles contract and glands either increase or decrease their rate of secretion.

6. A *stimulus* is any factor that causes a receptor to trigger impulses in a nerve pathway.

7. The brain, which is a specialized group of nerve cells, controls and coordinates the activities of the nervous system.

8. A nerve cell consists of *dendrites,* a *cell body,* and an *axon.* The dendrites are short, highly branched fibers that receive impulses and conduct them toward the cell body. The cell body, or cyton, contains the nucleus and cell organelles. It carries out most of the metabolic activities of the nerve cell and controls the growth of the cell. The axon is a long, thin fiber that extends from the cell body and carries impulses away from the cell body to other neurons or to effectors.

9. The *synapse* is the junction between the terminal branch of one neuron and the membrane of the adjoining neuron.

10. *Sensory neurons* carry impulses from receptors toward the spinal cord and brain. *Motor neurons* carry impulses from the brain and spinal cord toward effectors. *Associative neurons,* or *interneurons,* relay impulses from one neuron to another in the brain and spinal cord.

11. *Nerves* are bundles of axons or dendrites that are bound together by connective tissue. *Sensory nerves* carry impulses from receptors toward the spinal cord and brain; *motor nerves* carry impulses from the brain and spinal cord toward effectors; and *mixed nerves* are made up of both sensory and motor fibers.

12. In the resting neuron, the outside of the membrane has a positive charge and the inside has a negative charge.

13. The difference in electrical charge across the nerve-cell membrane is maintained by the sodium-potassium pump. At rest, the nerve-cell membrane is permeable to potassium ions, but not to sodium ions. Potassium ions are pumped into the cell, but they tend to diffuse back out. Sodium ions are pumped out of the cell, but they cannot easily diffuse back through the membrane. Thus they accumulate outside the cell. This results in an excess positive charge (due to the accumulated sodium ions) outside the membrane and an excess negative charge inside the membrane.

14. In the area of the impulse, the inside of the nerve cell is positively charged, while the outside is negatively charged.

15. In the area of the impulse, the membrane is highly permeable to sodium ions so that there is a high concentration of sodium ions inside the membrane.

16. In the area of the impulse, the change in ion distribution results in a reversal of polarity in the membrane. The outside of the membrane becomes negative and the inside positive. This results in a flow of electrical current that affects the permeability of adjacent areas of the membrane. Sodium ions pass through the membrane in the new region of increased membrane permeability and cause the polarization there to become reversed. In this way the reversal of polarization, the nerve impulse, travels down the length of the axon membrane.

17. The rate of impulse conduction is faster in myelinated fibers because the myelin acts as an insulator and the impulse travels by jumping from one node of Ranvier to the next.

18. Each type of nerve cell has a minimum level of sensitivity, or threshold, so that a stimulus whose strength is below this threshold level will not cause the cell to fire, or initiate impulses. Any stimulus whose strength is above the threshold level will cause the nerve cell to fire. Thus a nerve cell will either be triggered to produce impulses or not, depending only on whether a stimulus is above or below the threshold strength.

19. Recognition of different types of stimuli depends on the particular nerve pathways that carry the impulses and on which part of the brain receives the impulses. It is the brain that analyzes and interprets the impulses.

20. Stimulus strength is determined in two ways. First, a stronger stimulus causes more impulses to be transmitted each second—that is, the frequency of impulses is higher. Second, because different neurons have different thresholds, a stronger stimulus causes a larger number of neurons to fire.

21. At the synapse, the terminal branch of an axon ends in a synaptic knob. A tiny space, the synaptic cleft, separates the membrane of the synaptic knob from the membrane of the adjacent neuron. The synaptic knob is filled with small vesicles containing a substance that acts as a neurotransmitter.

22. When an impulse reaches the synaptic knob, it causes the release of the neurotransmitter from the vesicles of the knob. The neurotransmitter diffuses across the synaptic cleft and triggers impulses in the adjacent neuron.

23. With a stronger stimulus, impulses arrive at the synaptic knob with greater frequency. This causes the release of more neurotransmitter into the synaptic cleft, which in turn initiates more impulses per second in the adjacent neuron.

24. In a nerve pathway, a single neuron may transmit impulses to and receive impulses from a large number of neurons. Some of the impulses it receives may be excitatory and some may be inhibitory. The cell body averages these impulses, and impulses may be initiated or not, depending on the overall results of this averaging. Thus, neurons fire or don't fire, depending on the total information they receive. The firing of some neurons can inhibit the firing of other neurons. The behavior of an organism is the result of the great number of synaptic circuits formed when neurons are stimulated or inhibited.

25. At the neuromuscular junction, the axon of a motor neuron ends in structures called *motor end plates*. The motor end plates contain synaptic vesicles and are separated from the adjacent muscle fiber by a gap.

26. When impulses reach a motor end plate, they cause the synaptic vesicles to release a chemical transmitter, which diffuses across the gap between the end of the axon and the membrane of the muscle fiber. The transmitter increases the permeability of the muscle to sodium, which initiates impulses that travel down the muscle membrane and cause the muscle fiber to contract.

27. Some drugs interfere with the functioning of acetylcholine at the neuromuscular junction, resulting in paralysis of the muscles. Stimulants aid in synaptic transmission, while depressants work by blocking the formation of norepinephrine.

28. Protozoans respond to such stimuli as food, light, and irritating chemicals. They can distinguish between food and nonfood, move away from irritating chemicals, and change direction to avoid solid matter in their path.

29. The nervous system of the hydra is in the form of a nerve net. A stimulus to any part of the system elicits a coordinated response in the whole animal.

30. The central nervous system of the earthworm consists of a brain and a pair of ventral nerve cords that enlarge into ganglia in each body segment. The peripheral nervous system includes all the nerves that branch out from the central nervous system.

31. The nervous system of the grasshopper is basically the same as that of the earthworm. It includes a brain, a pair of ventral nerve cords, and ganglia, as well as nerves branching out from the central nervous system. The main difference is that sense organs of the grasshopper are more highly developed than those of the earthworm. The grasshopper has eyes, antennae, and taste organs.

Answers to Test Your Understanding

1. In the area of an impulse, the membrane polarity becomes reversed as sodium ions from the outside of the membrane diffuse through the membrane to the inside. The reversal of polarity causes an electrical current that changes the membrane permeability in the adjacent membrane, and sodium ions pass through the membrane in that region, reversing the polarity there. At the synapse, the impulse causes synaptic vesicles in the synaptic knob to release neurotransmitter into the synaptic cleft. The neurotransmitter diffuses across the cleft and initiates impulses in the adjacent nerve cell membrane by changing its permeability to sodium ions.

2. Excitatory neurotransmitters include acetylcholine, norepinephrine, histamine, and glutamic acid. Inhibitory neurotransmitters include serotonin, epinephrine, and glycine.

3. The neurotransmitter released at a synapse may be excitatory or inhibitory. Thus synapses control the passage of impulses through a nerve pathway.

Chapter 15

Rationale

Students are usually fascinated by the complexity of the human nervous system. The chapter begins with a discussion of the central nervous system. The protective coverings of the brain and spinal cord are described. The location, structure, and function of the cerebrum, cerebellum, and medulla are discussed. The anatomy of the spinal cord and its functions are considered.

The following section deals with the peripheral nervous system. Special attention is given to the parasympathetic and sympathetic divisions of the autonomic nervous system. Stress the homeostatic functions of and antagonistic relationship between the two divisions of the autonomic nervous system.

The sense receptors of the human body are presented in some detail. Both the structure of the eye and ear and the physiological basis for vision, hearing, and balance are explained. The section concludes with a discussion of the receptors of the skin, the taste buds, and the olfactory receptors.

The last part of the chapter discusses human behavior and learning. Reflexes, habits, and instincts are studied. The discussion of conditioned responses and habits affords the teacher an opportunity to stress the way good habits can be made and bad ones broken. The latest findings on memory are reviewed.

Audiovisual Materials

"Autonomic Nervous System," (17 min., color) IFB.
"Exploring the Human Brain," (18 min., color) BFA.
"Miracle of the Mind," (26 min., color) McGraw-Hill.
"Nervous Control of Behavior," (16 min., color) McGraw-Hill.
"Pavlov's Experiment—The Conditioned Reflex," (10 min., b&w) Coronet.
"Senses and Perception: Links to the Outside World," (18 min., color) EBE.
"Sensory World," (33 min., color) CRM.
"The Ears and Hearing," (22 min., color) EBE.
"The Eye," (11 min., color) FI.
"The Eyes and Seeing," (19 min., color) EBE.
"The Human Body: The Brain," (16 min., color) Coronet.
"The Human Body: Nervous System," (13 min., color) Coronet.
"The Human Body: Sense Organs," (18 min., color) Coronet.
"The Nose (Structure and Function)," (11 min., color) EBE.
"The Skin as a Sense Organ," (12 min., color) IFB.

Answers to Test Your Learning

1. The skull protects the brain; the vertebrae protect the spinal cord; and the meninges protect both the brain and the spinal cord.

2. Cerebrospinal fluid is found between the meninges, in the ventricles of the brain, and in the central canal of the spinal cord. It cushions the delicate nervous tissue against shock.

3. The major source of energy for the brain is glucose.

4. The cerebrum is the largest part of the brain. It is divided into two halves, the right and left cerebral hemispheres. The outer surface of the cerebrum is highly folded. The ridges of the surface are called *convolutions*. The outer layer of the cerebrum is the gray matter, which is made up of the cell bodies of motor neurons and associative neurons. The inner layer of the cerebrum is the white matter, which is made up of myelinated nerve fibers.

5. The cerebral cortex performs sensory, motor, and associative functions. The sensory areas of the cortex receive and interpret impulses from the sense receptors of the body. The motor areas initiate impulses that are responsible for all voluntary movements of the body. The associative areas of the brain are responsible for memory, learning, and thought.

6. The myelinated fibers of the white matter form bundles, or tracts, that enter the cerebral cortex and serve to connect it with the other parts of the brain. There is also a tract that connects the right and left cerebral hemispheres so that there is an exchange of information between the two.

7. At some point, nerve fibers leaving the cerebral hemispheres cross over to the opposite side of the brain or spinal cord. Thus fibers from the left side of the brain control the right side of the body, and fibers from the right side of the brain control the left side of the body.

8. The cerebellum is located behind and beneath the cerebrum. Like the cerebrum, it is divided into two hemispheres with the gray matter on the outside and white matter on the inside.

9. The cerebellum coordinates and controls all voluntary movements and some involuntary movements. (Impulses for voluntary movements are initiated by the cerebral cortex.) The cerebellum also maintains balance and muscle tone.

10. Beneath the cerebellum and continuous with the spinal cord is the medulla. Running through the medulla are nerve fibers that connect the spinal cord to the various other parts of the brain. The medulla controls such involuntary functions as breathing, heartbeat, blood pressure, movement and secretion in the digestive tract, coughing, and sneezing.

11. The spinal cord extends from the base of the brain down through the vertebrae of the spinal column. A cross section of the spinal cord shows an inner H-shaped region of grey matter surrounded by an outer region of white matter. The gray matter contains associative neurons and the cell bodies of motor neurons. The white matter contains myelinated fibers that carry impulses between all parts of the body and the spinal cord and brain.

12. The spinal cord connects the nerves of the body with the brain and controls certain reflexes.

13. The peripheral nervous system includes all the neurons and nerve fibers outside the brain and spinal cord, including the spinal nerves from the spinal cord and the cranial nerves from the brain.

14. There are 12 pairs of cranial nerves.

15. The two divisions of the peripheral nervous system are the *somatic nervous system* and the *autonomic nervous system*.

16. The somatic nervous system contains both sensory and motor neurons that connect the central nervous system to skeletal muscles, the skin, and the sense organs. It is also responsible for body movements over which there is some conscious awareness or voluntary control.

17. The autonomic nervous system is made up of motor neurons.

18. The autonomic nervous system controls such vital body functions as the heartbeat rate, the diameter of arteries, breathing movements, movements of the digestive organs, and secretion by certain glands, such as the sweat glands.

19. A *plexus* is a cluster of ganglia.

20. The two divisions of the autonomic nervous system are the *sympathetic nervous system* and the *parasympathetic nervous system*. The two systems function antagonistically. Most organs receive impulses from both systems. The sympathetic system generally helps the body to deal with emergency situations by accelerating certain body activities and slowing down others. The parasympathetic system generally promotes normal, relaxed body functioning. Where impulses from one system increase the activity of an organ, impulses from the other system decrease the activity of that organ.

21. The outer layer, or "white," of the eye is the *sclera*. In the front of the eye, the sclera bulges outward and becomes the transparent *cornea*. Just beneath the sclera is the *choroid coat,* the darkly pigmented middle layer of the eye. At the front of the eye the choroid coat forms the *iris,* the colored part of the eye. In the center of the iris is an opening called the *pupil*. Behind the iris is the *lens*. The innermost layer of the eye is the *retina*. Between the cornea and the lens is a cavity filled with *aqueous humor*. The cavity behind the lens is filled with *vitreous humor*.

22. Light entering the eye passes through the cornea, pupil, aqueous humor, lens, and vitreous humor, and forms an image on the retina at the back of the eye.

23. The rods and cones are the light-sensitive structures in the retina. Rods are responsible for vision in dim light and provide only black-and-white vision. Cones are responsible for color vision, but function only in bright light.

24. Retinal is a light-sensitive pigment that is synthesized from vitamin A. It is involved in both black-and-white and color vision. In the rods and in each of the three different kinds of cones, retinal combines with a different protein. Each of the proteins binds differently with the retinal, and it is the type of bonding that allows the retinal to respond to different colors and intensities of light. When light strikes the rod or cone, it breaks the chemical bond between the retinal and the protein, which initiates impulses in sensory neurons. The impulses pass to the brain where they are interpreted.

25. Sound waves collected by the outer ear pass down the auditory canal to the eardrum. They cause the eardrum to vibrate, and the vibrations are transmitted across the middle ear by the hammer, anvil, and stirrup. Vibrations of the stirrup cause vibrations in the oval window, which in turn causes the fluid within the cochlea to vibrate.

26. The movement of the fluid in the cochlea causes vibration in specialized hair cells lining one of the membranes within the cochlea. This initiates impulses in nerve endings around the hair cells. These impulses travel over the auditory nerve to the cerebrum, where they are interpreted as sound.

27. As the head changes position, the fluid in the semicircular canals also changes position. This causes movement of hairlike projections that stimulate nerve endings and initiate impulses that travel to the cerebellum and then to the cerebrum. Impulses from the cerebrum and cerebellum correct the position of the body.

28. The sense receptors in the skin are sensitive to touch, pressure, pain, heat, and cold.

29. Taste buds are located within papillae, which are small projections on the surface of the tongue. Each taste bud consists of a number of sense cells and opens to the surface of the tongue through a pore. There are four different types of taste buds, each type sensitive to one of four basic tastes—sweet, sour, salt, and bitter. When a taste bud is stimulated by a substance in solution on the tongue, impulses from the nerve fibers branching throughout the structure are carried over sensory pathways to the brain, where they are interpreted.

30. Odor is detected when molecules of a gaseous substance enter the nose, dissolve in the mucus, and stimulate the olfactory receptors. Impulses from the olfactory cells are carried by the olfactory nerves to the brain, where they are interpreted.

31. *Behavior* is the response of an organism to stimuli. Innate behavior is determined by heredity. Acquired behavior is learned.

32. A *reflex* is an involuntary, automatic response to a given stimulus. Examples of reflexes include blinking, sneezing, coughing, heartbeat, peristalsis, knee-jerk, and breathing movements.

33. The first step in this reflex arc is that a receptor in the skin is stimulated by the heat. The receptor initiates impulses in a sensory neuron, which carries impulses to the spinal cord. Within the spinal cord, the sensory neuron synapses with an associative neuron, which synapses with a motor neuron. (Impulses are also carried to the brain, but this is not part of the reflex arc.) The motor neuron transmits impulses to muscles that move the body away from the heat.

34. An *instinct* is a complex, inborn behavior pattern.

35. A *conditioned response* is a reflex act that occurs in response to a new stimulus.

36. A *habit* is a learned, routine activity that an individual can perform with little or no conscious thought. Writing, talking, and tying shoes are common habits.

37. All voluntary behavior is controlled by the cerebrum.

38. *Momentary memory* is memory that is retained for a few minutes at most. *Short-term memory* can be recalled for periods of several hours. *Long-term memory* can last weeks or years.

Answers to Test Your Understanding

1. The cerebrum, cerebellum, and semicircular canals of the ears play a role in maintaining balance and position.

2. A *reflex response* is an inborn response to a particular stimulus. A *conditioned response* is a reflex response that occurs in response to a new stimulus as the result of learning. An *instinct* is an inborn behavior pattern. A *habit* is learned behavior that has become automatic through practice.

3. Emergency situations stimulate the sympathetic division of the autonomic nervous system. When the sympathetic system is stimulated, certain body activities, such as heartbeat rate and respiratory rate, are accelerated, and others, such as peristalsis, are slowed.

4. While you are reading, impulses traveling over sensory pathways from the eye reach the part of the cerebrum involved with vision, and from there pass through associative neurons to other parts of the cerebral cortex concerned with associative functions, such as thought and memory. During reading, impulses from the brain pass to the eyes, controlling the eye movements associated with reading. Writing involves the eyes and visual area of the cerebrum, and also the associative and motor areas of the cerebrum, the cerebellum, spinal cord, and nerves running into the arm and hand.

Chapter 16

Rationale

This chapter focuses on the role of the endocrine system in the regulation of body functions. It begins with a comparison of the mechanisms of nervous and endocrine coordination. The control of hormone secretion by negative feedback is carefully described and illustrated. The one-messenger and two-messenger models of hormone action are described.

The hormones of the pituitary, thyroid, parathyroid, and adrenal glands and the pancreas, ovaries, testes, stomach, small intestine, thymus, and pineal gland are all discussed. The effects of over- and undersecretion of the hormones are also covered. Note that detailed discussion of the reproductive hormones is deferred until Chapter 23, which covers human reproduction.

Audiovisual Materials

"Endocrine Glands," (11 min., b&w) EBE.

"Prostaglandins: Tomorrow's Physiology?" (22 min., color) Upjohn.

Answers to Test Your Learning

1. The nervous system operates by means of electrochemical impulses in a network of nerve fibers and chemical transmitters that cross synaptic clefts. The nervous system acts quickly and directs its messages to specific parts of the body. The endocrine system, on the other hand, consists of a number of glands that produce substances called hormones. The hormones are released into the bloodstream and carried to all the tissues of the body. The amount of time needed for these substances to travel to their target tissues and produce an effect is much longer than that required for a nervous response. However, the effects of hormones can last longer—hours, days, or years.

2. An *exocrine gland* discharges its secretions into ducts (the liver, for example, secretes bile into the bile duct). An *endocrine gland* discharges its secretion directly into the bloodstream (the thyroid gland, for example, secretes thyroxin into the blood).

3. The tissues whose functions are affected by a particular hormone are the target tissues of that hormone. The hormone may stimulate the target tissue and increase its activities, or it may inhibit the target tissue and decrease its activities. Hormones change the rates of certain biochemical reactions. They may start, speed up, slow down, or stop the reactions.

4. The body processes regulated by hormones are metabolism, maintenance of homeostasis, growth, and reproduction.

5. A thermostat is controlled by negative feedback.

6. In the one-messenger model, the hormone enters the body cells. In the target cells there are specific receptor proteins not found in nontarget cells. The hormone combines with receptor proteins and forms an active factor that alters the rate of some chemical reaction in the cell, thereby producing the hormonal effect. In the two-messenger model, the hormone combines with receptors on the membrane surface of the target cell. This causes enzymes in the membrane to produce a second messenger (cyclic AMP), which enters the cell and produces the hormonal effect. The same second messenger may be produced by a number of different types of cells. However, its effects within the cell varies from one cell type to another.

7. *Hypersecretion* is the production of an abnormally high level of hormone. *Hyposecretion* is the production of an abnormally low level of hormone.

8. The secretion of hormones by the anterior pituitary is controlled by the hypothalamus. The hypothalamus produces hormones called *releasing factors* that control the release of hormones by the anterior pituitary.

9. *Thyroid-stimulating hormone* stimulates the production and release of thyroxin by the thyroid. *Adrenocorticotropic hormone* stimulates the production and release of hormones by the adrenal cortex. *Growth hormone* controls growth and affects most of the body tissues. *Follicle-stimulating hormone* stimulates the development of egg cells in the ovary. In males it controls production of sperm in the testes. *Luteinizing hormone* causes the release of eggs from the ovaries. It also affects the production of sex hormones in both males and females. *Prolactin* stimulates the secretion of milk by the mammary glands at the end of pregnancy.

10. The two hormones released by the posterior pituitary are *oxytocin* and *vasopressin*. They are produced by nerve cells in the hypothalamus. They pass down the axons of the nerve cells to the posterior lobe of the pituitary for storage and eventual release.

11. Oxytocin stimulates contraction of the uterus during labor. Vasopressin controls the reabsorption of water in the kidneys.

12. *Thyroxine* regulates the rate of metabolism in the body. *Calcitonin* is involved in the regulation of the blood calcium level.

13. When the concentration of thyroxin in the blood falls below a certain level, the hypothalamus is stimulated to produce TSH-releasing factor, which stimulates the anterior pituitary to secrete TSH. TSH stimulates the release of thyroxine by the thyroid. Increasing levels of thyroxine in the blood inhibit the production of releasing factor by the hypothalamus, which inhibits production of TSH, and thereby decreases the stimulation of the thyroid. Thus, by negative feedback the concentration of thyroxine in the blood controls the system by which it is produced.

14. The four tiny parathyroid glands are embedded in the back of the thyroid gland.

15. *Parathormone* regulates calcium and phosphate metabolism.

16. The concentration of calcium ions in the blood must be kept constant within relatively narrow limits for the normal functioning of nerves and muscles.

17. The adrenal glands are located on the tops of the kidneys.

18. The adrenal medulla secretes epinephrine (adrenalin) and norepinephrine (noradrenalin). Both hormones are involved in stimulating the so-called ''fight-or-flight'' reaction. They both constrict the blood vessels of the body. Epinephrine increases the rate of heartbeat, blood pressure, breathing rate, blood clotting rate, and sweating.

19. The secretion of hormones by the adrenal medulla is controlled by the sympathetic nervous system.

20. *Cortisol* affects carbohydrate, protein, and fat metabolism. It affects the synthesis of glucose in the liver and other tissues and is one of the hormones that controls blood glucose levels. *Aldosterone* and related compounds maintain normal mineral balance in the blood. By controlling the concentrations of sodium and potassium ions, aldosterone also controls the volume of the intercellular fluid and the blood.

21. The pancreas is both an endocrine gland and an exocrine gland. The exocrine portions secrete digestive juices into the pancreatic duct. The endocrine portions consist of small clusters of cells, the islets of Langerhans, that secrete the hormones insulin and glucagon.

22. The alpha cells secrete glucagon and the beta cells secrete insulin.

23. Insulin affects glucose metabolism. When the blood glucose level is high, the beta cells are stimulated to secrete insulin, which promotes the passage of glucose into the body cells, thereby lowering the blood glucose level. It also promotes the conversion of glucose to glycogen in the liver and skeletal muscle, and in fatty tissues it promotes the conversion of glucose to fat. It also increases the rate of oxidation of glucose within cells.

24. The effects of glucagon on glucose metabolism are generally opposite to those of insulin. When the blood glucose level falls below a certain level, the alpha cells of the pancreas secrete glucagon, which stimulates the conversion of glycogen to glucose in the liver. This glucose quickly diffuses out of the liver into the bloodstream. When the supply of liver glycogen is exhausted, glucagon causes the conversion of amino acids and fatty acids to glucose.

25. Diabetes occurs when the islets of Langerhans fail to produce enough insulin and the amount of glucose that can enter the body cells is greatly reduced. As a result, the concentration of glucose in the blood rises, and the excess sugar is excreted in the urine. Symptoms of diabetes include loss of weight despite increased appetite, thirst, and general weakness. Proper diet and daily injections of insulin can control the disease.

26. The ovaries produce *estrogen* and *progesterone*. During development, estrogen stimulates the development of the female reproductive system. Estrogen also promotes the development of the female secondary sex characteristics, and together with progesterone it regulates the menstrual cycle.

27. The major hormone secreted by the testes is *testosterone*. During development, testosterone stimulates the development of the male reproductive system. It also promotes the development of the male secondary sex characteristics.

28. The lining of the stomach secretes the hormone *gastrin,* which stimulates the flow of gastric juice. The lining of the small intestine secretes the hormone *secretin,* which stimulates the flow of pancreatic juice.

29. The thymus is located in the upper chest cavity near the heart.

30. During childhood the thymus secretes the hormone *thymosin*. Thymosin is thought to stimulate development of T lymphocytes, which are important in immunity. The thymus appears to serve no function in adults.

31. The pineal gland is attached to the base of the brain.

32. The pineal gland secretes the hormone *melatonin*. In frogs melatonin acts on pigment cells; in rats it inhibits the functioning of the ovaries and testes. In humans it is thought to inhibit sexual development in males and possibly also in females.

33. *Prostaglandins* are ''local hormones'' that produce their effects in the cells in which they are synthesized without ever entering the bloodstream.

34. Prostaglandins are thought to modify the effects of other hormones. They influence a wide variety of metabolic activities, including heartbeat, blood pressure, excretion of urine, and contraction of the uterus during childbirth.

Answers to Test Your Understanding

1. (A) Oversecretion of parathormone.
(B) Undersecretion of growth hormone.
(C) Oversecretion of thyroxin.
(D) Undersecretion of thymosin.
(E) Undersecretion of insulin.

2. When the blood glucose level is high, the beta cells of the pancreas secrete insulin, which promotes the passage of glucose from the blood into the body cells, thereby lowering the blood glucose level. When the blood glucose level is low, the alpha cells of the pancreas secrete glucagon, which stimulates the conversion of glycogen to glucose in the liver. This glucose diffuses out of the liver into the bloodstream, raising the glucose level.

3. When the blood level of calcium drops, the parathyroids are stimulated to secrete parathormone, which causes the release of calcium from bone into the plasma. When the blood calcium concentration rises above a certain level, calcium is removed from the blood and stored in bone. Excess calcium can also be excreted by the kidneys and intestines.

4. Fright causes the adrenal medulla to secrete epinephrine and norepinephrine, which increase the rate and strength of the heartbeat.

Chapter 17

Rationale

This chapter covers plant nutrition as well as bacterial photosynthesis and chemosynthesis. Since these topics are discussed on a molecular level, they are difficult, and diagrams are used wherever possible to supplement the presentation.

Photosynthesis is introduced by a description of the scientific investigations that led to an understanding of this important process. The chemistry of photosynthesis, including both light and dark reactions, is explained on a simplified level. Environmental factors that affect the rate of photosynthesis are also covered. A brief discussion of heterotrophic nutrition in plants and bacterial photosynthesis and chemosynthesis closes the chapter.

Students are often interested in insectivorous and parasitic plants. Questions may lead to a discussion of differences in soils in woodlands and bogs, the habitats of insectivorous plants.

Audiovisual Materials

''How Green Plants Make and Use Food,'' (11 min., color) Coronet.
''Light and Color,'' (14 min., color) EBE.
''Photosynthesis,'' (21 min., color) EBE.
''Photosynthesis: Chemistry of Food Making,'' (13 min., color) Coronet.
''Photosynthesis: The Biochemical Process,'' (14 min., color) Coronet.

Answers to Test Your Learning

1. *Van Helmont* found that plants grow and gain weight without taking anything from the surrounding soil. In van Helmont's experiment the only material he added to the growing plant was water, so he concluded that new plant material comes from water. *Priestley* discovered that a plant could restore freshness to air that had been "damaged" by a burning candle. *Lavoisier* showed that oxygen was removed from air by burning and that for air to support burning or animal life, oxygen has to be present. *Ingenhousz* found that plants restore air only in sunlight. *Senebier* found that plants take in carbon dioxide only in sunlight and that in the dark they use oxygen from the air. *Mayer* stated that during photosynthesis plants convert light energy to chemical energy.

2. Light is a form of electromagnetic radiation and travels through space in waves. The various colors of light differ from one another in wavelength. Although light travels in waves, it also behaves as though it were made of particles. These particles are called *photons*. Each photon carries a definite amount of energy.

3. Generally, when light is absorbed by a material, its energy is changed to heat, which is radiated away. When some materials absorb light, the energy is transferred to an electron of an atom of the material, raising the electron to a higher energy level.

4. A pigment is a substance that absorbs light of particular wavelengths.

5. When light of certain wavelengths strikes a photosynthetic pigment, the absorbed energy raises the energy level of electrons in the chlorophyll. The energy gained is used to split water into hydrogen and oxygen.

6. The most important photosynthetic pigments are chlorophylls a and b.

7. Chlorophyll absorbs violet, blue, red, and orange light and reflects green and yellow light. It is the light reflected by the chlorophyll that gives plants their green color.

8. These pigments absorb light of wavelengths not absorbed by chlorophyll. The energy they absorb is transferred to chlorophyll.

9. The membranes of the chloroplasts play an integral part in the reactions of photosynthesis, and without them, the reactions will not occur. They contain electron acceptors and other molecules necessary for photosynthesis.

10. In respiration, glucose and oxygen are used to produce energy, carbon dioxide, and water. In photosynthesis, carbon dioxide, water, and energy from light are used to produce glucose and oxygen.

11.

$$\text{Energy} + 6CO_2 + 12H_2O \xrightarrow[\text{enzymes}]{\text{chlorophyll}} C_6H_{12}O_6 + 6O_2 + 6H_2O$$

12. In the light reactions, the energy absorbed from light raises the energy level of certain electrons in the chlorophyll. The energy is released in a stepwise fashion and used to split water into hydrogen and oxygen. The hydrogen is picked up by the coenzyme $NADP^+$ and the oxygen is given off to the environment. Some of the energy from light is also used to produce ATP.

13. In the dark reactions, ATP and $NADPH_2$ from the light reactions are used to synthesize organic compounds from carbon dioxide.

14. PGAL is both a reactant and a product of the dark reactions. One molecule of glucose is synthesized from two molecules of PGAL in plant cells. Plants can also use PGAL in the synthesis of fats and amino acids. In glycolysis, PGAL is an intermediate formed from the breakdown of glucose.

15. Photosynthesis occurs most rapidly at a temperature of about 35°C. Above this temperature, the rate declines steeply. The rate of photosynthesis increases as light intensity increases to about one-third the strength of summer sunlight. Beyond this point, the rate declines. An increase in the concentration of carbon dioxide tends to stimulate photosynthesis until it reaches about ten times the normal atmospheric concentration. Beyond this point, the rate of photosynthesis decreases. Water shortage causes a decrease in the rate of photosynthesis because the stomates close to conserve water, which prevents the gas exchange necessary for photosynthesis. Magnesium and nitrogen are minerals needed for the formation of chlorophyll. Other minerals affect other metabolic processes. A shortage of any necessary mineral can affect the whole metabolism of the plant.

16. The roots of parasitic plants such as dodder are modified to enter the tissues of the host from which the parasite draws its nutrients and water.

17. Insect-eating plants most commonly grow in bogs or marshes. The acidic water of these habitats tends to reduce the rate of decay, thereby limiting the supply of nitrogen. The plants obtain the nitrogen they need from the insects they capture.

18. In bacterial photosynthesis water is not the source of hydrogen for the dark reactions. Instead, hydrogen comes from other sources, such as hydrogen sulfide.

19. *Chemosynthesis* is a form of autotrophic nutrition carried on by a few types of bacteria. In chemosynthesis, energy for the synthesis of organic compounds is obtained from the oxidation of inorganic compounds, not from light.

Answers to Test Your Understanding

1. Chlorophyll absorbs almost all wavelengths of visible light except green and yellow, which are reflected. The reflected green and yellow wavelengths give plants their green color. The chlorophyll masks the presence of other pigments. In the fall when chlorophyll production ceases, the other pigments present in the leaf, including xanthophyll and carotene, show up. These pigments give the leaves their bright fall colors.

2. In photosynthesis, light energy from the sun is converted to chemical energy. The energy in fossil fuels, including, coal, oil, and natural gas, was produced by photosynthesis. With the development of new technology, the process of photosynthesis could be harnessed for the synthesis of synthetic fuels using the free energy from the sun. Also, plants could be used to produce ethyl alcohol or methane gas, which can be used as fuels.

3. Green plants use water as a source of hydrogen. When water is split by the light reactions, the hydrogen is picked up by hydrogen acceptors and the oxygen is released into the environment. Purple sulfur bacteria use hydrogen sulfide (H_2S) as a source of hydrogen. When the compound is split, sulfur is released as a by-product.

4. Plants, like animals, carry on cellular respiration for the breakdown of nutrients. Carbon dioxide is one of the end products of these reactions. Some carbon dioxide is used in photosynthesis, but the rest is released into the environment.

Chapter 18

Rationale

This chapter opens with a description of the different types of plant tissues, their structure and functions. The presentation of this material can be greatly enhanced by the projection of transparencies and the use of wall charts or microscope demonstrations during class discussion.

Next, the structure and function of roots, stems, and leaves are covered. Many types of roots, stems, and leaves are available in nature or at the grocery store. Appropriate demonstrations will reinforce the text material. To supplement class activity, ask students to collect entire plants or plant organs as examples to be displayed in class. A class herbarium might prove interesting to students.

Audiovisual Materials

"Angiosperms—The Flowering Plants," (21 min., color) EBE.

"Evolution of Vascular Plants: The Ferns," (17 min., color) EBE.

"Origin of Land Plants: Liverworts and Mosses," (14 min., color) EBE.

"The Growth of Plants," (21 min., color) EBE.

Answers to Test Your Learning

1. *Roots* anchor a plant and absorb water and minerals from the soil. *Stems* hold the leaves and expose them to the sun, display flowers, and hold fruits and seeds. *Leaves* are the site of photosynthesis. *Flowers* and *cones* are the reproductive organs of most higher plants.

2. *Meristematic tissue* is the only type of tissue capable of cell division in a mature plant. This type of tissue is found in the growing tips of roots and stems.

3. *Epidermis* is a protective tissue that forms the outer layer of leaves, green stems, and roots. In plant parts found aboveground the epidermis is covered by cutin. *Cork* is a protective tissue that covers the surface of woody stems.

4. *Xylem* conducts water and minerals from the roots upward through the stems and into the leaves of the plant. Mature xylem cells are usually dead. The cell walls form continuous tubes from the roots through the stems and leaves. Xylem consists of two types of cells. *Tracheids* have small openings in the cell walls that are aligned with the pits of other cells. Water and minerals can pass freely from one cell to the next. *Vessel cells* have no end walls. Stacked end-to-end, they form long, continuous tubes.

Phloem conducts food and other dissolved materials both upward and downward throughout the plant. It is composed of *sieve cells* and *companion cells*. Sieve cells have cytoplasm but no nucleus, and the end walls contain openings. They are stacked one on the other. Companion cells have nuclei and are thought to control the transport activities of sieve cells.

5. *Parenchyma* is made up of unspecialized, thin-walled cells and is found in roots, stems, leaves, and fruits. In leaves and young stems, it contains chloroplasts for photosynthesis. In roots, fruits, and stems, the cells store food. *Collenchyma* cells are similar to parenchyma cells, but are elongated and have thickened cell walls. They strengthen and support plant organs. They sometimes contain chloroplasts. *Sclerenchyma* cells are thick-walled and are found where support is needed. When mature, they contain no cytoplasm.

6. A *primary root* is the first structure to emerge from a sprouting seed. A *secondary root* is a new branch that develops from a primary root.

7. A *tap root system* is one in which the primary root grows rapidly and remains the largest root of the root system. The root is thick and fleshy and grows deep into the soil. A *fibrous root system* develops when branching secondary roots are as large as or larger than the primary root. An *adventitious root system* originates from stems or leaves.

8. The *root cap* is a thimble-shaped group of cells that forms a protective covering for the delicate meristematic tissue behind it. Crushed root cap cells release a lubricating fluid that aids the passage of the root through the soil. The *meristematic zone* is a region of actively dividing cells behind the root cap. All the other cells of the root are formed from these cells. The *elongation zone*, which is behind the meristematic zone, is a region in which cells grow longer and push the root tip forward. In the *maturation zone*, which is behind the elongation zone, the cells differentiate, developing into mature, functioning cells of various types of root tissues.

9. See Figure 18-10 (page 299) for a drawing of a cross section of a root tip. The *epidermis* controls the absorption of water and minerals. Root hairs increase the surface area for absorption. The *cortex* is involved in food storage and transport of water. The *endodermis* controls the movement of water into the central cylinder. The *pericycle* is a layer of parenchyma cells from which secondary roots originate. The *xylem* and *phloem* transport water and dissolved substances throughout the plant.

10. Woody stems contain thick, tough tissue. Herbaceous steams are soft, green, and juicy.

11. A cotyledon is a modified leaf that contains stored food and is found within a seed.

12. In monocots, the seeds contain one cotyledon. In dicots, the seeds contain two cotyledons.

13. See Figure 18-11 (page 301).

14. See Figure 18-12 (page 301).

15. The terminal bud produces new tissues, causing the stem to increase in length. Vascular cambium produces new xylem and phloem, increasing the diameter of the stem.

16. Lenticels are openings that extend from the internal tissues through the epidermis of a stem. Exchange of gases occurs through the lenticels.

17. See Figure 18-13 (page 301).

18. Annual rings are the xylem cells produced during a growing season. The cells produced by the vascular cambium during the spring are larger and lighter in color than those formed during the summer.

19. *Heartwood* is xylem that no longer conducts water. Its primary function is support. *Sapwood* is relatively new xylem that functions in water conduction and lies adjacent to the cambium. Both heartwood and sapwood have been formed by the cambium.

20. See Figure 18-15 (page 303).

21. Woody monocot stems become woody from the thickening of the walls of the pith cells.

22. Most growth occurs at the tip of the stem and involves the terminal bud. Woody monocots show little growth in stem diameter.

23. The *blade* is the thin, flat, broad surface of a leaf. The *petiole* is the stalk that attaches the leaf to the stem. The *veins* of the leaf contain the xylem and phloem.

24. The upper and lower surfaces of the leaf are covered by the epidermis. A waxy cuticle on top of the epidermis prevents water loss. Stomates allow gas exchange through the epidermis. Guard cells regulate the opening and closing of the stomates. The mesophyll layer beneath the epidermis is the site of photosynthesis. The palisade mesophyll is made up of tightly packed cells containing many chloroplasts. Below the palisade mesophyll is the loosely packed spongy mesophyll. Air spaces between the cells of this layer are continuous with stomate openings of the lower epidermis. A network of veins containing xylem and phloem is found within the mesophyll layer.

Answers to Test Your Understanding

1. In roots, many cells are produced in the meristematic zone of the root tip. These cells enlarge in the elongation zone, which increases the length of the root. Cell division in the cambium, a meristematic tissue, increases the diameter of the root. A stem increases in length by division of the meristematic cells in the terminal bud. Growth in diameter is caused by cell division of the vascular cambium. New twigs and leaves grow from the terminal and lateral buds.

2. Plants take in oxygen and get rid of carbon dioxide by diffusion of these gases through the stomates of the leaves and the lenticels of stems. Water vapor is lost by evaporation through the stomates and lenticels.

3. *Herbaceous dicot stems* are generally soft and green. There is an outer layer of epidermis. Inside the epidermis is the cortex, which contains cells that serve in food storage and support. Inside the cortex is a ring of vascular bundles, which are made up of phloem cells, cambium, and xylem cells. The center of the stem is filled with pith, which contains stored food.

Woody dicot stems are hard but flexible. In woody dicots the xylem and phloem are arranged in concentric rings. The xylem ring is innermost, then comes the cambium, and next is the phloem. The production of new xylem during each growing season produces annual rings. In mature woody dicot stems, the center of the stem is filled with nonfunctioning xylem called *heartwood*. The outermost layer of a woody dicot stem is the bark.

4. Plant stems connect the roots to the branches and to the leaves, flowers, and fruits. They make it possible for the leaves to receive the maximum amount of light for photosynthesis and support the aboveground parts of the plant.

Chapter 19

Rationale

This chapter covers the life processes of plants except for photosynthesis, which was dealt with in Chapter 17. Transpiration and translocation are discussed. There is a section on excretion that explains the removal, storage, and reuse of various types of wastes.

Following is a discussion of plant nutrients and the organic compounds that plants produce. This section presents an opportunity to emphasize the special uses of plant products. Ask students to contribute articles for a bulletin board of plant products. The final sections of the chapter deal with plant hormones. Tropisms and photoperiodism are presented in sufficient detail for a basic understanding of the topics. Students may wish to set up simple tropism demonstrations.

Audiovisual Materials

"Adaptation in Plants," (16 min., color or b&w) IU.

"Plant Tropisms and Other Movements," (11 min., color) Coronet.

"The Redwood Trees," (15 min., color) Arthur Barr Productions.

Answers to Test Your Learning

1. Green plants are able to synthesize organic nutrients by photosynthesis, while animals must obtain organic nutrients from the environment.

2. *Transpiration* is the loss of water vapor from the plant, mostly through the stomates of the leaves.

3. The inner walls of the guard cells are thicker than the outer walls. When water enters the guard cells, the uneven thickness of the cell walls causes them to buckle outward, creating an opening between them, the stomate. When the guard cells lose water, they regain their former shapes, and the stomate closes.

4. Photosynthesis in the guard cells produces soluble carbohydrates, such as glucose. This reduces the concentration of water in the guard cell cytoplasm. Water from the surrounding epidermal cells enters the guard cells by osmosis, which causes the cells to swell and buckle outward, opening the stomate. Within the guard cells, enzyme-controlled reactions can convert soluble carbohydrates into insoluble starch, which has no osmotic effect. Water then leaves the guard cells, they become less turgid, and the stomate closes.

5. Xylem cells are not living.

6. *Adhesion* is an attractive force between unlike molecules. *Cohesion* is an attractive force between like molecules. *Capillary action* is the upward movement of a liquid in a tube of narrow diameter. The upward movement takes place because of adhesion between the water molecules and the walls of the tube and because of cohesion between water molecules, whereby water molecules moving up the tube pull other water molecules along.

7. *Root pressure* is an osmotic pressure in the root cells that causes water to rise in the continuous tube of the xylem cells.

8. *Transpiration pull* is the process by which water is thought to rise in a continuous column through the xylem of the plant. Cohesive forces hold the water molecules together in the column. As water molecules evaporate from the top of the column in the leaves, other water molecules are pulled up from below to replace them. Water molecules move into the xylem of the roots, keeping the column intact.

9. *Translocation* is the movement of dissolved materials through the plant.

10. Sugars, minerals, and various other dissolved substances are transported in the phloem.

11. The movement of water and minerals in the xylem is a passive, mechanical process because xylem cells are dead. In the phloem, the cells are alive and movement of materials is very rapid. In the xylem, materials move only upward, while in the phloem, movement can be in any direction. According to the *pressure flow theory*, the rapid movement of materials in the phloem occurs because of differences in osmotic pressure in the column of sieve tube cells.

12. Plants carry on cellular respiration both day and night. Some of the oxygen produced by photosynthesis during the day is used in cellular respiration. The rest is excreted through stomates and lenticels. When photosynthesis is not occurring, oxygen is taken in from the air. Carbon dioxide is produced by cellular respiration. During the day, some is used in photosynthesis, and the rest is excreted through the stomates and lenticels.

13. Nitrogenous wastes are often reused in the plant. The amino group is removed and the nitrogen is used in the synthesis of other compounds. Some wastes are stored in vacuoles, and some are stored as crystals. Actively dividing meristematic cells grow away from their waste materials.

14. Plants need water, carbon dioxide, nitrogen, and minerals, such as magnesium, iron, phosphorus, calcium, sulfur, copper, and zinc.

15. Plants can synthesize amino acids, proteins, carbohydrates, lipids, nucleic acids, and vitamins. Some plants also synthesize special substances used by humans.

16. *Auxins* affect the growth of all types of plant tissues. High auxin concentrations stimulate the growth of stems but inhibit root growth. Low auxin concentrations stimulate root growth. Auxins produced by the terminal bud inhibit the growth of lateral buds for a distance along the stem. Auxins influence the development of flowers and fruits and control the dropping of leaves and fruits. *Gibberellins* affect plant growth and the development of fruits and seeds. They cause stems to grow early in the spring, seeds to sprout, and fruits to grow; in some plants they affect flowering. *Cytokinins* stimulate cell division, growth, and differentiation.

17. In a positive tropism, the plant grows toward the stimulus. In a negative tropism, the plant grows away from the stimulus.

18. *Phototropism* is the bending of a plant toward a light source. The bending is caused by an uneven concentration of auxins in the plant tissues. *Geotropism* is the growth response to gravity. Roots generally exhibit positive geotropism and grow down into the earth in the direction of gravitational pull. Stems grow up, away from the force of gravity. *Hydrotropism* is a growth response to water. *Chemotropism* is growth toward or away from a chemical.

19. *Photoperiodism* is the response of a plant to the changing duration of light and darkness during the course of the year. Photoperiodism influences flowering and the dropping of leaves in the autumn.

Answers to Test Your Understanding

1. A water molecule passes from the root hair into the root cortex, through the endodermis, and into the central cylinder, where it enters the xylem. In the xylem the water molecule moves up through the root and stem and into a vein of a leaf. From the vein, it moves into the leaf mesophyll and evaporates from the leaf through the stomate.

2. The materials in the phloem move at a faster rate than can be explained by simple diffusion. Furthermore, different substances in adjacent sieve tube cells can move in opposite directions. The substances can also move against the concentration gradient. The speed and flexibility of movement in the phloem indicates that active transport is involved rather than just simple diffusion.

3. The growth of the plant toward light occurs because of an uneven distribution of auxins in the stem. The auxin concentration is higher on the shady side of the stem than on the lighted side. This stimulates cell growth of the side away from the light source and the increased cell growth on this side causes the stem to bend toward the light.

4. The capacity to respond to environmental change is important to survival. Hormones influence the growth of a plant toward or away from environmental stimuli. For example, the growth of a stem toward light allows maximum photosynthesis. Roots growing in the direction of gravity and toward water anchor the plant and ensure maximum water supply. Different parts of the plant life cycle are also influenced by hormones.

Chapter 20

Rationale

This chapter offers a detailed description of mitotic cell division. The structure and function of the chromatin and chromosomes are presented. Each stage of mitosis is carefully described and diagrammed. The differences in mitosis in plant and animal cells are explained. The section on asexual reproduction covers binary fission in bacteria and protozoa, budding in yeast and hydra, and spore formation in yeast and bread mold. There is also a description of regeneration. The chapter concludes with a discussion of vegetative reproduction. Both natural vegetative reproduction and artificial vegetative reproduction are covered.

Audiovisual Materials

''Asexual Reproduction,'' (17 min., color) IU.
''Cell Biology: Mitosis and DNA,'' (16 min., color) Coronet.
''Mitosis,'' 2nd ed., (14 min., color) EBE.
''Mitosis,'' (9 min., color) IFB.
''Mitosis and Meiosis,'' (20 min., color) McGraw-Hill.

Answers to Test Your Learning

1. *Reproduction* is the process by which living things produce new individuals like themselves.

2. In asexual reproduction there is only one parent, and no special reproductive cells or organs are involved. Sexual reproduction involves the union of two nuclei from special sex cells, which are usually produced by two separate parent organisms.

3. *Mitosis* is the process by which the nucleus divides. *Cytoplasmic division* is the process by which the cytoplasm of the cell is divided into two parts, each containing one of the newly formed nuclei and about half of the other contents of the parent cell. *Mitotic cell division* includes both nuclear and cytoplasmic division.

4. The hereditary material is DNA, which is located in the cell nucleus.

5. The nucleus is important because it is the control center of the cell and contains the hereditary material.

6. In nondividing cells, the DNA is found in the chromatin, the dark-staining nuclear material that consists of a network of long, thin, twisted threads. In dividing cells, the chromatin becomes organized into rodlike structures called chromosomes.

7. During *interphase* the cell is growing and the chromosomes and centrioles replicate. Interphase lasts from the end of one cell division to the beginning of the next. The chromosomes are not visible.

During *prophase* the doubled, rodlike chromosomes become visible, the centrioles migrate to opposite poles of the cell, the spindle is formed, and the nuclear membrane and nucleolus disappear.

During *metaphase* the chromosomes line up across the equatorial plane and the double chromosomes separate into two daughter chromosomes.

During *anaphase* the two sets of daughter chromosomes separate and move to opposite poles of the cell.

During *telophase* the chromosomes reach the poles, elongate, uncoil, and gradually assume the threadlike appearance of chromatin. The spindle and asters disappear, a nuclear membrane forms around each daughter nucleus, and the nucleoli reappear.

8. In animal cells, cytoplasmic division often begins during late anaphase and is completed during telophase. It is accomplished by a pinching-in of the cell membrane.

9. Mitotic cell division in plant cells differs from mitotic cell division in animal cells in two ways. First, plant cells do not have centrioles and therefore no asters form. Second, in telophase in plant cells, the spindle fibers thicken and form a cell plate that grows outward to join the cell wall, thus dividing the cell in half.

10. Interphase is the longest phase of mitosis.

11. In animals, mitosis is most frequent in the cells that are least specialized. Embryonic cells divide frequently. In adults, bone marrow cells and skin epithelial cells divide frequently. Highly specialized cells, such as nerve and muscle, seldom or never divide. In plants, mitosis is most frequent in root tips and other meristematic tissues.

12. In unicellular organisms, it is thought that an increase in cell size triggers cell division.

13. In cancer cells, mitotic division is abnormal. The cancer cells divide more rapidly than normal cells, and in some cases, each division results in the formation of more than two daughter cells.

14. In a bacterial cell, the single chromosome replicates, and a cell wall forms near the center of the parent cell, dividing it into two daughter cells, each containing one of the replicated chromosomes. When an ameba reaches full size, it rounds up, and the nucleus undergoes mitosis. Then the cytoplasm in the middle of the cell pinches in producing two daughter cells. In the paramecium, the micronucleus and macronucleus divide by mitosis. The oral groove, gullet, and contractile vacuole also replicate. The cytoplasm divides when the middle of the cell pinches in.

15. In budding, the parent organism divides into two unequal parts, while in binary fission, the parent organism divides into two approximately equal parts.

16. In yeast, the nucleus moves toward the side of the cell, the cell wall bulges outward forming a bud, and the nucleus undergoes mitosis. One daughter nucleus remains in the parent cell, while the other moves into the bud. A cell wall forms between the parent cell and the bud.

In the hydra, undifferentiated cells on the side of the parent undergo repeated mitotic divisions, forming a bud that consists of a small mound of cells. In a few days the bud develops into a small, complete hydra that eventually separates from its parent. In yeast, the bud may remain attached to the parent cell, or it may separate from it.

17. Spores are small cells that are surrounded by a protective wall that can withstand unfavorable environmental conditions for long periods of time. When conditions become favorable, a spore can give rise to a new organism.

18. In yeast, when conditions are unfavorable, the nucleus and cytoplasm undergo two cell divisions, forming four spores. These are enclosed within the original cell wall, or spore case. The spore case eventually bursts, releasing the spores. In bread mold, spores are produced in spore cases on specialized stalks that grow upward from the surface of the mold. When mature, the walls of the spore case break open and thousands of tiny spores are released and carried away by air currents.

19. *Regeneration* is the ability of an organism to regrow lost body parts.

20. Relatively simple animals, such as the hydra, planaria, and starfish, have the greatest regenerative powers.

21. Vegetative reproduction is the process by which roots, stems, or leaves give rise to a new plant.

22. A *bulb* is a short underground stem surrounded by thick, fleshy leaves that contain stored food. As the plant grows, small new bulbs sprout from the old one. Each new bulb can give rise to a new plant. *Corms* resemble bulbs but do not have leaves. Corms are short, stout underground stems that contain stored food. A *tuber* is an enlarged portion of an underground stem that contains stored food. Along the surface of a tuber are indentations called "eyes." The eyes are tiny buds, each of which is capable of giving rise to a new plant. A *runner* is a horizontal stem with buds that grows along the surface of the ground. A new plant grows where a bud from the runner touches the soil. A *rhizome* is a stem that grows horizontally underground. It is usually thick and fleshy and contains stored food. Along the rhizome are enlarged areas called *nodes*. The upper portion of the node gives rise to leaf-bearing branches while the lower portion forms roots.

23. A new plant can be produced from a *cutting,* which can be a stem, leaf, or root. In *layering,* a stem is bent over so that part of it is in contact with the soil. Roots grow down into the soil and new branches grow upward, forming a new plant. In *grafting,* a stem or bud is removed from one plant and joined permanently to the stem of a closely related plant.

Answers to Test Your Understanding

1. In unicellular organisms, mitotic cell division is the most common means of reproduction. In multicellular organisms, mitotic cell division is necessary for growth and for replacement of cells. In very simple multicellular organisms it may be a means of asexual reproduction.

2. Vegetative propagation ensures the growth of new plants exactly like the parent. It takes less time for a new plant to develop by vegetative propagation than it does from seed. Vegetative propagation is the only way that seedless fruits can be grown. Grafting can be used to increase fruit yield.

3. Stems or buds from three different types of apple trees are grafted onto the same tree.

4. (A) Geraniums can be produced from stem cuttings.

(B) African violets can be produced from leaf cuttings.

(C) White potatoes can be produced from a piece of a white potato that contains an eye.

(D) Tulips can be produced from bulbs.

Chapter 21

Rationale

The chapter begins with a comparison of asexual and sexual reproduction and a discussion of the biological advantages of sexual reproduction. The difference between diploid and monoploid chromosome numbers is explained, and the stages of meiosis are carefully described and diagrammed.

A discussion of sexual reproduction in protists is followed by a general introduction to sexual reproduction in animals. Oogenesis and spermatogenesis are described, as are fertilization and zygote formation. External and internal fertilization are described and compared, and the chapter ends with a brief description of parthenogenesis.

Audiovisual Materials

"Basic Nature of Sexual Reproduction," (15 min., color) IU.

"Heredity and Adaptive Change: Sex Cell Formation," (16 min., color) EBE.

"Meiosis," (12 min., color) IFB.

"Meiosis," (15 min., color) EBE.

"Sexual Reproduction and Species Survival," (16 min., color) McGraw-Hill.

Answers to Test Your Learning

1. In asexual reproduction only a single parent is involved, and all offspring are identical to the parent. Sexual reproduction generally involves two parents, and the offspring are not identical to either parent. Variations introduced by sexual reproduction can be helpful to survival of the species.

2. Variation increases the possibility that some individuals of a species will be better adapted than others to survive short-term and long-term changes in the environment. Variations also enable certain individuals in a population to move into new environments.

3. The body, or somatic, cells of an organism are usually diploid, while the sex cells, or gametes, are monoploid.

4. Homologous chromosomes are a pair of chromosomes that are similar in size and shape and control the same hereditary characteristics.

5. Meiosis reduces the chromosome number by half, from diploid to monoploid.

6. In *synapsis* the four strands of a pair of doubled homologous chromosomes twist about each other. These entwined chromosome pairs consisting of four chromatids are called *tetrads*. The process of separation of the tetrad is called *disjunction*.

7. During the first meiotic division, the chromosomes replicate and the homologous chromosomes of each tetrad separate, so that each of the two daughter cells has half the number of chromosomes of the parent cell. However, each chromosome is already in replicated form.

8. During the second meiotic division, the chromosomes do not replicate. The double-stranded chromosomes separate, and each of the resulting cells is monoploid and contains single-stranded chromosomes.

9. In protists there are no distinct male and female cells. However, there are usually two different mating types, or plus and minus strains. Apparently there are biochemical and chromosomal differences between different mating types.

10. During conjugation in spirogyra two filaments of opposite strains lie side-by-side. Projections develop on the sides of adjacent cells. Where these projections meet, the walls break down, and a passageway, or conjugation tube, opens between the cells of the two filaments. The contents of the cell of the active strand flow through the conjugation tube and fuse with the nucleus and cytoplasm of the adjacent passive cell, forming a diploid zygote. Each zygote secretes a thick wall that protects it during its dormant season and becomes a zygospore.

11. During conjugation, a plus and a minus paramecium stick together in the region of their oral grooves, and a protoplasmic bridge forms between them. In each cell, the macronucleus disappears and the micronucleus divides by meiosis. One of the newly formed monoploid micronuclei from each paramecium moves across the protoplasmic bridge into the opposite cell, where it fuses with a micronucleus of that cell. Both cells now contain a diploid micronucleus. The conjugating paramecia separate, and the new micronuclei undergo several mitotic divisions. These divisions result in the formation of new macronuclei and micronuclei. Both organisms then divide twice without nuclear division, and eight new organisms are produced.

12. The ovaries produce the female gametes, or egg cells, while the testes produce the male gametes, or sperm cells.

13. A *hermaphrodite* is an organism that contains both testes and ovaries and can produce both eggs and sperm.

14. Within the ovary, *oogonia* develop into *primary oocytes*, which undergo the first meiotic division. As a result of this division, the cytoplasm of the cell is divided unequally—most goes to the *secondary oocyte*. The other daughter cell, the *first polar body*, is very small. Each of these cells is monoploid. In the second meiotic division, the secondary oocyte divides unequally into a large cell called the *ootid* and another polar body. The first polar body may also divide into two polar bodies. The ootid develops into a mature egg, and the polar bodies die and disintegrate.

15. One mature egg is produced from each oogonium.

16. In spermatogenesis, a *spermatogonium* increases in size to become a *primary spermatocyte*. The primary spermatocyte undergoes the first meiotic division, forming two monoploid cells of equal size called *secondary spermatocytes*. Each secondary spermatocyte undergoes the second meiotic division, forming four *spermatids*, which develop into mature sperm.

17. Each spermatogonium gives rise to four sperm.

18. Eggs are round and nonmotile. They contain a nucleus and stored food. Eggs are always larger than the sperm of the same species. Most sperm cells are microscopic. A typical sperm is made up of a head, a middle piece, and a long, thin tail.

19. As sperm approach an egg, they encounter a chemical that stimulates them to move faster and aids in their attachment to the surface of the egg. When a sperm comes in contact with an egg, the acrosome releases enzymes that dissolve an opening through the protective membranes around the egg. This allows the head of the sperm to enter the egg. The sperm cell nucleus moves through the cytoplasm and fuses with the egg nucleus to form a diploid zygote.

20. External fertilization is limited to aquatic animals. It is found in almost all aquatic invertebrates, most fish (not sharks), and many amphibians.

21. In external fertilization, large numbers of gametes are produced to overcome the many hazards of the environment.

22. Internal fertilization is characteristic of land-dwelling animals. It is also found in some aquatic animals, including sharks and lobsters.

23. In internal fertilization the eggs are well protected and the chances of fertilization are much greater than they are when the gametes are simply released into the water.

24. *Parthenogenesis* is the development of an unfertilized egg into an adult animal.

Answers to Test Your Understanding

1. Mitotic cell division results in daughter cells that are identical to the parent cell and have the same number of chromosomes. Meiotic cell division produces daughter cells with half the number of chromosomes of the parent cell. In mitosis, the chromosomes replicate and the cell divides in half. In meiosis the replication of the chromosomes is followed by two cell divisions.

2. In oogenesis an oogonium develops into one mature egg and three nonfunctional polar bodies. In spermatogenesis a spermatogonium develops into four functional sperm. In the female, all the oogonia of the individual are present at birth. No others are produced. Then from puberty until menopause one oogonium develops into an egg each month. In the male, on the other hand, spermatogonia develop in the testes by mitosis throughout childhood. After sexual maturity, some spermatogonia divide by mitosis to produce more spermatogonia, while others undergo meiosis to produce mature sperm.

3. If the gametes did not contain the monoploid number of chromosomes, the chromosome number would double with each fertilization.

4. Some of the problems of external fertilization are that: the egg and sperm may not meet; the eggs or young may be eaten by other animals; or they may die because of unusual water temperature, inadequate oxygen, pollutants, etc. With internal fertilization the most serious problem is in timing of fertilization. Both eggs and sperm live only a short while, and in most animals fertilization can only occur at certain times. Thus mating must occur during those periods.

Chapter 22

Rationale

The chapter begins with a detailed discussion of cleavage, blastula formation, gastrulation, and the formation of the three germ layers. Next, growth and differentiation are examined. Then the role of the nucleus and cytoplasm in development and the role of neighboring cells in differentiation are discussed. The chapter concludes with a discussion of external development in water and on land and internal development. A detailed description of the internal structure of the chicken egg and its extraembryonic membranes is given. There is a comparison of development in placental and nonplacental mammals.

Audiovisual Materials

"Amphibian Embryos (Frog, Toad, and Salamander)," (16 min., color) EBE.

"Birth of the Red Kangaroo," (21 min., color) IFB.

"Chick Embryo: Life is Born," (15 min., color) McGraw-Hill.

"Development of the Chick: Extraembryonic Membranes," (20 min., color) IU.

"Development and Differentiation," (20 min., color) CRM.

"Reproduction Among Mammals," (11 min., b&w) EBE.

"The Chick Embryo: From Primitive Streak to Hatching," (13 min., color) EBE.

"The Fish Embryo: From Fertilization to Hatching," (12 min., color) EBE.

"The Frog," (12 min., color) EBE.

"The Sea Urchin: From Egg to Adult," (16 min., color) McGraw-Hill.

Answers to Test Your Understanding

1. *Cleavage* is a series of cell divisions that occurs in the zygote immediately after fertilization.

2. The *morula* consists of a solid ball of cells. The *blastula* is a hollow sphere that is generally one cell layer thick.

3. The eggs of frogs and chickens contain a lot of yolk. In eggs of this type the cells undergoing cleavage are found at one pole of the embryo and the yolk at the other.

4. In gastrulation the cells on one side of the blastula push in to form a two-layered embryo called the *gastrula*. The outer layer of cells in the gastrula is the *ectoderm* and the inner layer is the *endoderm*. A third cell layer, the *mesoderm*, forms between them. The ectoderm, mesoderm, and endoderm are the three germ layers.

5. *ectoderm:* nervous system; lining of mouth, nostrils, and anus; epidermis of skin

mesoderm: bones and muscle; blood and blood vessels; reproductive and excretory systems; dermis of skin

endoderm: lining of digestive tract, trachea, bronchi, and lungs; liver and pancreas; thyroid and parathyroids; urinary bladder

6. In most animals, the blastopore becomes the anus. The second opening of the digestive system—the mouth—forms where the primitive gut cavity (archenteron) breaks through at the opposite end of the developing embryo.

7. *Differentiation* is the series of changes that transforms the unspecialized embryonic cells into the specialized cells, tissues, and organs of the organism.

8. It appears that the control of development involves an interaction between the DNA of the chromosomes and various constituents of the cytoplasm. As a result of this interaction different parts of the DNA are switched on and off in different cells, and this in turn determines the direction of cellular differentiation.

9. *Embryonic induction* is the process by which certain parts of the developing embryo (the *organizers*) induce other structures to differentiate.

10. Nourishment for the embryo is supplied by yolk in the egg. Oxygen from the surrounding water diffuses into the egg, while wastes from the embryo diffuse out of the egg into the water.

11. Some advantages of external development in water are that the egg contains all the nutrients the embryo needs and that oxygen can be obtained and wastes gotten rid of by simple diffusion. Also, once the eggs are laid and fertilized, no further parental care is generally necessary. Some disadvantages are that water is required for fertilization and development and that although large numbers of eggs are produced, most are destroyed before development is completed.

12. The egg of a bird contains large amounts of yolk within a hard, calcium-containing shell. The embryo is surrounded by four membranes that protect it and carry out necessary life processes.

13. The *chorion* aids in gas exchange. The *allantois* collects the metabolic wastes of the embryo. The *amnion* contains the amniotic fluid, which acts as a cushion and protects the embryo from shocks. The *yolk sac* produces blood vessels that transport food to the embryo.

14. The shelled egg is waterproof and provides the embryo with a self-contained aquatic environment. It provides good protection for the embryo, contains all food necessary for development, and allows diffusion of oxygen and carbon dioxide.

15. The *placenta* is a structure that connects the developing embryo to the uterus and through which the embryo obtains food and oxygen and gets rid of wastes.

16. In placental mammals development occurs in the uterus.

17. In pouched mammals development begins in the uterus and is completed in a pouch on the outside of the mother's body.

Answers to Test Your Understanding

1. The fertilized egg undergoes a series of cell divisions (cleavage) during which no cell growth occurs. This results in the formation of a solid ball of cells, which is the *morula* stage. As cleavage continues, the cells undergo a rearrangement resulting in the formation of a hollow, fluid-filled sphere. At this stage the embryo is called a *blastula*. Mitotic division continues, eventually reaching a stage where division is accompanied by growth and by movements of cells that establish the shape of the embryo. The cells on one side of the blastula push inward, forming a two-layered embryo called the *gastrula*.

2. In organisms in which fertilization and development are external and in which there is little or no parental care, tremendous numbers of gametes must be produced to ensure the survival of even a few offspring from a mating. In organisms in which fertilization and development are internal, relatively few eggs are produced but many sperm are produced to ensure fertilization. In these organisms the chances of survival of each fertilized egg are much greater than in eggs that undergo external development. Parental care helps to ensure survival of the young.

3. For normal development to occur, the cells of the embryo must do more than just grow and divide. They must move around for the embryo to develop its characteristic shape and they must differentiate to form all the tissues and organs. The movement and differentiation of the cells involves an interaction between the DNA of the nucleus and constituents of the cytoplasm. In different cells certain parts of the nuclear DNA are functional while other parts are nonfunctional. This is one factor controlling cell differentiation. Another factor is the presence of organizers. Organizers are groups of cells that affect the differentiation of nearby cells.

4. External development in water involves the production of tremendous numbers of gametes. Behavioral adaptations are necessary to ensure that the male and female gametes are released together so that there is some chance of fertilization. Even when a large number of eggs are fertilized, environmental hazards kill many of the developing embryos. Animals that reproduce on land generally have internal fertilization. In those that undergo external development the eggs are generally surrounded by a protective covering. With internal fertilization fewer gametes are produced because the chances of fertilization are better. Care of the young by the parents further ensures survival of some of the young. Internal fertilization and internal development provide the highest rate of survival for the young.

Chapter 23

Rationale

Chapter 23 deals with human reproduction It opens with a detailed discussion of the anatomy and physiology of the male and female reproductive systems. The stages and regulation of the menstrual cycle are presented. Fertilization, implantation, and development are discussed next. The role of the placenta and extraembryonic membranes are described. There is a discussion of the events of birth. The chapter ends with a brief explanation of multiple births.

The topic of human reproduction usually elicits many questions from the students. Discussion of these questions and many of the topics in this chapter require care and sensitivity on the part of the teacher.

Audiovisual Materials

"Biography of the Unborn," (17 min., color) EBE.
"Female Cycle," (8 min., color) FI.
"Hormone Controls in Human Reproduction," (16 min., color) McGraw-Hill.
"How Life Begins," (46 min., color) McGraw-Hill.
"Human Reproduction," 2nd ed. (20 min., color) McGraw-Hill.
"Reproduction Among Mammals," (11 min., b&w) EBE.
"The Fertilization Process (Problems and Phases)," (16 min., color) McGraw-Hill.
"The Human Body: Reproductive System," (14 min., color) Coronet.
"VD: A New Focus," (20 min., color) AEF.
"VD Quiz: Getting the Right Answers," (20 min., color) AEF.

Answers to Test Your Learning

1. The testes produce sperm and the male sex hormone testosterone.

2. Testosterone is responsible for the secondary sex characteristics of males, including body hair, muscle development, and deepness of voice.

3. The testes are located in the *scrotum*. The scrotum, which is a sac located outside the body walls, keeps the testes at a slightly lower temperature than the rest of the body. This lower temperature is necessary for the production of viable sperm.

4. Immature sperm are produced in the *seminiferous tubules* of the testes. From there they pass to the *epididymis,* where they are stored until they mature. From the epididymis the sperm pass into the *vas deferens* and then into the *urethra,* which passes through the penis to the outside of the body.

5. Secretions are added to the sperm by the *seminal vesicles, Cowper's glands,* and the *prostate gland.*

6. Semen consists of the sperm plus the secretions of the seminal vesicles, Cowper's glands, and the prostate gland.

7. The ovaries produce eggs and secrete the female sex hormone estrogen.

8. Estrogen is responsible for the female secondary sex characteristics, such as breasts, broadened pelvis, and pattern of fat distribution. It also is one of the hormones that regulates the menstrual cycle.

9. The two ovaries are located deep in the lower part of the abdomen.

10. From the follicle in the ovary, the egg enters and passes down the Fallopian tube into the uterus. The degenerating egg then passes through the cervix, down the vagina, and out of the body.

11. The menstrual cycle involves the maturation and release of an egg from the ovaries, the build-up of the uterine wall in preparation for implantation, and the breakdown of the uterine wall if fertilization and implantation do not occur.

12. *Menopause* is when the menstrual cycle ceases. This usually occurs between the ages of 40 and 50.

13. During the *follicle stage* one of the follicles in the ovaries develops and matures. As the follicle develops, the lining of the uterus thickens with mucus and a rich supply of blood vessels. This stage lasts 10 to 14 days.

During the *ovulation stage* the follicle ruptures and releases a mature egg. This usually takes place in about the middle of the cycle.

During the *corpus luteum stage* the follicle fills with cells, forming a yellow body called the corpus luteum. During this period the uterine lining is maintained and continues to thicken, and no new follicles mature. This stage lasts 10 to 14 days.

During the *menstruation stage* the corpus luteum and thickened lining of the uterus both break down. The extra layers of the uterine lining, the unfertilized egg, and a small amount of blood pass out of the body through the vagina. This is called *menstruation* and lasts about 3 to 5 days.

14. Fertilization generally occurs while the egg is in the oviduct.

15. When a sperm reaches an egg, it breaks through the membrane surrounding the egg, and the sperm nucleus enters the egg cell cytoplasm. Once this has occurred, the membranes around the egg change so that no other sperm can enter the egg. The sperm nucleus moves to the egg nucleus and two nuclei fuse. The resulting cell is the zygote.

16. After fertilization, the zygote undergoes cleavage and develops into a blastula. Meanwhile, it is moving down the oviduct toward the uterus. Some 5 to 10 days later it enters the uterus, where the outer layer of embryo cells secretes enzymes that digest part of the thick uterine lining. The embryo becomes implanted at this spot. After implantation, the embryo undergoes gastrulation.

17. *Pregnancy* is the period during which the developing baby is carried in the uterus. The term *embryo* is used to refer to a developing human from the time of fertilization until it is about 8 weeks old. From that point until birth it is called a *fetus*.

18. A hormone secreted by the chorion prevents the breakdown of the corpus luteum, which continues to secrete high levels of progesterone. The progesterone maintains the thickened uterine wall.

19. The placenta is formed from chorionic villi and the lining of the uterus.

20. In the placenta nutrients and oxygen diffuse from the mother's blood into the fetus' blood, while wastes diffuse from the fetus' blood into the mother's blood. Thus the placenta allows the fetus to obtain nutrients and oxygen from the mother and to get rid of wastes.

21. The umbilical cord, which contains fetal blood vessels, connects the fetus to the placenta.

22. The *chorion* is involved in implantation and the formation of the placenta. The *amnion,* which is filled with fluid, surrounds the fetus. The fluid provides a stable environment and cushions the fetus against shocks. The *allantois* and *yolk sac* form the umbilical cord.

23. When the fetus is ready to be born, the uterine muscles begin slow, rhythmic contractions and the opening of the cervix expands. When the cervix is fully expanded, the contractions force the fetus out of the uterus into the vagina and then out of the mother's body. The amniotic membrane bursts, and the fluid that is released eases the passage of the baby through the birth canal.

24. The afterbirth consists of the placenta and amnion, which are expelled from the mother's body by additional uterine contractions.

25. *Identical twins* result from a single fertilized egg that has split in two very early in development. *Fraternal twins* are produced from two eggs fertilized by different sperm at the same time.

Answers to Test Your Understanding

1. FSH from the pituitary controls the development of follicles in the ovary. Maturing follicles secrete estrogen, which causes thickening of the uterine lining. High estrogen concentrations inhibit the production of FSH and stimulate secretion of LH by the pituitary. LH causes ovulation and development of the corpus luteum. The corpus luteum secretes progesterone, which maintains growth of the uterine lining and inhibits development of new follicles. If fertilization does not occur, secretion of LH decreases and the corpus luteum breaks down, which in turn decreases the level of progesterone. Without the progesterone, the uterine lining breaks down and menstruation occurs. During menstruation, a new follicle is maturing in the ovary and the cycle begins again.

2. Only one sperm enters the egg because as soon as the sperm enters, the membrane around the egg changes, preventing the entrance of any other sperm.

3. If the pituitary does not secrete adequate FSH, no follicles will mature in the ovary and the menstrual cycle will not occur.

4. During pregnancy, the menstrual cycle is suppressed. The thickened lining of the uterus is maintained by progesterone secreted by the corpus luteum. The placenta also secretes hormones that maintain pregnancy. Oxytocin affects uterine contractions during labor and prolactin affects the secretion of milk by the mammary glands.

Chapter 24

Rationale

Chapter 24 describes the life cycles of the major plant groups—mosses, ferns, and seed plants. The chapter begins with a discussion of alternation of generations. The life cycles of mosses and ferns are then described.

The life cycles of gymnosperms and angiosperms are described in detail. The chapter ends with a discussion of seed dispersal and seed dormancy and germination. Audiovisual materials and class demonstrations of appropriate plants will enhance presentation of this material. You may want to have students collect various types of seeds, emphasizing dispersal mechanisms.

Audiovisual Materials

"Angiosperms—The Flowering Plants," (21 min., color) EBE.
"Evolution of Vascular Plants," (17 min., color) EBE.
"Flowers at Work," (11 min., color) EBE.
"Gymnosperms," (17 min., color) EBE.
"Mosses, Liverworts and Ferns," (12 min., color) Coronet.
"Pollen Germination and Tube Growth," (4 min., color) Modern Learning Aids.
"Pollination and Fertilization in Flowering Plants," (7 min., color) Modern Learning Aids.
"Seed Dispersal," (15 min., color) EBE.
"Seed Germination," (15 min., color) EBE.
"Sexual Reproduction in Ferns," (11 min., color) Modern Learning Aids.
"The Liverwort: Alternation of Generations," (15 min., color) Coronet.

Answers to Test Your Learning

1. The *gametophyte* is the monoploid, gamete-producing stage in the life cycle of a plant. The *sporophyte* is the diploid, spore-producing stage.

2. Plants whose life cycles have a sporophyte stage and a gametophyte stage are said to shown an *alternation of generations*.

3. The gametophyte generation is dominant in mosses.

4. In the moss life cycle there are male and female gametophytes. In the male gametophyte, the reproductive organ is the *antheridium,* which produces sperm. In the female gametophyte the reproductive organ is the *archegonium,* which produces eggs. Sperm released from the antheridium swim through rain or dew to reach the egg in the archegonium. Fertilization of the egg produces a diploid sporophyte, which grows directly from the archegonium. It is a leafless stalk with a capsule at the tip. Monoploid spores are produced by meiosis in the capsule. Each spore can produce a new monoploid gametophyte.

5. The sporophyte stage is dominant in ferns.

6. In the fern sporophyte there is an underground stem called a *rhizome*. True roots grow downward from the lower surface of the rhizome, while fronds, or leaves, grow upward from the upper surface. Spore-producing sori are found on the backs of some fronds.

The fern gametophyte, or prothallus, is a small, heart-shaped structure that contains both an antheridium and an archegonium. Rootlike rhizoids extend from the lower surface and anchor the plant.

7. In the sori of the sporophyte plant monoploid spores are produced by meiosis. The spores are released, and under favorable conditions each will germinate to form a prothallus containing both antheridium and archegonium. An egg is fertilized by a sperm from another prothallus, and the fertilized egg develops into a new sporophyte plant.

8. In the life cycles of both mosses and ferns the sperm must swim through water to reach the egg. Without water, fertilization cannot occur.

9. pines, spruce, hemlocks

10. The reproductive structures of gymnosperms are *cones*. The female cone is called the *seed cone,* while the male cone is called the *pollen cone*.

11. The sporophyte generation is dominant in gymnosperms.

12. Pollen, the male gametophyte, is released from the pollen cone and lands on a sticky material near the micropyle of the ovule, which is the female gametophyte. From the pollen grain a pollen tube grows into the micropyle. Two sperm cells pass into the ovule. One sperm fertilizes the egg, which develops into the plant embryo. The ovule, which contains the plant embryo, develops into seed. The seed is eventually released from the seed cone and under favorable conditions develops into a new sporophyte plant, which produces pollen or eggs by meiosis.

13. The sporophyte generation is dominant in angiosperms.

14. See Figures 24-6 (page 391), and 24-7 and 24-8 (page 392).

15. The *pedicel* supports the flower and connects it to the stem of the plant. The *receptacle* is the expanded end of the pedicel from which the flower grows. The *sepals* are leaflike structures that surround the base of the flower and protect it before it opens. The *petals* are modified leaves found within the sepals and surrounding the stamens and pistils. The *stamens* are the male reproductive organs of angiosperms, while *pistils* are the female reproductive organs.

16. Within the anthers of the stamens, monoploid spores are produced by meiosis. The spores develop into pollen grains, each containing two monoploid nuclei.

The ovary of the pistil contains one or more ovules. In each ovule four monoploid spores are produced by meiosis. Three of the spores degenerate, and the remaining spore divides by mitosis to form the female gametophyte, or embryo sac, which contains seven cells. One cell near the micropyle serves as the egg.

17. *Pollination* is the transfer of pollen from an anther to a stigma. *Self-pollination* is the transfer of pollen from an anther to a stigma on the same plant. *Cross-pollination* is the transfer of pollen from the anther of one plant to the stigma of another plant.

18. When a pollen grain becomes stuck on a stigma, it breaks open and a pollen tube grows down through the stigma and style and through the micropyle into the ovary. The growth of the pollen tube is controlled by the tube nucleus of the pollen grain. The tube nucleus and the generative nucleus pass from the pollen grain down the pollen tube. During this time the generative nucleus divides to form two monoploid sperm nuclei. The two sperm nuclei enter the embryo sac. One sperm fertilizes the egg, forming the diploid zygote, and the other fuses with two polar nuclei to form the triploid *endosperm nucleus*.

19. The ovary and associated structures form the fruit.

20. The seed, which develops from an ovule, consists of a seed coat, the embryo, and the endosperm. The seed coat develops from the wall of the ovule. The plant embryo develops from the fertilized egg, and the endosperm forms from the endosperm nucleus.

21. The plant embryo consists of one or two cotyledons, the epicotyl, hypocotyl, and radicle. Cotyledons are modified leaves. In some seeds they are greatly thickened and contain stored food for the embryo. The epicotyl, which is located above the cotyledons, gives rise to the terminal bud, leaves, and upper part of the stem. The hypocotyl, which is the part of the embryo below the cotyledons, gives rise to the lower part of the stem. The radicle, the lower-most part of the hypocotyl, gives rise to the roots.

22. *Cotyledons* are modified leaves that make up part of the plant embryo. In some types of plants they contain stored food that is used to nourish the developing embryo.

23. In some plants the fruits burst, scattering the seeds over a wide area. In some, the seeds are very light and are scattered by the wind. Some seeds are carried away from the parent plant by water, some become attached to the fur of passing animals. Some fruits are eaten by birds or mammals and the indigestible seeds later deposited along with digestive wastes.

24. It is important for survival of the species. If seeds were not scattered but remained instead around the parent plant overcrowding would result and the competition for natural resources would result in the death of any new plants.

25. Seed germination is affected by temperature and availability of water and oxygen. Some seeds may require light to germinate.

26. *Dormancy* is a period during which the seed will not germinate even if environmental conditions are favorable. The length of the dormant period varies from one seed to another, even within the same species. Thus if harsh environmental conditions kill some germinating seeds, others still in a dormant phase will survive.

Answers to Test Your Understanding

1. Mosses and ferns need water for fertilization to occur because the sperm must swim to the egg. In gymnosperms and angiosperms the pollen tube serves as a passageway between the sperm and the egg.

In gymnosperms and angiosperms the embryo is enclosed within a seed, while mosses and ferns do not produce seeds.

2. In gymnosperms the seeds develop on the female cone. In angiosperms the seeds are enclosed within a fruit.

3. In mosses, the gametophyte generation is dominant. In ferns, gymnosperms, and angiosperms, the sporophyte generation is dominant.

4. To botanists, a fruit is a seed-containing structure that develops from the ovary of a flower. String beans, olives, tomatoes, and cucumbers are fruits. In popular usage the term is applied to sweet-tasting fruits. The term *vegetable* has no scientific meaning.

5. Bean seeds are dicots in which nutrients are stored only in the cotyledons. In the developing bean seedling, the epicotyl gives rise to the terminal bud, the leaves, and the upper part of the stem. The hypocotyl gives rise to the lower part of the stem, and the radicle gives rise to the roots.

Corn is a monocot, and each kernel is a complete fruit that contains one seed. The embryo is partially surrounded by endosperm. Nutrients are stored both in the endosperm and in the cotyledon. In the developing corn seedling, the epicotyl gives rise to the stem and leaves, while the hypocotyl and radicle give rise to the roots.

Chapter 25

Rationale

This chapter deals with the basic principles of heredity. Mendel's experiments with pea plants are described and his principles of dominance, segregation, and independent assortment are explained. Modern genetic terminology, simple probability, and the Punnett square are smoothly integrated into the discussion. The use of the test cross is explained. The chapter ends with a discussion of incomplete dominance and multiple alleles.

Audiovisual Materials

"Genetics: Mendel's Laws," (14 min., color) Coronet.
"Heredity," (11 min., b&w) EBE.
"Mechanism of Inheritance," (14 min., color or b&w) McGraw-Hill.
"Mendel's Experiments," (30 min., b&w) Association Sterling Films.

Answers to Test Your Learning

1. genetics

2. Genes are found on the chromosomes of the nucleus. They are composed of DNA.

3. Gregor Mendel conducted the first scientific studies of heredity in the 1850s and 1860s.

4. Pea plants were a good choice for research because they are easy to grow, mature quickly, and have sharply contrasting traits. Also, the structure of the flower allows the scientist to carry out artificial cross-pollination under controlled conditions.

5. Mendel found that pea plants showed one of two forms of certain traits and that he could isolate plants that were pure-breeding for those traits. He crossed plants that were pure for contrasting traits. For example, he crossed pure tall plants with pure short plants. He collected the seeds produced by these crosses, carefully separating those from different plants. He kept complete records and analyzed his results mathematically.

6. The F_1, or first filial, generation is the first generation of offspring from a cross.

7. All members of the F_1 generation showed one of the two contrasting traits of the parents. For example, in the cross between pure short and pure tall plants, all offspring were tall.

8. A *hybrid* is the offspring of a cross between pure parents showing contrasting traits.

9. According to the principle of dominance, when organisms pure for contrasting traits are crossed, all their offspring will show the dominant trait.

10. According to the principle of segregation, in successive generations recessive factors can be separated from the dominant factors and recombined to produce the recessive trait.

11. Mendel's results were explained by the discovery that the hereditary information is carried on the chromosomes. The separation of homologous chromosomes during meiosis and their recombination by fertilization explained Mendel's principal of segregation.

12. *Alleles* are different genes for the same trait. An organism in which both alleles for a particular trait are the same is *homozygous* for that trait. If the two alleles are different, the organism is *heterozygous*.

13. The genetic makeup of an organism is its *genotype*. The traits that an organism develops as the result of its genotype are its *phenotype*.

14. If there are several possible events that might occur, and no one of them is more likely to occur than any other, then they will all occur in equal numbers over a large number of trials.

15. The Punnett square is a diagram that can be used to show the results of any genetic cross.

16. In a hybrid cross, the offspring show a phenotype ratio of 3:1—3 dominant to 1 recessive. The genotype ratio is 1:2:1—1 homozygous dominant, 2 heterozygous, and 1 homozygous recessive.

17. The principle of independent assortment states that the genes for different traits are separated and distributed to gametes independently of one another. In the dihybrid cross, Mendel crossed a plant that was pure for both dominant traits with a plant pure for both recessive traits. As expected, in the F_1 generation all offspring showed both dominant traits. In the F_2 generation, each trait calculated separately showed the 3:1 ratio. This led Mendel to believe that factors are inherited independently of one another.

18. 9:3:3:1 (9 dominant-dominant; 3 dominant-recessive; 3 recessive-dominant; and 1 recessive-recessive)

19. A test cross is used to determine whether an organism that shows the dominant trait is pure dominant or hybrid.

20. The organism in question is mated with an organism showing the recessive trait. If any of the offspring show the recessive trait, the test organism was hybrid.

21. *Incomplete dominance* is a type of inheritance in which both alleles contribute to the phenotype of a heterozygous individual.

22. Inheritance of flower color in the Japanese four-o'clock shows incomplete dominance. A cross between a plant with red flowers and a plant with white flowers results in offspring with pink flowers. In Andalusian chickens, a cross between a chicken with black feathers and one with white feathers results in offspring with feathers in which there are patches of black and patches of white.

23. For some traits, more than two different alleles exist in a species. Blood type in humans involves multiple alleles.

24. An individual can have only two alleles for any one trait.

Answers to Test Your Understanding

1. B = black b = brown
S = short hair s = long hair

(A) In a cross between a homozygous black guinea pig (BB) and a brown guinea pig (bb) all the offspring will be black (Bb).

(B) In a cross between two dihybrid black short-haired guinea pigs, the offspring show a ratio of 9 black, short-haired (dominant-dominant) to 3 black long-haired (dominant-recessive) to 3 brown short-haired (recessive-dominant) to 1 brown long-haired (recessive-recessive).

2. B = brown eyes b = blue eyes

(A) In a cross between a heterozygous brown-eyed father (Bb) and a blue-eyed mother (bb), the offspring would be 50 percent brown-eyed and 50 percent blue-eyed. The brown-eyed offspring would be heterozygous (Bb) and the blue-eyed would be homozygous recessive (bb).

(B) father = Bb mother = Bb children = bb

3. Both sets of parents could have produced offspring with blood type AB. However, only the parents with types AO and BO could have produced the child with type O blood.

4. Cross the plant with one showing the recessive traits—wrinkled green seeds. If any of the offspring show the recessive traits, the test plant was heterozygous for the trait.

Chapter 26

Rationale

Chapter 26 covers modern genetic theory. It opens with Sutton's chromosome theory. This is followed by a discussion of sex determination and sex-linked traits. Gene linkage, crossing-over, multiple-gene inheritance, and the role of the environment in gene expression are covered. Gene and chromosomal mutations are defined, and the various types of chromosomal mutations are described. The chapter closes with discussions of human heredity and genetic diseases and the genetic techniques used in plant and animal breeding.

Audiovisual Materials

"Genetics: Chromosomes and Genes," (15 min., color) Coronet.
"Genetics: Improving Plants and Animals," (13 min., color) Coronet.
"Heredity and Environment," (11 min., color or b&w) Coronet.
"Human Heredity," (22 min., color) Churchill.
"Improving Strains of Livestock," (13 min., b&w) EBE.
"It Runs in the Family," (30 min., b&w) Association Sterling Films.

Answers to Test Your Learning

1. Sutton explained Mendel's dihybrid experiment by stating that the genes for yellow or green seeds are on one chromosome and the genes for wrinkled or round seeds are on another. In this way independent assortment could occur.

2. An *autosome* is any of the chromosomes of a cell except the sex chromosomes.

3. In males the sex chromosomes consist of one X and one Y chromosome. In females there are two X chromosomes. All eggs contain an X chromosome. A sperm, on the other hand, may contain either an X or a Y chromosome. If the egg is fertilized by a sperm carrying an X chromosome, the new individual will be female (XX). If the sperm carries a Y chromosome, the new individual will be male (XY).

4. *Drosophila* are tiny and can be cultured in a small space. A female produces up to 300 offspring from a single mating. This is important because test results could not be considered valid with only a few offspring. The life cycle of the fruit fly is completed in about 14 days. Thus many generations can be studied in a relatively short time. Fruit flies have only four pairs of chromosomes, and the salivary glands contain giant chromosomes that are easy to see and study.

5. Sex-linked genes are genes found only on the X chromosome. Sex-linked genes were discovered by T.H. Morgan in his studies of the trait for white eyes in fruit flies.

6. In the cells of a male, there is only one X chromosome, while in a female there are two. If an abnormal gene is present on one X chromosome in a female, there may be a normal gene on the homologous chromosome that will counteract or mask the effect of the abnormal gene. In a male, however, there is no homologous chromosome, so any abnormal gene on the X chromosome is expressed in the phenotype of the individual.

7. Linked genes are genes located on the same chromosome.

8. Crossing-over is the exchange of parts between homologous chromosomes. It occurs during synapsis in meiosis.

9. Crossing-over is an important source of variation among offspring.

10. Gene maps show the sequence of genes on a chromosome. They are based on the frequency with which the genes become separated by crossing-over.

11. Multiple genes are two or more independent pairs of genes that affect the same trait.

12. Himalayan rabbits have black fur on their ears, noses, feet, and tails, while the rest of the body is white. This color pattern is produced by a gene that causes the deposition of black pigment where the body temperature falls below 33°C.

13. A *mutation* is a new trait that appears suddenly. A *mutant* is an individual who first shows the new trait.

14. In a gene mutation a new allele for an existing trait suddenly appears on the chromosome that carries the gene. A chromosomal mutation involves a change in the structure of an entire chromosome or a change in the number of chromosomes within the cells of an organism.

15. *Translocation* is the transfer of a chromosome segment to a nonhomologous chromosome. *Inversion* involves the rotation of a piece of a chromosome so that the order of genes is reversed. *Addition* involves the breaking off of a chromosome segment and its attachment to the homologous chromosome. *Deletion* is the breaking off of a chromosome segment, resulting in the loss of some genes.

16. Nondisjunction is the failure of the chromosomes to separate normally after synapsis. The cells of the new organism may have an extra chromosome or may be missing a chromosome. Down's syndrome, Turner's syndrome, and Klinefelter's syndrome are caused by nondisjunction.

17. *Polyploidy* is a condition in which the cells contain some multiple of the normal chromosome number.

18. Studies of human genetics are difficult because the time between generations is so long, the number of offspring produced is so small, and no controlled experiments are possible.

19. In *sickle-cell anemia* the hemoglobin of the red blood cells is abnormal, which affects its oxygen-carrying capacity. The red cells have an abnormal shape, which causes them to clump in the small blood vessels. In *phenylketonuria* the lack of an enzyme causes products of phenylalanine metabolism to accumulate in the body, damaging the brain and causing mental retardation. *Tay-Sachs disease* results from the lack of an enzyme necessary for lipid metabolism in the brain. The lipids accumulate in the brain cells and destroy them.

20. Genetic counseling gives prospective parents an accurate idea about the risks they carry of having a child with a genetic defect.

21. In *amniocentesis* a needle is inserted into the amniotic sac and a small sample of the amniotic fluid is withdrawn. This fluid contains cells from the baby, which are cultured and subjected to various tests designed to detect genetic defects. In *karyotyping* a photograph is taken of a fetal cell undergoing mitosis. The photograph is enlarged and the chromosomes examined for abnormalities.

22. *Selection* is choosing certain plants or animals for breeding to perpetuate their desirable characteristics. *Inbreeding* is the mating of closely related individuals to perpetuate specific traits. *Outbreeding* is the mating of unrelated individuals to introduce new, desirable genes into the population.

23. Close relatives are generally prohibited from marrying because harmful recessive genes may thereby be brought together and expressed. Inbreeding may increase the number of homozygous genes.

24. Mutations are used by plant and animal breeders to improve their stock. When a mutant organism carrying a desirable new trait appears, breeders try to perpetuate this trait in their stock.

Answers to Test Your Understanding

1. (A) In a marriage between a color-blind male and a normal female, all the female offspring would be carriers for color blindness and all the male offspring would be normal.

(B) In a marriage between a normal male and a color-blind female, all the female offspring would be carriers and all the male offspring would be color-blind.

2. If these genes had been located on the same chromosomes, they would not have assorted independently, although they might occasionally have been separated by crossing-over. In general the two traits being studied would have been inherited together.

3. From studies of spermatogenesis in grasshoppers Sutton realized that the chromosomes that separated during meiosis were the same chromosomes that had united during fertilization. On reviewing Mendel's work he realized that Mendel's factors, or genes, might be carried on the chromosomes, and that the results of Mendel's dihybrid cross could be explained if the genes for the two traits studied were carried on different chromosomes.

Morgan, in studies on *Drosophila,* discovered the existence of sex-linked traits. He also noted that certain traits appeared to be inherited together and concluded that the genes for these traits were located on the same chromosome—they were linked. However, in a small percentage of cases the linked genes separated during meiosis. Morgan discovered that this was caused by the exchange of parts between homologous chromosomes during meiosis, a process he called *crossing-over*.

4. For traits involving multiple alleles the trait is controlled by one pair of genes located on homologous chromosomes. However, there are more than two possible forms of the genes (alleles) for the trait. For traits involving multiple genes, there is more than one pair of genes affecting the trait.

Chapter 27

Rationale

Molecular genetics relates hereditary processes to the biochemical nature of the gene. The chapter opens with a description of the research that resulted in the identification of DNA as the genetic material. The chemical composition of DNA is reviewed and the work of Watson and Crick on the structure of DNA is presented. DNA replication is described.

The next section deals with proteins and cellular activities. The importance of enzymes and the one gene—one enzyme hypothesis of gene function are described. Protein synthesis is described in detail, including the genetic code, messenger RNA, transfer RNA, ribosomal RNA, and the assembly of polypeptides.

The following sections deal with the gene. The control of gene transcription in *E. coli* is described, and gene mutations, cytoplasmic DNA, and transformation and transduction are discussed. The chapter closes with sections on genetic engineering, plasmids, recombinant DNA, and cloning.

Audiovisual Materials

"Assault on Life," (50 min., color) Time-Life Films.
"Between the Living and Non-living," (29 min., b&w) IU.
"Cytoplasmic Heredity," (30 min., color or b&w) McGraw-Hill.
"DNA: Molecule of Heredity," (16 min., color or b&w) EBE.
"Smaller Than Life," (39 min., color) Time-Life Films.
"Stop or Go: An Experiment in Genetics," (29 min., color) IU.

Answers to Test Your Learning

1. In Griffith's key experiment, he mixed dead type S bacteria with live type R bacteria. When this mixture was injected into mice, the mice developed pneumonia and died. Live type S bacteria were found in the tissues of the dead mice. This indicated that in some way material from the dead type S bacteria had transformed the live type R bacteria into type S.

2. They identified the transforming material in Griffith's experiment as DNA.

3. Hershey and Chase tagged the DNA of some phages with radioactive phosphorus and the protein coats of other phages with radioactive sulfur. The phages were then exposed to bacterial cultures. When the bacterial cells were examined, it was found that they contained large amounts of radioactive phosphorus, but little sulfur. This indicated that the DNA of the phage enters the bacterial cell and that the DNA carries the genetic information for making more phages.

4. DNA is made up of the sugar deoxyribose, phosphate groups, and nitrogenous bases. The bases found in DNA are the purines adenine and guanine and the pyrimidines cytosine and thymine.

5. According to the Watson-Crick model, DNA consists of two parallel chains of sugar-phosphate groups. Pairs of bases link the chains together, and the whole structure is coiled to form a double helix.

6. The two strands of DNA are said to be complementary because in the pairing of bases adenine and thymine bond only to each other and cytosine and guanine bond only to each other. Thus, wherever there is an adenine in one chain there is a thymine in the other, etc.

7. In replicating, the double DNA strand separates to form two single strands, like opening a zipper. Complementary nucleotides become bonded to the exposed nitrogen bases, thereby forming two complete double strands identical to the original.

8. Like DNA, RNA is made up of nucleotides. RNA nucleotides contain the sugar ribose instead of the deoxyribose found in DNA. In RNA, thymine is replaced by uracil. Like thymine, uracil bonds only with adenine. The other three nitrogen bases are the same in both nucleic acids. Unlike DNA, RNA molecules are single-stranded.

9. Enzyme production in the cell is controlled by the hereditary material.

10. In their experiments, Beadle and Tatum used the bread mold *Neurospora,* which can normally grow on a minimal medium. Beadle and Tatum irradiated the mold with X rays to produce mutations. After exposure to X rays, the mold could not survive on a minimal medium. If amino acids were added, some of the molds could grow. By adding the amino acids one at a time, Beadle and Tatum were able to separate the molds that needed one particular amino acid. The inability to produce a particular amino acid meant that the mold had lost the gene needed to make an enzyme involved in the synthesis of that amino acid.

11. According to the one gene—one polypeptide hypothesis, each gene directs the synthesis of one specific polypeptide chain.

12. The hereditary information is encoded in the sequence of the nucleotides in DNA.

13. A *codon* is a group of three nitrogen bases that specifies an amino acid.

14. The synthesis of mRNA is similar to DNA replication. The two strands of DNA separate temporarily. Complementary RNA nucleotides take their places along one of the exposed strands. When the assembled RNA sequence reaches the end of the polypeptide message, it becomes detached from the DNA strand.

15. *Transcription* is the copying of a genetic message from DNA into a molecule of mRNA.

16. Transfer RNA is found in the cell cytoplasm. There are twenty different kinds of tRNA, and each one will pick up only one type of amino acid. In protein synthesis, the tRNA carries a specific amino acid to a particular place specified by the mRNA.

17. A ribosome consists of protein and two different rRNA subunits. The protein for the ribosome is synthesized in the cytoplasm and then migrates into the nucleus. In the nucleoli, the protein and the two rRNA subunits are combined to form complete ribosomes.

18. The assembly of a polypeptide takes place in the cytoplasm using the information carried in the mRNA. Ribosomes become attached to the mRNA strand at intervals along its length. Where the ribosome is attached to the mRNA, a tRNA carrying the amino acid specified by the mRNA becomes attached temporarily to the mRNA. The amino acid brought into position by the tRNA joins the last amino acid in the forming chain and separates from the tRNA. The ribosome then moves along to the next codon on the mRNA.

19. The production of the three lactose-digesting enzymes in *E. coli* is controlled by three structural genes. When these genes are functioning, the enzymes are synthesized. When they are not functioning, the enzymes are not synthesized. The activity of the structural genes is controlled by an operator gene, and the activity of the operator gene is in turn controlled by a protein repressor. When lactose is not present in the cell, the repressor protein, which is produced constantly, binds with the operator, which prevents the structural genes from producing the enzymes. When lactose is present in the cell, some lactose molecules bind with the repressor. The operator is turned on and the structural genes are transcribed, resulting in the synthesis of the lactose-digesting enzymes.

20. A gene mutation is a change in the sequence of bases along a DNA strand.

21. Gene mutations may occur because of random errors in DNA replication. They may also be caused by mutagenic agents, such as X rays, mustard gas, and chloroform.

22. Gene mutations can involve the addition or deletion of an entire nucleotide or they can involve the substitution of one base for another.

23. Sickle-cell anemia is caused by the change of one base in the gene that controls the production of one of the polypeptide chains in the hemoglobin molecule.

24. Chloroplasts and mitochondria contain DNA.

25. Chloroplasts and mitochondria can replicate, or reproduce themselves.

26. In *transformation,* living bacteria take in DNA from dead bacteria, and the DNA causes traits of the dead bacteria to show up in the living bacterial cells. In *transduction* pieces of DNA are transferred from one bacterial cell to another by viruses.

27. *Recombinant DNA* is DNA in which a new gene has been inserted or attached.

28. *Plasmids* are ring-shaped segments of DNA found mainly in bacteria. Plasmids are being used to transfer new genes to bacterial cells. The new gene is inserted into the plasmid, and the bacterial cells are then exposed to the altered plasmid. When the plasmid is taken into a bacterium, the transplanted genes begin to be expressed, and the protein they specify is synthesized.

29. A *clone* is a group of individual organisms that have exactly the same genes.

Answers to Test Your Understanding

1. Each gene of an organism directs the synthesis of an enzyme or part of an enzyme. Every reaction in a living cell requires the presence of a specific enzyme. Genes control cell metabolism by controlling the synthesis of enzymes.

2. *Messenger RNA* is synthesized on strands of DNA in the nucleus. The genetic information in the DNA is encoded in the base sequence of the mRNA. The mRNA migrates into the cytoplasm, where this information is used for the synthesis of polypeptides. *Transfer RNA,* like mRNA, is formed on DNA strands in the nucleus. Each type of tRNA carries a particular amino acid for use in the synthesis of a polypeptide. *Ribosomal RNA* is formed from DNA in the nucleoli of the cell. It combines with a specific protein to form ribosomes, which function in protein synthesis.

3. The pairing of complementary bases occurs in DNA replication, RNA synthesis, and in the matching of codon and anticodon in the synthesis of a polypeptide.

4. Griffith discovered bacterial transformation in his experiments with type R and type S bacteria. Avery, MacLeod, and McCarty found that the transforming factor was DNA. Hershey and Chase found that in the infection of bacteria by bacteriophages, it is DNA from the phage that enters the bacterial cell and controls the production of new phages.

Chapter 28

Rationale

This chapter covers the evidence of organic change and early theories of evolution. It begins with a study of fossils. The formation of fossils and the fossil record are discussed. This is followed by sections on absolute dating, the geologic time scale, and evidences of evolution from comparative anatomy, comparative embryology, and comparative biochemistry and immunology.

Lamarck's theory of evolution is presented, and the chapter ends with a detailed discussed of Darwin's work.

Audiovisual Materials

"Charles Darwin," (24 min., color) UC.

"Darwin's Finches: Clues to the Origin of Species," (10 min., color) IU.

"Galapagos: Islands for Evolutionary Discovery," (20 min., color) FI.

"Natural Selection," (16 min., color) EBE.

"Story in the Rocks," (18 min., color) Shell Oil Co. (film division).

Answers to Test Your Learning

1. *Geologic evolution* is the continuous process of change undergone by the earth. *Organic evolution* is the continous process of change undergone by living things.

2. A *fossil* is the actual remains or any trace of an organism that lived at some time in the past.

3. (A) Fossils can be preserved in amber. Amber is formed from a sticky resin produced by trees. Insects trapped in the resin are often found in the amber. (B) Intact remains of various animals have been preserved in ice for thousands of years. (C) Hard parts of animals that are made up mostly of minerals may remain unchanged for millions of years. (D) In some cases the original substances of an organism are dissolved away and replaced by minerals from the water in which the remains lie. This process is called *petrifaction*. (E) In lakes and seas, dead organisms sink to the bottom and are gradually buried by particles of sand or mud. The sand or mud later hardens into rock. The remains of the organisms decay, but their shapes are preserved in the rock as a hollow *mold*. If the mold later becomes filled with minerals that harden into rock, the hardened minerals form a *cast*. (F) Impressions made by living things in mud may remain when the mud hardens into rock. Such impressions are called *imprints*.

4. Sedimentary rock generally forms at the bottom of shallow seas or in oceans along the shorelines of continents. Sediments in the water sink to the bottom, building up thick deposits. The material slowly hardens into rock by chemical processes combined with the great pressures exerted by the weight of the sediments. Different types of sediments deposited during the long, slow buildup show up in the rock as distinct layers.

5. In sedimentary rock, the lower layers were deposited earlier than the upper layers. Fossils in the lower layers represent organisms that lived at an earlier time than the fossils in the upper layers. *Correlation* is the process of matching rock layers in one location with rock layers in another location. Correlation makes it possible to establish the relative ages of rocks and fossils in nearby locations. *Index fossils* are fossils of species that flourished for a time over wide regions of the earth and then disappeared. Rock layers containing fossils of such organisms must have been formed during the period these organisms were in existence. By means of these index fossils, it is possible to match the relative ages of sedimentary rocks in widely separated parts of the earth.

6. Radioactive dating is based on the fact that certain elements have radioactive isotopes. These isotopes decay at a fixed rate into stable isotopes of other elements. The time required for half the atoms in a sample of a radioactive element to decay is called the half-life of that element. Radioactive dating is based on a comparison of the amounts of the radioisotope present in the sample and the amounts of the stable end product of decay. The actual age of a rock sample can be calculated by radioactive dating.

7. The geologic time scale shows the major events of the earth's history. The major subdivisions of the earth's history are the eras, which are divided into periods and epochs. The types of living things that flourished during each time period are listed.

8. The major eras of the geologic time scale are the Cenozoic, Mesozoic, and Paleozoic eras.

9. The fossil record became abundant during the Paleozoic era (during the Cambrian period).

10. *Homologous structures* are structures that are found in different kinds of organisms and that have the same basic arrangement of parts and a similar pattern of embryonic development. The presence of homologous structures is considered evidence of an evolutionary relationship among the organisms that possess them. *Analogous structures* are structures found in different types of organisms. They are similar in function or outward appearance but not in basic structure or pattern of embryonic development. The presence of analogous structures does not indicate any relationship between the organisms in which they are found.

11. *Vestigial structures* are the remnants of structures that were functional in some ancestral form. They are generally reduced in size and serve little or no function in modern animals. However, the presence of vestigial structures is considered good evidence of an evolutionary relationship between a modern animal and the ancestral form.

12. Embryos of related organisms show similar patterns of development, indicating a common evolutionary origin. The more closely related the organisms, the longer they will resemble each other during development.

13. Related organisms show similarities in their biochemical makeup, particularly in DNA and protein structure. Immunological reactions also provide evidence of evolutionary relationships. Using special antigen-antibody reactions, the closeness of the relationship between two organisms can be measured by the amount of precipitate that forms.

14. Lamarck's theory of evolution included the principle of use and disuse. According to this principle, the more an animal used a particular part of the body, the stronger and better developed it became. Parts that were not used became weak and were underdeveloped. The second part of Lamarck's theory of evolution was the inheritance of acquired characteristics. According to Lamarck, the characteristics an organism developed through use and disuse were passed on to its offspring.

15. Weismann showed that cutting the tails off mice for generation after generation had no effect. The mice were still born with tails. The acquired characteristic was not passed on.

16. During his voyage on the *Beagle* Darwin observed that: (A) There was a gradual change in each species as he traveled down the long coast of South America. (B) The fossils he found were not the same as any living animals, but there were similarities suggesting that the fossils might be related to modern forms. (C) The species on the Galapagos Islands resembled species on the mainland, but differed in certain characteristics.

17. According to Malthus, the human population tends to increase geometrically, while the food supply increases arithmetically at best.

18. By the process of natural selection, Darwin meant that organisms with favorable variations would be better able to survive and reproduce than organisms without these variations.

19. Alfred Russel Wallace

20. The main points of Darwin's theory of evolution are: (A) *Overproduction*. Most species produce more offspring than are needed to maintain the population. (B) *Struggle for existence*. The offspring of each generation must compete both among themselves and with other species for living space and food. Therefore, only a small fraction can possibly survive long enough to reproduce. (C) *Variation*. In the members of any species there are differences, or variations. (D) *Survival of the fittest*. Because of variations, some individuals will be better equipped to survive and reproduce than others. In the competition for existence, the better-adapted individuals will have a better chance of living long enough to reproduce. (E) *Natural selection*. Survival of the fittest can act as a kind of natural selection. The individuals that are better-adapted to their environment will survive and reproduce in greater numbers than those that are less fit. The offspring of these individuals inherit the favorable variations. (F) *Evolution of new species*. Over many generations, certain variations gradually accumulate in the species and others disappear. Eventually the accumulated changes become so great that the population represents a new species.

21. According to the theory of natural selection, the original giraffe population would have had predominantly short necks, and they would have eaten grass and other low-growing plants. However, neck length varied among members of the population. When low-growing plants became scarce, those giraffes with longer necks could obtain more food than the others by eating leaves from trees. These animals would therefore be more likely to survive and reproduce. Their offspring would inherit the favorable variation of a longer neck. The longer the neck, the higher a giraffe could reach for leaves on the trees. Thus, as a result of natural selection, the average neck length of the giraffe gradually increased.

22. Darwin's theory of evolution does not explain the origin and transmission of variation and does not distinguish between hereditary variations and those caused by environmental factors, which are not inherited.

Answers to Test Your Understanding

1. The theory of organic evolution is supported by evidence from fossils, from studies of comparative anatomy (homologous and vestigial structures), from comparative embryology, and from comparative biochemistry and immunology.

2. According to Darwin's theory, variations among members of a species make some individuals better adapted to survive and reproduce than others. The helpful variations will be passed on to their offspring. The gradual accumulation of variations in a population eventually results in the development of a new species.

3. The presence of homologous structures and vestigial structures can provide evidence of evolutionary relationships between organisms. The presence of homologous structures in two different types of organisms shows that they share a common ancestry. The presence of vestigial structures can provide information about what type of organism a modern organism is descended from. The presence of analogous structures cannot provide evidence of any type of evolutionary relationships.

4. Lamarck thought that evolution was brought about first, by use and disuse of various structures, and then by inheritance of acquired characteristics. Darwin theorized that evolution occurred as a result of natural selection, which resulted in the accumulation of variations in a population. According to Darwin, these accumulated variations eventually led to the evolution of a new species.

Chapter 29

Rationale

This chapter begins with a discussion of variations in populations. The work of Hugo de Vries on mutation is described. This is followed by sections on sources of variation, population genetics, gene frequencies, differential reproduction, and the Hardy-Weinberg law. Next is a short discussion of adaptations. There is a detailed description of speciation, including geographic and reproductive isolation, polyploidy, adaptive radiation, and convergent evolution. The sections on observed natural selection include industrial melanism, bacterial resistance to antibiotics, and insect resistance to DDT.

The chapter ends with a discussion of the origin of life. First early beliefs are covered. The experiments of van Helmont, Redi, van Leeuwenhoek, Needham, Spallanzani, and Pasteur are described. Then the modern theory of the origin of life, the heterotroph hypothesis, is presented.

Audiovisual Materials

''Adaptation Between Organism and Environment,'' (16 min., color) McGraw-Hill.

''Adaptive Variations in Insects,'' (16 min., color) McGraw-Hill.

''Evolution and the Origin of Life,'' (36 min., color) CRM.

''Evolution in Progress (Industrial Melanism),'' (18 min., color) UC.

''Natural Selection and Adaptation,'' (29 min., color) McGraw-Hill.

''Origin of Life: Chemical Evolution,'' (11 min., color) EBE.

''Theories on the Origin of Life,'' (14 min., color) EBE.

Answers to Test Your Learning

1. De Vries believed that an unexplained change in the hereditary material, which he called a *mutation,* caused the appearance of new traits. According to de Vries, the important changes or adaptations leading to new species did not occur slowly over many generations, but instead occurred rapidly as a result of mutations.

2. According to modern genetic theory, variations within a species arise from: gene mutations, chromosomal mutations, crossing-over, recombination, and immigration and emigration in populations.

3. A *population* is a group of organisms of the same species living in the same area and capable of interbreeding. *Population genetics* is the study of the changes in the genetic makeup of populations.

4. Modern studies of evolution concentrate on populations rather than individuals because populations evolve, while individuals do not.

5. If the frequency of a gene in a population is 75 percent, it means that 75 out of 100 individuals in the population have that particular gene.

6. The *gene pool* is the total of all the genes in a population.

7. *Differential reproduction* means that better-adapted individuals live longer and produce more offspring than less well-adapted individuals.

8. Differential reproduction does affect the gene frequencies in a population. As a result of differential reproduction, the genes for favorable variations will increase in the population.

9. The Hardy-Weinberg law states that under certain conditions, the gene frequencies in a population will not change from generation to generation.

10. For the Hardy-Weinberg law to hold true, the following conditions must exist: (A) The population must be large. (B) Individuals must not migrate into or out of the population. (C) Mutations must not occur. (D) Reproduction must be random.

11. The Hardy-Weinberg law is useful because it shows that where gene frequencies are changing, evolution is occurring.

12. An *adaptation* is an inherited trait or modification that improves the chance of survival and reproduction of an organism in a given environment. The wings of birds and insects are structural adaptations. The venom of snakes is a physiological adaptation. The migration of birds is a behavioral adaptation.

13. *Camouflage* protects the organism by allowing it to blend into the environment. *Warning coloration* ensures that the animal is easily recognized by potential enemies. In *mimicry* one organism is protected from its enemies because it resembles another, unrelated species that is not desirable prey for the enemy species.

14. If the geographic range of a population is very large, the differences in environmental conditions in various parts of the range will exert different selective pressures and lead to different adaptive characteristics in the population. Eventually, the species will consist of separate populations with different gene pools. Although the populations at the extreme ends of the range may not be able to interbreed, adjacent populations can mate and produce normal offspring. The different populations across the range are then considered subspecies, or varieties, of the same species.

15. *Speciation* is the formation of new species.

16. Speciation is a two-step process, first involving geographic isolation and then reproductive isolation. When two parts of a population become separated, their gene pools evolve separately as each becomes adapted to its particular environment. When the differences between the two isolated groups become so great that they cannot interbreed even if they could get together, the geographic isolation has been replaced by reproductive isolation, and the two groups are considered to be separate species.

17. Polyploid organisms are generally plants, and they contain more than the usual number of chromosome sets. When polyploidy occurs and the organisms can interbreed only with other polyploids, they are considered to be a new species.

18. *Adaptive radiation* is the process by which an ancestral species evolves into a number of different species, each occupying a different habitat. This spreading or radiation of organisms into different environments is accompanied by adaptive changes to the new way of life. The finches that Darwin saw on the Galapagos Islands are an example of adaptive radiation.

19. *Industrial melanism* is the term used to describe the development of dark-colored organisms in a population exposed to industrial air pollution.

20. Both light-colored and dark-colored moths existed in the original population. The dark color is a mutation that occurs at a constant, low frequency. Before England became industrialized, the light-colored moths blended well with the lichens that covered tree bark. Because of this camouflage, birds that feed on the moths could not easily find the light-colored moths, but the dark moths were easily seen and eaten. Thus, in this situation, the light-colored moths had a reproductive advantage. With industrialization, pollution killed the light-colored lichens and blackened the tree bark. When this occurred, the light-colored moths lost their protective coloration and no longer blended with the trees. Consequently, they became easy prey for birds. The dark-colored moths now had a reproductive advantage because the blackened trees offered them good camouflage. Through natural selection, more dark moths survived and reproduced than light moths. Kettlewell's study showed that through natural selection, the trait that makes the organism best adapted to the environment is preserved.

21. The Lederbergs grew bacteria on an agar medium. Using a velveteen cloth, they picked up some bacteria from each colony and transferred them to a second agar plate that contained the antibiotic streptomycin. Normally, this antibiotic prevents bacterial growth. However, a few colonies did develop. In comparing the new streptomycin-resistant colonies with the original colonies, the Lederbergs found that the streptomycin-resistant bacteria had been present in the original colonies. This experiment showed that the resistance to streptomycin had not arisen as a result of exposure to the antibiotic. The gene for this trait had already existed in a few of the bacteria. In the presence of streptomycin, these genes provided an adaptive advantage for the organisms that possessed them.

22. A small proportion of the insect population had genes that made them resistant to DDT. In the presence of DDT, nonresistant insects were killed. Because of differential reproduction, whole populations of resistant insects arose.

23. *Abiogenesis,* or *spontaneous generation,* is the belief that living organisms can arise spontaneously from nonliving matter over the course of a few days or weeks.

24. The ancient Egyptians believed that the mud of the Nile River gave rise to frogs and snakes. The ancient Greeks believed that an active principle was responsible for life and that this active principle was present in mud. They thought that eels could arise from mud.

25. Van Helmont's experiment supports the theory of spontaneous generation.

26. Redi set up three jars containing meat. One jar was left open, and maggots appeared on the meat. The second jar was tightly sealed, and no maggots appeared on the meat. The third jar was covered with fine gauze that allowed air to enter the jar, but kept out flies. The flies deposited eggs on the gauze, and the eggs developed into maggots. No maggots appeared inside the jars. Therefore, Redi concluded that maggots arise from eggs laid by flies and do not arise spontaneously from decaying meat. Redi's experiments disproved the theory of spontaneous generation.

27. The discovery of microorganisms led many scientists to the conclusion that although larger animals might not arise from nonliving matter, microorganisms could.

28. Needham boiled flasks containing chicken, lamb, and corn broth for a few minutes to kill any microorganisms. He then sealed the flasks with corks. After a few days he examined the broths and found that they contained microorganisms. This experiment was used to support the theory of spontaneous generation.

29. Spallanzani repeated Needham's experiments, but he boiled the contents of the flasks for a much longer time. No living organisms later appeared in the broths. Spallanzani's results helped to disprove the theory of spontaneous generation.

30. Pasteur filled flasks with nutrient broth and heated the necks of the flasks. He drew the necks of the flasks into a long S shape, and left the ends of the necks open. The contents of the flasks were then sterilized by boiling. Air could still get into the flasks, but the contents of the flasks remained sterile because microorganisms in the air were trapped in the long necks of the flasks. This experiment finally put an end to the idea of spontaneous generation.

31. According to the heterotroph hypothesis, the atmosphere of the primitive earth consisted of hydrogen, water vapor, ammonia, and methane.

32. Sources of energy thought to have been present on the primitive earth include: heat given off by the earth itself; radiation from the decay of radioactive elements; electrical energy from lightning; ultraviolet light; visible light; and X rays from the sun.

33. Miller constructed an apparatus in which he placed hydrogen, water vapor, ammonia, and methane. Boiling water in the apparatus forced these gases to circulate past sparking electrodes. After a week, Miller found that the apparatus contained urea, amino acids, hydrogen cyanide, and organic acids, such as lactic acid and acetic acid. This experiment demonstrated that the organic substances that make up living things could have been produced in nature under the conditions thought to have existed on the primitive earth.

34. According to the heterotroph hypothesis, the inorganic compounds of the primitive atmosphere dissolved in the hot seas, where they reacted to form various organic compounds. In the water, it is suggested that protein complexes developed into aggregates, or *coacervates*. The coacervates, which had a sort of limiting membrane, became more complex and developed an anaerobic biochemical system to release energy from various types of organic molecules, which were absorbed from the environment. Eventually, these coacervates, which are now described as heterotrophs, developed the capacity to split in half and to grow. Heterotrophs became more and more complex. Eventually, organisms developed that could use light energy for the synthesis of ATP. In later organisms, the use of light to synthesize ATP became coupled with reactions in which carbon dioxide and water were used in the synthesis of carbohydrates. These photosynthetic organisms changed the environment by adding oxygen to the atmosphere. Still later, organisms developed that could carry on aerobic respiration.

Answers to Test Your Understanding

1. Some factors that can change gene frequencies in a population are: the migration of organisms into or out of the population; the appearance of mutations; nonrandom, or differential, reproduction.

2. Any factor that affects the gene frequencies in a population can be involved in the evolution of a new species. Such factors include the occurrence of mutations, migration of organisms into or out of the population, and differential reproduction. Factors that can produce a selective pressure leading to differential reproduction include changes in the environment and competition for existing resources. Variations will accumulate more readily in the gene pool of a relatively small, isolated population than in the gene pool of a very large, extended population.

3. (A) Anaerobic heterotrophs. (B) Anaerobic autotrophs. (C) Aerobic autotrophs. (D) Aerobic heterotrophs.

4. Answers will vary.

Chapter 30

Rationale

This chapter opens with a discussion of the kingdom Monera. There is a comparison of procaryotic and eucaryotic cells, followed by a general description of blue-green algae and bacteria. The life functions of the bacteria are discussed in detail, along with the role of bacteria in disease and decay. The discussion of the kingdom Protista includes some of the algae, the protozoa, and the slime molds. The chapter concludes with sections on viruses and viral diseases.

Audiovisual Materials

"Bacteria," (19 min., color) EBE.
"Bacteria, Friend and Foe," (11 min., color) EBE.
"Bacteria Laboratory Study," (15 min., color) IU.
"Protist Ecology," (12 min., color) Modern Learning Aids.
"Protist Physiology," (13 min., color) Modern Learning Aids.
"Protist Reproduction," (10 min., color) Modern Learning Aids.
"Protozoa: Structures and Life Functions," (16 min., color) Coronet.
"Viruses: Threshold of Life," (13 min., color) Coronet.

Answers to Test Your Learning

1. The kingdom Monera includes the blue-green algae and bacteria.

2. Procaryotic cells lack a membrane-bounded nucleus and other membranous organelles. The DNA is usually concentrated in one region of the cell. Many enzyme-controlled reactions take place on infoldings of the cell membrane. In procaryotes, flagella consist of parallel strands of protein twisted around each other.

3. Blue-green algae are either unicellular or filamentous. Their cell walls are often surrounded by a slime sheath. They contain the pigments phycocyanin and chlorophyll, and various species also have a number of other pigments. The cytoplasm contains storage granules filled with proteins and carbohydrates. Some blue-green algae can convert atmospheric nitrogen into usable forms. Only asexual reproduction has been observed in these organisms.

4. Bacterial cells are surrounded by a cell wall and many also have a slimy capsule. The cells contain no distinct nucleus and there are no mitochondria, Golgi bodies, endoplasmic reticulum, or lysosomes. DNA is present as one circular molecule. Ribosomes are scattered throughout the cytoplasm. Bacteria may be unicellular, or they may be found in pairs or in chains.

5. *Cocci* are spherical bacteria. *Bacilli* are rod-shaped bacteria. *Spirilla* are spiral.

6. *Facultative anaerobes* can live both in the presence or absence of free oxygen. *Obligate anaerobes* cannot live in the presence of free oxygen.

7. Heterotrophic bacteria obtain food from the environment. They are either saprophytes, feeding on dead plants and animals, or parasites, obtaining nutrients from living organisms.

8. (A) The disease-causing organisms must be found only in animals that have the disease. (B) These organisms must be isolated from the diseased animals and grown in pure culture. (C) Organisms from the culture injected into a healthy, susceptible animal must produce the disease. (D) The microorganisms isolated from the infected test animals must be the same as the original microorganisms.

9. Bacteria, along with fungi, are the major organisms of decay in nature. They make possible the recycling of materials from the remains of dead plants and animals.

10. Like plants, euglenoids contain chloroplasts and carry on photosynthesis. Like animals, the cells lack cell walls and have flagella. In the absence of light, they obtain nutrients from the environment.

11. The euglena is a green, unicellular protist with two flagella. It is surrounded by a cell membrane. Inside the cell membrane is a flexible pellicle, which gives the organism its shape. The cell has a large central nucleus and numerous small chloroplasts. Food reserves are stored in the pyrenoid. One of the flagella is long and is used for locomotion. The other is short and nonfunctional. The bases of the flagella are within an inpocketing called the *reservoir*. Near the reservoir is a contractile vacuole and a light-sensitive eyespot.

12. The yellow-green and golden brown algae contain chlorophyll and yellow-brown pigments. Most are unicellular, and they have one or two flagella. Some are marine, but most are freshwater organisms. They store food as oils or carbohydrates. The cell walls contain silicon.

13. Diatoms are unicellular organisms that contain one or more chloroplasts. They lack flagella. The cell wall of a diatom is made up of two halves that fit together like the top and bottom of a box. When diatoms die, they sink to the ocean floor. In some places the shells accumulate and form rocklike deposits known as *diatomaceous earth*.

14. Dinoflagellates are unicellular organisms found mainly in the ocean. Some are photosynthetic and some are heterotrophic. Many have a cellulose cell wall that is in the form of plates. These organisms have two flagella, one running in a groove around the middle of the cell, and the other extending from one end of the organism. Dinoflagellates store food as starch or oil.

15. Sarcodina—pseudopods. Ciliata—cilia. Mastigophora—flagella. Sporozoa—nonmotile.

16. amebas, foraminiferans, radiolarians

17. Amebic dysentery is transmitted when amebas in an infected person form cysts that pass out of the body with the digestive wastes. Other people become infected when they ingest water or food containing these encysted amebas.

18. Ciliates are complex unicellular organisms with cilia on their outer surface. The cilia may cover the entire outer surface of the organism, or they may be arranged in rows (cirri) or in clumps (membranelles). There is a protective outer covering called a pellicle. Some ciliates have trichocysts beneath the pellicle. Food enters the organism through the oral groove. The cytoplasm contains food vacuoles, contractile vacuoles, and two types of nuclei.

19. The *macronucleus* controls normal cell metabolism. The *micronucleus* functions in sexual reproduction.

20. Members of the phylum Mastigophora have one or more flagella, which are used in locomotion. The flagella have the typical 9+2 arrangement of microtubules. Zooflagellates reproduce both asexually and sexually. Some are free-living, but most are parasitic.

21. Sporozoans are parasitic and obtain nutrients from their hosts.

22. The malarial parasite is transmitted to humans by the bite of the female *Anopheles* mosquito. The *Plasmodium* cells reproduce asexually in human tissues and form spores. The spores invade red blood cells and multiply further. Every 48 to 72 hours they break out of the red cells and invade new ones. Some spores eventually develop into gametocytes. When the infected human is bitten by another mosquito, the gametocytes pass into the mosquito with the blood. If it is a female *Anopheles* mosquito, the gametocytes develop into gametes in the mosquito's stomach. Fertilization occurs, and the resulting zygote divides to form thousands of infective cells. These cells migrate to the salivary glands of the mosquito.

23. The plasmodium stage in the true slime molds is a multinucleate mass—the cytoplasm contains many nuclei not separated by cell membranes. When conditions become unfavorable, the plasmodium stops moving and develops stalked, spore-producing fruiting bodies. In the fruiting bodies, haploid spores are produced by meiosis. The spores are eventually released, and those landing in suitable environments germinate to form flagellated gametes. Two gametes fuse to form a zygote. The nucleus of the zygote undergoes repeated mitotic divisions and forms a new plasmodium.

24. In the cellular slime molds, spores give rise to haploid ameboid cells, which divide and produce more haploid ameboid cells. When conditions become unfavorable, the separate cells come together and form a *pseudo-*

plasmodium in which the individual cells are still distinguishable. The pseudoplasmodium forms fruiting bodies that produce spores. There does not appear to be a diploid stage in the life cycle of cellular slime molds.

25. Basically, a virus consists of a protein coat that surrounds a core of nucleic acid. In some viruses the nucleic acid is DNA and in others it is RNA.

26. When a virus enters a host cell, it appears to take over the biochemical machinery of the cell and use it to produce more virus particles.

27. The human body has several mechanisms to protect itself from viral infections. Viruses act as antigens and trigger an immune response in which antibodies are produced. The antibodies destroy the invading viruses. Some lymphocytes also react with virus-infected cells and destroy them. Interferon also protects the body from virus infections. It blocks the production of viral nucleic acid in the cells.

Answers to Test Your Understanding

1. The procaryotic nature of moneran cells distinguishes them from the cells of all other organisms. In cells of all other organisms there is a distinct, membrane-bounded nucleus and an assortment of membranous organelles. Moneran cells lack these features.

2. Blue-green algae are photosynthetic organisms and contain the pigments phycocyanin and chlorophyll; some blue-greens also contain other pigments. Some blue-green algae exist as single cells, others form filaments. They do not have flagella. Sexual reproduction has not been found in blue-greens.

Except for a few species, bacteria do not contain photosynthetic pigments and must obtain nutrients from the environment. Bacterial cells are found singly, in pairs, and in chains. Many bacterial cells have flagella. Reproduction is generally asexual, but sexual reproduction does occur. Most bacteria are aerobic, but some are facultative anaerobes and some are obligate anaerobes. A few types of bacteria carry on photosynthesis and a few are chemosynthetic.

3. Answers will vary.

4. In nature bacteria play an essential role in the cycle of materials by breaking down the remains of dead organisms. Certain bacteria are involved in the nitrogen cycle, which is essential to living things. For humans, bacteria are both helpful and harmful. They are a source of many useful antibiotics. They are used in the production of cheeses, sauerkraut, and pickles. They also cause many diseases and spoil foods.

Chapter 31

Rationale

The chapter opens with a brief introduction to the plant kingdom and a discussion of the problems of land-dwelling plants. The following sections describe the general characteristics of green, brown, and red algae and bryophytes. The chapter continues with a discussion of the tracheophytes. Most major groups of vascular plants are covered. The final sections of the chapter deal with the fungi.

Audiovisual Materials

''Angiosperms—The Flowering Plants,'' (21 min., color) EBE.

''Evolution of Vascular Plants: The Ferns,'' (17 min., color or b&w) EBE.

''Fungi,'' (16 min., color or b&w) EBE.

''Gymnosperms,'' (17 min., color) EBE.

''Life of Molds,'' (20 min., color) Association Sterling Films.

''Mosses, Liverworts and Ferns,'' (12 min., color) Coronet.

''Origin of Land Plants: Liverworts and Mosses,'' (14 min., color) EBE.

''Seed Plants: Diversity in Adaptation,'' (10 min., color) Coronet.

''Simple Plants: Algae and Fungi,'' (13 min., color) Coronet.

''Simple Plants: The Algae,'' (18 min., color or b&w) EBE.

Answers to Test Your Learning

1. The most serious problems for land plants are obtaining and conserving water. Land plants also need strong supporting tissues to stand upright against the force of gravity, and they need special reproductive mechanisms that enable the sperm to reach the egg without water.

2. *Chlamydomonas, Spirogyra, Ulva, Acetabularia, Halimeda, Valonia*

3. *Chlamydomonas* is a unicellular organism with two flagella. The cell contains one large chloroplast, a pyrenoid body, and two contractile vacuoles.

4. The brown algae are multicellular organisms that range in size from microscopic to more than 50 meters in length. They contain chlorophyll and other pigments. The cell wall is composed of cellulose. Food reserves are stored in the form of polysaccharides or oil. The life cycle shows an alternation of generations. Brown algae are found mainly in cold ocean waters.

5. The red algae are mostly multicellular and are generally smaller than brown algae. They usually grow in deeper water attached to some surface. Their chloroplasts contain chlorophyll and other pigments. They have a complex life cycle that includes an alternation of generations. The cell walls of red algae contain cellulose and other substances.

6. Mosses, liverworts, and hornworts are members of the phylum Bryophyta.

7. Bryophytes are nonvascular land plants. Without xylem, bryophytes have no supporting tissues so they are very short. Bryophytes do not have true organs, and the cells that make up their various structures are all similar. There are rootlike rhizoids that grow into the soil. The rhizoids absorb water and minerals and anchor the plant. Other branches grow upward, forming stemlike shoots and leaves. Because they lack vascular tissues bryophytes must live in moist environments. Reproduction in bryophytes also requires water. The gametophyte generation is dominant.

8. The phylum Tracheophyta includes whisk ferns, club mosses, horsetails, ferns, and seed plants.

9. The tracheophytes, the vascular plants, are the dominant modern land plants. All tracheophytes contain the vascular tissues xylem and phloem in the sporophyte generation. The gametophyte generation is greatly reduced. The gymnosperms and angiosperms are seed-producing plants, while the other tracheophytes are spore-producing.

10. The whisk ferns do not have true leaves or roots. The plant body consists of an underground stem anchored by rhizoids. Aboveground, there are green stems that carry on photosynthesis. The ends of these stems are Y-shaped and sporangia form at the tips of some branches. The life cycle shows an alternation of generations.

11. The spore-producing structures of club mosses are called *strobili*.

12. The horsetails have true roots and leaves and green, hollow stems. Leaves grow only at certain points on the stem. Cone-shaped strobili form at the ends of some stems. Horsetails are generally less than 1 meter in height.

13. Ferns have underground, horizontal stems, or *rhizomes*. True roots grow downward from the rhizome, while leaves, or *fronds,* grow upward. The only aboveground part of the fern is the fronds. The internal structure of ferns is similar to that of seed plants. However, fern stems contain no cambium. Ferns reproduce both asexually and sexually, and their life cycle shows an alternation of generations.

14. The two types of seed plants are *gymnosperms* and *angiosperms*.

15. Gymnosperms include conifers, cycads, and gingkoes.

16. Conifers are cone-bearing plants with leaves in the form of needles. Most conifers remain green throughout the year. Sequoias and redwoods, which are conifers, are the oldest and largest trees in the world.

17. The angiosperms, the flowering plants, are divided into two groups—monocots and dicots. The seeds of monocots contain one cotyledon, while the seeds of dicots contain two cotyledons.

18. Fungi are nonphotosynthetic organisms. The bodies of most fungi are made up of threadlike *hyphae*. The hyphae form a tangled mass called the *mycelium*. The cell walls in fungi are composed of chitin. In some fungi the hyphae are only partially divided by cell walls, and in some they are not divided at all. Fungi reproduce both sexually and asexually. Asexual reproduction involves the formation of spores.

19. *Rhizopus* obtains nutrients through *rhizoids,* rootlike hyphae that anchor the fungus, secrete digestive enzymes, and absorb nutrients. Reproduction is usually asexual by spore formation. The spores are produced in sporangia at the tips of sporangiophores, which are reproductive hyphae. When the spores germinate, they give rise to new mycelia. Sexual reproduction is by conjugation. Conjugation only occurs between hyphae of two different strains (plus and minus). Where the hyphae touch, the end walls break down, and the nuclei of opposite strains fuse to form several diploid nuclei. A hard wall forms around the nuclei and associated cytoplasm to form a zygospore. Under favorable conditions, the zygospore germinates and eventually gives rise to a new sporangiophore.

20. The water molds have motile, flagellated spores. The male and female gametes are structurally different. The cell walls are composed of cellulose. There are no cellular partitions in the hyphae. The diploid generation is the prominent generation.

21. cup fungi, powdery mildews, morels, truffles, blue and green molds, yeasts

22. mushrooms, bracket fungi, puffballs, rusts, smuts

23. The mushroom is actually a fruiting body. The mycelium grows below the surface. The mushroom consists of a stalk and a cap. The under-surface of the cap contains many gills on which spores are produced.

24. A lichen is made up of an alga and a fungus that live together. The algal cells are embedded within the mycelium of the fungus. The fungus is usually a sac fungus, while the alga may be green or blue-green.

25. Lichens play an important role in soil formation. They begin the breakdown of rock.

Answers to Test Your Understanding

1. **(A)** Plant cells contain chlorophyll in chloroplasts; fungal cells do not. Plants show an organ level of organization, having roots, stems, and leaves; fungi are made of cells that form threadlike hyphae. In plants, the cell walls are composed of cellulose; in fungi they are generally composed of chitin.

(B) Plants are autotrophs; fungi are heterotrophs, mostly saprophytes.

(C) Plants and fungi differ in their modes of nutrition and in some aspects of their reproductive process. However, their other life functions are similar.

(D) Answers will vary.

2. Ferns and seed plants are better adapted for life on land than bryophytes because they have conducting tissues—xylem and phloem—that can transport materials efficiently throughout the plant. Seed plants are better adapted than either ferns or bryophytes because they do not need water for reproduction. The sperm travels to the egg through the pollen tube instead of swimming through water.

3. Members of the plant kingdom are thought to have arisen from the green algae. Also, like plants, the green algae contain chlorophyll in chloroplasts and their cell walls are composed of cellulose. The brown and red algae are multicellular and show some structural specialization. Thus they are also classified with plants.

4. Club mosses, horsetails, and ferns were abundant during the Carboniferous period.

Chapter 32

Rationale

This chapter offers a comprehensive view of the lower invertebrates. The chapter opens with an introduction to the animal kingdom, including some of the general characteristics of animals and an explanation of symmetry. The taxonomic survey begins with the sponges. With this group and with each subsequent phylum the general structural characteristics and life functions are discussed in some detail. The other phyla covered in this chapter are the coelenterates, flatworms, roundworms, segmented worms, and mollusks.

Audiovisual Materials

"Animals Without Backbones," (11 min., color) Coronet.

"Adaptive Radiation: The Mollusks," (18 min., color) EBE.

"First Many-Celled Animals," (17 min., color) EBE.

"Flatworms," (16 min., color) EBE.

"Segmentation—Annelid Worms," (16 min., color) EBE.

"Sponges and Coelenterates; Porous and Sac-like Animals," (10 min., color) Coronet.

"Stinging-Celled Animals: Coelenterates," (17 min., color) EBE.

"The Invertebrates," (14 min., color) Coronet.

"Worms—Flat, Round, and Segmented," (15 min., color) Coronet.

Answers to Test Your Learning

1. *Zoology* is the branch of biology that deals with the study of animals. An *invertebrate* is an animal that does not have a backbone. A *vertebrate* is an animal that has a backbone. A *larva* is a young animal whose body form is very different from that of the adult of the species.

2. In *spherical symmetry* any section through the center of the sphere will divide the animal into matching halves. In *radial symmetry* any lengthwise cut down the central axis divides the animal into matching halves. In *bilateral symmetry* there is one cut that can divide the body into two symmetrical halves, which are mirror images of each other.

3. *Dorsal* refers to the upper side or back of the animal. *Ventral* refers to the lower side or belly of the animal. *Anterior* refers to the front or head end, while *posterior* refers to the rear or tail end.

4. sponges

5. Adult sponges are generally found attached to some object on the floor of the ocean.

6. The outer layer of the sponge body consists of thin, flat cells and is pierced by numerous pores. The inner layer consists of flagellated *collar cells* that line the central cavity. Between these two layers is a middle layer of jellylike material that contains ameboid cells. *Spicules* are also present in the middle layer.

7. Water is drawn into the sponge through the pores and circulated in the central cavity by the beating of the flagella of the collar cells. From the central cavity the water passes out of the sponge through the osculum.

8. As water passes through the sponge, food particles are captured, ingested, and digested by the collar cells. Some digestion is completed in the ameboid cells of the middle layer, which then carry nutrients to other parts of the sponge. In respiration, gases are exchanged by diffusion between the water and the body cells. Wastes from the cells diffuse into the water passing through the sponge and leave with the water passing out through the osculum.

9. In sexual reproduction each sponge produces both male and female gametes. However, the sperm pass out of the sponge through the osculum. The sperm then enter another sponge through the pores and fertilize eggs found in the middle layer. The zygotes develop into free-swimming larvae that pass out of the sponge through the osculum. Asexual reproduction occurs by budding or by the formation of *gemmules,* which consist of a group of cells enclosed by a tough outer covering.

10. hydras, jellyfish, sea anemones, corals

11. The body forms of coelenterates include the *polyp*—hydra, corals, and sea anemones—and the *medusa*—jellyfish.

12. *ectoderm, mesoglea,* and *endoderm.*

13. *Cnidoblasts* are stinging cells used for defense and capturing food. Within the cnidoblast is a *nematocyst,* a small, fluid-filled capsule that contains a coiled thread. When a cnidoblast is stimulated, the nematocyst is discharged, and the thread entangles the prey. Some nematocysts contain poison that paralyzes the prey.

14. In coelenterates, food is captured by the tentacles and passed into the mouth. In the gastrovascular cavity extracellular digestion occurs. Small food particles are then engulfed by cells lining the cavity and digestion is completed within the cells. Nutrients are circulated by diffusion. Wastes pass out of the cells and into the water by diffusion. The exchange of respiratory gases between the cells and the water also occurs by diffusion.

15. Corals are small polyps that grow in colonies. Each coral is surrounded by a hard calcium-containing skeleton.

16. The life cycle of *Aurelia* includes both medusa and polyp forms. In the medusa form the sexes are separate. Sperm from the male are released into the water. Some enter the gastrovascular cavities of females where fertilization occurs. The zygote develops into a free-swimming larva. The larva eventually settles to the bottom and develops into a polyp. The polyp grows and eventually produces medusas by asexual reproduction.

17. Platyhelminthes

18. bilateral symmetry

19. planaria, flukes, and tapeworms

20. Flatworms show an organ and organ system level of organization.

21. In feeding, the pharynx extends out through the mouth and sucks small bits of food into the digestive cavity. Most digestion takes place in vacuoles in the cells lining the intestine. Digested food diffuses to all the cells of the body, and indigestible materials are expelled through the pharynx and mouth.

22. The excretory system consists of a series of tubules that run the length of the body. Flame cells in the side branches of the tubules remove excess water and liquid wastes from the body and pass them into ducts that empty through small excretory pores on the dorsal surface.

The nervous system includes a small brain from which two nerve cords run the length of the body along either side. Transverse nerves connect the two cords.

Planaria are hermaphroditic, but there is no self-fertilization. Instead, two planaria mate and exchange sperm. Fertilization is internal and the fertilized eggs are shed in capsules. The eggs hatch into tiny worms.

23. Flukes are parasitic flatworms. Adult flukes live in the blood vessels of the human intestine and bladder. They lay thousands of eggs that pass out of the body with digestive wastes. Eggs landing in water hatch into free-swimming larvae, which then infect a certain species of snail. They later leave the snail and infect streams, rice paddies, and irrigation ditches. On contact with humans, the flukes bore through the skin, beginning the cycle again.

24. Beef tapeworms are long, ribbonlike parasitic flatworms. They have excretory, nervous, and reproductive systems, but lack a mouth and digestive system. They live as parasites in the intestine and absorb nutrients through their skin. The tapeworm is held in place by suckers on the head. Below the head and neck are segments called *proglottids,* which are produced by budding. The proglottids contain male and female reproductive organs, and periodically, segments filled with fertilized eggs detach from the worm, and pass out of the intestine with digestive wastes. Cattle eat food contaminated with eggs, the eggs develop into larvae that eventually form dormant capsules in the muscle. When a human eats contaminated meat, the capsule is digested, releasing the tapeworm.

25. Nematoda

26. Roundworms, which are bilaterally symmetrical, have elongated cylindrical bodies that are tapered at both ends.

27. Free-living roundworms are found in fresh and salt water and in soil. Parasitic roundworms are found in most kinds of plants and animals.

28. Flatworms have only one opening in their digestive system—the mouth. Roundworms have a complete digestive system with two openings. Food enters the mouth and wastes leave through the anus.

29. trichina, filaria, pinworms, and hookworms

30. Adult trichina worms live in the intestines of hogs. When the worms reproduce, the larvae invade the muscles of the hog, where they become enclosed in cysts. Humans become infected when they eat pork that has not been completely cooked. The encysted worms in the meat are not killed. Instead, the larvae are released in the human digestive tract, grow into adults, and reproduce sexually. The newly produced larvae enter the person's muscles and become encysted.

31. Annelida

32. Annelids have a tube-within-a-tube body plan. The inner tube is the digestive tract and the outer one is the body wall. The body is divided into segments, or metameres.

33. *Metamerism* is the division of the body into metameres, each containing more or less the same internal structures. The *coelom* is the body cavity between the outer body wall and the digestive tube.

34. In *Nereis* parapodia are paddlelike extensions found on most segments and used in locomotion and as a surface for gas exchange.

35. Sexes are separate in *Nereis*. During the mating season, eggs or sperm develop in the body cavity. They pass out of the body into the water where fertilization occurs. A zygote develops into a trochophore larve, which eventually develops into a worm.

36. Most leeches obtain nourishment from the blood of their prey.

37. The class Bivalvia includes clams, oysters, and mussels. The class Gastropoda includes snails and slugs. The class Cephalopoda includes squids and octopuses.

38. Bivalves have a two-part shell. Most gastropods have a single shell, often coiled. Cephalopods have no shell (octopus) or a small internal shell (squid or cuttlefish). The nautilus is a cephalopod with a coiled shell.

39. The *foot* is a muscular structure that functions in locomotion. The *mantle* is a fold of skin that surrounds the body organs. In the squid and octopus, the mantle is muscular and is used in locomotion, while in shelled mollusks, the mantle secretes part of the shall. The *radula* is a rasping, tonguelike organ found in all mollusks except bivalves. It can be extended out through the mouth and is used to scrape off food particles.

40. Clams are filter feeders. Food particles in the water become trapped by mucus on the gills. They are transported by the cilia to the mouth and then pass through the rest of the digestive system.

In respiration, water entering the incurrent siphon passes over the gills, where the exchange of respiratory gases occurs. Cilia move the water over the gills.

Clams have an open circulatory system consisting of a heart and blood vessels. Blood leaving the heart is carried by vessels to the body tissues. There it flows into sinuses and bathes the tissues directly. From the sinuses, the blood flows into vessels that carry it to the gills. After the exchange of respiratory gases, the blood flows back to the heart.

A pair of kidneys removes organic wastes from the blood and releases them into the water leaving the animal through the excurrent siphon.

In clams, the sexes are separate. Sperm leave the male through the excurrent siphon and enter the incurrent siphon of the female. Fertilization of the eggs occurs on the gills. The young develop in the water, passing through several larval stages before becoming adults.

41. Land snails glide along on a layer of mucus secreted by the foot. They feed on plant material that they rub off with their radula.

42. Most cephalopods have little or no shell. The mouth is surrounded by tentacles. Their bodies are streamlined for swimming. Locomotion is accomplished with a jet of water from the mantle cavity. The eyes of cephalopods are similar to those of vertebrates.

Answers to Test Your Understanding

1. Sponges have a low level of organization. Although their cells show some specialization, they do not form true tissues. Flatworms, on the other hand, have true tissues, organs, and organ systems, including digestive, excretory, nervous, and reproductive systems.

2. Porifera: asymmetrical; Coelenterata: most adults are radially symmetrical; Platyhelminthes: bilateral symmetry; Nematoda: bilateral symmetry; Annelida: bilateral symmetry; Mollusca: bilateral symmetry.

3. Both annelids and mollusks have a trochophore larva, which is thought to show an evolutionary relationship between them.

4. Answers will vary.

Chapter 33

Rationale

The chapter opens with a discussion of the general characteristics of the arthropods. The crayfish is then described as a typical crustacean. The external and internal anatomy and the life functions of the crayfish are presented in considerable detail. There is a brief discussion of the general characteristics of centipedes and millipedes, followed by a description of the arachnids. Next the chapter focuses on the insects. There is a brief account of the structural variations found among insects. Then, using the grasshopper as a representative insect, external anatomy and reproduction and development are discussed. There is a short section on insect classification, followed by a discussion of the economic importance of insects.

The chapter concludes with a description of the structure and life functions of echinoderms.

Audiovisual Materials

"Animal Life: Echinoderms," (17 min., color) EBE.
"Animal Life: The Jointed-Legged Animals," (19 min., color) EBE.
"Arthropods: Insects and Their Relatives," (11 min., color) Coronet.
"Crayfish: Life Cycle," (10 min., color) Coronet.
"Crustaceans," (14 min., color) EBE.
"Echinoderms," (13 min., color) McGraw-Hill.
"Echinoderms: Sea Stars and Their Relatives," (17 min., color) EBE.
"Insect Metamorphosis," (14 min., color) IU.
"Insects," (11 min., color) EBE.
"The Life Cycle of Insects: Complete Metamorphosis," (20 min., color) IFB.
"The Life Cycle of Insects: Incomplete Metamorphosis," (17 min., color) IFB.
"The Sea Urchin," (16 min., color) McGraw-Hill.

Answers to Test Your Learning

1. The five major classes of the phylum Arthropoda are: Crustacea, Chilopoda, Diploda, Arachnida, and Insecta.

2. Five characteristics shared by all arthropods are: jointed legs; an exoskeleton composed of chitin; a segmented body; a well-developed nervous system with a distinct brain and ventral nerve cord; and an open circulatory system.

3. *Molting* is the process in which the exoskeleton is shed and replaced by a new, larger one.

4. Crustaceans include lobsters, crayfish, shrimp, water fleas, barnacles, and sow bugs.

5. The crayfish has two main body regions—the cephalothorax and the abdomen. The paddle-shaped last segment of the abdomen is called the *telson*. Starting from the anterior end, the paired appendages are: antennules, antennae, mandibles, maxillae, maxillipeds, chelipeds, four pairs of walking legs, swimmerets, and uropods.

6. The antennules function in touch, taste, and balance. The antennae are used for touching and tasting. The mandibles crush food. The maxillae handle food. The maxillipeds touch, taste, and handle food. The chelipeds are the claws used for food-getting and defense. The walking legs are used for walking. The swimmerets are used for swimming; in females they are used to carry the eggs and the newly hatched young. The uropods and the telson together form a fan-shaped tail that is used for rapid backward movement.

7. Crayfish feed on dead animals and on living animals they catch with their chelipeds. Food crushed by the mandibles is passed to the mouth by the maxillae and maxillipeds. From the mouth it passes down the esophagus into the stomach, where it is ground up by the gastric mill. The resulting fine food particles are digested by enzymes and passed into the digestive glands, where nutrients are absorbed into the blood. Undigested material passes through the intestine and out the anus.

8. In the open circulatory system of the crayfish, the heart is surrounded by the *pericardial sinus*. Blood in the pericardial sinus enters the heart through three pairs of *ostia*. The ostia close, the heart contracts, and blood is pumped out through vessels to all parts of the body. The vessels open into sinuses so that the blood bathes the cells and the exchange of oxygen, nutrients, carbon dioxide, and wastes takes place. Eventually the blood collects in the *sternal sinus* and is channeled to the gills, where it picks up oxygen and gets rid of carbon dioxide. The exchange of respiratory gases between the gills and the environment takes place by diffusion. From the gills, the blood returns to the pericardial sinus.

The *green glands* in the head are the excretory organs of the crayfish. They remove wastes from the blood and excrete them from the body through an opening near the base of the antennae.

9. Extending from the brain are two nerve cords that encircle the esophagus and join ventrally to form a double nerve cord. In each segment the cord enlarges into ganglia. The sensory organs of the crayfish include a pair of compound eyes, antennules, antennae, and sensory hairs on the body. The sense organs of equilibrium are found in the statocysts.

10. In the fall, sperm are transferred from the male to the seminal receptacle of the female. The sperm are stored until spring, when the female lays hundreds of eggs that have been fertilized by the stored sperm. The eggs become attached to the female's swimmerets. After 5 or 6 weeks the eggs hatch, but the young remain attached to the swimmerets for several more weeks.

11. Centipedes have a distinct head followed by a long, wormlike body made up of many similar segments. All body segments except the first and last two have one pair of legs. The head has mouthparts and one pair of antennae. The first body segment has poison claws with which the centipede bites its victim. Centipedes, which feed on insects, are active at night.

12. Millipedes have a distinct head and a long, wormlike body made up of many segments. Except for the last two segments, millipedes have two pairs of legs per segment. The head bears a pair of antennae and various mouthparts. Millipedes feed on decaying organic matter.

13. The class Arachnida includes spiders, scorpions, ticks, mites, and daddy longlegs.

14. The body of an arachnid consists of two regions—the cephalothorax and the abdomen. There are six pairs of jointed appendages attached to the cephalothorax. The first pair of appendages are the fanglike chelicerae, which are used to pierce the prey and to suck out its body fluids. Poison glands associated with the chelicerae are used to inject a poison that paralyzes the prey. The second pair of appendages, the pedipalps, are sensitive both to chemicals and to touch. They hold the food and are used by the male in reproduction. The last four pairs of appendages are the walking legs.

15. The respiratory organs of arachnids are *book lungs,* which consist of a series of leaflike plates containing blood vessels. The book lungs are located in chambers on the underside of the abdomen. Air drawn into the chambers through slits in the abdomen circulates between the plates. Gas exchange occurs between the blood circulating in the plates and the air in the chamber.

In reproduction, sperm from the male are transferred to the seminal receptacle of the female. As the female lays the eggs, they are fertilized and wrapped in a cocoon. The cocoons may be carried around until the young hatch or they may be deposited on the ground. In some spiders, the sperm are enclosed in a case, which is deposited on the ground. The case is then taken up by the female and placed in a body opening called a *gonopore*.

16. The spinnerets are used to spin silk produced by silk glands in the abdomen.

17. Insects are biologically successful because they: can fly; show a variety of adaptations that allow them to live in almost all environments and to obtain food from a variety of sources; have a very high reproductive rate; are small.

18. All insects have three body regions—a head, thorax, and abdomen. On the head are one pair of antennae, several pairs of mouthparts, and a pair of compound eyes. On the thorax are three pairs of walking legs; in flying insects, the wings are also on the thorax. There are no appendages on the abdomen.

19. Mouthparts can be modified for chewing or sucking. Some insects have flattened bodies, others have plump bodies, etc. Legs show modifications for jumping, swimming, walking upside down, collecting pollen, etc.

20. The head of the grasshopper is made up of six fused segments. On the sides of the head are two large compound eyes. Between the compound eyes are three simple eyes, or ocelli. On the front of the head are a pair of jointed antennae. The labrum, or upper lip, and the labium, or lower lip, function in holding the food. The mandibles are used to bite off and chew food. The maxillae hold the food. Sensory palps on the maxillae and labium feel and taste food. Beneath the lower lip is a tonguelike organ.

21. The thorax consists of three segments. Each segment bears a pair of legs. The first two pairs of legs are used in walking. The third pair is modified for jumping. Attached to the last two segments of the thorax are two pairs of wings. The outer pair, the forewings, serves as a protective covering for the inner pair, the hindwings, which are used in flight.

22. The ten pairs of *spiracles* on the abdomen and thorax are the openings of the tracheae, or breathing tubes. The *tympana* are the organs of hearing.

23. In grasshoppers, the male transfers sperm into the body of the female, where they are stored in the seminal receptacle. Eggs leaving the ovary enter the oviduct and are fertilized as they pass out of the body. The female digs a hole in the ground with her ovipositor and deposits the eggs in the hole. The eggs are deposited in the fall, but do not hatch until spring.

24. Grasshoppers, crickets, and cockroaches undergo incomplete metamorphosis. The three stages of development are the egg, the nymph, and the adult. The nymph resembles the adult but is smaller and is missing some of the structures of the adult. The eggs of most insects undergo complete metamorphosis. Moths, butterflies, beetles, bees, and flies show complete metamorphosis. The four stages of development in this group are the egg, larva, pupa, and adult. The larva is generally wormlike, and the pupa is enclosed in a cocoon and undergoes a rearrangement of body form to produce the adult.

25. Neurosecretory cells in the brain secrete *brain hormone,* which stimulates production of *molting hormone*. Molting hormone stimulates periodic molting of the exoskeleton. The transformation of the larva into more mature forms is inhibited by *juvenile hormone*. As long as juvenile hormone is secreted, the larva can molt, but it will not pupate. At the end of the larval period, the secretion of juvenile hormone decreases. At the time of the next molt, the larva forms a pupa. During the pupal stage the body changes, and at the end of pupation, the adult emerges.

26. Orthoptera: grasshopper and cricket; Coleoptera: ladybug beetle, cotton boll-weevil; Lepidoptera: cabbage butterfly and silkworm moth; Diptera: housefly and mosquito; Hemiptera: giant waterbug and bedbug; Hymenoptera: honeybee and ant.

27. Insects are harmful in that they destroy crops and transmit both plant and animal diseases. Insects are helpful in that they pollinate many plants and produce such things as honey, lac, and silk.

28. Insects can be controlled either by chemical insecticides or by various biological methods of control. Biological methods of insect control may involve releasing sterile males into the population, introducing natural enemies of the insect pest, or using sex attractants to lure insects into traps.

29. Echinodermata

30. Echinoderms are marine animals found mainly on the ocean floor. Some are sessile, but most are motile. The larvae are bilaterally symmetrical, while the adults are radially symmetrical. Echinoderms have an internal skeleton made up of hard, calcified plates that are embedded in the body wall. Spiny projections on the plates stick out through the ectoderm.

31. The echinoderms are thought to be more closely related to vertebrates than other invertebrates because their pattern of development is more like that of vertebrates. In the embryo, the blastopore becomes the anus and the mouth forms later opposite the anus. This developmental pattern is typical of vertebrates and is found in no other invertebrate group.

32. The water-vascular system of the starfish consists of a series of canals and tube feet. Sea water enters through the sieve plate and passes through the stone canal into the ring canal. A radial canal runs into each arm from the ring canal. Connected to each radial canal are many small tube feet. Each tube foot has a bulblike structure at one end and a sucker at the opposite tip. The bulbs are within the body, but the rest of the tube foot extends out from the bottom surface of each arm.

33. Locomotion in the starfish involves the coordinated action of hundreds of tube feet. When the bulb of a tube foot contracts, water is forced out into the rest of the tube foot, causing it to elongate. When the tube foot touches a surface, its sucker holds fast. The tube foot then contracts, forcing the water back up into the bulb. When a number of tube feet contract together, the starfish is pulled forward.

In feeding, the starfish wraps its arms around both sides of a clam or oyster, attaches tube feet to each shell, and pulls. Eventually, the mollusk tires and its shells open slightly. The starfish extends its stomach out through its mouth and into the opening between the mollusk's shells. Enzymes partially digest the soft body parts of the mollusk. The food is taken into the stomach, and the stomach is pulled back into the starfish, where digestion is completed.

34. Respiration occurs by diffusion of gases across the tube feet and the skin gills, which are small, fingerlike extensions from the body surface. Circulation of materials is carried out by the coelomic fluid, which bathes the body organs and supplies them with nutrients and oxygen and removes wastes. Sexes are separate in starfish. Gametes are shed into the water through openings in the central disk. Fertilization occurs in the water, and the zygote develops into a bilaterally symmetrical, free-swimming larva. After several weeks, the larva becomes attached to a solid surface and develops into a small starfish.

Answers to Test Your Understanding

1. The arthropod exoskeleton is tough, lightweight, and waterproof, and it provides good protection for the soft body parts. It also functions in locomotion. However, because it cannot grow, it must be shed periodically, leaving the animal in a highly vulnerable condition until the new exoskeleton hardens.

2. The body of a spider is divided into a cephalothorax and an abdomen, while an insect has three distinct body regions—the head, thorax, and abdomen. The head of an insect has a pair of antennae, while the spider has no antennae. Spiders have four pairs of legs, while insects have three pairs. The respiratory organs of spiders are book lungs, while insects have a system of tracheal tubes.

3. There are more insects than any other group of animals. Insects live in almost all land environments and a few even live in water.

4. Spiders trap their prey in a web. Then they use their chelicerae to inject a poison that paralyzes the prey. They feed by sucking out the body fluids of the prey.

Chapter 34

Rationale

The chapter begins with a discussion of the characteristics that distinguish vertebrates from other animals. A brief description of the urochordates and cephalochordates is followed by a detailed discussion of the general characteristics of vertebrates and the difference between cold-blooded and warm-blooded animals.

The following sections deal with the jawless, cartilaginous, and bony fishes. There is a fairly complete description of the structure and life functions of bony fishes. The amphibians are covered next. The structure and life processes of the frog are described in detail. The chapter concludes with a discussion of the reptiles and their adaptations for life on land. Crocodiles, alligators, turtles, lizards, and snakes are described.

Audiovisual Materials

"Amphibians," (10 min., color) Coronet.
"Animal Life: What Is a Fish?" (17 min., color) EBE.
"Animal Life: What Is a Reptile?" (18 min., color) EBE.
"Animal Life: What Is an Amphibian?" (11 min., color) EBE.
"Fish and their Characteristics," (10 min., color) Coronet.
"Fish in a Changing Environment," (11 min., color) EBE.
"Reptiles," (14 min., color) EBE.
"The Chordates: Diversity in Structure," (13 min., color) Coronet.

Answers to Test Your Learning

1. Chordates have a dorsal hollow nerve cord, a notochord, and paired gill slits.

2. Larval tunicates are motile, tadpolelike organisms that show all three chordate characteristics. Adult tunicates are sessile, soft-bodies animals. They lack the dorsal, hollow nerve cord and notochord that are present in the larva. Water entering the incurrent siphon of the adult tunicate passes into the pharynx and through the gill slits in the walls of the pharynx, where gas exchange occurs. The water then passes into the atrium and out of the animal through the excurrent siphon. The gill slits also trap food particles and pass them into the digestive tract.

3. Adult lancelets show the three characteristic chordate structures. Water enters the body of the lancelet through the mouth, passes into the pharynx and through the gill slits, where gas exchange occurs. Water leaves the body through the atrial pore. Food particles pass directly into the digestive system, and digestive wastes are excreted through the anus.

4. Vertebrates are distinguished from other chordates by the presence of a spinal column made up of vertebrae.

5. (A) The anterior part of the dorsal, hollow nerve cord is enlarged into a brain. (B) The body is divided into a head, neck, and trunk. (C) In most, a tail is present at some stage of development. (D) There is a jointed, internal skeleton and two pairs of appendages. (E) The circulatory system is closed, the heart has two to four chambers, and the red blood cells contain hemoglobin. (F) Gas exchange takes place in gills or lungs. (G) The body covering is skin.

6. In ectothermic, or cold-blooded, animals, the body temperature varies with the temperature of the environment. Fishes, amphibians, and reptiles are cold-blooded. In endothermic, or warm-blooded, animals, the body temperature remains relatively constant regardless of the temperature of the environment. Birds and mammals are warm-blooded.

7. The jawless fishes have long, snakelike bodies with smooth skin and no scales. They have two single fins and a tail fin. They lack the paired fins, true jaws, and scales of other fishes. The skeleton of jawless fishes is composed of cartilage, and the notochord persists throughout life.

8. Lampreys are external parasites on other fish. They attach themselves to the fish with their round, suckerlike mouth, then they use the teeth on their tongue to gnaw a hole in the body of their victim. They obtain nutrients from the blood and body fluids they suck from the fish. Lampreys spawn in freshwater streams. The fertilized eggs hatch into larvae that live in the mud of the streams. After several years the larvae mature into adults, which live only a year or two.

9. Sharks, rays, and skates are members of the class Chondrichthyes. In this class, the skeleton is made of cartilage and traces of the notochord are present in the adult. These fish have movable upper and lower jaws equipped with rows of sharp teeth.

10. Skates and rays have flattened, winglike bodies with whiplike tails. Sharks are streamlined fish. The skin of the shark is covered with embedded, toothlike, placoid scales.

11. Bony fishes have skeletons made of bone, paired fins, and overlapping scales.

12. In bony fishes there are four pairs of gills on each side of the body. Water enters through the mouth, passes over the gills, and then out of the body. As water passes over the gills, there is an exchange of respiratory gases between the water and the blood in the gills. Bony fishes have a two-chambered heart consisting of an atrium and a ventricle. Blood from the heart passes to the gills, where it picks up oxygen and gives off carbon dioxide. From the gills it passes to the rest of the body before it is returned to the heart.

13. The swim bladder acts as a float to regulate the buoyancy of the fish. By increasing or decreasing the amount of gas in the swim bladder, the fish can change the density of its body, enabling it to remain suspended in the water at any depth.

14. Amphibians share the following characteristics: the skin is generally thin and contains mucus-secreting glands; there are two pairs of limbs, which are used for walking, jumping, and/or swimming; there is a pair of nostrils connected to the mouth cavity; there is a three-chambered heart; the young show a distinct larval form different from the adult.

15. The two main groups of amphibians are the tailed amphibians, such as salamanders, and the tailless amphibians, such as frogs.

16. The frog has a short, broad body with a pair of short forelegs and a pair of long, muscular hindlegs. The toes of the front legs are not webbed; the hindlegs have webbed toes and are adapted for jumping and swimming. The upper surface of the frog is green-brown, while the underside is whitish. The two eyes have three eyelids, one of which is transparent. Behind each eye is a tympanic membrane. On the tip of the head is a pair of nostrils.

17. The frog rapidly flips out its tongue, which is attached at the front end of the lower jaw, and catches insects in flight.

18. From the mouth, food passes through the esophagus into the stomach, where digestion begins. From the stomach, food enters the small intestine. The pancreas and liver secrete digestive juices that pass through ducts into the small intestine. Most digestion and absorption take place in the small intestine. Undigested food passes from the small intestine into the large intestine and then into the cloaca, which empties to the outside of the body. The cloaca also serves as a passageway for urine and for eggs and sperm.

19. The frog has a three-chambered heart consisting of two thin-walled atria and a muscular ventricle. Oxygenated blood from the lungs is carried to the left atrium by the right and left pulmonary veins. Three large veins empty blood from all other parts of the body into a thin-walled sac that empties into the right atrium. Both the right and left atria empty blood into the ventricle. Thus, blood pumped out of the ventricle is a mixture of oxygenated blood from the left atrium and deoxygenated blood from the right atrium. Blood from the ventricle passes through arteries to the capillaries of the body and is returned to the heart through veins.

20. The respiratory surfaces of the frog include the lungs, the lining of the mouth, and the skin. The frog uses its lungs to meet most of its oxygen requirements. The moist skin serves as a respiratory surface in air and when the frog is underwater. When frogs are hibernating the skin acts as the respiratory surface. The lungs and mouth function in respiration only when the frog is breathing air.

21. The central nervous system consists of the brain and spinal cord. The cranial nerves from the brain and the spinal nerves from the spinal cord and their branches make up the peripheral nervous system.

22. In the female, eggs produced in the ovaries enter the oviducts and are stored in sacs until they are released from the body through the cloaca. In the male, the testes produce sperm, which pass to the kidneys through tubules. From the kidneys, the sperm are carried by the ureters to the cloaca. During mating, the sperm are discharged from the male through the cloaca.

23. A tadpole is small and fishlike, with a long tail, gills, and no legs. Metamorphosis of the tadpole into the adult frog involves the development of legs, the absorption of the tail, the disappearance of gills, and the development of lungs and a three-chambered heart.

24. Reptiles share the following characteristics: the fertilized egg is enclosed in a tough, leathery shell; the skin is dry and covered with scales; except for snakes, reptiles have two pairs of legs; most have a three-chambered heart; they have well-developed lungs protected by a ribcage; nitrogenous wastes are excreted as uric acid.

25. Crocodiles have long snouts, powerful jaws with large teeth, and long, powerful tails. A pair of nostrils at the tip of the snout enables them to lie submerged in water with only the tip of the snout and eyes projecting above the surface. All the structural features described are good adaptations for defense.

26. The two parts of the turtle shell are the *carapace* and the *plastron*.

27. Turtles grab and tear food with the hard, sharp edges of their beak. They feed on plants and small animals.

28. Most lizards have two pairs of legs while snakes have no legs. Lizards have movable eyelids and external ear openings, while snakes have immovable eyelids and no external ear openings. The scales of the lizard are almost uniform in size, while those of the snake vary.

29. The forked tongue of the snake picks up odor-bearing particles of the prey. The particles are identified by *Jacobson's organs* in the roof of the mouth. Some snakes have heat-detecting *pit organs* on their head. These organs are used to track and strike the prey. Snakes also have sense organs in the skull that respond to vibrations.

30. Snakes feed on mice, rats, frogs, toads, insects, fish, and other small animals from their environment. Some snakes eat only living animals, swallowing them alive. Others kill their prey before swallowing them. Some snakes crush or strangle their victims before eating them, and some poison their victims.

31. *Neurotoxins* attack nervous tissues and cause paralysis, while *hemotoxins* break down red blood cells and blood vessels.

Answers to Test Your Understanding

1. *Jawless fishes* have long, snakelike bodies and smooth skin. They lack the paired fins, movable jaws, and scales of other fishes. The skeleton is composed of cartilage and the notochord persists throughout life. *Cartilaginous fishes* have a skeleton made entirely of cartilage, and traces of the notochord are present in the adult. The upper and lower jaws are movable and have several rows of sharp teeth. The *bony fishes* have skeletons made of bone, paired fins, and protective, overlapping scales.

2. Reptiles are better-adapted than amphibians for life on land for several reasons. They do not need water for fertilization. Fertilization is internal, and the embryo is enclosed in a leathery shell. The skin of reptiles is waterproof, which protects them from excessive water loss. The heart and lungs of reptiles are more efficient than those of amphibians, and the excretion of uric acid and urine in the form of a semisolid paste is an excellent adaptation for conserving water.

3. Cold-blooded animals cannot maintain a constant internal temperature. Their body temperature fluctuates with the temperature of their environment. When the outside temperature drops below a certain point, reptiles cannot be active because their metabolism slows down. Thus, the geographic range of reptiles is limited to tropical, subtropical, and temperate zones, where the average temperature is high enough for the animals to be active. In temperate zones, reptiles and other cold-blooded animals become inactive during cold weather.

4. Vertebrates are biologically successful because they have a very highly developed nervous system and sense organs, an internal skeleton, and efficient circulatory, excretory, respiratory, and reproductive systems.

Chapter 35

Rationale

The chapter opens with a discussion of birds. The general characteristics of birds are described, including their various structural adaptations. Then the internal structure of birds is presented in some detail. Next, the general characteristics of mammals are described. The three different kinds of mammals—monotremes, marsupials, and placental mammals—are discussed briefly. The major orders of placental mammals are presented.

The chapter ends with a look at human origins. The characteristics that distinguish humans from other primates are described, and the fossil evidence of human origins is presented.

Audiovisual Materials

"Australian Marsupials," (15 min., color) McGraw-Hill.

"Dr. Leakey and the Dawn of Man," (26 min., color) National Geographic Society.

"Mammals," (16 min., color) McGraw-Hill.

"Search for Fossil Man," (24 min., color) National Geographic Society.

"The Living Bird," (14 min., color) IFB.

"The Living Mammal," (17 min., color) IFB.

"Whales, Dolphins, and Men," (51 min., color) Time-Life Films.

Answers to Test Your Learning

1. All birds have feathers, a spindle-shaped body, one pair of wings and one pair of legs, hollow bones, a four-chambered heart, and a mouth in the form of a horn-covered beak or bill. Birds lack teeth and a urinary bladder. The females produce shell-covered eggs.

2. Feathers protect the skin from wear, support the bird in flight, and provide excellent insulation. A typical feather consists of a flat area, or *vane,* and a central shaft, or *rachis*. Each vane consists of numerous closely spaced barbs and each barb has numerous barbules that hook onto the barbules of adjacent barbs.

3. Air enters the respiratory system through the *nostrils* and passes down the *trachea,* which divides into two *bronchi*. One bronchus enters each lung. The bronchi pass through the lungs to the *posterior air sacs*. A system of small *air tubes* leads from the posterior air sacs into the lungs. The air tubes divide and subdivide many times, making close contact with capillaries in the lungs. Oxygen-rich air from the posterior sacs is forced through the fine air tubes in the lungs, where gas exchange occurs. The oxygen-poor air enters the *anterior air sacs,* and then passes back up the trachea and out of the body.

The circulatory system of birds is very similar to that of humans. There is a four-chambered heart with complete separation of oxygenated and deoxygenated blood, and a complete system of vessels—arteries, capillaries, and veins.

4. Birds need large amounts of food to provide energy for flight.

5. Food is taken into the *mouth,* where it is mixed with saliva. It then passes down the *esophagus* to the *crop,* where it is stored and softened. From the crop it passes into the first portion of the *stomach,* where it is partially digested by gastric juice. It then enters the *gizzard,* where it is ground up between pebbles. From the gizzard the food moves into the *intestine,* where digestion is completed and nutrients are absorbed into the bloodstream. Undigested food enters the short *rectum* and leaves the body through the *cloaca*.

6. Unlike all other vertebrates, mammals nourish their young with milk produced by mammary glands and the body surface has hair.

7. *Incisors* are for cutting, the *canines* are for tearing, and the *premolars* and *molars* are for grinding.

8. The three different types of mammals are the *monotremes,* the *marsupials,* and the *placental mammals*.

9. Insectivora—moles and shrews; Rodentia—mice and beavers; Lagomorpha—rabbits and hares; Chiroptera—brown bats and vampire bats; Cetacea—whales and dolphins; Edentata—anteaters and armadillos; Proboscidea—African and Asiatic elephants; Artiodactyla—pigs and deer; Perissodactyla—horses and rhinoceroses; Carnivora—dogs and bears.

10. The characteristics used to distinguish humans from other primates are the size and shape of the skull, jaws, and teeth; the shape of the pelvis; and the position of the foramen magnum.

11. *Ramapithecus, Australopithecus afarensis, Australopithecus africanus, Australopithecus robustus, Homo habilis, Homo erectus, Homo sapiens*. Neanderthal man and Cro-Magnon man are classified as varieties of *H. sapiens*.

12. Cro-Magnon man lived in caves and dwellings made of rock, wood, and hides. These early humans made finely chipped stone and bone tools, including axes, knives, awls, chisels, and scrapers. They also made fishing hooks, needles, and spear points. They wore clothing sewn from animal hides, drew on the walls of caves, and buried their dead in a ritualistic fashion. Their skeletons were the same as those of modern humans.

Answers to Test Your Understanding

1. The monotremes are egg-laying mammals. The embryos develop in eggs with leathery shells and containing a large amount of yolk. In marsupials the young are born in a very immature condition. They crawl into a pouch on the mother's body, and they complete their development in the pouch. In placental mammals, the young develop within the uterus of the mother. During this period they receive nourishment from the mother through the placenta.

2. Warm-blooded animals can be active during all seasons and can live in cold climates.

3. In birds, structural adaptations for flight include: the modification of the forelimbs as wings; strong, hollow, lightweight bones; strong breast muscles; a highly efficient respiratory system; feathers; a compact and efficient digestive tract.

4. (A) Cetacea; (B) Rodentia; (C) Perissodactyla; (D) Edentata (E) Primates; (F) Insectivora; (G) Carnivora; (H) Lagomorpha; (I) Chiroptera.

5. Humans have become the dominant animal species because of their intelligence and adaptability.

6. They made and used a wide variety of tools; they used and controlled fire; and they buried their dead in a ritualistic manner.

Chapter 36

Rationale

The chapter opens with a discussion of the abiotic factors of the environment, and then covers the organization of living things in populations, communities, and ecosystems. The following sections deal with nutritional and energy relationships in ecosystems. The topics covered include autotrophic and heterotrophic nutrition, symbiotic relationships, the roles of producers, consumers, and decomposers, food chains and food webs, and the pyramids of energy and biomass.

The following sections describe the cycles of materials in nature. The limited nature of the earth's resources and the reuse of materials by successive generations of living things are stressed. There is a brief discussion of competition in ecosystems, and the chapter ends with a description of change in ecosystems.

Audiovisual Materials

"An Ecosystem: A Struggle for Survival," (22 min., color) National Geographic Society.

"Coral Reef," (23 min., color) National Geographic Society.

"Plant-Animal Communities: Ecological Succession," (13 min., color) Coronet.

"Plant-Animal Communities: Interrelationships," (12 min., color) Coronet.

"Plant-Animal Communities: Physical Environment," (10 min., color) Coronet.

"Pond Life Food Web," (10 min., color) National Geographic Society.

"Succession: From Sand Dune to Forest," (16 min., color) EBE.

"The Community," (11 min., color) EBE.

"What is Ecology?" (11 min., color) EBE.

Answers to Test Your Learning

1. *Ecology* is the branch of biology that deals with the interactions between organisms and their environment.

2. The *biotic factors* include all the living organisms in the environment and their effects on other living things. The *abiotic factors* are the nonliving factors in the environment, including water, oxygen, light, temperature, soil, and inorganic and organic nutrients.

3. Both intensity and duration of sunlight vary with latitude. Areas around the equator receive sunlight of the strongest intensity, while the North and South Poles receive light of the weakest intensity. Areas around the equator receive about 12 hours of daylight throughout the year. In the winter at the poles, the sun never rises above the horizon, and in the summer it never sets below the horizon. In regions between the equator and the poles the relative lengths of day and night vary with the season.

4. Temperature patterns on the earth's surface vary with latitude and altitude. They are also affected by the presence of nearby major geographic features, such as mountains or an ocean.

5. The areas around the equator have the warmest average temperatures, while the areas at the North and South Poles are the coldest.

6. Precipitation patterns vary with altitude and latitude, and they are also affected by nearby geographic features.

7. Soil formation begins with the breakdown of rock by weathering and by the action of bacteria, fungi, lichens, and other soil-forming organisms. The breakdown of dead organisms adds organic matter to the rock particles. Over a long period of time, as the rock particles get smaller and more organic matter is added, three distinct soil layers appear. The uppermost layer is *topsoil,* which includes organic matter and living organisms. Beneath the topsoil is the *subsoil,* which consists of rock particles, various inorganic compounds, and water-soluble materials carried downward from the topsoil. The bottommost layer consists of bits of rock broken off from the parent bedrock.

8. A *population* consists of all the individuals of a particular species that live and interbreed in a given area. A *community* consists of all the populations in a given area. An *ecosystem* includes a community and its physical environment.

9. The *biosphere* is the portion of the earth in which living things exist. The biosphere includes portions of the *lithosphere,* which is the solid part of the earth's surface; the *hydrosphere,* which includes water on and under the earth's surface and the water vapor of the air; and the *atmosphere* which is the mass of air surrounding the earth.

10. A *herbivore* is an animal that feeds only on plants. Rabbits, cattle, horses, sheep, and deer are herbivores.

11. A *carnivore* is an animal that feeds only on other animals. Lions, sharks, hawks, and wolves are carnivores.

12. *Predators* attack and kill their prey, while *scavengers* feed on dead animals that they find. Tigers, cougars, and owls are predators, while vultures and hyenas are scavengers.

13. Humans, bears, raccoons, rats, and pigs are *omnivores*.

14. *Saprophytes* are organisms that obtain nutrients by breaking down the remains of dead plants and animals. Bacteria and fungi are the most numerous saprophytes.

15. A *symbiotic relationship* is one in which two different types of organisms live in a close association that benefits at least one of them.

16. In *mutualism* both organisms benefit from their association. Examples include termites and the wood-digesting microorganisms they contain and cows and the microorganisms in their digestive tracts. In *commensalism* one organism benefits while the other is not affected either way. Examples are the remora fish and sharks and barnacles and whales. In *parasitism* one organism benefits from the association and the other is harmed. Examples are tapeworms in digestive systems of animals and strangler figs growing on trees.

17. Most producers carry on photosynthesis, using energy from light to synthesize organic nutrients. Consumers are heterotrophs; they must obtain ready-made organic nutrients. Some consumers feed on autotrophs (producers), while others feed on lower-level consumers. Decomposers break down the remains of dead organisms, releasing substances that can be reused by other members of the ecosystem.

18. A food chain is a series of organisms through which food energy is passed. Producers form the base of the food chain. First-level consumers (herbivores) are animals that feed on plants. Second-level consumers are carnivores that feed on the first-level consumers. A food web illustrates the complicated feeding relationships in an ecosystem. A food web consists of a number of interconnected food chains.

19. The total amount of energy available in an ecosystem is greatest at the producer level and decreases sharply with each higher feeding level. The pyramid of energy represents the amount of energy at each feeding level. Because the total amount of available energy decreases with each higher feeding level, the total mass of living organisms that can be supported at each level decreases too. Thus available energy determines the pyramid of biomass.

20. Atmospheric nitrogen is converted to forms usable by most living things by the process of *nitrogen fixation*. In nitrogen fixation, which is carried out by the nitrogen-fixing organisms, atmospheric nitrogen is converted to nitrites and nitrates, which plants can use in the synthesis of proteins.

21. Decomposers break down the remains of dead plants and animals. One of the breakdown products is ammonia, which is converted by nitrifying bacteria to nitrates. Nitrates can be used by plants.

22. Nitrogen is returned to the atmosphere by the denitrifying bacteria.

23. *Carbon fixation* is the incorporation of carbon dioxide from the atmosphere into organic compounds. This is accomplished by photosynthesis.

24. In the carbon cycle, carbon dioxide is removed from the atmosphere by photosynthesis and returned by cellular respiration. Carbon dioxide is also released into the atmosphere by the burning of fossil fuels.

25. The carbon dioxide content of the atmosphere has increased because of the increased burning of fossil fuels.

26. In the oxygen cycle, oxygen is released into the atmosphere by photosynthesis and removed from the atmosphere by cellular respiration.

27. The water cycle involves the cycling of water between the surface of the earth and the atmosphere. There are no chemical changes in the water cycle, only the evaporation of water from the earth's surface and the condensation of water vapor in the atmosphere, resulting in the return of water to the surface as precipitation.

28. The *habitat* of an organism is the particular part of the environment in which it lives. The role of a species in an ecosystem is its *niche*.

29. *Interspecific competition* arises when the niches of two species in an ecosystem overlap. Eventually, one of the species is eliminated from the ecosystem.

30. *Intraspecific competition* is competition between members of the same species.

31. An ecosystem can be stable and self-sustaining if: there is a constant source of energy; there are organisms in the ecosystem that can use the energy for the synthesis of organic compounds; there is a cycle of materials between living organisms in the ecosystem and the environment.

32. *Ecological succession* is the gradual replacement of an existing community by a new community.

33. *Dominant species* are the species that exert the greatest effect on the environment and on other members of the community. A *climax community* is a stable community that is not replaced unless it is upset by a catastrophic event, such as a fire.

34. Succession on land begins with the slow formation of soil by weathering and the action of pioneer organisms, such as bacteria, fungi, and lichens. As the rock particles are broken down and the soil gains organic matter, mosses appear and eventually grasses and annual plants begin to grow in the area. When these plants die, the breakdown of their remains makes the soil richer. Small shrubs grow, then tree seedlings take root. One type of community succeeds another until a climax community is established.

35. Bacteria, fungi, and lichens are pioneer organisms.

36. Succession in a pond begins when sediments and debris accumulate on the lake bottom, making the pond shallower. The growth of plants around the edges of the pond gradually extend the banks inward. The more plants living in and around the pond, the more debris accumulates on the bottom when they die. Thus the pond fills in, and as succession continues it becomes a marsh and then dry land, eventually becoming part of the surrounding community.

Answers to Test Your Understanding

1. The amount of energy available in a food web decreases sharply with each higher feeding level. Only about 10 percent of the energy at one feeding level is available for the organisms of the next feeding level. Thus, above a certain level there is not enough available energy to support another group of organisms.

2. In an environment the supply of resources is limited. Living organisms incorporate substances from the environment into their bodies. If these substances were not returned to the environment, the supply would eventually be exhausted.

3. The intensity of sunlight is greatest at the equator and decreases with increasing latitude. The length of daylight around the equator is about 12 hours per day throughout the year. At the poles the sun never sets below the horizon in the summer and never rises above the horizon in the winter. Between the equator and the poles the length of daylight varies with the season. The warmest average temperatures are around the equator. With increasing latitude or increasing altitude the average temperature decreases. Annual precipitation patterns vary with latitude and altitude and are affected by large, nearby geographic features. In most areas around the equator there is heavy rainfall throughout the year. Most deserts are at latitudes of 30°N and 30°S.

4. Answers will vary. Some type of plant community could probably exist.

Chapter 37

Rationale

This chapter covers the biomes of the earth. The physical conditions, the type of climax community present, and the animal life of each type of biome are detailed. The tundra, taiga, temperate deciduous forests, grasslands, deserts, tropical rain forests, and marine and freshwater biomes are discussed.

Audiovisual Materials

"A Forest in the Clouds," (20 min., color) National Geographic Society.
"A Tidal Flat and its Ecosystem," (20 min., color) National Geographic Society.
"Plant-Animal Communities: Changing Balance of Nature," (10 min., color) Coronet.
"The Changing Forest," (18 min., color) McGraw-Hill.
"The Ocean Shore," (15 min., color) Modern Learning Aids.
"The Pond," (20 min., color) IFB.
"The Prairie," (18 min., color) IFB.
"The Sea," (26 min., color) EBE.
"The Spruce Bog," (22 min., color) McGraw-Hill.
"World in a Marsh," (21 min., color) McGraw-Hill.

Answers to Test Your Learning

1. A *biome* is a large geographic region showing a particular type of climax community.

2. The tundra extends across the northern parts of North America and Europe and Siberia.

3. The tundra has a very low average temperature and a very short growing season—about 60 days. Permafrost is characteristic of this region. Although there are only 10 to 12 centimeters of precipitation a year, the region contains many bogs and ponds because of the low rate of evaporation.

4. Vegetation in the tundra is limited to lichens, mosses, grasses, sedges, and shrubs. Animals include reindeer, musk oxen, caribou, wolves, Arctic hares, Arctic foxes, lemmings, snowy owls, and ptarmigans.

5. The taiga is a belt south of the tundra that extends across North America, Europe, and Asia.

6. The taiga has cold winters in which the ground is covered with deep snow. The growing season is about 120 days. The earth thaws completely during the summer, and there are many ponds and bogs.

7. Pines, firs, and spruce are the dominant vegetation of the taiga. However, some deciduous trees, shrubs, and flowering plants are present. Animals of the taiga include moose, wolves, bears, lynx, deer, elk, wolverines, martens, snowshoe hares, porcupines, rodents, birds, and many insects.

8. There is temperate deciduous forest south of the taiga in eastern North America and Europe. In this biome the winters are cold and the summers are hot and humid. Rainfall averages 75 to 150 centimeters a year.

9. Trees common to the temperate deciduous forest include oak, maple, hickory, beech, chestnut, and birch. There are also shrubs and various flowering plants. Animals include wolves, gray foxes, bobcats, deer, raccoons, squirrels, chipmunks, and a wide variety of birds and insects.

10. Grasslands are found in North America, Asia, South America, and Africa. They are usually found in the interior of a continent. Grasslands have 25 to 75 centimeters of rainfall a year and occur in both temperate and tropical climates.

11. The natural vegetation includes many species of grasses and wild flowers. Wetter areas have shrubs. Animals of the North American grasslands are coyotes, badgers, rattlesnakes, prairie dogs, jackrabbits, and ground squirrels, as well as birds and insects. In the past there were buffalo and antelopes. In Africa, grasslands are populated by zebras, giraffes, gazelles, lions, birds, and insects.

12. Rainfall in the desert is less than 25 centimeters a year. Temperatures in the desert may vary as much as 30°C during a 24-hour period.

13. Desert plants include cacti, yuccas, mesquite, sagebrush, and creosote bush. Desert animals include rodents, fennecs, birds, snakes, spiders, and insects.

14. Tropical rain forests are found in areas around the equator. They receive 200 to 400 centimeters of rain a year. Temperatures remain at about 25°C throughout the year.

15. In the rain forest, the tree cover is very dense so that little light reaches the ground. The treetops form a dense canopy about 50 meters high. Shorter, shade-tolerant trees grow below the canopy. The trees generally have shallow root systems that enable them to absorb nutrients and water from the thin layer of topsoil. Many trees have braces or prop roots that help to keep the trunks upright. Numerous species of vines, epiphytes, cacti, orchids, and ferns grow in the rain forest. Animals include monkeys, bats, rodents, birds, snakes, lizards, tapirs, antelopes, deer, spiders, and insects.

16. Increasing altitude generally produces climatic effects similar to increasing latitude.

17. There is no problem about the availability of water. However, in fresh water, excess water must be excreted, and in salt water, excess salt must be excreted. Variations in temperature are less in water than on land.

18. Sessile marine organisms include sponges, sea anemones, corals, and barnacles. Free-floating marine organisms include protists, algae, copepodes, jellyfish, and worms. Free-swimming marine organisms include squid, fishes, turtles, seals, and whales.

19. The phytoplankton are the major producers of the oceans.

20. The *intertidal zone* is an area along the shoreline that is covered by water at high tide and uncovered at low tide. Seaweeds, clams, crabs, starfish, sand fleas, worms, barnacles, and mussels live in the intertidal zone. The *littoral zone* includes the shallow waters above the continental shelf. Many types of organisms live in this zone, including algae, fish, oysters, mussels, crabs, barnacles, worms, and sea cucumbers. The *open water zone* is beyond the continental shelf and is very deep. The upper layer has plankton, fish, porpoises, squids, and whales. Below the photic zone, all organisms are heterotrophic.

21. In fast-moving streams, the bottoms consist mainly of rocks and gravel. Most organisms are found in calmer, shallow areas near the banks. In such areas, algae grow on rocks and there are many insects and insect larvae. Fish and floating algae are found in all parts of the stream. In slow-moving streams, muddy sediment accumulates on the bottom, and many animals live in the bottom mud. Animals living along the banks of the stream catch fish and other animals from the stream.

22. *Swamps* are low wet areas in which the vegetation includes trees and shrubs. *Bogs* are shallow bodies of water that contain sphagnum moss. In bogs, the water tends to be acid, which slows the rate of decay and reduces the cycling of nitrogen.

Answers to Test Your Understanding

1. Desert plants have widespread, shallow roots that enable them to absorb the maximum amount of water when it is available. Many desert plants store water in their tissues. Others complete their life cycle during the brief rainy season. Plants of the tropical rain forest have no problems with obtaining or conserving water. However, many of the trees have shallow root systems because nutrients are present mainly in the thin layer of topsoil.

2. In tropical rain forests the soil is poor because dead organisms decay quickly and the materials released by decomposition are rapidly taken up by the plants. Materials not absorbed by the plants are quickly washed away by the frequent rains.

3. Animals living in the tundra are faced by a very limited food supply and long, very cold winters. Animals of the desert are faced with a severely limited supply of water and very high daytime temperatures.

4. Marine organisms do not have a problem with water balance either because the salt concentration in their tissues is the same as that of the water or because they have some mechanism for excreting excess salt.

5. The intertidal zone contains seaweeds, clams, crabs, sand fleas, barnacles, mussels, starfish, and various shore birds. The littoral zone contains algae, fish, oysters, mussels, crabs, barnacles, worms, and sea cucumbers. In the open ocean, the upper layer includes plankton, large fish, porpoises, squids, and whales.

Chapter 38

Rationale

The chapter opens with a discussion of human activities that can damage the environment. Population growth, urbanization, agricultural practices, and various types of pollution are covered. The following sections deal with current attempts to restore the environment. Topics discussed include pollution control, conservation of natural resources, soil, forests, and wildlife, and the biological control of pests.

Audiovisual Materials

"Conservation and Balance in Nature," (18 min., b&w) IFB.

"Food and People," (25 min., b&w) EBE.

"Man's Impact on the Environment," (20 min., color) Modern Learning Aids.

"Population Ecology," (19 min., color) EBE.

"Problem of Conservation—Air," (15 min., color) EBE.

"The Garbage Explosion," (15 min., color) EBE.

Answers to Test Your Learning

1. Human ecology deals with the relationship between humans and the environment.

2. In many industrialized countries, both the birth rate and the death rate have declined, resulting in a stable but older population. In many underdeveloped countries, the death rate has dropped but the birth rate has remained high, resulting in rapid population growth.

3. If human population growth continues at the present rate, food will eventually become the limiting factor, and starvation will become a means of population control in some parts of the world.

4. Movement of the population to cities has resulted in the loss of productive farmland, which is now used for other purposes.

5. Poor farming practices have depleted soil nutrients in many areas and left them without a covering of vegetation, resulting in erosion.

6. *Pollution* is the addition of substances to the environment that make it less fit for living things.

7. Small amounts of organic wastes added to waterways can be broken down by bacteria in the water. The breakdown of large amounts of organic wastes, however, results in a depletion of oxygen from the water. This kills off fish and other types of aquatic organisms. Organic wastes that are plant nutrients can result in premature aging of lakes and ponds, or *eutrophication*.

8. *Biological magnification* is the accumulation of larger and larger quantities of toxic substances in the bodies of organisms at each higher level of the food chain.

9. Thermal pollution occurs when water from a stream is used to cool industrial equipment and then returned to the stream. Because the water has absorbed heat from the equipment it is much warmer than normal when it is returned to the stream.

10. *Sulfur dioxide* irritates the respiratory system. It also produces acid rain, which can destroy building stone and change the pH of lakes, killing aquatic organisms. *Hydrogen sulfide* is toxic at high concentrations. *Carbon monoxide* causes drowsiness at low concentrations and death at high concentrations. *Nitrogen oxide, ozone, hydrocarbons,* and *photochemical smog* are irritants to the respiratory system and the eyes, and they also damage plant tissues.

11. In a *temperature inversion* a layer of cool air becomes trapped beneath a layer of warmer air. The warm air acts as a lid, preventing the upward movement of air from the earth's surface. Pollutants accumulate in the cool layer.

12. Solid wastes can be burned in incinerators equipped with pollution-control devices or they can be buried in sanitary landfills.

13. Chemical pesticides can contaminate air and water, killing other organisms besides pests. Some are highly toxic to humans. Some of the pesticides do not break down rapidly and enter food chains, where they become concentrated in the bodies of higher-level consumers by the process of biological magnification.

14. If an organism is introduced into an area in which it has no natural enemies, there may be nothing to control its population increase.

15. Emission controls and the use of unleaded gasoline have reduced air pollution from automobiles. Treatment of industrial waste gases has also helped air pollution. Sewage treatment plants have reduced pollution of waterways. Efforts are also being made to stop the indiscriminate dumping of toxic wastes.

16. *Renewable natural resources* include air, water, soil, sunlight, and living things. *Nonrenewable natural resources* include coal, oil, natural gas, metals, and minerals.

17. *Erosion* is the removal of soil by wind or water.

18. *Cover crops* are crops that are planted to cover a whole field and that have a fibrous root systems. Cover crops hold the soil in place. In *strip cropping* cover crops are planted between the rows of row crops, thereby keeping the whole field covered. *Terracing* is the construction of flat areas for planting on a hillside. In *contour farming,* rows are plowed across the slopes, following the contour of the land. *Windbreaks* are rows of trees used to prevent wind erosion. In *crop rotation* different crops are grown in succeeding years to prevent the depletion of soil nutrients.

19. Soil depletion is prevented by crop rotation and by the use of fertilizers.

20. Techniques being used in forest conservation include sustained-yield tree cutting, block cutting, strip cutting, and selective harvesting of trees. In reforestation programs cut areas are planted with seeds or seedlings of a particular type.

21. Wildlife conservation practices include the establishment of hunting and fishing laws, game and bird preserves, fish hatcheries, and legal protection for endangered species.

22. Biological methods of pest control involve the introduction of natural enemies to control pests, use of viruses or bacteria against insects and worms, crop rotation, use of pheromones to lure insects into traps, and the release of sterile males into the population.

23. Biological methods of pest control tend to be more specific than chemical methods and they have less of an effect on the environment.

Answers to Test Your Understanding

1. Answers will vary.

2. Answers will vary. The food supply and environmental pollution are possibilities.

3. Various forms of pollution have already proved to be serious health hazards. As the world's population increases, the potential for damage by humans to the environment increases too.

4. It is important to prevent the extinction of plant and animal species for several reasons. First, they may be a necessary part of a food chain or web. We don't know what interrelationships may exist in nature. The organism might have traits that are not of any known use at this time, but which might be useful in the future.

BIOLOGY
THE STUDY OF LIFE

William D. Schraer
Chairperson
Science Department
Middletown High School
Middletown, New York

Herbert J. Stoltze
Professor of Biology
Northeastern Illinois University
Chicago, Illinois

Cebco Standard Publishing
9 Kulick Road, Fairfield, New Jersey 07006
a Standex company

Technical Consultants

Donald Deters
University of Texas
(Respiration)

Gary B. Ellis
University of Texas
(Vertebrates)

Kenneth R. Miller
Brown University
(Photosynthesis)

M.V. Parthasarathy
Cornell University
(Plant structure and function)

Irwin Rubenstein
University of Minnesota
(The cell)

Charles F. Stevens
Yale University
(Nervous and endocrine systems)

Daryl Sweeney
University of Illinois
(Invertebrates)

Marjorie B. Zucker
New York University School of Medicine
(Circulatory systems)

ACKNOWLEDGMENTS

The authors are indebted to many individuals whose comments, suggestions, and criticisms during the writing of the manuscript helped to create a better textbook. The authors especially acknowledge the assistance of Dr. Eugene McArdle, Betty Mishkin, Dr. Herbert Lamp, Gerri Leffner, William Conrad, and Ray Smith.

We wish to express our appreciation of the thorough review of sections of the manuscript given by the technical consultants. It must be stressed, however, that the authors bear the sole responsibility for the accuracy of the content of the final product.

The authors also wish to give special thanks to the following teachers who reviewed a trial section of the text during its development, answered a questionnaire, and offered many useful comments and suggestions: Carole Brenkacz, West Seneca East Senior High School, West Seneca, New York; Brenda L. Dorsey, York Community High School, Elmhurst, Illinois; Karen L. Fout, Fenwick High School, Middletown, Ohio; Richard L. Gaume, Plain Local Schools, Canton, Ohio; Norm Grimes, Columbian High School, Tiffin, Ohio; Emiel Hamberlin, Du Sable High School, Chicago, Illinois; Sister M. Francis Hopcus, Pomona Catholic High School, Pomona, California; Mic Jaeger, East Union High School, Manteca, California; Harold Pratt, Jefferson County Schools, Lakewood, Colorado; Helen Louise Shafer, Science and Technology Magnet School, Dallas, Texas; Russell H. Stanhope, Worcester Public Schools, Worcester, Massachusetts; Harlow B. Swartout, Woodstock High School, Woodstock, Illinois; Robert C. Wallace, Reavis High School, Burbank, Illinois; Melanie Wojtulewicz, Whitney M. Young Magnet High School, Chicago, Illinois.

The authors are grateful for the help and guidance given to them by their editors Deena Cloud and Bertram Coren.

Finally, but surely not least in importance, is our gratitude to our wives, Beverley Schraer and Golda Stoltze, and our children, Lynann Schraer and Jonathan, Barry, and Sarah Stoltze, for their patience and encouragement.

William D. Schraer
Herbert J. Stoltze

Design and Illustration
ASSOCIATED DESIGNERS
George A. Bakacs, *Art Director*

Supplementary features developed by
EDUCATIONAL CHALLENGES, INC.
Alexandria, Virginia

ISBN: 0-88320-714-1

1 3 5 7 9 10 8 6 4 2

Learning Biology with the Help of this Book

To the student:

Science is made up of two parts. One part of science is its facts. When a seed is planted under the right conditions, it grows into a plant. That is a fact of biology. The other part of science is its ideas and theories. The explanation of how a seed develops into a plant is an idea or theory of biology, not a fact. The idea of evolution is another example of a theory, not a fact.

Ideas are really what science is all about. But to understand the ideas, you need to know the facts on which the ideas are based. You also need to follow the reasoning that leads from the facts to the ideas.

This book has been planned to make the facts of biology clear and the ideas of biology understandable. Each chapter has special aids to help you along the path from facts to ideas. You will find it easier to learn from this book if you know what these special features are and how to use them. Look at any chapter and notice the following things:

Learning goals for each main section. These are statements of things you should be able to do after studying the section. If you can do them, you know you have mastered the topic.

Boldface words. These are the important new terms you need to know. They are explained in the text where they appear in bold type. Most of them are also defined in the Glossary at the back of the book.

Chapter summary. This will help you quickly review the important facts and ideas of the chapter. If you are uncertain about any point, go back and read about it again.

New vocabulary list. This will help you check up on your learning of the new words in the chapter. If necessary, use the Index to find where they are explained, or use the Glossary to review their meanings.

Chapter questions. Notice that the "test your learning" questions are keyed to the numbered sections of the chapter. Check your answers by referring to the corresponding sections.

If you become especially interested in any topic, there are suggestions for independent research at the end of the chapter and a list of books and articles for further reading starting on page 686.

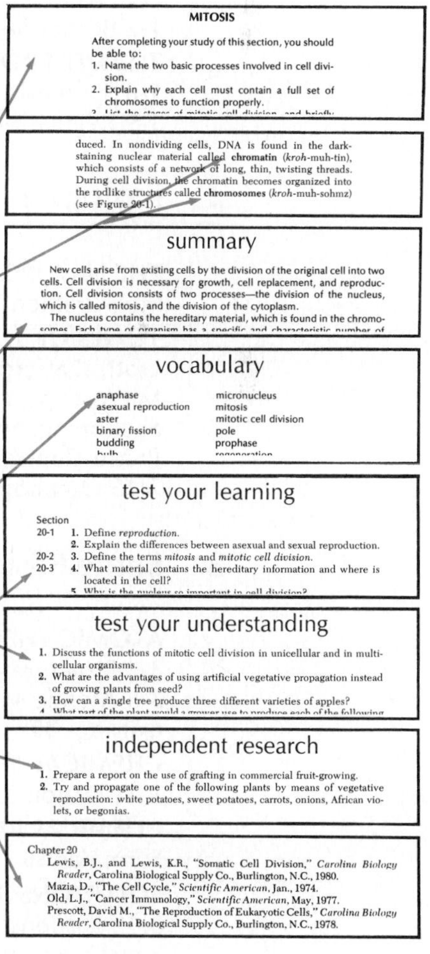

MITOSIS
After completing your study of this section, you should be able to:
1. Name the two basic processes involved in cell division.
2. Explain why each cell must contain a full set of chromosomes to function properly.
duced. In nondividing cells, DNA is found in the dark-staining nuclear material called chromatin (kroh-muh-tin), which consists of a network of long, thin, twisting threads. During cell division, the chromatin becomes organized into the rodlike structures called chromosomes (kroh-muh-sohmz) (see Figure 20-1).
summary
New cells arise from existing cells by the division of the original cell into two cells. Cell division is necessary for growth, cell replacement, and reproduction. Cell division consists of two processes—the division of the nucleus, which is called mitosis, and the division of the cytoplasm.
The nucleus contains the hereditary material, which is found in the chromo-
vocabulary
anaphase
asexual reproduction
aster
binary fission
budding
micronucleus
mitosis
mitotic cell division
pole
prophase
test your learning
Section
20-1 1. Define reproduction.
2. Explain the differences between asexual and sexual reproduction.
20-2 3. Define the terms mitosis and mitotic cell division.
20-3 4. What material contains the hereditary information and where is located in the cell?
test your understanding
1. Discuss the functions of mitotic cell division in unicellular and in multicellular organisms.
2. What are the advantages of using artificial vegetative propagation instead of growing plants from seed?
3. How can a single tree produce three different varieties of apples?
independent research
1. Prepare a report on the use of grafting in commercial fruit-growing.
2. Try and propagate one of the following plants by means of vegetative reproduction: white potatoes, sweet potatoes, carrots, onions, African violets, or begonias.
Chapter 20
Lewis, B.J., and Lewis, K.R., "Somatic Cell Division," Carolina Biology Reader, Carolina Biological Supply Co., Burlington, N.C., 1980.
Mazia, D., "The Cell Cycle," Scientific American, Jan., 1974.
Old, L.J., "Cancer Immunology," Scientific American, May, 1977.
Prescott, David M., "The Reproduction of Eukaryotic Cells," Carolina Biology Reader, Carolina Biological Supply Co., Burlington, N.C., 1978.

CONTENTS

UNIT 1 INTRODUCTION TO BIOLOGY

UNIT 2 ANIMAL MAINTENANCE

10 The Blood 160

11 Respiratory Systems 176

12 Excretion 192

13 Support and Locomotion 206

Chapter

UNIT 3 PLANT MAINTENANCE

UNIT 4 REPRODUCTION AND DEVELOPMENT

24 Sexual Reproduction in Plants 384

UNIT 5 GENETICS

25 Mendelian Genetics 402

26 Modern Genetics 418

Chapter

27 Molecular Genetics 434

UNIT 6 EVOLUTION

28 Evidence of Organic Change 456

29 Theories of Evolution 476

UNIT 7 DIVERSITY OF LIVING THINGS

Chapter

UNIT 8 ECOLOGY

Special Features

sidelights

frontiers of biology

careers

historical notes

UNIT 1
INTRODUCTION TO BIOLOGY

chapter 1

The Nature of Life

INTRODUCTION TO BIOLOGY

The word **biology** is easy to define. It is the study of living things. Let us consider what this might mean. Think for a minute or two about the different kinds of living things you know by sight. You may want to jot them down under various headings, such as domestic animals, wild animals, ocean life, insects. Don't forget the plants you know—for example, trees, wildflowers, garden flowers, house plants, weeds. If you take the time to do it, you may come up with quite a long list—probably 100 kinds, at least.

Suppose you wanted to find out everything you could about the living things you know. You might expect it to take quite a long time. Yet, the living things you know are only a tiny fraction of all that exist. Biologists have found more than a million different kinds of life on earth. You may wonder how you can possibly learn very much about a million different things in one year of biology.

Actually, you are going to learn a great deal about every one of them by reading just a few pages of this chapter. The reason is that despite the great *diversity* of life, there is also a great *unity* of life. All living things are alike in many ways. We are going to begin the study of biology by talking about these similarities.

Figure 1-1. Forest in Summer.

LIVING AND NONLIVING THINGS

After completing your study of this section, you should be able to list eight general characteristics that distinguish living from nonliving things.

1-1 Characteristics of Life

Just what do we mean when we say that something is alive? Look at Figure 1-1. It is a fairly common sight—the edge of a woods. Do you see a dead tree in the picture? What makes you think so?

Now look at Figure 1-2. This is a similar scene during the winter in one of the colder parts of the country. Are all these trees dead? They certainly look like the dead tree in Figure 1-1. But they are probably not dead. In the spring, tiny buds at the ends of twigs will grow into leaves. The trees will once again show signs of life.

Figure 1-2. Forest in Winter.

The growth of new leaves on a tree is a sign of life. What other signs of life can you think of? Biologists have not been able to agree on a simple definition of life that fits all cases. But they have agreed on what the "signs of life" are. Taken together, these characteristics or activities become the definition of life.

Each individual living thing is called an **organism** (*or*-guh-nih-zum). All organisms have the following characteristics.

1. Living things are highly organized and contain many complex chemical substances.
2. Living things are made up of one or more **cells,** which are the smallest units that can be said to be alive.
3. Living things use energy.
4. Living things have a definite form and a limited size.
5. Living things have a limited life span.
6. Living things grow.
7. Living things respond to changes in the environment.
8. Living things reproduce.

Nonliving objects may show one, or even a few, of these characteristics, but they never show all of them.

1-2 Borderline Cases

It is a human trait to try to define and classify the things we find in the world around us. But the world doesn't seem to be made to suit our wishes. Our definitions and classifications often have fuzzy edges. There are usually borderline cases that fit partly into one category and partly into another. This is especially true of our attempts to define life. There are things in the world that cannot clearly be called "living" or "nonliving." One example is the viruses—objects that can be stored like chemicals in a bottle, but when inside a living cell can reproduce more of themselves. Viruses can reproduce, but they do not otherwise carry on any of the processes of life. Another example is a plant seed. Many seeds can be kept in a package for years without undergoing any change. When supplied with water and other suitable conditions, they develop into living plants. Is the seed in the package alive?

The best answer to the question may be that it doesn't really matter whether we say a seed is living or not. There is a far more important and, we think, more interesting question: How does a seed develop into a living plant? You will be trying to answer this kind of question in your study of biology.

THE LIFE PROCESSES

After completing your study of this section, you should be able to:

1. Name and define eight general processes by which the life of organisms is maintained.
2. Define the term *metabolism*.

We have mentioned some of the general characteristics of living things. Living things carry on certain activities that are also characteristics of life. In this section we will briefly describe the functions or processes that organisms perform in order to stay alive. These life processes are nutrition, transport, respiration, synthesis and assimilation, growth, excretion, regulation, and reproduction. We will find as we go along that everything we learn about living things is related in some way to these life processes. No matter how different individual organisms may be, they all must carry on these activities. This is the common thread that ties all living things together and makes them basically alike.

Figure 1-3. Nutrition in Animals. Animals must obtain food from the environment.

1-3 Nutrition

Every organism takes materials from its environment and changes them into forms it can use. This activity is called **nutrition** (noo-*trish*-un). Substances that an organism can use for energy or for growth and repair are called **nutrients** (*noo*-tree-unts).

There are two basic types of nutrition. In one kind of nutrition, the organism can produce its own complex nutrients from simple substances in the environment. All the green plants and some bacteria and other one-celled organisms are able to make their own nutrients in this way.

Organisms that cannot make their own nutrients must obtain them in the form of food from the environment. All animals must find their nutrients already made in their environment (see Figure 1-3).

The taking in of food from the environment is called *ingestion* (in-*jes*-chun). Generally, the nutrients in food are not in forms that the organism can use directly. The nutrients are chemically too complex, and the organism must first break them down into simpler forms. The breakdown of complex food materials into simpler forms that can be used by an organism is called *digestion* (dy-*jes*-chun). The elimination of indigestible material from the digestive tract is called *egestion* (ih-*jes*-chun).

Stress that the materials that form digestive wastes have never been part of the body cells.

1-4 Transport

Transport is the process by which usable materials are taken into the organism *(absorption)* and distributed throughout the organism *(circulation)*. Wastes and other products of the life processes are also transported from one place to another within the organism. In the smallest organisms there is no real transport system. Usable materials are absorbed directly into the organism from the environment. Wastes pass from the organism directly back into the environment. In most animals there is a highly specialized circulatory system for carrying needed materials to all parts of the organism and carrying wastes away. In plants, there are also specialized conducting structures that carry substances from the roots and leaves to all parts of the plant.

1-5 Respiration

All the life processes require a constant supply of energy. Organisms obtain the energy they need by releasing the chemical energy stored in nutrients. The process by which this is accomplished is called **respiration** (res-puh-*ray*-shun).

Respiration involves a complex series of chemical reactions. In one type of respiration, sugar is broken down to produce water and carbon dioxide. This is called *aerobic* (er-*roh*-bik) *respiration* because it requires oxygen from the air. *Breathing* is the process by which air is drawn into the body and waste gases are eliminated. Most organisms make use of aerobic respiration to release the energy they need. Some simple organisms carry on *anaerobic* (an-uh-*roh*-bik) *respiration*, which does not require oxygen.

1-6 Synthesis and Assimilation

Organisms are able to combine simple substances chemically to form more complex substances. This process is called **synthesis** (*sin*-thuh-sis). The substances used in synthesis are generally products of the digestion of complex food materials.

One of the results of synthesis is to produce materials that can become part of the structure of an organism. In this way, the organism can repair or replace worn-out parts and can also grow. The incorporation of materials into the body of the organism is called **assimilation** (uh-sim-uh-*lay*-shun).

1-7 Growth

Growth is the process by which living organisms increase in size. It is one result of assimilation of nutrients. In one-celled organisms, growth is simply an increase in the size of the cell. In organisms made up of many cells, growth is usually the result of an increase in the number of cells. In animals, growth generally follows a particular pattern and ends after a certain period of time. Some plants, on the other hand, continue growing throughout life.

1-8 Excretion

Every organism produces waste substances that it cannot use and that may be harmful if allowed to accumulate in the body. The removal of these wastes is called **excretion** (ek-*skree*-shun).

1-9 Regulation

Regulation is the process by which an organism maintains a stable internal environment in a constantly changing external environment. The maintenance of a stable internal environment is called **homeostasis** (hoh-mee-oh-*stay*-sis).

In animals, regulation is accomplished by two specialized systems—the *nervous system* and the *endocrine* (*en*-duh-krin) *system.* The nervous system consists of a network of specialized cells that carry messages, or impulses, throughout the organism. The endocrine system consists of a number of glands that secrete chemicals called *hormones.* Both nerve impulses and hormones can bring about changes in the organism in response to changes in either the internal or the external environment. There is no nervous system in plants, but there are parts of the plant that produce hormones. These hormones enable the plant to respond to various changes in the environment.

1-10 Reproduction

Reproduction is the process by which living things produce new organisms of their own kind. Unlike the other life processes, reproduction is not necessary for the continued life of an individual organism. However, it is necessary for the continued existence of that kind of organism.

There are two types of reproduction—*asexual* (ay-*sek*-shuh-wul) *reproduction* and *sexual* (*sek*-shuh-wul) *reproduction.* In asexual reproduction there is only one parent, and all offspring are identical to that parent. In sexual reproduction there are two parents, and the offspring are not identical to either parent.

1-11 Metabolism

All the chemical reactions of the life processes of an organism are called its **metabolism** (muh-*tab*-uh-liz-um). Metabolism includes processes that build complex substances from simpler ones and processes that break down complex substances into simpler ones. Metabolism also involves the continuous release and use of energy. Many biologists consider metabolic activity to be the single most important characteristic of life.

summary

Biology is the study of living things. There are more than a million different kinds of living things on earth. Although they vary in many respects, they all show certain basic characteristics that distinguish them from nonliving things. A few things, including viruses and seeds, are impossible to classify definitely as either living or nonliving—they show characteristics of both. Living things carry on certain activities that are characteristics of life. These activities include nutrition, transport, respiration, synthesis and assimilation, growth, excretion, regulation, and reproduction. Metabolism includes all the chemical reactions of the life processes.

vocabulary

assimilation
biology
cell
excretion
growth
homeostasis
metabolism
nutrient
nutrition
organism
regulation
reproduction
respiration
synthesis
transport

test your learning

Section		
1-1	**1.**	Define the term *organism.*
	2.	List the eight characteristics of living things.
1-2	**3.**	Would you classify viruses and seeds as living or nonliving? Give the reasons for your answer.
1-3	**4.**	Define the terms *nutrition, nutrient, ingestion,* and *digestion.*
1-4	**5.**	Describe the process of transport, including absorption and circulation.
1-5	**6.**	By what process do organisms obtain the energy they need?
	7.	What is the difference between aerobic and anaerobic respiration?
1-6	**8.**	Define the terms *synthesis* and *assimilation.*
1-7	**9.**	How does growth occur in many-celled organisms?
1-8	**10.**	By what life process are metabolic wastes removed from an organism?
1-9	**11.**	Define the term *homeostasis.*
	12.	How do the nervous and endocrine systems function in regulation?
1-10	**13.**	What is the difference between asexual and sexual reproduction?
1-11	**14.**	Define the term *metabolism.*

test your understanding

1. Can you think of any nonliving thing that shows more than four of the characteristics of living things?
2. How does breathing differ from respiration?
3. List the life processes that are involved in transforming food into part of the body of a living organism.

independent research

1. Write a report about one of the following characteristics of living things:
   A. Living things are made up of cells.
   B. Living things use energy.
   C. Living things have a definite form and limited size.
   D. Living things have a limited life span.
   E. Living things grow.
   F. Living things respond to changes in the environment.
2. Using library reference books for information, describe the process by which each of the following organisms obtains nutrients: maple tree, tiger, bread mold, tapeworm.
3. For class discussion, prepare a report on viruses, including their structure and life functions and how they differ from living things.

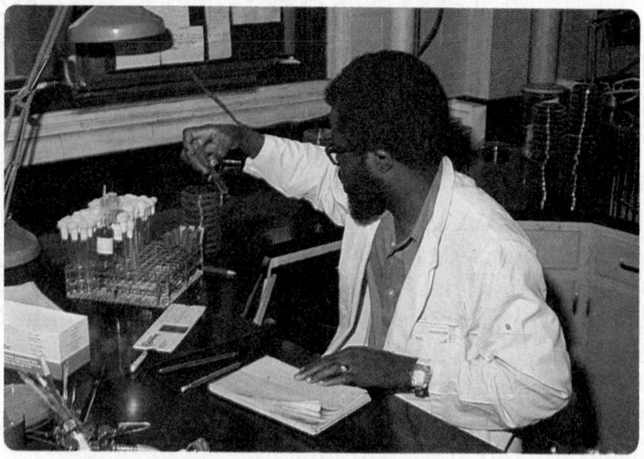

chapter 2

Biology as a Science

THE NATURE OF SCIENCE

After completing your study of this section, you should be able to:
1. State the essential steps of a scientific investigation.
2. Explain what is meant by a controlled experiment.
3. Define the terms *hypothesis* and *theory*.

Figure 2-1. Observation. Biologists often observe organisms in nature. Such studies provide information that cannot be obtained in a laboratory setting.

2-1 The Scientific Method

Broadly speaking, all science is an attempt to understand the world we live in. By this we mean that science goes beyond simple observation and description of objects and events. It tries to find general principles that explain why things are as they are and why things happen the way they do. There are so many different kinds of phenomena to be explained, and so many unanswered questions, that scientists have had to become specialists—physicists, chemists, astronomers, earth scientists, biologists, and so on. Within each of these major fields, there are numerous subdivisions. Today, few scientists have the knowledge or the time to make investigations beyond a narrow field of interest.

Scientists in all fields approach their problems in the same way. When a scientist announces a finding or proposes a new idea, other scientists may repeat the work or test its conclusions. This universal approach to scientific problems is called the **scientific method.** Its main features are the same in all areas of science.

Defining the problem. The first task of the investigator is to define the problem to be studied. A problem should be limited enough in scope so that it can be investigated with some chance of clear-cut results. At the start of a research project, the investigator will usually search through all available literature on the topic. The investigator thus gathers information on the topic and avoids unnecessary duplication of work already done.

Observation. Since the goal of science is to explain what is observed, every investigation must include observations. In biology, some observations may simply be descriptions of an organism or its parts or of ways the organism behaves in its natural environment (see Figure 2-1). However, most scientific observations are made by means of experiments. In an experiment, the investigator sets up a situation in which a particular kind of observation can be made. The investigator makes certain changes in the situation and observes the results. In biology, research often involves the use of **controlled experiments.** In a controlled experiment, the same experiment is set up in duplicate. A single factor is then changed in one setup, but not in the other. Any difference in the results of the two experiments can be assumed to be caused by the factor that was changed. The setup in which no change was made is called the *control* (see Figure 2-2).

Measurement. In the early history of science, observations were generally imprecise. One thing might be described as larger than another, or an event might be described as more likely to happen at warm temperatures than at cold temperatures. Today we recognize that such vague observations are not very useful. The heart of modern science is accurate measurement and the statement of results in numerical, or quantitative, form. To obtain precise, quantitative results, scientists use many special tools and instruments.

Recording and reporting observations. For progress to occur in any field of science, there must be no secrecy, no withholding of information. The materials and procedures used in all investigations, as well as all observations and results, must be recorded accurately and reported in full detail. If an experiment cannot be repeated by other investigators, the reported results of the original investigation cannot be considered valid.

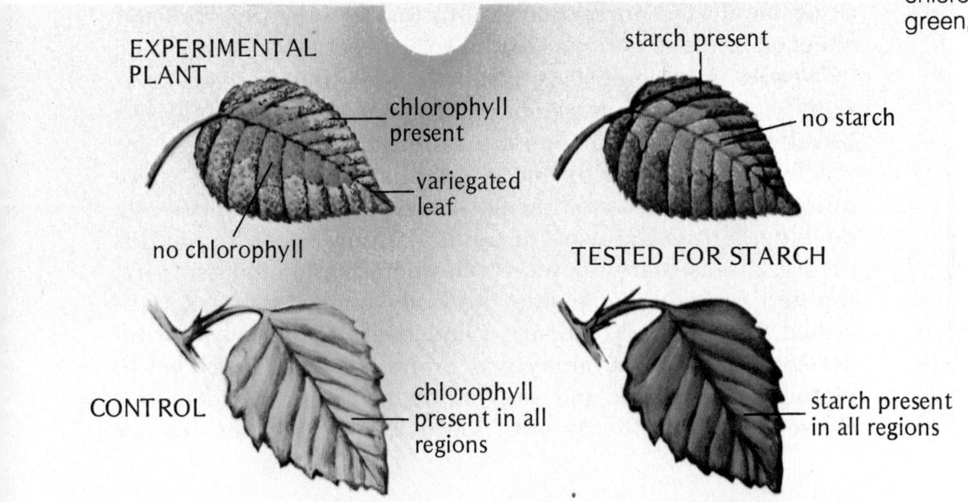

Figure 2-2. A Controlled Experiment. In a leaf that is partly green, starch is produced by photosynthesis only in the green regions (those that contain chlorophyll). In a leaf that is entirely green, starch is produced in all regions.

When a research project has been completed, the investigator may write a paper describing it and submit the paper to a scientific journal. These journals are usually publications of scientific societies specializing in a particular branch of science. The journals serve as a source of information on recent developments in various scientific fields.

The search for patterns or regularities. In working on a research problem, the investigator must repeat experiments many times so that many sets of results are obtained. Performing an experiment only once or twice does not provide enough data for a valid conclusion. Once enough data has been collected, it must be arranged in a logical way. It may reveal a pattern or some definite relationship between one factor and another in the experiment.

Hypotheses. Regularities in the results of experiments are interesting and useful. They tell you what can be expected from other experiments of the same kind. But they do not by themselves *explain* anything. What scientists really want to know is *why* a particular pattern is observed. They want to know what causes the pattern to occur. It is here that human reasoning, guesswork, or inspiration enters. The investigator, or someone else studying the reported pattern, may have an idea as to why the pattern exists. This idea is called a **hypothesis** (hy-*pahth*-uh-sis). A hypothesis is a possible explanation of an observed set of facts.

A hypothesis may seem very logical. It may explain everything that is known about a certain problem. But until it is tested by further experiments, it remains just a hypothesis—a logical guess. A hypothesis cannot be tested just by carrying out more experiments of the same kind. That would only verify the pattern, not the hypothesis about its cause. A good hypothesis will predict other kinds of patterns that may not have been looked for. Experiments will then be performed to look for these other predicted effects. The hypothesis is accepted as probably correct if all its predicted effects are observed, and if it never fails. A hypothesis can never be completely proved. It may at any time be disproved by a single experiment! (Of course, that experiment must be repeated and checked to make sure its results are correct.)

Theories. A hypothesis is usually an idea limited to observations in a particular investigation. Explanations that apply to a broad range of phenomena are called **theories.** Theories are much harder to come by and to establish than hypotheses. An example of a well-tested theory is the germ theory of disease, developed from the work of Louis Pasteur. According to this theory, diseases are the effects of microscopic organisms living and reproducing inside the body of the diseased individual. The nature of disease had been completely misunderstood before this theory was proposed. The theory led to methods of treating and preventing many human diseases. However, it is a theory with limits. Many diseases are not

Table 2-1. Prefixes of the Metric System.

mega-	one million	1,000,000
kilo-	one thousand	1,000
deci-	one-tenth	0.10
centi-	one-hundredth	0.01
milli-	one-thousandth	0.001
micro-	one-millionth	0.000001

caused by germs. The world is still waiting for a theory that will account for the so-called degenerative diseases, such as arthritis, diabetes, cancer, and heart disease.

2-2 Scientific Measurement

Measurements in scientific investigations are usually expressed in units of the **metric system.** In this system, the basic unit of length is the meter; the unit of mass or weight is the gram; the unit of volume is the liter; and the unit of temperature is the Celsius degree, or kelvin. In the customary system of measurement used in daily life in the United States, units of different size have different names. For example, inches, feet, yards, and miles are all units of length. For a particular measurement we choose the unit that is most convenient. Thus we express the size of a sheet of paper in inches; the dimensions of a room in feet; and the distance between cities in miles. In the metric system, a simpler method is used to make units of convenient size. A prefix is attached to the unit name to make it larger or smaller. The most commonly used prefixes are defined in Table 2-1. The measurements of some familiar objects in metric units are shown in Figure 2-3.

The biologist has a need for small units because of the small size of the structures in living cells. Many of these structures are no more than a few millionths of a meter (micrometers) in length or diameter. Since so many measurements in biology are in this range, biologists often use a shorter name, the micron, in place of the micrometer. One micron (symbol, μ) is the same as one micrometer, or one-millionth of a meter. It is also equal to one-thousandth of a millimeter (0.001 mm).

Another small unit of length sometimes used for cell structures is the Angstrom unit (symbol, Å). One Angstrom unit is one ten-thousandth of a micron.

Figure 2-3. Some Representative Metric Measurements.

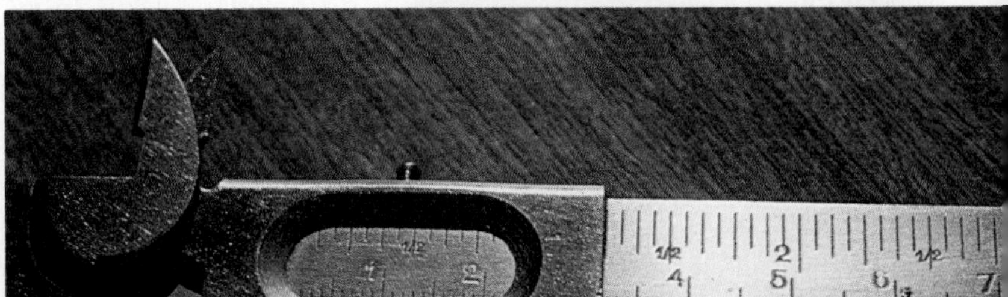

TOOLS OF THE BIOLOGIST

After completing your study of this section, you should be able to:

1. State why instruments are necessary for scientific research.
2. Name and state the function of the parts of a compound microscope.
3. Explain how to find the magnifying power of a compound microscope.
4. Define and state the importance of resolution in a microscope.
5. Describe the steps in preparing a specimen for examination with a microscope.
6. State the special characteristics and uses of the stereomicroscope, the phase-contrast microscope, and the electron microscope.

2-3 The Need for Instruments

Observation and measurement are the backbone of scientific investigation. The observations that can be made by the unaided senses are quite limited. Therefore, every branch of science makes use of instruments that increase the range and accuracy of the human senses. Even in daily life we use instruments to help our senses. Eyeglasses are an obvious example. But we also use thermometers, measuring cups, scales, and rulers. We seldom think of these things as scientific instruments, but that is what they are. In this section of the text we will describe a few of the important instruments that are used in biological research.

Figure 2-4. A Simple Microscope. A magnifying glass is a simple microscope.

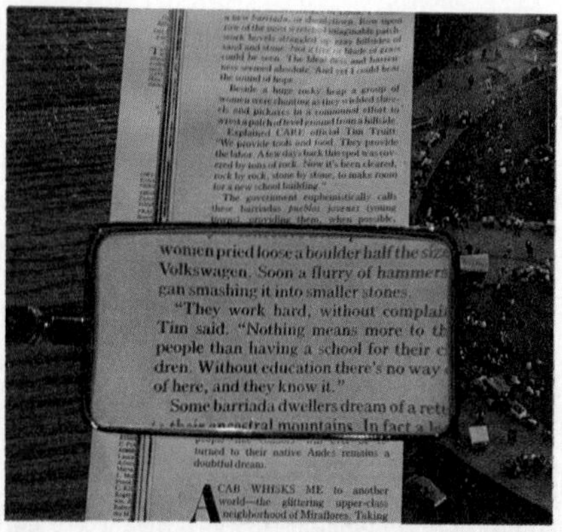

2-4 The Optical Microscope

A **microscope** is any device that enables us to see small details in an object by apparently enlarging it. What we see when we use a microscope to examine an object is called an **image.** The ratio of the image size to the object size is the **magnification,** or *magnifying power,* of the instrument. Microscopes that make use of light to produce enlarged images are called **optical microscopes.** Optical microscopes depend on the fact that light rays change direction when they pass from one transparent medium into another. Optical microscopes contain lenses, which are pieces of glass with curved surfaces. The lenses cause light rays from an object to bend in such a way as to produce an enlarged image.

2-5 The Simple Microscope

The **simple microscope** is what we know as a magnifying glass (see Figure 2-4). It consists of a single lens. Lenses of this type were used as early as the tenth century. They are still used by biologists to identify specimens in the field and for quick observations not requiring the high magnifications of a laboratory instrument.

2-6 The Compound Microscope

A compound microscope is one that uses two lenses (see Figure 2-5). One lens produces an enlarged image that is further magnified by the second lens. A compound microscope has an optical system, a mechanical system, and a light system.

The optical system. The lenses make up the **optical system** of the compound microscope. The two lenses of the optical system are the *objective* and the *ocular* (ahk-yuh-ler), or *eyepiece*. In modern microscopes, the objective and the ocular each consist of several lenses combined to give the desired optical properties. However, as far as the operation of the instrument is concerned, each set of lenses acts like a single lens.

A compound microscope usually has two or more objective lenses of different magnifying powers. A *low-power objective* is used first to locate the region of the specimen to be examined. A *high-power objective* is then moved into position if further magnification is wanted. The microscope usually has just one ocular. However, in some cases the ocular may be removed and replaced by another of different power.

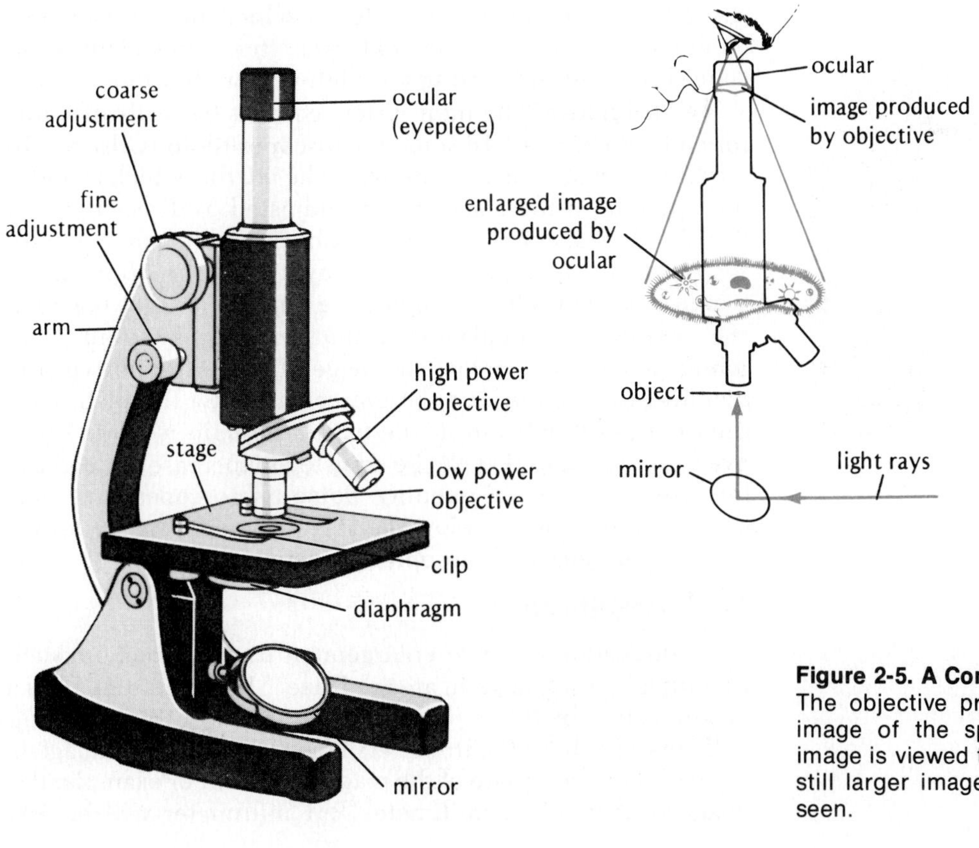

Figure 2-5. A Compound Microscope. The objective produces an enlarged image of the specimen. When this image is viewed through the ocular, a still larger image of the specimen is seen.

The mechanical system. The **mechanical system** consists of the structural parts that hold the specimen and lenses and permit focusing of the image.

The *base* is the structure on which the microscope stands. Most of the other mechanical parts are attached to the *arm.* The *stage,* which is a platform coming out from the arm, has a round opening over which the specimen is placed. The specimen is usually mounted on a glass or plastic *slide* for observation. Two *clips* attached to the stage hold the slide in place. Attached to the top of the arm is the cylindrical *body tube,* which holds the lenses. The eyepiece, which you look through when using the microscope, is at the top of the body tube. At the bottom of the body tube is a revolving *nosepiece,* which holds the objective lenses. The objectives are changed by turning the nosepiece.

Focusing the microscope. To focus the microscope, two adjustment knobs are used. The large knob is the *coarse adjustment,* which is used for approximate focusing of the low-power objective. The smaller knob is the *fine adjustment,* which is used for final focusing of the low-power objective and for all focusing of the high-power objective. Both adjustment knobs vary the distance between the objective and the specimen by moving either the body tube or the stage. The specimen is in focus when the image is sharpest for the observer. When the high-power objective is in position, it generally lies very close to the slide on which the specimen is mounted. For this reason, only the fine adjustment knob should be used in focusing the high-power objective.

The light system. The light system consists basically of a mirror and a diaphragm. In some microscopes there is also a substage illuminator and a condenser. The *mirror,* which is under the opening in the stage, can be adjusted to direct light up through the specimen into the objective. In some microscopes, light is supplied directly by a *substage illuminator,* which is a small electric light. The amount of light reaching the objective is regulated by the *diaphragm* (*dy*-uh-fram), which is mounted below the stage. There are two types of diaphragms: the *disc diaphragm* consists of a flat plate with different-sized holes in it; the *iris diaphragm* is made up of overlapping plates that can be adjusted to increase or decrease the size of the central opening. Some microscopes have *condensers* located in or below the stage. Condensers are lenses that concentrate the light on the specimen.

2-7 Magnification

Magnification refers to enlargement in one direction, such as length, not a change in area or "size." If a microscope has a magnification of 100×, the image of a line 1 millimeter long will appear to be 100 millimeters long. The area of an image is increased by the square of the magnification. For example, the image of a square 1 millimeter × 1 millimeter will be 100 millimeters × 100 millimeters. The square has an area of 1 square millimeter. Its image has an area of 10,000 square millimeters. Students are sometimes confused by this difference between the enlargement of a line and the enlargement of an area.

In a compound microscope, the total magnification can be found by multiplying the magnifying power of the objective by the magnifying power of the ocular. In student microscopes, the power of the high-power objective is often 43×, and that of the ocular is 10×. With the high-power objective in use, the total magnifying power of the microscope is 43 × 10, or 430×. This means that the distance between two points in the image is 430 times greater than it is in the actual object.

Some student microscopes have an oil-immersion objective (97X), which is used for viewing very small specimens, such as bacteria. To reduce light loss between the objective and slide at this high magnification, a drop of oil with optical properties is placed on the slide. The tip of the objective is lowered into the oil and focused.

2-8 Resolution

The microscope does not add detail to objects. The details are always there. What the microscope does is to spread the details apart so the human eye can make them out. To the unaided eye, two tiny spots close together blend into one. We cannot see them as separate spots. Under the microscope, these two spots are seen farther apart. Now we can see them separately.

The ability of a microscope to show two points that are close together as separate images is called its **resolution** (rez-uh-*loo*-shun), or *resolving power*. Resolution is another term for sharpness of an image. It does no good to increase the magnifying power of a microscope if its resolving power is not also increased. If only the magnification is increased, the image gets larger, but you cannot make out any more detail. Small blurred spots simply become larger blurred spots.

Up to a point, the resolving power of a microscope depends on the precision and quality of the lenses. However, there is a limit to the resolving power of any optical lens system. An optical microscope cannot distinguish two points that are less than 0.2 micrometers apart. This limit of resolving power is the result of the properties of light. Light is not affected by spacing that small, so it carries no information about the spacing. The two points might just as well be one. This property of light sets a limit on what can be discovered through the optical microscope about the structure of cells. This limit remained until the development of electron microscopes in the 1930s. The electron microscope is described later in this chapter.

Start a class discussion on what is meant by a "high-quality" lens. Quality lenses are precision-ground glass plates that transmit images with a minimum of distortion.

2-9 Fixation, Sectioning, and Staining

A specimen to be observed under the compound microscope must be thin enough so that light can pass through it. Most biological materials are too thick to allow the passage of light. For this reason they must first be fixed, which hardens them, and then sliced into thin sections. Fixation is done by first cutting the material into relatively small pieces, and then

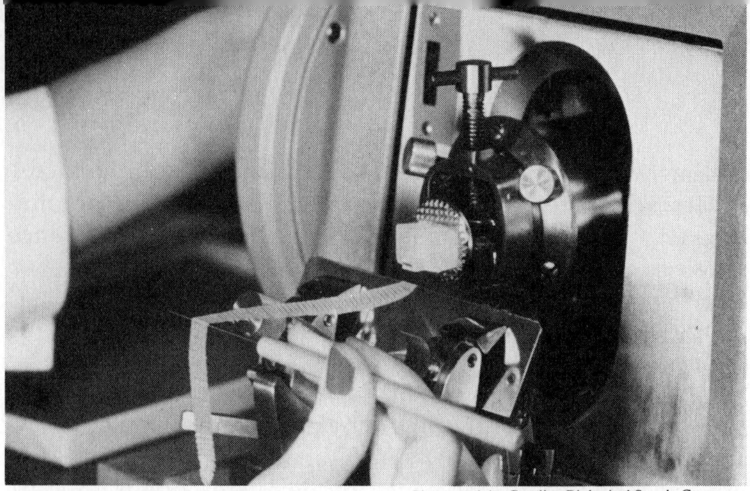

Photograph by Carolina Biological Supply Company

Figure 2-6. A Microtome. A microtome is used to slice thin sections of material.

allowing it to soak in a fixative, such as formalin. The fixed material is then embedded in soft wax or plastic, which is allowed to harden. The wax or plastic holds the material in place so that it can be sliced, or *sectioned.* The instrument used for slicing thin sections is called a *microtome* (see Figure 2-6).

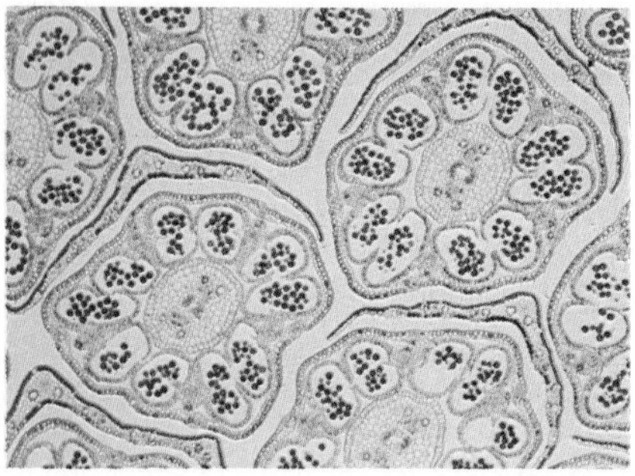

Figure 2-7. Stained Cell. Stains make visible various structures within the cell.

The thin sections are then usually attached to a glass slide and stained. Without staining, relatively little structural detail of biological specimens can be observed with the compound microscope. However, by using one or more colored stains, which are taken up only by certain structures in the section, the details can be seen (see Figure 2-7). There are some stains, called *vital stains,* that can be used with living tissues. They are taken in by the tissue, but they do not kill it, and the structural details can be seen with the microscope.

2-10 The Stereomicroscope

The **stereomicroscope,** or **binocular microscope,** has an ocular and an objective for each eye. It provides a three-dimensional image of the specimen being viewed. The magnifying power of stereomicroscopes varies from about 6× to about 50×. This type of microscope is used mainly in studying the external structure of small plants and animals. In laboratories, dissections may be carried out under the stereomicroscope (see Figure 2-8).

Figure 2-8. The Stereomicroscope.

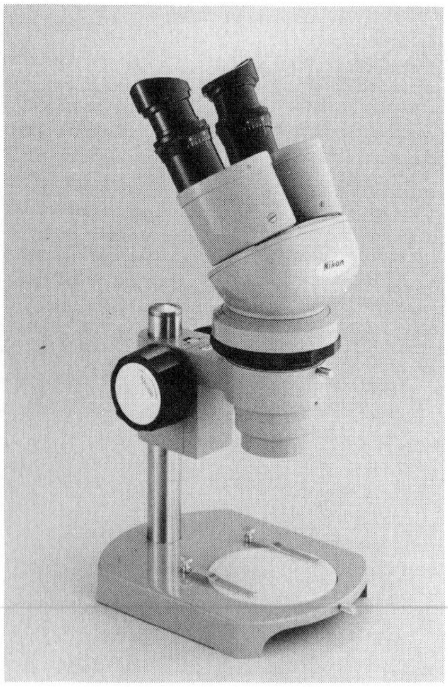

2-11 The Phase-Contrast Microscope

The reason we are able to use our eyes to distinguish one object from another is that the objects affect light waves in different ways. The eyes and the brain then use the differences in the light waves to "see" the two objects separately. One difficulty with the ordinary optical microscope is that the different structures in living cells are nearly transparent to light. The structures have the same effect on the color or brightness of light passing through them. As a result, we cannot distinguish the structures.

As already mentioned, one solution to this problem is staining. But staining usually kills living organisms. There is another solution. Structures may have the same effect on the color and brightness of light, but different effects on the *speed* of light passing through them. This difference causes the light waves to become "out of phase." The eye cannot detect a difference in the phase of light waves, but an optical system can be made that will make such differences visible. This is the basis of the **phase-contrast microscope.** This instrument is quite complex, but it makes structures in living cells visible that cannot be seen with ordinary light microscopes (see Figure 2-9).

Photograph by Carolina Biological Supply Company

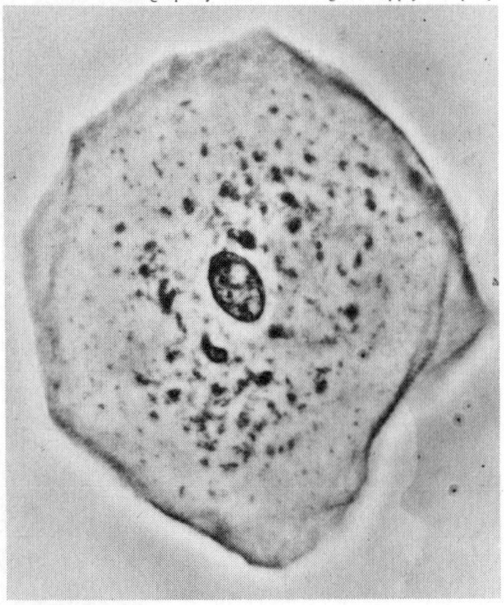

Figure 2-9. Cell Seen with Phase-Contrast Microscope.

2-12 The Electron Microscope

With the **electron microscope** it is possible to obtain magnifications of more than 250,000 times with useful resolution (see Figure 2-10). In place of the light beams and optical lenses of the light microscope, the electron microscope has an electron beam and electromagnetic lenses. The electron beam is directed through a vacuum chamber containing a series of electromagnets, which serve as lenses to focus the electron beam. When the electrons hit the specimen, some pass through, some are absorbed, and some are scattered. Those that pass through are focused on a screen similar to a television screen for viewing. Denser portions of the specimen will absorb more electrons than less dense portions, and will thus appear darker on the viewing screen. Electron microscopes also contain cameras, which can photograph the image of the specimen.

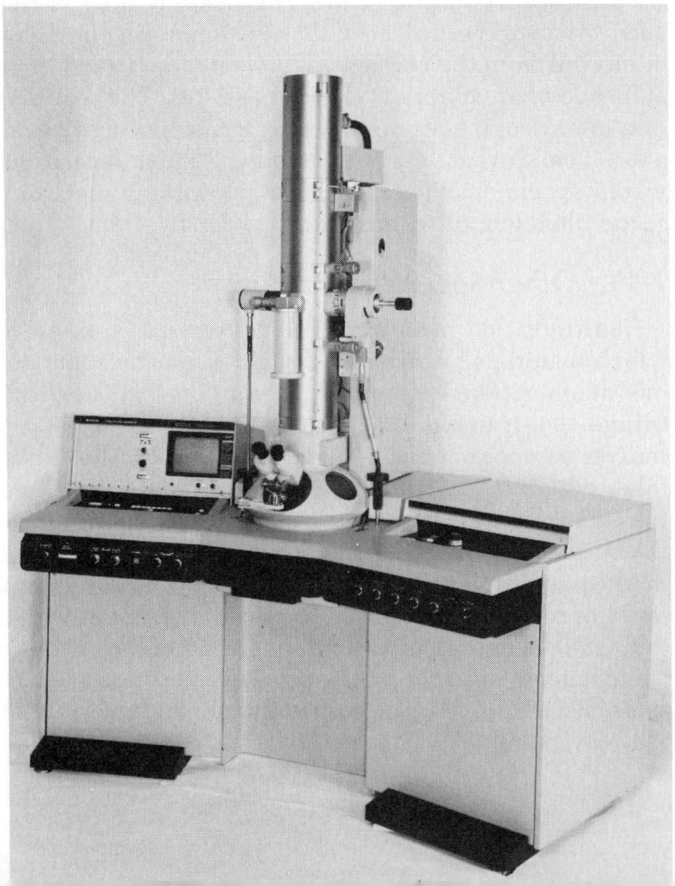

Figure 2-10. An Electron Microscope.

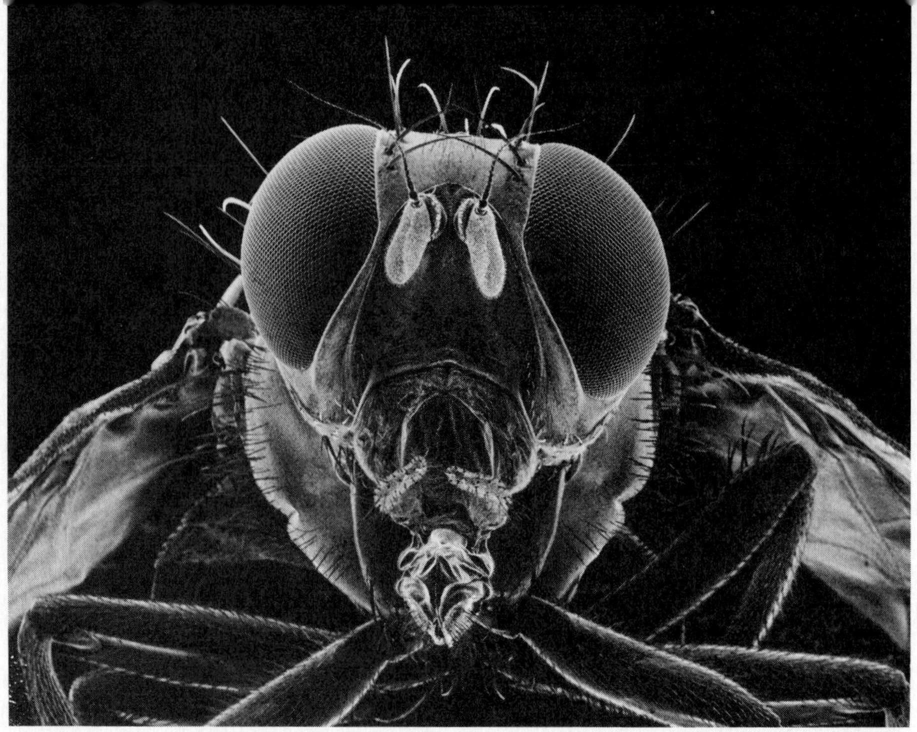

Figure 2-11. Mediterranean Fruit Fly Seen with Scanning Electron Microscope.

Ask students to do some library research for a class discussion comparing the uses in research of the various types of microscopes.

Specimens to be viewed in an electron microscope must be completely dried, embedded in plastic, and sliced into very thin sections (no more than 1 micron in thickness). The sections are then mounted on fine grids. Often, the specimen is coated with a very thin layer of heavy metal to provide increased contrast.

The *scanning electron microscope* operates in a somewhat different way. This microscope uses an electron beam that has been focused to a fine point. The beam is then passed back and forth over the surface of the specimen. Electrons reflected or ejected from the surface are collected and used to produce an image of great depth (see Figure 2-11). The scanning electron microscope does not have great magnifying power. However, it can reveal very fine details of the surface structure of whole specimens. There are many scanning electron microscope photographs in this text.

sidelights

Scientists have found that the images produced by various kinds of microscopes can be greatly enhanced by introducing video cameras and computers into the systems. The image from the microscope is picked up by the video camera, processed by an image-processing computer, and displayed on a screen. This technique was originally developed to handle photographs from space satellites. The image-processing computer can be adjusted to sharpen blurred images or to increase the contrast between light and dark areas.

2-13 Other Special Techniques

Centrifugation (sen-truh-fyoo-*gay*-shun) is a process by which materials of different densities can be separated from one another. The instrument used to do this is called a **centrifuge** (*sen*-truh-fyooj). The material that is to be separated into its component fractions is suspended in liquid in a test tube, which is put into the centrifuge. The centrifuge spins the tube around. The heaviest particles in the liquid settle to the bottom the fastest. The next-heaviest form a layer on top of the heaviest, and so on. The lightest layer is left on top. Each layer, or fraction, can then be removed by itself from the tube.

The *ultracentrifuge* is much more powerful than a regular centrifuge. It spins at rates of from 40,000 to 100,000 revolutions per minute. It can be used to separate very light particles, including the various parts of the cell, from one another.

In **microdissection** (my-kroh-dis-*ek*-shun), very small instruments are used to perform various operations on living cells (see Figure 2-12). This work must be done under a microscope. First, a *micromanipulator* (my-kroh-muh-*nip*-yuh-lay-ter) is attached to the microscope stage. This apparatus controls the tiny tools used in microdissection. Among the tools that can be used with the micromanipulator are *microelectrodes,* which are used to measure or produce electrical currents in the cell; *microknives* or *microneedles,* which are used to remove cell structures; and *micropipettes* (my-kroh-py-*pets*), which are used to introduce materials into, or remove materials from, the cell.

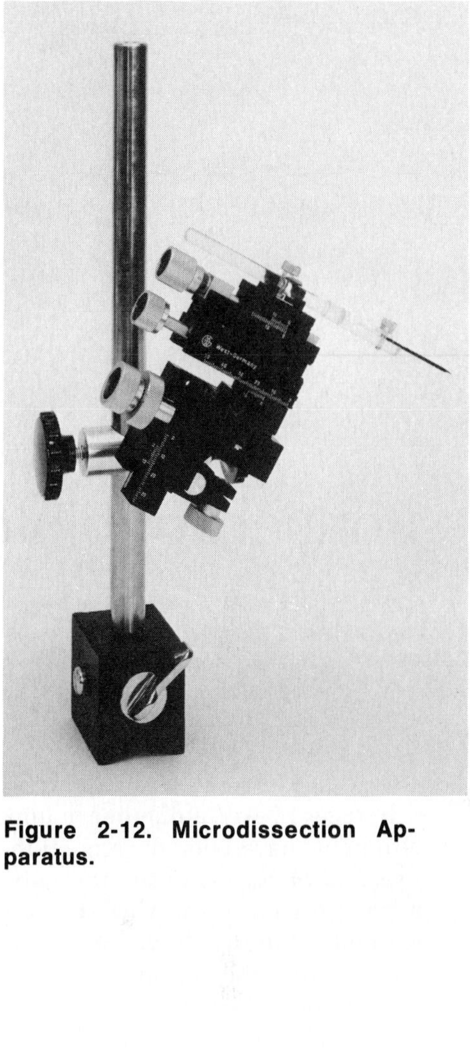

Figure 2-12. Microdissection Apparatus.

Tissue culture is a technique for maintaining living cells or tissues in a culture medium outside the body. Cells from living organisms are placed in culture tubes and bathed in fluid containing all necessary nutrients, oxygen, etc. Cells grown in tissue culture are used in many types of biological and medical research.

Chromatography (kroh-muh-*tog*-ruh-fee) and *electrophoresis* (ih-lek-truh-fuh-*ree*-sis) are both sensitive processes used for separating and analyzing mixtures of chemical substances. In chromatography the mixture to be separated is placed on a material to which it adheres. A solvent is then introduced. Those substances that adhere most loosely to the material will be carried away first in the solvent. Those substances that adhere most tightly will be carried away last. In this way the different substances in the mixture separate. If the test substances are colored, they will form colored bands or spots. If they are colorless, they can be sprayed with chemicals that give them a color. The rate at which a given substance moves in a given solvent is a characteristic of that substance. By comparing the distance that the test substances have moved with the pattern of known substances, the test substances can be identified.

Electrophoresis is a technique used to separate substances whose particles have an electrical charge. An electric current is run through a trough of liquid containing the test mixture. Different substances move at different rates in the electrical field. In this way the substances that make up the test mixture are separated. Again, the rate at which each substance moves is a characteristic of that substance.

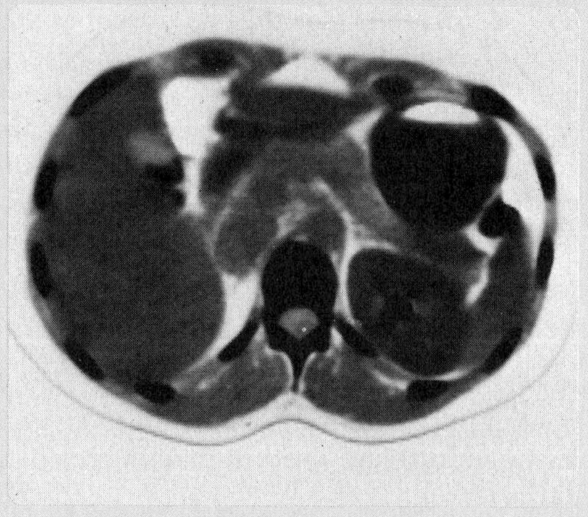

frontiers of biology

In recent years, a number of important new instruments have been developed that allow scientists and physicans to see through the surface of a living organism and view its internal structures without surgery. New techniques use light, sound, and other forms of radiation to pass the barriers of the skin.

The CAT scan (computed axial tomography) uses a rotating beam of X rays to provide a detailed view of a particular part of the human body. The different tissues of the body vary in density and therefore absorb different amounts of X rays. The greater the amount of X ray absorbed, the less is transmitted by, or passes through, the tissue. Sensors located beneath the body detect the X rays that pass through the tissues. A computer uses the information from the sensors to produce an image of the tissues being examined. The CAT scanner is very sensitive and can distinguish between tissues of very similar densities. It has become widely used in the diagnosis of a number of types of disorders, particularly those involving the brain and spinal cord, kidneys, lungs, and liver. CAT scans make it possible to avoid a number of more dangerous diagnostic tests and gives the physician a clear picture of internal structures without surgery.

Ultrasound is sound waves above the frequencies that can be detected by the human ear. Diagnostic techniques using ultrasound are employed in cases where exposure to X rays could be harmful, most frequently in viewing a developing baby in the uterus of a pregnant woman. Waves of ultrasound beamed at the mother's body strike the various internal structures, which vary in density. Some of the sound waves are reflected off the surfaces of these structures. Sensors detect the returning sound waves, and using this information, an image of the internal structures is produced by a computer and displayed on a viewing screen. From this image, a physician can tell the size and position of the baby and whether it is developing normally.

summary

The approach to scientific problems used by scientists in all fields is called the scientific method. According to this method, the first task of the investigator is to define the problem to be studied. Next, the investigator must set up experiments in which the factors to be studied can be observed. Biological research often involves the use of controlled experiments. Experimental observations may include precise numerical measurements, which are made with special instruments. All materials and procedures used in the experiments, as well as observations, must be fully and accurately recorded. The results of an experiment may lead to the development of a hypothesis—a possible explanation of an observed set of facts. Hypotheses may lead to the development of a theory, which is an explanation for a broader range of phenomena.

In scientific investigations, measurements are usually expressed in units of the metric system. In this system, the basic unit of length is the meter; the unit of mass is the gram; the unit of volume is the liter; and the unit of temperature is the Celsius degree.

The instruments most commonly used by biologists are microscopes. These include simple microscopes, compound microscopes, binocular microscopes, phase-contrast microscopes, and electron microscopes. Other techniques used in biological research are centrifugation, microdissection, tissue culture, chromatography, and electrophoresis.

vocabulary

binocular microscope
centrifugation
centrifuge
compound microscope
controlled experiment
electron microscope
hypothesis
image
light system
magnification
mechanical system
metric system
microdissection
microscope
optical microscope
optical system
phase-contrast microscope
resolution
scientific method
simple microscope
stereomicroscope
theory
tissue culture

test your learning

Section	
2-1	**1.** Describe the basic steps of the scientific method.
	2. Define the terms *hypothesis* and *theory.*
2-2	**3.** Name the basic units of measurement of the metric system.
2-3	**4.** Why are instruments needed in scientific research?
2-4	**5.** Define the term *microscope.*
	6. What is an optical microscope, and how does an optical microscope work?
2-5	**7.** What is the common name for a simple microscope?
	8. How many lenses does a simple microscope have?
2-6	**9.** How many lenses does a compound microscope have?
	10. Describe the optical system of a compound microscope.
	11. What are the functions of the mechanical system of the compound microscope?
	12. What parts are used to focus the compound microscope?
	13. Briefly describe the general procedure for focusing the compound microscope.
	14. What parts make up the light system of the compound microscope, and what are their functions?
2-7	**15.** Define the term *magnification.*
	16. How is the total magnification of a compound microscope calculated?
2-8	**17.** Define the term *resolution.*
2-9	**18.** What must be done to a specimen before it can be studied with a compound microscope?
2-10	**19.** What is a binocular microscope, and what is it used for?
2-11	**20.** How does a phase-contrast microscope work?
	21. What advantage does a phase-contrast microscope have over an ordinary compound microscope?
2-12	**22.** How does an electron microscope differ from an optical microscope?
	23. What major advantage does an electron microscope have over an optical microscope?
2-13	**24.** Describe each of the following special techniques: ultracentrifugation, microdissection, tissue culture, chromatography, and electrophoresis.

test your understanding

1. Discuss the importance of a control in biological experiments.

2. What is the value of a hypothesis?

3. At the toy counter, sales clerks often stress the high magnification of a toy microscope. What important factor about microscopes are they neglecting to mention?

4. In a student microscope, the magnification of the ocular is 10×, the low-power objective is 10×, and the high-power objective is 40×. The diameter of the field with the low-power objective is 2 millimeters. What is the diameter of the field using the high-power objective?

independent research

1. Select an instrument used in biological research and write a report discussing its structure and use.
2. Ask your teacher for permission to use a microscope, a slide, and a cover slip. Obtain some pond water. Put a few drops on the slide, and cover with cover slip. Draw as detailed pictures as you can of the small organisms that you observe. Make descriptive notes to accompany your drawings. Use reference books recommended by your teacher to identify these organisms.
3. Read a book by or about a famous scientist describing his or her research. Compare the work method and sequence with the scientific method described in Chapter 2.

chapter 3

Some Basic Ideas of Chemistry

In this century great progress has been made in understanding the processes of life. These processes are chiefly chemical. The student of biology today needs to know some of the basic principles of chemistry. This chapter will present those facts and terms of chemistry that we will be using frequently. They concern atoms, compounds, and simple chemical reactions. You may have already learned most of this information in previous science classes. In that case, the chapter will be mainly a refresher.

ATOMIC THEORY OF MATTER

After completing your study of this section, you should be able to:

1. Define the terms *element* and *compound.*
2. Recognize the names and chemical symbols of the most common elements.
3. Describe the structure of the atom.
4. Define the terms *atomic number, isotope,* and *atomic mass.*
5. Briefly describe the process of radioactivity, and explain how radioisotopes and other isotopes are used in biological and chemical research.
6. Describe the arrangement of electrons in the space around the nucleus.

3-1 Elements and Compounds

As you can see just by looking around you, the world is made of many different substances. Hundreds of thousands of different substances are known. Hundreds of thousands of others can probably exist. Chemistry tells us that all of these different kinds of matter are made of **atoms** combined in various ways. We will have more to say later about atoms.

In spite of the very large number of different substances, there are only about 100 different kinds of atoms. Some substances are made entirely of one kind of atom. These substances are called **elements.** Iron, for example, is an element. All iron consists entirely of iron atoms. Oxygen is an element made entirely of oxygen atoms. Since there are about 100 different kinds of atoms, there are about 100 different elements.

Most substances are **compounds.** In a compound, there are two or more kinds of atoms combined in definite proportions. For example, water is a compound made of hydrogen atoms and oxygen atoms in the proportion of 2 to 1. In water, there are always two hydrogen atoms for each oxygen atom.

There is no way of knowing, just by inspecting a substance, whether it is an element (made of a single kind of atom) or a compound (made of two or more kinds of atoms) (see Figure 3-1). For example, the gas oxygen is an element; the gas carbon dioxide is a compound. However, there are chemical means of deciding whether something is a compound. Compounds can be separated into the elements that make them up. Carbon dioxide, for example, can be separated into carbon and oxygen. Carbon and oxygen cannot be separated into anything else. They are pure elements in themselves.

Chemists have given names and symbols to all the elements. The symbols are a convenient shorthand for showing the makeup of compounds and for showing what happens during chemical reactions. Table 3-1 lists the names and symbols of the elements that are important in biological processes. You

Figure 3-1. Elements and Compounds. Glass (top) can look very much like diamond (bottom). However, diamond is a crystalline form of the element carbon. Glass is a mixture of compounds consisting chiefly of sodium, silicon, and oxygen.

Table 3-1. Elements of Importance in Biology. The Latin name is given when the symbol is derived from it.

Name of element	Symbol	Atomic number	Name of element	Symbol	Atomic number
hydrogen	H	1	phosphorus	P	15
carbon	C	6	sulfur	S	16
nitrogen	N	7	chlorine	Cl	17
oxygen	O	8	potassium (*kalium*)	K	19
sodium (*natrium*)	Na	11	calcium	Ca	20
magnesium	Mg	12	iron (*ferrum*)	Fe	26

will find it useful to learn these symbols. Notice that most of them are abbreviations or initials of the name of the element in English. The others come from the Latin names of the elements. These are elements that were known to scientists several hundred years ago, when Latin was used for most scholarly writing. Names of elements are not capitalized, but the first letter of the symbol is capitalized.

3-2 Structure of Atoms

The idea that matter is made of atoms is a very old one, going back about 2500 years to the philosophers of ancient Greece. The early concept of an atom was that it was an extremely small particle that could not be changed in any way. Research in the twentieth century has shown that atoms are not the hard, solid balls they were first imagined to be. They consist of still smaller particles. Each atom has a very small central portion called the **nucleus.** The nucleus contains particles called **protons** (*proh*-tahnz) and **neutrons** (*noo*-trahnz). In the space outside the nucleus, there are other particles called **electrons** (ih-*lek*-trahnz).

Electrons. The electrons are the parts of an atom that determine its chemical properties. When atoms combine to form compounds, they do so by shifting some of their electrons. An important feature of an electron is that it carries an electric charge. There are two kinds of electric charge—positive and negative. The electron has a negative charge. All electrons have the same amount of electric charge. This is usually called one unit of charge.

Protons. The nucleus of every atom contains one or more protons. A proton has a positive charge of one unit. That is, it has the same amount of charge as an electron, but of opposite sign. However, a proton has almost 2,000 times as much mass, or weight, as an electron.

Neutrons. With the exception of the hydrogen atom, every atomic nucleus also contains neutrons. A neutron has almost exactly the same mass as a proton, but no electric charge.

3-3 Atomic Number

The number of protons in the nucleus of an atom is called its **atomic number.** Each different atomic number represents a different element. For example, an atom of hydrogen has 1 proton in its nucleus (see Figure 3-2). Therefore, the atomic number of hydrogen is 1. The nucleus of an oxygen atom has 8 protons. Therefore, the atomic number of oxygen is 8. Each atom has the same number of electrons as protons. The hydrogen atom has 1 electron; the oxygen atom has 8 electrons. In each atom, the total positive charge of the protons is balanced by the equal number of negative charges of its electrons. Therefore, an atom is normally electrically neutral.

sidelights

In the 1930s, about 15 years after the discovery of the electron, proton, and neutron, physicists discovered a particle that resembled an electron but had a positive, rather than a negative, electrical charge. This new particle was called a *positron.* Following the discovery of the positron, several other types of particles were found, some in laboratory experiments and some in nature. These particles include the neutrino, which has no electrical charge; positive and negative muons; photons; positive, negative, and neutral pions; the antiproton, which has a negative electrical charge; and the antineutron which has no electrical charge, but which has magnetic properties opposite to those of the neutron.

Particles such as the positron, antiproton, and antineutron make up *antimatter,* matter in which the atomic particles have properties opposite to those of ordinary atomic particles. When particles of antimatter collide with particles of ordinary matter, they annihilate each other, releasing energy in the process. In our solar system, particles of antimatter are quickly destroyed by collision with particles of ordinary matter. However, there may be galaxies made up of antimatter elsewhere in the universe.

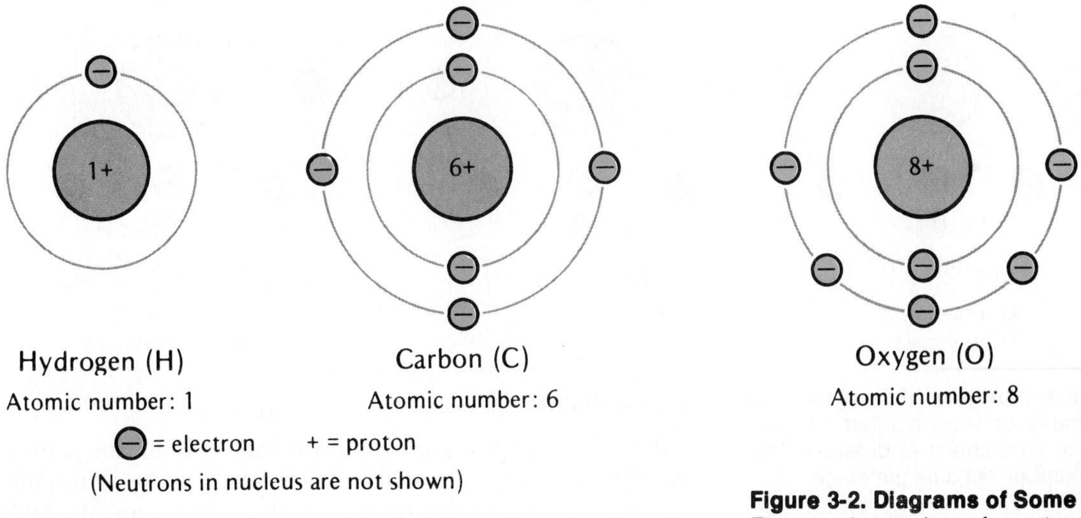

Figure 3-2. Diagrams of Some Atoms. The atomic number of an atom equals the number of protons in its nucleus. It also equals the number of electrons surrounding the nucleus. These diagrams are not supposed to be pictures of what atoms would look like if they could be seen.

3-4 Isotopes

The number of neutrons in an atom does not have a definite relation to its atomic number. Atoms of an element may have different numbers of neutrons. For example, most hydrogen atoms have no neutrons. The nucleus is simply a single proton (see Figure 3-3). However, there are also hydrogen atoms with 1 neutron in the nucleus, and others with 2 neutrons. Although these atoms are not exactly alike, they behave the same chemically. That is true because they all have only one electron, and it is the electrons in an atom that determine its chemical properties. Therefore, these three kinds of atoms are all considered to be atoms of the element hydrogen. These varieties of hydrogen, which differ only in the number of neutrons in their atomic nuclei, are called **isotopes** (*i*-suh-tohps) of hydrogen.

All elements have isotopes. For example, the most common variety of oxygen atom has 8 neutrons in its nucleus. But there are other varieties that occur naturally with 9 and 10 neutrons. Other isotopes of oxygen, with 6, 7, and 11 neutrons, have been produced artificially.

The isotopes of hydrogen are called protium (^{1}H), deuterium (^{2}H), and tritium (^{3}H). ^{1}H accounts for more than 98% of natural hydrogen. Deuterium oxide, or heavy water, is used in nuclear reactors. Tritium, which is radioactive, is used as a tracer in biological research.

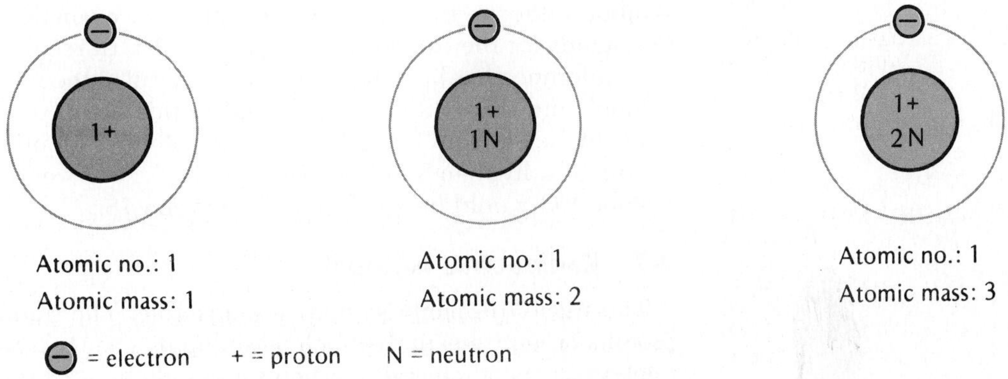

Figure 3-3. Isotopes of Hydrogen. The atomic number is the same for all isotopes of the same element. Only the number of neutrons in the atomic nucleus is different for each isotope.

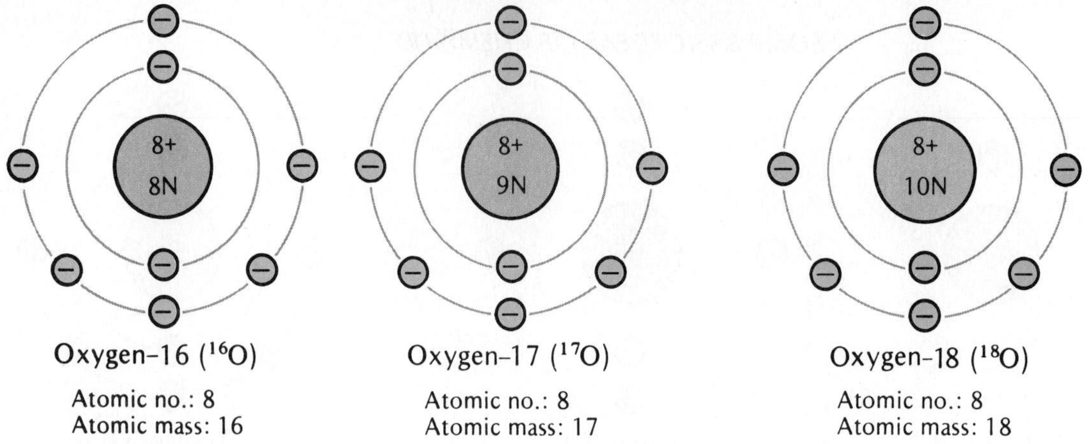

Figure 3-4. Isotopes of Oxygen. The atomic mass, or mass number, of each isotope of an element is different. The atomic number remains the same.

3-5 Atomic Mass

Recall that protons and neutrons have about the same mass, and that this mass is about 2,000 times as large as the mass of an electron. Since the protons and neutrons are packed into the nucleus, just about all the mass of an atom is in its nucleus. If we think of each proton and neutron as having one unit of mass, the mass of an atom is equal to the sum of its protons and neutrons. This sum is called the **atomic mass** of the atom, or its **mass number.** The mass number of an atom with 9 protons and 10 neutrons is 19. Isotopes of the same element have the same atomic number, but different mass numbers (see Figure 3-4). The three isotopes of hydrogen have mass numbers of 1, 2, and 3. The three natural isotopes of oxygen have mass numbers of 16 (8 + 8), 17 (8 + 9), and 18 (8 + 10).

3-6 Symbols of Isotopes

Before the discovery of isotopes, the symbol of a chemical element was used to represent any atom of that element. Since all atoms of an element were thought to be exactly alike, this was considered enough to identify the atom. The symbol O, for example, was used to represent an atom of oxygen. This is still done when it does not matter which isotope of oxygen is meant. When it is necessary to distinguish one isotope from another, a small number is placed next to the chemical symbol to show the mass number of the isotope. The number is written as a superscript; that is, it is placed slightly above the symbol, either to the left or to the right. For example ^{18}O or O^{18} stands for the oxygen isotope of mass 18. In recent years, the preference has been to put the superscript at the left of the symbol, and this is the practice used in this book. When the name of the element is spelled out, the isotope is identified by means of a hyphen and the mass number. For example, the isotope ^{18}O would be spelled out as oxygen-18.

3-7 Radioactive Isotopes

The nuclei of many isotopes are unstable. The number of protons or neutrons in the nucleus suddenly changes, and the nucleus gives off charged particles and radiation. In this process the atom changes to another isotope, usually an isotope of a different element. The process is called **radioactivity** (ray-dee-oh-ak-*tiv*-uh-tee). It was discovered by Henri Becquerel in 1896 during experiments with minerals containing the element uranium.

There are three types of natural radiation: alpha particles are helium nuclei, consisting of 2 protons and 2 electrons; beta particles are electrons; and gamma radiation, a form of electromagnetic radiation, consists of high-energy X rays.

All the isotopes of the heaviest elements (those with atomic numbers greater than 83) are radioactive. These elements have no stable forms. But even the elements that do have stable isotopes also have some radioactive isotopes. Most of these are made artificially in nuclear reactors or by bombardment of the elements with high-speed atomic particles.

Radioactivity is not a chemical process. We mention it here because radioactivity is an important means of studying biological processes. The reason for this is that radioactive isotopes, or **radioisotopes** (ray-dee-oh-*i*-suh-tohps), can be detected and their amounts measured by instruments sensitive to the radiations they emit. Radioisotopes can thus be used to follow materials in the body and to detect abnormalities in the size, shape, or function of organs (see Figure 3-5). They can also be used to study biochemical reactions in living organisms. The atoms of the radioisotope act as *tracers*, or tagged atoms. They can be detected and followed as they move from one compound to another. Thus the detailed chemical steps of a process can be determined.

Isotopes need not be radioactive to serve as tracers. They can be detected by their different masses in an instrument called a *mass spectrometer* (spek-*trahm*-uh-ter). Oxygen-18, a stable isotope, has been used in this way to study the process of photosynthesis.

careers

Radiology, or nuclear medicine, is a field of medicine in which radioisotopes and various forms of radiation are used in the diagnosis and treatment of disease. A radiologist is a medical doctor who has completed several years of additional training in this field.

Radiologists are often assisted by technicians, who actually carry out many of the tests. Radiologic technicians must be high school graduates and have at least 2 years of specialized technical training.

3-8 Electron Structure of Atoms

The electrons in an atom are located in the space surrounding the nucleus. They are arranged in **shells**, or energy levels, at different distances from the nucleus. Modern atomic theory states definite rules for the distribution of an atom's electrons

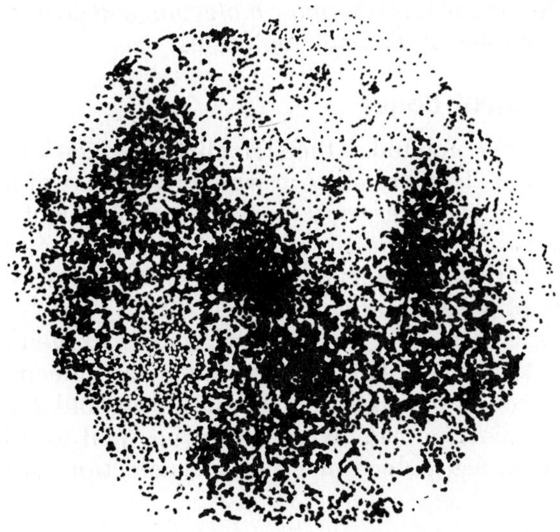

Figure 3-5. Use of Radioactive Iodine in Diagnosing Thyroid Disorders. Iodine is specifically taken up by the cells of the thyroid gland. This photo shows where iodine has been concentrated in thyroid cells (dark spots).

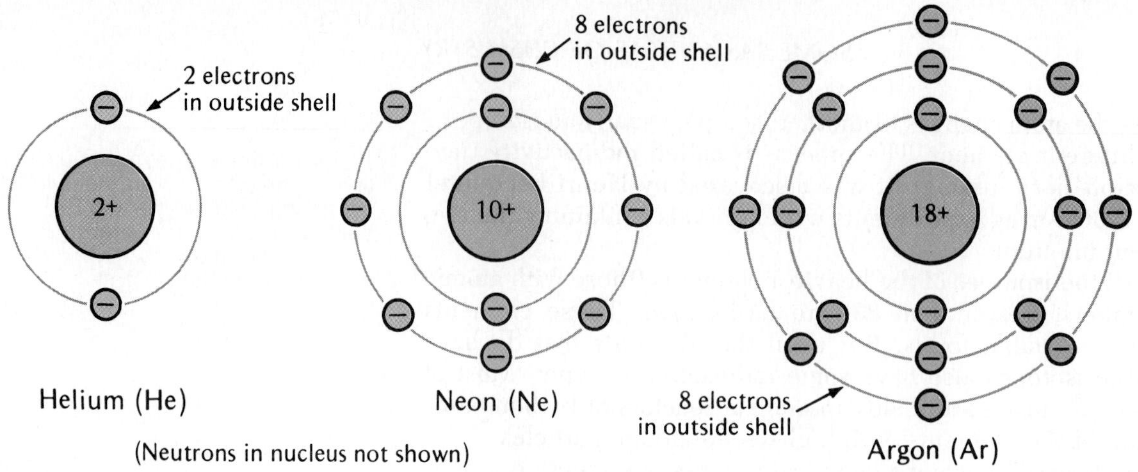

Figure 3-6. Inert Elements. In the inert elements, the outside electron shells are filled to capacity.

among its shells. We need not go into the details of this theory. All we need to know is that the first shell can hold only 2 electrons. When it has 2 electrons, it is said to be filled. An atom with more than 2 electrons has more than one shell. In all such atoms, the outside shell can hold only 8 electrons. If the outside shell has fewer than 8 electrons, it is unfilled.

A filled outside shell is a very stable arrangement. Elements that already have filled outside shells are chemically inactive. Except for a few special cases, they do not form compounds with other elements. They are all gases under ordinary conditions. Examples are helium, neon, and argon. The structures of these atoms are shown in Figure 3-6.

Atoms that do not have filled outside shells can form compounds with other elements. When atoms combine to form compounds, their outside electrons are rearranged to give each atom a filled outside shell. The ways in which this can happen are described in the next section.

CHEMICAL BONDING

After completing your study of this section, you should be able to:

1. Describe the formation of covalent and ionic bonds.
2. Define the term *diatomic molecule,* and give several examples of diatomic molecules.

3-9 Covalent Bonds

Water is a compound of the elements hydrogen and oxygen. It consists of chemical units in which two atoms of hydrogen and one atom of oxygen are joined together. A unit of this kind, in which two or more atoms are combined and act as a single particle, is called a **molecule** (*mahl*-ih-kyool). Let us see how a molecule of water is formed.

The structures of a hydrogen atom and an oxygen atom are shown in Figure 3-7. The hydrogen atom has 1 electron. This electron occupies shell no. 1. This shell can hold 2 electrons. One more electron can be added to the shell to fill it. The oxygen atom has 8 electrons. Two of its electrons are in shell

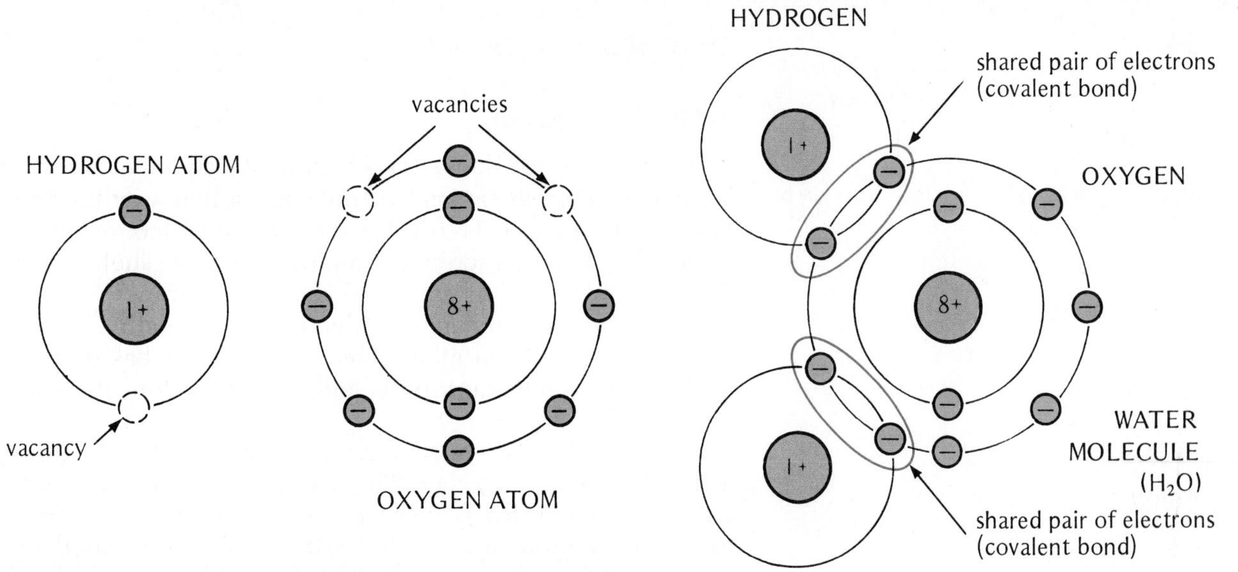

no. 1, which is therefore filled. The other 6 electrons are in shell no. 2. This shell, being the outside shell, can hold 8 electrons. Two more electrons can be added to the shell to fill it.

Figure 3-7 includes a diagram of a water molecule, showing two hydrogen atoms combined with one oxygen atom. Each hydrogen atom is sharing its electron with the oxygen atom. At the same time, the oxygen atom is sharing one of its electrons with each hydrogen atom. In other words, each hydrogen atom is sharing a pair of electrons with the oxygen atom. In this arrangement, the outside shells of all three atoms are filled (2 electrons in each hydrogen atom, 8 in the oxygen atom).

The sharing of a pair of electrons by two atoms produces a force of attraction that holds the atoms together. This force of attraction is called a **chemical bond.** When a chemical bond is formed by the sharing of electrons, it is called a **covalent** (koh-*vay*-lent) **bond.** In a molecule of water there are two covalent bonds holding the molecule together.

Figure 3-8 shows the electron structure of the element chlorine. The outside shell of a chlorine atom has 7 electrons. The chlorine atom needs only one more electron to fill its outer shell. It can fill this shell by sharing a pair of electrons with a hydrogen atom. When this happens, a molecule of the compound hydrogen chloride is formed. This molecule is held together by a covalent bond between the chlorine atom and the hydrogen atom (see Figure 3-8).

Figure 3-7. Electron Shells of Hydrogen and Oxygen. The hydrogen atom can accept one electron in its outside shell. The oxygen atom can accept two electrons in its outside shell. By sharing two pairs of electrons, the outside shells of the three atoms in the water molecule are filled. Each pair of shared electrons forms a single covalent bond.

In a covalent bond between two unlike atoms, the shared electrons may spend more time in orbit around one nucleus than the other. This occurs in polar compounds, such as water.

Figure 3-8. Structures of the Chlorine Atom and Hydrogen Chloride. Chlorine needs one electron to fill its outer shell. In hydrogen chloride, a covalent bond is formed by the sharing of one pair of electrons.

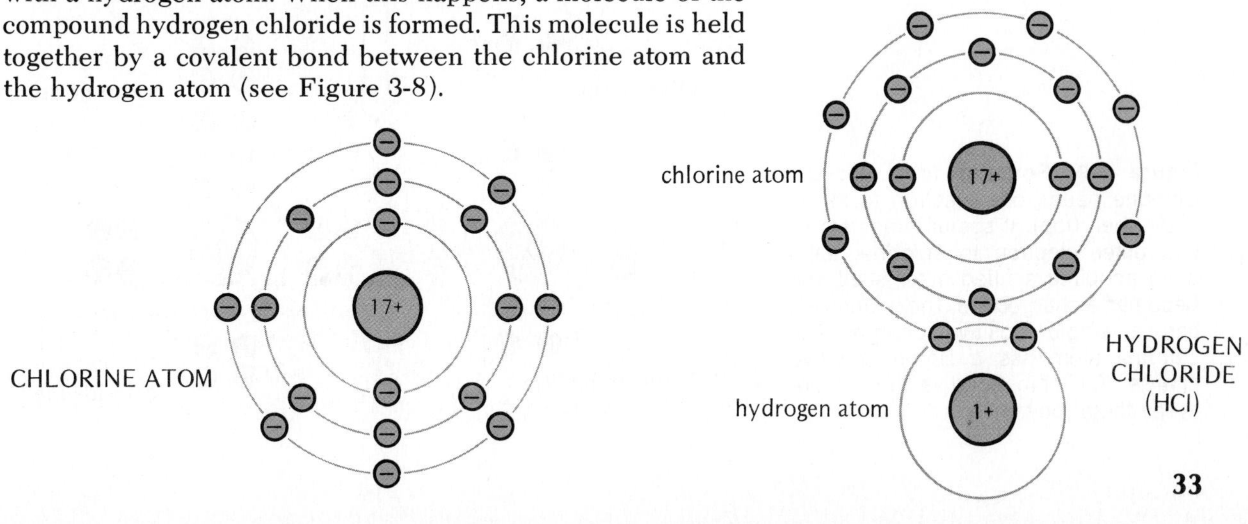

3-10 Ionic Bonds

Figure 3-9 (top) shows the electron structures of a sodium atom and a chlorine atom. The outside shell of a sodium atom has only 1 electron. To fill this shell, 7 more electrons would be needed. Could a sodium atom fill its outside shell by combining with a chlorine atom and sharing electrons? No, there is no way for this to happen. Electrons are usually shared in pairs, one from each atom. The sodium atom has only one outside electron to contribute, and could therefore share only one pair.

However, the sodium atom can *transfer* its outer electron to a chlorine atom altogether. This will fill the outer shell of the chlorine atom. At the same time, the sodium atom, having lost its outer electron, will be left with a new outer shell of 8 electrons. Thus, the outer shell of the sodium atom will also be a filled shell (see Figure 3-9, bottom).

When the chlorine atom acquires an extra electron from the sodium atom, the chlorine atom acquires an excess negative charge of 1 unit. An atom that acquires an excess charge in this way is called an **ion** (*i*-ahn). The chlorine atom has become a chlorine ion with a negative charge of 1 unit. The chlorine ion (also called the chlor*ide* ion) is represented by the symbol Cl^-.

When a sodium atom gives up an electron, it is left with an excess positive charge of 1 unit. It becomes a sodium ion, represented as Na^+.

One of the laws of electric charge is that particles with opposite charges attract each other. When a sodium atom loses an electron to a chlorine atom, the two ions that form are attracted to each other. The force of attraction between two ions is called an **ionic** (i-*ahn*-ik) **bond.** The compound of

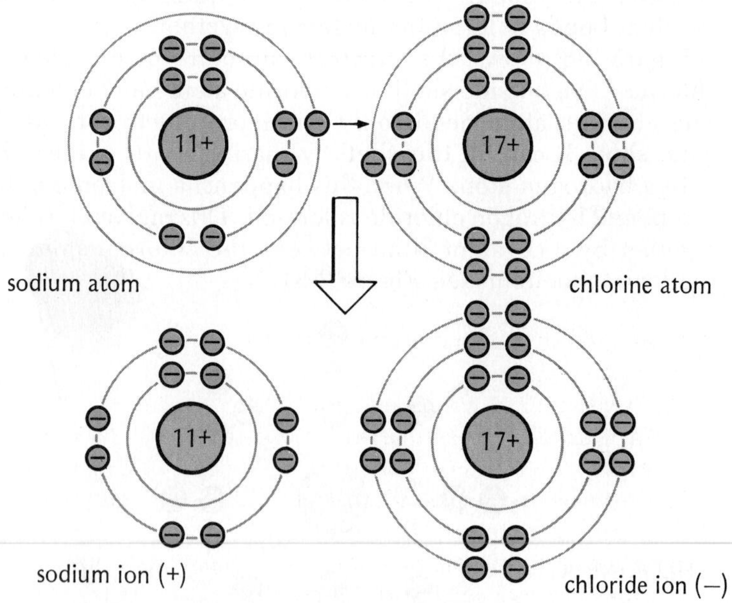

Figure 3-9. Forming Ionic Bonds. Chlorine needs one electron to fill its outer shell (top). If sodium transfers its one outer electron to chlorine, each atom acquires a filled outer shell and becomes a charged ion. The sodium ion has a single positive charge. The chlorine atom has a single negative charge. An ionic bond is formed between them (bottom).

sodium and chlorine, called sodium chloride, consists of sodium and chlorine ions held together by ionic bonds. Note, however, that the sodium and chlorine ions do not form molecules (see Figure 3-10). Molecules are formed only when atoms share electrons and form covalent bonds. In sodium chloride, the ions remain separate. Each sodium ion is attracted to several chlorine ions around it. Each chlorine ion is attracted to several sodium ions around it. Materials with this type of structure are called *crystals*. No distinct molecules are present in crystals.

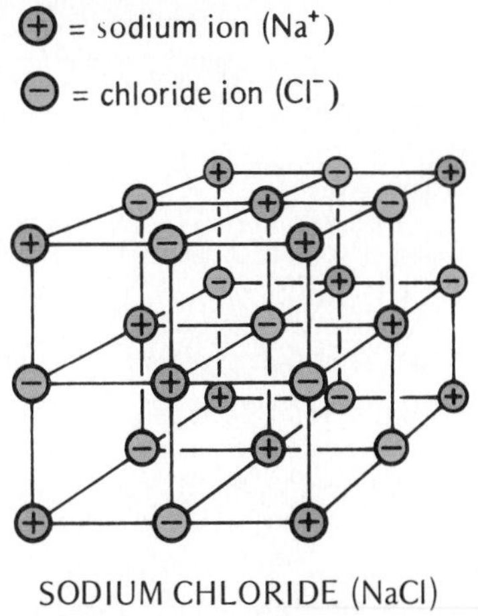

Figure 3-10. Structure of Sodium Chloride. Ionic compounds do not form molecules. Each ion is attracted to several oppositely charged ions around it.

3-11 Diatomic Molecules

Atoms of the same element sometimes form covalent bonds with each other, forming molecules consisting of two atoms. These are called **diatomic** (dy-uh-*tahm*-ik) **molecules.** Most elements that form diatomic molecules are gases under ordinary conditions. They include hydrogen, oxygen, nitrogen, and chlorine (see Figure 3-11).

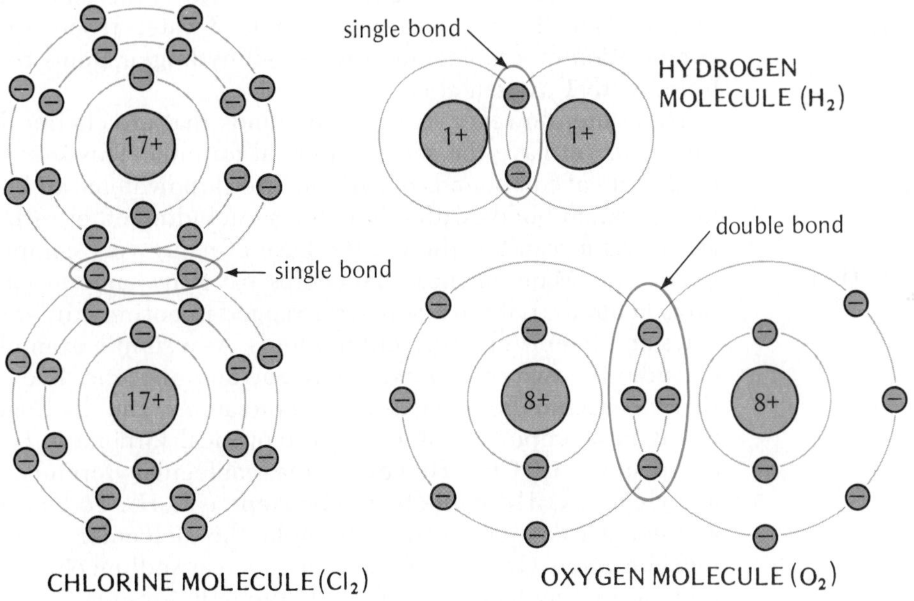

Figure 3-11. Diatomic Molecules of Some Gases. Two chlorine atoms form one covalent bond in a diatomic molecule, as do two hydrogen atoms. Two oxygen atoms form two covalent bonds in a diatomic molecule.

CHEMICAL REACTIONS

After completing your study of this section, you should be able to:

1. Define and give examples of the following: empirical formula, molecular formula, and structural formula.
2. Describe the types of changes that occur when a chemical reaction takes place.
3. Write out a simple balanced chemical equation and label the reactants and the products.

3-12 Chemical Formulas

Every compound consists of atoms combined in definite proportions. In water, for example, the proportion is 2 hydrogen atoms to 1 oxygen atom. In sodium chloride, the proportion is 1 sodium atom to 1 chlorine atom. This information about a compound can be given by its chemical formula. In a chemical formula, each element is represented by its chemical symbol. The proportions in which the atoms combine are shown by subscripts—small numbers written after the symbol and slightly below the line. The subscript 1 is not written in the formula, but is understood when no other subscript is shown. For example, the formula for water is H_2O, while the formula for sodium chloride is NaCl.

A formula that shows the simplest proportions of atoms in the compound is called an **empirical** (em-*pih*-rih-kul) **formula.** A formula that shows the composition of a molecule of a compound is called the **molecular** (muh-*lek*-yuh-ler) **formula** of the compound. In many cases the molecular formula is the same as the empirical formula. For example, H_2O is the molecular formula as well as the empirical formula of water. It shows the composition of a molecule of water—2 hydrogen atoms combined with 1 oxygen atom.

There are, however, many compounds that are chemically different, yet have the same empirical formula. This is especially true of compounds of carbon. The carbon atom can form four covalent bonds with other atoms, including other carbon atoms. As a result, carbon is the base of many very complex molecules. Many of these molecules have the same *proportions* of atoms, but the atoms are arranged in entirely different ways and in entirely different numbers. As a simple example, consider the two compounds acetylene and benzene. Each of these compounds consists of carbon atoms and hydrogen atoms in a proportion of 1:1. The empirical formula of both compounds is CH. However, the molecular formula of acetylene is C_2H_2, while that of benzene is C_6H_6. To identify a molecular compound by its formula, the molecular formula must be given. (In ionic compounds, such as sodium chloride, there are no molecules. Therefore, the only formula that can be written is the empirical formula.)

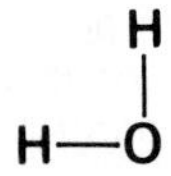

WATER (H_2O)

ACETYLENE (C_2H_2)

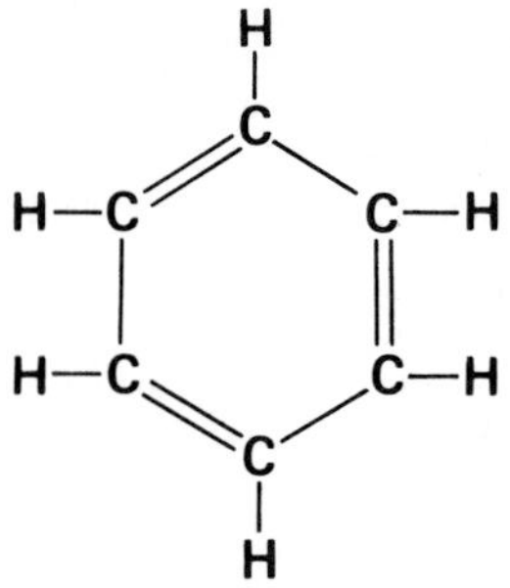

BENZENE (C_6H_6)

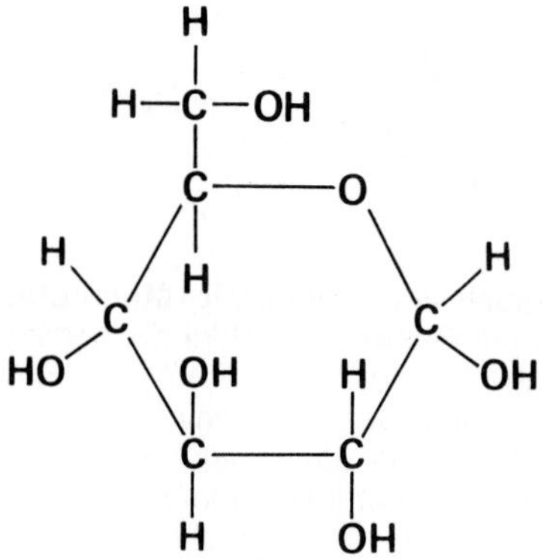

GLUCOSE ($C_6H_{12}O_6$)

Figure 3-12. Structural Formulas. Note that every carbon atom in a structural formula has four bonds connected to it.

3-13 Structural Formulas

A **structural formula** is a kind of molecular formula that shows not only the number and kind of atoms in a molecule, but also how they are bonded to one another. In a structural formula, each pair of shared electrons—that is, each covalent bond—is shown by a short line joining the atoms that are connected by the bond. The structural formulas of water, acetylene, and benzene are shown in Figure 3-12, along with the structural formula of glucose. Glucose is one of the sugars made by plants during photosynthesis. It is the chief source of energy for living things.

Note that the formula of glucose includes several OH symbols. The covalent bond between the O and the H has been omitted. This is often done to simplify structural formulas that contain certain common groups of atoms.

3-14 Chemical Equations

Every compound is a combination of atoms of certain elements bonded to one another in definite proportions and patterns. Chemical bonds can be broken, and atoms can form new bonds in new combinations, forming different substances. Whenever this happens, we say that a *chemical change*, or **chemical reaction,** has occurred. The substances that were present before the reaction started are called the **reactants** (ree-*ak*-tunts). The new substances produced by the reaction are called the **products.**

A chemical reaction can be represented by a **chemical equation.** In a chemical equation, the formulas of the reactants are shown at the left and the products at the right. Plus signs are used to join the reactants and to join the products. An arrow points from the reactants to the products.

As an example, consider the equation for the formation of water from hydrogen and oxygen. The reactants are hydrogen (H_2) and oxygen (O_2). Note the use of the molecular formulas rather than the atomic symbol alone. The reason for this is that hydrogen and oxygen, when uncombined with other elements, exist in the form of diatomic molecules. The product is water (H_2O). We can start writing the equation as follows:

$$H_2 + O_2 \longrightarrow H_2O$$

This equation says that 1 molecule of hydrogen (H_2) reacts with 1 molecule of oxygen (O_2) to produce 1 molecule of water (H_2O). However, if we examine this equation carefully, we see that there is something wrong with it. There are 2 atoms of oxygen in the molecule O_2 on the left, but only 1 atom of oxygen in H_2O on the right. One atom of oxygen is missing. The equation cannot be telling the whole story. A more accurate equation is the following:

$$2H_2 + O_2 \longrightarrow 2H_2O$$

This equation says that 2 molecules of hydrogen react with 1 molecule of oxygen to produce 2 molecules of water. In this equation all the atoms are accounted for. There are 4 H's and 2 O's on the left, and 4 H's and 2 O's on the right.

An equation in which the numbers of atoms of each kind are the same on both sides of the reaction is called a *balanced equation.* Chemical equations are almost always written in balanced form. The numbers placed in front of the formulas in order to balance the equation are called *coefficients* (koh-uh-*fish*-ents). A coefficient applies to the entire formula. It multiplies all the atoms shown in the formula.

Here is the balanced equation for the breakdown of glucose, the chemical reaction that provides most of the energy for living organisms:

$$\underset{\text{glucose}}{C_6H_{12}O_6} + \underset{\text{oxygen}}{6O_2} \longrightarrow \underset{\text{carbon dioxide}}{6CO_2} + \underset{\text{water}}{6H_2O}$$

We will discuss this reaction in some detail in a later chapter.

SOLUTIONS AND SUSPENSIONS

After completing your study of this section, you should be able to define the following terms and give an example of each: *mixture, solution, solvent, solute, suspension, colloidal dispersion.*

3-15 Mixtures

Figure 3-13. A Mixture. In a mixture of salt and iron filings, each substance retains its own properties. A magnet can remove the iron filings from the dry mixture. If the mixture is placed in water, the salt will dissolve, leaving the iron filings behind.

In every compound, the atoms or ions are joined by chemical bonds. The atoms or ions are present in fixed proportions and in a definite arrangement in space. It is possible, however, for substances to be physically mingled, but without forming new chemical bonds. The result is called a **mixture.** The substances in a mixture may be present in any proportions, and the proportions can change as one of the substances is added to or removed from the mixture. Another characteristic of mixtures is that the different substances in the mixture retain their usual properties.

Consider, for example, a mixture of table salt (sodium chloride) and iron filings. If this mixture is placed in water, the salt will dissolve, as it normally does. The iron filings will remain undissolved. On the other hand, a magnet will attract the iron filings in the mixture and remove them, leaving the salt behind (see Figure 3-13).

The substances in a mixture may be spread uniformly throughout the mixture. Such a mixture is said to be *homogeneous* (hoh-muh-*jee*-nee-us). Air, for example, is a homogeneous mixture of several different gases, including nitrogen, oxygen, carbon dioxide, water vapor, and a few others.

3-16 Solutions

Broadly speaking, any homogeneous mixture can be called a **solution.** However, the term is usually used for mixtures that are liquid. The liquid substance that makes up the bulk of the solution is called the **solvent.** The other substances, which are dissolved in the solvent, are called **solutes** (*sahl*-yoots). Solutes may be solids, liquids, or gases before they are dissolved in

Emphasize that the solute is dissolved in the solvent. As a demonstration, dissolve a small quantity of potassium permanganate ($KMnO_4$) (solute) in 100mL of water (solvent).

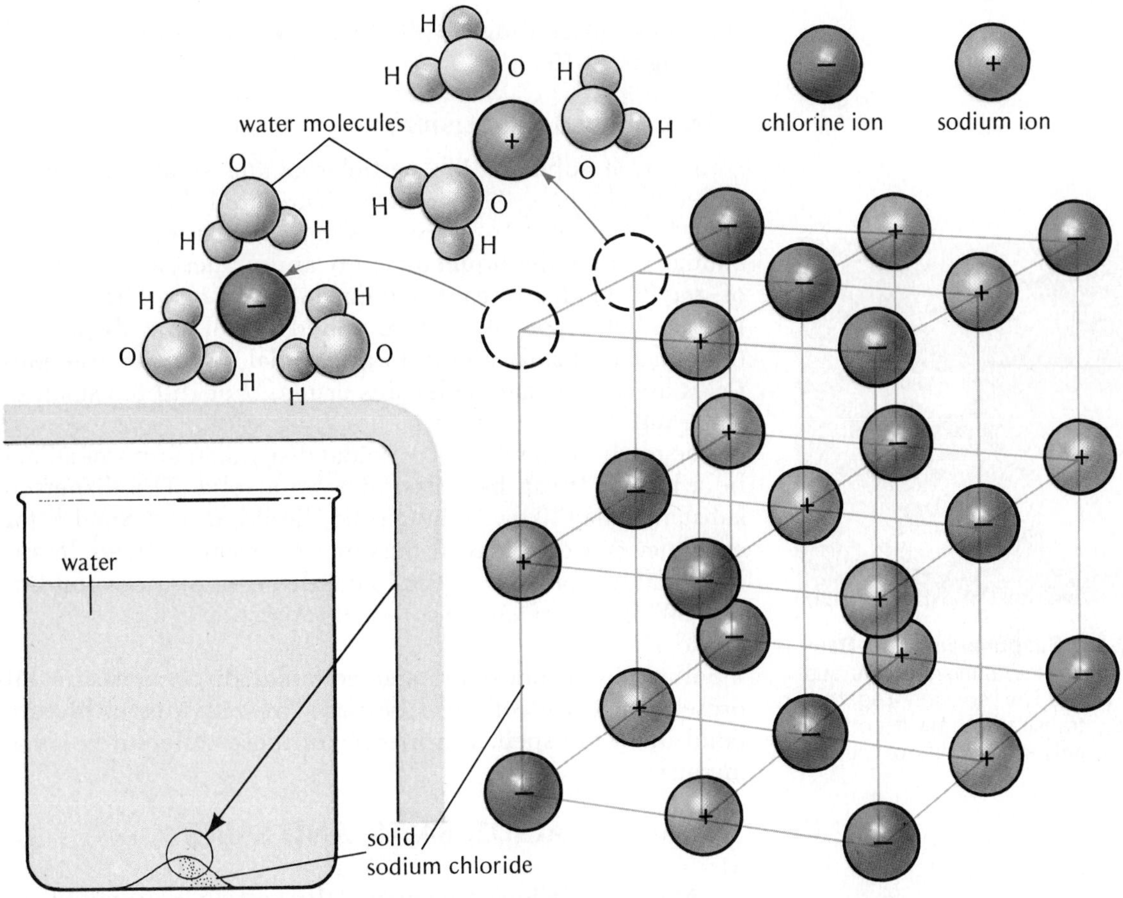

Figure 3-14. Dissociation of an Ionic Compound. When sodium chloride is placed in water, the structure of the salt breaks down. The compound separates into its individual ions, which become surrounded by water molecules. A solution of sodium chloride in water is formed.

the solvent. The most common solvent is water, and most solutions are made with water.

When molecular substances dissolve in a liquid, the substance separates into its individual molecules. The solute is spread through the solvent in the form of separate molecules. When ionic substances dissolve, the compound breaks up into its ions. Thus, when sodium chloride dissolves in water, it breaks up into sodium and chlorine ions (see Figure 3-14). This process is called *dissociation* (dis-soh-see-*ay*-shun). It can be represented by the following equation:

$$NaCl \longrightarrow Na^+ + Cl^-$$

We will see in later chapters that many important processes in living cells and tissues depend upon the presence of ions.

3-17 Suspensions

There are, as you know, many substances that do not dissolve in water to any noticeable extent. For example, sand is insoluble in water. If you put some in a pail of water and stir the water vigorously, the sand will form a cloudy mixture with the water. If you let this mixture stand, the particles of sand will gradually settle to the bottom of the pail. A mixture that separates on standing is called a **suspension** (suh-*spen*-shun) (see Figure 3-15).

3-18 Colloidal Dispersions

In a true solution, the particles of the solute are either molecules or ions. They remain distributed through the solvent indefinitely. In a suspension, the particles are large enough to give the liquid a cloudy appearance, and the force of gravity gradually causes them to settle out. There is an intermediate type of mixture called a **colloidal dispersion** (kuh-*loyd*-ul dis-*per*-zhun). In a colloidal dispersion, the particles are larger than molecules or ions, but still too small to settle out.

Figure 3-15. Suspensions and Solutions. Note the cloudiness of the suspension (left). The solution (right) is completely transparent, but it contains some undissolved particles of the solute.

The medium in which a colloidal dispersion forms need not be a liquid. It can be a gas, or even a solid. The dispersed substance may likewise be a solid, liquid, or gas. Smoke, for example, is a colloidal dispersion of carbon particles in air. Milk and mayonnaise are colloidal dispersions of several liquids. Whipped cream is a colloidal dispersion of a gas (air) in a liquid.

Solutions, suspensions, and colloidal dispersions are all present in living cells and tissues. The activities of life depend upon the special properties of these different types of mixtures.

Protoplasm is a colloid in which particles are dispersed in water.

ACIDS, BASES, AND SALTS

After completing your study of this section, you should be able to:

1. Define and compare the terms *acid* and *base,* and give an example of each.
2. Describe what happens in a neutralization reaction.
3. Explain the meaning of the pH scale and what is indicated by pH values of 1, 7, and 14.
4. Explain how indicators are used.

3-19 Acids

There are many compounds that are molecular in the dry state, but form ions when dissolved in water. An important group of these compounds is the **acids** (*as*-idz). All acids contain hydrogen covalently bonded to another atom or group of atoms. When these compounds are dissolved in water, the hydrogen breaks loose as a hydrogen ion, H^+. The rest of the molecule forms a negative ion.

Acid solutions have a sour taste. Vinegar contains acetic acid, citrus fruits contain citric acid, and grapes contain tartaric acid.

A simple example of an acid that is important to our life activities is hydrochloric acid, HCl. In its dry state, this compound is a gas consisting of HCl molecules. However, when it dissolves in water, it separates into H^+ and Cl^- ions:

$$HCl \xrightarrow[\text{water}]{\text{in}} H^+ + Cl^-$$

Any substance that produces hydrogen ions in solution is called an acid. It is the presence of hydrogen ions that gives acids their particular properties.

3-20 Bases

A compound that produces *hydroxyl* (hy-*drahk*-sul) *ions* (OH^-) when dissolved in water is called a **base.** Many bases in the dry state are ionic compounds. Sodium hydroxide (NaOH) is an example. This is a solid compound consisting of sodium and hydroxyl ions. When it is dissolved in water, it separates into its ions.

$$NaOH \xrightarrow[\text{water}]{\text{in}} Na^+ + OH^-$$

A few bases are not ionic compounds in the dry state, but they do produce hydroxyl ions when dissolved in water. Ammonia, for example, is a molecular gas, NH_3. When dissolved in water, it reacts with the water to produce OH^- ions:

$$NH_3 + H_2O \longrightarrow NH_4^+ + OH^-$$

The positive ion, NH_4^+, is called the ammonium ion. The solution of ammonia in water is called ammonia water, or ammonium hydroxide. You are probably familiar with this base as a cleaning agent.

Notice that one of the H's in NH_4^+ comes from the water molecule. This H is detached from the water molecule without its electron. It therefore carries a positive charge, and it is this that gives the ammonium ion its positive charge. The part of the water molecule left behind is an O and an H with an extra electron. It is a hydroxyl ion (OH^-). If the formula for water is written HOH, the reaction with NH_3 is a little easier to understand:

$$NH_3 + HOH \longrightarrow NH_4^+ + OH^-$$

3-21 Neutralization

When solutions of an acid and a base are mixed, a reaction occurs. The hydrogen ions from the acid combine with the hydroxyl ions from the base to form molecules of water:

$$H^+ + OH^- \longrightarrow HOH \text{ (or } H_2O)$$

If the quantities of acid and base are just right, all the H^+ and OH^- ions will combine, and there will be no excess of either one in the solution. The solution will be neither an acid nor a base. It is said to be neutral. The process of reacting an acid and a base to produce a neutral solution is called **neutralization** (noo-truh-luh-*zay*-shun).

Acids and bases are both caustic; that is, in concentrated solutions they can damage living tissue, as well as nonliving materials. When an acid or a base is accidentally spilled, the best way to reduce or prevent harm is to neutralize the substance with its opposite. An acid can be neutralized with a base; a base can be neutralized with an acid.

3-22 Salts

When an acid and a base react, their hydrogen and hydroxyl ions combine to form water molecules. These two ions are therefore removed from the solution; that is, they are no longer present as separate ions. However, the negative ions of the acid and the positive ions of the base are still present. For example, when hydrochloric acid reacts with sodium hydroxide, sodium and chlorine atoms remain in the solution. In other words, this neutralization reaction produces a solution of sodium chloride.

$$HCl + NaOH \longrightarrow Na^+ + Cl^- + HOH$$

The sodium chloride can be obtained from the solution by evaporating the water.

The compound produced by a neutralization reaction between an acid and a base is called a **salt.** Sodium chloride, or table salt, is actually only one of many different salts that can be formed. Most of the substances in food that are called minerals are salts. Salts provide many essential ions for body processes.

In addition to sodium, other necessary ions supplied in food are potassium, calcium, phosphorus, iron, and iodine.

3-23 Dissociation of Water

We have said that water is a molecular compound, H_2O. However, at any given moment a small fraction of the molecules in water are dissociated into hydrogen and hydroxyl ions:

$$H_2O \longrightarrow H^+ + OH^-$$

Since each water molecule furnishes one hydrogen ion and one hydroxyl ion, the number of ions of each kind in pure water is the same. Water is therefore neutral; it has no excess of either H^+ or OH^- ions. However, it does have a certain concentration of H^+ ions (and the same concentration of OH^- ions).

The water molecules that do not dissociate separate the ions of a dissolved substance. Water molecules are polar. The positive pole attracts negative ions and the negative pole attracts positive ions. This causes separation of the ionic compound.

3-24 The pH Scale

If an acid is dissolved in water, the concentration of H^+ ions increases. At the same time, the concentration of OH^- ions decreases. This happens because some of the excess H^+ ions combine with OH^- ions, forming undissociated water molecules. (Remember that there are always some H^+ and OH^- ions in water.) If a base is dissolved in water, the OH^- ion concentration increases. This causes a reduction in H^+ ion

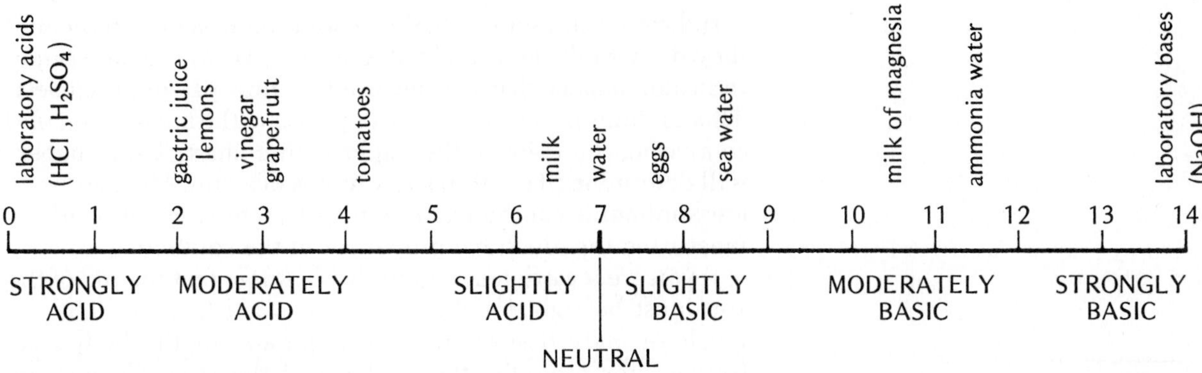

Figure 3-16. The pH Scale. Each change of one unit on this scale is a change of ten times in the degree of acidity. For example, a pH of 4 is ten times as acid as a pH of 5.

concentration. This means that in acid solutions the H^+ concentration is greater than it is in pure water. In basic solutions, the H^+ concentration is smaller.

The H^+ concentration is indicated by a unit called **pH.** The pH scale has been set up in such a way that high concentrations of H^+ (acid solutions) correspond to low values of pH (see Figure 3-16). Low concentrations (basic solutions) correspond to high pH values. The pH scale runs from 0 (highly acid) to 14 (highly basic). A neutral solution has a pH of 7. This is the pH of pure water.

Whether a solution is acid or basic can be determined by means of indicators. An **indicator** is a substance that changes color when the pH goes above or below a certain value. *Litmus* (*lit*-mus) *paper*, for example, turns red when the pH is moderately acid (below 5); it turns blue when the pH is at least slightly basic (above 8) (see Figure 3-17). Methyl orange changes from yellow to red in fairly acid solutions (ph below 3). *Phenolphthalein* (*feen*-ul-*thal*-leen) changes from colorless to red in fairly basic solutions (pH above 10).

Demonstrate the use of indicators, such as litmus paper and phenolphthalein. Use indicators to measure the pH of vinegar, orange juice, ammonia water, and soap.

Figure 3-17. Common Indicators. Litmus (left) turns red in acid solutions and blue in basic solutions. Phenolphthalein (center) changes from colorless to red in basic solutions. Methyl orange (right) is red in strong acids, changing to yellow in weaker acids.

Indicators can show whether a solution is acid or basic, but they do not tell the actual value of the pH. There are special indicator papers that can be used to find pH more closely. This is done by moistening the paper with the solution and comparing the color of the paper with a chart. These papers will determine pH within a few tenths of a unit. More accurate measurements can be made with pH meters, which work by measuring the electrical properties of the solution.

If you are a gardener, you probably know that the pH of the soil must be right for the plants you want to grow. The pH levels of body tissues are also important for the body's activities. For example, the contents of the stomach must be slightly acid for digestion to proceed normally. Maintaining the right pH levels in different parts of the body is part of homeostasis.

summary

All matter is made up of atoms. The nucleus of the atom contains protons and neutrons. In the space around the nucleus are electrons. Electrons have a negative electrical charge, protons have a positive electrical charge, and neutrons have no electrical charge. Elements are substances made up of only one kind of atom. Compounds are made up of two or more elements combined in definite proportions.

The atomic number of an atom is the number of protons in its nucleus. Each element has a different atomic number. All atoms of an element have the same number of protons, but the number of neutrons can vary. Atoms that have the same number of protons, but different numbers of neutrons, are different isotopes of the same element. The mass number of an atom is equal to the sum of its protons and neutrons. Thus, different isotopes of the same element have the same atomic number but different mass numbers. Many elements have radioactive isotopes.

The electrons of an atom are found at various distances from the nucleus in different shells. For all atoms with more than 2 electrons, the outermost shell can hold up to 8 electrons. If the outermost shell is not filled, the atom can form compounds with other elements. When atoms combine to form compounds, the electrons in the outer shell are rearranged to give each atom a filled outer shell. A chemical bond may be formed by the sharing of a pair of electrons by two atoms (a covalent bond) or by the transfer of one or more electrons from one atom to another (an ionic bond).

In a chemical formula each element is represented by its chemical symbol. An empirical formula shows the simplest proportions of atoms in the compound. A molecular formula shows the composition of a molecule of a compound. A structural formula shows how the atoms of a molecule are bonded to one another. A chemical equation shows what happens in a chemical reaction.

A mixture is formed when substances are physically mixed together but no new chemical bonds are formed. Liquid mixtures are often called solutions. Solutions do not separate on standing. A mixture of a liquid and another substance that separates on standing is a suspension. In a colloidal dispersion, the solute particles are larger than the molecules or ions of a solution, but they are too small to settle out.

A substance that produces hydrogen ions in solution is an acid. A substance that produces hydroxyl ions in solution is a base. A reaction between an acid and a base that produces a neutral solution is called neutralization. Neutralization reactions produce water and a salt. Hydrogen ion concentration is indicated by a unit called pH. Neutral solutions have a pH of 7. Acids have a pH of less than 7, and bases have a pH of more than 7.

vocabulary

acid
atom
atomic mass
atomic number
base
chemical bond
chemical equation
chemical reaction
colloidal dispersion
compound
covalent bond
diatomic molecule
electron
electron shell
element
empirical formula
indicator
ion
ionic bond
isotope
mass number
mixture
molecular formula
molecule
neutralization
neutron
nucleus
pH
product
radioactivity
radioisotope
reactant
salt
solute
solution
solvent
structural formula
suspension

test your learning

Section		
3-1	**1.**	What is an element?
	2.	What is a compound? How can you determine whether a substance is a compound or an element?
3-2	**3.**	Describe the structure of an atom.
3-3	**4.**	What is indicated by the atomic number of an element?
3-4	**5.**	In what way do different isotopes of the same element differ from one another?
3-5	**6.**	How do you determine the atomic mass of an element?
3-6	**7.**	Write the symbols for the isotopes of oxygen having mass numbers 16, 17, and 18.
3-7	**8.**	What changes occur when a radioactive isotope disintegrates?
	9.	How are radioisotopes used in studying biological processes? How are isotopes that are not radioactive used as tracers?
3-8	**10.**	Describe the arrangement of electrons around the nucleus of the atom.
	11.	How many electrons are in a filled outer shell?
3-9	**12.**	What is a chemical bond?
	13.	Describe a covalent bond.
3-10	**14.**	What is an ion?
	15.	Describe an ionic bond.
3-11	**16.**	What is a diatomic molecule?
3-12	**17.**	What is the difference between an empirical formula and a molecular formula?
3-13	**18.**	What is a structural formula?
3-14	**19.**	What is a balanced equation? Write a balanced equation showing what happens in the reaction of sodium (Na) with chlorine (Cl_2).
3-15	**20.**	What is a mixture? A homogeneous mixture?
3-16	**21.**	Define the terms *solution, solute,* and *solvent.*
	22.	What happens when a molecular substance dissolves in a liquid?
	23.	What happens when an ionic compound dissolves in a liquid?
3-17	**24.**	What is a suspension?
3-18	**25.**	How does a colloidal dispersion differ from a suspension?
3-19	**26.**	What is an acid?
3-20	**27.**	What is a base?
3-21	**28.**	What happens in a neutralization reaction?
3-22	**29.**	What substances are formed in a neutralization reaction?
3-23	**30.**	What ions are formed by the dissociation of water?
	31.	Is water an acid, a base, or neutral? Why?
3-24	**32.**	What is the pH scale?
	33.	What is an indicator?

test your understanding

1. The atomic number of lithium (Li) is 3. The atomic mass of lithium is 7.
   A. How many neutrons does an atom of lithium have?
   B. How many protons? How many electrons?
   C. How many electrons are in its outermost shell?
   D. Is the outer shell filled?
   E. Write a balanced equation showing the reaction of lithium and chlorine to form lithium chloride. (Li combines with Cl in the same way as Na.)
   F. Does lithium chloride have ionic or covalent bonds?
2. Compare the properties of a mixture, a solution, a suspension, and a colloidal dispersion.
3. Protons, neutrons, and electrons are particles that make up atoms.
   A. Which type of particle determines the chemical properties of the atom?
   B. Which type of particle determines what element the atom is?
   C. Which type of particle determines what isotope of the element the atom is?

independent research

1. Prepare a report on biologically important ions in humans. Include examples of how excesses or deficiencies of certain ions affect body function.
2. Prepare a report on the uses of acids, bases, and salts in common household products.

chapter 4

Chemical Compounds of Life

At one time it was believed that there was something special about the chemistry of life. Many chemists were sure that the substances found in living things could never be made in a laboratory. They thought, in other words, that the laws of ordinary chemistry did not apply to the chemistry of organisms. Today we know that this was a false idea. There is nothing going on in a cell that cannot be explained by the same principles that apply to chemistry in a test tube. The only difference is that most of the compounds in living cells are enormously complex. The reactions among these compounds are also very complicated. In this chapter you will become familiar with the kinds of compounds that play an important part in life processes. This will help you understand these processes when they are discussed in later chapters.

ORGANIC COMPOUNDS

After completing your study of this section, you should be able to:

1. List the major elements found in organic compounds.
2. Explain why organic compounds are generally larger and more complex than inorganic compounds.
3. Name the four major types of organic compounds found in living cells.

4-1 Definition of Organic Compounds

Organic (or-*gan*-ik) **compounds** are compounds that contain carbon. They almost always contain hydrogen, and usually contain oxygen and nitrogen. Organic compounds may also contain phosphorus and sulfur, as well as small amounts of calcium, iron, sodium, chlorine, and potassium. They are called organic compounds because they are found in nature only in the bodies or in the remains and products of living organisms. However, many organic compounds can be produced in chemical laboratories.

Organisms contain some inorganic compounds in addition to organic compounds. Inorganic compounds do not usually contain carbon. (Carbon dioxide, CO_2, is one exception.) Some common inorganic compounds found in living organisms are water, carbon dioxide, salts, bases, and inorganic acids such as hydrochloric acid.

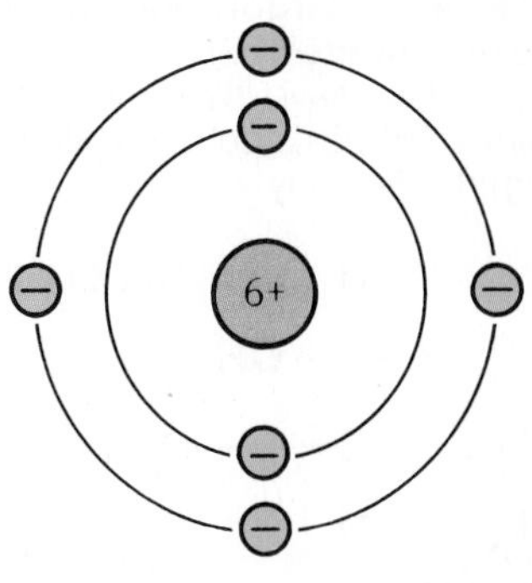

Figure 4-1. Structure of the Carbon Atom. The four electrons in the outer shell allow a carbon atom to form four covalent bonds. This special characteristic accounts for the unlimited variety of organic compounds.

4-2 Structure and Types of Organic Compounds

The big difference between the organic compounds of living organisms and the inorganic compounds found in the nonliving world is the size and complexity of many organic molecules. The reason for this is found in the electron structure of the carbon atom. The carbon atom has 6 electrons. Two of these electrons occupy the first shell, leaving 4 electrons for the second shell (see Figure 4-1). This means that the carbon atom can fill its outer shell with 8 electrons by forming 4 covalent bonds with other atoms. Each bond involves the sharing of one electron from the carbon atom and one electron from another atom bonded to the carbon. The atoms bonded to a carbon atom may be other carbon atoms. The carbon atoms may be bonded into long chains, with other groups or chains of atoms branching from the main chain. Carbon atoms may also be bonded into rings with side branches, or with connections to other rings. The possible size and variety of these arrangements is unlimited.

Emphasize that in organic compounds, each covalent bond formed by a carbon atom consists of one electron from carbon and one from the other atom.

In organic compounds, each carbon atom forms four bonds with other atoms. In many cases the bond is double; that is, there are two bonds between the same pair of atoms. In a few cases a pair of carbon atoms are joined by a triple bond. Figure 4-2 illustrates simple examples of single, double, and triple carbon-to-carbon bonds.

Although the total number of organic compounds is extremely large, they can be classified into a fairly small number of types. Four types of organic compounds will be discussed in this chapter—carbohydrates, lipids, proteins, and nucleic acids.

Figure 4-2. Bonds Between Carbon Atoms. Carbon atoms can form single bonds (top), double bonds (middle), and even triple bonds (bottom).

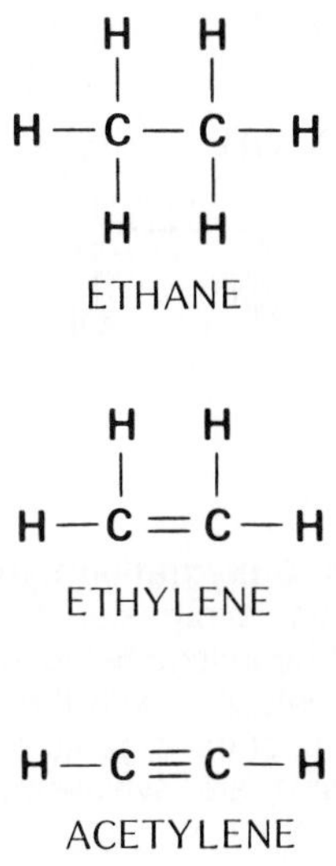

CARBOHYDRATES

After completing your study of this section, you should be able to:

1. Describe the basic chemical makeup of carbohydrates.
2. Name three monosaccharides and give their empirical and molecular formulas.
3. Describe the process of dehydration synthesis.

Figure 4-3. Structures of Some Monosaccharides. Glucose, fructose, and galactose have the same empirical formula ($C_6H_{12}O_6$), but their atoms are arranged differently.

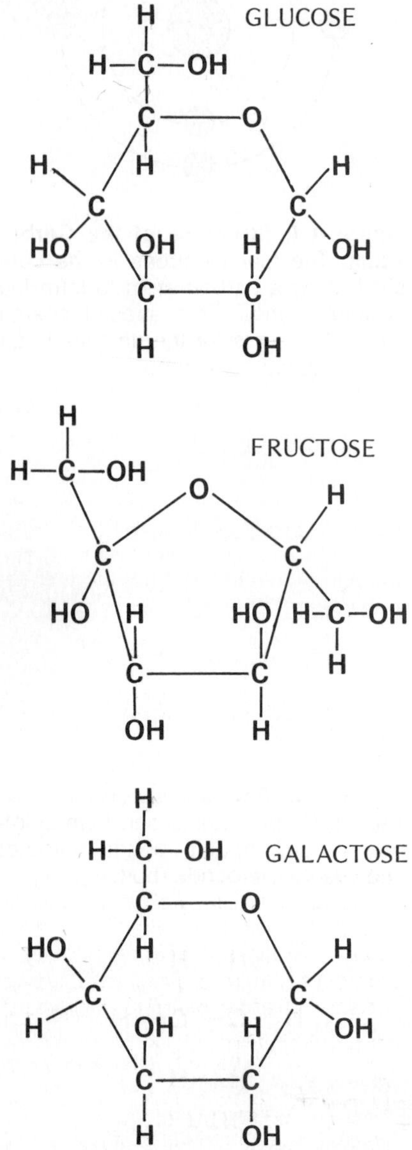

4. Define the terms *disaccharide, polysaccharide,* and *polymer.*
5. Name three polysaccharides found in living organisms and explain the function of each.
6. Describe the process of hydrolysis.

4-3 Characteristics of Carbohydrates

Carbohydrates (kar-boh-*hy*-drayts) are compounds of carbon, hydrogen, and oxygen in which the ratio of hydrogen to oxygen is the same as in water (2 atoms of hydrogen to 1 atom of oxygen). The simplest carbohydrates are the simple sugars, or **monosaccharides** (mahn-uh-*sak*-uh-ryds). They have the empirical formula CH_2O, but no sugar molecule is actually that simple. The most common monosaccharides have the molecular formula $C_6H_{12}O_6$. However, the atoms of the molecule may be arranged in several different structures, each corresponding to a different sugar. Figure 4-3 shows the structural formulas of three of these sugars—glucose, fructose, and galactose. Simple sugars with 5 carbons ($C_5H_{10}O_5$) and 4 carbons ($C_4H_8O_4$) also exist. The names of sugars end in *-ose.*

The sugars are biologically important because they contain large amounts of energy. This energy can be released by breaking the sugars down, in the presence of oxygen, to carbon dioxide and water. Nearly all organisms use glucose as a source of energy.

4-4 Dehydration Synthesis

Sugar molecules can be bonded together by a process called **dehydration synthesis** (dee-hy-*dray*-shun *sin*-thuh-sis). The

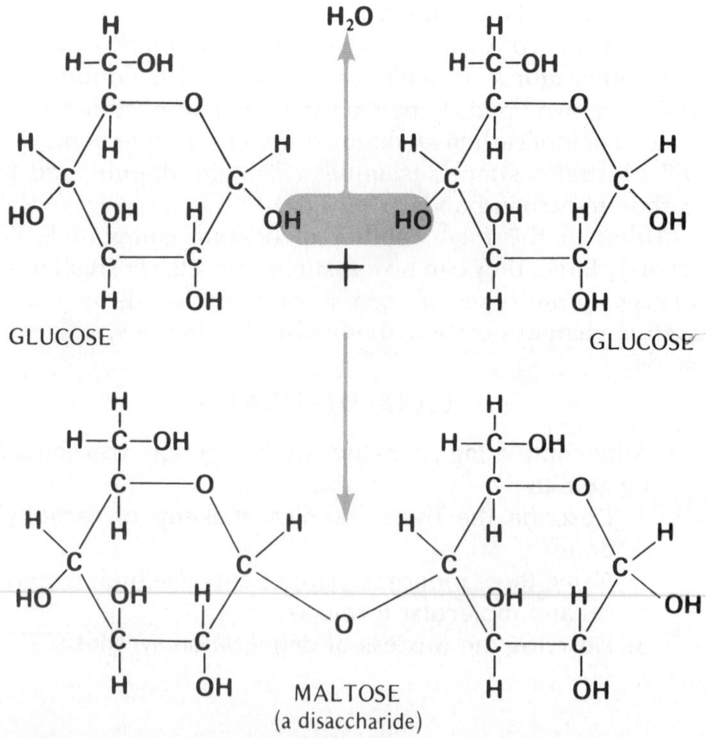

Figure 4-4. Dehydration Synthesis. In dehydration synthesis, two simple molecules bond together to form a more complex molecule, with the release of water. Many of the organic compounds in organisms are synthesized in this way.

bond forms where an OH group is present in each molecule. One OH combines with the H from the other OH, forming a molecule of water, and the two molecules become joined through the remaining O (see Figure 4-4).

Synthesis means "putting together" and dehydration means "removing water." Thus, dehydration synthesis means "putting together by removing water." In living cells, dehydration synthesis is brought about by the action of enzymes. It is an important process in making many of the organic compounds that the organism needs.

The molecule formed by joining two simple sugars is called a double sugar, or **disaccharide** (dy-*sak*-uh-ryd). The disaccharide formed by the dehydration synthesis shown in Figure 4-4 is maltose.

4-5 Polysaccharides

Simple sugars can be joined together by dehydration synthesis to form **polysaccharides** (pahl-ee-*sak*-uh-ryds), or long chains of repeating sugar units. Large molecules consisting of chains of repeating units are called **polymers** (*pahl*-uh-merz). The polysaccharides are examples of sugar polymers.

Organisms store excess sugar in the form of polysaccharides. In plants, this form of stored sugar is called **starch.** Starch is found in seeds and in roots and stems specialized for food storage. In humans, surplus sugar is stored in the liver as the polysaccharide **glycogen** (*gly*-kuh-jen), sometimes called "animal starch." Other types of polysaccharides form tough structural parts of organisms. For example, *cellulose* (*sel*-yuh-lohs), is a polysaccharide found in plants, while *chitin* (*kyt*-un) is a polysaccharide that makes up the shells of insects.

Glycogen molecules are large and highly branched. Although soluble in water, glycogen is suitable for a storage product because it cannot pass through cell membranes.

4-6 Hydrolysis

Chains of sugar molecules may be broken apart by the process called **hydrolysis** (hy-*drahl*-uh-sis). In this type of reaction, a water molecule is returned to the place from which it was removed in dehydration synthesis (see Figure 4-5). The bond between the two molecules is broken, and the original

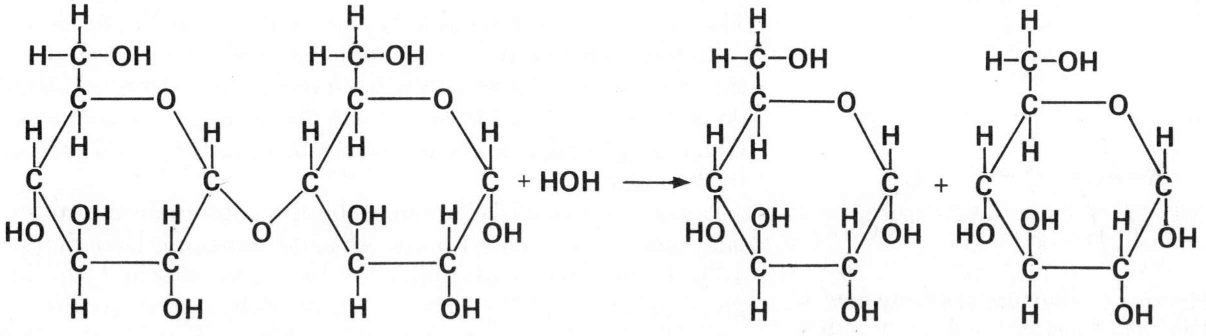

MALTOSE (a disaccharide) + WATER ⟶ GLUCOSE + GLUCOSE

Figure 4-5. Hydrolysis. A complex molecule can be broken down into smaller, simpler molecules by the addition of a water molecule. Hydrolysis is the most common process by which organisms change organic compounds into more usable forms.

OH groups are restored. Hydrolysis can be repeated on long chains until an entire polysaccharide has been split into its simple sugars.

LIPIDS

After completing your study of this section, you should be able to:

1. Name the three most common types of lipids.
2. Describe the basic chemical structure of a fatty acid molecule.
3. Explain what is meant by a saturated, unsaturated, and polyunsaturated fat.
4. Explain the relationship between saturated fats in the diet, cholesterol, and circulatory disorders.
5. Describe the functions of lipids in plants and animals.

4-7 Chemical Composition of Lipids

Lipids (*lip*-idz) include the substances commonly called fats, oils, and waxes. Like carbohydrates, they are made up of carbon, hydrogen, and oxygen. However, in lipids there is relatively less oxygen than in carbohydrates. One result of this difference is that gram for gram, fats yield more energy than carbohydrates when they are broken down.

Fats and oils are formed from the combination of fatty acids and glycerol. A **fatty acid** molecule consists of a chain of carbon atoms to which hydrogen atoms are bonded. At one end of the chain there is a *carboxyl* (kar-*bahk*-sul) *group*, -COOH.

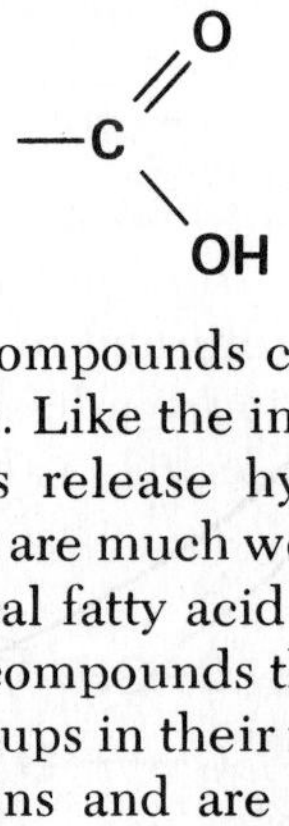

Fatty acids and other compounds containing carboxyl groups are called *organic acids*. Like the inorganic acids discussed in Chapter 3, these acids release hydrogen ions in solution. However, organic acids are much weaker than inorganic acids. The structure of a typical fatty acid is shown in Figure 4-6.

Alcohols are organic compounds that resemble bases in having one or more OH groups in their molecules. However, they do not release OH^- ions and are therefore not true bases. **Glycerol** (*glis*-uh-rohl) is an alcohol that has three OH groups in its molecule.

A molecule of fat is produced by the combination of three fatty acid molecules with one glycerol molecule (see Figure 4-7). Each fatty acid molecule becomes attached to the glycerol at one of the OH groups by dehydration synthesis. Three molecules of water are released for each molecule of fat that is formed.

Figure 4-6. Structure of a Fatty Acid. A fatty acid consists of a chain of carbon and hydrogen atoms with a carboxyl group at one end.

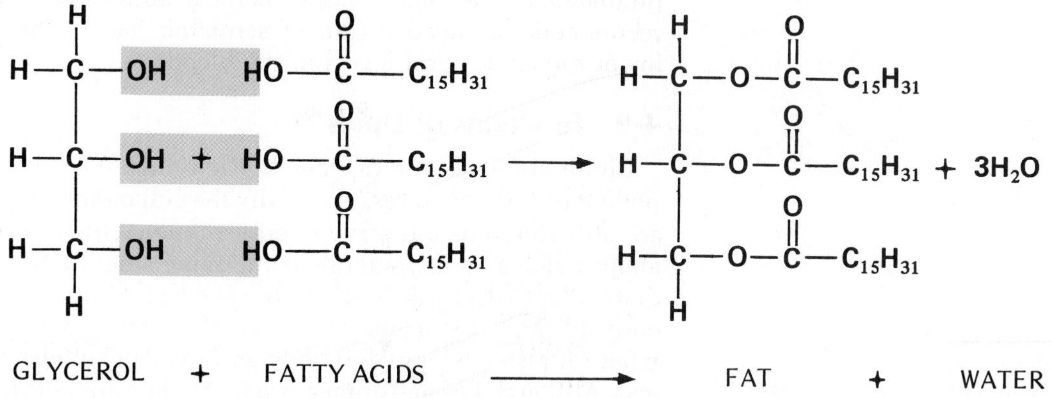

Figure 4-7. Synthesis of a Fat. A molecule of fat is formed by the dehydration synthesis of three fatty acid molecules and one glycerol molecule.

Fats as they occur in nature are almost always combinations of two or three different fatty acids with glycerol. Some fats are liquids at ordinary temperatures. These are usually called oils (animal oils or vegetable oils, depending on their source). *Waxes* are lipids formed by the combination of fatty acids with alcohols other than glycerol.

4-8 Saturated and Unsaturated Fats

If all the carbon-to-carbon bonds in a fatty acid are single bonds, the acid is said to be saturated. Fats formed from such acids are called **saturated** (*satch*-uh-rayt-ed) **fats** In **unsaturated fats,** one or more pairs of carbon atoms in the fatty acid molecules are joined by a double bond, or even a triple bond. A fat that has just one unsaturated bond in its molecule is called *monounsaturated.* A fat that has chains with more than one double or triple carbon bond is called *polyunsaturated.* A typical unsaturated fatty acid is illustrated in Figure 4-8.

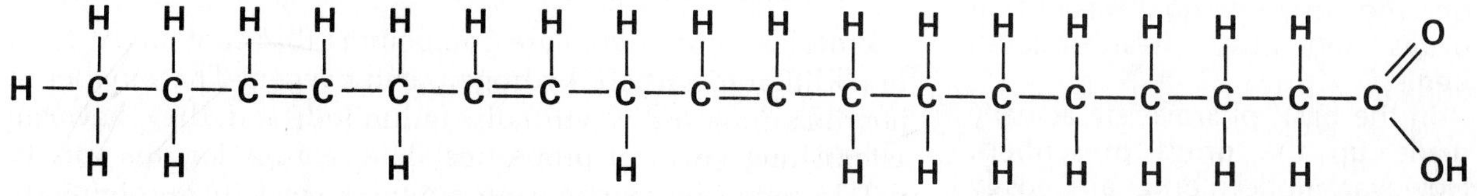

Figure 4-8. Structure of an Unsaturated Fatty Acid. An unsaturated fatty acid contains at least one double, or even triple, carbon bond.

In a saturated fatty acid, each carbon atom along the chain is bonded to two hydrogen atoms. (The carbon at the start of the chain is bonded to three hydrogens.) An unsaturated acid of the same length will have fewer hydrogen atoms. Unsaturated fats can be changed to saturated fats by adding hydrogen to them. This process is called *hydrogenation* (hy-drahj-uh-*nay*-shun).

Cholesterol (kuh-*les*-tuh-rohl) is an essential compound found in most animal tissues. However, it plays an important part in the buildup of deposits that harden and narrow the arteries. This condition can lead to heart attacks and strokes. There is evidence that saturated fats, such as those found in butter and meat, tend to increase the amount of cholesterol

Cholesterol is normally synthesized in the body, mainly in the liver. In addition to its role in membrane structure, it is a precursor of various steroid hormones, including progesterone, testosterone, estradiol, and cortisol. Bile salts are breakdown products of cholesterol.

produced in the body. Many medical authorities therefore recommend reduced intake of saturated fats in the diet to lower the cholesterol levels in the blood.

4-9 Functions of Lipids

Lipids are important in many life activities. They are a component of cell structures, especially the cell membranes. They are also stored as a reserve energy supply. They can furnish about twice as much energy as the same amount of carbohydrate. Plants store oils in seeds. Some examples are peanut oil, corn oil, and castor oil. Mammals store fat under the skin, where it also cushions the body and insulates it against heat loss. Although fats are storage products, they are not stored for long periods of time in animal tissue. Instead, they are constantly being broken down and then replaced. Investigations have shown that mice, for example, replace about one-half of their stored fat each week.

PROTEINS

After completing your study of this section, you should be able to:

1. List the functions of proteins in living organisms.
2. Illustrate the general molecular structure of an amino acid.
3. Describe the formation of a peptide bond.
4. List three shapes that protein molecules can have, and describe in general how polypeptide chains can form such shapes.

careers

Pharmacists, or druggists, are people who prepare and dispense drugs prescribed by physicians and dentists. They also advise people on the use of nonprescription drugs and other health-related items.

In the past, pharmacists actually made up the drugs prescribed. However, modern drugs are mostly produced by large manufacturers.

Pharmacists must be graduates of an accredited college of pharmacy. The pharmacy course is generally 5 years, and includes courses in biology and chemistry, as well as pharmacology, which is the study of drugs and their effects. To become a licensed pharmacist, graduates of pharmacy schools must serve a one-year internship under the supervision of a registered pharmacist and pass a state board examination.

4-10 The Nature of Proteins

Proteins (*proh*-teenz) are compounds that contain nitrogen in addition to carbon, hydrogen, and oxygen. The number of possible proteins is virtually unlimited, and they have an astonishing range of properties. The reasons for this variety will become clear when we examine the way that proteins are constructed.

It is the existence of proteins that makes life possible in its present degree of complexity. A few examples of the countless functions of proteins are:

1. *Structural parts* of cells and of body tissues, such as hair and nails, and the tough materials of cartilage and connective tissue.
2. *Pigments* in the blood, skin, and eyes.
3. *Hormones*, the chemical messengers that regulate body functions.
4. *Contractile material* of muscle tissues.
5. *Antibodies*, which protect the body against foreign substances and disease organisms.

6. *Enzymes,* which enable complex chemical reactions to take place in the body with precision and speed.

To understand how proteins are able to do all this and much more, let us examine their chemical structure.

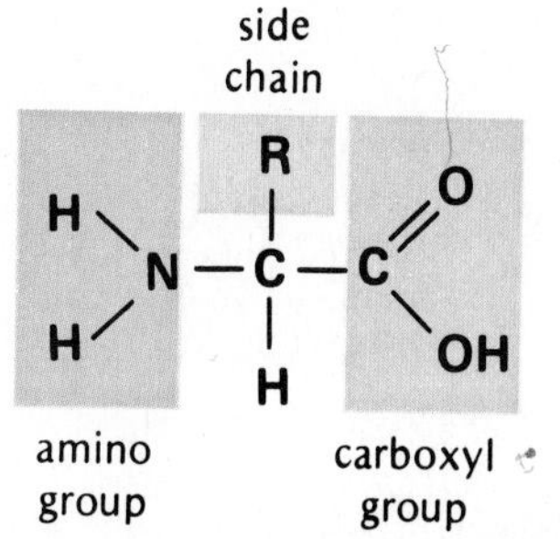

Figure 4-9. Structure of an Amino Acid. The side chains of the 20 amino acids give each its special chemical properties.

4-11 Amino Acids

Amino (uh-*mee*-noh) **acids** are the structural units of proteins. An amino acid is a relatively simple compound (see Figure 4-9). It consists of a central carbon atom to which are bonded:

1. A carboxyl group, COOH.
2. An **amino group,** NH_2.
3. A single hydrogen atom.
4. A side chain, symbolized by the letter R, which is different in each amino acid. In the simplest amino acid, glycine, the side chain is just another H. In alanine, it is a CH_3 group. Other side chains are more complex, and some contain sulfur and phosphorus. But none of the amino acid molecules is especially large. There are 20 different amino acids that are found as parts of proteins.

Point out that an enormous variety of proteins can be produced by the different combinations of 20 amino acids.

4-12 The Peptide Bond

Two amino acids may be bonded together by dehydration synthesis. The bond forms between the amino group of one amino acid and the carboxyl group of the other, with the loss of one water molecule. The bond is called a **peptide** (*pep*-tyd) **bond,** and the resulting molecule is called a **dipeptide.** The formation of a dipeptide is illustrated in Figure 4-10.

Figure 4-10. Formation of a Peptide Bond. A dehydration synthesis reaction between two amino acids links them together in a peptide bond. The molecule is called a dipeptide.

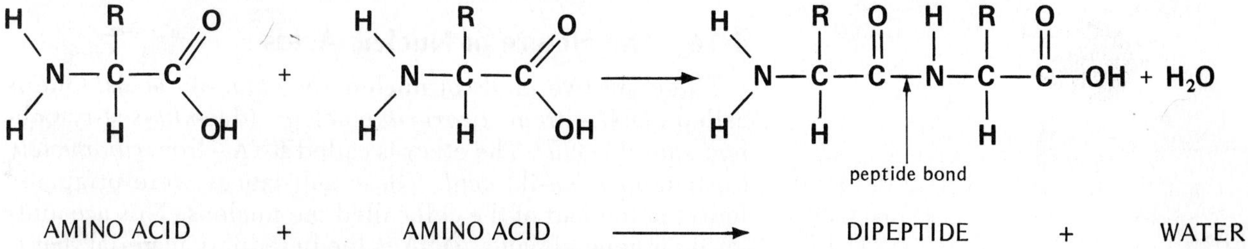

Amino acids can be added on at either end of a dipeptide in the same way, forming a chain of amino acids. Such a chain is called a **polypeptide.** All proteins are made of polypeptides.

4-13 The Structure of Proteins

Amino acids can be linked together in any sequence whatever and in chains of varying length. Each different sequence makes a different protein. Furthermore, the chains can fold and twist in space, making structures of many different shapes. Typical shapes of protein molecules are coils or helixes, pleated sheets, and globules. Often, adjacent sections of a folded chain become bonded to each other by what are

The function of a protein is a result of its three-dimensional structure, or conformation. Conformation, in turn, is determined by the amino acid sequences and the reactions that occur between neighboring amino acids and those that are far apart in the sequence. If its three-dimensional structure is disturbed, the protein ceases to function. It is denatured.

called *cross-links.* The variations in shape and formation of cross-links make possible an enormous variety of proteins.

All protein molecules are large in terms of the number of atoms and amino acid units they contain. The smallest protein molecules have about 50 amino acids, or about 1,000 atoms. The largest have over 100,000 amino acids and millions of atoms.

Determining the actual sequence of amino acids in a particular protein is obviously a difficult task. The first protein structure to be determined was that of insulin. It was accomplished by Frederick Sanger, at Cambridge University, England, in 1954. Sanger later received the Nobel Prize for this work. The molecular structures of several hundred proteins have since been worked out by painstaking methods. These methods include breaking the molecule chemically into successively smaller pieces and identifying the amino acid at the end of each broken section. Machines are now being developed that will automatically analyze a protein and print out its amino acid sequence.

NUCLEIC ACIDS

After completing your study of this section, you should be able to:

1. Name the two types of nucleic acids found in cells, and describe where they are found and their functions.
2. Describe the structure of each type of nucleic acid, including the type of sugar each contains, the types of bases, and the shapes of the molecules.

4-14 The Nature of Nucleic Acids

There are two kinds of **nucleic** (noo-*klay*-ik) **acids.** One is called **DNA**—from *deoxyribonucleic* (dee-*ahk*-see-ry-boh-noo-*klay*-ik) *acid).* The other is called **RNA**—from *ribonucleic* (*ry*-boh-noo-*klay*-ik) *acid.* These substances were originally found in the part of the cell called the nucleus. This accounts for their general name. DNA is the hereditary material that is transmitted from one generation to the next during reproduction. Working together with RNA, it directs and controls the development and activities of all the cells of an organism. The way in which this is done is the subject of Chapter 27.

4-15 The Structure of DNA and RNA

The general structure of a nucleic acid molecule is that of a very long chain of repeating units. The backbone of the chain consists of two alternating chemical units. One unit is a 5-carbon sugar (deoxyribose in DNA, ribose in RNA). The other is the phosphate group, PO_4. In human cells, a single DNA molecule may have as many as 3 *billion* of these units!

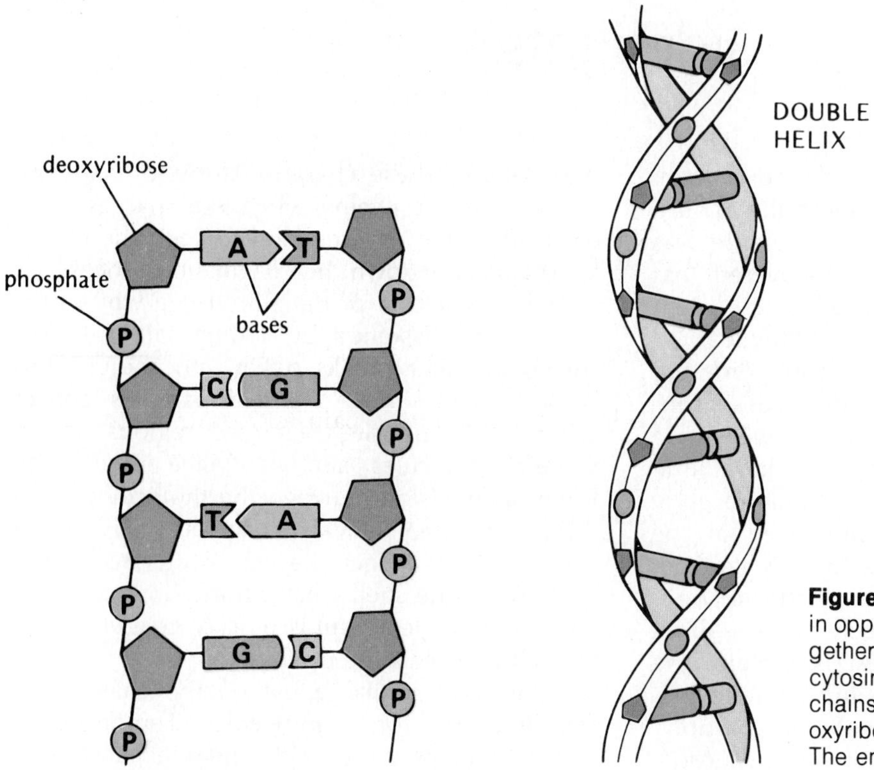

Figure 4-11. DNA Molecule. The bases in opposite side chains of DNA bond together, adenine (A) with thymine (T) and cytosine (C) with guanine (G). The side chains are formed of alternating deoxyribose and phosphate groups (P). The entire molecule is coiled to form a double helix.

Attached to the sugar groups along one side of the chain, there are chemical groups called bases. In DNA, there are only four different bases that may be attached to the chain. They are *adenine* (*ad*-uh-neen), *thymine* (*thy*-meen), *cytosine* (*syt*-uh-seen), and *guanine* (*gwah*-neen). **Just as amino acids may be arranged in any sequence in a polypeptide chain, the** four kinds of bases can be attached in any sequence along the length of the DNA molecule. As we will see in Chapter 27, the sequence of bases acts as a code that determines what proteins will be made in the cell. The proteins in turn determine the nature and activities of the cell.

A DNA molecule consists of two chains side by side, with the bases on opposite chains bonded together. In this bonding, an adenine is always bonded to a thymine. A cytosine is always bonded to a guanine (see Figure 4-11). The entire molecule is coiled into the form called a *double helix* (*hee*-liks). The double helix is coiled upon itself many times. A human DNA molecule would be about 4 centimeters long if it were stretched out in a straight line. By repeated coilings it is able to fit into tiny structures within the cell.

An RNA molecule is similar in chemical composition to DNA, but it has certain differences. The RNA molecule consists of only one chain, or strand, of bases. The sugar in RNA is ribose, not deoxyribose. And the base thymine is replaced by *uracil* (*yoor*-uh-sil). As we will see in Chapter 27, RNA is involved in protein synthesis.

sidelights

Nobody knows when humans started to cook their foods. It happened long before the earliest written records, most likely soon after fire was brought under control. People discovered that food was easier to eat and tasted better when it was heated over a fire. Gradually they learned the best ways to prepare and cook different foods. They invented sauces and used seasonings to make eating a pleasure as well as a necessity. Still, even the best cooks have little idea why their methods work. It is only recently that scientists have become interested in the processes that go on when a food is cooked.

Take, for example, the simple matter of boiling an egg. Egg white is largely water—about 88 percent. Nearly all the rest is protein, the chief protein in egg white being albumin. Albumin, like all proteins, is made up of polypeptides—long chains of amino acids. At room temperature or below, each chain is tightly folded upon itself many times. Adjacent lengths of the chain are held together by a weak kind of chemical bond called a hydrogen bond.

Heating a protein changes the shape of its molecule, a process called **denaturation.** Boiling an egg causes denaturation of the albumin in the egg white. At the temperature of boiling water, the denaturation of albumin is quite drastic. All the hydrogen bonds are broken, and the molecule untwists. The polypeptide chain becomes a long, floppy structure. Many of the side groups of the amino acids become exposed, rather than being concealed in the interior of the folded molecule. In this extended form, the chains tend to become bonded to one another rather than to themselves, a process call **coagulation.** The final result is the semisolid, elastic material of cooked egg white. Chemically, the albumin has hardly been changed at all, but physically, it is a different material.

It takes 10 to 15 minutes to hard-boil an egg. The amino-acid chains do not attach to one another quickly, even after they have been opened out. One reason for this is that the chains have electrical charges scattered along their length. These charge distributions are the same on all the chains. Since like charges repel each other, the charges tend to keep the chains apart and slow down the coagulation process.

The coagulation of denatured egg-white protein can be hastened by adding salt. Salt dissolved in water breaks down into sodium and chloride ions. These charged particles collect around the oppositely charged regions of the protein molecules and neutralize them. The force of repulsion between the molecules is reduced and they quickly coagulate. Salt in the water will not affect the egg white inside the shell. But if the shell cracks in the boiling water, any white that leaks out is quickly coagulated by the salt and seals the opening.

Acids have similar effect on the charge distribution on protein molecules. Lemon juice, which contains citric acid, and vinegar (acetic acid) can be used in place of salt to help coagulate egg white.

Did you ever whip egg white? This is denaturation of protein done by hand, without benefit of heat, salt, or acid. Whipping works because the protein chains on the surface of the egg white are already partly stretched out by surface tension—a molecular pull that is present at the surface of every liquid. As you whip the egg white, you continually bring fresh molecules to the surface, where they are opened up by surface tension. The whipping action also creates a tangle of coagulated protein molecules in which air becomes trapped. The end result is a light, airy foam with which you can make meringues, souffles, and very light cakes.

However, the least amount of fat or oil in the mixing bowl prevents the egg white from whipping properly. The reason for this is that oil greatly weakens the surface tension of water. Since egg yolk is about 30 percent fat, a bit of egg yolk in the white you plan to whip is disastrous. If, in separating the eggs to make a meringue or a souffle, some yolk gets into the whites, it may be a good idea to change your plans and make scrambled eggs instead.

ENZYMES

After completing your study of this section, you should be able to:

1. Explain the functions of enzymes in living cells.
2. Describe the lock-and-key model of enzyme action.
3. Explain the effects on enzyme action of temperature, pH, and enzyme and substrate concentrations.
4. Define the term *coenzyme*.

4-16 Importance of Enzymes

Most biochemical reactions of living cells will not occur in the absence of enzymes. Enzymes increase the rates of the reactions they catalyze by at least a million times.

Enzymes (*en*-zymz) are protein substances that make it possible for the chemical reactions of life to go on in living cells. There is a major difference between chemical reactions of inorganic substances and the reactions of organic compounds in living things. Consider, for example, the burning of gasoline in an automobile engine. The gasoline vapor is admitted to the engine cylinder, it is ignited by a spark, and the vapor completely burns in a fraction of a second. In fact, the burning is so rapid that it produces a small explosion, which helps to drive the engine.

The chemical reactions of life are nothing like that. It is true that glucose is "burned" to release energy in the cell. But the "burning" occurs in dozens of small steps. In some of these steps, a small part of a molecule is removed. In others, a small group of atoms is added on. In still others, atoms are just rearranged within the molecule. These steps must occur with great precision and in the right order. They must also occur at ordinary temperatures inside the cell and must not give off large amounts of heat. Otherwise, the cell would be destroyed.

Enzymes make all of this possible in the living cell. For each step of a reaction, there is a particular enzyme that brings it about. Enzymes enter into a chemical reaction only temporarily—just long enough to cause it to happen. Enzymes are not changed by the reaction. They remain to be used again and again for the same chemical step with other molecules. A substance that affects a reaction without being changed itself is called a **catalyst** (*kat*-uh-list). Enzymes are organic catalysts.

Enzymes are highly specific in their action. Each enzyme catalyzes only one particular reaction involving specific substrates.

The substance that an enzyme acts upon is called its **substrate** (*sub*-strayt). The names of enzymes usually end with the suffix *-ase,* and the name is often derived from the name of the substrate. For example, the enzyme that acts to split maltose into two glucose molecules is called maltase. Enzymes that break down proteins into shorter polypeptides or into separate amino acids are called *proteases* (*proh*-tee-ay-zez). Enzymes that break down lipids are called *lipases* (*ly*-pay-zez).

4-17 How Enzymes Work

Many experiments have shown that the ability of enzymes to act as catalysts depends on their shape. Somewhere on the

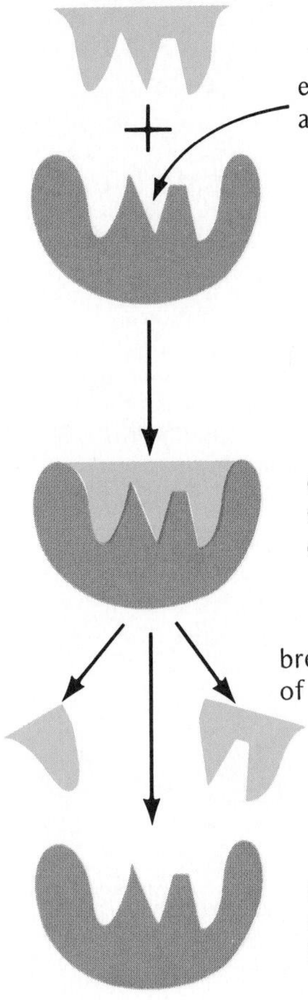

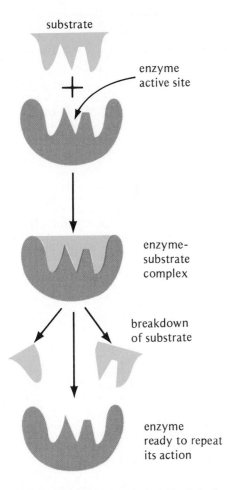

Figure 4-12. Lock-and-Key Model of Enzyme Action. In this theory of enzyme action, the substrate molecule fits into the active site on the enzyme, forming an enzyme-substrate complex. During this close association between enzyme and substrate the enzyme catalyzes a reaction in its substrate. When the reaction is finished, the enzyme and reaction product separate.

surface of each enzyme there is a region called the **active site.** The substrate molecules fit the shape of the active site (see Figure 4-12). When the substrate molecule comes in contact with the active site of the enzyme, it forms a temporary union with the enzyme. This is called an *enzyme-substrate complex.* During this time, the enzyme may break bonds within the substrate molecule and thus separate it into two smaller molecules.

An enzyme may also cause two molecules to join. In this case, there are two substrates. Each fits into the active site in such a way that they are brought into close contact. This enables bonds to form, joining the two substrate molecules.

The theory of enzyme action in which the enzyme and substrate fit together at an active site is called the *lock-and-key model.* The notched surface of a key can open only one lock. In a similar way, the shape of the active site of an enzyme fits the shape of only certain substrates. Thus, each enzyme can catalyze a reaction only of those substrates.

4-18 Characteristics of Enzyme Action

The following statements are generally true of enzyme action.

1. *Small amounts of an enzyme can cause the reaction of large quantities of substrate.* The time required for an enzyme-substrate complex to form and a reaction to occur is very short. A single enzyme molecule can catalyze thousands of substrate reactions each second. Thus, only small amounts of any enzyme need be present in a cell at any given time.

2. *Enzymes enable cell reactions to proceed at normal temperatures.* Many chemical reactions that occur very slowly at ordinary temperatures can be speeded up by raising the temperature. However, high temperatures would destroy living cells. Enzymes speed up reactions in the cell without requiring high temperatures.

3. *Enzymes work best at certain temperatures.* Enzyme action depends on the random motion of molecules, which brings the substrates into contact with the enzymes. This random motion increases as the temperature rises. If the temperature is low, the rate at which enzyme-substrate complexes form will be low (see Figure 4-13). The effect of the enzyme

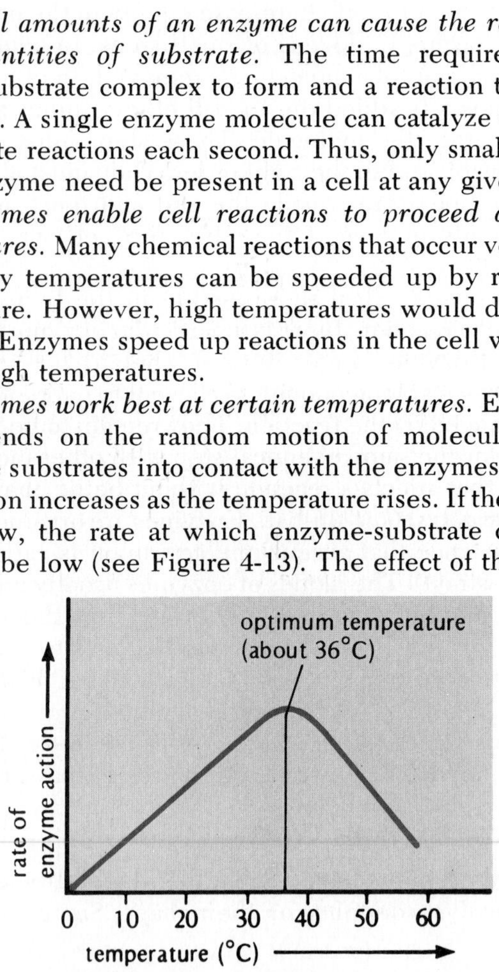

Figure 4-13. The Effect of Temperature on the Rate of Enzyme Action.

will therefore be reduced. At somewhat higher temperatures, the enzyme becomes more effective, because complexes are forming at a faster rate. At still higher temperatures, however, the enzyme protein starts to break down, a process called *denaturation.* The shape of the enzyme molecule changes, its active site no longer fits the substrate molecule, and it loses its effectiveness. There is therefore a particular temperature—the *optimum temperature*—at which enzyme effectiveness is greatest. Optimum temperatures for enzymes in living cells are usually close to the normal cell temperature.

4. *Each enzyme works best at a certain pH.* The effectiveness of an enzyme depends on the pH of the surrounding medium (see Figure 4-14). The pH of the contents of the

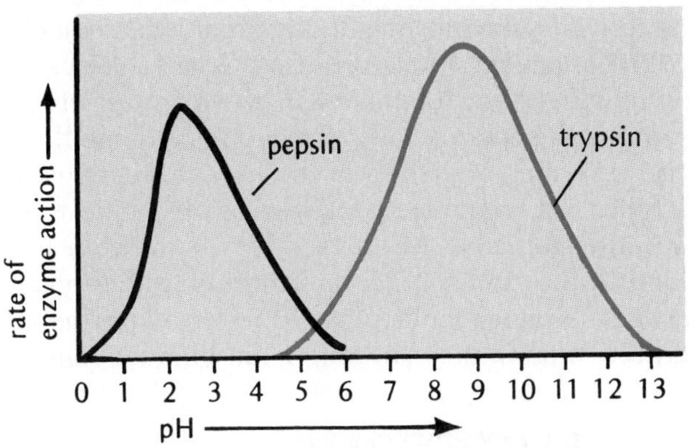

Figure 4-14. The Effect of pH on the Rate of Enzyme Action.

human stomach, for example, is slightly acid. The enzyme pepsin, which starts the digestion of proteins in the stomach, is most effective at this pH level. The pH in the intestine is slightly basic. Here the enzyme trypsin, which continues the digestion of proteins, works best.

Many enzyme-catalyzed reactions involve the transformation of energy. Such reactions occur in photosynthesis and cellular respiration. Energy from ATP is used in muscle contraction and active transport processes.

5. *The rate of an enzyme-controlled reaction depends on the concentrations of enzyme and substrate.* If relatively little enzyme is present, the number of substrate molecules it can act on in a given time is limited. Increasing the amount of enzyme will increase the rate at which the reaction products are formed (see Figure 4-15). When, however, all the substrate molecules are being acted on, a further increase in enzyme concentration will have little or no effect on output. Likewise, when all the enzyme molecules and substrate molecules are

Figure 4-15. The Effects of Enzyme and Substrate Concentration on the Rate of Enzyme Action.

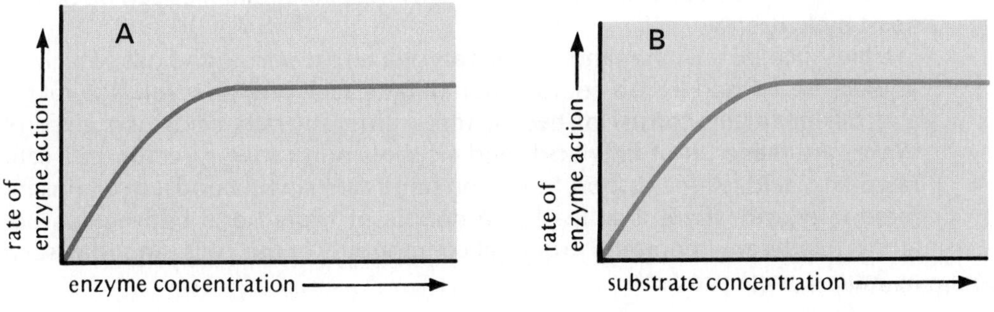

Enzyme activity can be inhibited by certain small molecules and ions. In living cells, this type of inhibition serves as a control mechanism. Various drugs and toxic substances also act as enzyme inhibitors. Some inhibitors bind irreversibly to the enzyme, while with other inhibitors the reaction is reversible. Some reversible inhibitors bind to the active site (competitive inhibitors) while others bind to other positions on the enzyme (noncompetitive inhibitors).

in the process of reaction, adding more substrate will have no effect on rate of output.

6. *Some enzymes need substances called coenzymes in order to function.* **Coenzymes** (koh-*en*-zymz), which are organic substances but are not proteins, enable enzymes to perform their catalytic function. Some coenzymes are built into the structure of an enzyme. Others are separate molecules. During the formation of the enzyme-substrate complex, the coenzyme is altered in a way that assists the reaction. After the reaction, the coenzyme is restored to its original form. It is now known that some vitamins are needed in the body because they are coenzymes or because coenzymes are made from them in the cell.

7. *Some enzymes function inside the cell, others act outside the cell.* All enzymes in a living organism are made by the cells of the organism. Most of these enzymes are used within the cell in which they are made. However, some enzymes are passed out of the cell to catalyze reactions outside the cell. All digestive enzymes produced in the human digestive tract are of this type. For example, pepsin is made inside the cells of glands in the stomach wall. It then leaves the cells and mixes with food in the stomach. Here, proteins in the food are broken down to simpler molecules, which can later be absorbed through cell membranes and enter the bloodstream.

summary

Organic compounds are compounds containing carbon. Most organic compounds also contain hydrogen. Organic molecules are often much larger and more complex than inorganic molecules. Their size and complexity is possible because of the chemical nature of the carbon atom.

Carbohydrates are organic compounds containing carbon, hydrogen, and oxygen. The proportion of hydrogen to oxygen in these molecules is 2:1, the same as in water. The simplest carbohydrates are the simple sugars, or monosaccharides, which have the empirical formula CH_2O. These sugars can be bonded together to form more complex compounds by dehydration synthesis. The molecule formed by joining two monosaccharides is a disaccharide. Long chains of repeating sugar units called polysaccharides can be formed from simple sugars by dehydration synthesis. Sugars are used as a source of energy for the cell, while polysaccharides serve both as food storage products and as structural materials. Chains of sugar molecules can be broken apart by hydrolysis.

Lipids include fats, oils, and waxes. Fats, which are solids, and oils, which are liquids, are formed from a combination of fatty acids and glycerol. Natural fats and oils generally consist of two or three different fatty acids and glycerol. Waxes are made up of fatty acids and alcohols other than glycerol. In a saturated fatty acid, all the carbon-to-carbon bonds are single bonds. In an unsaturated fatty acid, there is at least one double or triple bond between carbon atoms. Lipids are important structural components of the cells, and they serve as food storage products.

Proteins serve as structural materials, pigments, hormones, antibodies, enzymes, and contractile materials. Proteins are made up of chains of amino acids, which are bonded together by dehydration synthesis. The bond between adjacent amino acids is a peptide bond. There are 20 different amino acids, and the sequence of the amino acids is characteristic of the particular protein. A protein may contain several polypeptide chains, which can fold and twist in space. Thus protein molecules can be very large and very complex in form.

The nucleic acids are DNA and RNA. DNA contains the hereditary information, which is transmitted from one generation to the next during reproduction. DNA and RNA together control the synthesis of cell proteins, which in turn determine the nature and activities of the cell.

Nucleic acids are made up of very long chains of repeating units. DNA molecules consist of two chains bonded together, with the entire double chain coiled into a double helix. The RNA molecule consists of only a single chain.

Enzymes are proteins that serve as catalysts, making it possible for the biochemical reactions of the cell to occur at great speed and at normal temperatures. According to the lock-and-key model of enzyme action, the substrates fit into active sites on the enzyme. While the substrate and enzyme are joined, the enzyme may break bonds in the substrate molecule, or it may join substrate molecules together, forming a larger molecule.

vocabulary

active site
amino acid
amino group
carbohydrate
catalyst
cholesterol
coenzyme
dehydration synthesis
dipeptide
disaccharide
DNA
enzyme
fatty acid
glycerol
glycogen
hydrolysis
lipid
monosaccharide
nucleic acid
organic compound
peptide bond
polymer
polypeptide
polysaccharide
protein
RNA
saturated fat
starch
substrate
unsaturated fat

test your learning

Section		
4-1	1.	What elements are most commonly found in organic compounds?
4-2	2.	How many covalent bonds can a carbon atom form?
4-3	3.	What is the proportion of hydrogen to oxygen in carbohydrate molecules?
	4.	What is the empirical formula for monosaccharides?
	5.	Why are sugars biologically important?
4-4	6.	Describe the process of dehydration synthesis.
	7.	What type of compound is formed when two monosaccharides are joined by dehydration synthesis?
4-5	8.	What is a polysaccharide?
	9.	Name several polysaccharides found in plants and animals.
4-6	10.	Describe the hydrolysis reaction by which a polysaccharide can be broken down.
4-7	11.	Describe the chemical makeup of a fat.
	12.	Define the following terms: *lipid, oil, wax, fatty acid, glycerol.*
4-8	13.	What is the difference between a saturated and an unsaturated fatty acid?
	14.	What is the process of hydrogenation?
	15.	Why do many medical authorities suggest that the eating of saturated fats be limited?
4-9	16.	List several functions of lipids in living organisms.
4-10	17.	List several functions of proteins in living organisms.
4-11	18.	Show the basic structure of an amino acid.
	19.	How many different amino acids are found in proteins?
4-12	20.	Describe the formation of a peptide bond.
	21.	What is a dipeptide? A polypeptide?
4-13	22.	What structural features make possible the great variety of protein molecules?
4-14	23.	Name the two types of nucleic acids.
	24.	What are the functions of the nucleic acids?
4-15	25.	Describe the general structure of each type of nucleic acid, including the basic differences between the two.
4-16	26.	What is an enzyme, and why are enzymes important in biological reactions?
	27.	How are most enzymes named?
4-17	28.	Explain the lock-and-key model of enzyme action.
4-18	29.	Briefly describe how enzyme action is affected by the following: temperature, pH, enzyme concentration, and substrate concentration.
	30.	What is a coenzyme?

test your understanding

1. Why are the molecules of organic compounds generally much larger and more complex than molecules of inorganic compounds?
2. Discuss the functions of polysaccharides in plants and animals.
3. Why do advertisements for many margarines and cooking oils emphasize the fact that their product is polyunsaturated?
4. Name the four bases found in DNA. Explain the importance of the sequence of these bases in DNA molecules.
5. Explain the importance of enzymes in the metabolism of living cells.

independent research

1. Prepare a report on dietary sources of protein, fats, and carbohydrates.
2. Prepare a report on the role of cholesterol in diseases of the blood vessels. Include a discussion of the ongoing controversy over the role of dietary cholesterol in such diseases.
3. Illustrate or construct a model of a short segment of a DNA molecule.

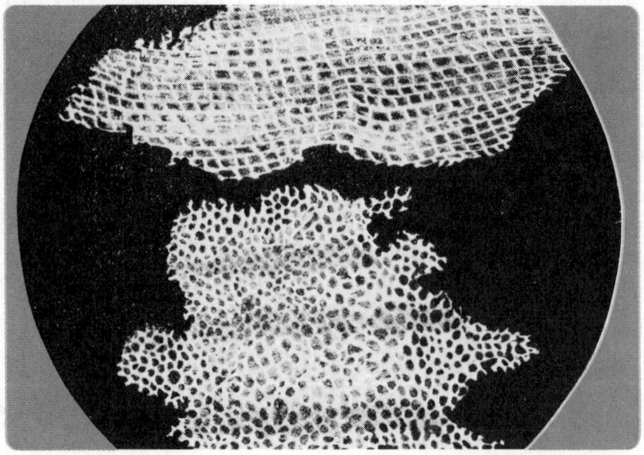

chapter 5

The Cell

THE CELL THEORY

After completing your study of this section, you should be able to:

1. Describe the contributions of the following scientists to the development of the cell theory: Robert Hooke, Anton van Leeuwenhoek, Robert Brown, Matthias Schleiden, Theodor Schwann, and Rudolf Virchow.
2. State the cell theory and explain its importance.

All living things are made up of small, individual units called **cells.** Some organisms consist of just one cell. Others contain billions of cells. In all cases, however, the life processes of the organism are actually carried on by its cells. To understand the workings of living things, we must first understand what goes on inside the cell.

5-1 Historical Development of the Cell Theory

The individual cells of most organisms cannot be seen with the naked eye. It was not until the mid-1600s that microscopes were used to study biological materials. **Robert Hooke** examined thin slices of cork and other plant tissues with a microscope and found that they were made up of boxlike structures, which he called *cells.* What Hooke saw was only the walls of dead cells. He never studied living materials in which the contents of the cells were to be seen. Hooke's findings were published in 1665 in his book *Micrographia.* The microscopes that Hooke used were compound microscopes, similar in principle to those we use today (see Figure 5-1).

However, they produced magnifications of only about 30×.

At the same time that Hooke was making and using compound microscopes, **Anton van Leeuwenhoek** (*lay*-ven-huk) was making single-lens microscopes of amazing power. Several of his microscopes still exist, and some have magnifying powers of more than 200×. Looking at drops of pond water with these microscopes, Leeuwenhoek saw living organisms that no one else had ever seen. We now know that many of them were one-celled organisms. Leeuwenhoek also observed and described human sperm cells and blood cells. In 1683 he described what must have been bacteria—the smallest kind of living cell. However, Leeuwenhoek did not know that he was seeing single cells, and he drew no conclusions about the cellular nature of organisms.

It was not until the early 1800s that the cellular nature of biological materials began to receive attention. In 1824, **Henry Dutrochet** (doo-troh-*shay*) proposed that all living things were composed of cells. However, the actual nature of living cells was still not known.

In 1831, **Robert Brown** noted that the small, dense, round body that had been observed in cells by other microscopists was a common feature of all plant cells. He called this structure the *nucleus*. The major role of the nucleus in cell function was not recognized at this time.

In 1838, **Matthias Schleiden** (*shly*-den) theorized that all plants were made up of cells. In the following year, **Theodor Schwann** (shvahn) proposed that all animals were also made up of cells. In the same year, **Johannes Purkinje** (per-*kin*-jee) used the term "protoplasm" to refer to the jellylike material that fills the cell. The last part of the cell theory was expressed by **Rudolph Virchow** (*vihr*-koh) in 1855, when he stated that all new cells arise only from existing cells.

In 1861, **Max Schultze** (shults) defined protoplasm as "the physical basis of life," and proposed that it was found in the cells of all types of organisms. At about the same time, **Felix Dujardin** (doo-zhar-*dahn*) recognized the existence of one-celled organisms. He also expressed the idea that protoplasm was associated with all forms of life. **Justus von Liebig** (*lee*-big) described protoplasm as consisting mainly of water, with the rest of the substance being proteins, fats, and carbohydrates.

By the end of the 1800s, biologists had discovered many of the structures found within the cell, including the chromosomes, which contain the hereditary information. They were also able to describe in detail the events of cell division, in which one cell divides, forming two cells.

5-2 Summary of the Cell Theory

The ideas that are generally called the **cell theory** are:

1. *All organisms are made up of one or more cells and the products of those cells.* An organism may be a single cell.

Figure 5-1. Robert Hooke's Compound Microscope.

Some organisms have structures or tissues that lose their cellular structures, becoming syncytial or coenocytic. Skeletal muscle fibers are syncytial. They are formed originally from a single cell that divides repeatedly. During development the cell membranes between daughter cells disappear, producing the multinucleate fiber. The plasmodium of many slime molds is a multinucleate mass. Multinucleate forms are also found among the red algae. Many fungi show incomplete divisions between adjacent cells.

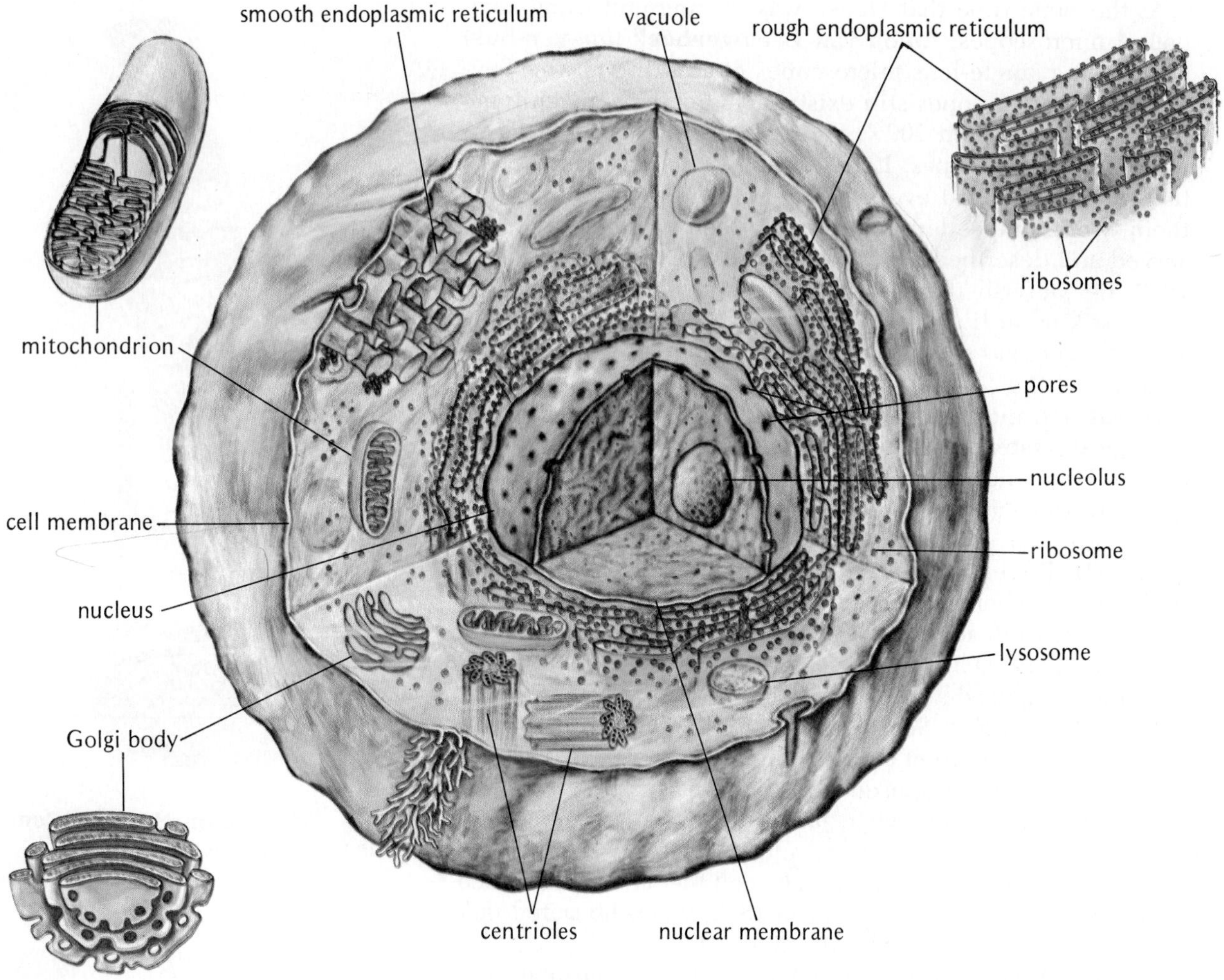

Figure 5-2. Generalized Structure of an Animal Cell.

Examples are protozoans, such as the ameba and paramecium, and bacteria. In many-celled organisms there may be intercellular material made by the cells.

2. *All cells carry on their own life activities.* The life activities of a many-celled organism are the combined effect of the activities of its individual cells.
3. *New cells can arise only from other living cells by the process of cell division or reproduction.* Reproduction of a many-celled organism is brought about by reproduction of certain of its cells.

CELL STRUCTURE

After completing your study of this section, you should be able to:

1. Describe the structures and functions of the following cell parts: cell wall, cell membrane, nucleus, and cytoplasm.

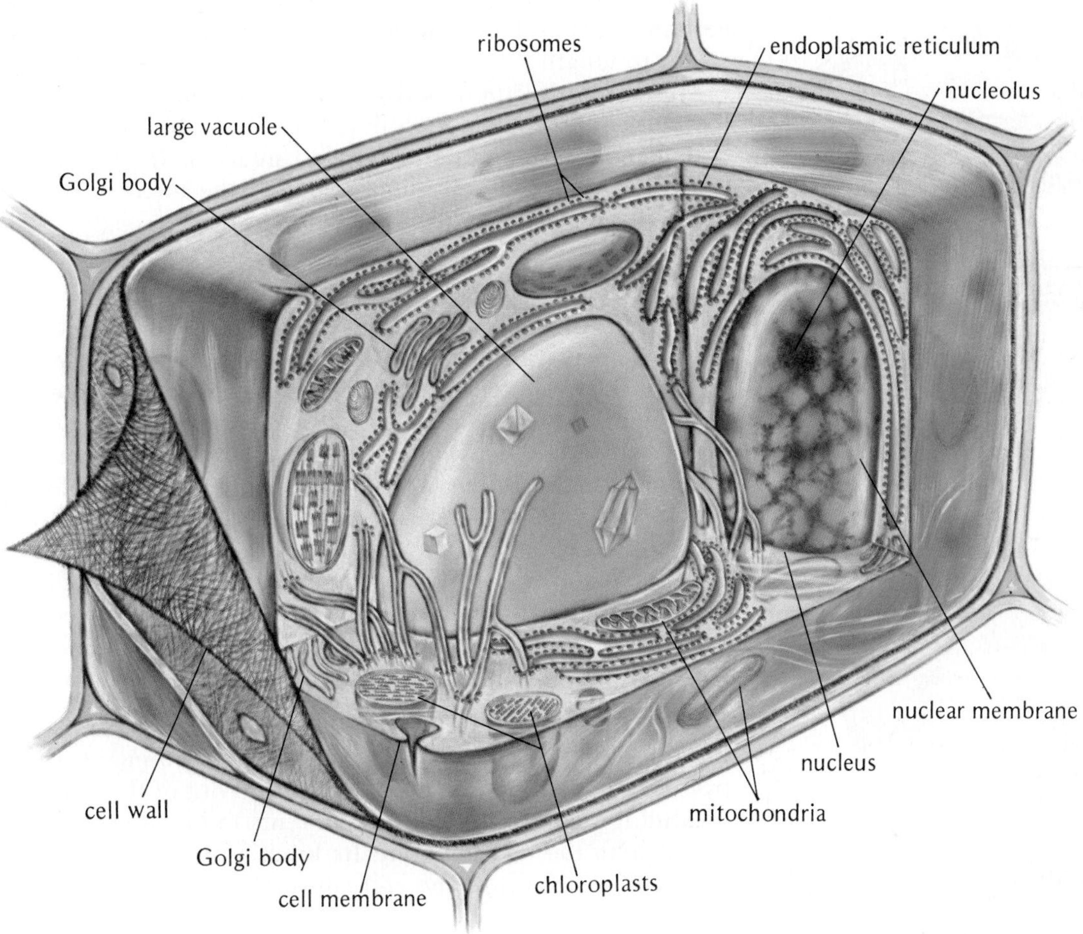

Figure 5-3. Generalized Structure of a Plant Cell.

2. Describe the structures and functions of the following cell organelles: endoplasmic reticulum, ribosomes, lysosomes; mitochondria, plastids, vacuoles, centrioles, microfilaments, microtubules, and cilia and flagella.
3. Contrast and compare the general structures of an animal cell and a plant cell.

5-3 General Characteristics of Cells

All processes necessary for life are carried on by the cells. In addition, the cells of many-celled organisms are generally highly specialized to perform specific functions. There are nerve cells that can carry messages, muscle cells that can shorten, glandular cells that produce certain substances, and so on. Figure 5-2 shows the general structure of an animal cell and Figure 5-3 shows the general structure of a plant cell. However, actual animal and plant cells will show variations from these structures.

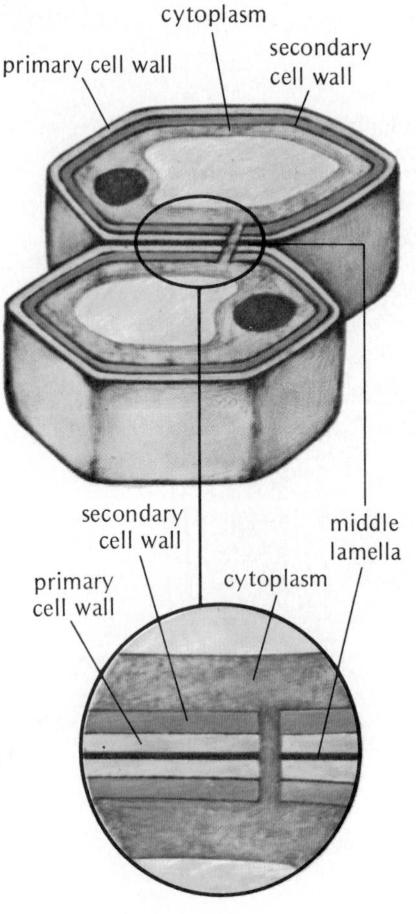

Figure 5-4. Structure of the Cell Wall. The primary cell wall, which is formed by the young plant cell, stretches as the cell grows. In the woody parts of the plant, full-grown cells produce a thick secondary cell wall inside the primary cell wall. The middle lamella is a layer that forms between adjacent cells and holds them together.

Cells vary in size and shape as well as in internal structure. Most cells are between 10 and 30 micrometers in diameter. However, chicken egg cells may be 6 centimeters across, and certain nerve cells may have extensions that are more than 1 meter in length.

All cells are surrounded by a cell membrane that separates the cell contents from the environment. All but the simplest cells contain a membrane-bounded nucleus. In all cells the space between the cell membrane and the nucleus is filled with a fluid material called the cytoplasm.

5-4 Cell Walls

The cells of plants and various microorganisms are enclosed by a rigid **cell wall,** which is outside the cell membrane. The cell wall gives the cell its shape and also provides protection (see Figure 5-4). In plants, this wall is composed largely of **cellulose** (*sel*-yuh-lohs). In other organisms it may contain other compounds. The cell wall has many small openings that allow the free passage of materials to and from the cell membrane. Thin strands of cytoplasm sometimes extend through the walls of adjacent cells, possibly allowing the direct passage of materials from one cell to another. Animal cells do not have a cell wall.

5-5 The Cell Membrane

The **cell,** or **plasma** (*plaz*-muh), **membrane** separates the interior of the cell from the surrounding environment. It controls the movement of materials into and out of the cell, thus making it possible for the cell contents to be chemically different from the environment. Its function is also to keep the internal conditions of the cell constant—to maintain homeostasis.

Permeability of the cell membrane. The cell membrane is selectively permeable, or **semipermeable** (sem-ee-*per*-mee-uh-bul). That is, some substances pass freely through it. Other substances can pass through only to some slight extent or only at certain times. And still other substances cannot pass through it at all. Through its selective permeability the cell membrane regulates the chemical composition of the cell. The semipermeable nature of the membrane results from the chemical and electrical properties of its molecules. The passage of materials through cell membranes is discussed in detail later in this chapter (page 79).

Structure of the cell membrane. The cell membrane is a two-layered structure composed of lipids and proteins (see Figure 5-5). The two layers are lipids, and the proteins are embedded in them. Some of the proteins are on the outer surface of the double membrane, some are on the inner surface, and some are thought to extend through the membrane. In electron micrographs there appears to be a light middle layer. This middle layer consists of the "tail ends" of the lipid molecules.

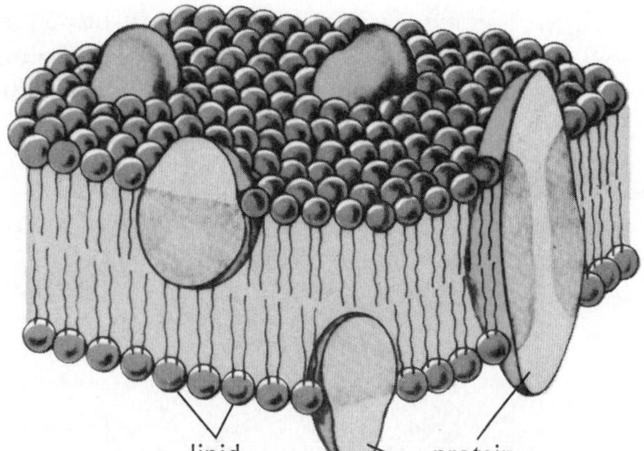

Figure 5-5. Structure of the Cell Membrane.

These ends are chemically different from the rest of the lipid molecule. They stain differently, thereby producing the appearance of a middle layer.

The proteins of the membrane are believed to be important in controlling the passage of substances through the membrane. In some cells the membrane proteins are thought to be involved in the pumping of various ions into and out of the cell. In nerve cells, they are involved in the transmission of messages, or impulses, along the cell membrane.

Pinocytosis and phagocytosis. Materials that cannot pass through the cell membrane may be taken into the cell by processes called pinocytosis and phagocytosis. In **pinocytosis** (pin-uh-sy-*toh*-sis), or "cell drinking," liquid from the surrounding medium or very small particles are taken into the cell. Where the substance is in contact with the surface of the cell membrane, the membrane forms an inpocketing or pouch (see Figure 5-6). The outer surface of the cell membrane closes over, and the pouch pinches off, forming a sac, or vacuole, within the cell. Inside the cell, the vacuole may open, releasing its contents.

In **phagocytosis** (fag-uh-sy-*toh*-sis), large particles or even small organisms are ingested into the cell. In this process, extensions of the cell called *pseudopods* (*sood*-uh-pahdz) flow around the particle to be taken in. When the particle has been surrounded, the membrane pinches off, forming a vacuole within the cell. Both phagocytosis and pinocytosis require the use of energy by the cell.

Figure 5-6. Pinocytosis. In pinocytosis, inpocketings in the cell membrane close over, leaving vacuoles in the cytoplasm.

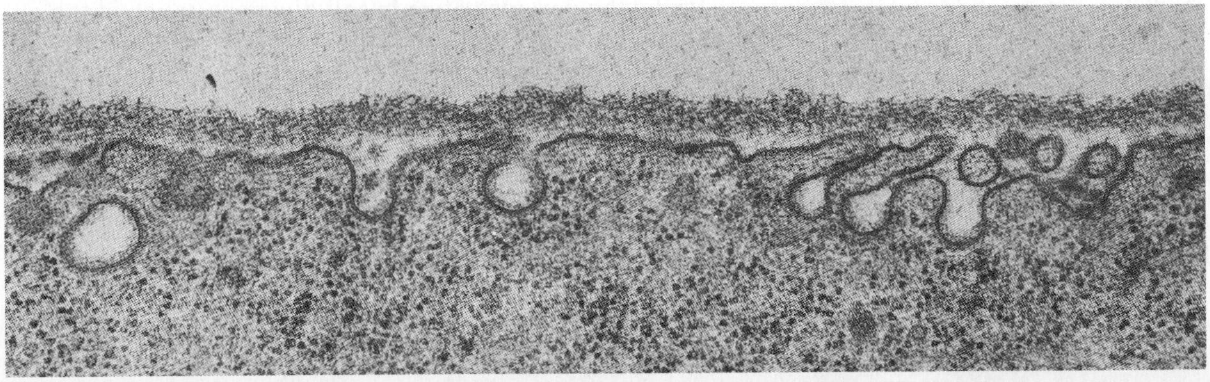

Figure 5-7. Electron Micrograph of the Cell Nucleus. The nuclear membrane and its pores are clearly visible. The round, dark structure within the nucleus is the nucleolus.

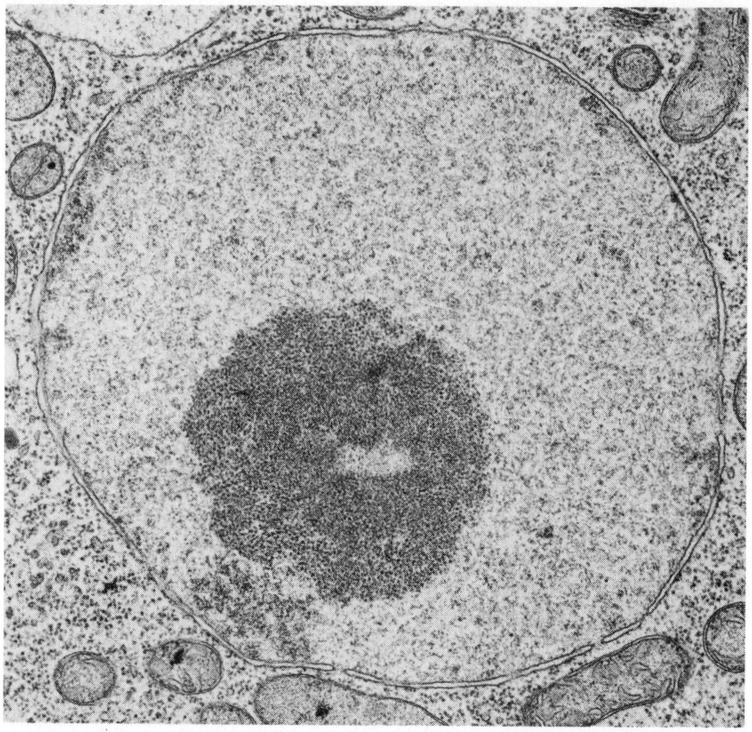

5-6 The Nucleus

The cell **nucleus** (*noo*-klee-us) is a round, dense body surrounded by a membrane (see Figure 5-7). The nucleus serves as the control center for cell metabolism and reproduction. If it is removed, the cell dies.

The nuclear membrane, like the cell membrane, is a selectively permeable double membrane. Unlike the cell membrane, the nuclear membrane has pores that can be seen in electron micrographs. The opening and closing of these pores allow the passage of certain substances into and out of the nucleus. The selective permeability of the nuclear membrane allows the contents of the nucleus to remain chemically different from the rest of the cell.

Within the nucleus are one or more **nucleoli** (noo-*klee*-uh-ly) (singular, **nucleolus**). These are dense, granular bodies that disappear at the beginning of cell division and reappear at the end. They are made up of DNA and protein. Nucleoli are the sites of production of ribosomes (see below).

During the periods between cell divisions, much of the nucleus is filled with chromatin. **Chromatin** (*kroh*-muh-tin) is the material of the **chromosomes** (*kroh*-muh-sohmz) in the form of long, very thin threads. During cell division, the chromatin shortens by coiling and becomes thick enough to be clearly visible as separate chromosomes. The chromosomes contain the hereditary material of the cell. Nucleoli are often formed at a particular location on a specific chromosome. This area is called the *nucleolar organizer*.

careers

Cytotechnologists are members of a medical laboratory team. Using microscopic and other techniques, they examine tissue sections obtained from patients for signs of cellular abnormalities. The cytotechnologist generally works under the supervision of a pathologist, a physician whose specialty is the effects of disease and injury on body tissues.

Most cytotechnologists work in hospitals or in private medical laboratories. A career as a cytotechnologist requires two years of college study, including biology courses, and a one-year course at an approved school of cytotechnology.

5-7 The Cytoplasm

All the material within the cell between the cell membrane and the nucleus is the **cytoplasm** (*syt*-uh-plaz-um). The cytoplasm is a watery material in which are dissolved many of the substances involved in cell metabolism. Many of the chemical reactions of cell metabolism take place in the cytoplasm. Also found in the cytoplasm are a variety of specialized structures called **organelles** (or-guh-*nelz*). Each type of organelle carries out a specific function in cell metabolism. We will discuss the various organelles on the following pages.

5-8 Endoplasmic Reticulum and Ribosomes

The **endoplasmic reticulum** (en-duh-*plaz*-mik rih-*tik*-yuh-lum) consists of a system of fluid-filled canals or channels enclosed by membranes. These canals generally form a continuous network throughout the cytoplasm (see Figure 5-8). The canals of the endoplasmic reticulum serve as a path for transport of materials through the cell. In addition, the membranes of the network provide a large surface area on which many biochemical reactions are thought to occur. Also, the endoplasmic reticulum divides, or partitions, the cell into compartments, making it possible for a number of different reactions to be going on at the same time.

The membranes of the endoplasmic reticulum are similar in structure to the cell membrane and nuclear membrane. It has been observed that in places the membranes of the endoplasmic reticulum are continuous with the outer portion of the nuclear membrane. There are two types of endoplasmic reticulum—*rough* and *smooth*. In rough endoplasmic reticulum, the outer surfaces of the membranes are lined with tiny particles called ribosomes. The ribosomes give the membrane a granular appearance. On smooth endoplasmic reticulum there are no ribosomes.

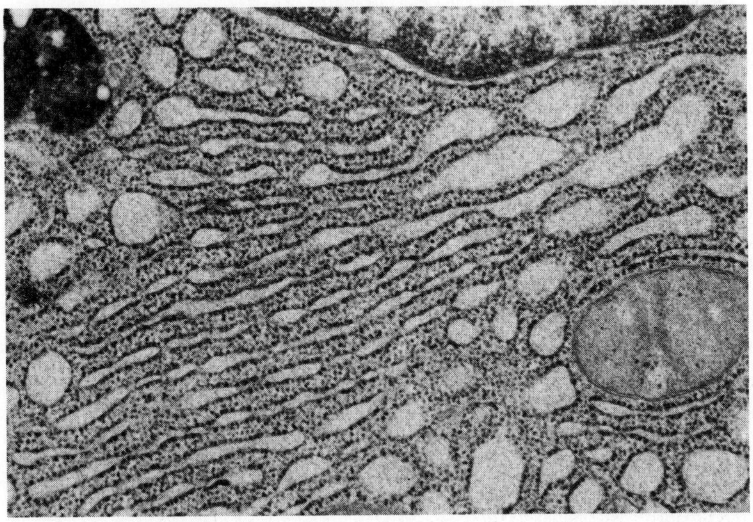

Figure 5-8. Rough Endoplasmic Reticulum. The membranes of the rough endoplasmic reticulum are lined with ribosomes.

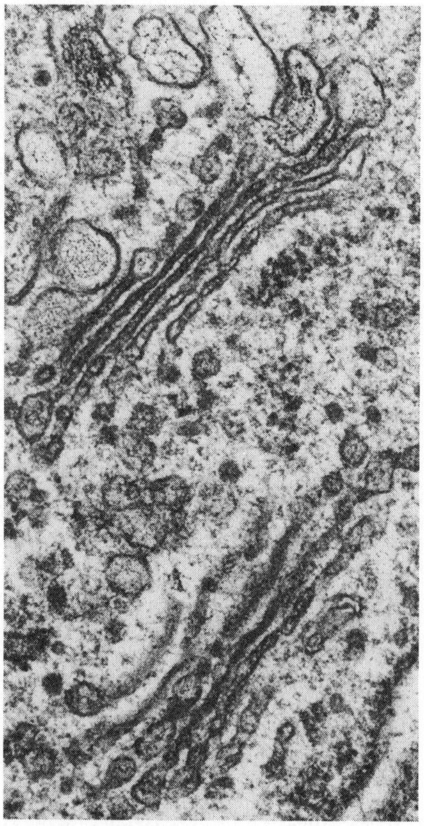

Figure 5-9. Golgi Bodies.

Ribosomes (*ry*-buh-sohmz) are the sites of protein synthesis in the cell. They are found both free in the cytoplasm and lining the membranes of the endoplasmic reticulum. In cells involved in the synthesis of proteins that are to be transported out of the cell, the ribosomes are mainly attached to the membranes of the endoplasmic reticulum. The proteins pass through these membranes into the canals, which carry them to the cell membrane and out of the cell. Where the products of protein synthesis are to be used within the cell, the ribosomes are generally free in the cytoplasm. Proteins synthesized on free ribosomes are usually enzymes that function in the cell cytoplasm.

5-9 Golgi Bodies

Golgi (*gohl*-jee) **bodies** consist of a stack of membranes forming flattened sacs and small spherical sacs, or vesicles (see Figure 5-9). Golgi bodies serve as packaging and storage centers for the secretory products of the cell. Animal cells generally have only one Golgi body, which is usually located near the nucleus. Plant cells may have up to several hundred Golgi bodies.

In some studies, connections between the Golgi body and the endoplasmic reticulum have been found. There is evidence that proteins synthesized on the ribosomes attached to the endoplasmic reticulum pass through the canals of the endoplasmic reticulum into the Golgi bodies. Here they are packaged in vesicles. The vesicles migrate to the cell surface, where their membranes fuse with the cell membrane. The materials in the vesicle are then released outside the cell. Cell secretory products other than proteins may also be packaged in the Golgi body. In plant cells, the Golgi bodies are thought to be involved in assembling materials for the cell wall.

5-10 Lysosomes

Lysosomes (*ly*-suh-sohmz) are small, saclike structures surrounded by a single membrane. These organelles contain strong digestive, or hydrolytic, enzymes. Lysosomes are thought to be produced by the Golgi bodies. They are found in most animal cells and in some plant cells. In one-celled organisms, lysosomes are involved in the digestion of food within the cell. In multicellular organisms, lysosomes serve several different functions. They break down worn-out cell organelles. In some animals they are part of the body's defense against disease. Lysosomes are present in white blood cells, which ingest disease-causing bacteria by phagocytosis. The lysosomes within the white cells break down the bacteria. Lysosomes are also involved in certain developmental processes. For example, as a frog develops from a tadpole to a mature frog, it loses its tail. Lysosomes are involved in the digestion and absorption of the tail.

5-11 Mitochondria

Mitochondria (myt-uh-*kahn*-dree-uh) (singular, **mitochondrion**) are round or slipper-shaped organelles surrounded by two membranes (see Figure 5-10). The inner membrane is highly folded, forming *cristae* (*kris*-tee) that extend into the mitochondrion itself. The cristae of the mitochondria provide a large surface area on which many biochemical reactions occur. Active cells, such as muscle cells, which use a lot of energy, contain large numbers of mitochondria. Because most of the energy needed by the cells is released in the mitochondria, this organelle is often called "the powerhouse of the cell." The process by which energy is released in mitochondria is called *cellular respiration*. Typical cells contain from 300 to 800 mitochondria, depending on their activity. Within the cell, the mitochondria are usually in motion, moving individually or in groups. They may also be found at specific locations within the cell. For example, in muscle cells, the mitochondria are found along the fibers that cause the muscle cell to contract. Mitochondria contain their own DNA and are capable of duplicating themselves.

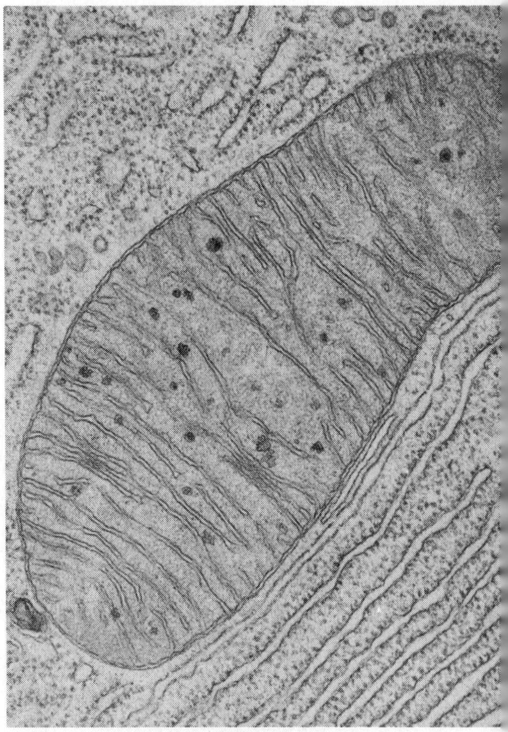

Figure 5-10. A Mitochondrion. The mitochondrion is surrounded by two membranes. Infoldings of the inner membrane form cristae.

Mitochondria may be found in clusters in the part of the cell with the highest metabolic activity. The activities of mitochondria are controlled both by nuclear DNA and by the DNA within the organelle.

5-12 Microtubules

Microtubules (my-kroh-*toob*-yoolz) are long, hollow, cylindrical structures. They are found in the cell cytoplasm, where they serve as a sort of "skeleton" for the cell, giving it shape (see Figure 5-11). They are found in centrioles, cilia, and flagella, and may also be involved in movement of the chromosomes during cell division. Microtubules are composed of a protein called **tubulin** (*toob*-yuh-lin). The molecules of this protein consist of two subunits that stack alternately in a helix. This gives the microtubule its form.

5-13 Microfilaments

Microfilaments (my-kroh-*fil*-uh-ments) are long, solid, threadlike organelles found in some types of cells. Most are composed of the protein **actin** (*ak*-tin) and are generally associated with cell movement. Microfilaments are thought to have the capacity to contract and to be involved in the movement of cytoplasm within the cell, a phenomenon known as

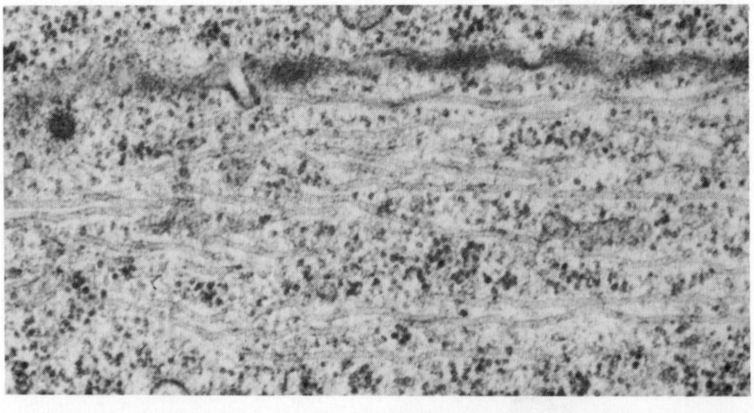

Figure 5-11. Microtubules. Microtubules are found in the cell cytoplasm and also in centrioles, cilia, and flagella.

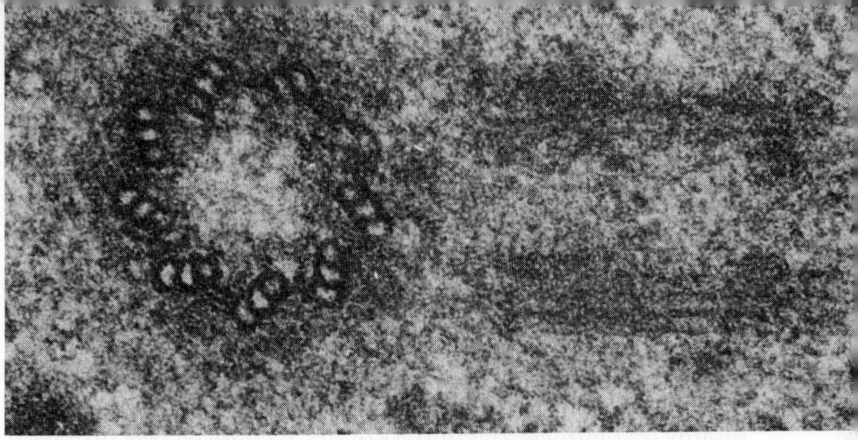

Figure 5-12. A Centriole. A centriole consists of a ring of nine groups of three microtubules.

cyclosis, or cell streaming. Actin microfilaments are also found in skeletal muscle cells and are involved in muscle contraction. Some microfilaments are not made of actin, and may serve as supporting structures for the cell.

5-14 Centrioles

Near the nucleus in animal cells there is a pair of cylindrical **centrioles** (*sen*-tree-ohlz) which lie at right angles to each other (see Figure 5-12). Each centriole consists of a ring of nine groups of three microtubules. Centrioles are involved in cell division in animal cells. They are also found in some algae and fungi, but not in plants.

5-15 Cilia and Flagella

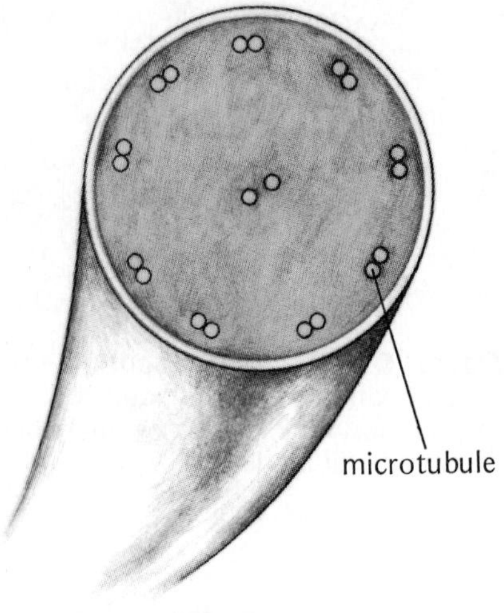

Figure 5-13. Structure of Cilia. Cilia arise from organelles called basal bodies that are structurally similar to centrioles. Each cilium contains a ring of nine pairs of microtubules with one pair of microtubules in the center.

Cilia (*sil*-ee-uh) and **flagella** (fluh-*jel*-uh) are hairlike organelles with the capacity for movement (see Figure 5-13). They extend from the surface of many different types of cells. Their structure is identical except that flagella are longer than cilia. There are usually only a few flagella on a cell, but cilia often cover the entire cell surface. In one-celled organisms, cilia and flagella are involved in cell movement. In larger, many-celled animals, ciliated cells serve to move substances over the surface of the cells.

Cilia and flagella arise from structures called *basal* (*bay*-sul) *bodies*. The structure of a basal body is similar to that of a centriole. The cilia and flagella are slightly different in structure from the basal body. They have a ring of nine pairs of microtubules, and in the center of the ring is another pair of microtubules.

5-16 Vacuoles

Vacuoles (*vak*-yuh-wohlz) are fluid-filled organelles enclosed by a membrane. Those found in plant cells are filled with a fluid called *cell sap*. In mature plant cells, there may be a single, very large vacuole that occupies most of the interior of the cell. In various microorganisms and simple animals, food is digested in special *food vacuoles* within the cells. Many of these organisms also have *contractile vacuoles* in which excess water from the cell collects. The water is periodically excreted from the cell directly into the environment. Vacuoles may also serve as storage sites for certain cell products.

5-17 Chloroplasts, Leucoplasts, and Chromoplasts

Chloroplasts, leucoplasts, and chromoplasts are all types of plastids. **Plastids** (*plas*-tidz) are membrane-enclosed organelles found in the cells of some protists and almost all plants. They are not present in the cells of animals or fungi. Like mitochondria, plastids are bounded by a double membrane and have systems of membranes within the organelle. There are three types of plastids. **Leucoplasts** (*loo*-kuh-plasts) are colorless plastids in which glucose is converted to starch, and in which starch and other plant nutrients are stored. **Chromoplasts** (*kroh*-muh-plasts) contain the pigments that give bright colors to fruits, flowers, and leaves. The pigments are synthesized within the chromoplasts. The most important type of plastids are **chloroplasts** (*klor*-uh-plasts), which contain the green pigment *chlorophyll* (*klor*-uh-fil). The chloroplasts are the site of photosynthesis, the food-making process of plants.

The inside of the chloroplast contains a system of double membranes called **lamellae** (luh-*mel*-ee) (see Figure 5-15). The lamellae form stacks called **grana** (*gray*-nuh). The pigments involved in photosynthesis are located in the membranes of the grana. The protein-containing material that fills the rest of the chloroplast is called the **stroma** (*stroh*-muh). Chloroplasts, like mitochondria, contain their own DNA and have the ability to duplicate themselves.

Like mitochondria, the activities of chloroplasts are controlled partially by nuclear DNA and partially by their own DNA. According to one hypothesis, mitochondria and chloroplasts were once free-living, primitive cells that developed a mutually beneficial relationship with other cells. This hypothesis is supported by the fact that these organelles contain their own DNA.

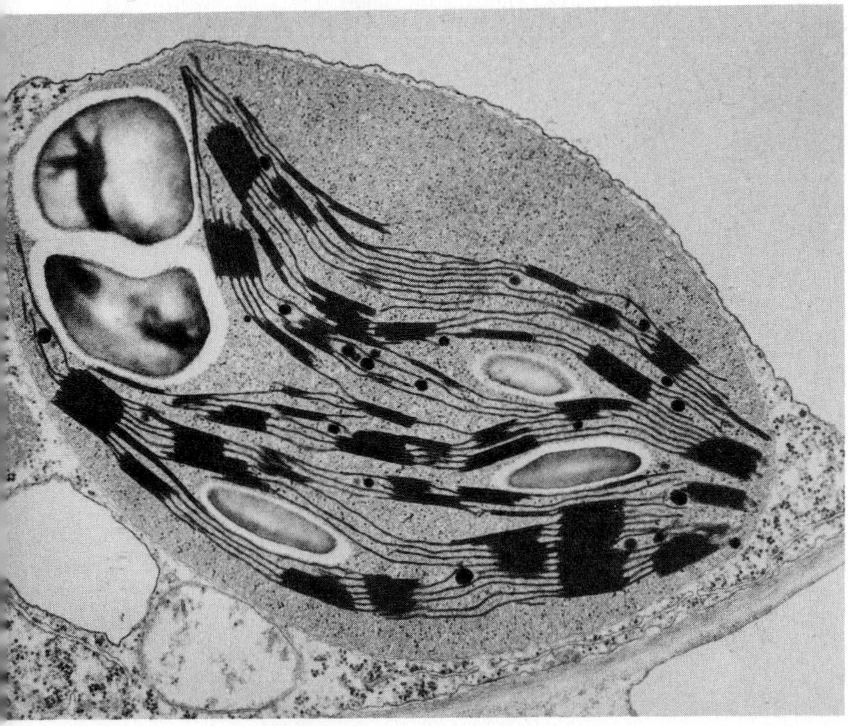

Figure 5-14. Electron Micrograph of Chloroplast. Within the chloroplast are grana, which are stacks of membranes, and large starch granules.

frontiers of biology

Since 1665 when Robert Hooke first viewed a thin slice of cork, researchers have relied on advances in microscope techniques for an increasingly detailed view of the cell. For nearly 300 years the light microscope was the basic tool for cell study. In the 1940s, the study of the cell took a giant step forward with the invention of the electron microscope.

The electron microscope can produce magnifications more than 100 times greater than the light microscope. However, materials to be viewed in standard electron microscopes must be sliced very thin (less than 0.2 micrometers). Thus, they reveal little about the structure of the cell cytoplasm, the material surrounding the nucleus and organelles. Standard electron microscope studies revealed the presence in the cytoplasm of elements that could serve as an internal "skeleton" for cell structure. These elements included microtubules, microfilaments, and fine strands of protein material.

Special high-voltage electron microscopes are now allowing researchers to view much thicker sections of biological materials, and with this has come a new view of the internal structure of the cell. These instruments are huge, weighing over 20 tons and standing more than 10 meters high. They use electrons with energies of a million electron volts, which can pass through specimens several micrometers in thickness. They can produce images of the internal structures of cells in the same way as X ray photographs show the internal structures of the body.

With the high-voltage electron microscope researchers have observed interconnected thin strands forming a three-dimensional lattice throughout the cytoplasm. This structure, called the microtrabecular lattice, is composed of fine protein filaments that can assemble and disassemble as cell conditions vary. These strands are connected to microtubules and microfilaments in the cell. The cell organelles appear to be suspended in the lattice, and it is possible that enzyme systems may also be bound to the strands of the lattice. By organizing organelles and enzyme systems the lattice would increase the efficiency of reactions occurring in the cell. It is thought that the lattice maintains the shape of the cell and plays a role in protein synthesis, cell differentiation, and the movement of materials within the cell.

The idea of the microtrabecular lattice as a structural and organizing element within the cell is still a new one. There are very few high-voltage electron microscopes being used in biological research, so there is relatively little available data on this subject.

PASSAGE OF MATERIALS THROUGH CELL MEMBRANES

After completing your study of the following section, you should be able to:

1. Relate the structure of the cell membrane to the passage of various types of substances through the membrane.
2. Describe the roles of diffusion, facilitated diffusion, and osmosis in the passage of materials into and out of cells.
3. Explain what is meant by semipermeable membrane, concentration gradient, turgor pressure, and plasmolysis.
4. Describe the effects of osmosis on cells placed in solutions containing different concentrations of water.
5. Compare passive transport with active transport.

5-18 Selective Permeability of the Cell Membrane

Certain types of substances pass through cell membranes more easily than others. For example, lipid molecules and molecules that dissolve in lipids, such as alcohol, ether, and chloroform, pass readily through cell membranes. Small molecules, such as water, glucose, amino acids, carbon dioxide, and oxygen, can pass freely through cell membranes. Large molecules, such as starch and proteins, cannot. Electrically neutral molecules enter and leave cells more easily than electrically charged ions. In addition, the permeability of cell membranes to certain substances varies from one type of cell to another. Even in the same cell, the permeability may vary from one moment to another. Thus, a given substance may pass freely through the cell membranes of one type of cell but not another, or it may pass through a cell membrane at one time, but be held back at another.

Some of the mechanisms by which substances move through cell membranes will be explained later in the chapter. Before considering these mechanisms, however, it is necessary to understand how molecules move from place to place and what determines the direction of their movement.

5-19 Diffusion

The molecules of gases and liquids are in constant motion. They move in all directions in straight lines until they collide with other molecules or the walls of their container. Collisions send them off in new directions so that their paths zigzag. As a result of this motion, the molecules of a substance tend to spread away from a region in which they are more concentrated to surrounding regions in which they are less concen-

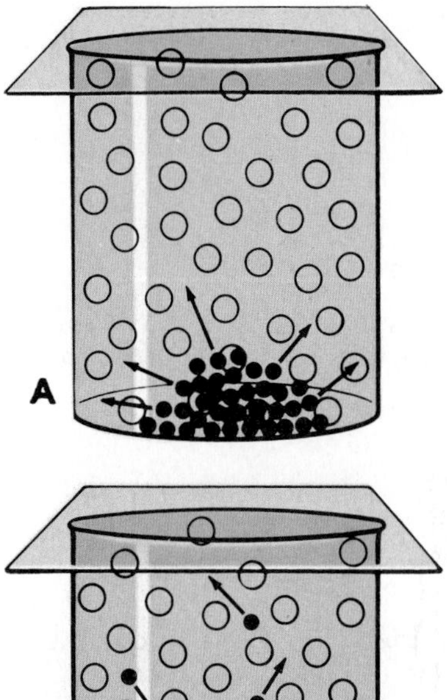

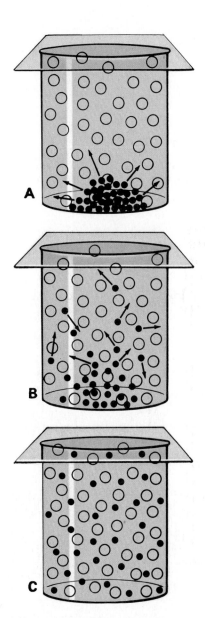

Figure 5-15. Diffusion. Because they are in constant motion, molecules in liquids and gases tend to move from regions where their concentrations are high (black dots, top) to regions where their concentrations are low (middle). This is diffusion. Eventually, the molecules become evenly distributed throughout the available space.

trated (see Figure 5-15). For example, if some instant coffee is placed at the bottom of a glass of hot water, a concentrated solution of coffee will form first near the bottom. However, the coffee molecules will gradually spread upward through the liquid. Similarly, if a perfume bottle is opened in one corner of a room, molecules of perfume will evaporate into the air near the bottle. At first, the odor will be noticeable only in the vicinity of the bottle. Eventually, the odor will spread to all parts of the room. Both of these examples illustrate the process of diffusion. **Diffusion** (dih-*fyoo*-zhun) is the movement of molecules or particles from an area of greater concentration to an area of lesser concentration. Diffusion occurs simply because the molecules are in constant random motion.

The difference in concentration between a region of greater concentration and a region of lesser concentration is called the **concentration gradient** (kahn-sen-*tray*-shun *gray*-dee-ent). Diffusion occurs only if there is a concentration gradient. As a result of diffusion the molecules eventually become evenly distributed throughout the available space. At this point no further change in concentration occurs. The molecules are still in motion, but there are now as many molecules moving out of any given area as are moving into the area. Such a situation is called an **equilibrium** (ee-kwuh-*lib*-ree-um). In the example with instant coffee in hot water, equilibrium is reached when every drop of water in the glass contains the same amount of coffee.

Diffusion is important in the movement of molecules into and out of cells. Depending on the concentration gradient, certain materials will either enter or leave cells by diffusion. Let us consider the role of diffusion in a cell that is using oxygen and producing carbon dioxide during respiration.

Both oxygen and carbon dioxide will be in solution inside the cell and also in the liquid medium surrounding the cell membrane. As the cell uses the oxygen dissolved in its cytoplasm, the concentration of oxygen inside the cell will decrease. The concentration outside the cell will at first not be affected. Therefore a concentration gradient toward the inside of the cell will develop across the cell membrane. As a result, there will be a net diffusion of oxygen into the cell. The opposite situation will develop with respect to carbon dioxide. As the cell produces carbon dioxide, its concentration inside the cell increases, while its concentration outside remains the same. Therefore a concentration gradient for carbon dioxide develops across the cell membrane toward the outside of the cell. A net diffusion of carbon dioxide out of the cell occurs. If the concentration gradients of oxygen and carbon dioxide were reversed, then oxygen would leave the cell and carbon dioxide would enter. Thus, the process of diffusion plays an important role in the entry and exit of molecules in living cells. It should be noted that several substances may be diffusing through the cell membrane at the same time.

5-20 Facilitated Diffusion

Some molecules diffuse through cell membranes at a faster rate than can be explained by diffusion alone. There is evidence that some of the proteins in the cell membrane have hollow centers that act as channels through the membrane. By twisting in one direction or the other, these protein channels may open wider or close down. When the channels are open, certain molecules are able to diffuse quickly through them. This process, which apparently makes temporary openings or pores in the cell membrane, is called **facilitated** (fuh-*sil*-uh-tay-ted) **diffusion.** Facilitated diffusion works only in the direction of the concentration gradient. It speeds up the normal movement of molecules from a region of higher concentration to one of lower concentration.

5-21 Osmosis

Up to this point we have been considering the diffusion of substances dissolved in water. A water solution is simply a mixture of water molecules and molecules of the dissolved substance. Water molecules are small. They can pass freely through a semipermeable membrane, just as other small molecules do. Therefore, water itself will diffuse through cell membranes. The direction of this diffusion will depend only on the concentration of water on opposite sides of the membrane. The diffusion of water across a semipermeable membrane from a region of high concentration of water to a region of low concentration of water is called **osmosis** (os-*moh*-sis).

What do we mean by the "concentration" of water? The meaning is the same as for any other substance—it is the amount of water present in a given volume.

Since two things cannot occupy the same space at the same time, the number of particles dissolved in a given amount of water determines the concentration of water molecules present. The concentration of water molecules is highest in pure water—water with nothing else in it. The more particles dissolved in a solution, the fewer the water molecules present in a given volume. For example, the concentration of water is higher in 100 ml of pure water than it is in 100 ml of a water and sugar solution.

Figure 5-16 shows an experiment that demonstrates osmosis. The glass bulb of a thistle tube is filled with a concentrated sugar solution. The bulb is then tightly covered with a semipermeable membrane of cellophane or sausage tubing, and placed in a jar of pure water. The membrane has pores through which the water molecules, but not the sugar molecules, can pass. The water concentration in the jar is 100 percent. The water concentration in the thistle tube is lower because the sugar solution contains fewer water molecules than the same volume of pure water. Since the water molecules can pass through the membrane, they move from

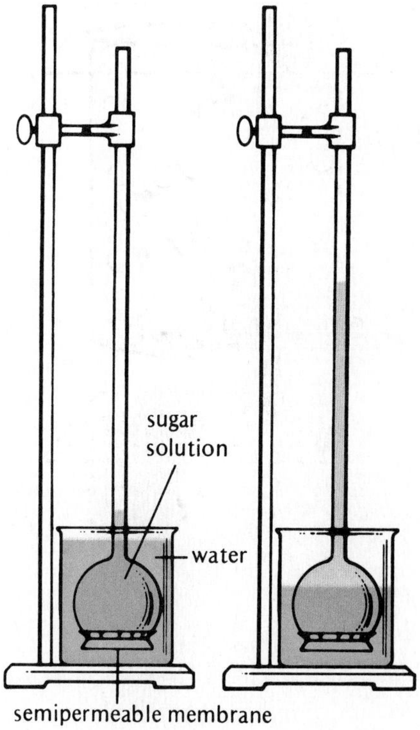

Figure 5-16. Demonstration of Effects of Osmosis. A thistle tube containing a concentrated sugar solution and covered with a semipermeable membrane is put in a beaker of pure water (left). The sugar molecules cannot pass through the semipermeable membrane, but the water molecules can. Water enters the thistle tube by osmosis, and the solution rises in the tube (right).

the area of higher concentration (the jar of pure water) to the area of lower concentration (the sugar solution in the thistle tube). As osmosis occurs, the level of liquid in the thistle tube rises.

5-22 Osmotic Pressure

In the osmosis experiment in Figure 5-16, the water eventually stops rising in the thistle tube. The reason for this is that rates of diffusion depend on pressure as well as concentration. If the difference in pressure between the two sides of the membrane increases, the rate of diffusion of water from the high-pressure side to the low-pressure side increases. As the water-sugar solution rises in the thistle tube, its weight results in increased pressure on the inside of the membrane. This increasing pressure causes the water to diffuse back across the membrane at a faster rate. Finally, an equilibrium is reached. Water molecules are still passing into the thistle tube because of the concentration gradient across the membrane. But they are passing out at the same rate because of the pressure gradient in the opposite direction. Thus there is no net change in the amount of water inside the thistle tube, and the water level in the tube remains constant. There is, however, a steady excess of pressure inside the thistle tube. This increased pressure resulting from osmosis is called **osmotic** (os-*mah*-tik) **pressure.**

5-23 Effects of Osmosis

The cytoplasm of cells consists mainly of water containing a wide variety of dissolved substances. Water can pass freely through the cell membrane in both directions. Whether there is a net movement of water into or out of the cell depends on the concentration gradient—whether there is a higher concentration of water on one side of the cell membrane than the other. Let us consider what happens to cells placed in solutions containing different concentrations of water (see Figure 5-17).

An **isotonic** (i-suh-*tahn*-ik) **solution** is one that has the same concentration of dissolved substances as a living cell placed in it. The concentration of water molecules in the cell and in an isotonic solution is the same. Since the concentration gradient is zero, there is no net gain or loss of water by the cell.

A **hypotonic** (hy-puh-*tahn*-ik) **solution** contains a lower concentration of dissolved substances than the cell. The concentration of water molecules is therefore higher in the hypotonic solution than it is in the cell. Since the concentration of water is higher outside the cell than inside, there is a net movement of water into the cell by osmosis. Animal cells swell and burst when placed in a hypotonic solution because of the osmotic pressure produced by the water that enters. When a plant cell is placed in a hypotonic solution, the excess water collects in the large vacuole, which swells to fill most of the interior of

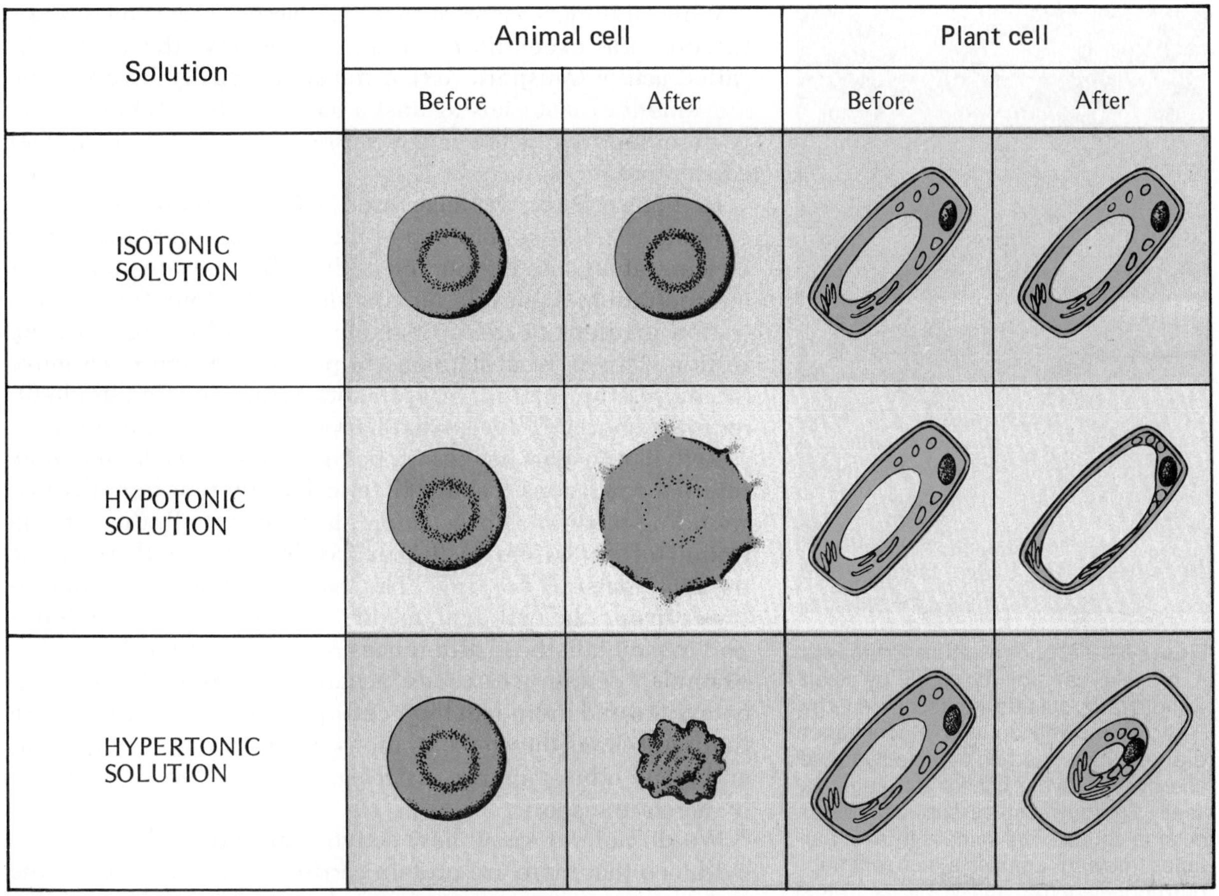

Solution
Animal cell
Plant cell
Before
After
Before
After
ISOTONIC SOLUTION
HYPOTONIC SOLUTION
HYPERTONIC SOLUTION

Figure 5-17. Effects of Osmosis on Living Cells. Cells placed in isotonic solutions show no osmotic effects. Cells placed in hypotonic solutions gain water. An animal cell swells; the vacuole in a plant cell expands. Cells placed in hypertonic solutions lose water. Animal cells shrink; the cytoplasm of plant cells contracts.

the cell. The rest of the cell contents are pushed against the strong, inflexible cell wall. This pressure in a plant cell is called **turgor** (*ter*-ger) **pressure.**

A **hypertonic** (hy-per-*tahn*-ik) **solution** contains a higher concentration of dissolved substances than the cell. The concentration of water molecules in a hypertonic solution is therefore lower than that of the cell. The concentration gradient results in a net movement of water out of the cell. Animal cells shrink when placed in a hypertonic solution. When a plant cell is placed in a hypertonic solution, the cytoplasm contracts into a ball within the cell wall. The shrinking of cytoplasm by osmosis is called **plasmolysis** (plaz-*mah*-luh-sis).

5-24 Passive and Active Transport

In diffusion and osmosis, no cellular energy is used to move substances into or out of the cell. Because these processes move materials across cell membranes without the expenditure of cellular energy, they are called **passive transport.** Numerous substances move into and out of the cell by passive transport, with the direction of movement determined only by the concentration gradient.

Figure 5-18. Concentration Gradients. A bicycle can roll downhill by itself, without any outside source of energy. Particles moving down a concentration gradient also need no outside supply of energy. A bicycle cannot roll uphill by itself. Energy must be supplied by an outside source. The same is true for particles moving against a concentration gradient—energy must be supplied from an outside source.

When the movement of materials across a cell membrane requires the expenditure of cellular energy, the process is called **active transport.** Active transport usually involves the movement of materials against a concentration gradient, that is, from an area of lower concentration to an area of higher concentration.

In Figure 5-18, we have used a hill to represent a concentration gradient. The top of the hill represents the higher concentration, and the bottom of the hill represents the lower concentration. A bicycle moving downhill along the concentration gradient needs no outside source of energy to keep rolling. This is what happens in passive transport. To move the bicycle up the hill, or against the concentration gradient, requires energy. This is what happens in active transport.

Active transport makes it possible for cells to maintain internal conditions that are chemically different from the surrounding medium. For example, in a nerve cell, the concentration of potassium is higher inside the cell than in the medium outside the cell. The concentration of sodium is lower inside the cell than outside. The cell uses active transport to maintain these differences in concentration. As another example, certain seaweeds accumulate minerals, such as potassium and iodine, in their cells in concentrations that are a thousand times the concentrations in ocean water. In humans and many other animals, wastes are removed from the blood by active transport.

We do not yet know how active transport works. There is evidence that there are protein carriers in the cell membrane that can transport certain molecules against a concentration gradient. This process, however, requires energy. It must therefore be coupled in some way to the production of energy in the cell.

ORGANIZATION OF CELLS IN LIVING THINGS

After completing your study of this section, you should be able to describe and compare the levels of organization and specialization in unicellular, colonial, and multicellular organisms.

5-25 Unicellular and Colonial Organisms

A cell, which is the smallest unit showing the characteristics of life, may exist alone, or it may be part of a larger organism made up of many cells. A cell that exists independently is regarded as a one-celled, or **unicellular, organism.** Many-celled, or **multicellular, organisms** may be made up of thousands, millions, or billions of cells.

Unicellular organisms are able to carry on all the life processes. They synthesize and obtain nutrients, break them down for energy, synthesize new materials, reproduce, and so on. Unicellular organisms include bacteria, protozoa, many algae, and some fungi. These organisms vary widely in size and in complexity of structure.

The simplest multicellular organisms are colonial forms, which consist of from a few cells to thousands of cells attached together. In some colonies, the cells are all alike, and each cell carries on all its own processes. Such colonies are like a group of unicellular organisms that are stuck together. Any of the cells has the capacity to reproduce and form a new colony.

In more complex colonies, the cells show specialization. That is, the cells forming the colony vary in their structure and function. Volvox, for example, forms spherical colonies that can include many thousands of cells (see Figure 5-19). However, only about twenty of these cells are capable of reproducing and forming new colonies. These are large cells found at the back of the colony. In the front of the colony are smaller cells containing large, light-sensitive organelles. These cells control the positioning and movement of the colony in the water. The cells of a volvox colony are connected together by thin strands of cytoplasm that run between them.

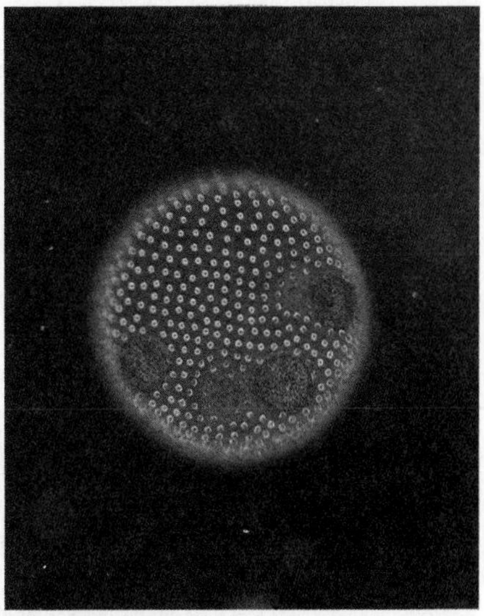

Figure 5-19. Volvox Colony.

5-26 Complex Multicellular Organisms

Cells. True multicellular organisms consist of millions or billions of cells of many different types. With organisms of increasing size and complexity, specialized structures are required to carry out the life processes and various other activities. Even millions of cells functioning individually are not adequate to perform these tasks. Thus, in more complex organisms, specialized cells are organized into larger units for the performance of certain functions in addition to their own life processes.

Tissues. In multicellular organisms, a group of cells that are structurally similar and perform the same function forms a tissue. Each cell in a tissue carries on its own life processes, but it also carries on some special processes related to the function of the tissue. In plants there are tissues that transport water and nutrients throughout the plant, tissues that cover and protect the parts of the plant, tissues that contain chloroplasts and carry on photosynthesis, and so on. The structures and functions of plant tissues are discussed in Chapter 18 (page 294). Complex multicellular animals contain a greater variety of tissues than plants, and many of these tissues are more highly specialized than plant tissues.

Table 5-1 lists the main types of tissues found in animals. Most animal tissues are a form of either epithelial tissue or connective tissue. Muscle, nerve, and blood are highly specialized tissues that do not belong to either of these groups.

Epithelial tissues cover body surfaces and line body cavities and organs. They also form glands. They are generally in the form of sheets of closely packed cells. The simplest epithelial

Type of tissue	Structure	Functions	Location
Epithelium (epithelial tissue)	Cells arranged in sheets one or more cell layers in thickness	Protection (outer layer of skin) Absorption (inner lining of intestine) Secretion (glands)	Lines cavities Covers surfaces Forms glands
Connective tissue	Consists of cells and fibers embedded in a formless "ground sub-substance," or matrix	Support of other tissues, including epithelium, and of organs Connects or binds tissues and organs together	Throughout body
Adipose tissue	Specialized ovoid fat cells in connective tissue fibers	Adipose connective tissue stores fat	Throughout body; found in large numbers in some areas
Bone and cartilage		Bone and cartilage are connective tissues that make up the skeleton. They support the body and give it form, and, with muscles, are responsible for movement.	Bone: found in skeleton Cartilage: found in skeleton, trachea, outer ear, nose
Blood	Specialized connective tissue—matrix is fluid	Transport of nutrients, wastes, oxygen, and carbon dioxide throughout body	Within vessels of the circulatory system
Nerve tissue	Consists of specialized cells, called neurons, which are bound together by connective tissue to form nerves	Conduction of impulses	Nerves and sense receptors throughout body
Muscle tissue	Individual cells or fused cells bound together by connective tissue to form bundles or sheets	Skeletal muscle: voluntary movement of body part Smooth muscle: involuntary movement of internal organs Cardiac muscle: makes up heart and is responsible for beating of heart	Skeletal muscles Internal organs Heart

Table 5-1. Types of Animal Tissues.

tissues consist of sheets only one cell layer thick. More complex forms consist of several cell layers. Sheets of epithelial tissues generally rest on a network of fibers that form a basement membrane. The basement membrane supports the sheets of cells.

Connective tissues support other body tissues and bind tissues and organs together. They give the body form. In connective tissues, unlike epithelial tissues, the cells are widely separated. The space between them is filled with various types of substances. For example, in bone, the bone-producing cells secrete the hard, bony material, which fills the spaces between the cells. In tendons, which connect muscles to bones, there are dense bundles of tough elastic fibers.

Muscle tissues are specialized for contraction, or shortening. There are three types of muscle tissues. Cardiac muscle tissue is found only in the heart. Skeletal muscle tissue makes up the muscles that are attached to the bones of the skeleton. Movement of these muscles is under voluntary control by the animal. Smooth muscle tissue is found in various organs of the body, such as the stomach, intestines, and blood vessels. Contraction of smooth muscles is involuntary and automatic. (Skeletal and smooth muscle are discussed in Chapter 13.) The structure and function of blood is discussed in Chapter 10. The structure and function of nervous tissue is discussed in Chapter 14.

Organs and organ systems. A group of tissues that works together to perform a specific function forms an **organ.** The eye, which contains nerves, light-sensitive cells, muscles, and blood vessels, is an organ.

A group of organs that work together to perform a specific function forms an **organ system.** An example of an organ system is the digestive system, which includes the mouth, esophagus, stomach, intestines, pancreas, liver, etc.

Although the parts of a multicellular organism can be described in terms of separate cells, tissues, organs, and organ systems, all these parts must function together for the organism to carry on its life processes.

summary

Cells are the basic units of structure and function in living things. As stated in the cell theory, all living things are made up of cells, and all cells arise from preexisting cells. All cells are surrounded by a semipermeable cell membrane and are filled with a fluid material called cytoplasm. All but the simplest cells contain a distinct, membrane-bounded nucleus.

The cells of plants and various microorganisms are surrounded by a rigid cell wall, which supports and protects the cell. In cells of other organisms the cell membrane is the outermost structure. This membrane controls the passage of materials into and out of the cell. The cell nucleus contains the hereditary material, the chromosomes, and the nucleolus, which is involved in the production of ribosomes.

Within the cytoplasm are various types of specialized structures, the organelles. The major organelles include the endoplasmic reticulum, which transports material from the cell; the ribosomes, which are the site of protein synthesis; Golgi bodies, which function in the storage and packaging of cell secretions; mitochondria, which are the site of cell respiration; plastids, which include chloroplasts, the site of photosynthesis; and lysosomes, which contain digestive enzymes. Cilia and flagella are hairlike organelles that extend from the cell surface and are capable of movement.

The movement of materials through cell membranes takes place by diffusion, osmosis, and processes involving active transport. Diffusion is the movement of molecules or particles from an area of greater concentration to an area of lesser concentration. It occurs because the molecules are in random motion. Osmosis is the diffusion of water across a semipermeable membrane from a region of high concentration of water to a region of low concentration of water.

Diffusion and osmosis are both types of passive transport. Passive transport processes take place without the expenditure of energy by the cell. In active transport, on the other hand, the movement of materials across the cell membrane is accomplished only with the expenditure of energy by the cell.

Organisms that consist of only one cell are unicellular, while those consisting of many cells are multicellular. The simplest multicellular organisms are colonies, which consist of a number of similar cells attached together. In complex multicellular organisms, most cells are specialized, both in structure and in function. Groups of similar cells that work together to perform a specific function form tissues. Groups of tissues that work together to perform a certain function form organs. Groups of organs working together to perform a certain function form organ systems.

vocabulary

active transport
cell
cell membrane
cell theory
cell wall
centriole
chloroplast
chromatin
cilia
concentration gradient
cytoplasm
diffusion
endoplasmic reticulum
equilibrium
facilitated diffusion
flagellum
Golgi body
hypertonic solution
hypotonic solution
isotonic solution
lysosome
microfilament
microtubule
mitochondrion
nucleolus
nucleus
organ
organ system
osmosis
osmotic pressure
passive transport
phagocytosis
pinocytosis
plasma membrane
plasmolysis
plastid
ribosome
semipermeable
tissue
turgor pressure
vacuole

test your learning

Section

5-1 **1.** Briefly describe the contributions of Hooke, van Leeuwenhoek, Brown, Schleiden, Schwann, and Virchow to the development of the cell theory.

5-2 **2.** State the cell theory.

5-3 **3.** What structure surrounds all cells?

4. What fluid material fills space within the cell?

5-4 **5.** What is the cell wall of plants composed of?

6. Describe the functions of the cell wall.

5-5 **7.** What is the function of the cell membrane?

8. What is a semipermeable membrane?

9. Describe the structure of the cell membrane.

10. Describe the processes of pinocytosis and phagocytosis.

5-6 **11.** What is the function of the nucleus?

12. Describe the structure of the nucleus.

13. How does the nuclear membrane differ from the cell membrane?

14. Describe the structure of the nucleolus and explain its function.

5-7 **15.** What are the functions of the cytoplasm?

5-8 **16.** Describe the structures and functions of smooth and rough endoplasmic reticulum.

17. What is the function of the ribosomes?

5-9 **18.** Describe the structure and function of Golgi bodies.

5-10 **19.** Describe the structure and functions of lysosomes.

5-11 **20.** Describe the structure and function of a mitochondrion.

21. How are new mitochondria thought to be formed in a cell?

5-12 **22.** What function do microtubules serve in the cell cytoplasm?

23. Describe the structure and chemical makeup of a microtubule.

5-13 **24.** Describe the structure and function of microfilaments.

5-14 **25.** What substructures make up a centriole, and how are these substructures arranged?

26. What types of cells contain centrioles, and what function do the centrioles serve?
5-15 27. Compare the structures of cilia and flagella.
28. Compare the functions of cilia and flagella.
5-16 29. What are vacuoles, and what functions do they serve in plant cells, in animal cells, and in microorganisms?
5-17 30. Name the three types of plastids, and briefly give the functions of each.
31. Describe the internal structure of a chloroplast.
5-18 32. What kinds of molecules pass easily through a cell membrane?
5-19 33. Define the terms *diffusion*, *concentration gradient*, and *equilibrium*.
34. What role does diffusion play in the passage of materials across the cell membrane?
5-20 35. Briefly explain the process of facilitated diffusion.
5-21 36. Define the term *osmosis*.
5-22 37. What is osmotic pressure?
5-23 38. Briefly describe what happens to cells placed in a hypotonic solution. A hypertonic solution. An isotonic solution.
5-24 39. What is the difference between passive transport and active transport?
40. Why is active transport important in maintaining the biochemical composition of the cell?
5-25 41. Explain what is meant by unicellular and colonial organisms, and give an example of each.
5-26 42. Describe the level of cellular organization in a complex, multicellular animal.

test your understanding

1. Describe the structures and the physical processes that determine the biochemical composition of the cell and its organelles.
2. Compare the role of the concentration gradient in diffusion, osmosis, facilitated diffusion, and active transport. Which of these processes require the expenditure of energy by the cell?
3. Name the structures within the cell that have the capacity to reproduce themselves.
4. How do colonial organisms differ from multicellular organisms?

independent research

1. Select one of the cytoplasmic organelles, and prepare an in-depth report on its structure and functions.
2. Prepare a report on the transport of substances through the cell membrane. Include recent theories on the relationship between the molecular structure of the membrane and the passage of materials across it.
3. Prepare a report on the structure of a complex colonial organism, such as the Portuguese man-of-war.

chapter 6

Classification of Living Things

6-1 Chapter Introduction

There are approximately 1.5 million different kinds of living organisms known today, and each year several thousand more are identified. Some experts believe that there may be as many as 10 million different kinds of organisms in existence. They vary in form from bacteria 5 micrometers in diameter to redwood trees over 100 meters tall.

To deal with this huge number of diverse organisms, biologists identify and name them according to an established international system. This makes it much easier for scientists to communicate with one another about the types and characteristics of living things. The branch of biology that deals with the classification and naming of living things is **taxonomy** (tak-*sahn*-uh-mee).

CLASSIFICATION

After completing your study of this section, you should be able to:

1. Explain the function of classification systems.
2. Describe the history of taxonomy, including the works of Aristotle, Theophrastus, John Ray, and Carolus Linnaeus.
3. List in order from broadest to narrowest the classification categories used in modern biology.
4. Explain the system of nomenclature used in modern biology.

5. Explain how the modern view of a species differs from the earlier view.
6. Describe the types of evidence used by taxonomists to determine relationships between groups of organisms.
7. Use a taxonomic key to identify an unknown organism.

Figure 6-1. Organization in a Supermarket. Think of how long you could search for a single item if all the products in a supermarket were arranged randomly.

6-2 Classification Systems

The function of any classification system is to allow you to find the object or information you are looking for without checking every item in a large group. In many situations that we deal with every day, objects or information is organized or classified into groups. To help you understand what is involved in classification, let us consider the arrangement of goods in a supermarket.

A large supermarket carries 7,000 to 10,000 items (see Figure 6-1). If these items were placed on the shelves at random, shopping for the week might take an entire day, or even longer. However, finding the items you need can be done in a relatively short time because related items are arranged together in groups. First, items are grouped into broad categories, such as frozen food, meat, produce, cleaning supplies, paper goods, and dairy products. Each of these departments is subdivided into a series of smaller related categories. For example, the frozen food department has separate sections for vegetables, juices, cakes, fish, TV dinners, and ice cream. Each of these sections is further subdivided. The ice cream section is divided into half-gallons, quarts, pints, and cups. Within each size range, the ice cream may be grouped by flavor.

Figure 6-2. An Early Classification System. Aristotle grouped organisms as air-dwellers, land-dwellers, and water-dwellers.

Once you are familiar with the organization of the supermarket, it is easy to locate a particular item. Or if the market manager gets a new kind of frozen cake, it is a simple matter to place it with the other frozen cakes. In a similar manner, the classification system used in modern biology enables biologists to identify an organism and place it in its proper group with related organisms.

6-3 Early Classification Schemes

In all early attempts at classification, living things were separated into two major groups—the plant kingdom and the animal kingdom. These two groups were then subdivided in various ways. In the Bible, for example, plants were divided into grasses, herbs, and trees, while animals were classified as fish, creeping creatures, fowl, beasts, and cattle.

In the 4th century B.C., the Greek philosopher **Aristotle** (*ar*-uh-stot-ul) made a study of animals; another philosopher, **Theophrastus** (thee-uh-*fras*-tus), studied plants. Aristotle grouped animals mainly according to the kind of environment in which they lived. Thus there were air-dwellers, land-dwellers, and water-dwellers (see Figure 6-2). Theophrastus grouped plants according to stem structure. Thus there were herbs with soft stems, shrubs with several woody stems, and trees with a single woody stem. Using these crude subdivisions of the plant and animal kingdoms, these two men identified and classified more than 500 kinds of plants and 500 kinds of animals.

The classification systems of Aristotle and Theophrastus worked only for the relatively small number of organisms en-

countered in everyday life. However, during the 1400s and 1500s, explorers such as Columbus, Magellan, and Vasco de Gama returned home from their travels with many new types of organisms. The development of the microscope in the 1500s led to the discovery of many new organisms not visible to the unaided eye. As the number of different known organisms increased, the need for a more effective classification system became clear.

The next major advance in classification was made in the mid-1600s by the English naturalist **John Ray.** In his travels through England and Europe, Ray identified and classified more than 18,000 different types of plants. He also classified the members of several different animal groups. Ray was the first to use the term **species** (*spee*-sheez) for each different kind of organism. Ray defined a species as a group of organisms that were structurally very similar and that passed these characteristics on to their offspring (see Figure 6-3). Closely related species were included together in a broader group called a **genus** (*jee*-nus) (plural, genera) (see Figure 6-4). Related genera were arranged, in turn, in still broader groups.

Figure 6-3. Varieties of Cats. The Persian cat (left), Siamese cat (center), and alley cat (right) all belong to the same species, *Felis catus.*

Figure 6-4. Closely Related Species of the Genus *Canis*. These animals belong to different, closely related species, but to the same genus. (A) The German shepherd dog is *Canis familiaris;* (B) the wolf is *Canis lupus;* (C) the coyote is *Canis latrans;* and (D) the dingo is *Canis dingo.*

A

B

C

D

Figure 6-5. Categories in the Modern Classification System.

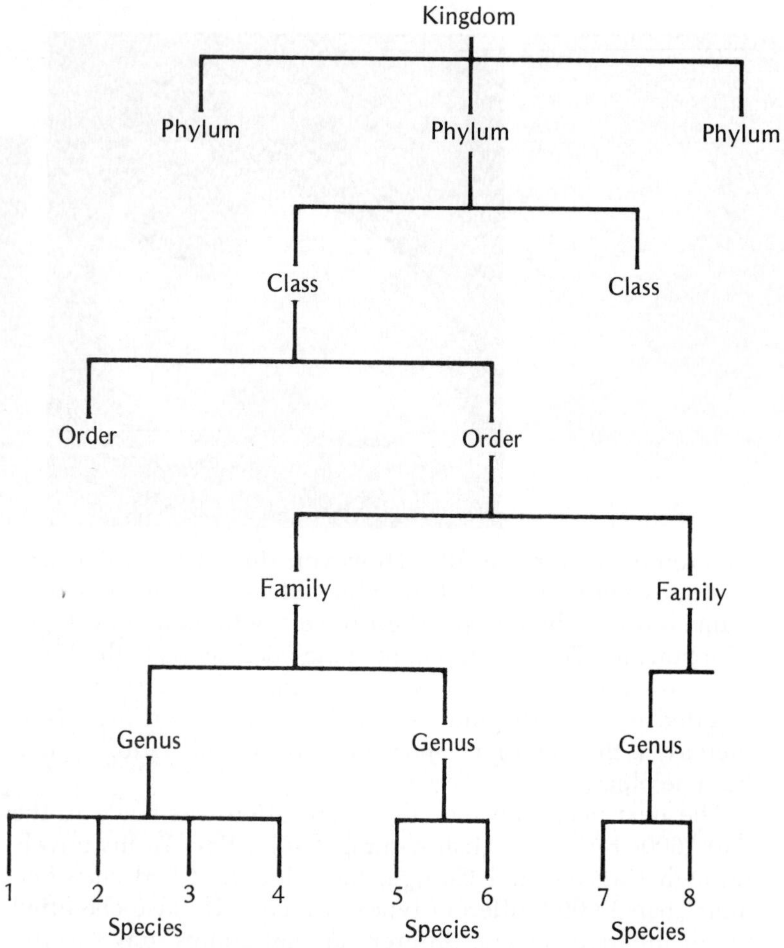

The Swedish botanist **Carolus Linnaeus** (luh-*nee*-us) is generally recognized as the founder of modern taxonomy. Linnaeus established methods for classifying and naming organisms that are still used. In his highly workable system, plants and animals were arranged in such a way that they could be identified easily. Like Ray, Linnaeus used structural similarities as a basis for his classification system.

6-4 Classification Categories

Classification categories are sometimes subdivided. For example, a phylum may be divided into several subphyla.

Between the time of Linnaeus and the present, taxonomists have added several categories to the classification system. The broadest and most inclusive category is the kingdom. The narrowest category is the species. In classifying living things, biologists now use the following categories: **kingdom, phylum** (*fy*-lum) (plural, phyla), **class, order, family, genus,** and **species.**

As shown in Figure 6-5, related species are grouped in a genus; related genera are grouped in a family; related families are grouped in an order; related orders are grouped in a class; related classes are grouped in a phylum; and related phyla are grouped in a kingdom. Each species—that is, each type of

Category	Human	Chimpanzee	Dandelion	Housefly
KINGDOM	Animalia	Animalia	Plantae	Animalia
PHYLUM	Chordata	Chordata	Tracheophyta	Arthropoda
CLASS	Mammalia	Mammalia	Angiospermae	Insecta
ORDER	Primates	Primates	Asterales	Diptera
FAMILY	Hominidae	Pongidae	Compositae	Muscidae
GENUS	*Homo*	*Pan*	*Taraxacum*	*Musca*
SPECIES	*Homo sapiens*	*Pan troglodytes*	*Taraxacum officinale*	*Musca domestica*

Table 6-1. Classification of Some Familiar Organisms.

organism—belongs to one kingdom, one phylum, one class, one order, one family, and one genus. Table 6-1 shows the complete classification for several different species.

6-5 Nomenclature

The system for naming organisms is called **nomenclature** (*noh*-men-klay-chur). The modern system for naming organisms was devised by Linnaeus. Before Linnaeus, each species was identified by its genus name followed by a number of Latin words that described the species. In some cases a string of eight or ten words followed the genus name. In his books, Linnaeus identified each species by its genus name followed by only one descriptive word (both in Latin). Within each genus, no two species could be described by the same word. This is the system that is still in use.

This two-word system of identifying each kind of organism is known as **binomial** (by-*noh*-mee-ul) ("two names") **nomenclature.** It is equivalent to our system of using two names to identify a person—a family name and a given (or first) name. The genus name is like a person's family, or last, name, while the species name is like his or her first name.

In modern biology, each kind of organism has a two-word Latin name, which is its scientific name. The first word is its genus name, the second identifies the species within that genus. Most large plants and animals also have common names. However, for several reasons these names are not suitable for scientific use. For one thing, common names are often confusing and inexact. A starfish, for example, is not a fish. Also, one species may have several different common names. The blue jay *Cyanocitta christata* is also known as the blue coat, the corn thief, and the nest robber. In other cases, the same common name is used for two or more different species. More than a dozen different species of plants are commonly known as raspberries. Finally, common names vary from language to language. An English "dog" is a Spanish "perro" and a Japanese "inu." However, the scientific name *Canis familiaris* is understood by biologists everywhere.

6-6 Taxonomic Keys

A **taxonomic key** is a tool used to identify and classify organisms. Most keys consist of a series of paired statements, each describing a certain characteristic. These characteristics are generally the presence or absence of certain structures. For example, an animal may or may not have a spinal column. If it has a spinal column, it may or may not have lungs. If it has lungs, its body may or may not be covered with hair. If it has hair, its posture may or may not be erect, and so on. By choosing from a series of paired characteristics, an unknown organism can be placed in successively smaller groups until, through the process of elimination, it is either finally identified as a member of a known species or established as a previously unknown species. Of course, it is necessary to arrange the key statements so that they apply to smaller and smaller groupings. A key would not work if a minor difference were applied before a major one. For example, examining the body of an animal for hair must not be done before looking for a spinal column and all the other listed distinctions. To see how a key works, use the key in Figure 6-6 to identify the leaves on page 97.

Figure 6-6. A Taxonomic Key for the Identification of Leaves.

To identify the leaves on page 97, use the following classification key. Begin at the top of the key with items 1A and 1B. Choose the statement that best describes the leaf. At the end of that statement, there is a number in parentheses, which refers to the number of the next pair of choices you should go to. Again, choose between the paired statements. If another number is indicated, proceed to that pair of statements, and choose between them. Eventually, the name of the tree will follow the statement. Continue this process until all the leaves have been identified.

1A. Leaves needlelike (2)
1B. Leaves broad with flattened blade (6)
- **2A.** Needles up to 2.5 cm long: yew *(Taxus canadensis)*
- **2B.** Needles 5 cm or longer (3)

3A. Needles 5 to 12.5 cm long (4)
3B. Needles more than 12.5 cm long (5)
- **4A.** Needles in clusters of two: Scotch pine *(Pinus sylvestris)*
- **4B.** Needles in clusters of four or five: white pine *(Pinus strobus)*

5A. Needles in clusters of two: black pine *(Pinus nigra)*
5B. Needles in clusters of three: ponderosa pine *(Pinus ponderosa)*
- **6A.** Leaves divided into separate leaflets (little leaves) (7)
- **6B.** Leaves in one piece, no leaflets (8)

7A. Leaves with five to seven leaflets, bottom pair smallest: shagbark hickory *(Carya ovata)*
7B. Leaves with thirteen to forty-one leaflets; edges of leaflets with one or two coarse teeth: tree of heaven *(Ailanthus altissima)*
- **8A.** Leaf edge smooth, lacking saw-teeth or lobing: flowering dogwood *(Cornus florida)*
- **8B.** Leaf edge saw-toothed, wavy, or lobed (9)

9A. Leaves saw-toothed; veins like barbs on a feather: beech *(Fagus grandifolia)*
9B. Leaves three to five lobes; veins radiating from central point: sugar maple *(Acer saccharum)*

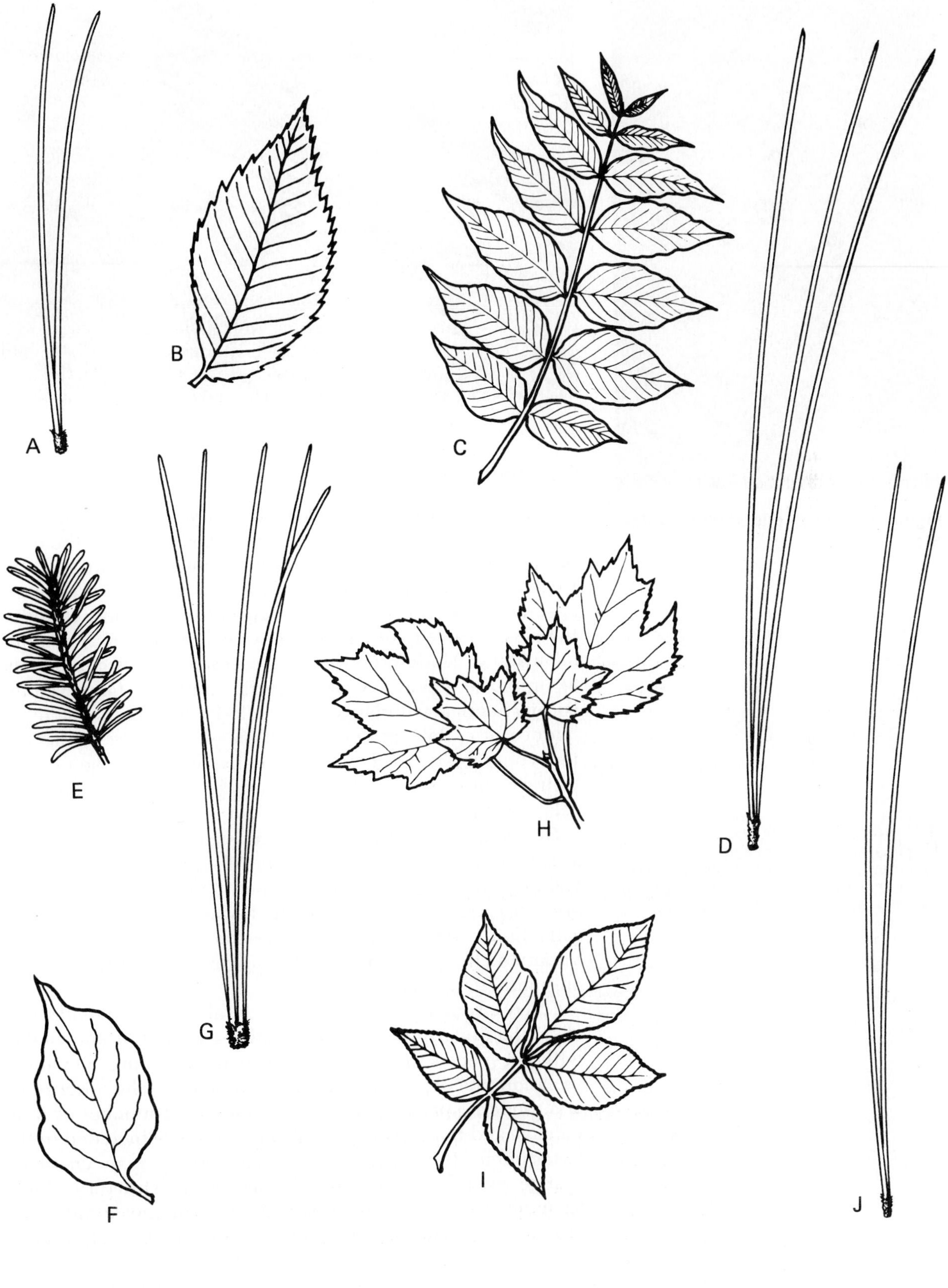
A
B
C
D
E
F
G
H
I
J

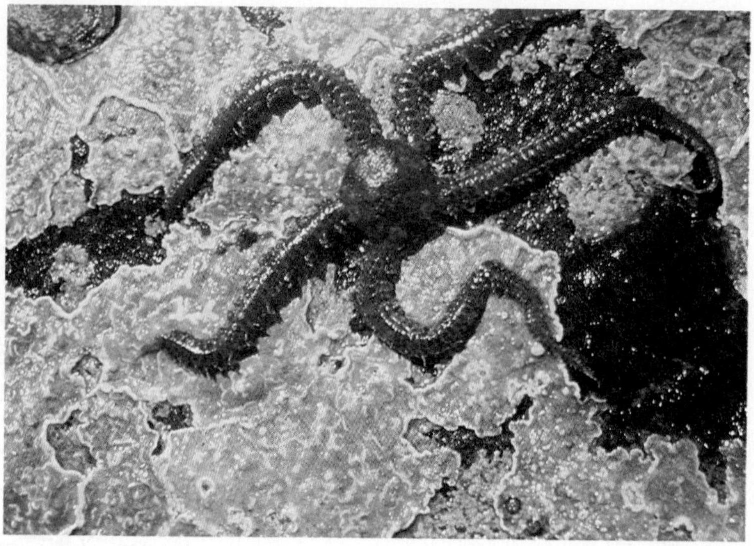

Figure 6-7. Fossil and Modern Brittle Star.

6-7 Modern Taxonomy

Evidence used in classification. In early systems of classification, species were organized into larger groups on the basis of structural similarities. Structural similarities are still the first thing considered in deciding how to classify different species. However, these are often not enough to determine the closeness of relationships. Physical features may even be misleading. Modern taxonomists use other kinds of evidence to support the evidence of structural similarity. One example is biochemical similarity, particularly the amino acid sequence of certain proteins. Another is similarity in the patterns of embryo development. Fossils, which are the remains or traces of extinct organisms, may also provide evidence of relationships between species (Figure 6-7).

Modern taxonomic systems are based on the theory of evolution. Related organisms share a common ancestor at some point in their evolution. The more recent the divergence from the common ancestral form, the closer the relationship.

Definition of a species. In the past, each species was viewed as a constant and unchanging form. The description of an animal or plant species was based on a single specimen, called a *type specimen.* This type specimen was placed in a museum collection, where it served as the standard for that species. Variations from the type specimen were considered to be of only minor significance.

Today a species is viewed as a natural group, or *population,* of similar organisms that interbreed in nature. It is known that within a species there may be a considerable range of natural variation (the organisms are not all identical). The description of a modern species is therefore based on a number of individuals, and the most important variations are included in the description. It is also known that species may gradually change over long periods of time. From structure alone, taxonomists may find it difficult to say whether a particular group of organisms is one species whose members show great variation, or whether the group is actually two or more species. This problem is resolved by using the modern definition of a species. If the organisms interbreed in nature, they belong to the same species.

MAJOR TAXONOMIC GROUPS

After completing your study of this section, you should be able to name the five kingdoms used in classification in this book, and give a brief description of each.

6-8 Kingdoms of Organisms

In all early classification schemes, living things were divided into two major groups, or kingdoms—plants and animals. This system works well with large organisms. Trees, grass, flowers, and shrubs are obviously plants, while frogs, fish, insects, birds, and cats are obviously animals. However, some organisms show both plantlike and animal-like characteristics. The euglena, for example, is a unicellular organism that carries on photosynthesis like a plant and moves about by means of a flagellum like an animal. It is difficult to assign such organisms to one kingdom or the other.

To solve the problem of classifying organisms that are not distinctly animals or plants, taxonomists have added new kingdoms to the modern classification systems. However, there is no general agreement as to how many additional kingdoms are needed and which organisms should be placed in them. Each possible arrangement has some advantages and some disadvantages. There does not seem to be any completely satisfactory way of classifying the simplest organisms.

Table 6-2. Organization of the Five-Kingdom Classification System.

CHARACTERISTICS OF THE FIVE KINGDOMS*					
Characteristics	Monera	Protista	Fungi	Plantae	Animalia
Nuclear membrane	Absent	Present	Present	Present	Present
Mitochondria	Absent	Present	Present	Present	Present
Ability to perform photosynthesis	Some do	Some do	No	Yes	No
Ability to move	Some motile, some not	Some motile, some not	No	No	Yes
Body form	Unicellular	Unicellular or Multicellular	Unicellular or Multicellular	Multicellular	Multicellular
Reproductive structures	Unicellular	Unicellular	Multicellular	Multicellular	Multicellular
Nutrition	Absorption, photosynthesis, or chemosynthesis	Absorption, photosynthesis, or ingestion	Absorption	Photosynthesis	Ingestion
Nervous system	Absent	Absent	Absent	Absent	Present
Example	Bacteria, blue-green algae	Protozoa	Fungi	Plants	Animals

*In the four-kingdom system, the fungi are classified as plants. In the three-kingdom system, some protists are classified as animals, while the rest of the protists and the fungi are classified as plants.

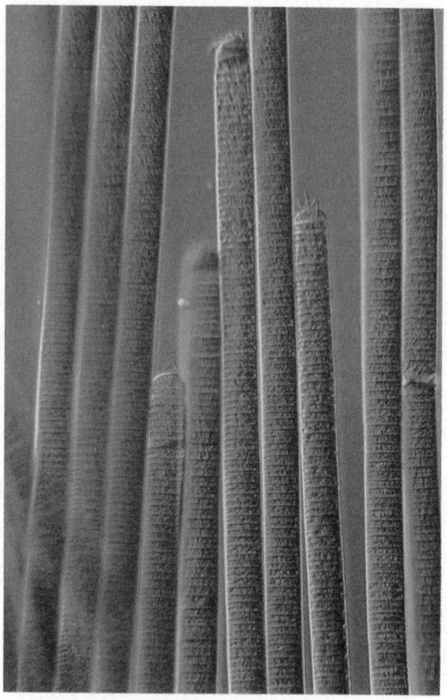

Figure 6-8. **Representative of the Kingdom Monera.** Blue-green algae of the genus *Oscillatoria* form chains of connected cells.

Figure 6-9. **Representative of the Kingdom Protista.** A colony of two species of stentors, which are protozoans.

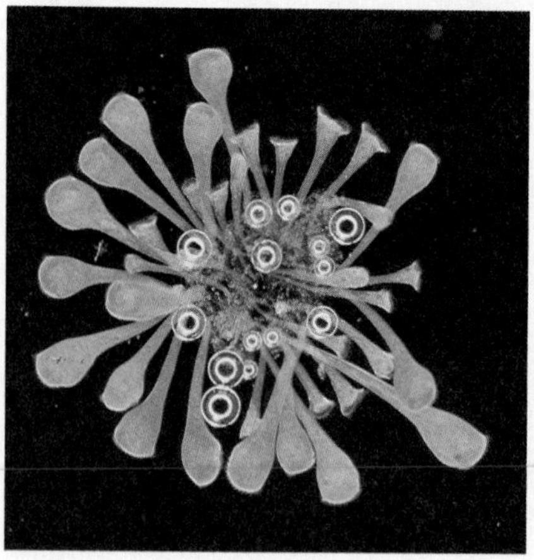

In this book we use a five-kingdom system of classification. The five kingdoms are Monera, Protista, Fungi, Plantae, and Animalia. This system emphasizes certain very basic differences among large groups of organisms. It also simplifies somewhat the classification within the kingdoms. The general characteristics of the five kingdoms are described briefly in the following sections (also see Table 6-2).

6-9 Kingdom Monera

The distinguishing characteristic of members of the kingdom **Monera** (muh-*ner*-uh) is that their cells do not have an organized nucleus with a nuclear membrane. These organisms are mostly unicellular, although some form chains, clusters, or colonies of connected cells. The cells lack most of the organelles found in other cell types, such as mitochondria, Golgi bodies, and lysosomes. The kingdom Monera includes only two phyla—the bacteria and the blue-green algae (*al*-jee). Most bacteria do not carry on photosynthesis and must obtain nutrients from the environment. Blue-green algae, on the other hand, do contain chlorophyll and carry on photosynthesis (see Figure 6-8). However, the chlorophyll is not in chloroplasts within the cells.

6-10 Kingdom Protista

Like the monerans, members of the kingdom **Protista** (proh-*tist*-uh) are either unicellular or very simple multicellular organisms (see Figure 6-9). Unlike the monerans, protist cells contain a membrane-bounded nucleus and many different types of organelles. There are many different types of protists. Among the more important ones are several groups of algae, which resemble plants in having cells with cell walls; the *protozoa* (proh-tuh-*zoh*-uh), which resemble animals in being able to move around and in lacking cell walls; and the euglenalike organisms, which are like protozoa but can carry on photosynthesis.

6-11 Kingdom Fungi

The members of the kingdom **Fungi** (*fun*-jy) are a unique group of organisms (see Figure 6-10). In the past, members of this group were usually included in the plant kingdom. However, differences between the fungi and plants have led many biologists to place the fungi in a separate kingom. Fungi contain no chlorophyll and cannot synthesize their own food. Some fungi are unicellular, while others have an unusual multicellular form. The cells of the fungi have a distinct nucleus surrounded by a nuclear membrane and many different organelles.

Figure 6-10. Representative of the Kingdom Fungi. Chicken-of-the-woods is a brightly colored fungus.

6-12 Kingdom Plantae

The plants, members of the kingdom **Plantae** (*plan*-tee), include the mosses, liverworts, and vascular plants (see Figure 6-11). Unlike monerans, protists, and fungi, almost all plants show a true tissue and organ level of organization. Plants cannot move around from place to place on their own. Nearly all plants carry on photosynthesis. The chlorophyll in plant cells is found in chloroplasts.

6-13 Kingdom Animalia

Animals, members of the kingdom **Animalia** (an-uh-*mal*-yuh), generally show an organ and organ system level of organization. During at least some part of their life cycle, most animals can move about from place to place on their own. Animals do not carry on photosynthesis, and they must obtain

Figure 6-11. Representatives of the Kingdoms Plantae and Animalia. The daisy is a plant, while the katydid is an insect, a member of the animal kingdom.

COMPARISON OF PLANTS AND ANIMALS.		
Characteristic	Plants	Animals
nutrition	Most are autotrophs–photosynthetic	Heterotrophs
motility	Nonmotile	Usually motile during at least one stage of development
cell structure	Cell wall, chloroplasts, and large vacuoles present; centrioles lacking	Lack cell wall, chloroplasts, and large vacuoles; small vacuoles and centrioles present
body structure	Only a few types of organs present; no organ systems	Many types of organs present; organs organized into organ systems
growth pattern	Rate of growth and shape of organism depend on environmental conditions and vary within wide limits	Size and shape of adult closely regulated and vary within narrow limits
sensitivity	Lack nervous system or specialized sensory organs; responses to stimuli are slow and limited	Nervous system and sensory organs present; very responsive to stimuli

Table 6-3. Characteristics of Plants and Animals.

food from the environment. The characteristics of plants and animals are shown in Table 6-3.

A more complete list of the taxonomic groups is found on pages 682 - 684.

summary

The branch of biology that deals with the classification and naming of living things is taxonomy. Early attempts at classification divided living things into two major groups—plants and animals. These large groups were then subdivided in various ways.

Carolus Linnaeus established methods for classifying and naming organisms so that they could be easily identified. His system of classification was based on the presence of structural similarities among related organisms. Linnaeus identified each species by two Latin names—its genus name plus a single descriptive species name. His system of binomial nomenclature is still in use.

In modern classification, organisms are classified in graded series of categories. From the broadest to the narrowest these categories are: kingdom, phylum, class, order, family, genus, and species.

In the five-kingdom system of classification, the kingdoms are: Monera, which includes bacteria and blue-green algae; Protista, which includes the protozoa, some of the algae, and slime molds; Fungi; Plantae, which includes red, brown, and green algae, mosses, liverworts, and vascular plants; and Animalia.

Modern taxonomists view a species as a natural group of similar organisms that interbreed in nature. Within such a population, there may be considerable variation among the members.

vocabulary

Animalia
binomial nomenclature
class
evolution
family
fossil
Fungi
genus
kingdom
Monera
nomenclature
order
phylum
Plantae
Protista
species
taxonomic key
taxonomy

test your learning

Section

6-1 **1.** What branch of biology deals with the classification and naming of organisms?

6-2 **2.** Why is it helpful to identify, classify, and name all types of organisms?

6-3 **3.** Briefly describe the systems of classification of Aristotle, Theophrastus, John Ray, and Carolus Linnaeus.

4. Who was the first to use the term *species* to refer to each type of organism?

6-4 **5.** List the modern classification categories in order from the narrowest to the broadest.

6-5 **6.** Explain the system of binomial nomenclature.

6-6 **7.** Explain briefly how a taxonomic key is used.

6-7 **8.** What types of evidence are used by modern taxonomists in determining relationships between different types of organisms?

9. What is the modern definition of a species?

6-8 **10.** Why have modern taxonomists added new kingdoms in their classification schemes?

6-9 **11.** What are the distinguishing characteristics of members of the kingdom Monera? Name two members of this group.

6-10 **12.** Describe the basic characteristics of members of the kingdom Protista. Name several members of this group.

6-11 **13.** Describe the basic characteristics of fungi.

6-12 **14.** Describe the basic characteristics of plants.

6-13 **15.** Describe the basic characteristics of animals.

test your understanding

1. Using sources other than this textbook, give the complete classification from phylum through species for a honeybee and a sugar maple.
2. Besides the starfish, which is mentioned in Section 6-5 of the text, can you think of five other organisms whose common names are misleading and not in agreement with their correct classification?
3. Why are all dogs considered to be members of the same species?
4. Why is the system of binomial nomenclature, in which each type of organism has two Latin names, so useful to biologists?

independent research

1. Use a field guide to identify three different types of trees or birds in your area.
2. Write a report discussing the advantages and disadvantages of the two-, three-, four-, and five-kingdom systems of classification.
3. Write a report on the use of similarities in protein structure in determining relationships between groups of organisms.

UNIT 2
ANIMAL MAINTENANCE

chapter 7

Cellular Respiration

CHAPTER INTRODUCTION

After completing your study of this section, you should be able to define the term *cellular respiration* and explain the importance of this process for living organisms.

7-1 The Release of Energy

All living things need a continuous supply of energy to carry on their life activities and thus stay alive. Some of this energy is needed for physical or mechanical work. A flying bird needs energy just as an airplane does. A beaver building a dam, or a worm burrowing in the soil, needs energy just as construction or earth-moving equipment does. Even tree frogs singing on a spring evening use energy just as a transistor radio does. Most movements of living things require energy. Energy is also needed for less obvious purposes. The synthesis of complex compounds from simpler ones usually requires chemical energy. As we saw in Chapter 5, the transfer of materials across cell membranes may also require energy.

In recent years we have all become conscious of the importance, and the cost, of energy for doing the work of our industrial civilization. Although some of this energy is obtained from falling water (hydroelectric power plants), some from nuclear energy, and some directly from solar radiation, most of it comes from the burning of fuels, such as oil, gas, and coal. Burning a fuel releases energy in the form of heat and light. The heat can then be used to run engines and electric generators, turning the heat energy into other forms of energy. The burning of fuel is a chemical process in which carbon and hydrogen in the fuel combine with oxygen from the air, forming carbon dioxide and water. The fuels contain stored chemical energy, which is released mostly as heat during the chemical changes of burning.

7-2 Energy for Living Things

Living things rely upon chemical energy stored in their food. Carbohydrates are the foods most commonly broken down for energy. This energy is released, in most cases, by chemical changes resembling burning. However, organisms cannot use energy in the form of heat. The energy released by the breakdown of food must be preserved in chemical form. Only in this form can it be used to perform some necessary function, such as movement, synthesis, or active transport. Energy in the form of heat is usually wasted energy. Excessive heat will damage or kill most organisms. For that reason, the breakdown of food and the release of energy in living organisms does not occur by direct reaction between the carbohydrates and oxygen. Instead, it occurs in a series of many small chemical steps.

The release of energy stored in food is accomplished inside the individual cells of every organism. The entire process is called **cellular respiration.** In this chapter we will examine the process by which the cell releases energy from food and makes it available for the life functions of the cell itself and for the organism as a whole.

STORAGE AND TRANSFER OF ENERGY

After completing your study of this section, you should be able to:

1. Describe the role of ATP in energy transfer and storage in the cell.
2. Explain where the energy for ATP production comes from in the cell.
3. Define the terms *oxidation* and *reduction*.
4. Explain what happens in an oxidation-reduction reaction.
5. Explain the function of hydrogen acceptors in cellular respiration.

7-3 ATP and ADP

Energy released during cellular respiration is not used directly. It is first "packaged" in molecules of a compound called *adenosine triphosphate* (uh-*den*-uh-seen try-*fahs*-fayt), abbreviated **ATP.** Figure 7-1 shows the structure of the ATP molecule. The main part of the molecule is composed of a molecule of adenine joined to a molecule of ribose. Adenine is one of the nitrogen bases found in DNA and RNA. Ribose is the 5-carbon sugar found in RNA. The combination of the two

sidelights

Although humans and most other mammals must maintain a constant body temperature, bats, woodchucks, chipmunks, and some other small mammals withstand the low temperatures of winter by hibernating. They spend the winters sleeping in burrows or nests. Their body temperatures drop almost to freezing, and their metabolic rates drop almost to zero. In ground squirrels, for example, the rate of heartbeat drops from 350 beats per minute to 3 or 4 during hibernation.

Animals that hibernate store food in their bodies in the form of fat over the summer. During hibernation they may lose half their body weight as the stored food is used for cellular respiration.

Recent research indicates that hibernation is controlled by a protein in the blood, which has been called HIT (for hibernation induction trigger). It is thought that HIT is produced in the brains of hibernating animals. When the substance isolated from the brain of a hibernating ground squirrel was injected into the bloodstream of a rat, the rat's body temperature dropped 10° and its rate of oxygen consumption dropped 35%. Similar effects have been observed on monkeys and other animals.

It is possible that studies on hibernation could eventually lead to various medical applications, for example in heart surgery, where the body temperature of the patient must be lowered to slow the heartbeat.

Although ATP is the compound most commonly involved in the storage and transfer of energy, other compounds also have the capacity to transfer phosphate groups and can serve the same function. These compounds include phosphoenolpyruvate, acetyl phosphate, and creatine phosphate.

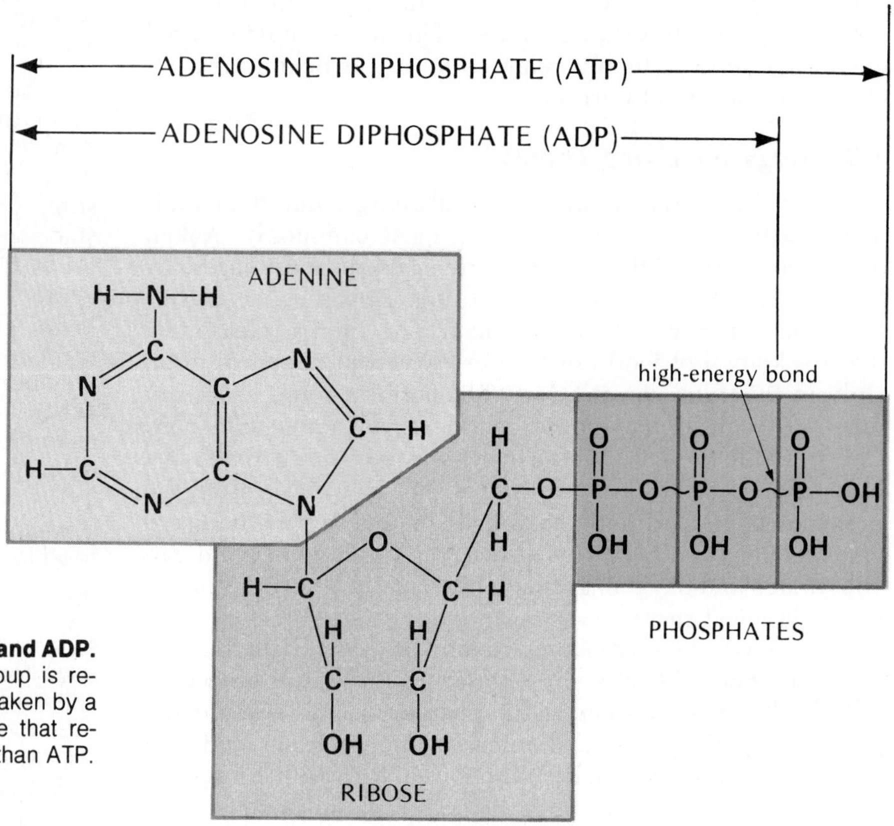

Figure 7-1. Structure of ATP and ADP. When the third phosphate group is removed from ATP, its place is taken by a hydrogen atom. The molecule that remains, ADP, has less energy than ATP.

is called *adenosine.* There are three phosphate groups bonded end-to-end to the adenosine in ATP. You will recall that phosphate groups are also part of the structure of DNA and RNA. It is interesting that the cell uses these same molecular units for different purposes. There are many examples of such multiple uses of chemical groups in the chemistry of life.

The important part of the ATP molecule as far as energy storage is concerned is the bond linking the last phosphate group to the molecule. This bond is shown as a wavy line. This symbol means that the bond contains a relatively large amount of energy. It is called a **high-energy bond.** When the third phosphate is detached from ATP and bonded to another compound, it transfers energy to the other compound. This transfer is called *phosphorylation* (fahs-for-uh-*lay*-shun). Phosphorylation is a common way for chemical energy to be transferred in biochemical reactions (see Figure 7-2).

When one phosphate is removed from ATP, the remaining molecule is called *adenosine diphosphate,* or **ADP.** ADP is a compound in a lower energy state than ATP. Its second phosphate is attached through a high-energy bond, but this bond is used less often in the cell as a source of energy.

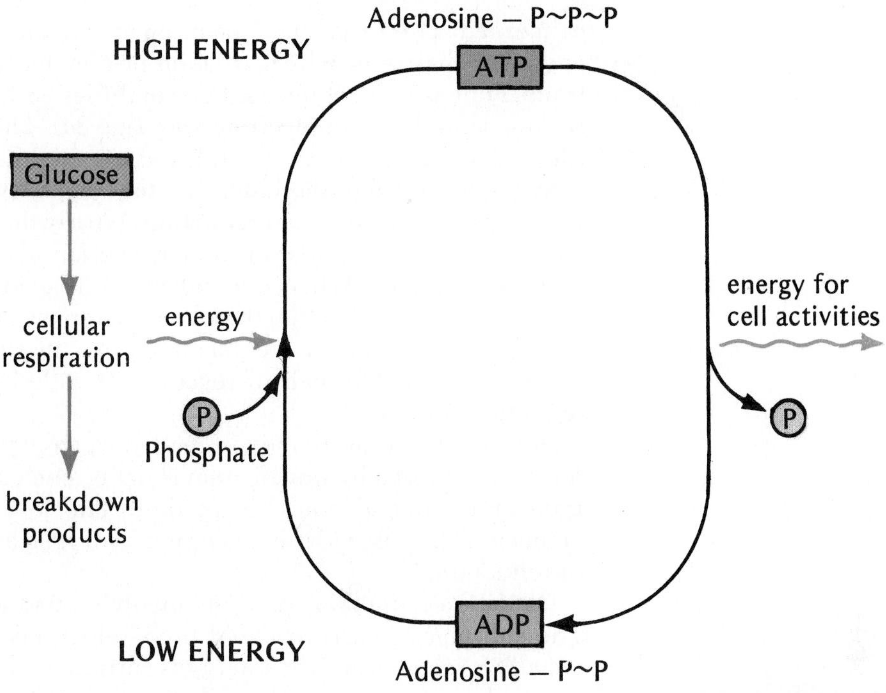

Figure 7-2. The Energy Cycle in the Cell. Energy obtained from the breakdown of glucose is used to attach a third phosphate to ADP, forming ATP and storing energy in it. When the third phosphate is detached from ATP, the stored energy can be used for cell activities. The low-energy ADP is returned for reuse. The energy from a single glucose molecule can form 36 molecules of ATP.

7-4 Source of Energy for ATP

During cellular respiration, energy released by the gradual breakdown of food molecules is used to attach a third phosphate to ADP, thus returning it to its high-energy state as a molecule of ATP. The ATP can then be sent to any part of the cell where its energy is needed for some chemical process.

The most common food substance from which cells obtain energy is the sugar glucose. Glucose is usually the starting point for cellular respiration. From the energy in a single molecule of glucose, a cell can produce up to 36 molecules of ATP from ADP. That is, the total energy that can be obtained by breaking down a molecule of glucose is actually divided into as many as 36 small units. If all this energy were released in a single burst, it would be too much for the cell to handle. There is no way the cell can use that much energy all at once. However, the amount of energy in a single molecule of ATP is just about right for the average reaction in the cell that requires energy. Thus the packaging of energy in these small units is convenient and efficient for the needs of the cell.

It was originally thought that 38 ATP could be formed from the breakdown of one glucose molecule, including 6 ATP from the 2 $NADH_2$ formed in glycolysis. However, $NADH_2$ cannot pass through the mitochondrial membrane, so the H's are carried through the membrane by other molecules. Inside the mitochondrion, they are picked up by FAD, forming $2FADH_2$. Only 4 ATP are produced from these H's, so the maximum number of ATP formed from one glucose molecule is 36, not 38.

7-5 Oxidation-Reduction Reactions

It is interesting to follow the main steps by which the energy in glucose is used to generate ATP. The idea of chemical oxidation and reduction can help you understand these steps. The term **oxidation** (ok-suh-*day*-shun) originally referred to combination with oxygen. Chemists later broadened the meaning of the term to include reactions that were like combination with oxygen as far as shifts of electrons were concerned. This broadened meaning of oxidation refers to any chemical change in which an atom or a molecule loses electrons. For example, when sodium combines with chlorine, the sodium atom loses an electron (see page 34). This is an example of oxidation. We say that the sodium atom is oxidized.

At the same time, the chlorine atom acquires an electron. Gaining electrons is called **reduction.** We say that the chlorine atom is reduced. Oxidation and reduction always occur as pairs of reactions. When one substance is oxidized, another must be reduced. That is, the electrons given up by the substance being oxidized are taken up by another substance being reduced. The pair of reactions is called an **oxidation-reduction reaction.**

In some oxidation-reduction reactions, an electron is transferred as part of a hydrogen atom. That is, one compound may transfer hydrogen atoms to another. The loss of hydrogen atoms is a form of oxidation. Gaining hydrogen atoms is a form of reduction.

Oxidation-reduction reactions involve a transfer of energy. The substance that is oxidized (loses electrons or hydrogen) usually loses energy. The energy is carried by the electrons or the hydrogen atoms to the substance that is reduced. This substance thus gains energy. In cellular respiration, almost all the energy released by the breakdown of glucose is at first carried off by hydrogen atoms. The oxidation of glucose in the cell is actually a loss of hydrogen atoms, not a reaction with oxygen.

7-6 Hydrogen Acceptors

The breakdown of glucose in cellular respiration occurs as a series of numerous chemical steps. A sequence of chemical reactions that leads to a particular result in the living cell is called a *biochemical pathway.* At several points in the pathway of cellular respiration, one of the compounds involved is oxidized by giving up hydrogen atoms. For this oxidation to occur, some other compound must accept the hydrogen and thus be reduced. Each of these oxidation-reduction steps requires the action of a specific enzyme. Since the enzyme cannot accomplish its task unless a *hydrogen acceptor* is present, the hydrogen acceptors act as coenzymes, which enable the enzymes to function.

One of the coenzymes that act as hydrogen acceptors in cellular respiration is represented as *NAD* (from its full name nicotinamide adenine dinucleotide). Another is *FAD* (flavin adenine dinucleotide). Each of these molecules can accept two hydrogen atoms, thus undergoing reduction:

$$\mathrm{NAD} + 2\mathrm{H} \longrightarrow \mathrm{NADH_2}^*$$
$$\mathrm{FAD} + 2\mathrm{H} \longrightarrow \mathrm{FADH_2}$$

*This is a simplified way of showing the reduction of NAD. The oxidized form of NAD actually carries a positive charge. A more accurate equation for its reduction is:

$$\mathrm{NAD^+} + 2\mathrm{H} \longrightarrow \mathrm{NADH} + \mathrm{H^+}$$

careers

In medical laboratories, there are medical technologists and technicians who work under the supervision of a physician or scientist performing various types of diagnostic tests.

Medical technologists do complicated diagnostic tests involving chemical analysis, microscopic examination of tissues, and cultures of body fluids to determine the presence of bacteria and other microorganisms. Medical technicians do less complicated work involving simpler equipment. They may, for example, do cell counts and operate automated testing equipment.

To become a medical technologist a person must have four years of college, including a year of actual clinical training. To be a medical technician, a person must complete a two-year program that includes clinical laboratory training. Medical technologists and technicians work in hospital and private laboratories, in doctor's offices, and in clinics, and some work for drug companies.

As the hydrogen atoms are transferred to the coenzymes, the coenzyme molecules also gain energy. The reduced coenzymes are thus carrying hydrogen and added energy. This is a temporary state of affairs. In another series of reactions, the coenzymes give up the hydrogen and return to their oxidized form. At the same time, the extra energy the coenzymes were carrying is used to form ATP from ADP. Oxygen acts as the final acceptor of the hydrogen, producing water. In the following sections we will examine some of the details of this process.

ANAEROBIC RESPIRATION

After completing your study of this section, you should be able to:

1. Explain the difference between aerobic respiration and anaerobic respiration.
2. Describe the basic reactions of glycolysis.
3. Describe the process of fermentation.

7-7 Types of Respiration

In the process of cellular respiration, glucose is broken down to simpler compounds. Energy stored in the chemical bonds of the glucose molecule is extracted and used to form ATP from ADP and phosphate.

In most organisms, respiration is carried on in the presence of free oxygen. Oxygen is obtained from the air or from water, in which it is dissolved. This type of respiration is called **aerobic** (uh-*roh*-bik) **respiration.** In aerobic respiration, glucose is completely oxidized to carbon dioxide and water, and the maximum amount of energy is extracted from it.

A number of one-celled organisms, including yeast and many forms of bacteria, can carry on cellular respiration in the absence of oxygen. This is called **anaerobic** (an-uh-*roh*-bik) **respiration.** In anaerobic respiration, only a partial breakdown of the glucose molecule occurs. Relatively little of the chemical energy in the glucose is extracted and stored as ATP.

The initial steps of both aerobic and anaerobic respiration are the same. We will therefore examine the chemical pathways of anaerobic respiration first.

7-8 Splitting of Glucose (Glycolysis)

The first steps in respiration are phosphorylation reactions. In these reactions, two phosphate groups are attached to the glucose molecule. These steps *require* energy. The energy and the phosphate groups are obtained by the breakdown of two ATP molecules to ADP. The energized glucose molecule then goes through a series of chemical reactions that split it into two molecules of a 3-carbon compound called phosphoglyceraldehyde (PGAL). PGAL is then oxidized by the loss of

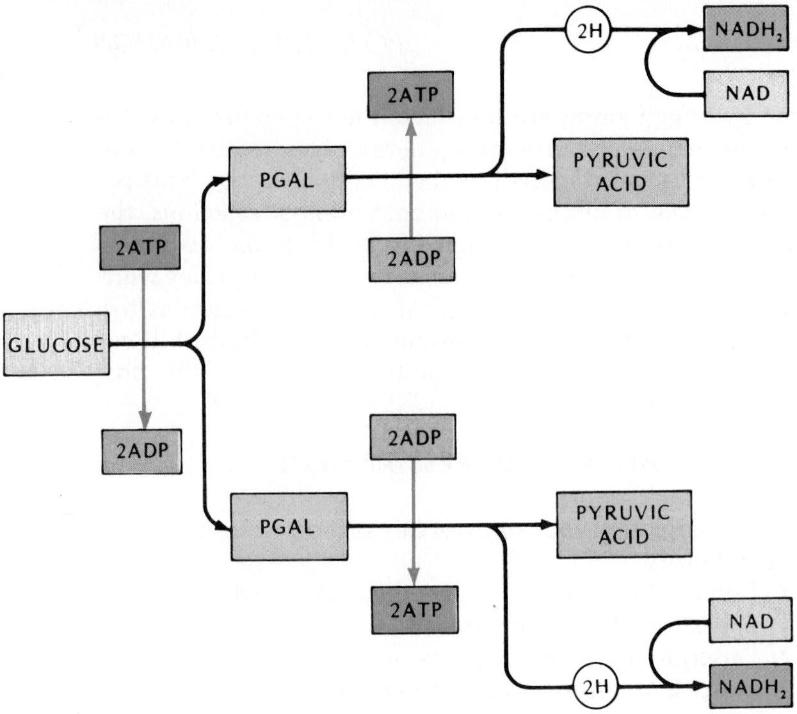

Figure 7-3. Glycolysis. During glycolysis, one molecule of glucose is split into two molecules of pyruvic acid. From these reactions, 4 ATP and 2 $NADH_2$ are produced. Since 2 ATP are used in phosphorylation reactions at the beginning of glycolysis, the pathway produces a net gain of 2 ATP.

two hydrogen atoms and changes to another 3-carbon compound called **pyruvic** (py-*roo*-vik) **acid**. The oxidation of PGAL releases energy. Some of this energy is used directly to form two ATP. At the same time the hydrogen removed from PGAL is accepted by NAD, forming $NADH_2$. The $NADH_2$ also carries some energy that is used to form ATP at a later stage. The entire process of breaking down the 6-carbon glucose molecule into two 3-carbon pyruvic acid molecules is called **glycolysis** (gly-*kahl*-uh-sis) (see Figure 7-3).

For each pyruvic acid molecule produced by glycolysis, two ATP are formed. Since the splitting of one glucose molecule produces two pyruvic acid molecules, a total of four ATP are formed per glucose molecule. However, two ATP are used to energize the glucose molecule. So the net energy output of glycolysis is two ATP for each molecule of glucose.

7-9 Fermentation

In anaerobic organisms, energy is obtained by the process of glycolysis. In this process, glucose is converted to pyruvic acid, and NAD is reduced to $NADH_2$. Several different chemical changes may follow, depending on the metabolism of the particular organism. In all cases the pyruvic acid accepts the hydrogens from $NADH_2$, oxidizing it to NAD so that it can be used again. However, no additional ATP is produced. At the same time the pyruvic acid is changed to other compounds. In yeast cells, the pyruvic acid is converted to ethyl alcohol and carbon dioxide (see Figure 7-4). In certain bacteria, such as those found in milk, the end product is lactic acid.

Glycolysis followed by the conversion of pyruvic acid to some other end product with no further release of energy is

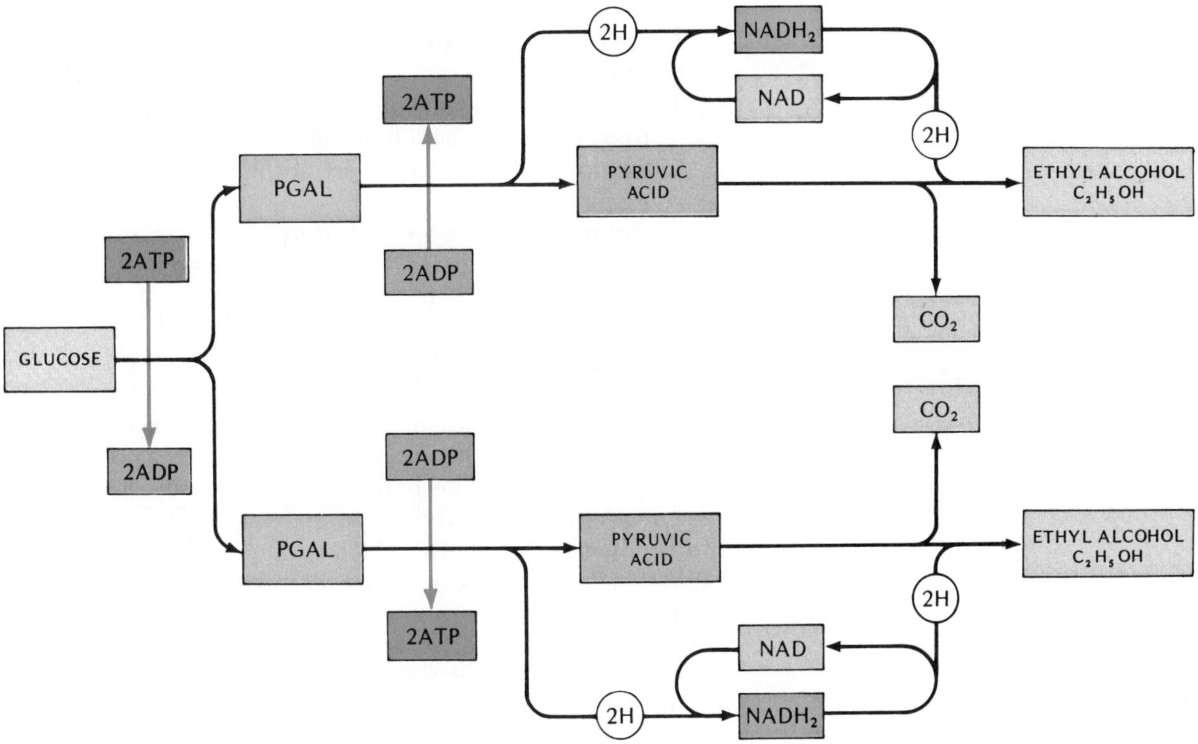

Figure 7-4. Fermentation. In the absence of oxygen, pyruvic acid produced by glycolysis gives up CO_2 and accepts 2H from $NADH_2$, forming ethyl alcohol. The result of this type of fermentation is the production of two ATP (net), two molecules of CO_2, and two molecules of ethyl alcohol per molecule of glucose.

Figure 7-5. Industrial Fermentation. In bread dough, yeast cells break down carbohydrates to carbon dioxide and alcohol. The carbon dioxide forms gas bubbles in the dough, causing it to "rise." The alcohol evaporates during baking (left). Yeasts are used to make beer, wine, and other alcoholic beverages. In this case, the alcohol produced by fermentation is the desired product. The carbon dioxide may or may not be retained in the beverage, depending on the particular processing used (right).

called **fermentation** (fer-men-*tay*-shun). Several industrial processes make use of natural fermentation (see Figure 7-5). Yeast fermentation is used in making bread; the carbon dioxide causes the bread to "rise." The manufacture of ethyl alcohol for beverages and other purposes is another well-known example.

AEROBIC RESPIRATION

After completing your study of this section, you should be able to:

1. **Describe the results of the Krebs cycle and the electron transport chain in aerobic respiration.**
2. **Compare the efficiency of aerobic and anaerobic respiration.**
3. **Define the term *oxygen debt*, and explain what happens in muscle during prolonged strenuous activity.**

7-10 The Importance of Oxygen

In anaerobic respiration, or fermentation, the only energy-yielding process is the formation of pyruvic acid from the splitting of glucose. The hydrogen accepted by NAD during this process is transferred to the pyruvic acid, producing an end product such as ethyl alcohol. The end products of fermentation have almost as much energy as the glucose from which they are made.

A cell that can use oxygen from the environment for its respiration can extract the energy remaining in these end products. It can do this because oxygen will accept the hydrogen removed during the oxidation of these compounds.

7-11 The Krebs Cycle

Aerobic respiration begins with glycolysis—the splitting of a molecule of glucose into two molecules of pyruvic acid, the reduction of two molecules of NAD to two molecules of $NADH_2$, and the net output of two molecules of ATP. These steps are the same in both aerobic and anaerobic respiration. In anaerobic respiration, the pyruvic acid accepts the hydrogen from $NADH_2$, ending the respiratory pathway. In aerobic respiration, the pyruvic acid undergoes further breakdown and energy release. Some energy is also obtained from the $NADH_2$ formed during glycolysis.

The remaining steps of aerobic respiration take place inside the mitochondria of the cell. The pyruvic acid produced by glycolysis enters the mitochondrion, where a series of reactions break it down to carbon dioxide and hydrogen. The carbon dioxide is given off as a waste product. The hydrogen is accepted by the coenzymes NAD or FAD. A mitochondrion has a double membrane (see page 75). The inner membrane is deeply folded and has a very large surface area. Research indicates that most of the enzymes, coenzymes, and other special molecules needed for aerobic respiration are located on this membrane surface. It is the presence of these molecules in an organized pattern on the membrane that makes the entire process possible.

The outer mitochondrial membrane is permeable to many small molecules and ions, but the inner membrane is not. The respiratory enzymes of the electron transport chain are found on the infoldings of the inner membrane, the cristae. The reactions of the Krebs cycle occur in the matrix, which fills the space between the cristae.

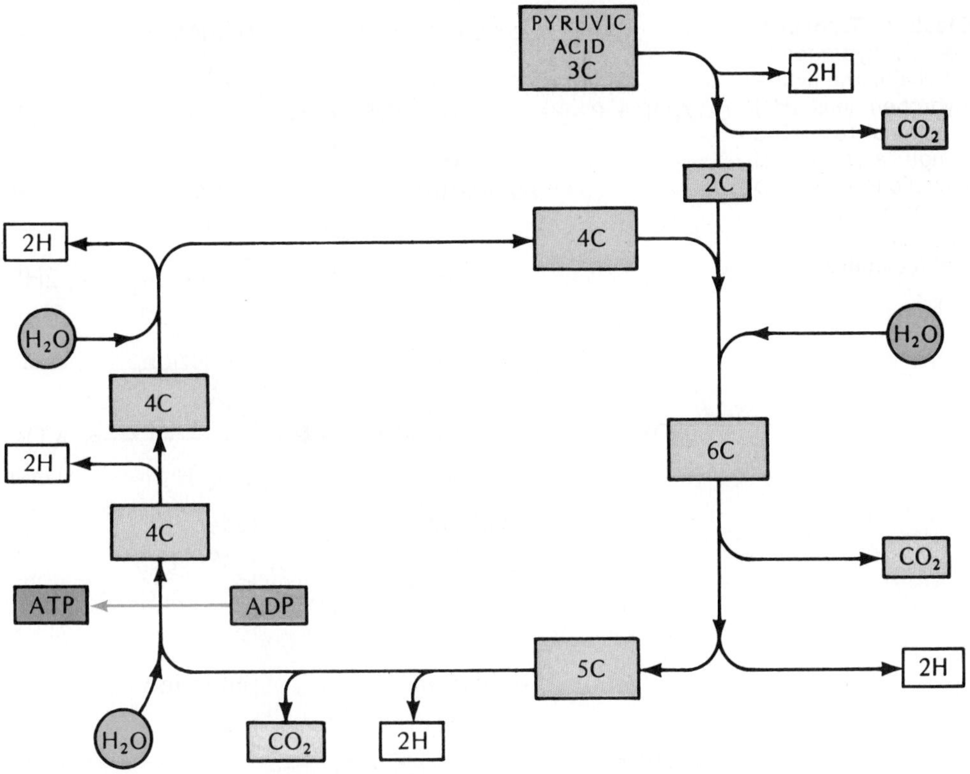

Figure 7-6. The Krebs Cycle. For each turn of the cycle, three molecules of carbon dioxide are produced from one pyruvic acid molecule (3C). Hydrogen is removed from the pyruvic acid by coenzymes. Note that three water molecules are used during the Krebs cycle.

The series of chemical reactions by which pyruvic acid is broken down is called the **Krebs cycle** (see Figure 7-6). Its details were discovered by Sir Hans Krebs of Oxford University in England. He received a Nobel Prize in 1953 for this accomplishment. Krebs found that the series of reactions has the form of a repeating cycle. Certain organic acid molecules that are part of the cycle are used over and over again. They are changed to other compounds during the cycle but are then changed back to their original form.

Each "turn" of the cycle breaks down one pyruvic acid molecule to three molecules of carbon dioxide and releases four pairs of hydrogen atoms. In addition, one pair of hydrogen atoms is removed from the pyruvic acid molecule before it enters the cycle. These hydrogen atoms are picked up by NAD, forming $NADH_2$. Almost all the chemical energy extracted from the pyruvic acid during the Krebs cycle is carried by the hydrogen and temporarily transferred to the reduced coenzymes. Only one ATP is produced directly by each turn of the cycle.

7-12 The Electron Transport Chain

We have seen so far that in aerobic respiration, two ATP are produced by the splitting of glucose into two molecules of pyruvic acid, and one ATP is produced by each turn of the Krebs cycle (two ATP for each glucose molecule). This is a

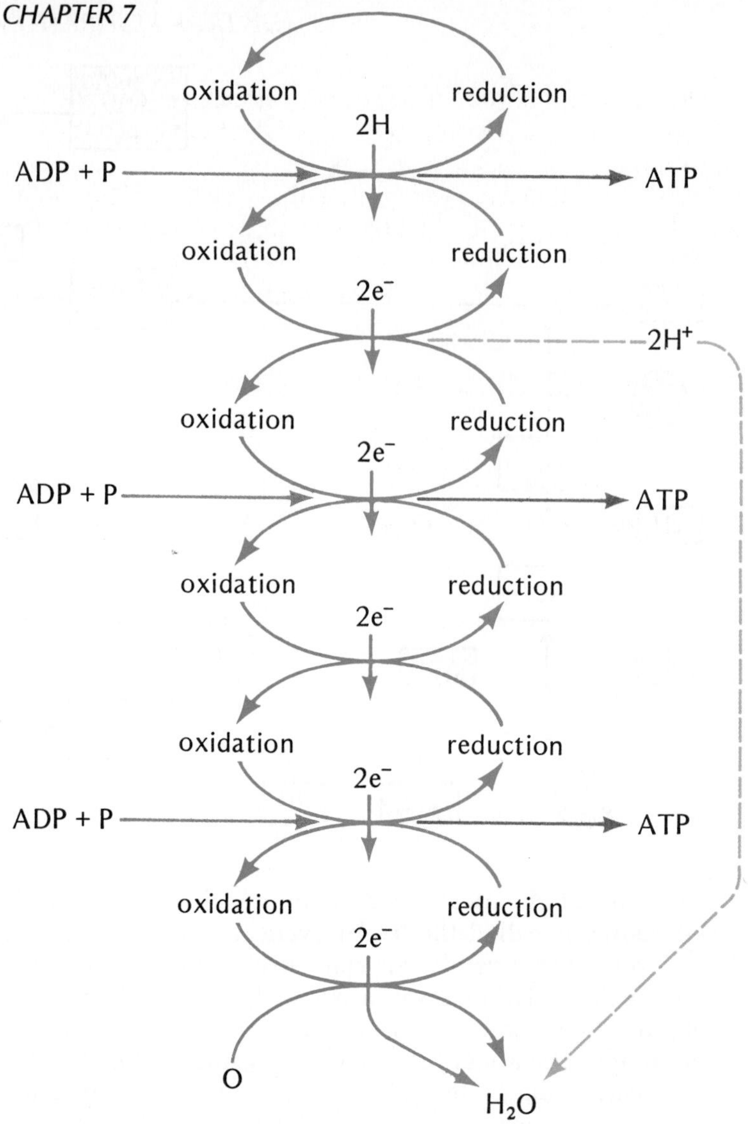

Figure 7-7. The Electron Transport Chain. Coenzymes deliver hydrogen to the electron transport chain. The hydrogen is split into hydrogen ions (H^+) and high-energy electrons (e^-). The electrons pass through a series of oxidation-reduction reactions, giving up energy to form ATP. At the end, the electrons, hydrogen ions, and free oxygen combine to form water molecules.

total of four ATP per glucose molecule. All the remaining energy released by the breakdown of glucose is carried by the hydrogen in $NADH_2$ and $FADH_2$. This energy is used to form ATP by a highly organized system of enzymes and coenzymes called the **electron transport chain.**

In the electron transport chain, a series of oxidation-reduction reactions take place. Hydrogen atoms are carried into the chain by $NADH_2$ and $FADH_2$. The electrons from the hydrogen atoms are then passed along from one compound to another (see Figure 7-7). At three places along the chain, the electrons give up some energy, and molecules of ATP are formed. Altogether, in most cells 32 ATP are produced by the electron transport chain for each molecule of glucose. Since 2 ATP come directly from glycolysis and 2 ATP from the Krebs cycle, aerobic respiration can produce a total of 36 ATP from each molecule of glucose.

The final step in this process involves free oxygen. Oxygen becomes the final hydrogen acceptor, combining with it to form water.

Ordinarily, the combination of hydrogen and oxygen to form water gives off large amounts of heat energy. In this case, however, the hydrogen has already given up most of its available energy, and the final combination with oxygen releases little heat.

Water produced by cellular respiration is called the *water of metabolism*. It may be used by the cell or it may be excreted as a waste product. For desert animals, such as the kangaroo rat, the water of metabolism is an essential source of water for survival.

7-13 Net Reactions of Aerobic Respiration

The net result of all the steps of aerobic respiration is usually summarized in the following chemical equation:

$$C_6H_{12}O_6 + 6\ O_2 \rightarrow 6\ CO_2 + 6\ H_2O + \text{Energy (36 ATP)}$$

This equation is somewhat oversimplified. Water is needed as a raw material for the Krebs cycle. In Figure 7-6 you can see three places where a molecule of water enters the cycle. Since the Krebs cycle runs twice for each glucose molecule, six molecules of water are needed for each glucose molecule that is broken down. This water should be shown as a raw material in the equation. The equation should therefore be written as follows:

$$C_6H_{12}O_6 + 6\ H_2O + 6\ O_2 \rightarrow 6\ CO_2 + 12\ H_2O + \text{Energy (36 ATP)}$$

7-14 Efficiency of Cellular Respiration

The oxidation of glucose is usually used as a measure of the energy output of cellular respiration. In anaerobic respiration, the glycolysis pathway produces a net yield of two ATP per molecule of glucose. This type of respiration is relatively inefficient, leaving most of the potential energy of the glucose in the end products of fermentation. The method is, however, adequate for the energy needs of many simple organisms, such as yeast and bacteria.

Aerobic respiration yields almost 20 times as much energy per molecule of glucose as fermentation does. It is, moreover, a very efficient process. About 45 percent of the total energy that could theoretically be obtained from the oxidation of glucose is stored as ATP after aerobic respiration. In comparison, an automobile engine converts only about 25 percent of the chemical energy of its fuel to useful work.

7-15 Muscle Fatigue and Oxygen Debt

Some organisms that have the capacity for aerobic respiration can function by anaerobic respiration alone when free oxygen is not available. Yeast cells, for example, employ aerobic respiration when the supply of oxygen is ample, but they can live and grow by anaerobic respiration in the absence of oxygen. Muscle cells in humans and other animals normally

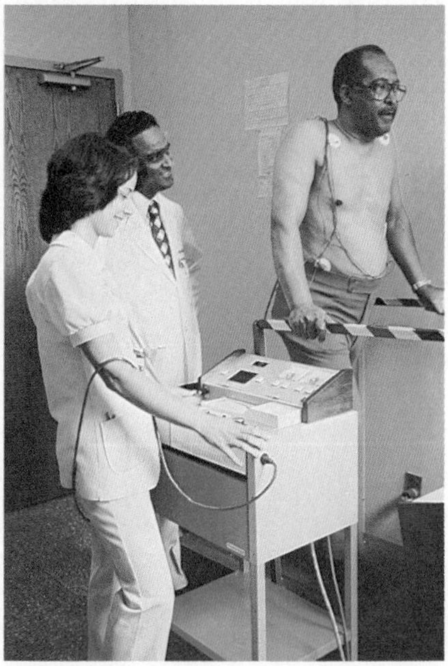

Figure 7-8. Stress Test. In an exercise stress test, a person's capacity to supply oxygen to the muscles is measured. Such tests provide information about the condition of the circulatory system.

rely on aerobic respiration for their energy needs. They can, however, function for a short time without oxygen, making do with the energy obtained from glycolysis alone.

During periods of intense or prolonged physical activity, the muscle cells may use oxygen faster than it can be supplied by the respiratory and circulatory systems (see Figure 7-8). When the oxygen supply gets too low, the electron transport chain cannot function. This means that $NADH_2$ and $FADH_2$ accumulate in the mitochondria and are not recycled. This forces the Krebs cycle to stop working.

Under these circumstances, the muscle cells continue to release energy by glycolysis, but the pyruvic acid becomes the acceptor for hydrogen and is converted to lactic acid. The accumulation of lactic acid in the muscle cells produces the sensation of fatigue and gradually reduces the ability of the cells to do their normal work.

The cells require a period of rest or reduced activity to recover to a normal condition. During this time, fresh supplies of oxygen allow the lactic acid to be oxidized back to pyruvic acid, and the accumulated hydrogen is passed down through the electron transport chain. The amount of oxygen needed to dispose of the lactic acid is called **oxygen debt.** You know that during periods of strenuous activity, the breathing and heart rates increase in order to deliver greater supplies of oxygen to the muscles. When the intense activity stops, the breathing and heart rates remain high for a time. During this time, extra supplies of oxygen are being delivered to pay back the oxygen debt of the previous period of exertion.

CATABOLISM AND ANABOLISM

After completing your study of this section, you should be able to define the terms *catabolism* and *anabolism*.

7-16 Breakdown of Substances in the Cell

The discussion of aerobic respiration has focused on the breakdown of glucose to furnish energy for the cell. The food of most organisms does not contain glucose in its simple form. The glucose is obtained by the breakdown, or digestion, of more complex carbohydrates. Cells that carry on aerobic respiration can also extract energy from other types of food substances, such as fats and proteins. These substances are broken down and converted into compounds that can enter the respiratory pathway at some intermediate point. Fatty acids and glycerol from the digestion of fats, as well as amino acids from the digestion of proteins, can enter the Krebs cycle.

The proteins and fats in the food supply of an organism are broken down by digestion for use within the body. However, even the proteins and fats that are part of the tissues of the organism are constantly being broken down and then formed again. In the cells of the human body, about half the body proteins are broken down and reformed every 80 days. Some proteins are replaced every 10 days. Some liver enzymes are destroyed and remade in periods as short as 2 hours.

All the processes that result in the breakdown of complex substances in the body are called **catabolism** (kuh-*tab*-uh-liz-um). This is the destructive phase of metabolism. The processes of catabolism are offset by the opposite phase of metabolism, called anabolism. **Anabolism** (uh-*nab*-uh-liz-um) involves the buildup or synthesis of materials needed for the continued functioning of the organism.

summary

All living things require energy to carry on their life processes. This energy is obtained by the release of chemical energy stored in food. Cellular respiration is the process by which chemical energy in food is converted into a form that can be used by cells. The substance most commonly broken down by cellular respiration is the sugar glucose. The energy released by the breakdown of glucose is packaged in molecules of ATP. ATP, in turn, can be broken down to provide energy for other metabolic processes.

In cellular respiration, the breakdown of glucose and the generation of ATP involve a series of reactions in which energy is transferred in a stepwise manner from one substance to another. These reactions are oxidation-reduction reactions.

Aerobic cellular respiration is carried on in the presence of oxygen, while anaerobic cellular respiration, or fermentation, occurs in the absence of oxygen. The pathways of both aerobic and anaerobic respiration begin with the breakdown of a 6-carbon glucose molecule to two molecules of the 3-carbon compound pyruvic acid. In this process, which is called glycolysis, there is a net gain of two ATPs, and four hydrogen atoms are transferred to the hydrogen carrier NAD.

In fermentation, the hydrogen atoms from NAD are transferred to pyruvic acid, which is converted to ethyl alcohol, lactic acid, or various other compounds. No further release of energy occurs.

In aerobic respiration, the 3-carbon pyruvic acid molecule enters the Krebs cycle, a series of reactions that break it down to three molecules of carbon dioxide; five pairs of hydrogen atoms are released. One ATP is formed in the Krebs cycle, and most of the energy of the pyruvic acid is in the five pairs of hydrogen atoms.

In another series of oxidation-reduction reactions carried out by the electron transport chain, the energy of the hydrogen atoms is used to form ATP. In the final reaction of this series, the hydrogen atoms combine with oxygen forming water.

Aerobic cellular respiration can yield up to 36 ATPs for each molecule of glucose broken down. Anaerobic respiration, or fermentation, yields only 2.

During prolonged physical activity, the body cannot pump oxygen to the cells as fast as it is needed. Without adequate oxygen, muscle cells can carry on a form of anaerobic respiration that produces lactic acid. The buildup of lactic acid in the tissues causes muscle fatigue. When oxygen becomes available, the oxygen debt is paid back. Lactic acid is oxidized back to pyruvic acid, which is then completely broken down by aerobic respiration.

Processes involving the breakdown of complex substances in the body are called catabolism, while the synthesis of materials needed by the body is called anabolism.

vocabulary

ADP
aerobic respiration
anabolism
anaerobic respiration
ATP
catabolism
cellular respiration
electron transport chain
fermentation
glycolysis
high-energy bond
Krebs cycle
oxidation
oxidation-reduction reaction
oxygen debt
pyruvic acid
reduction

test your learning

Section

7-1 **1.** What chemical and physical changes occur during the burning of fuels, such as coal and gas?

7-2 **2.** Why must the oxidation of food and the release of energy in living organisms take place in small chemical steps?

3. Define *cellular respiration*.

7-3 **4.** Describe the structure of the part of the ATP molecule that is important in energy storage.

5. What is the difference between ATP and ADP?

6. What happens in a phosphorylation reaction?

7-4 **7.** What happens to the energy released by cellular respiration?

8. Why is it advantageous for the cell to store energy in the form of ATP molecules?

7-5 **9.** Define the terms *oxidation* and *reduction*.

10. Explain what happens in an oxidation-reduction reaction.

7-6 **11.** Name two coenzymes used as hydrogen acceptors in cellular respiration.

7-7 **12.** How does anaerobic respiration differ from aerobic respiration?

7-8 **13.** Describe the process of glycolysis.
14. What is the net gain in ATP from glycolysis?
7-9 **15.** Describe the process of fermentation.
7-10 **16.** Why is oxygen important in cellular respiration?
7-11 **17.** In which cell organelle do the reactions of the Krebs cycle occur?
18. What happens to a molecule of pyruvic acid as it goes through the Krebs cycle?
19. What type of chemical reactions occur in the electron transport chain?
7-12 **20.** What happens to the hydrogen atoms from $NADH_2$ and $FADH_2$ in the electron transport chain?
21. What is the total number of ATP molecules that can be produced from the oxidation of one molecule of glucose?
22. What is the final hydrogen acceptor in the electron transport chain?
7-13 **23.** Write the chemical equation for the net reactions of aerobic respiration.
7-14 **24.** Compare the relative efficiencies of aerobic and anaerobic cellular respiration.
7-15 **25.** What happens to muscle cells when they run short of oxygen during prolonged physical activity?
26. What is oxygen debt?
7-16 **27.** What compounds besides glucose can enter the respiratory pathway?
28. Define the terms *catabolism* and *anabolism*.

test your understanding

1. Compare the amounts of energy released by aerobic respiration and fermentation. Why is less energy released by fermentation than by aerobic respiration?
2. What function does oxygen serve in aerobic respiration? What happens in the reaction sequence of aerobic respiration when oxygen is not available?
3. Describe the roles of ADP and ATP in cell metabolism.
4. Describe the roles of NAD and FAD in aerobic cellular respiration.
5. Describe what happens in human muscle cells during and after prolonged exercise.

independent research

1. Prepare a report on several types of bacteria, such as those that cause botulism and tetanus, that produce substances that are dangerous to humans. Discuss their methods of respiration and how they are affected by the presence or absence of free oxygen.
2. Prepare a report on the research of Hans Krebs leading to the discovery of the Krebs cycle.

chapter 8

Nutrition

NUTRITION

After completing your study of this section, you should be able to:

1. **Contrast autotrophic nutrition and heterotrophic nutrition.**
2. **Define *mechanical digestion* and *chemical digestion*.**
3. **Describe the functions of the six basic types of nutrients found in foods.**
4. **Define the terms *calorie* and *kilocalorie* and explain how the energy content of food is measured.**

8-1 Nutrients

All living organisms need food. It is from food that they obtain energy for their activities and materials for growth and repair. **Nutrition** is the process by which organisms obtain food, use it to carry on their life activities, and transform it into living tissues.

All foods contain **nutrients,** which are substances that can be used in metabolism. Some nutrients are simple, inorganic compounds, while others are more complex organic compounds. Some can be synthesized within the organism, and some must be taken in from the environment. Nutrients required by living organisms include proteins, carbohydrates, fats, vitamins, minerals, and water. Sources of these nutrients are given in Table 8-1.

In addition to nutrients, many foods contain bulky, indigestible materials called **roughage** (*ruhf*-idj). The main kind of roughage in human foods is cellulose. Cellulose is an indigestible material found in the cell walls of fruits, vegetables, and grains. Roughage stimulates the muscles of the digestive tube and thus keeps food moving through it.

8-2 Energy Content of Food

Living organisms need energy to carry on their life processes. This energy is provided in most cases by the chemical breakdown of carbohydrates, fats, and proteins obtained from food. As explained in the discussion of cellular respiration in Chapter 7, the energy is released in a series of small steps and stored in molecules of ATP for later use.

The total amount of energy released by the gradual breakdown of a given quantity of food by cellular respiration is the same as would be released by burning, which is a rapid process. The energy content of a food sample is the amount of energy given off by the complete breakdown of that sample. It

Table 8-1. Nutrients Important for Human Metabolism.

Nutrient	Importance	Sources
Carbohydrates (sugar and starch)	Supply energy for body functions	*Sugar:* fruit, table sugar, sweets, syrups, jelly *Starch:* bread, cereals, potatoes, rice, corn, beans, spaghetti
Fats & Oils	Supply energy; storage form of fuel in the body	Margarine, butter, bacon, cooking oils, fat in meat, nuts
Proteins	Growth and repair of body tissue; can supply energy	Meat, milk, fish, eggs, beans, peas
Water	Solvent in which chemical reactions take place; transport of materials	Drinking water and other beverages; most foods; product of metabolism
Minerals	Body building; regulation of metabolism	Meats, milk, vegetables, fruits
Calcium	Makes up bones and teeth; needed for normal muscle activity and blood clotting	Milk and dairy products, leafy vegetables, fruits
Phosphorus	Part of ATP, ADP, etc.; makes up bones	Milk and dairy products, leafy vegetables, fruits
Iron	Part of hemoglobin	Liver, red meat, eggs, green leafy vegetables
Iodine	Part of thyroid hormone	Sea food, iodized table salt
Vitamins	Many serve as coenzymes in metabolic reactions. Prevent deficiency diseases.	Varied diet
A	Growth, night vision	Vegetables, fruit
D	Needed for good teeth and bones. Prevents rickets.	Eggs, meat, milk
C	Keeps body tissues healthy. Prevents scurvy.	Citrus fruits, tomatoes
B (complex)	Coenzymes in cellular metabolism.	Liver, eggs, milk, enriched bread, cereals

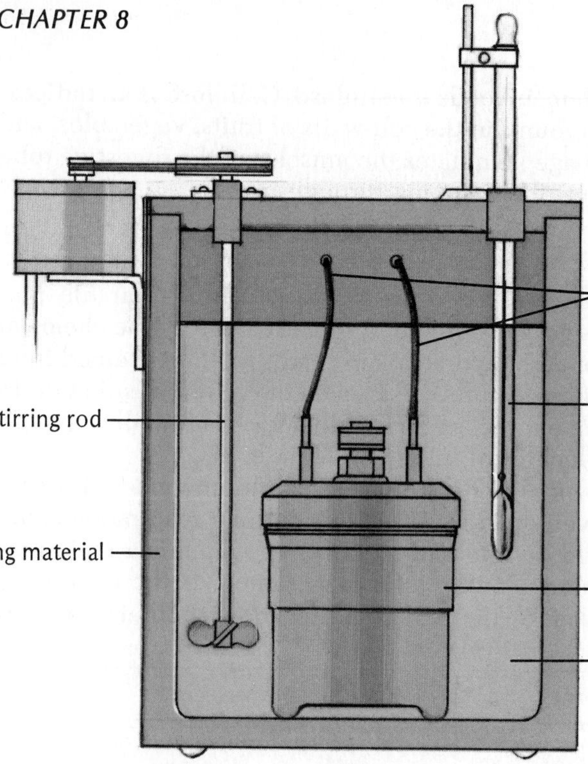

Figure 8-1. Calorimeter. In a calorimeter, a food sample is burned and the heat produced is measured. In this way, the energy content of the food can be determined.

is determined by completely burning a sample of the food and measuring the amount of heat given off. The instrument used to measure the energy content of a food sample is a **calorimeter** (kal-uh-*rim*-uh-ter) (see Figure 8-1).

The unit used in measuring the energy content of food is the **calorie** (*kal*-uh-ree). This is the amount of heat needed to raise the temperature of 1 g of water 1°C. The calorie is a very small unit that is not convenient for expressing the energy content of food. Instead, the unit used in measuring the energy content of food is the **kilocalorie** (*kil*-uh-kal-uh-ree). A kilocalorie is one thousand calories and is the amount of heat needed to raise the temperature of 1 kg of water 1°C. In tables giving the "calorie" content of foods, the unit is actually a kilocalorie.

With the use of a calorimeter, it has been determined that the amount of heat liberated by 1 gram of carbohydrate or 1 gram of protein is about 4 kilocalories. One gram of fat, on the other hand, releases 9 kilocalories. Fat contains more than twice as many calories as an equal weight of carbohydrate or protein. Now you can see why most reducing diets restrict fat intake. The energy contents of some common foods are shown in Table 8-2.

Individuals vary in their daily calorie requirements. In general, younger people need more calories than older people, males need more calories than females, and active people need more calories than inactive people. A person whose diet contains more calories than are needed gains weight. A person whose diet includes fewer calories than are needed loses weight.

8-3 Types of Nutrition

There are two basic ways that organisms obtain the **organic** nutrients they need. Some organisms are capable of **making,** or synthesizing, these nutrients from simple inorganic substances. Such organisms are **autotrophs** (*awt*-uh-trohfs). Green plants and green algae and various other types of microorganisms are autotrophs. Most autotrophs are photosynthetic—that is, they use energy from sunlight and carbon dioxide and water from the environment to make their own organic nutrients. However, certain types of bacteria are also autotrophs, but they do not use light as a source of energy. Instead, they obtain energy from special types of chemical reactions. Such organisms are called **chemotrophs** (*kee*-muh-trohfs). (The details of photosynthesis and chemosynthesis are discussed in Chapter 17.)

Heterotrophs (*het*-uh-ruh-trohfs) are organisms that cannot synthesize their own organic nutrients. All animals and cer-

Table 8-2. Energy Content of Some Common Foods.

Food	Portion	Calories
apple	1 medium (150g)	70
bacon	2 slices (16g)	100
banana	1 (150g)	85
bread, white	1 slice (23 g)	70
candy, bar	1 plain (57g)	300
carrot	1 cup (145g)	45
cheese, American	1 oz. (28g)	105
corn	1 cup (256g)	170
cupcake	1 (50g)	185
egg	1 large (50g)	80
frankfurter	1 (51g)	155
ham	3 oz. (85g)	245
hamburger	3 oz. (85g)	245
ice cream	½ cup	225
milk	1 cup (244g)	150
orange	1 (180g)	60
peas	1 cup (160g)	115
pork roast	3 oz. (85g)	310
potato	1 medium (130g)	105
tomato	1 medium (150g)	35

tain types of microorganisms are heterotrophs. Such organisms must take in, or ingest, food containing "ready-made" nutrients from other plants or animals.

8-4 Digestion

For a nutrient to be used by the cells of an organism, it must pass through the cell membranes. In general, the nutrient molecules in food are too large to pass through cell membranes. Thus, to be used by the cells, most food molecules must be broken down into smaller, simpler forms. The process by which food molecules are broken down is called **digestion** (dy-*jes*-chun).

The term *digestion* usually refers to the chemical breakdown of food substances into simpler compounds. In many organisms, pieces of food are first cut, crushed, or broken into smaller particles without being changed chemically. This treatment results in the mechanical breakdown of the food. Mechanical breakdown increases the surface area of the food particles. Chemical digestion is carried out by digestive enzymes, which act only on the surface of food particles. Thus, mechanical breakdown prepares the food for more rapid chemical digestion by exposing more food surface to the action of the digestive enzymes. Chemical digestion, like mechanical breakdown, takes place in stages. Large molecules are broken down into smaller molecules, and these in turn are broken down into still simpler forms. The usable, simplest products of digestion are the end products of digestion.

ADAPTATIONS FOR NUTRITION

After completing your study of this section, you should be able to:

1. **Contrast intracellular digestion and extracellular digestion.**
2. **Compare digestive processes in protozoa, hydra, earthworm, and grasshopper.**

8-5 Nutrition in Protozoa

Among the protozoa digestion is **intracellular** (in-truh-*sel*-yuh-ler)—that is, it occurs within the cell. However, members of this group show a variety of adaptations for food-getting. The ameba and paramecium are one-celled protozoans that live in water and feed on smaller organisms. Both have the ability to move, and they appear to be attracted to food by chemical stimuli.

Amebas crawl along solid surfaces by a flowing of cytoplasm into projections of the cell called pseudopods, or "false feet." When an ameba comes in contact with a food particle, pseudopods surround the particle (see Figure 8-2). The cell

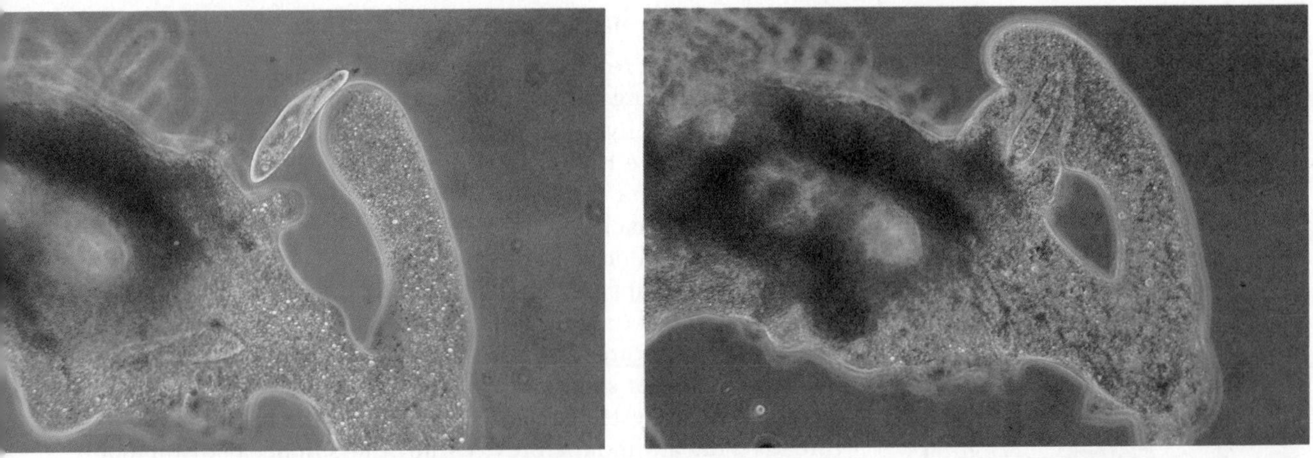

membranes of the pseudopods then join so that the particle is incorporated into the cell but is enclosed within a membrane. Although the food is within the cell, it is separated from the other cell contents by a membrane. It now is in a food vacuole that moves about within the cell cytoplasm. The food vacuole fuses with a lysosome, and digestive enzymes from the lysosome break down the food in the vacuole into forms usable by the cell. These products of digestion diffuse across the vacuole membrane into the cytoplasm. Indigestible materials remain in the food vacuole. The food vacuole eventually fuses with the cell membrane, and its contents are expelled from the cell.

Figure 8-2. Food-Getting in Ameba. As the ameba senses its food, a paramecium, its pseudopods reach out to surround it (left). The engulfed paramecium is enclosed in a food vacuole inside the ameba (right). Note that the ameba had already captured another paramecium.

The paramecium moves by the beating of hairlike cilia that cover the outside of the organism. The movement of the cilia also sweeps food particles down the **oral groove** into the **gullet** (*gul*-et) (see Figure 8-3). As food collects at the end of the gullet, the cell membrane bulges inward and pinches off, forming a food vacuole. The food vacuole travels through the cytoplasm. As in the ameba, the food vacuole fuses with a lysosome, which contains digestive enzymes. Digestion occurs within the vacuole, and the usable products diffuse into the cytoplasm. Indigestible material is discharged from the cell at the **anal** (*ayn*-ul) **pore.**

Figure 8-3. Food-Getting in Paramecium. Food particles are swept down the oral groove into the gullet by the beating of the cilia.

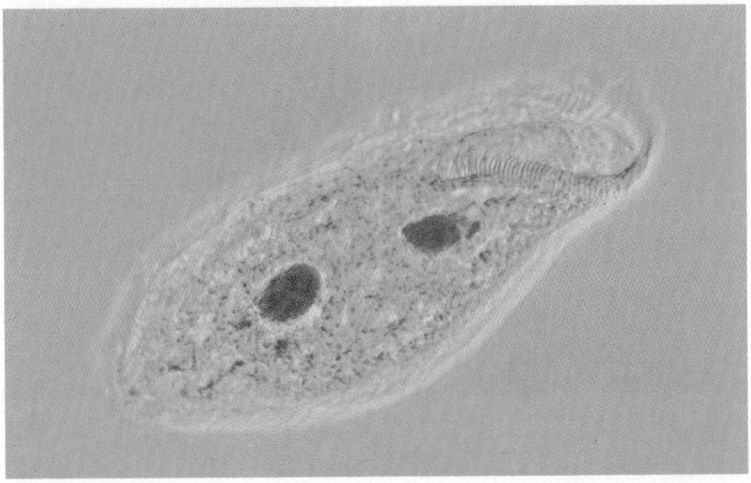

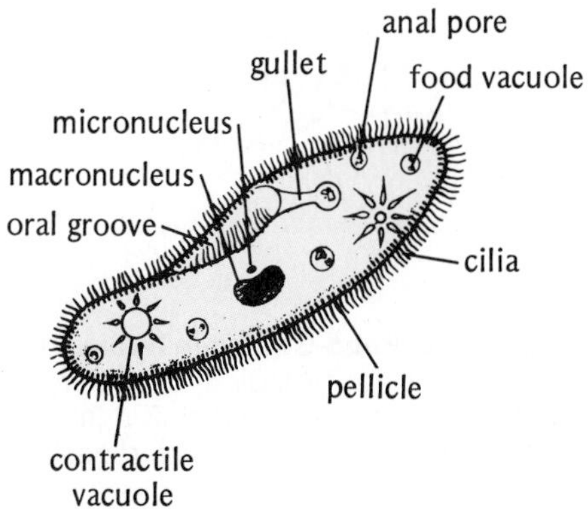

Figure 8-4. Structure of Hydra. The hydra body has two cell layers, the ectoderm and endoderm. Tentacles surround the mouth. The stinging cells of the tentacles each contain a nematocyst.

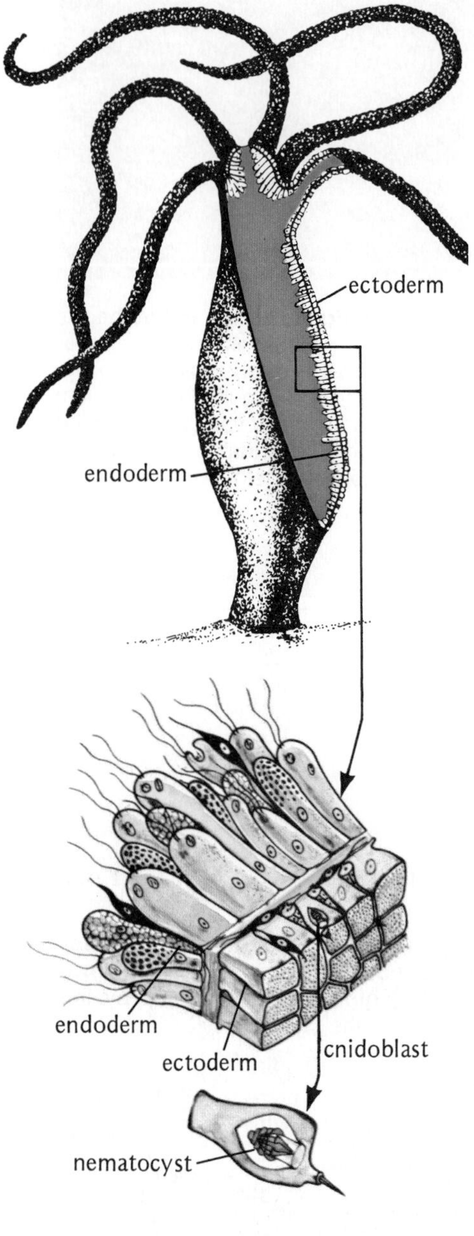

8-6 Nutrition in Hydra

The hydra is a relatively simple multicellular animal about 5 millimeters long from the tip of its tentacles to its base. The body of the hydra is a hollow cylinder made up of two layers of cells (see Figure 8-4). The outer layer is the **ectoderm** (*ek*-tuh-derm), and the inner layer is the **endoderm** (*en*-duh-derm). The tentacles, which surround the mouth, contain stinging cells called **cnidoblasts** (*nyd*-uh-blasts). Within each cnidoblast is a capsule called a **nematocyst** (neh-*mat*-uh-sist), which contains a coiled, hollow thread.

The hydra captures its food with its tentacles. When a water flea or some other small animal comes in contact with a tentacle, the nematocysts discharge their long threads. Some of the threads wind around the prey, while others inject a poison that paralyzes the animal. By movements of the tentacles, the food is stuffed through the mouth and into the **gastrovascular cavity**, where digestion begins (see Figure 8-5).

Digestion in hydra is both intracellular and extracellular. Extracellular digestion takes place outside the cells. Nutrients are then absorbed into the cells. Specialized cells in the endoderm secrete digestive enzymes into the gastrovascular cavity. These enzymes partially break down the food. Other endoderm cells have flagella, and the waving of these organelles

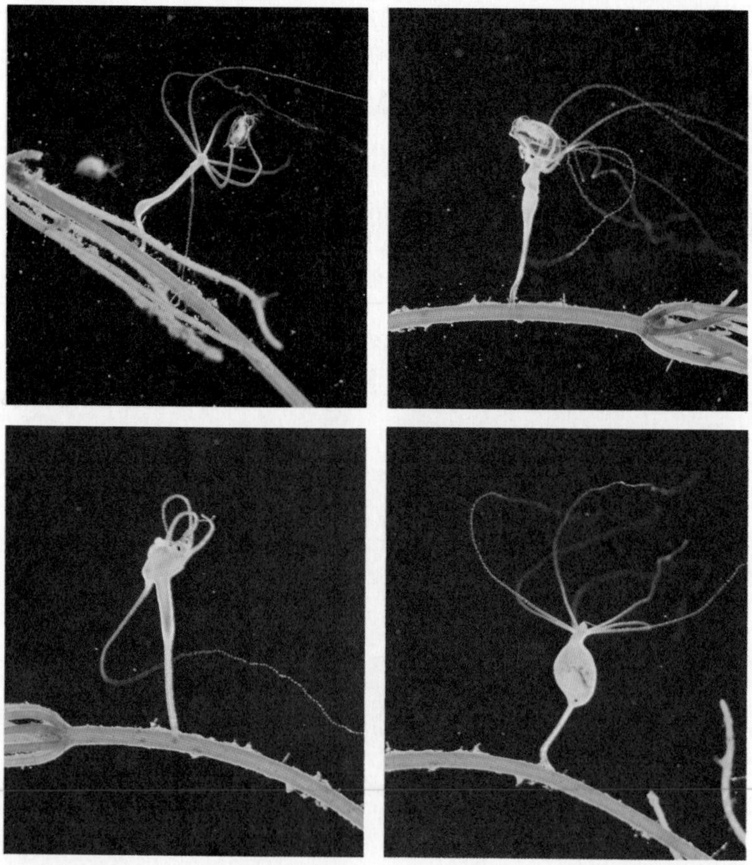

Figure 8-5. Food-Getting in Hydra. The hydra uses its tentacles to capture a water flea (daphnia) and stuff it into its gastrovascular cavity, where digestion will occur.

circulates the food particles through the gastrovascular cavity. Some endoderm cells form pseudopods and engulf, or phagocytize, the small food particles, thus forming food vacuoles. Digestion is completed by enzymes secreted into the food vacuoles. Since the hydra is only two cell layers thick, the end products of digestion pass easily from the cells of the endoderm into the cells of the ectoderm by diffusion. Wastes from the ectoderm cells diffuse directly into the surrounding water. Wastes from the endoderm diffuse back into the gastrovascular cavity and are carried out through the mouth by water currents.

The presence of the digestive cavity and the capacity for extracellular digestion in hydra are considered to be advances over the protozoa because they allow the coelenterates to feed on larger pieces of food.

Hydras can digest proteins and fats, but not carbohydrates.

8-7 Nutrition in the Earthworm

The earthworm is a complex multicellular animal with a "tube-within-a-tube" body plan. The inner tube is the digestive system, while the outer tube is the body wall (see Figure 8-6). The digestive tube, or **alimentary** (al-uh-*ment*-uh-ree) **canal,** has two openings—the mouth, through which food enters the body, and the **anus** (*ayn*-us) through which waste matter leaves. Food travels through the digestive system in one direction—from the mouth to the anus. The food is broken down both mechanically and chemically in the digestive tract. Usable nutrients are then absorbed into the body cells.

As earthworms burrow through the ground, they ingest large quantities of soil. They also come to the surface to eat leaf litter and other decaying plant matter. Food is pulled into the mouth by the sucking action of the muscular **pharynx** (*fa*-rinks). The food is then pushed through the digestive tube by waves of muscular contraction. From the pharynx, food passes through the **esophagus** (eh-*sahf*-uh-gus) into a round, thin-walled organ called the **crop.** The crop, which functions as a storage chamber, gradually releases food into the **gizzard** (*giz*-urd). The gizzard is a thick-walled grinding organ that

Figure 8-6. Digestive System of the Earthworm.

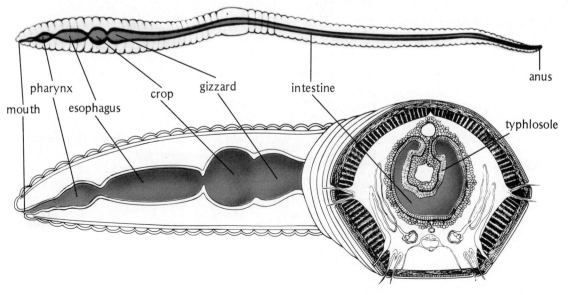

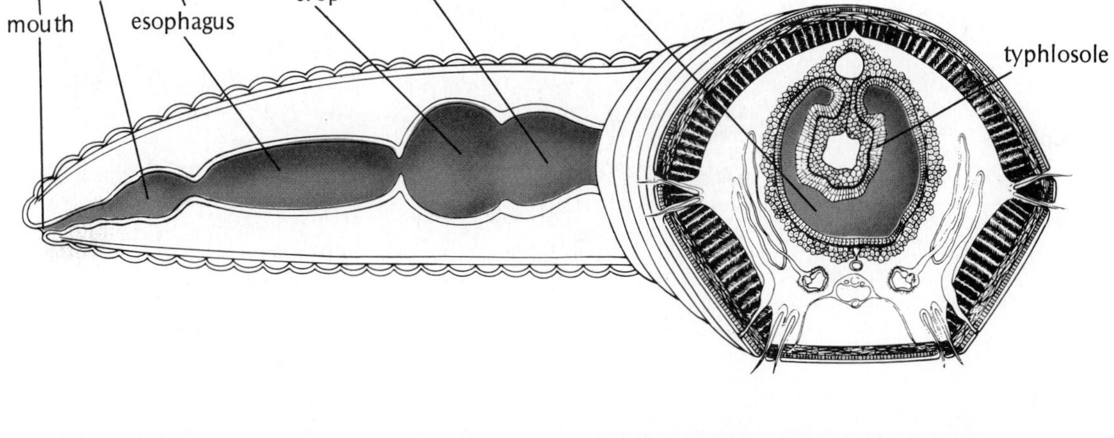

crushes the food. Mechanical breakdown is accomplished by the muscular movements of the gizzard, which grind the organic material against the sand grains from the soil. From the gizzard, the pastelike food mass passes into the long **intestine.**

Chemical digestion and absorption take place in the intestine. The surface area of the intestine is increased by a fold in the wall called the **typhlosole** (*tif*-luh-sohl). Cells lining the intestine secrete enzymes that break down large food molecules into smaller molecules. The products of digestion are absorbed by cells of the intestine and are picked up by the blood. The food molecules are transported in the blood to all parts of the body. Undigested materials and soil from which the food has been removed pass out of the worm through the anus.

8-8 Nutrition in the Grasshopper

The grasshopper, like the earthworm, has a tubular digestive system (see Figure 8-7). Food is broken down mechanically by the mouthparts, which are well-adapted for chewing leafy vegetation. In the mouth the food is mixed with **saliva** (suh-*ly*-vuh) secreted by the **salivary** (*sal*-uh-ver-ee) **glands.** The food then passes through the esophagus into the crop, where it is stored temporarily. From the crop the food passes into the muscular gizzard, where it is ground into smaller particles by the action of teethlike plates made of **chitin** (*kyt*-un). From the gizzard, food passes into the **stomach,** where chemical digestion takes place. Digestive enzymes produced by glands just outside the stomach pass into the stomach, where they act on food particles. The products of digestion are absorbed into the bloodstream through the stomach walls and are transported to all the cells of the body. Undigested material passes through the intestine and is stored temporarily in the **rectum** where water absorption occurs. The dried wastes are eliminated through the anus.

Figure 8-7. Digestive System of the Grasshopper.

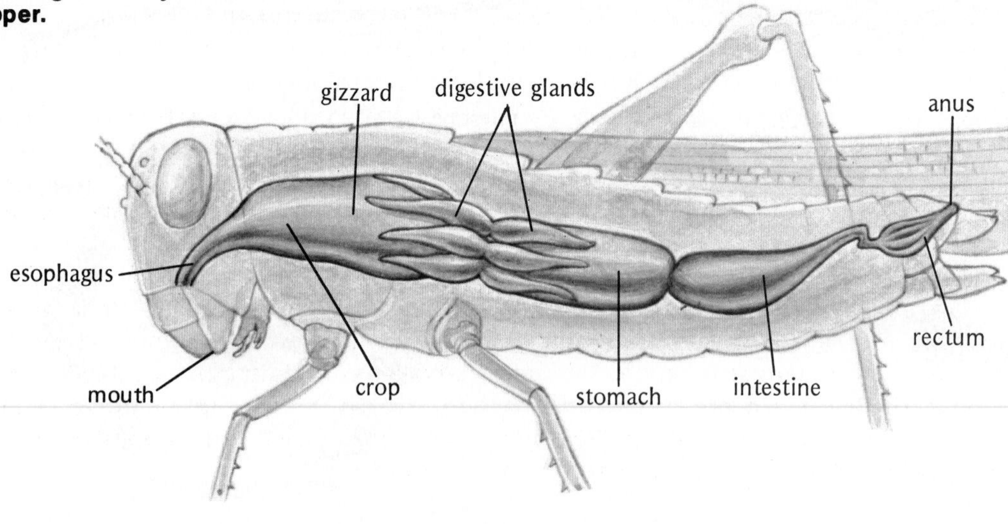

sidelights

Vitamins are necessary for good health. They are coenzymes or are converted into coenzymes, and they function with certain enzymes to catalyze metabolic reactions in the cells. A lack of a particular vitamin leads to the development of a particular deficiency disease.

The importance and nature of vitamins was not discovered until the early 1900s. However, at least one vitamin deficiency disease, scurvy, was recognized and treated in the mid-1700s. The Scottish physician James Lind realized that scurvy appeared where food supplies were scarce or highly restricted, as on a ship. He treated people suffering from scurvy with a variety of different foods, and found that they responded to a diet high in citrus fruits. Eventually, the British navy made a practice of giving its sailors lime juice to prevent scurvy, which is why British sailors became known as "limeys." In the 1890s, the Dutch physician Christiaan Eijkman discovered that a disease of chickens that was very similar to beriberi in humans could be caused or cured by particular diets.

Although it was known that scurvy and beriberi were caused by an absence of something in the diet, it was not until the early 1900s that the concept of vitamins, specific organic substances needed in the diet in small amounts, was developed.

In 1912, the Polish-American biochemist Casimir Funk found that the substance that prevented beriberi in chickens was an amine (a substance containing the $-NH_2$ group). Funk suggested the term "vitamine" for such substances. However, when it was discovered that other substances that served similar functions were not amines, the term became "vitamin." It is now known that beriberi is caused by a lack of thiaamine (a B vitamin) and scurvy by a lack of vitamin C.

Although it has been established that vitamins are needed in certain minimum amounts, a controversy has arisen over the theory that higher daily doses of vitamins can be even more beneficial to health. The U.S. Food and Drug Administration (the FDA) has established a "recommended daily allowance," or RDA, for each vitamin. These are the amounts that the FDA has found are needed by the average person to prevent vitamin deficiency diseases.

However, there are some nutritional researchers who feel that the FDA's allowances are much too low. They argue that much higher levels of vitamins are not only safe, but beneficial. They feel that it is not just a question of preventing deficiencies, but of giving large enough doses for individuals to reach optimal health. Some believe that vitamin therapy—very large doses (megadoses) of one or more vitamins—provides a wide variety of benefits for the body.

However, it does not necessarily follow that if small doses of vitamins are good for you, then large doses will be even better. Some vitamins (the B vitamins and vitamin C) are water-soluble. When these vitamins are taken in high doses, the excess is excreted from the body by the kidneys. Vitamin therapists argue that the water-soluble vitamins are safe in any amount since the body can get rid of the excess. This seems to be true of the B vitamins, but there is mounting evidence that large doses of vitamin C produce some ill effects before the body can excrete the excess.

Vitamins A, D, E, and K are fat-soluble. Excess fat-soluble vitamins are not simply excreted from the body. Instead they are stored in fatty tissues, and can accumulate to toxic levels. An excess of vitamin A can cause headaches, nausea, diarrhea, and fatigue. Still higher doses can cause increased pressure in the cerebrospinal fluid and brain damage. Vitamin D overdose can cause growth retardation and calcium deposits in children and serious kidney damage in adults. Some researchers now think that megadoses of vitamin E, which was once considered harmless in any amount, can also have toxic effects, including interfering with blood clotting.

Should you take large doses of vitamins to stay healthy? Most physicians and nutritionists feel that a good, balanced diet provides all the vitamins you need. If you don't eat a balanced diet, they may recommend a daily vitamin supplement containing RDA levels of the vitamins. Although some other experts believe that large doses of certain vitamins can be beneficial, even to people who eat well and are in good health, the evidence for this is disputed. Such large doses of vitamins, even those that are water-soluble, may be harmful.

HUMAN DIGESTIVE SYSTEM

After completing your study of this section, you should be able to:

1. Describe the functions of the various parts of the human digestive system—the mouth, esophagus, stomach, small intestine, liver, gallbladder, pancreas, and large intestine.
2. List the principle digestive enzymes, where they are produced, the type of food they act upon, and the end products of enzymatic breakdown.

Figure 8-8. Human Digestive System. Accessory digestive glands are also a part of the digestive system.

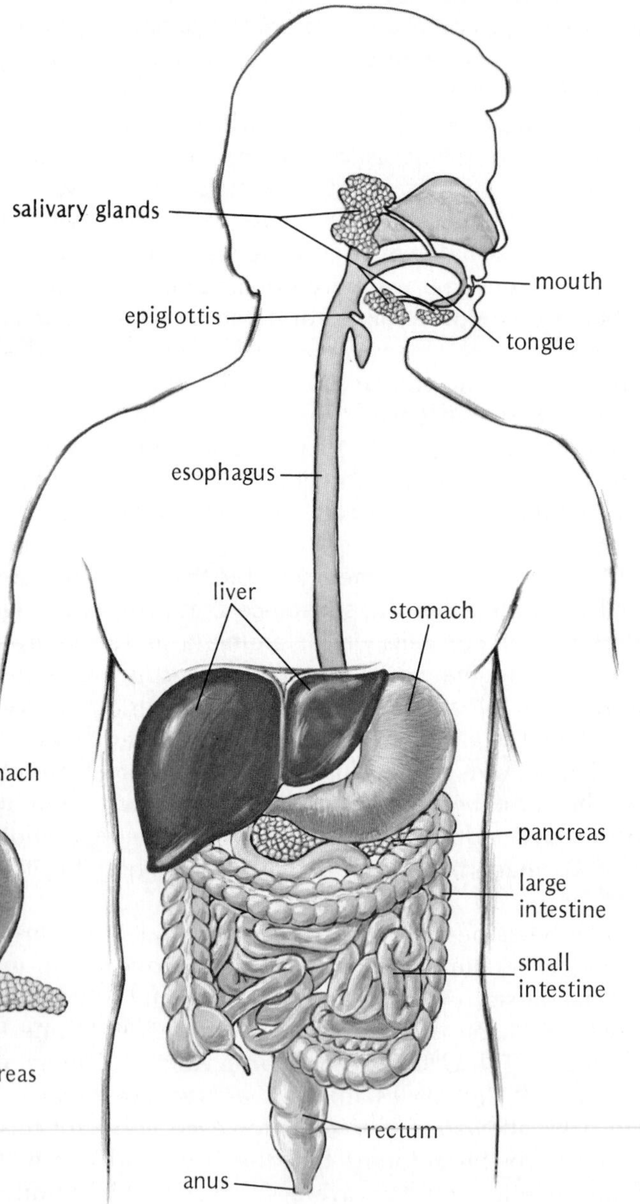

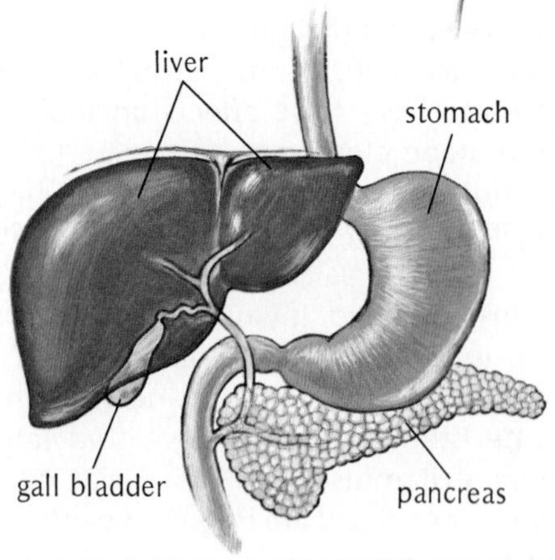

8-9 Parts of the Human Digestive System

The structure and function of the human digestive system is basically similar to that of the earthworm and the grasshopper. The digestive tube consists of a series of specialized organs, with different phases of digestion occurring in each organ. Food passes through the digestive tube in the following order: oral cavity (mouth), pharynx (throat), esophagus (gullet), stomach, small intestine, large intestine, rectum, and anus (see Figure 8-8). Several glands secrete digestive enzymes and juices into the digestive tube, where extracellular digestion occurs.

The digestive glands are groups of specialized secretory cells that are found in the lining of the alimentary canal or in separate accessory organs. The accessory glands lie outside the digestive tract. Their secretions pass into the digestive tract by way of a tube or duct. Food is never found within the accessory glands, only within the alimentary canal itself. The accessory glands include the salivary glands, the **liver,** and the **pancreas** (*pan*-kree-us).

Cells in the lining of the walls of the alimentary canal also secrete a slimy **mucus** (*myoo*-kus), which acts as lubricant for the food mass. It also provides a coating that protects the delicate cells of the digestive tube from the action of acid, digestive enzymes, and abrasive substances in the food.

8-10 The Mouth and Pharynx

Food enters the body through the mouth, where both mechanical breakdown and chemical digestion occur. Chunks of food are bitten off with the teeth and ground into pieces small enough to swallow. The tongue moves and shapes the food mass in the mouth.

As food is chewed, it is mixed with saliva, which is secreted into the mouth by three pairs of salivary glands. There are actually two types of saliva produced. One is a thin, watery secretion that wets the food. The other is a thicker, mucus secretion that acts as a lubricant and causes the food particles to stick together to form a food mass, or *bolus* (*boh*-lus). Saliva also contains a digestive enzyme called **ptyalin** (*ty*-uh-lin), or **salivary amylase** (*am*-uh-layz). This enzyme breaks down starch, which is a polysaccharide, into maltose, which is a disaccharide.

When the food has been chewed sufficiently, it is pushed by the tongue to the back of the throat, or pharynx (see Figure 8-9). This initiates the automatic swallowing reflex, which forces food into the esophagus, the tube leading to the stomach. However, air as well as food passes through the pharynx. The air must pass through the voice box, or **larynx** (*la*-rinks), and down the **trachea** (*tray*-kee-uh) to the lungs. To prevent food and liquids from entering the larynx, it is automatically closed off during swallowing by a flap of tissue

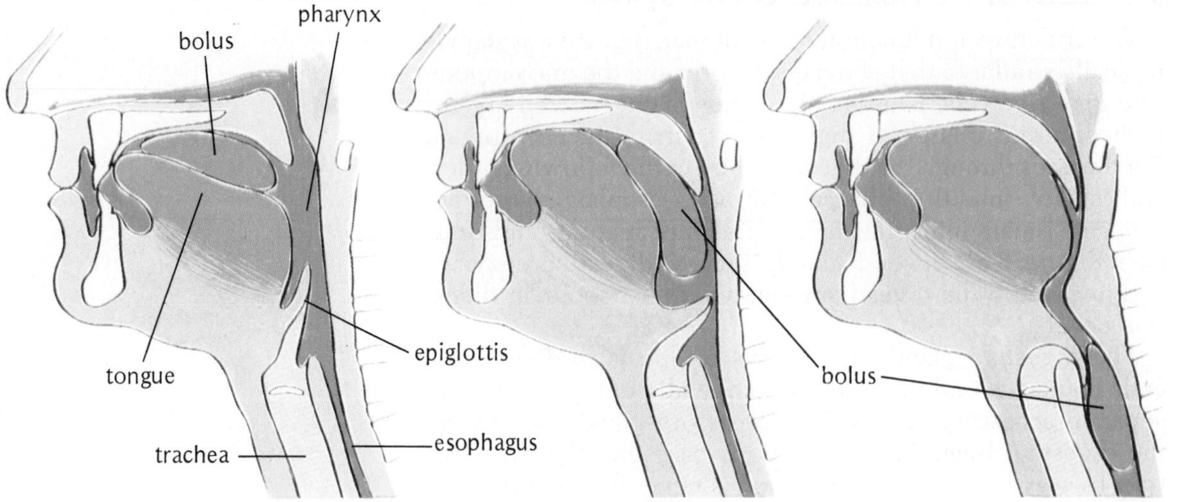

Figure 8-9. Swallowing. The epiglottis prevents food or liquid from entering the air passages during swallowing.

called the **epiglottis** (ep-uh-*glaht*-is). At the same time, breathing stops momentarily, and the passageways to the nose, ears, and mouth are blocked. When a person "swallows the wrong way" and food enters the trachea, it is brought back up into the throat by violent coughing.

8-11 The Esophagus

The esophagus is a tube through which food passes from the pharynx to the stomach. Beginning in the esophagus, the movement of food down the digestive tube is aided by alternate waves of relaxation and contraction in the muscular walls of the alimentary canal. This is called **peristalsis** (pehr-uh-*stahl*-sis). The muscles in front of the food mass relax, while those behind the food mass contract, pushing the food forward.

Aided by peristaltic contractions, food passes quickly down the esophagus. Where the esophagus opens into the stomach, there is a ring of muscle called a **sphincter** (*sfink*-ter). The sphincter acts as a valve and controls the passage of food from the esophagus into the stomach. When the wave of peristalsis reaches the sphincter, it relaxes and opens, and the food enters the stomach. The sphincter between the esophagus and the stomach is called the *cardiac sphincter*. During vomiting, a wave of peristalsis passes upward—reverse peristalsis—causing the cardiac sphincter to open, and the contents of the stomach to be "thrown up."

8-12 The Stomach

The stomach is a thick-walled, muscular sac that can expand to hold more than 2 liters of food or liquid. Food is stored temporarily in the stomach, and mechanical breakdown and chemical digestion occur there. Food is broken down mechanically into smaller particles by the contractions of the muscular stomach walls. The food mass is churned and mixed with gastric juice secreted by glands in the stomach walls.

The lining of the stomach contains two types of glands. **Pyloric** (py-*lor*-ik) **glands** secrete mucus, which covers the stomach lining and protects it from being digested. **Gastric** (*gas*-trik) **glands** secrete very acidic **gastric juice,** which has a pH of 1.5 to 2.5. This juice contains **hydrochloric** (hy-druh-*klor*-ik) **acid** (HCl) and the digestive enzyme **pepsin** (*pep*-sin). Pepsin is secreted in an inactive form called *pepsinogen* (pep-*sin*-uh-jen), which is activated after it is mixed with the hydrochloric acid. Pepsin breaks down large protein molecules into shorter chains of amino acids called **polypeptides** (pol-ee-*pep*-tydz).

Students may be interested in the work of Dr. William Beaumont on Alexis St. Martin, a hunter whose gunshot wound healed, leaving an opening into his stomach. Beaumont observed the effects of gastric juice on various kinds of foods, and the effects of different emotional states on the inner lining of the stomach.

Pepsin also curdles milk proteins—that is, it causes them to solidify. The liquid portion of milk passes quickly into the small intestine. The curdled proteins, however, remain in the stomach for a longer time, allowing digestion to occur. Without curdling, the milk proteins would pass through the stomach before any digestion had occurred.

Hydrochloric acid not only provides the proper pH for the functioning of pepsin, but also kills most bacteria present in food.

The breakdown of starch by ptyalin, which begins in the mouth, continues for some time after the food mass reaches the stomach. Gradually, however, the low pH of the acid in the stomach inactivates this enzyme, and starch breakdown stops.

When no food is in the stomach, only small amounts of gastric juice are present. When food is taken in, the flow of gastric juice increases. There are three mechanisms involved in stimulating the flow of gastric juice.

1. The thought, sight, smell, or taste of food stimulates the brain to send messages to the gastric glands, causing them to secrete moderate amounts of gastric juice.
2. Food touching the lining of the stomach stimulates the secretion of moderate amounts of gastric juice.
3. When a food mass enters the stomach, it stretches the stomach walls. This stretching, as well as the presence of proteins, caffeine, alcohol, and certain other substances, stimulates the lining of the stomach to secrete a hormone called **gastrin** (*gas*-trin) directly into the blood. (A *hormone* is a substance that is secreted directly into the bloodstream and that produces a specific effect on a particular tissue.) Gastrin stimulates the gastric glands to produce large amounts of gastric juice.

Liquids pass through the stomach in 20 minutes or less. Solids, on the other hand, must first be reduced to a thin, soupy liquid called **chyme** (kyme). The chyme passes in small amounts at a time through the *pyloric sphincter,* the muscle that controls the passage of food from the stomach into the small intestine. The stomach empties from 2 to 6 hours after a meal. Hunger is felt when an empty stomach is churning.

If the thick mucus layer that protects the stomach wall breaks down, a part of the stomach wall may be digested, and a painful ulcer develops. It is thought that some ulcers are caused by the oversecretion of gastric juice brought on by nervousness or stress. Ulcers are treated by diet, medication, or, in severe cases, by surgery.

8-13 The Small Intestine

The small intestine is a coiled tube about 6.5 meters long and about 2.5 centimeters in diameter. Most chemical digestion and almost all absorption occur here. Unlike the stomach with its acid secretions, fluids in the small intestine are generally alkaline.

In the small intestine, chyme is mixed with **bile** from the liver, **pancreatic** (pan-kree-*at*-ik) **juice** from the pancreas, and **intestinal juice** from glands in the wall of the intestine. These three secretions contain the enzymes and other substances necessary to complete digestion.

Peristalsis of the small intestine. When food is present, the small intestine is in constant motion. These peristaltic movements have four main effects: (1) they squeeze chyme through the intestine; (2) they mix the chyme with digestive enzymes; (3) they break down food particles mechanically; and (4) they speed up absorption of digestive end products by bringing the intestinal contents into contact with the intestinal wall.

Pancreatic juice. When the acid chyme from the stomach enters the small intestine, it stimulates cells in the intestinal lining to secrete two hormones into the blood. These hormones are *secretin* (sih-*kreet*-in) and *cholecystokinin* (koh-luh-sis-tuh-*ky*-nin). These hormones stimulate the pancreas to secrete pancreatic juice and pancreatic enzymes, which pass through the pancreatic duct into the upper part of the small intestine. Pancreatic juice contains sodium bicarbonate, which neutralizes the acid in the chyme and makes the pH of the contents of the small intestine slightly alkaline (pH 8). The enzymes secreted by the pancreas act on every major component of food—proteins, carbohydrates, fats, and nucleic acids.

Trypsin and chymotrypsin are secreted in inactive forms and are activated in the intestine.

The pancreatic enzymes include **amylase,** which hydrolyzes any remaining starch to maltose; **proteases** (*pro*-tee-ay-zez) (protein-splitting enzymes), including **trypsin** (*trip*-sin) and **chymotrypsin** (ky-muh-*trip*-sin), which continue the breakdown of large protein molecules begun in the stomach; and **lipase,** which breaks down fats.

Bile. The cells of the liver produce bile, which passes through ducts into the **gallbladder,** where it is stored. Bile passes from the gallbladder to the upper part of the small intestine through the **bile duct.** The release of bile from the gallbladder is stimulated by the hormone cholecystokinin, which also acts on the pancreas. Bile contains no enzymes, but it aids in the digestion of fats and oils by breaking them up into tiny droplets. This process, called **emulsification** (ih-mul-suh-fuh-*kay*-shun), increases the surface area for enzyme action. Since bile is alkaline, it aids in neutralizing the acid chyme from the stomach.

Intestinal juice. The walls of the small intestine contain millions of intestinal glands, which secrete intestinal juice. Intestinal juice contains enzymes that complete the digestion of carbohydrates, fats, and proteins.

In the small intestine, molecules of proteins, carbohydrates, and fats are broken down into the end products of digestion. Proteins are broken down into amino acids, carbohydrates into simple sugars, and fats into fatty acids and glycerol. A summary of the secretions of the human digestive system and their functions is given in Table 8-3 (page 138).

Within the vessels of the lymphatic system, the fatty acids and glycerol recombine, forming fat molecules. The fat molecules are added to the bloodstream when the lymph empties into veins near the heart.

Absorption. The small intestine is the site of **absorption.** Simple sugars, amino acids, vitamins, minerals, and other substances are absorbed through the wall of the small intestine into the blood vessels of the circulatory system. Fatty acids and glycerol are absorbed into tiny vessels of the lymphatic system called **lacteals** (*lak*-tee-uls) (see page 155).

The small intestine has a number of structural features that increase its surface area and make it ideally suited for absorption (see Figure 8-10). (1) The small intestine is very long. (2) Its lining has many folds. (3) The lining is covered with millions of fingerlike projections called **villi** (*vil*-ly). (4) The epithelial cells that make up the intestinal lining have **brush borders.** In the brush borders, the ends of the cells that face into the intestinal opening have tiny projections called **microvilli** that further increase the surface area.

Within each villus there is a network of blood capillaries, and in the center is a lacteal. The outer covering of each villus is a layer of epithelial cells with microvilli. During absorption, digested nutrients pass through the epithelial cells and enter either the capillaries or the lacteal. Absorption involves both diffusion and active transport.

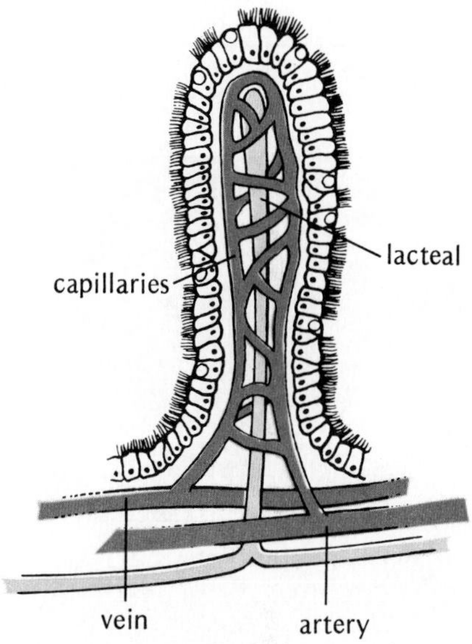

Figure 8-10. Cross Section of a Villus.

8-14 The Large Intestine

Undigested and unabsorbed materials pass from the small intestine through a sphincter into the large intestine. The large intestine is about 1.5 meters long and 6 centimeters in diameter. No digestion occurs in this portion of the digestive system.

On the lower right side of the abdomen, where the small intestine joins the large intestine, is a small pouch, the **appendix** (uh-*pen*-diks). The appendix plays no part in the functioning of the human digestive system. Occasionally, however, the appendix becomes infected, a condition known as **appendicitis** (uh-pen-duh-*sy*-tus). If the condition is not treated, the appendix may burst, spreading the infection.

One of the principal functions of the large intestine is the reabsorption of water from the food mass. During digestion, water is mixed with the food as it moves through the digestive system. The reabsorption of this water into the capillaries of

Organ	Secretions and enzymes	Function
Salivary glands	Saliva: amylase	Enzyme that breaks down starch into maltose.
Esophagus	Mucus	Aids passage of food down esophagus to stomach.
Stomach (gastric glands)	Gastric juice:	
	pepsin	Enzyme that breaks down proteins into smaller molecules (peptones and proteoses).
	hydrochloric acid	Necessary for effective action of pepsin on proteins.
Liver	Bile	Breaks down fat mechanically into small droplets (emulsification).
Pancreas	Pancreatic juice:	
	amylase	Enzyme that continues digestion of starch to disaccharides.
	trypsin	Enzyme that digests peptones and proteoses into peptides.
	lipase	Enzyme that digests fat droplets into fatty acids and glycerol.
Small intestine (intestinal glands)	Intestinal juice:	
	peptidases	Enzymes that break down peptides into amino acids.
	maltase	Enzyme that breaks down maltose (a disaccharide) into glucose (a monosaccharide).
Large intestine	-------	Absorbs water from undigested materials. Forms feces.

Table 8-3. Secretions and Digestive Functions of the Human Digestive System.

the large intestine helps the body conserve water. If too little water is absorbed, diarrhea results; if too much water is absorbed, constipation results.

A second function of the large intestine is the absorption of vitamins produced by bacteria that normally live in the large intestine. The vitamins are absorbed with the water. Intestinal bacteria live on undigested food material. They produce vitamin K, which is essential for blood clotting, and some of the B vitamins. When large doses of antibiotics destroy the intestinal bacteria, a vitamin K deficiency may result.

The third function of the large intestine is the elimination of undigested and indigestible material from the digestive tract.

This material consists of cellulose from plant cell walls, large quantities of bacteria, bile, and mucus, and worn-out cells from the digestive tract. As this material travels through the large intestine, it becomes **feces** (*fee*-seez). Fecal matter is stored in the last part of the large intestine, the **rectum,** and periodically eliminated, or defecated, through the anus.

summary

The process by which organisms obtain food and use it to carry on their life activities is nutrition. The substances in food that can be used in cell metabolism are nutrients. Some organisms can synthesize their own food. These organisms are autotrophs. Other organisms must obtain ready-made food from the environment. These organisms are heterotrophs. All animals are heterotrophs.

The nutrient molecules in food are generally too large and complex to be used by the cells. They must first be broken down into smaller and simpler molecules. This is done by the process of digestion. The nutrients required by living organisms include proteins, carbohydrates, fats, vitamins, and minerals, as well as water.

Energy to carry on life processes comes from the breakdown of fats, carbohydrates, and proteins. The unit used in measuring the energy content of food is the kilocalorie, which is the amount of heat needed to raise the temperature of 1 kg of water by 1°C.

In some of the most simple organisms, such as the protozoa, digestion is intracellular. Food particles are ingested into the cell and enclosed within a food vacuole, which separates them from the other cell contents. The food is broken down by digestive enzymes secreted into the vacuole. Usable nutrient molecules diffuse out of the vacuole for use by the cell. In all but the simplest animals, digestion is extracellular. Food enters a specialized digestive tube, and enzymes are secreted into the tube. Usable nutrients pass from the tube to the cells of the organism. Extracellular digestion occurs in the earthworm and grasshopper, as well as in humans.

Humans, like earthworms and grasshoppers, have a tube-within-a-tube body plan, with the inner tube being the digestive tube. The digestive tube consists of a series of specialized organs, each the site of a particular phase of digestion. The organs of the human digestive tube include the mouth, esophagus, stomach, small intestine, large intestine, rectum, and anus. The salivary glands, liver, and pancreas are accessory organs that secrete their products into the digestive tube.

vocabulary

absorption
alimentary canal
amylase
anal pore
anus
appendicitis
appendix
autotroph
bile
calorie
calorimeter
chemotroph
chyme
chymotrypsin
crop
digestion
ectoderm
emulsification
endoderm
epiglottis
esophagus
extracellular digestion
feces
gallbladder
gastric gland
gastrovascular cavity
gizzard
gullet
heterotroph
hydrochloric acid
intestinal juice
intestine
intracellular digestion
kilocalorie
lacteal
larynx
lipase
liver
mucus
nutrient
nutrition
oral groove
pancreas
pancreatic juice
pepsin
peristalsis
pharynx
protease
ptyalin
pyloric gland
rectum
roughage
saliva
salivary amylase
salivary gland
sphincter
stomach
trachea
trypsin
typhlosole
villus

test your learning

Section

8-1 **1.** Define the terms *nutrition* and *nutrient*.
2. Name the six types of nutrients needed by living organisms.

8-2 **3.** Define the terms *calorie* and *kilocalorie*.
4. How is the energy content of food determined?
5. How does the energy content of fat compare with that of an equal amount of protein or carbohydrate?

8-3 **6.** Explain the differing modes of nutrition in autotrophs, chemotrophs, and heterotrophs.

8-4 **7.** What is digestion, and why is this process necessary?
8. How does mechanical breakdown of food aid in digestion?

8-5 **9.** Describe food-getting, digestion, and elimination of wastes in the ameba and paramecium.

8-6 **10.** Describe food-getting, digestion, and elimination of wastes in the hydra.

8-7 **11.** Trace the path of food through the alimentary canal of the earthworm, explaining what happens in each part of the digestive tube.

8-8 **12.** List the parts of the digestive system of the grasshopper in order beginning with the mouth.

8-9 **13.** List the parts of the human digestive system, including the accessory glands.

14. What is the function of mucus in the human alimentary canal?
8-10 15. What are the functions of saliva and its enzyme ptyalin?
16. Describe the pathways of air and of food as they pass through the pharynx.
8-11 17. What structure connects the mouth and the stomach?
18. What causes food to move down the digestive tube?
8-12 19. Name the two types of glands in the stomach lining and their secretions.
20. What enzymes are present in the stomach, and what are their functions in digestion?
21. What mechanisms stimulate the flow of gastric juice?
22. What structures control the passage of food into and out of the stomach?
8-13 23. Name the three fluids that mix with food in the small intestine.
24. How does peristalsis affect the food mass in the small intestine?
25. What types of food are broken down in the small intestine?
26. What are amylases, proteases, and lipases?
27. What organ secretes bile? How does bile reach the small intestine? What is the function of bile in digestion?
28. Name the end products of digestion.
29. What structural features of the small intestine increase its surface area for absorption?
30. Which of the end products of digestion are absorbed into capillaries and which enter lacteals?
8-14 31. Describe the three major functions of the large intestine.

test your understanding

1. Why is food harder to digest when it has not been properly chewed?
2. Describe the breakdown of carbohydrates in the human digestive system beginning in the mouth.
3. Why is absorption in the small intestine important in human nutrition?
4. Why are the salivary glands, liver, and pancreas considered to be part of the digestive system?
5. How does removal of part, or even all, of the stomach affect a person's ability to digest and absorb food?

independent research

1. Many people take vitamin pills to supplement their diet. Write a report discussing the actual need and value of taking various vitamins.
2. Prepare a report on food additives, such as preservatives and dyes. Discuss their relative value and safety, as well as possible problems arising from their use.
3. Prepare a report on reducing diets. Discuss the advantages and disadvantages of current fad diets, as well as the requirements for a good basic reducing diet.

chapter 9

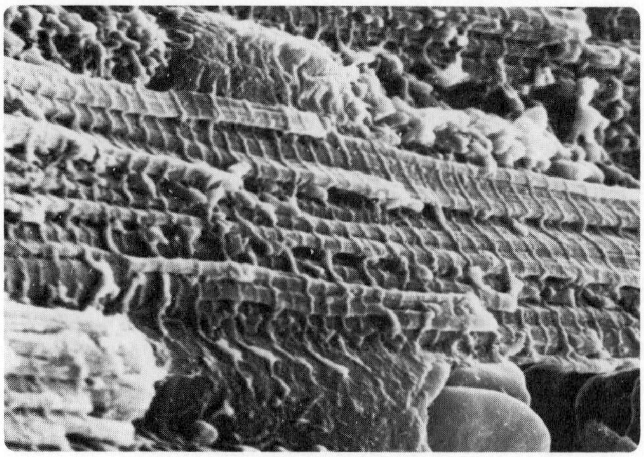

Transport

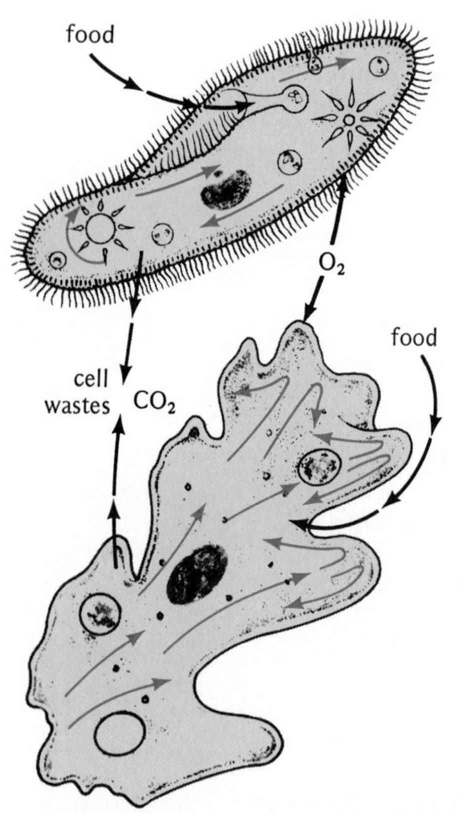

Figure 9-1. Transport in Ameba and Paramecium. In the paramecium (top) and ameba (bottom), the exchange of materials between the cells and the environment occurs by diffusion through the cell membrane.

9-1 Chapter Introduction

Every cell needs substances from the environment to carry on its life processes. To enter the cell, these substances must move across cell membranes. This passage of materials is called **absorption** (ab-*sorp*-shun). Once inside the cell, substances must be moved to the places where they are to be used or stored. In multicellular organisms, materials must also be moved from one cell to another and from one part of the organism to another. For example, oxygen and digested nutrients must be delivered to all cells of an organism. The movement of materials within a cell or between parts of an organism is called **circulation** (ser-kyoo-*lay*-shun). The term **transport** (*trans*-port) refers to all the processes by which substances pass into or out of cells and move within the organism.

In simple organisms, no cell is very far from the external environment. In such organisms the processes of diffusion and active transport, along with the streaming of the cytoplasm, are adequate to move materials both within cells and from one cell to another. However, these processes are too slow to carry materials long distances. In large or complex organisms, many cells are far from the external environment. Such organisms need a special circulatory system to move materials from one part of the organism to another. The circulatory system is the link between the cells of the organism and its environment.

A circulatory system has three components: (1) a fluid in which transported materials are dissolved; (2) a network of tubes or body spaces through which the fluid flows; and (3) a means of driving the fluid through the tubes or spaces. In animals, the fluid in the circulatory system is usually called **blood.** The organ that pumps blood through the system is called the **heart.**

ADAPTATIONS FOR CIRCULATION

After completing your study of this section, you should be able to:

1. Describe the process of transport in the ameba, paramecium, and hydra.
2. Compare the circulatory system of the earthworm with that of the grasshopper.

9-2 Transport in Protists

Protists have no circulatory system. Most are one-celled, and even in the colonial forms, most of the cells are in direct contact with the environment. Diffusion and active transport are adequate to transport materials between the organism and the external environment. Within the cell, the distribution of material is aided by **cyclosis** (sy-*kloh*-sis), which is the streaming of the cytoplasm.

In the ameba and paramecium, food vacuoles circulate through the cytoplasm by cyclosis (see Figure 9-1). As the food is digested, absorption takes place by diffusion or active transport across the food vacuole membrane.

9-3 Transport in Hydra

Simple multicellular animals, such as the hydra, can also get along without a circulatory system. The hydra lives in fresh water. Its body form is like a hollow sac (see Figure 9-2). The body wall of the hydra is composed of two layers of cells. The outer layer, the ectoderm, is in direct contact with the aquatic environment. The inner layer, the endoderm, lines the gastrovascular cavity. The endoderm is also in contact with water because water freely enters and leaves the gastrovascular cavity through the mouth. Therefore, both cell layers can exchange dissolved oxygen, nutrients, carbon dioxide, and wastes directly with their watery environment.

Nutrients from the gastrovascular cavity pass into the cells of the endoderm by active transport and diffusion. The outer layer of ectodermal cells absorbs nutrients from adjoining endoderm cells by diffusion. Within all cells, nutrients and other substances are circulated by cyclosis.

The muscular movements of the hydra as it stretches and contracts help to distribute materials within the gastrovascular cavity. This movement brings needed materials to all cells of the endoderm. It also prevents wastes from collecting near the surface of the endoderm. The flagella of endoderm cells also help move materials. Thus the gastrovascular cavity serves a circulatory function in hydra.

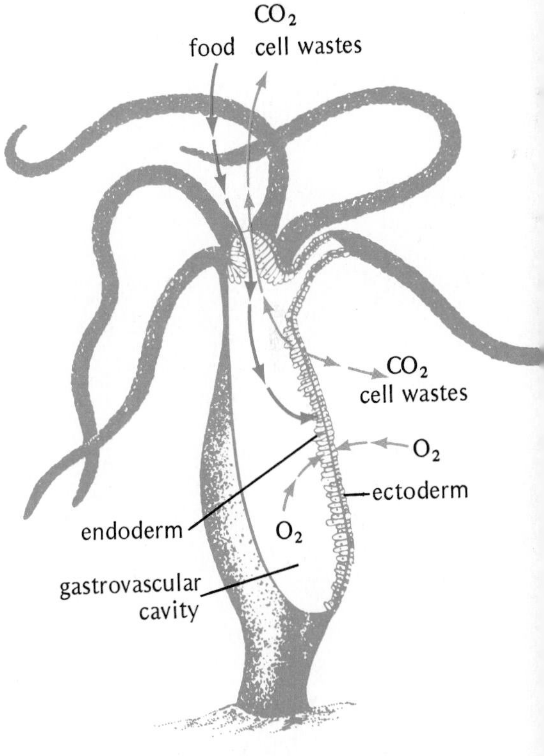

Figure 9-2. Transport in Hydra. In hydras, the cells of both layers of the body wall are in direct contact with the environment. The exchange of materials between the cells and the environment takes place by diffusion through the cell membranes.

9-4 Transport in the Earthworm

The earthworm is structurally much more complex than the hydra. It contains true organs and organ systems. Most of its cells are not in direct contact with the external environment.

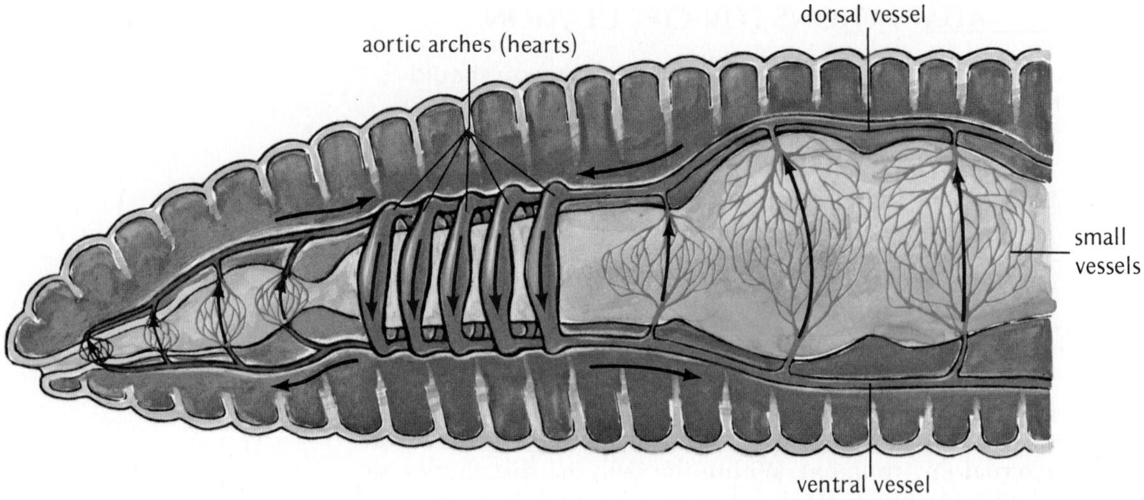

Figure 9-3. Circulatory System of the Earthworm. In the closed circulatory system of the earthworm, the blood is pumped through a system of vessels by the contractions of five pairs of "hearts."

The circulatory system of the earthworm makes possible the exchange of materials between the external environment and body cells.

The main features of the circulatory system of the earthworm are shown in Figure 9-3. The blood carries dissolved nutrients, gases, wastes, water, and other substances. It is red because it contains the red pigment **hemoglobin** (*hee*-muh-gloh-bin). Hemoglobin increases the oxygen-carrying capacity of the blood. The circulatory system of the earthworm is an example of a **closed circulatory system,** one in which the blood is always confined in vessels.

There are two major blood vessels in the earthworm—the *dorsal* (*dor*-sul) *vessel,* which runs along the top of the digestive tract, and the *ventral* (*ven*-trul) *vessel,* which runs below the digestive tract. These two vessels are connected near the anterior, or head, end of the worm by five pairs of blood vessels known as *aortic* (ay-*ort*-ik) *arches,* or "hearts." The pulsations of these heartlike blood vessels pump the blood from the dorsal vessel to the ventral vessel.

The ventral vessel divides into many smaller vessels that go to all parts of the body. These small blood vessels branch into still smaller and smaller vessels. The smallest blood vessels are the microscopic **capillaries** (*kap*-uh-ler-eez), which are so numerous that every cell in the body is near one. The exchange of materials between the blood and the body cells takes place through the walls of the capillaries. Dissolved materials diffuse across the thin walls of capillaries quite rapidly. The capillaries join to form larger vessels that carry the blood back to the dorsal vessel. The dorsal blood vessel contracts rhythmically, forcing the blood back into the aortic arches.

9-5 Transport in the Grasshopper

The grasshopper has an **open circulatory system.** In an open circulatory system, the blood is not always enclosed in blood

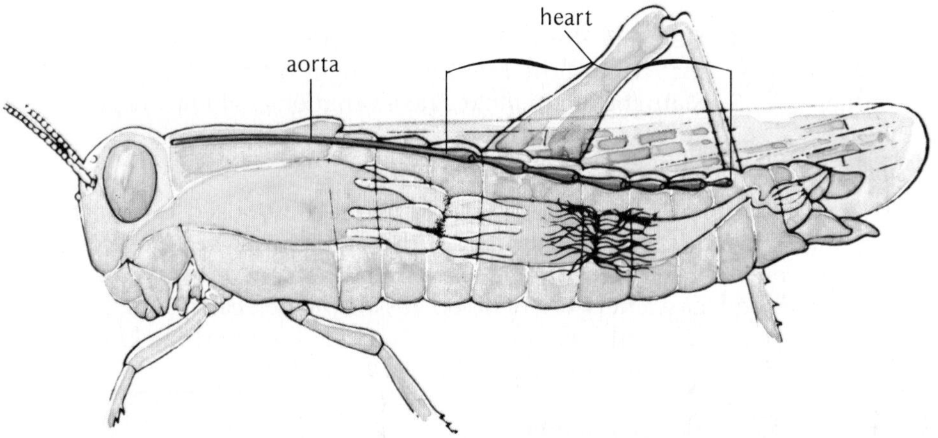

vessels, but flows into open spaces where it bathes the tissues of the body directly.

The blood of the grasshopper does not contain hemoglobin and is colorless. It serves mainly to transport food and nitrogen-containing wastes. It does not transport oxygen or carbon dioxide. Instead, these respiratory gases are transported in a series of tubes that are separate from the circulatory system.

The open circulatory system of the grasshopper is quite different from the closed system of the earthworm (see Figure 9-4). Along the upper, or dorsal, surface, above the digestive and reproductive systems, is a single vessel, the **aorta** (ay-*ort*-uh), and a tubular heart. Contraction of the heart, which is near the posterior, or rear, end of the animal, forces the blood forward through the aorta toward the head. In the head, the blood flows out of the aorta and trickles through the body spaces, or **sinuses** (*sy*-nuh-sez), and over the body tissues. The exchange of materials between the blood and the body cells takes place while the blood is in the sinuses. Blood is kept moving through the sinuses by breathing movements and other body movements. Eventually, the blood passes back into the heart through valvelike openings in the heart wall.

A basic characteristic of an open circulatory system is that the blood moves more slowly than in a closed circulatory system, where it is under pressure. However, open circulatory systems are efficient enough to meet the needs of insects and several other groups of animals.

Figure 9-4. Circulatory System of the Grasshopper. In the open circulatory system of the grasshopper, blood pumped by the tubular heart passes through the aorta and into the body spaces, where it bathes the body tissues.

THE HUMAN CIRCULATORY SYSTEM

After completing your study of this section, you should be able to:

1. Describe and compare the structures of an artery, a vein, and a capillary.
2. Identify the structures of the heart and describe their functions.
3. Trace the path of the blood through the heart.

4. Describe the heartbeat cycle and the mechanisms that control the rate and strength of the heartbeat.
5. State the factors that cause variations in blood pressure.

Humans, like other vertebrates, have a closed circulatory system. It is similar to that of the earthworm, but more complex. The system includes a single heart, which pumps the blood, and a network of blood vessels, which carries the blood to and from all the cells of the body. There are three kinds of blood vessels—arteries, veins, and capillaries.

9-6 Blood Vessels

Arteries. The blood vessels that carry blood away from the heart to the organs and tissues of the body are the **arteries** (*ar*-tuh-reez). The walls of arteries are thick and elastic. They contain layers of connective tissue, muscle tissue, and epithelial tissue (see Figure 9-5). As an artery enters a tissue or organ, it divides and subdivides many times to form smaller and smaller arteries. The smallest arteries are called **arterioles** (ar-*teer*-ee-olz).

Veins. The blood vessels that return blood from the body tissues to the heart are the **veins** *(vaynz)*. The smallest veins are called *venules* (*veen*-yoolz.) The venules join together to form veins, which also merge, forming larger and larger veins. The walls of veins are thin and only slightly elastic. Inside the veins are flaplike **valves** that allow the blood to flow in only

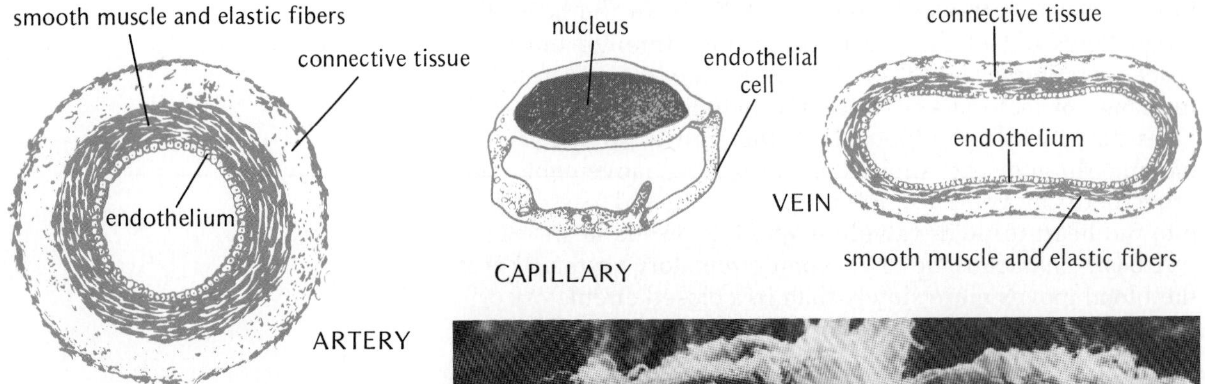

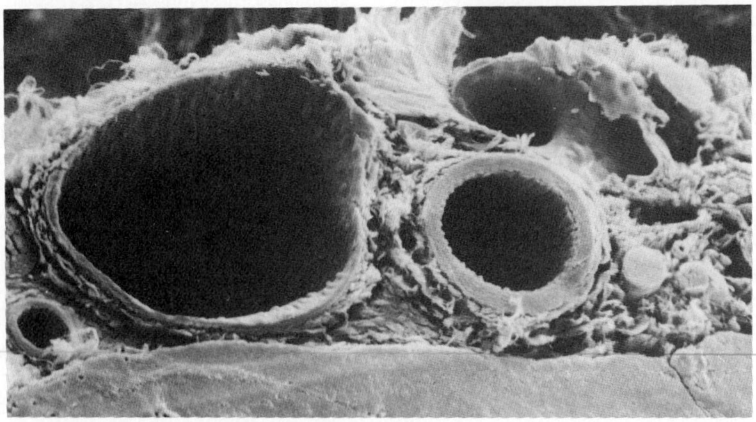

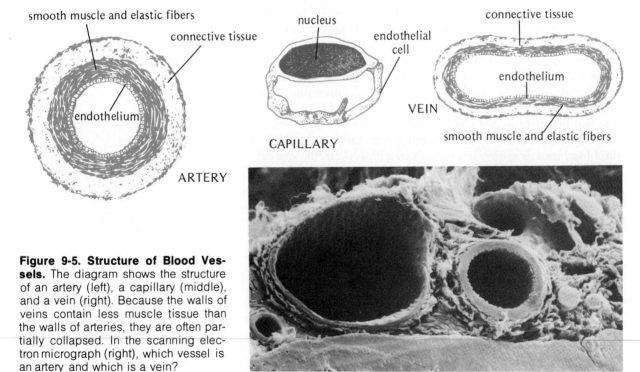

Figure 9-5. Structure of Blood Vessels. The diagram shows the structure of an artery (left), a capillary (middle), and a vein (right). Because the walls of veins contain less muscle tissue than the walls of arteries, they are often partially collapsed. In the scanning electron micrograph (right), which vessel is an artery and which is a vein?

one direction—toward the heart (see Figure 9-6). When the valves do not function properly, blood tends to accumulate within the vein. The walls of the vein become stretched and lose their elasticity. This condition is called *varicose* (*var*-uh-kohs) *veins*.

Capillaries. Arterioles and venules are connected by networks of microscopic capillaries. The walls of the capillaries consist of a single layer of epithelial cells. These vessels are so narrow that red blood cells pass through them in single file. Dissolved nutrients, wastes, oxygen, and other substances are exchanged between the blood and the body cells while blood flows through the capillaries.

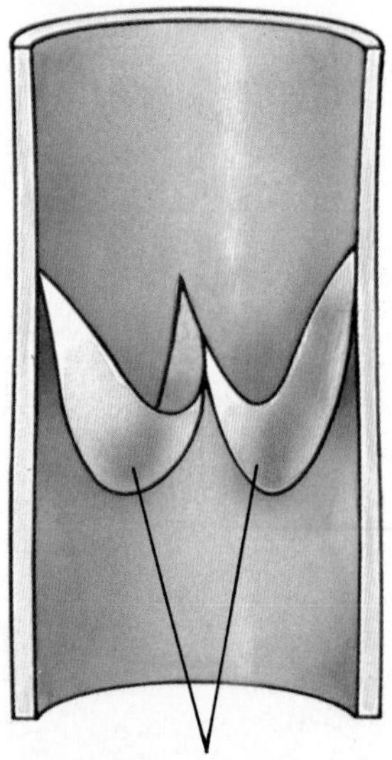

Figure 9-6. Valve in a Vein. This longitudinal section of a vein shows the cuplike valve that prevents the backflow of blood.

9-7 The Heart

The heart is a pump whose rhythmic contractions force the blood through the vessels. This muscular organ is somewhat larger than your fist and is located slightly to the left of the middle of the chest cavity. It is composed mostly of cardiac muscle. Microscope studies show that this tissue consists of individual cells, each with a single nucleus (see Figure 9-7). The cardiac muscle cells form a branching, interlocking network, which enables them to contract with great force.

The outside of the heart is surrounded by a tough protective membrane, the **pericardium** (per-uh-*kard*-ee-um). Internally, the heart is divided into four chambers (see Figure 9-8). The two upper, thin-walled chambers are the **atria** (*ay*-tree-uh), or **auricles** (*or*-ih-kulz). The two lower, thick-walled chambers are the **ventricles** (*ven*-trih-kulz). The right and left sides of the heart are separated by a partition called the **septum** (*sep*-tum).

Figure 9-7. Structure of Cardiac Muscle.

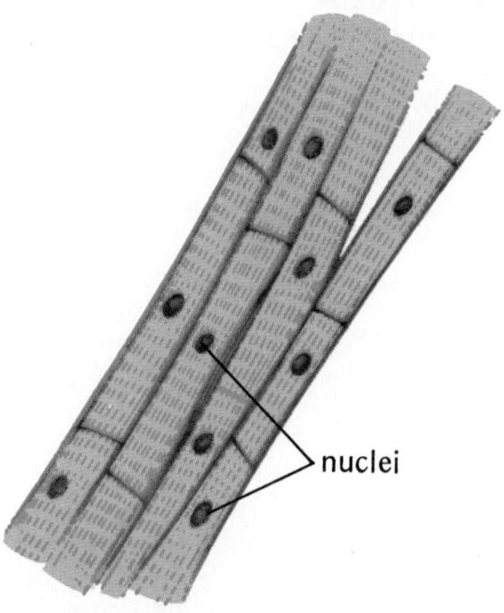

The flow of blood through the heart is controlled by four flaplike valves that allow the blood to flow in only one direction. Two of these valves, called the *atrioventricular* (ay-tree-oh-ven-*trik*-yoo-ler) or *A-V, valves*, allow blood to flow from the atria into the ventricles. They prevent the flow of blood from the ventricles into the atria. In the right side of the heart, the A-V valve is called the *tricuspid* (try-*kus*-pid) valve because it has three flaps. In the left side, it is called the *bicuspid* (by-*kus*-pid), or *mitral* (*my*-trul) *valve*. The other two valves, called the *semilunar* (sem-ee-*loon*-er) *valves*, allow blood to move from the ventricles into the pulmonary artery and the aorta. They prevent backflow from these arteries into the ventricles.

Actually, the heart is a double pump. The right side of the heart sends oxygen-poor blood to the lungs, while the left side sends oxygen-rich blood to the rest of the body.

The heartbeat cycle. The pumping action of the heart involves two main periods. During one of these periods, the heart muscle is relaxed. This period of relaxation is called **diastole** (dy-*as*-tuh-lee). During the other period, the heart muscle is contracting. The period of contraction is called **systole** (*sis*-tuh-lee).

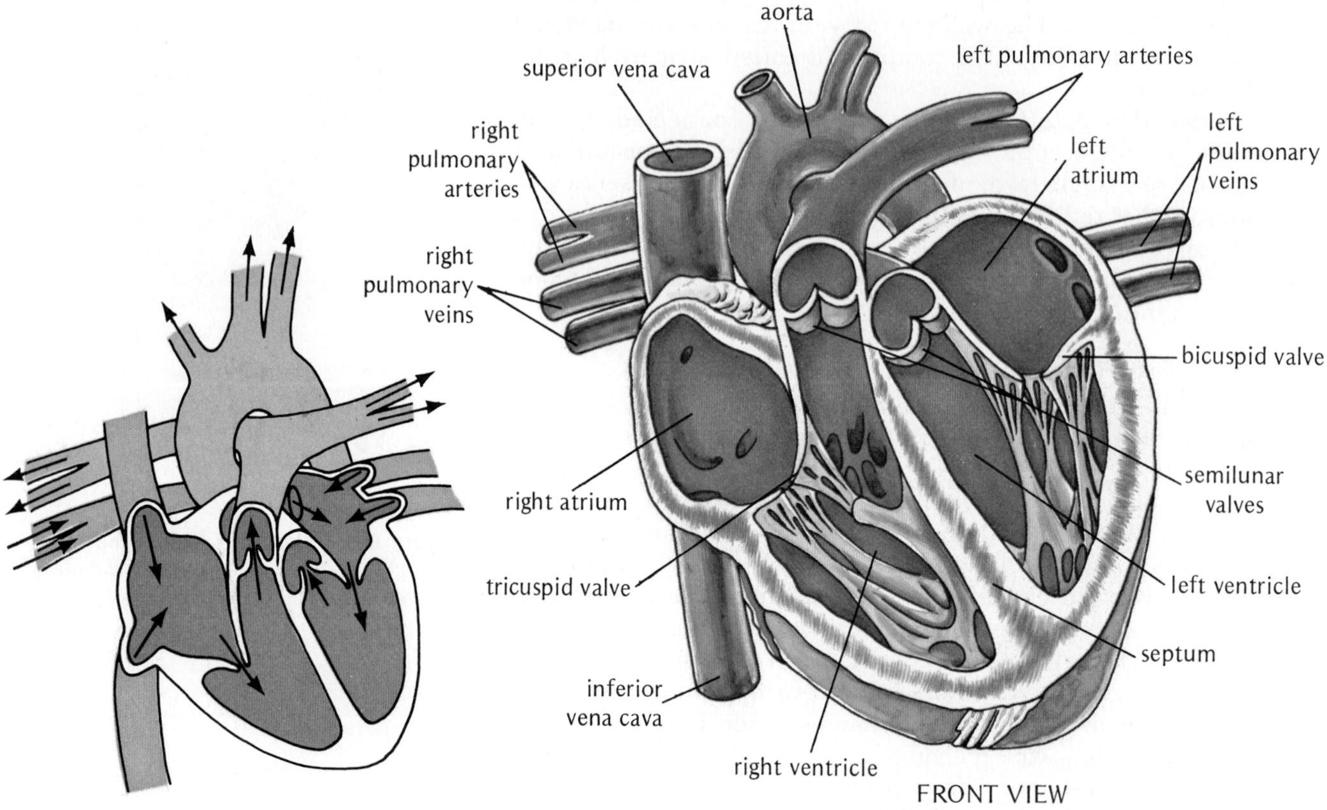

Figure 9-8. Structure of the Human Heart. The cross section of the heart (right) shows the four chambers, the valves, and the blood vessels that connect with the heart chambers. The small drawing above shows the path of the blood through the heart.

During diastole—the period of relaxation—the atrioventricular (A-V) valves are open. Blood flows from the atria into the ventricles. By the end of diastole, the ventricles are about 70 percent filled. Systole—the period of contraction—begins with contraction of the atria. The contraction of the atria forces more blood into the ventricles, filling them. The ventricles then contract. The pressure of this contraction closes the A-V valves and opens the semilunar valves. Blood flows out of the right ventricle into the pulmonary artery, which divides into two pulmonary arteries that lead to the lungs. Blood flows out of the left ventricle into the aorta, the largest artery of the body. The aorta branches and divides into many smaller arteries, which carry blood to all the body tissues.

While the ventricles are contracting, the atria relax. This permits blood to flow into the atria from the veins. Blood returning from the body tissues enters the right atrium. Blood returning from the lungs enters the left atrium. When the ventricles relax, a new period of diastole begins, and the cycle repeats.

Point out that the heart is a very efficient pump. Each day it pumps over 10,000 liters of blood and beats, assuming an average of 70 beats/minute, about 100,000 times.

As the heart valves open and close, they make a "lub-dup" sound that may be heard clearly through a stethoscope. The "lub" sound is produced by the closing of the tricuspid and bicuspid (A-V) valves. The "dup" sound is made by the closing of the semilunar valves. If any of the heart valves are damaged, there will be a leakage, or backflow, of blood at certain times during the heartbeat cycle. This produces abnormal heart sounds, commonly known as "heart murmurs."

Control of the heartbeat. The cardiac muscle that makes up the heart is different from the other muscle tissues of the body. Unlike other types of muscles, cardiac muscle fibers form a network, or lattice. The arrangement of muscle fibers is such that the atria are one functional unit and the ventricles are another.

The contraction of other types of muscle is controlled by the nervous system. Cardiac muscle, however, has a built-in, or innate, ability to contract. Even when it is removed from the body, the heart will keep beating for a while if kept in a special solution. Each heart-muscle fiber has its own innate rate of contraction. However, the heart must function as a unit. This is made possible by a structure in the heart called the **sinoatrial** (sy-no-*ay*-tree-ul) **node,** also called the **pacemaker.** The pacemaker is a specialized group of muscle cells in the wall of the right atrium. Contraction of the heart is initiated by electrical impulses from the pacemaker. A specialized system of fibers carries the impulses to all parts of the heart, causing the atria to contract first, and then the ventricles.

The minute electrical current produced each time the heart contracts can be recorded on a machine that produces an **electrocardiogram** (eh-lek-troh-*kard*-ee-o-gram), or **ECG** (see Figure 9-9). Physicians use electrocardiograms to check the health of the heart.

The rate of the heartbeat is regulated by certain nerves that enter the pacemaker. Impulses from the **vagus** (*vay*-gus) **nerves** slow down the pacemaker, while impulses from the **cardioaccelerator** (*kard*-ee-oh-ak-*sel*-uh-ray-tur) nerves speed up the pacemaker. The built-in rhythm of the heart is also affected by changes in body temperature and by certain chemicals circulating in the blood.

When the natural pacemaker of the heart does not function properly, the wires from a battery-powered electronic pacemaker can be attached surgically to the heart to regulate the heartbeat.

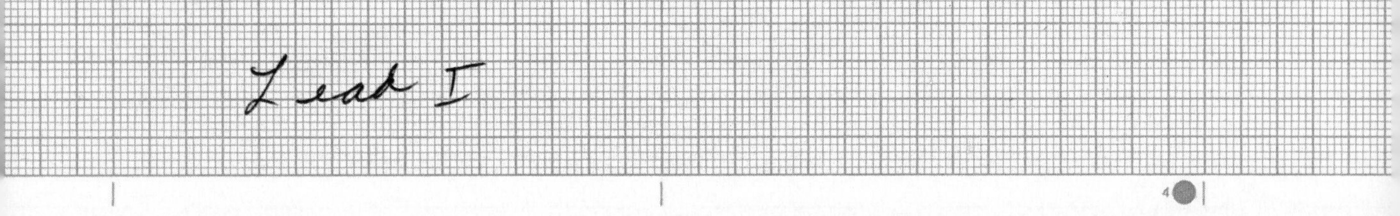

Figure 9-9. Electrocardiogram. The electrocardiogram records the changing electrical currents produced by the contractions of the heart. This electrocardiogram is from a normal heart.

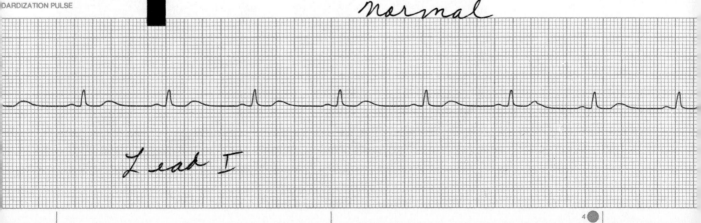

careers

Emergency medical technicians, or EMTs, are popularly known as "paramedics." They generally drive ambulances, and provide emergency treatment to victims of accidents, heart attacks, drowning, and other life-threatening events. They must determine the type of injury or illness and give appropriate emergency treatment when needed. Their job may include the control of bleeding, immobilization of fractures, administration of cardiopulmonary resuscitation, restoration of breathing, and treatment of shock. EMTs transport the patient to the hospital and provide the doctor with a full report on the treatment given and background of the case.

Emergency medical technicians work for police and fire departments, for private ambulance companies, and for hospitals. An EMT must pass a standard 81-hour course designed by the U.S. Department of Transportation. Such courses are given by police and fire departments as well as hospitals and colleges.

9-8 Blood Pressure and the Flow of Blood

The thick, muscular walls of the arteries are elastic. When the ventricles contract, blood is forced out under great pressure into the arteries. Because of their elasticity, arteries can expand and absorb this great pressure. As the ventricles relax, the pressure decreases. However, the elasticity of the artery walls helps to maintain the pressure between heartbeats. In this way, blood is kept flowing continuously. The **pulse** is the alternate expansion (high pressure) and relaxation (lower pressure) that can be felt in an artery each time the left ventricle contracts. Both the rate and the force of the heartbeat are reflected in the pulse.

The blood in the arteries is under pressure. Physicians measure arterial blood pressure with an instrument called a *sphygmomanometer* (sfig-moh-muh-*nahm*-uh-ter). Pressure is measured in terms of the height of a column of mercury in a tube in this instrument. During systole in an average adult at rest, the pressure is enough to support a column of mercury about 120 millimeters high. During diastole, the pressure drops, and the maximum height of the mercury is only about 80 millimeters. Blood pressure is commonly stated in the form of systolic pressure/diastolic pressure. Thus the normal blood pressure in a resting adult is 120/80. During exercise and time of stress, blood pressure increases.

High blood pressure, or *hypertension* (*hy*-per-ten-shun), is a condition in which the blood pressure remains much above normal throughout the heartbeat cycle. It is a serious and fairly common health problem. One frequent cause of high blood pressure is *atherosclerosis* (ath-uh-roh-skluh-*roh*-sis), a disease commonly called "hardening of the arteries." In this disease, deposits of cholesterol and other fatty materials collect on the inner walls of the arteries (see Figure 9-10). The

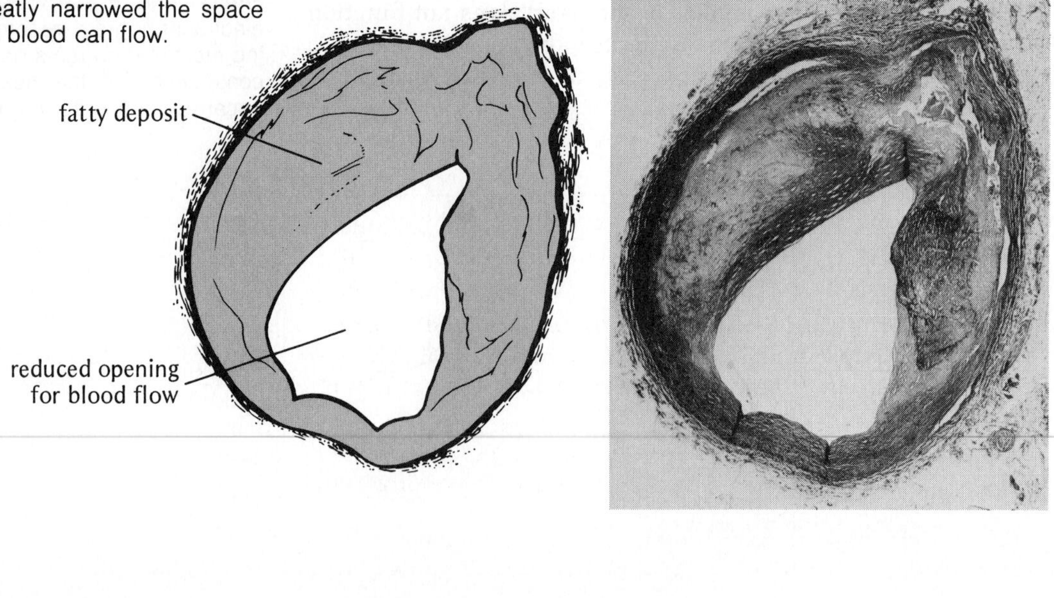

Figure 9-10. Atherosclerosis. The large deposit of fatty material in this artery has greatly narrowed the space through which blood can flow.

arteries become narrower and the walls inelastic, causing the blood pressure to increase. The condition puts a strain on both the heart and the blood vessels. If untreated, it can lead to heart attacks and strokes. Many studies indicate that the chance of developing atherosclerosis increases with the amount of cholesterol in the blood. This, in turn, seems to be related to the amount of fat, particularly animal fat, in the diet. Many physicians recommend that the amount of fat in the diet be kept low for this reason.

As the blood flows through the arteries, there is relatively little drop in pressure. However, there is a large drop when it reaches the arterioles. At the capillary ends of the arterioles there are rings of muscle, the *precapillary sphincters*, that control the blood flow through the capillaries. The capillaries are the most numerous blood vessels in the body. If all the capillaries were open at the same time, there would not be enough blood to fill them. The opening and closing of the precapillary sphincters directs the flow of blood to the parts of the body where it is needed. For example, when you run, the flow of blood into the capillaries of the skeletal muscles is increased, while the supply of blood to the capillaries of the digestive tract is decreased.

By the time blood reaches the veins, pressure is low. It is too low to return the blood to the heart, especially from the lower parts of the body. Blood flow in the veins is assisted by the squeezing action of the skeletal muscles as the body moves. As a contracting muscle presses against a vein, the blood in the vein is forced to move. The blood moves toward the heart, since the valves in the veins prevent flow in the opposite direction.

Standing at attention for an extended period causes blood to collect in the veins of the legs. Eventually, the blood supply to the brain may be affected, and fainting occurs. Walking or flexing the leg muscles forces the blood through the veins. Breathing movements also help to move blood through the veins because when the chest expands during inhalation, the reduced air pressure in the chest cavity draws blood into the chest veins and the atria.

PATHWAYS OF HUMAN CIRCULATION

After completing your study of this section, you should be able to:

1. **Trace the path of the blood through the pulmonary circulation and discuss the exchange of gases that occurs in the lungs.**
2. **Trace the path of the blood through the systemic circulation, including the coronary, hepatic-portal, and renal circulations.**

In the second century A.D., the Greek physician Galen proposed that blood flowed back and forth from the heart to the rest of the body through the veins. It was not until 1628 that the English physician William Harvey proposed the correct pathway for blood circulation. Harvey demonstrated that the heart pumps blood to the organs through arteries and that veins carry blood back to the heart. He thought that connections between the ends of tiny arteries and the ends of tiny veins must exist, but he could not find these connecting ves-

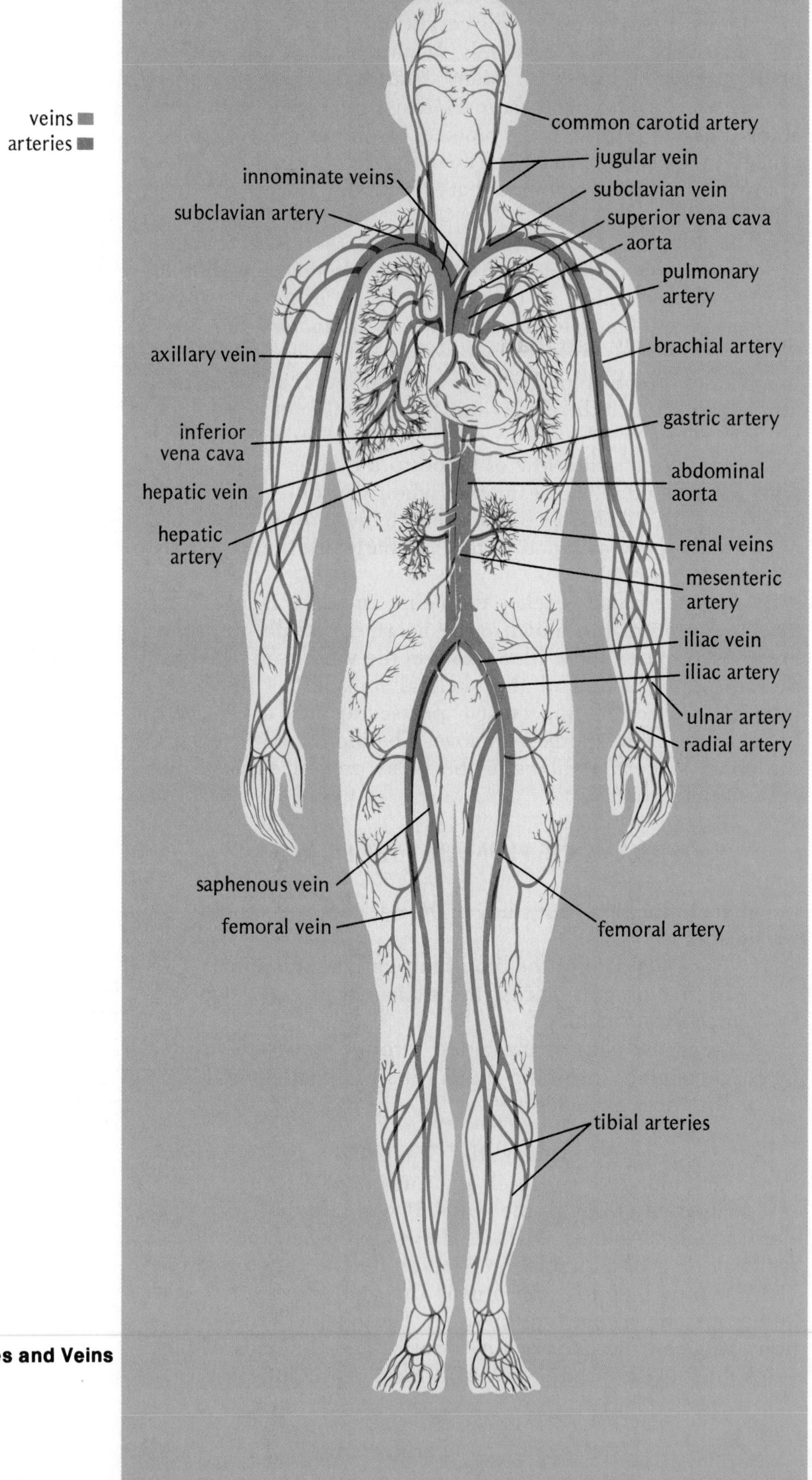

Figure 9-11. Major Arteries and Veins of the Human Body.

sels. In 1660, the Italian anatomist Marcello Malpighi demonstrated that capillaries connect arteries to veins. Thus, Harvey's theory of the circulation of the blood was proved correct.

The major arteries and veins of the human circulatory system are shown in Figure 9-11.

As shown in Figure 9-12, the two major pathways of the blood are the **pulmonary** (*pul*-muh-ner-ee) **circulation** and the **systemic** (sis-*tem*-ik) **circulation.** The pulmonary circulation carries blood between the heart and the lungs. The systemic circulation carries blood between the heart and the rest of the body.

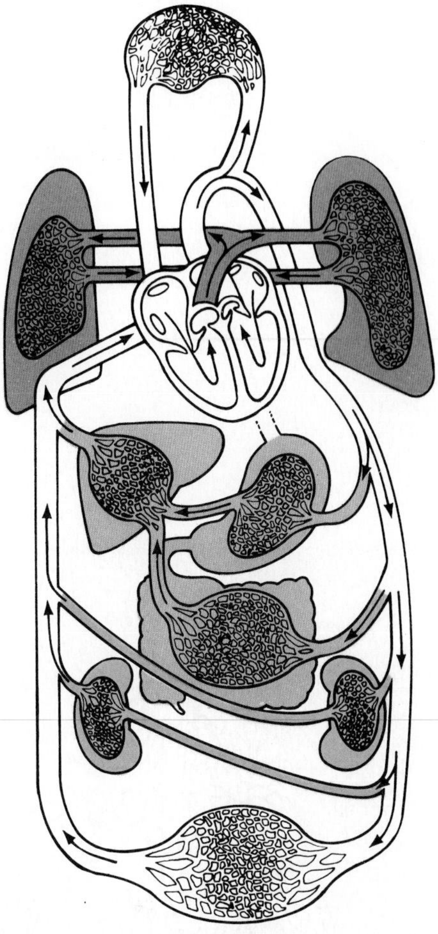

9-12. Pulmonary and Systemic Circulations. The pulmonary circulation includes the flow of blood between the heart and the lungs. The rest of the pathways, including the hepatic-portal and renal circulations, make up the systemic circulation.

9-9 Pulmonary Circulation

Blood returning to the heart from the body tissues is low in oxygen and high in carbon dioxide. This blood enters the right atrium and flows into the right ventricle. The right ventricle pumps it through the pulmonary arteries to the lungs. The pulmonary arteries are the only arteries that carry oxygen-poor blood. All other arteries carry oxygen-rich blood. As the blood travels through the capillaries in the lungs, it gains oxygen and gets rid of carbon dioxide. The pulmonary capillaries merge into pulmonary veins, which carry the oxygen-rich blood to the left atrium of the heart. The pulmonary veins are the only veins that carry oxygen-rich blood. All other veins carry oxygen-poor blood.

9-10 Systemic Circulation

From the left atrium the blood enters the left ventricle. The systemic circulation begins in the left ventricle of the heart. The powerful left ventricle has thicker walls than the other chambers of the heart because it pumps blood throughout the body. From the left ventricle, the blood is pumped out into the aorta. The aorta branches, forming arteries that serve all parts of the body. The arteries divide and subdivide, forming smaller and smaller vessels, and finally forming capillaries. Every cell in the body is near a capillary. The exchange of materials between the blood and the body tissues takes place through the walls of the capillaries. Capillaries merge to form veins, which ultimately return the blood to the heart. The largest veins of the body, the **superior vena cava** (*vee*-nuh *kay*-vuh) and the **inferior vena cava,** empty into the right atrium of the heart. The superior vena cava returns blood from the head, arms, and chest; the inferior vena cava returns blood from the lower body regions.

The systemic circulation includes three subdivisions of special importance—the **coronary** (*kar*-uh-ner-ee) **circulation,** the **hepatic-portal** (heh-*pat*-ik *port*-ul) **circulation,** and the **renal** (*reen*-ul) **circulation.**

Coronary circulation. The coronary circulation supplies blood to the muscle of the heart. The right and left coronary arteries branch off the aorta just after the aorta leaves the

About 25% of the blood pumped by the left ventricle travels through the coronary circulation.

heart. The coronary arteries run down either side of the heart, with branches entering the heart muscle. Within the heart, the arteries divide, eventually forming capillaries. The veins that drain the heart muscle empty directly into the chambers of the heart, mostly the right atrium. The cells of the heart require a constant supply of nutrients and oxygen. When a coronary artery is blocked by a blood clot or fat deposit, a heart attack can occur.

Hepatic-portal circulation. Generally, blood travels through only one set of capillaries before it returns to the heart. An exception is the hepatic-portal circulation, which transports blood from the digestive tract to the liver. Blood passing through the capillaries of the digestive tract picks up nutrients. Veins draining these capillaries do not lead directly back to the heart. Instead, they form the portal vein, which goes to the liver. Within the liver, the vein divides into smaller veins and then into vessels similar to capillaries—the hepatic sinuses. Fluids, nutrients, and even blood proteins diffuse easily out of the blood and into intercellular spaces in the liver. Blood in the sinuses of the liver is collected by a number of hepatic veins, which empty into the inferior vena cava.

The hepatic-portal circulation serves a vital homeostatic function. As blood passes through the liver, excess glucose is absorbed by the liver cells and converted to glycogen, which is then stored. If no food has been eaten for a time, the blood reaching the liver from the digestive tract will be low in glucose. The liver then converts some of its stored glycogen to glucose, which diffuses out of the liver cells and into the blood. Thus, the liver helps to maintain the blood glucose concentration at a constant level.

Renal circulation. One of the functions of the blood is to carry off the wastes of the body tissues. These wastes must be disposed of, or excreted. The gaseous waste product carbon dioxide is carried by the pulmonary circulation to the lungs and is excreted there. Other wastes are removed from the blood and excreted by the kidneys. The renal circulation is the special branch of the systemic circulation that carries blood to and from the kidneys.

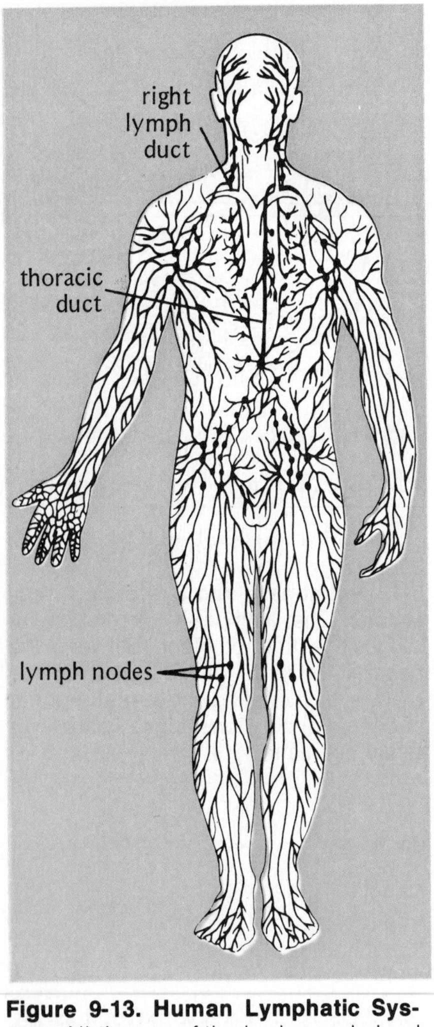

Figure 9-13. Human Lymphatic System. All tissues of the body are drained by vessels of the lymphatic system.

HUMAN LYMPHATIC SYSTEM

After completing your study of this section, you should be able to:

1. Describe the formation, composition, and function of intercellular fluid.
2. Identify the structures of the lymphatic system and explain their functions.

9-11 Intercellular Fluid

All the cells of the body are bathed in a colorless, watery

fluid called the **intercellular** (in-ter-*sel*-yoo-ler), or **interstitial** (in-ter-*stish*-ul), **fluid.** This fluid serves as a medium for the exchange of materials between the capillaries and the body cells. All substances exchanged between the blood and the body cells must diffuse through the intercellular fluid.

The intercellular fluid is formed from the liquid part of the blood (plasma) that diffuses out of the capillaries. It consists mostly of water and salts, but also contains proteins and nutrients. Diffusion of intercellular fluid into the body tissues occurs at the arteriolar end of the capillaries. At the venous end of the capillaries, most of the intercellular fluid and some of the substances it contains diffuse back into the capillaries. However, some of the fluid and all of the proteins remain outside the capillaries.

9-12 Structure and Function of the Lymphatic System

Excess fluid and proteins from the intercellular spaces are returned to the blood by a system of vessels called the **lymphatic** (lim-*fat*-ik) **system** (see Figure 9-13). Without the lymphatic system, the constant loss of fluid from the blood would drain the circulatory system, and the body tissues would be flooded. The lymphatic system begins in the body tissues with lymph capillaries, microscopic tubes that are closed at one end. The walls of these tubes are only one cell layer thick. Openings between the cells allow intercellular fluid and proteins to pass readily into the lymphatic vessels. The fluid inside the vessels is called **lymph.** Like veins, lymphatic vessels have flaplike valves that allow the lymph to flow only in one direction. Muscular activity squeezes the lymph vessels and pushes the lymph along.

The lymphatic capillaries merge to form larger and larger vessels. Eventually, all the lymph from the lower part of the body, the left side of the head and chest, and the left arm flows into the *thoracic* (thuh-*ras*-ik) *duct*, the largest lymphatic vessel in the body. Lymph from the thoracic duct is emptied into a large vein at the left side of the neck. All lymph from the right side of the head, the right arm, and the right side of the chest enters the *right lymph duct*, which drains into a large vein on the right side of the neck. In this way, fluid and proteins lost from the blood in the capillaries is returned to the circulation.

The lymph vessels in the villi of the small intestine are called lacteals. The products of fat digestion enter the lacteals and eventually enter the circulating blood with the lymph.

At various places along the lymphatic vessels there are **lymph nodes,** or **lymph glands,** which play an important role in the body's defense against disease (see Figure 9-14). They filter foreign matter from the lymph, preventing cancer cells, bacteria, and other disease-causing organisms, from entering the bloodstream. They also produce some types of white

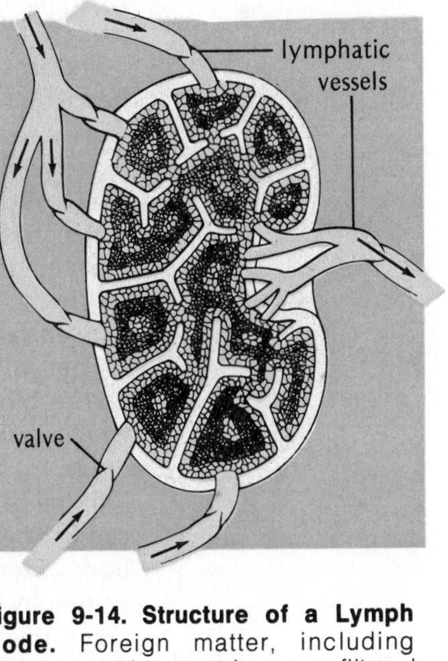

Figure 9-14. Structure of a Lymph Node. Foreign matter, including disease-causing organisms, are filtered out of the lymph in the lymph nodes.

blood cells (lymphocytes) whose products can destroy bacteria and other foreign substances. In the area of an infection, the lymph node may become enlarged and sore. These "swollen glands" indicate that the body is fighting an infection.

Lymphoid tissue like that found in lymph nodes is also found in the *spleen*, an organ located near the stomach. In the spleen, the lymphoid tissues filter out bacteria and worn-out red cells from the blood.

summary

The process of transport involves absorption, the movement of materials across cell membranes, and circulation, the movement of materials within cells or between parts of an organism. The movement of materials within the cell takes place by diffusion and may be aided by cyclosis. It may also involve active transport. In one-celled and simple multicellular organisms these processes are adequate for circulation of materials. In larger and more complex organisms, specialized circulatory systems carry materials to and from all cells.

In open circulatory systems the blood is not confined within vessels throughout the system. Instead, it flows out of the vessels into body spaces, where it bathes the body tissues directly. It eventually seeps back into the vessels. Such systems are found in insects. In closed circulatory systems, the blood is confined within vessels. It is pumped through the vessels by the rhythmic contraction of the heart. All vertebrates have closed circulatory systems.

Humans have a closed circulatory system consisting of a four-chambered heart that pumps the blood and a complex network of blood vessels that carries the blood throughout the body. These vessels are of three types: arteries, which carry blood away from the heart to all parts of the body; veins, which return the blood from the body tissues to the heart; and capillaries, which are small vessels that connect arteries and veins.

Except for the pulmonary vessels, blood in the arteries is rich in oxygen and nutrients, while blood carried by the veins is poor in oxygen and contains high concentrations of metabolic waste products.

The two major pathways of the blood are the pulmonary circulation, which carries blood between the heart and the lungs, and the systemic circulation, which carries blood between the heart and all parts of the body except the lungs.

Some of the fluid, proteins, and nutrients of the blood diffuse through the capillary walls, forming intercellular fluid, which bathes all the cells of the body. Excess intercellular fluid and proteins are returned to the circulatory system by the lymphatic system, a system of vessels arising in the body tissues. Once the intercellular fluid enters the vessels of the lymphatic system it is called lymph. Lymph empties from the vessels of the lymphatic system into large veins near the heart.

Scattered throughout the lymphatic system are lymph nodes, which filter foreign materials, including disease-causing organisms, from the blood and destroy them. Thus, the lymphatic system is part of the body's defense system against disease.

vocabulary

absorption
aorta
arteriole
artery
atrium
auricle
blood
capillary
circulation
closed circulatory system
coronary circulation
cyclosis
diastole
electrocardiogram
heart
hemoglobin
hepatic-portal circulation
inferior vena cava
intercellular fluid
interstitial fluid
lymph
lymphatic system
lymph gland
lymph node
open circulatory system
pacemaker
pericardium
pulmonary circulation
pulse
renal circulation
septum
sinoatrial node
sinus
superior vena cava
systemic circulation
systole
transport
valve
vein
ventricle
venule

test your learning

Section

9-1 **1.** Define the term *transport*, and describe the two processes involved in transport.

2. What is the function of a circulatory system?

3. What are the basic parts of a circulatory system?

9-2 **4.** What processes are involved in the circulation of materials in an ameba or paramecium?

9-3 **5.** How do the cells of the hydra obtain nutrients and oxygen and get rid of wastes?

9-4 **6.** What is a closed circulatory system?

7. Describe the circulatory system of the earthworm.

9-5 **8.** What is an open circulatory system?

9. Describe the circulatory system of the grasshopper.

9-6 **10.** Describe and compare the structures and functions of the three types of human blood vessels.

9-7 **11.** Name the four chambers of the human heart and give the function of each.
12. Name the valves of the human heart, and give the location and functions of each.
13. Describe the path of the bloodflow through the heart.
14. What are the two phases of the heartbeat cycle, and what occurs during each phase?
15. How is the heartbeat initiated? How is the rate of the heartbeat controlled?
9-8 **16.** What is the pulse?
17. What controls the flow of blood through the capillary beds?
18. In which type of vessel is the blood pressure the highest? In which is it the lowest?
19. What forces the blood through the arteries? Through the veins?
9-9 **20.** Describe the pathway of the pulmonary circulation.
21. Explain the function of the pulmonary circulation.
9-10 **22.** What parts of the body are served by the systemic circulation?
23. What are the three major subdivisions of the systemic circulation and what are their functions?
9-11 **24.** What is intercellular fluid and how does it form?
9-12 **25.** Describe the structure of the lymphatic system.
26. What are the functions of the lymphatic system?

test your understanding

1. What advantages does a closed circulatory system have over an open circulatory system for large animals?
2. Compare the structure of the human circulatory system with that of the grasshopper.
3. What happens when the walls of the arteries lose their elasticity?
4. Describe the relationship between the circulatory system and the lymphatic system.
5. Trace the path of the blood through the human body from the right big toe through the heart and back to the toe.

independent research

1. Prepare a report on one of the following topics:
   A. The experiment of William Harvey.
   B. The role of diet in cardiovascular diseases.
   C. Risk factors and cardiovascular diseases.
   D. Cardiopulmonary resuscitation (CPR).
2. Prepare a report on one of the following career opportunities. If possible, interview an individual who works in the field. A tape recorder will be very helpful for the interview. Be sure to prepare your questions in advance.
   A. Intensive-care nurse.
   B. Cardiologist.
   C. ECG technician.
   D. Vascular surgeon.
3. Obtain a beef, sheep, or hog heart from a butcher. Make a drawing of its external structure, adding a written description of its major features. Dissect the heart and describe its internal structure.

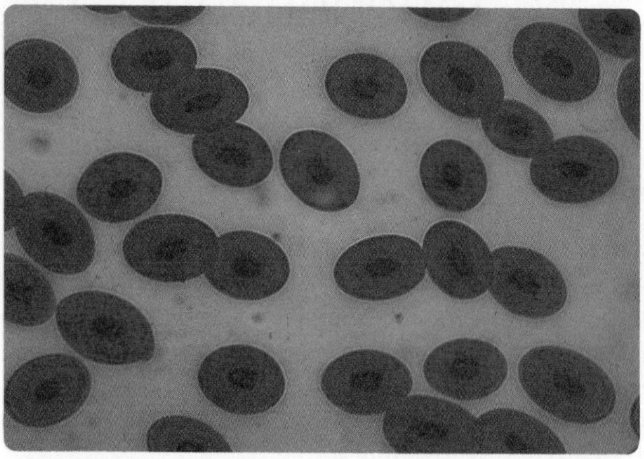

chapter 10

The Blood

10-1 Chapter Introduction

Blood is the liquid tissue of transport in humans and other vertebrates. Because it is a liquid, blood can transport dissolved and suspended materials. It carries respiratory gases, nutrients, cellular wastes, and regulatory substances, such as enzymes and hormones.

Blood contributes to the regulation of all bodily functions. It maintains and regulates the chemical state, pH, and water content of cells and body fluids. Blood is also involved in the regulation of body temperature.

Blood protects the body. The white blood cells and certain substances found in the blood protect the body from disease-causing microorganisms. The ability of the blood to clot protects the circulatory system from collapse that could be caused by loss of fluid from a wound.

COMPOSITION OF BLOOD

After completing your study of this section, you should be able to describe the different parts of the blood and explain the functions of each.

The average human body contains about 5.5 liters of blood. Blood is a unique tissue in that it is made up of cells suspended in a liquid, the **plasma** (*plaz*-muh). Plasma accounts for about 55 percent of the total volume of the blood, while the cells, or *formed elements*, make up about 45 percent. The formed elements include red blood cells, white blood cells, and platelets. Red blood cells account for most of the volume of the formed elements.

10-2 Plasma

Plasma is a clear, straw-colored liquid (see Figure 10-1). It consists mainly of water (over 90 percent) and dissolved proteins (7 percent). It also contains salts, glucose, amino acids, fatty acids, vitamins, hormones, and cellular wastes.

The three types of protein found in blood plasma are **albumin** (al-*byoo*-min), **globulins** (*glahb*-yoo-linz), and **fibrinogen** (fy-*brin*-uh-jen). Albumin, which is the most abundant of the plasma proteins, causes an osmotic gradient that regulates the diffusion of plasma out of the capillaries into the intercellular spaces. The globulins serve a number of different functions. Some globulins are involved in the transport of proteins and other substances from one part of the body to another. Other globulins, particularly the gamma globulins, play a major role in the body's defense against infection. Fibrinogen is important in the clotting of blood.

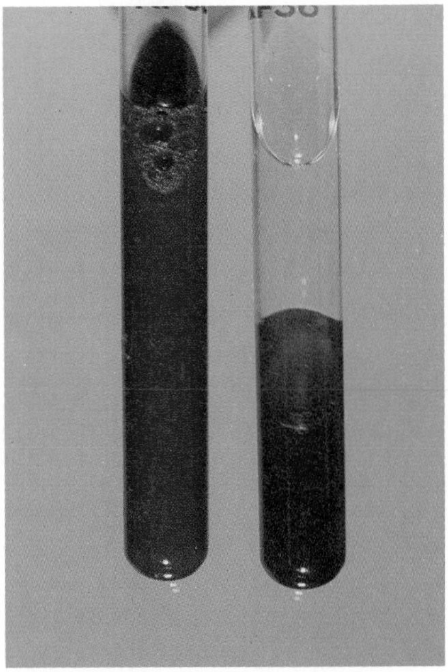

Figure 10-1. Plasma. When whole blood (left) is centrifuged, the cells collect at the bottom of the test tube, leaving the clear, straw-colored plasma at the top (right).

10-3 Red Blood Cells

Red blood cells, or **erythrocytes** (eh-*rith*-ruh-syts), are by far the most numerous of the cells in the blood (about 5 million per cubic millimeter of blood). Their major function is to transport oxygen from the lungs to the body tissues and carbon dioxide from the body tissues to the lungs. Red blood cells are disk-shaped cells that are thinner in the center than around the rim (see Figure 10-2). However, they easily change shape. They are filled with the iron-containing pigment hemoglobin, which gives blood its characteristic red color. Hemoglobin functions in the transport of oxygen and carbon dioxide. (This is discussed in detail in Chapter 11.)

During the development of the human embryo, red blood cells are produced by various organs, including the liver, spleen, and lymph nodes. After birth, however, they are normally produced only by the bone marrow. Mature red blood

The flattened shape of the red cells exposes the maximum surface area for the exchange of oxygen and carbon dioxide.

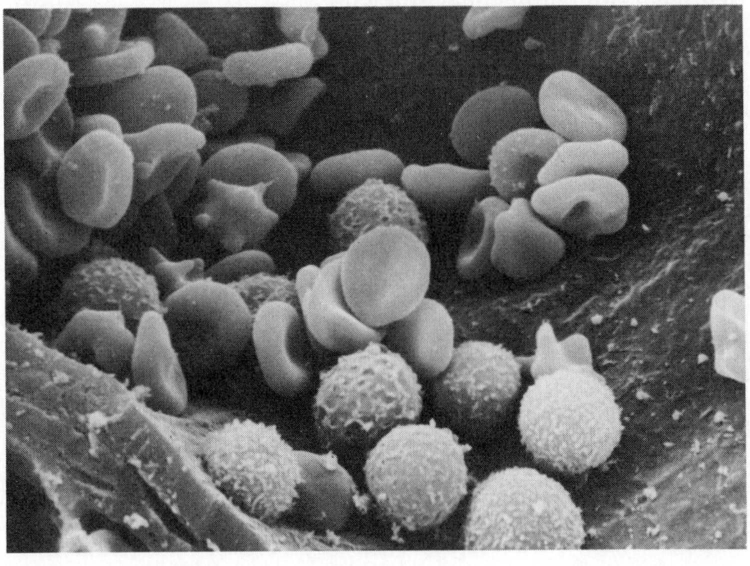

Figure 10-2. Scanning Electron Micrograph of Red Blood Cells and White Blood Cells. The red cells are mostly disk-shaped and thinner in the center than around the outside. The white cells are larger and spherical.

cells contain no nucleus. They live for about 120 days. Worn-out red cells are removed from the circulation by the liver and spleen and broken down. The iron from the hemoglobin molecule is reused by the body.

Anemia (uh-*nee*-mee-uh) is a condition in which a person has too few red blood cells or insufficient hemoglobin. In anemia, the cells of the body do not receive an adequate supply of oxygen. Some forms of anemia can be treated by injections of vitamin B_{12} or by eating iron-rich foods.

10-4 White Blood Cells

The **white blood cells,** or **leukocytes** (*loo*-kuh-syts), protect the body against infection by bacteria and other microorganisms. White cells are larger than red cells, and unlike red cells, they contain one or more nuclei (see Figure 10-2). Leukocytes are produced by the bone marrow and by lymphatic tissues. The mature leukocytes enter the bloodstream. Leukocytes can squeeze through the walls of the capillaries and move through the body tissues. When there is an infection at a particular site in the body, the leukocytes collect there.

Structurally, there are several different kinds of white blood cells. However, in terms of function, leukocytes fall into two groups. One type acts as **phagocytes** (*fag*-uh-syts), engulfing microorganisms and other matter (see Figure 10-3). The second type is involved in the production of *antibodies* (*ant*-ih-bod-eez), which are protein molecules that attack foreign substances or microorganisms that enter the body.

In leukemia, the number of white blood cells can increase to 1 million or more per mm^3.

Normally, there are only 6,000 to 8,000 white blood cells per cubic millimeter of blood. However, when there is an infection in the body, the number may increase to 30,000 per cubic millimeter. Among the phagocytic leukocytes, most can ingest from 5 to 25 bacteria before they die. The pus that forms at the site of an infected wound consists mainly of white blood cells that have died after ingesting bacteria.

Leukemia (loo-*kee*-mee-uh) is a form of blood cancer in which there is an uncontrolled increase in the number of white blood cells. Some forms of leukemia can now be controlled or even cured by drugs.

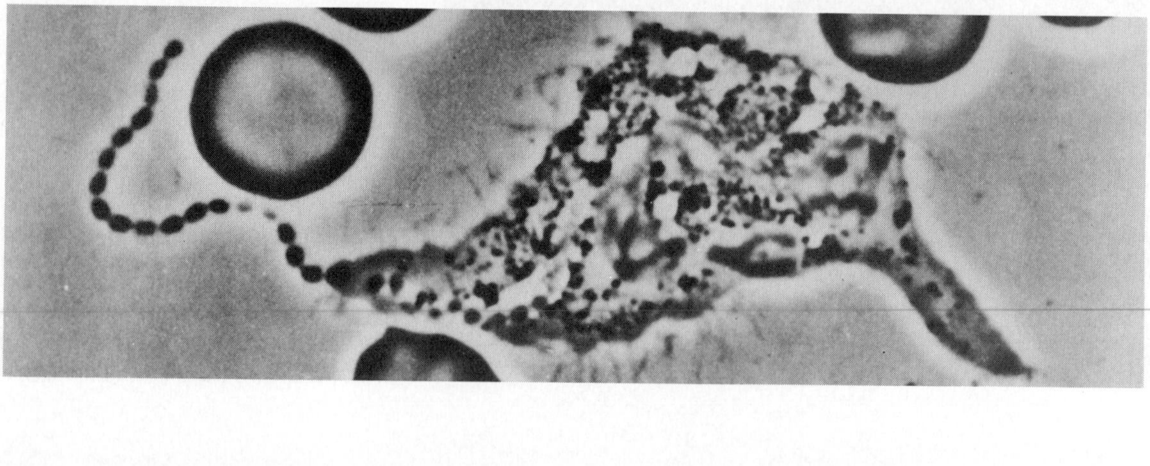

Figure 10-3. White Blood Cell Engulfing a Chain of Bacteria.

Figure 10-4. Scanning Electron Micrograph of Blood Platelets.

10-5 Platelets

Platelets (*playt*-lets) are small, round or oval fragments of a type of blood cell formed in the bone marrow. A platelet, which has no nucleus, consists of a bit of cytoplasm surrounded by a cell membrane (see Figure 10-4). There are generally from 200,000 to 400,000 platelets per cubic millimeter of blood. Platelets trigger the blood clotting process.

BLOOD CLOTTING

After completing your study of this section, you should be able to describe the process of blood clotting.

10-6 The Clotting Process

When a blood vessel is broken, the escape of blood is stopped by the formation of a solid mass that plugs up the hole, a blood clot. The solidification of blood is called **clotting**. Clotting is carried out primarily by the platelets and the plasma protein fibrinogen. The overall process of blood clotting may be summarized as follows:

1. Clotting is started by the release of a substance called *thromboplastin* (throm-boh-*plas*-tun) from the wall of the injured blood vessel.
2. As soon as the vessel is injured, platelets begin to stick to the broken vessel wall. The platelets also secrete a substance that makes other passing platelets sticky so that a solid plug begins to build up.
3. A complex series of enzyme-controlled reactions occurs that eventually converts the plasma protein *prothrombin* (proh-*throm*-bin) to *thrombin*.
4. Thrombin, which is an enzyme, converts the plasma protein fibrinogen into insoluble strands of *fibrin* (*fy*-brin) (see Figure 10-5). Thrombin also makes platelets sticky so that the hole in the vessel wall becomes filled with a mass of platelets and fibrin strands.
5. Red blood cells become trapped in the mass of fibrin strands and platelets and fill in the wound. As water evaporates from the clot, it hardens into a scab.

Figure 10-5. Fibrin Strands and Trapped Red Blood Cells.

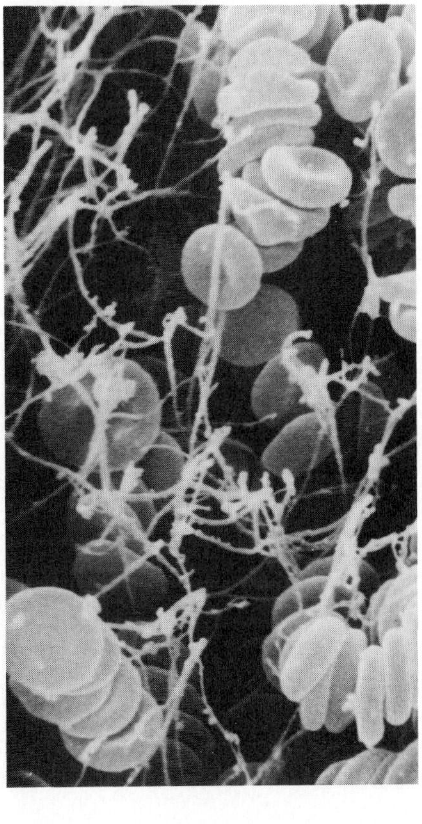

6. The wound is repaired by the growth of cells called *fibroblasts* (*fy*-broh-blasts) and by an outer layer of epithelial cells.

Clotting must be prevented if blood is to be used for transfusions. Calcium ions are necessary for many of the clotting reactions and are present in plasma. If sodium citrate is added to blood, calcium ions bind to the citrate and clotting cannot occur. Citrated blood is used for most blood transfusions.

10-7 Clotting Problems

There are various conditions in which the blood does not clot normally. This can lead to excessive bleeding, or *hemorrhaging* (*hem*-uh-rij-ing), from minor injuries. A tendency to bleed excessively may be caused by a deficiency of platelets in the blood, by a vitamin K deficiency (vitamin K is needed for the synthesis of prothrombin), or by a hereditary disease called *hemophilia* (hee-muh-*fil*-ee-uh) in which one of the clotting factors is missing from the blood.

While clotting is a major defense against loss of blood, it must occur only where and when it is needed. Two factors prevent clots from forming in the blood as it circulates through the blood vessels. First, the structure of the inner wall of the blood vessels prevents activation of the clotting reaction. Second, there are chemicals in the blood that act as *anticoagulants* (ant-ih-koh-*ag*-yuh-lunts) and prevent clot formation. Heparin is a powerful anticoagulant that may be used as a drug after surgery to prevent the formation of blood clots. It is normally present in the blood in low concentrations. It is produced by a number of different types of cells in the body, particularly in the tissues that surround the capillaries of the lungs and the liver.

Sometimes a clot does form within a blood vessel. When such a clot is attached to the vessel wall, it is called a *thrombus*. If a thrombus forms in an artery, the supply of blood to the organ fed by that artery could be cut off or reduced, with possibly disastrous effects. If a thrombus breaks loose, it forms an *embolus* (*em*-buh-lus), a clot that travels through the bloodstream. An embolus is very dangerous. It may eventually clog an artery to a vital organ, particularly the heart, lungs, or brain. A clogged coronary artery can cause a heart attack; a clogged artery to the brain can cause a stroke.

IMMUNITY

After completing your study of this section, you should be able to:

1. Explain how immunity works.
2. Compare inborn immunity with acquired immunity and active immunity with passive immunity.
3. Discuss the involvement of the immune system in allergies, transplant rejection, and autoimmune diseases.

10-8 Defenses Against Disease

The body has a number of general defenses against disease-causing organisms. The unbroken skin protects against the invasion of microorganisms. The acid of the stomach kills many microorganisms in food. Many microorganisms that do succeed in entering the body tissues are engulfed and destroyed by phagocytes. However, **immunity** (ih-*myoo*-nuh-tee), which is resistance to infection by a particular microorganism, is the strongest of the body's defenses. Immunity is defined as the ability of the body to resist a particular disease.

Although it is only recently that the actual mechanisms of immunity have been discovered, it has been known for hundreds of years that people who recover from certain diseases are unlikely to get them again—they are immune to those diseases. Smallpox was such a disease. (It has been wiped out in this century.) However, since it was often fatal, contracting smallpox was not a desirable way to acquire immunity to it.

In the 18th century, milkmaids often contracted a mild disease called cowpox, which was like smallpox in some ways. Many people believed that anyone who had had cowpox could not get smallpox. In 1796, Edward Jenner, an English physician, decided to test this theory. He took some fluid from a milkmaid's cowpox sores and injected it into a small cut that he made in the skin of a young boy. The boy developed the usual mild case of cowpox. After the boy recovered, Jenner treated his skin in the same way with material from the sores of a smallpox victim. The boy remained healthy. He had apparently become immune to smallpox. From this experiment Jenner developed the method of vaccination to give people immunity to smallpox. The method was later extended to the prevention of many other diseases.

Cowpox and smallpox are caused by closely related viruses so that immunity to cowpox also produces immunity to smallpox. However, this "cross immunity" between cowpox and smallpox is unusual. In general, immunity to one disease has no effect on immunity to any other disease.

10-9 How Immunity Works

The basis of immunity lies in the body's ability to distinguish between "self" (its own cells and molecules) and "nonself" (foreign cells and molecules). This recognition is based on differences in certain large molecules between one organism and another. When foreign cells or molecules enter the body, they are recognized as "nonself" by the immune system, which attempts to destroy or neutralize them. The immune system includes a type of white blood cells called **lymphocytes** (*lim*-fuh-syts) and various tissues of the lymphatic system (lymphoid tissues). The reaction of the immune system to the presence of foreign cells or molecules is called the **immune response.**

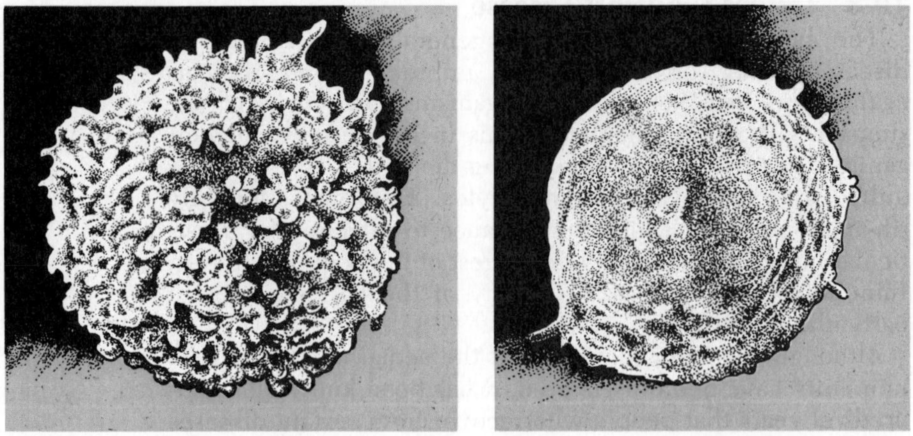

Figure 10-6. B and T Lymphocytes.

Antigens. Any substance that can cause an immune response is called an **antigen** (*ant*-ih-jun). Most antigens are proteins, but carbohydrates and nucleic acids may also be antigens. Most microorganisms and most **toxins** (poisonous substances produced by bacteria) contain substances that are antigens. Each human body contains a unique combination of proteins that no other human has. As a result, tissue from one person transplanted into another will contain "foreign" proteins that act as antigens. The presence of antigens in the body brings about an immune response that acts to destroy the antigens or the foreign tissue carrying them.

Lymphocytes and antibodies. The recognition and destruction of antigens present in the body tissues is carried out by the lymphocytes. Lymphocytes are produced originally in the bone marrow of developing embryos. They enter the bloodstream, pass into the body tissues, and finally collect in the lymphoid tissues. There are two types of lymphocytes—*B lymphocytes* and *T lymphocytes* (see Figure 10-6).

Before they become established in the lymphoid tissue, both B and T lymphocytes undergo "processing" at special sites in the lymphatic system. Without this processing, they cannot recognize antigens. It is estimated that there are between 10,000 and 100,000 different kinds of antigen receptors on human lymphocytes. However, each individual lymphocyte has receptors for only one kind of antigen. When an antigen enters the body, only those lymphocytes with receptors that recognize that particular antigen become activated. Depending on the antigen, B lymphocytes, T lymphocytes, or both may be stimulated.

Plasma cells generally live only a few days, but they produce antibodies at an extremely rapid rate—about 2,000 molecules per second.

When B lymphocytes are activated by antigens, they enlarge and undergo repeated cell divisions, forming two different types of cells—**plasma cells** and **memory cells.** Plasma cells secrete **antibodies**, which are proteins that react specifically with antigens and inactivate them (see Figure 10-7). Antibodies have active sites that fit a particular site on a par-

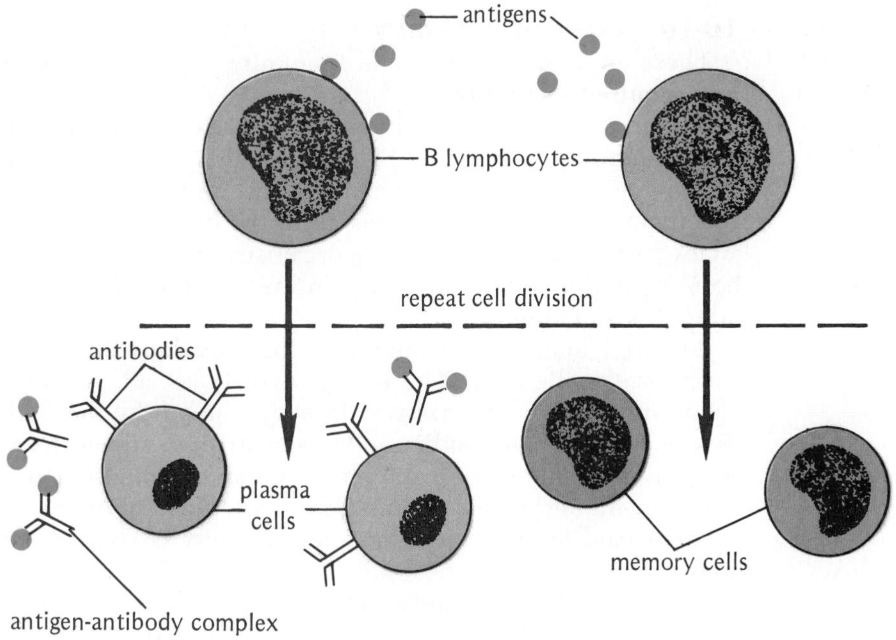

Figure 10-7. Antibody Formation by B Lymphocytes. B lymphocytes stimulated by the presence of a particular antigen in the blood undergo various cellular changes followed by repeated cell divisions. Some of the stimulated B lymphocytes form antibody-producing plasma cells; others form memory cells.

ticular antigen. There are several different classes of antibodies, and they inactivate antigens in different ways (see Table 10-1).

The memory cells produced by the activated B lymphocytes remain in the lymphoid tissue. If the same antigen enters the body again, the memory cells immediately begin to produce antibodies against it, thereby providing immunity to that disease.

When a T lymphocyte is stimulated by the presence of an antigen, it also undergoes rapid cell division, forming more lymphocytes sensitive to that antigen. Some of these newly formed T lymphocytes remain in the lymphoid tissue and serve as memory cells. The rest pass from the lymphoid tissue into the circulatory system and body tissues. When they come in contact with the antigens to which they are sensitive, they combine with them and destroy them.

The viruses that cause colds and the flu are constantly changing, and new antibodies must be produced to fight each new form.

Table 10-1. Types of Antigen-Antibody Reactions.

Agglutination	Antigens are bound together into clumps by antibodies and thereby inactivated.
Precipitation	Antibodies combine with antigens, and the resulting complex settles out of solution.
Neutralization	Antibodies combine with antigens, inactivating the toxic site of the antigen molecule.
Lysis	Antibodies cause the cell membranes of antigenic microorganisms to burst.
Complement system	The complement system is a group of enzymes present in the plasma in inactive form. The presence of the antigen-antibody complex activates these enzymes, which attack the antigenic material.

10-10 Types of Immunity

There are two basic types of immunity—**inborn immunity** and **acquired immunity.**

Inborn, or innate, immunity to some diseases is present at birth. There are several types of chemicals in the blood that destroy certain types of microorganisms, and there are also specific antibodies that are present in the blood at birth that attack particular disease-causing organisms. Humans have inborn immunity to many microorganisms that cause diseases in other types of animals.

Acquired immunity is immunity that develops during an individual's lifetime. There are two types of acquired immunity—active and passive. In **active immunity** the body produces its own antibodies and/or sensitized lymphocytes to attack a particular type of antigen. In **passive immunity** a person is given antibodies obtained from the blood of either another person or an animal. Passive immunity is "borrowed" immunity.

Active acquired immunity may develop as the result of having a disease. For example, a person who has had chicken pox rarely gets the disease a second time. Memory cells remaining in the body tissues quickly produce antibodies or lymphocytes if the chicken pox virus invades the body again.

Active immunity may also develop through the use of a **vaccine** (vak-*seen*). A vaccine consists of dead or weakened bacteria or viruses or modified bacterial toxins. In each case, the organism or toxin can still stimulate the immune system, but it can no longer cause disease. Thus, when the vaccine is injected into the body, the immune system responds to the presence of the antigens and produces antibodies or activated lymphocytes against them. In this way a person develops an immunity to a disease without actually suffering through it. As a rule, active acquired immunity develops slowly, but lasts for years. With some vaccines, it is necessary to give periodic "booster shots" to keep the antibody level high.

Passive immunity is only temporary, and generally does not last for more than a month because the body destroys the borrowed antibodies. However, it is fast-acting, and it is used to help people who have been exposed to a serious disease or who have come down with such a disease.

Antibodies are proteins of the gamma globulin type. For passive immunity, the gamma globulin fraction of blood from a number of different people is used.

Maternal immunity is a form of passive immunity. Antibodies from the mother enter the baby's blood before birth and provide immunity. They are also present in the mother's milk. Maternal immunity protects a child against most infectious diseases for the first few months of its life.

Interferon is a protein manufactured by body cells when they are attacked by viruses. This substance is carried in the bloodstream and blocks the production of viral DNA in the uninfected cells of the body. In this way it protects the uninfected cells from infection by the invading virus. Much research on the possible use of interferon in the prevention and cure of disease is being conducted. Unfortunately, interferon from other animals is not effective in humans. Scientists are trying to find ways to stimulate the body's own production of interferon.

10-11 Disorders of the Immune System

Disorders of the immune system appear to be involved in allergies, arthritis, cancer, and various other human diseases. The immune system may also be involved in the aging process.

A basic property of the immune system is that the cells of an individual's immune system do not react with the other cells of the body and destroy them. This property is called **tolerance.** It is thought that tolerance develops in the processing of the lymphocytes during embryonic development and just after birth. During processing, all lymphocytes sensitive to the antigens of the body's own cells are destroyed by constant exposure to these antigens.

There are various diseases in which the tolerance of a person's immune system breaks down, and antibodies and sensitized lymphocytes develop against the body's own antigens. Such diseases are called **autoimmune** (aw-toh-im-*yoon*) **diseases.** In rheumatic fever, for example, an immune response against the tissues of the heart and joints develops after exposure to a particular type of streptococcus bacteria. Another type of streptococcus causes an immune response to develop against kidney tissue.

Many people suffer from **allergies** (*al*-ur-jeez), such as hay fever and asthma. Allergies are caused by the production of antibodies against antigens that are not in themselves dangerous and do not bother most people. Such antigens include dust, penicillin, various foods, pollen, bee stings, and animal fur. Typical symptoms of allergy include a runny nose, swollen eyes, sneezing, coughing, and rashes (hives). These symptoms are generally caused by the release of a substance called *histamine* (*his*-tuh-meen) by the body cells following an antigen-antibody reaction. *Antihistamines* are drugs that are used to counteract the effects of histamine.

Experiments have shown that T lymphocytes attack cancer cells because the surfaces of these cells contain abnormal proteins that are recognized as antigens. This suggests that the body is normally protected from cancer by the immune response. There is evidence that some cancers develop when there is a deficiency in the immune response.

10-12 Transplants

When an organ or tissue, such as a heart, kidney, or skin, is transplanted from one person (the *donor*) to another (the *recipient*), the transplant is soon recognized by the recipient's immune system as "nonself," or foreign. This activates the immune response, and the organ or tissue is destroyed, a response called *rejection*. Rejection appears to take place in two steps. First, the transplanted tissue is invaded by T lymphocytes; then antibodies produced by B lymphocytes cause the disintegration of the tissue. In transplants between identical twins there is generally no rejection because their tissue proteins are identical.

The immune response to a transplant can be lessened by matching the tissue proteins of the donor as closely as possible to those of the recipient. In addition, the immune response may be controlled by the use of drugs that knock out the immune system. However, this leaves the patient highly susceptible to infection.

HUMAN BLOOD GROUPS

After completing your study of this section, you should be able to:

1. Describe the biochemical basis of human blood groups.
2. Discuss the significance of the ABO blood groups and Rh factors in transfusions and in pregnancy.

10-13 ABO Blood Groups

Before the discovery of blood groups, transfusions of blood from one person to another were occasionally attempted. The results were sometimes helpful, but at other times fatal. In the early 1900s the Austrian physician Karl Landsteiner succeeded in showing that there are four major types of human blood. If the wrong types are mixed in a transfusion, the red blood cells from the donor may clump together, a process called **agglutination** (uh-gloot-un-*ay*-shun). This clogs the blood vessels and causes kidney failure. The agglutination of the red cells is the result of an antigen-antibody reaction.

The blood groups first discovered by Landsteiner are those of the ABO system. Since that time, more than 100 other blood groups have been discovered. The **ABO blood group** involves the presence of certain antigens on the surface of the red blood cells. There are two antigens involved, called A and B. In any individual's blood, the red cells may have only A antigens (type A blood); only B antigens (type B blood); both A and B antigens (type AB blood); or neither A nor B antigens (type O blood). In addition, the blood plasma contains antibodies that react with the antigens the blood does *not* have. In other words, it has antibodies that will detect the presence of "foreign" red cells. Thus type A blood contains anti-B antibodies. Type B blood contains anti-A antibodies. Type AB blood does not have either of these antibodies. Type O blood has both. These facts are summarized in Table 10-2.

The A and B antigens are called **agglutinogens** (uh-*gloot*-in-uh-jenz). The antibodies that react to them are called **agglutinins** (uh-*gloot*-in-inz). If blood containing red cells with

frontiers of biology

In recent years, scientists working in the United States and Japan have developed a substance that can be used as artificial blood. This substance, which is called Fluosol, is a white fluid that is chemically similar to Teflon. Fluosol serves only one of the many functions of whole blood, but in emergencies, it is the most important function of blood—it carries oxygen. The oxygen-carrying capacity of artificial blood is much greater than that of real blood. In fact, the oxygen-carrying capacity of this fluid is so great that a mouse can live completely submerged in it. The mouse does not die from lack of oxygen as it would if submerged in water.

Fluosol belongs to a class of chemical compounds called fluorocarbons. These compounds were developed during World War II by scientists working on the atomic bomb. The scientists were looking for oxygen-carrying substances to be used in the separation of uranium isotopes.

Unlike red blood cells, which can be stored for only 3 weeks, artificial blood can be stored for 3 years. It contains no antigens so there is no problem with matching blood types. It contains none of the disease-causing organisms that may be present in real blood. One problem with artificial blood is that it only remains in the circulation for about 11 hours. By the end of that period, it has been broken down into waste gases and exhaled from the body through the lungs. Thus repeated injections of the fluid have to be administered if it is needed for longer periods of time.

Artificial blood has been tested on animals, but its use in humans is still highly experimental. However, it has been tried successfully both in the United States and in Japan. In the United States, its use has been limited to surgery patients who, for religious reasons, refuse to receive transfusions of real blood.

Because of its excellent oxygen-carrying capacity, scientists are experimenting with artificial blood for a number of possible uses. One of the most important could be its use in victims of heart attack and stroke, where it could provide more oxygen to the damaged tissues, thereby reducing tissue damage. Organs to be used in transplants appear to keep better in artificial blood than in real blood.

Table 10-2. Antigens and Antibodies of the ABO System.

Blood type	Antigens	Antibodies
O	none	Anti-A and Anti-B
A	A	Anti-B
B	B	Anti-A
AB	A and B	none

one of these antigens is mixed with blood containing the corresponding antibody, the antibody will react with the antigen and cause the red cells to clump together, or agglutinate (see Figure 10-8).

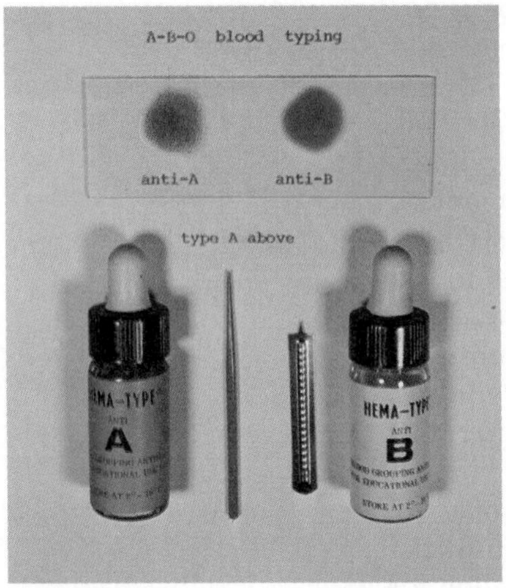

Figure 10-8. Blood Typing. When type A blood is mixed with anti-A antiserum, clumping of the red cells occurs. No clumping occurs when type A blood is mixed with anti-B antiserum.

10-14 Transfusions

For a blood transfusion to be safe, the recipient's blood must not contain antibodies that will react with antigens of the ABO system in the donor blood. Knowing this, it is a simple matter to decide which types of blood can be safely given to each type of recipient. The results are shown in Table 10-3. Note particularly that a person with type AB blood can receive a transfusion of any type, since type AB blood contains no antibodies. People with AB blood are therefore called **universal recipients.** Type O blood, on the other hand, can be given to any recipient because type O blood has no antigens. People with type O blood are called **universal donors.**

In emergency situations, plasma is used for transfusions instead of whole blood. The plasma restores blood volume and maintains blood pressure. The advantages of plasma are that no blood typing is necessary, and the plasma can be frozen and stored for long periods of time.

10-15 Rh Factors

The **Rh factors** are another group of antigens found on the surface of red blood cells. These antigens were discovered by Karl Landsteiner in 1940. They were called Rh factors because they were first found in rhesus monkeys. Unlike the ABO system, which includes only two different antigens, the

Table 10-3. Matching Blood Types for Transfusions.

Recipient		Donor
Type O	Can safely receive	Type O
Type A	Can safely receive	Type A or O
Type B	Can safely receive	Type B or O
Type AB	Can safely receive	Type A, B, AB, or O

Rh system includes eight possible antigens. Some of these can cause severe agglutination reactions in transfusions, while the others cause little or no reaction. A person whose red blood cells contain one or more of the Rh factors that do cause transfusion reactions is said to be Rh-positive, or Rh+. A person whose red blood cells do not contain Rh factors that cause transfusion reactions is said to be Rh-negative, or Rh−. In the United States, about 85 percent of the population is Rh+, while 15 percent is Rh−.

In the ABO system, antibodies against other blood types develop spontaneously shortly after birth. However, anti-Rh antibodies do not develop spontaneously, but only after exposure to the Rh antigens. An Rh+ individual can receive both Rh+ and Rh− blood. The first time an Rh− person receives Rh+ blood, there are no ill effects. However, this transfusion stimulates the formation of anti-Rh antibodies. If a second transfusion of Rh+ blood is given, a serious antigen-antibody reaction may occur. In matching blood types for transfusions, the Rh factor must be taken into account as well as the ABO system.

The Rh factor may present a special problem during pregnancy when the mother is Rh− but the child has inherited Rh+ blood from its father. During birth there may be some leakage between the child's circulatory system and the mother's circulatory system. Some Rh antigens enter the mother's blood, which then begins to form anti-Rh antibodies. In later pregnancies, antibodies from the mother's blood enter the baby's blood. If the child is Rh+, the antibodies destroy the baby's red blood cells. In recent years a treatment has been developed that can eliminate the Rh problem in pregnancies. Within 72 hours after the birth of an Rh+ child, the Rh− mother is given an injection of anti-Rh antibodies. These antibodies destroy any Rh antigens that have entered the mother's blood from the baby's blood. In this way the mother's body is not stimulated to produce its own anti-Rh antibodies, and consequently there is no problem with the next Rh+ baby.

Stress that since the leakage occurs during birth, that child would not be affected by the antibodies that develop in the mother. However, all succeeding Rh+ children would be. Without the injection of anti-Rh antibodies the mother's body forms its own antibodies about 3 days after delivery.

summary

Blood is a liquid tissue that carries materials to and from the cells of the body. The liquid portion, the plasma, contains suspended red blood cells, white blood cells, and platelets. The plasma, which is mostly water, also contains dissolved proteins, salts, glucose, amino acids, fatty acids, vitamins, hormones, and cellular wastes. Red blood cells, or erythrocytes, transport oxygen from the lungs to all the body tissues, and carbon dioxide from the body tissues to the lungs. White blood cells, or leukocytes, protect the body from infection by microorganisms. Platelets are cell fragments that are involved in clotting, the process by which breaks in blood vessels are plugged up.

Immunity, the ability of the body to resist a particular disease, is a function of the immune system. This system includes white blood cells called lymphocytes

and certain lymphoid tissues. Lymphocytes respond to the presence of antigens either by attacking them directly or by producing antibodies. The antibodies react specifically with the antigens and destroy them. Most antigens are proteins. Basically, the functioning of the immune system involves its ability to recognize foreign cells and materials—antigens—as not being a natural part of the organism.

Humans are born with immunity to some diseases. This is inborn, or innate, immunity. Immunity to other diseases develops over a lifetime. This is acquired immunity.

Failures of the immune system to function normally are involved in a wide variety of diseases, including allergies, autoimmune diseases, and possibly cancer. The immune system is also responsible for the rejection of transplants. The transplanted tissues contain foreign proteins that are attacked by antibodies and lymphocytes.

There are a number of different types of human blood, depending on the presence of particular antigens on the red cells and antibodies in the plasma. When transfusions are given, the blood type of the donor must be matched with that of the recipient. Otherwise, an antigen-antibody reaction occurs in which the red cells agglutinate. In terms of transfusions, the blood types of recipient and donor must be matched for both ABO and Rh antigens.

vocabulary

ABO blood groups
acquired immunity
active immunity
agglutination
agglutinin
agglutinogen
albumin
allergy
anemia
antibody
anticoagulant
antigen
autoimmune disease
clotting
erythrocyte
fibrinogen
globulin
immune response
immunity
inborn immunity
interferon
leukocyte
lymphocyte
maternal immunity
memory cell
passive immunity
phagocyte
plasma
plasma cell
platelet
red blood cell
Rh factor
tolerance
toxin
universal donor
universal recipient
white blood cell

test your learning

Section
10-1 1. List the functions of the blood.
10-2 2. Name the liquid portion of the blood and describe its composition.
10-3 3. Describe the structure and functions of the red blood cells.
4. What is hemoglobin and what function does it serve?
10-4 5. Describe the structure and functions of the white blood cells.
6. What is a phagocyte?

10-5 7. Describe the structure and function of the platelets.
10-6 8. Describe the sequence of events in blood clotting.
10-7 9. What prevents the blood from clotting within the blood vessels?
10. What is hemophilia?
10-8 11. Describe three of the body's defenses against disease.
10-9 12. What is the basis of immunity?
13. What is an antigen?
14. Describe the two ways in which lymphocytes destroy antigens.
10-10 15. Explain the difference between inborn and acquired immunity.
16. How does active acquired immunity develop?
17. How does passive acquired immunity develop?
10-11 18. What are autoimmune diseases?
19. What is an allergy?
10-12 20. What causes the rejection of organs transplanted from one person to another?
10-13 21. What causes agglutination in some transfusions?
22. List the four blood types of the ABO system. For each type give the antigens present on the cells and the antibodies present in the plasma.
10-14 23. For each of the four blood types of the ABO system, list the types of blood that may be safely received in transfusions.
10-15 24. What is meant by an Rh+ blood type?
25. Under what circumstances is the Rh factor a problem during pregnancy?

test your understanding

1. In the treatment of certain allergies, such as hay fever, the patient may be given a series of injections containing small amounts of the allergy-causing antigen. Explain how this treatment can help to cure the allergy symptoms.
2. Why are the chances of a blood clot forming within the circulatory system increased just after surgery?
3. Using your knowledge of the immune response, explain why organ transplants between identical twins are generally successful.
4. Why can an Rh− person safely receive one transfusion of Rh+ blood as long as the ABO system is properly matched, while a single transfusion of the wrong ABO type can prove fatal?
5. How does a vaccine against a viral or bacterial disease work?

independent reseach

1. Prepare a report on one of the following topics:
   A. autoimmune diseases
   B. allergies
   C. organ transplants
   D. interferon
2. Prepare a report on the life and scientific contributions of one of the following scientists:
   A. Edward Jenner
   B. Charles Drew
   C. Karl Landsteiner
   D. Jonas Salk
   E. Albert Sabin

chapter 11

Respiratory Systems

CHAPTER INTRODUCTION

After completing your study of this section, you should be able to:

1. Define the term *respiration*.
2. Explain what is meant by a respiratory surface, and list the characteristics of such a surface.

11-1 Respiration

In the process of *cellular respiration* nutrients are broken down and energy is released (see Chapter 7). In all but a few organisms, cellular respiration is aerobic—it requires oxygen. The end products of aerobic cellular respiration are carbon dioxide and water. Thus, all organisms that carry on aerobic cellular respiration have the problem of obtaining oxygen from the environment and getting rid of carbon dioxide. The process by which a living organism exchanges oxygen and carbon dioxide with its environment is called **respiration.**

11-2 The Respiratory Surface

The exchange of oxygen and carbon dioxide between an organism and its environment involves the passage of these gases through a boundary surface. The surface through which gas exchange takes place is called the **respiratory surface.** A respiratory surface must have the following basic characteristics: (1) It must be thin-walled so that diffusion can occur easily. (2) It must be moist because the oxygen and carbon dioxide must be in solution. (3) It must be in contact with an environmental source of oxygen. (4) In most multicellular organisms, it must be in close contact with the system that transports dissolved materials to and from the cells of the organism.

Gas exchange through the respiratory surface takes place by diffusion (see page 79). The direction of the gas exchange is determined by the concentration gradients of the gases on either side of the respiratory surface. As oxygen is used up inside the organism's tissues, more oxygen diffuses in. When the carbon dioxide concentration builds up within the tissues, this gas diffuses out. The larger the area of the respiratory surface, the greater the amount of gas exchange that can occur.

Examine the characteristics of the respiratory surfaces in each type of organism discussed in the chapter.

In protists and very small multicellular animals, the diffusion of respiratory gases can take place directly between the cells and the environment. In larger animals, most of the body cells are not in contact with the environment, and direct diffusion cannot serve as the mechanism of gas exchange. In addition, larger animals often have an outer protective layer, such as scales, feathers, or skin, that prevents any significant gas exchange. Therefore, large multicellular animals have their respiratory surfaces in specialized organs or systems.

ADAPTATIONS FOR RESPIRATION

After completing your study of this section, you should be able to:

1. Describe the respiratory surfaces of protozoa and hydra and the processes by which respiratory gases are exchanged in these organisms.
2. Explain why specialized respiratory systems are necessary in large multicellular animals.
3. Describe the function of respiratory pigments.
4. Describe and contrast the respiratory process in earthworms, grasshoppers, and gill breathers.

The major differences in overall respiratory activity among various types of animals is the method by which they exchange oxygen and carbon dioxide with their environments. Protists and animals show a variety of adaptations for the exchange of respiratory gases with their environment.

11-3 Respiration in Protozoa

Respiration is relatively simple in protozoa. The exchange of gases takes place directly through the body surface—the cell membrane. In the ameba and paramecium, oxygen dissolved in the surrounding water passes through the cell membrane into the cytoplasm by diffusion (see Figure 11-1). The carbon dioxide formed by cellular respiration diffuses out of the cytoplasm into the surrounding water.

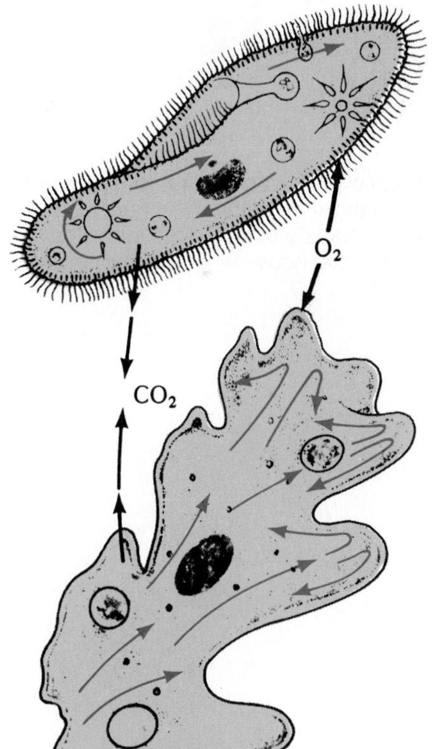

Figure 11-1. Respiration in Ameba and Paramecium. The exchange of respiratory gases in the ameba (top) and paramecium (bottom) takes place directly through the cell membrane.

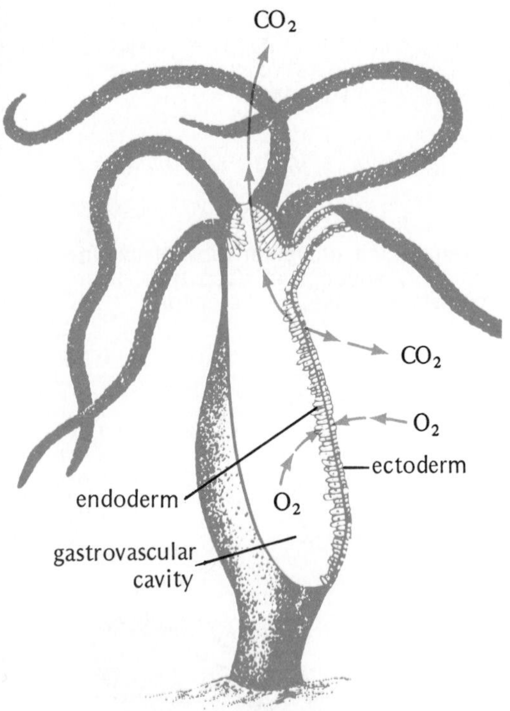

Figure 11-2. Respiration in Hydra. The exchange of respiratory gases in the hydra takes place by direct diffusion between the body cells and the environment.

11-4 Respiration in Hydra

The cells of the two layers that make up the body of the hydra are in direct contact with water (see Figure 11-2). Because of the small size and simple structure of the hydra, the exchange of respiratory gases can take place by direct diffusion between the body cells and the environment. There are no special structures for gas exchange in the hydra.

11-5 Respiration in Large Multicellular Animals

A large multicellular animal must exchange relatively large quantities of gases across a respiratory surface. Animals that live submerged in water have different respiratory problems from animals that breathe air. First, the concentration of dissolved oxygen in water is seldom higher than 0.5 percent, whereas the oxygen concentration in air is about 21 percent. (The oxygen that is chemically part of the water molecules is, of course, not available for respiration. Only the free dissolved oxygen can be used.) Second, diffusion of oxygen occurs much more slowly in water than in air. Consequently, to obtain adequate oxygen, an animal living underwater must continuously move a large volume of water across its respiratory surface.

Gases must be in solution before they can diffuse across living membranes. Therefore, air-breathing animals are faced with the problem of keeping their respiratory surfaces moist. Most air-breathing animals have respiratory systems that extend inward into the interior of the organism. This protects the respiratory surface and makes it possible for the air to be moistened before it reaches the respiratory surface.

11-6 Respiratory Pigments

Many multicellular animals have protein pigments in the blood that carry oxygen and carbon dioxide between the respiratory surface and the body cells. These pigments enable the blood to carry more oxygen and carbon dioxide than plain water can. For example, 100 milliliters of water can carry about 0.2 milliliters of oxygen and 0.3 milliliters of carbon dioxide. Hemoglobin, the most common respiratory pigment, is an efficient carrier of respiratory gases. It enables 100 milliliters of human blood to carry about 20 milliliters of oxygen and 30 to 60 milliliters of carbon dioxide. (These are not the volumes of the gases when in solution, but their equivalent volumes as gases in the air.)

11-7 Respiration in the Earthworm

In earthworms, which live in moist soil, the skin is the respiratory surface (see Figure 11-3). It is thin and is kept moist by mucus secreted by special cells. It is supplied with an abundance of capillaries. Oxygen diffuses from the air in the soil through the moist skin into the capillaries. Blood in the

Figure 11-3. Respiration in the Earthworm. The moist skin of the earthworm is its respiratory surface. Gases are exchanged with the environment through the skin and are carried to and from the body cells by the blood.

capillaries picks up the oxygen and transports it to the cells of the body. The blood plasma contains the red pigment hemoglobin, which aids in the transport of oxygen. At the body cells, the blood picks up carbon dioxide and carries it to the capillaries in the skin. The carbon dioxide diffuses through the skin into the air.

Damp soil keeps the earthworm's skin moist and helps its respiratory system to work efficiently. If earthworms are exposed to air, their skin soon dries out and they suffocate. When the weather is dry, they burrow deeper until they reach moist soil. Rain, however, is a problem for earthworms because their burrows become flooded, and they cannot obtain adequate oxygen from water. They have to leave their flooded burrows to avoid drowning.

11-8 Respiration in the Grasshopper

The respiratory system in grasshoppers is unusual. Blood does not play a role in the transport of oxygen or carbon dioxide. Instead, air is carried directly to all the cells of the body through a system of branching air tubes called **tracheae** (*tray*-kee-ee), or **tracheal tubes.** Air enters and leaves the grasshopper's body through ten pairs of openings called **spiracles** (*speer*-uh-kulz) (see Figure 11-4). From each spiracle, the tracheal tubes branch repeatedly into smaller and smaller tubes. The fluid-filled ends of these microscopic air tubes are in direct contact with the body cells and are the actual respiratory surface. Here oxygen in the air diffuses from the tracheal tubes to the body cells, and carbon dioxide diffuses from the body cells into the tracheal tubes.

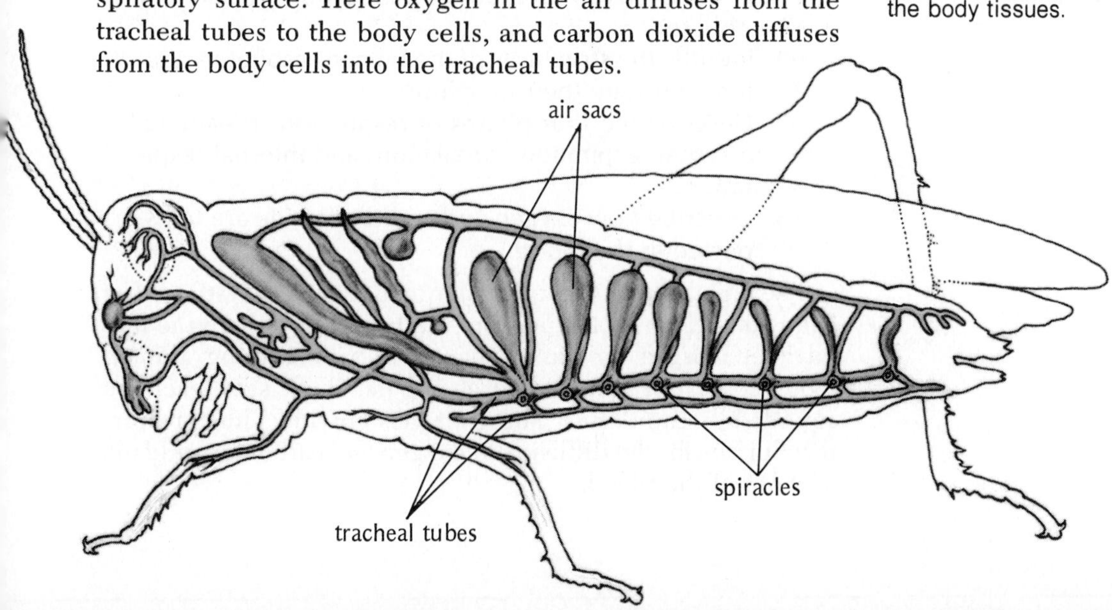

Figure 11-4. Respiratory System of the Grasshopper. In the grasshopper, air enters and leaves the animal through the spiracles. A branching system of tracheal tubes carries the air to and from the body tissues.

Figure 11-5. Gills of a Fish. The thin filaments of a gill are richly supplied with blood vessels and provide a large surface area for the exchange of respiratory gases.

Air is pumped into and out of the tracheal system by contraction of the grasshopper's muscles. During inhalation, the abdomen expands, and air is sucked into the tracheal tubes through the first four pairs of anterior spiracles. Several large air sacs connected to these tubes aid in this pumping action. During exhalation, the abdomen contracts, the four pairs of anterior spiracles close, and air is squeezed out of the tracheal tubes through the six posterior pairs of spiracles.

The system of tracheal tubes is relatively efficient for respiration in small animals. However, in a large animal it would not be possible to move the necessary volume of gases through such a system. Grasshoppers and other insects are all small, and the system of air tubes is adequate for their needs. Giant insects are found only in science fiction.

11-9 Gill Respiration

Gills are the respiratory organs of many aquatic animals, including fish, clams, oysters, and lobsters (see Figure 11-5). Gills are thin filaments of skin that generally grow out of the body. They are covered with a thin layer of cells and are richly supplied with blood vessels. They provide a large surface area for gas exchange. As water passes over the gills, dissolved oxygen diffuses from the water across the thin membrane and into the blood, which transports it to all parts of the body. Carbon dioxide from the blood diffuses out of the gills and into the water. There must be a continuous flow of water over the gills. If the water flow is stopped, the animal will die from lack of oxygen.

HUMAN RESPIRATORY SYSTEM

After completing your study of this section, you should be able to:

1. Identify the structures of the human respiratory system and state their functions.
2. Describe the four phases of respiration: breathing, external respiration, circulation, and internal respiration.
3. Describe how oxygen and carbon dioxide are transported in the blood.

The human respiratory system consists of a system of air tubes that carry air to and from the **lungs.** Lungs are the most advanced organ for gas exchange in air-breathing animals. They consist of many small chambers, or air sacs, each surrounded by capillaries. These air sacs provide a huge respiratory surface for the diffusion of oxygen and carbon dioxide into and out of the blood.

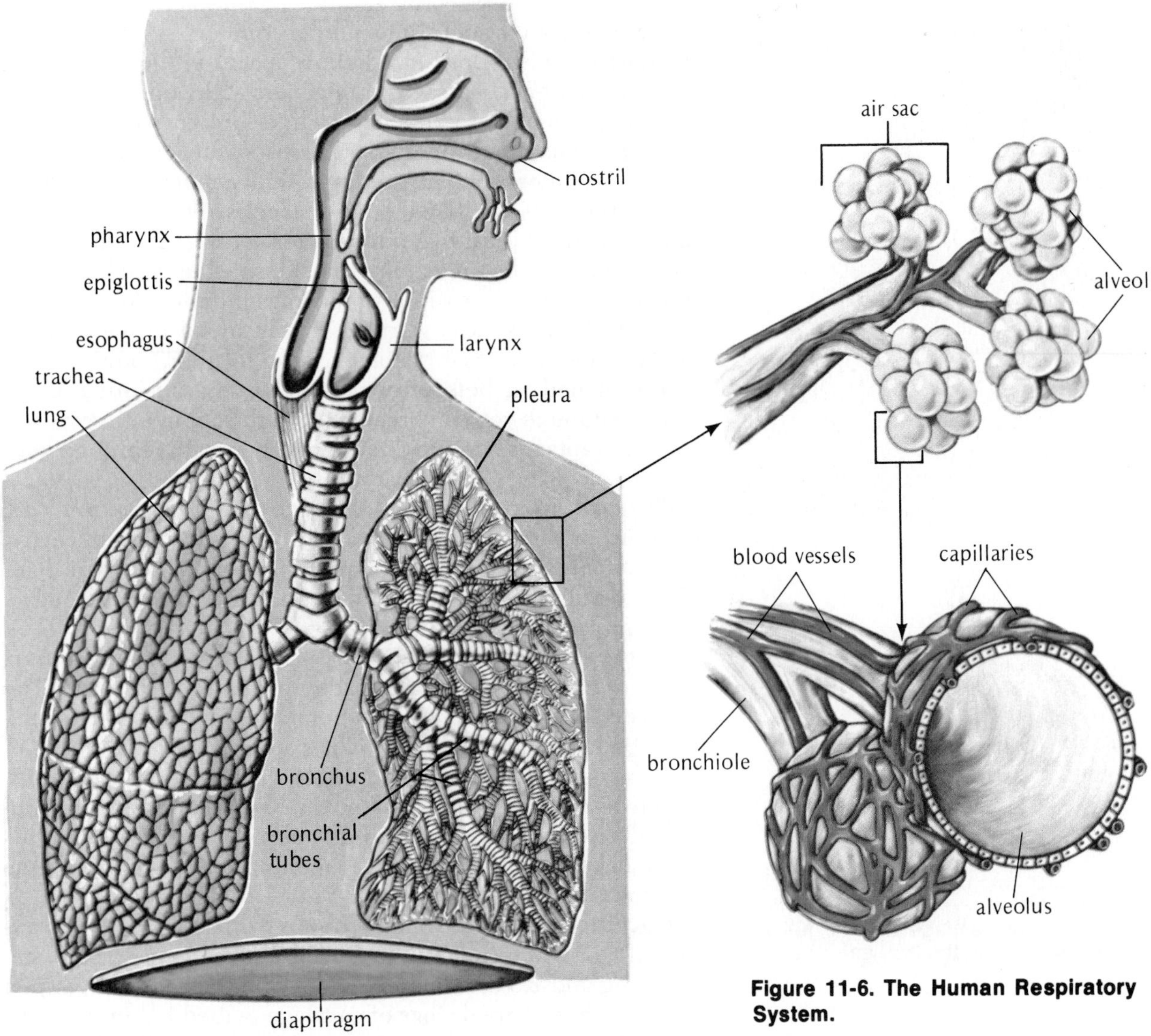

Figure 11-6. The Human Respiratory System.

11-10 Structure of the Human Respiratory System

The human respiratory system consists of the lungs and all the air passages that lead to them (see Figure 11-6). The lungs occupy a large portion of the chest cavity. They are separated from the abdominal cavity by the **diaphragm** (*dy*-uh-fram), a muscle that forms the floor of the chest cavity. Each lung is completely enclosed by a two-layered membrane called the **pleura** (*plur*-uh). One layer of the pleural membrane closely covers each lung, while the other layer is in contact with the diaphragm and other organs of the chest cavity. A lubricating fluid between the layers allows the lungs to move freely in the chest during breathing.

The air passages conduct air from the environment to the respiratory surface in the lungs. These passages include the nose, pharynx, trachea, bronchi, and bronchioles.

The nose. Air normally enters the respiratory system through the **nostrils,** which lead into hollow spaces in the nose called the **nasal** (*nay*-zul) **passages.** Long hairs at the openings of the nostrils prevent the entrance of large foreign particles. The walls of the nasal passages, like the rest of the air passageways in the respiratory system, are lined with a mucous membrane made up mainly of ciliated epithelial cells. Other cells secrete mucus, a sticky fluid that traps bacteria, dust, and other particles in the air. The mucus also moistens the air. Just below the mucous membrane is a rich supply of capillaries. As air passes through the nose, it is warmed by the blood in these capillaries. Thus, the nasal passages serve to filter, moisten, and warm inhaled air before it reaches the delicate lining of the lungs. Although you can breathe through your mouth, you lose these advantages if you do not regularly breathe through your nose.

Pharynx. From the nasal passages, air passes into the **pharynx,** or throat, which is located behind the mouth cavity. The *adenoids* (*ad*-uh-noydz) and *tonsils* (*tahn*-sulz) are lymphoid tissues found in the throat. They are part of the body's defense against infection.

Larynx. From the pharynx, air passes into the **larynx** (*lar*-inks), or voice box, which is made up largely of cartilage. The larynx is located at the upper end of the trachea, which is the air tube leading to the lungs. The vocal cords are two pairs of membranes that are stretched across the interior of the larynx. As air is exhaled, vibrations of the vocal cords can be controlled to make sounds. During swallowing, food and liquids are blocked from entering the opening of the larynx by the epiglottis.

The rings of cartilage can be felt by gently squeezing the trachea.

Trachea. The larynx is continuous with the **trachea** (*tray*-kee-uh), or windpipe. The trachea is a tube about 12 centimeters long and 2.5 centimeters wide. The trachea is kept open by horseshoe-shaped rings of cartilage embedded in its walls. Like the nasal passages, the trachea is also lined with a ciliated mucous membrane (see Figure 11-7). Normally, the

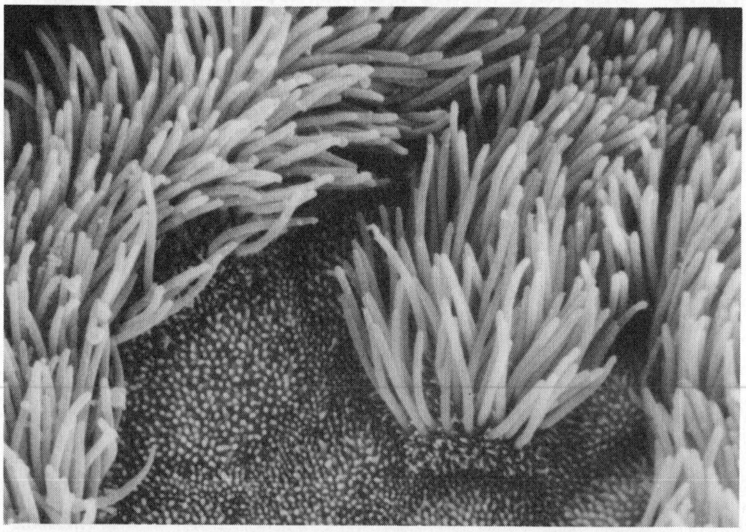

Figure 11-7. The Lining of the Trachea. The cilia of the cells lining the trachea beat rhythmically, moving mucus and foreign particles toward the pharynx.

cilia move mucus and trapped foreign matter to the pharynx, where they are expelled from the air passageways and usually swallowed.

As many people have discovered, the respiratory system is not designed to handle tobacco smoke. Smoking paralyzes the cilia. Just one cigarette stops the movement of the cilia for about 20 minutes. Furthermore, tobacco smoke increases the production of mucus in the air passages. A smoker's cough is the body's attempt to remove the excess mucus.

Bronchi. In the middle of the chest, the trachea divides into two cartilage-ringed tubes called **bronchi** (*brahn*-kee). The bronchi enter the lungs and branch in treelike fashion into smaller tubes called **bronchial** (*brahn*-kee-ul) **tubes** (see Figure 11-6).

Bronchioles. As the bronchial tubes divide and subdivide, their walls become thinner, and they gradually lose their cartilage. Finally, they become a network of microscopic tubes called **bronchioles** (*brahn*-kee-ohlz).

Air sacs and alveoli. Each bronchiole ends in a space called an **air sac.** An air sac resembles a cluster of grapes (see Figure 11-6). Each air sac contains several cup-shaped cavities called **alveoli** (al-*vee*-uh-ly) The walls of the alveoli, which are only one cell thick, are the respiratory surface. They are thin and moist and are surrounded by a rich network of capillaries. It is through these walls that the exchange of oxygen and carbon dioxide between blood and air occurs. It has been estimated that the lungs contain about 300 million alveoli, with a total surface area of about 70 square meters. This would be 40 times the surface area of the skin.

Besides irritating the trachea and bronchi, smoking interferes with the uptake of oxygen in the air sacs. When cigarette smoke is inhaled, about one-third of the particles remain in the alveoli. Phagocytic cells called **macrophages** (*mak*-ruh-fay-jez) can slowly remove many of the particles (see Figure 11-8). However, an excess of particles from smoking or air

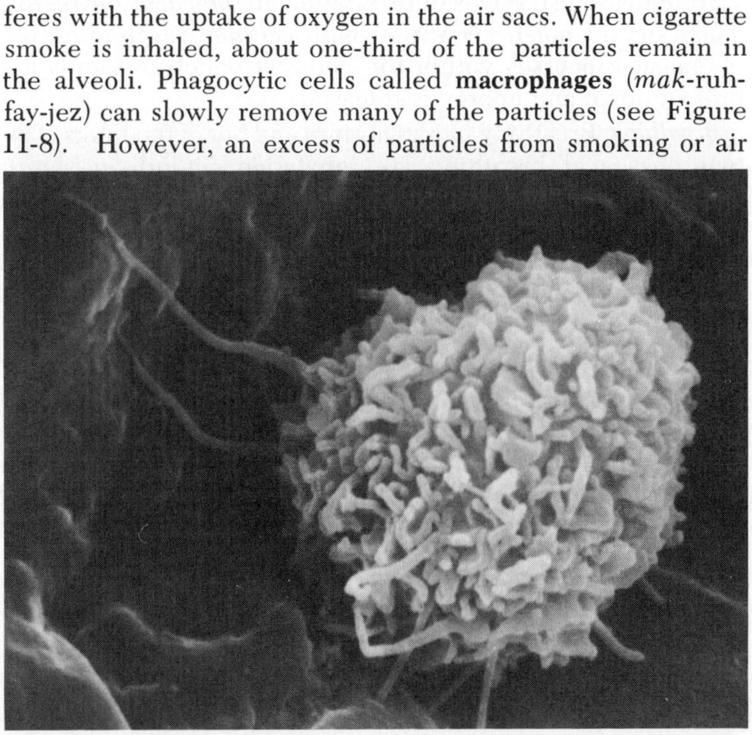

Figure 11-8. Lung Macrophage. The phagocytic macrophages ingest foreign particles. However, when an excess of particles accumulate, the macrophages become overwhelmed and can no longer prevent damage to the lungs.

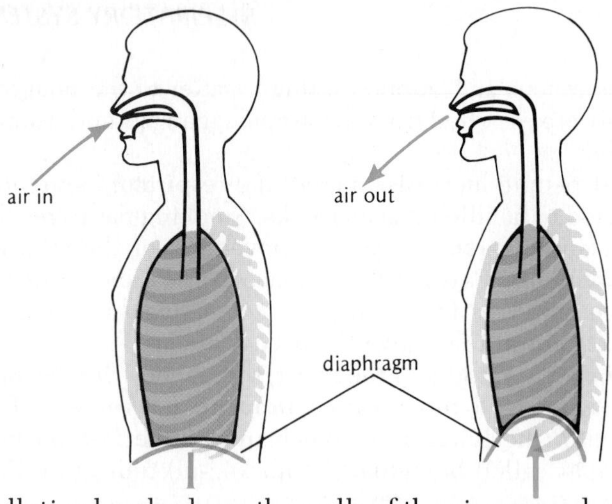

Figure 11-9. Breathing. During inhalation (left), the ribs are pulled up and out, the diaphragm is pulled down, and the chest cavity is enlarged. Because the pressure in the chest is reduced, air is forced into the lungs. During exhalation (right), the diaphragm and chest muscles relax, and the size of the chest cavity is decreased. This increases the pressure in the chest, and air is squeezed out of the lungs.

pollution breaks down the walls of the air sacs and causes the formation of inelastic, scarlike tissue. This greatly reduces the functional area of the respiratory surface and may lead to a disease called emphysema.

11-11 Phases of Human Respiration

In humans, respiration can be divided into four distinct phases.

1. **Breathing** is the movement of air into and out of the lungs.
2. **External respiration** is the exchange of oxygen and carbon dioxide between the air and the blood in the lungs.
3. **Circulation** is the carrying of dissolved gases by the blood to and from the body cells.
4. **Internal respiration** is the exchange of oxygen and carbon dioxide between the blood and the body cells.

Note that these stages of respiration are *physical* processes. They should not be confused with *cellular* respiration, the chemical processes within the cells by which nutrients are broken down and energy is released.

Breathing. Breathing moves air into and out of the lungs. The two phases of breathing are **inhalation** (in-huh-*lay*-shun), which draws air into the lungs, and **exhalation** (eks-huh-*lay*-shun), which expels air from the lungs. Since the lungs contain no muscle tissue, they are not capable of independent movement. However, they are elastic, and during breathing they are forced to expand or contract by the movement of the diaphragm, ribs, and rib muscles, and by the force of air pressure.

Inhalation is the active phase of breathing. As the ribs are pulled up and out and the diaphragm is pulled downward, the chest cavity is enlarged (see Figure 11-9). As a result, the pressure within the chest cavity is reduced. External air (at atmospheric pressure) rushes down the air passageways into the air sacs, forcing the lungs to expand.

Exhalation is the passive phase of breathing. The diaphragm relaxes and pushes upward, and the rib muscles relax, causing the ribs to drop. This decreases the size of the chest cavity and increases the pressure on the lungs. Thus, air is squeezed out of the lungs.

Normal rates of breathing vary from about 12 to 25 times per minute. One of the effects of smoking is to increase the breathing rate.

Be sure to discuss the harmful effects of cigarette smoking.

Although breathing can be controlled voluntarily to some extent, it is basically an involuntary process. It is controlled by the *respiratory center* in the brain. There are also special structures in the aorta and several other large arteries that are sensitive to the concentrations of oxygen and carbon dioxide in the blood. These *chemoreceptors* send messages to the respiratory center. When the carbon dioxide concentration in the blood increases, the respiratory center of the brain is stimulated. Nerves from the respiratory center carry impulses to the diaphragm and chest muscles that increase the rate and depth of breathing. This lowers the carbon dioxide concentration and increases the oxygen concentration of the blood.

During heavy muscular exertion, lactic acid is produced as well as carbon dioxide. This increases the acidity of the blood. The increased acidity also stimulates the respiratory center of the brain and increases the rate of breathing.

External and internal respiration. External respiration is the exchange of oxygen and carbon dioxide between the air and the blood in the lungs (see Figure 11-10). After inhalation, the concentration of oxygen in the alveoli is higher than the concentration of oxygen in the blood. Oxygen dissolves into the moist lining of the alveoli and diffuses from the region of higher concentration (the alveoli) to the region of lower concentration (the blood). Independently, carbon dioxide diffuses in the opposite direction—out of the blood and into the alveoli.

Figure 11-10. External and Internal Respiration. In human body tissues, all cells exchange gases with the internal environment by diffusion across the moist cell membranes. The gases are transported to and from the lungs by the blood and the circulatory system. Exchange with the external environment occurs by diffusion across moist cell membranes in the alveoli of the lungs.

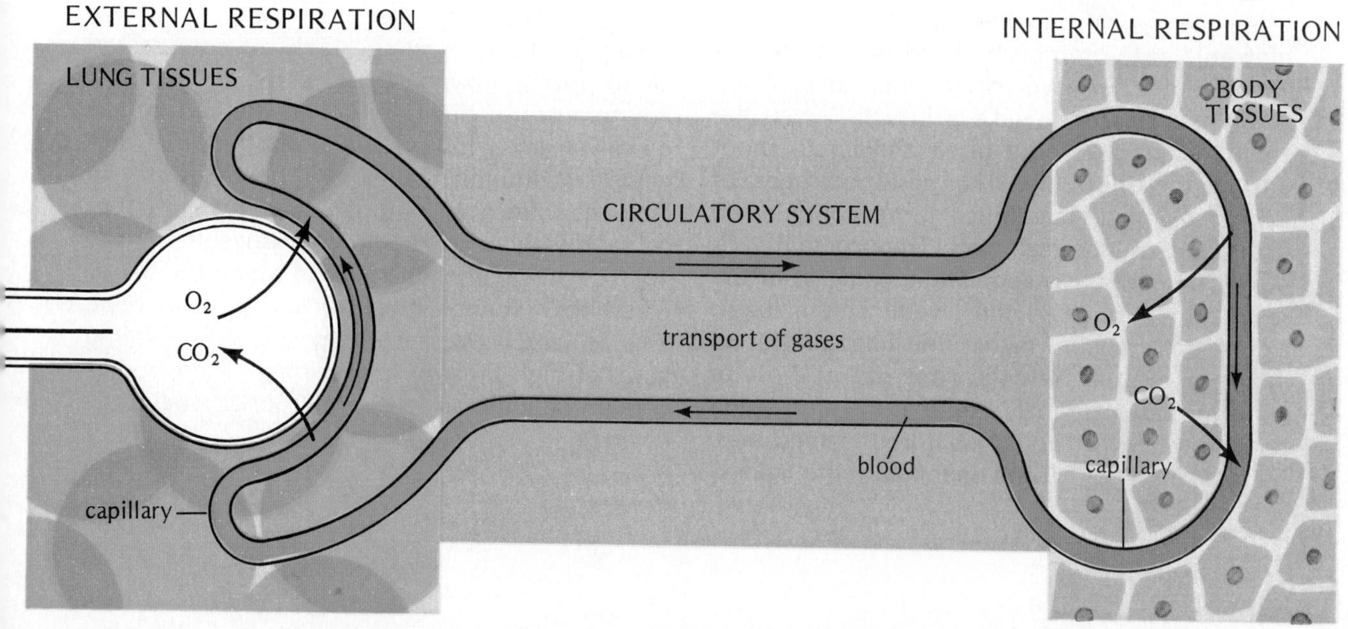

sidelights

Marine mammals, including whales, dolphins, porpoises, seals, and sea lions, must breathe air, but they dive hundreds of meters below the ocean's surface in search of food. Seals have been observed to dive as deep as 600 meters and to stay submerged for 70 minutes. Whales have been found at depths of over 1,000 meters, and they have been observed to stay submerged for as long as 75 minutes.

Marine mammals are well adapted to their environment in terms of body form. Their bodies are sleek and streamlined. Movement of the strong tail propels them through the water. The modified forelimbs, the flippers, serve for balancing and steering the animal. The respiratory and circulatory systems show adaptations for life in the sea. In seals and sea lions, which spend time on shore or on ice floes, the head resembles that of a dog, and the nasal openings are in the front of the head. In whales, dolphins, and porpoises, which spend their lives completely in water, the nasal opening is called the blowhole, and it is located on the top of the head. The blowhole must be out of the water when the animal breathes. The location of the blowhole at the top of the head means that the animal does not have to lift much of its body above the surface to take a breath. When the animal exhales, a spout of air and liquid shoot out of the blowhole. The nasal passages of marine mammals are much more complicated than those of land mammals. They contain various adaptations that keep water away from the respiratory surface — the alveoli of the lungs.

Research has shown that the lungs of marine mammals are relatively the same size as those of land-dwelling mammals, and that the air needed for a long, deep dive is not stored in the lungs. In fact, in many diving mammals, the animal exhales before or shortly after diving. In some, the lungs become almost completely collapsed during a dive.

The circulatory system shows a number of adaptations for diving. The heart of diving mammals is relatively the same size as in land-dwelling mammals, but the size and pattern of arteries and veins is different. The increased size of veins, in particular, results in an increased volume of blood in the body. In adddition, the number of red blood cells per milliliter of blood is much higher in marine mammals than in land-dwelling mammals, and the concentration of hemoglobin in the red cells is also much greater. These adaptations greatly increase the oxygen-carrying capacity of the blood. There is also the so-called "diving response," which alters the pattern of blood flow in the body. In the diving response, the blood flow is directed to the heart and brain and away from the less sensitive tissues of the body. The rate of the heartbeat is greatly slowed during the dive, and other metabolic processes also slow down. These adaptations allow the animal to stay underwater for long periods of time.

Human divers must use tanks of compressed air to provide oxygen for dives of more than a few minutes. If divers return to the surface too quickly from a long, deep dive, they may develop a condition called the bends from the large quantities of nitrogen gas that have become dissolved in the body tissues (see page 187). Diving mammals do not develop the bends when they surface quickly from a deep dive. This is largely because they are not inhaling gases at high pressure underwater. Their bodies contain only the air left in their lungs when they dived.

As the blood is pumped through the vessels of the body by the beating of the heart, oxygen-rich blood from the lungs is carried to the body tissues and oxygen-poor blood from the tissues is returned to the lungs.

Internal respiration is the exchange of oxygen and carbon dioxide between the blood and the body cells. In the capillaries of the body tissues, oxygen diffuses from the blood through the intercellular fluid to the body cells; carbon dioxide diffuses from the cells through the intercellular fluid into the blood. Each gas diffuses from a region of higher concentration to a region of lower concentration.

Oxygen transport. Most oxygen is transported from the lungs to the body tissues by the hemoglobin in the red blood cells. It is not dissolved in the plasma to any great extent. Hemoglobin is a unique iron-containing protein. Its most important characteristic is that it combines readily with oxygen. However, the oxygen is loosely held, and the reaction is reversible, depending on the oxygen concentration. In the lungs, where the oxygen concentration is high, hemoglobin (Hb) combines with oxygen (O_2) to form *oxyhemoglobin* (HbO_2). When the blood reaches the capillaries of the body tissues, where the oxygen concentration of the surrounding tissues is low, the oxyhemoglobin breaks down into oxygen and hemoglobin. The oxygen diffuses from the blood into the body cells, where it is used in cellular respiration.

Blood low in oxygen is a dark red or dull purple color because of the hemoglobin. Blood rich in oxygen is a bright red color because of the oxyhemoglobin.

Carbon dioxide transport. Cellular respiration produces carbon dioxide. Thus the concentration of carbon dioxide is greater in the body cells than in the capillary blood. Therefore, the carbon dioxide diffuses out of the cells and into the blood. Carbon dioxide is transported by the blood to the lungs in several ways .

When carbon dioxide diffuses into the blood, it combines with water, forming carbonic acid.

$$CO_2 + H_2O \longrightarrow H_2CO_3$$

The H_2CO_3 quickly breaks down (ionizes), forming hydrogen ions and bicarbonate ions.

$$H_2CO_3 \longrightarrow H^+ + HCO_3^-$$

These reactions are speeded up by the presence of an enzyme in the red blood cells. Most of the carbon dioxide (about 70 percent) is carried in the plasma in the form of bicarbonate ions.

Some of the carbon dioxide (about 20 percent) is carried in the red blood cells as carboxyhemoglobin.

$$CO_2 + Hb \longrightarrow HbCO_2$$

sidelights

As a diver descends deeper and deeper beneath the surface of the water, the pressure increases enormously. At a depth of 11 meters the pressure is twice as great as at sea level. At 22 meters the pressure is three times as great, and so on. To prevent the lungs from collapsing, the diver must breathe air that is under pressure. At increased pressures, the volume of gases is compressed. For example, 1 liter of air at sea level is compressed to ½ liter at a depth of 11 meters.

When a diver breathes pressurized air for long periods of time, large amounts of compressed nitrogen become dissolved in the body fluids and tissues. The greater the depth of the diver, the greater the amount of nitrogen in the body. If the diver suddenly returns to the surface, where the pressure is much less, the nitrogen is no longer compressed, and it forms bubbles in the body fluids and tissues. This condition, called the "bends," or decompression sickness, is very painful and can be fatal if the bubbles affect the lungs or nervous system.

The bends can be avoided if decompression is gradual. Divers returning to the surface from depths of more than about 12 meters must do so gradually, with stops of varying lengths at certain depths. These stops give the body a chance to get rid of the nitrogen gradually.

A small amount of carbon dioxide (about 10 percent) is carried in solution in the plasma.

All these reactions are reversible, and in the lungs carbon dioxide is released.

11-12 Diseases of the Respiratory System

You may wish to discuss air pollution here instead of lumping it with other environmental problems in Chapter 38. You can discuss the effects of air pollutants on the respiratory system.

The following list includes some of the common disorders of the respiratory system.

1. *Asthma* (*az*-muh) is a severe allergic reaction in which contraction of the bronchioles makes breathing difficult.

2. *Bronchitis* is an inflammation of the linings of the bronchial tubes. The passageways to the alveoli become swollen and clogged with mucus. The condition is generally marked by severe coughing and by difficulty in breathing.

3. *Emphysema* (em-fuh-*zee*-muh) is a condition in which the lungs lose their elasticity. The walls of the air sacs break down, reducing the respiratory surface. Emphysema is marked by shortness of breath.

4. *Pneumonia* (noo-*moh*-nyuh) is a condition in which the alveoli become filled with fluid, preventing the exchange of gases in the lungs.

5. *Lung cancer* is a disease in which tumors (masses of tissue) form in the lungs as a result of irregular and uncontrolled cell growth. Numerous studies have demonstrated a definite relationship between lung cancer and smoking.

Smokers also run a greater risk of developing bronchitis and emphysema than nonsmokers.

summary

Respiration is the exchange of carbon dioxide and oxygen between a living organism and its environment. This gas exchange takes place by diffusion through the organism's respiratory surface, which must be thin-walled and moist. In very simple organisms the exchange of gases takes place through the cell membrane. Complex multicellular animals require complex respiratory and transport systems to carry the gases between the environment and the cells. In many animals, including humans, the blood contains a pigment that increases its capacity to carry respiratory gases.

In earthworms, the respiratory surface is the moist skin, which is well-supplied with capillaries. The blood contains the pigment hemoglobin, which carries oxygen and carbon dioxide. In grasshoppers, the circulatory system is not involved in carrying respiratory gases. Instead, there is a system of tubes called tracheae that carry the air to and from the body cells. Air enters and leaves the system through openings called spiracles. In fish and many other aquatic animals, the respiratory organs are gills, which are thin filaments of skin that grow out from the body. The exchange of respiratory gases occurs as water flows over the gills.

In humans, the respiratory system consists of the lungs and a system of tubes that carry air to and from the lungs. Within the lungs are millions of tiny thin-walled alveoli, each surrounded by capillaries. The exchange of respiratory gases takes place through the walls of the alveoli. Oxygen diffuses through the walls into the capillary blood, while carbon dioxide from the blood diffuses out of the capillaries and through the walls into the alveoli.

Respiration in humans can be divided into four phases: breathing, which is the movement of air into and out of the lungs; external respiration, which is the exchange of respiratory gases that takes place in the lungs; circulation, which is the transport of respiratory gases between the lungs and the cells of the body; and internal respiration, which is the exchange of respiratory gases between the blood and the body cells.

vocabulary

air sac
alveolus
breathing
bronchial tube
bronchiole
bronchus
diaphragm
epiglottis
exhalation
external respiration
gill
inhalation
internal respiration
larynx
lung
macrophage
nasal passage
nostril
pharynx
pleura
respiration
respiratory surface
spiracle
trachea

test your learning

Section		
11-1	1.	What is respiration?
11-2	2.	What is a respiratory surface, and what characteristics must a respiratory surface have?
	3.	What determines the direction of movement of gases across the respiratory surface?
11-3	4.	What is the respiratory surface in protozoa, and how is gas exchange with the environment accomplished?
11-4	5.	How do the cells of hydra obtain oxygen and get rid of carbon dioxide?
11-5	6.	Why must aquatic animals move large volumes of water over their respiratory surfaces?
11-6	7.	Explain the function of hemoglobin in the blood.
11-7	8.	Describe the respiratory surface and the process of respiration in the earthworm.
11-8	9.	Describe the structure of the respiratory system of the grasshopper, and explain how it functions.
11-9	10.	What are gills, and how do they function in respiration?
11-10	11.	Describe the position of the lungs in the chest in humans.
	12.	What functions do the nasal passages serve in the human respiratory system?
	13.	What is the larynx and where is it located?
	14.	Trace the path of the air from the nasal passages to the alveoli.
	15.	What is the respiratory surface in the human lung?
	16.	How does tobacco smoke damage the lungs?
11-11	17.	What are the four phases of respiration in humans?
	18.	Describe what happens to the chest and lungs during inhalation and during exhalation.
	19.	What is accomplished by breathing?
	20.	What factors affect the rate of breathing?
	21.	What happens during external respiration and during internal respiration?
	22.	Describe the transport of oxygen in the blood from the lungs to the body cells.
	23.	Describe the transport of carbon dioxide in the blood from the body cells to the lungs.
11-12	24.	Briefly describe each of the following conditions: asthma, bronchitis, emphysema, and pneumonia.

test your understanding

1. Why is the respiratory surface in humans and other land-dwelling animals located within the body? Would an internal respiratory surface also be suitable for a fish? Explain.
2. Distinguish between the following processes: cellular respiration, breathing, internal respiration, and external respiration.

3. Trace the path of oxygen from the air into a body cell.
4. What happens to the oxygen and carbon dioxide concentrations in your blood if you hold your breath? What happens if you breathe deeply and rapidly?

independent research

1. Write a report on one of the following topics:
   A. deep-sea diving and the "bends"
   B. artificial lung machines
   C. asthma
2. Prepare a report on one of the following career opportunities:
   A. inhalation therapist
   B. speech therapist
   C. air pollution control technician

   If possible, interview a person who works in the field. A tape recorder is very helpful in doing the interview. Be sure to prepare your questions in advance.

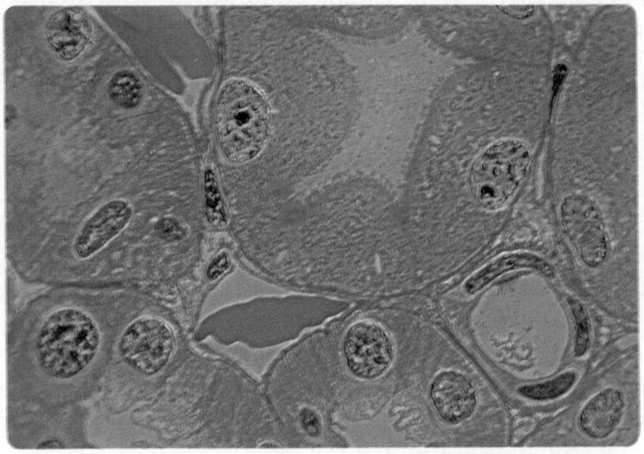

chapter 12

Excretion

CHAPTER INTRODUCTION

After completing your study of this section, you should be able to:

1. Define the term *excretion*.
2. List the major metabolic wastes and name the processes by which they are formed.

12-1 Importance of Excretion

Organisms can carry out their life processes only if the chemical environment of their internal fluids is kept constant within certain limits. However, as the cells carry on their life processes, wastes are produced. These wastes are the end products of metabolism. For example, in cellular respiration nutrients are oxidized, and the energy released is stored in the form of ATP. However, carbon dioxide and water are also produced, and these end products are wastes that must be removed from the organism. **Excretion** (ek-*skree*-shun) is the process by which the wastes of cellular metabolism are removed from the organism.

The excretory organs regulate the chemical makeup of the blood and other body fluids by removing metabolic wastes and excess materials. They also help to maintain a constant body temperature by removing excess heat. The excretory organs function together with the circulatory, nervous, and endocrine systems in maintaining a constant internal environment—they maintain homeostasis.

12-2 Major Metabolic Wastes

The most important of the cellular wastes are carbon dioxide, water, nitrogenous wastes, and mineral salts. Carbon dioxide and water are formed during cellular respiration. Water is also produced by dehydration synthesis (see page 50). Nitrogenous wastes in the form of ammonia, urea, or uric acid are produced by the breakdown of amino acids. Mineral salts, such as sodium chloride and potassium sulfate, accumulate during metabolism. All these wastes are poisons in high concentrations.

Unlike freshwater amebas, saltwater amebas do not have contractile vacuoles. However, if the medium in which they are kept is gradually made less and less salty, contractile vacuoles form.

In addition to the wastes of metabolism, the excretory system must also remove any excess water, salts, or other substances that accumulate within the organism.

Many people confuse excretion with elimination. Elimination, or *defecation* (def-uh-*kay*-shun) is the removal from the digestive tract of unabsorbed and undigested food in the form of *feces*. Since these materials never enter the body cells, they are not metabolic wastes.

ADAPTATIONS FOR EXCRETION

After completing your study of this section, you should be able to:

1. List the metabolic wastes of protozoa and hydra and explain how each type of waste is removed from the cell.
2. Explain the function of the contractile vacuole in freshwater protozoa.
3. Describe and compare the excretory structures and products of the earthworm and the grasshopper.

12-3 Excretion in Protozoa

Excretion in protozoa is a relatively simple process. Wastes diffuse through the cell membrane into the surrounding watery environment. Metabolic wastes include carbon dioxide, mineral salts, and ammonia. Ammonia (NH_3) is the chief nitrogenous waste of microorganisms and many aquatic multicellular animals. Although ammonia is highly toxic to cells, it is very soluble in water. Thus, ammonia can easily be excreted as a waste product if plenty of water is available to wash it away.

Water continuously enters the cells of freshwater protozoans, such as ameba and paramecium, by osmosis. Some water is also produced as a by-product of cellular respiration. Excess water must be "pumped out" of the cell against a concentration gradient. The excess water collects in contractile vacuoles, which periodically burst at the cell membrane, ejecting the excess water from the cell (see Figure 12-1). This action, which involves active transport, maintains the normal water balance in the cell.

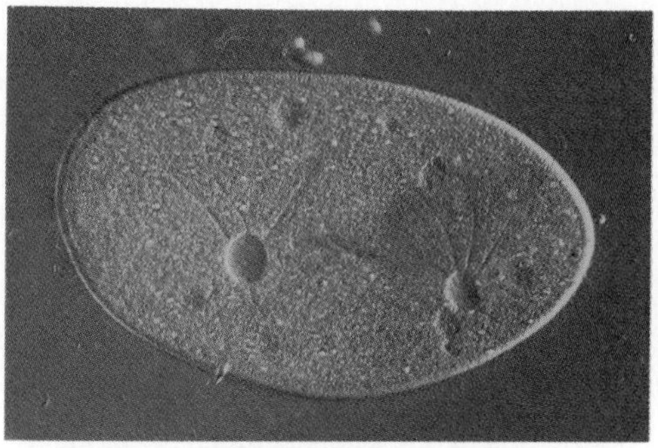

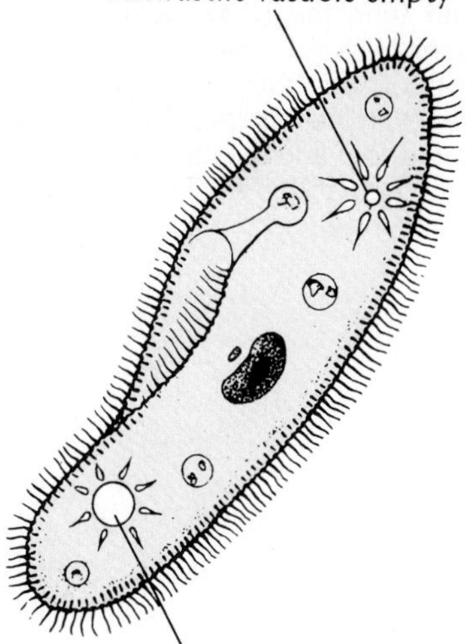

Figure 12-1. Water Balance in the Paramecium. Water continuously enters the paramecium and other freshwater protozoa by osmosis. Water balance is maintained by means of contractile vacuoles. Excess water collects in the vacuoles and is periodically ejected from the organism.

12-4 Excretion in Hydra

The hydra is a very small animal, and its structure is such that most of its cells are in contact with the water of its environment. Hence, the metabolic wastes, including carbon dioxide, ammonia, and mineral salts, diffuse directly through the cell membrane of each cell into the surrounding water.

Hydras are freshwater organisms, and water tends to enter their cells by osmosis. However, no contractile vacuole has been observed in the cells of the hydra. Excess water may be pumped out through the cell membrane by active transport.

12-5 Excretion in the Earthworm

When most of the cells of an animal are not in contact with the external environment, the removal of metabolic wastes requires special excretory organs. The excretory organs of the earthworm are the **nephridia** (nih-*frid*-ee-uh). These structures are found in pairs, one on each side, in most of the segments of the earthworm's body (see Figure 12-2). Each nephridium occupies parts of two adjacent segments.

Some of the cellular wastes diffuse directly into the fluid in the body cavity of the earthworm. This fluid, which contains useful substances in addition to wastes, enters the funnel-like opening of the nephridium and is moved through it by the beating of cilia. The fluid travels through a tubule to the major part of the nephridium in the next segment. This part consists of several coiled loops and a large bladder with an opening to the outside of the body, the *nephridiopore* (nih-*frid*-ee-oh-por). The coiled loops of the nephridium are surrounded by a network of capillaries. Wastes from the bloodstream pass out of the capillaries and into the nephridium. Useful substances from the body fluid, such as glucose and water, are reabsorbed

Figure 12-2. Excretory System of the Earthworm. A pair of nephridia surrounded by capillaries is found in almost every segment of the earthworm. Fluid from the body cavity enters the nephridia and useful substances are reabsorbed into the bloodstream. Wastes in the form of urine pass through the bladder and are discharged from the body through the nephridiopores.

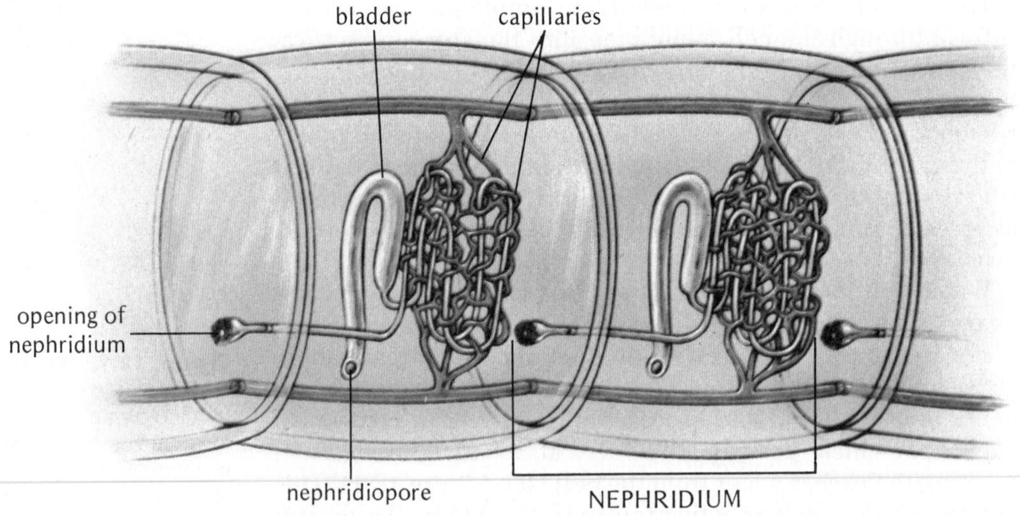

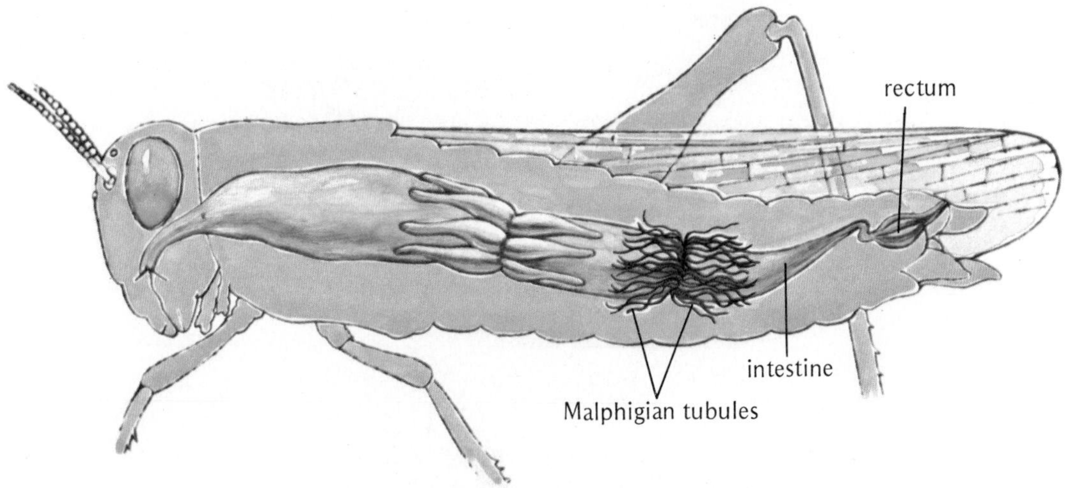

Figure 12-3. Excretory System of the Grasshopper. The Malpighian tubules of the grasshopper remove wastes from the blood by diffusion and active transport. A dry nitrogenous waste product, uric acid, is eliminated with the feces through the anus.

into the blood. The wastes in the nephridium are discharged through the nephridiopore as a dilute solution called **urine** (*yur*-en).

The wastes excreted by the nephridia include water, mineral salts, ammonia, and **urea** (yuh-*ree*-uh), which is formed from ammonia and carbon dioxide. Like ammonia, urea is very soluble in water. However, it is less toxic to cells than ammonia.

In the earthworm, carbon dioxide is excreted through the moist skin (see page 178).

12-6 Excretion in the Grasshopper

The excretory organs of grasshoppers and other insects are the **Malpighian** (mal-*pig*-ee-en) **tubules** (see Figure 12-3). Insects have open circulatory systems. Thus, the slender excretory tubules are bathed directly by the blood, which circulates freely within the body spaces. Wastes and other substances from the blood enter the tubules by diffusion and active transport. From the tubules they pass into the large intestine. Water, nutrients, and other useful substances are reabsorbed both in the tubules and in the digestive tract, and are returned to the body fluids. The dry nitrogenous waste product, **uric** (*yur*-ik) **acid,** is eliminated from the body through the anus along with the feces.

Of all the nitrogenous wastes, uric acid is the least toxic. In fact, because it is insoluble in water, it is almost completely harmless. It is excreted as a solid or semisolid by birds and reptiles, as well as insects. Because its removal from the body of an organism requires almost no water, the excretion of uric acid helps to conserve water in land animals whose water supply is limited.

Carbon dioxide diffuses from the body tissues into the tracheal tubes and then out of the grasshopper through the spiracles (see page 179).

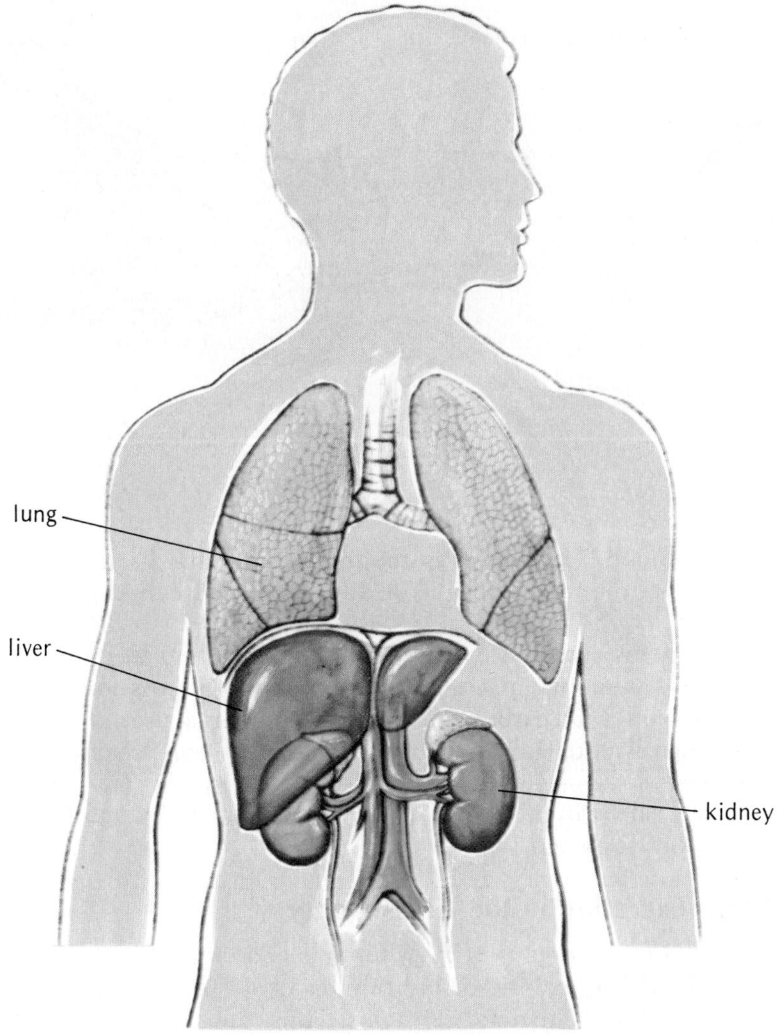

Figure 12-4. Organs of the Human Excretory System. The organs of excretion in humans include the liver, kidneys, lungs, and skin.

EXCRETION IN HUMANS

After completing your study of this section, you should be able to:

1. Identify the principal metabolic wastes of the human body.
2. Describe the excretory functions of the liver.
3. Draw and label the parts of the human urinary system, including a nephron, and explain the function of each.
4. Describe the process of urine formation.
5. Explain the excretory functions of the lungs.
6. Describe the structure and functions of the skin.

The complex and highly developed excretory system of humans plays a major role in the maintenance of homeostasis. The principal metabolic wastes of humans are carbon dioxide, urea, water, and mineral salts. The organs of excretion are the liver, kidneys, lungs, and skin (see Figure 12-4).

12-7 Role of the Liver in Excretion

The role of the liver in digestion was discussed in Chapter 8. As an excretory organ the liver performs a number of functions that regulate the composition of body fluids.

Detoxification. A major function of the liver is the removal of harmful, or toxic, substances from the blood. Within the liver these substances are converted into inactive or less toxic forms. Thus the liver purifies, or *detoxifies,* the blood. The inactive substances formed in the liver are then released back into the bloodstream and are eventually excreted from the body by the kidneys.

Excretion of bile. Bile is synthesized by the cells of the liver. It consists of bile salts, cholesterol, and part of the hemoglobin molecule from worn-out red blood cells. Since some of the constituents of bile are metabolic wastes, bile is considered an excretory product. Bile passes from the liver to the small intestine, where it functions in the digestion and absorption of fats. In the last part of the small intestine, almost all the bile salts are reabsorbed into the blood and returned to the liver. From the liver, they again pass to the small intestine. Thus, bile salts are reused. The rest of the bile passes into the large intestine and is eliminated from the body in the feces.

Urea formation. Amino acids are both the building blocks and breakdown products of proteins. However, excess amino acids cannot be stored in the body. Instead, in the liver the amino group (NH_2) is removed, a process called *deamination* (dee-am-uh-*nay*-shun). The amino group is converted to ammonia (NH_3), while the remainder of the amino acid molecule is either converted to pyruvic acid and used as an energy source in cellular respiration or converted to glycogen or fat for storage (see Figure 12-5).

Figure 12-5. Fate of Excess Amino Acids in the Body. Excess amino acids undergo deamination, in which the amino group is removed and converted to ammonia. The ammonia is quickly converted to urea, which is excreted from the body. The carbon skeleton of the amino acid can be converted to pyruvic acid and used in cellular respiration or it can be converted to glycogen or fat and stored.

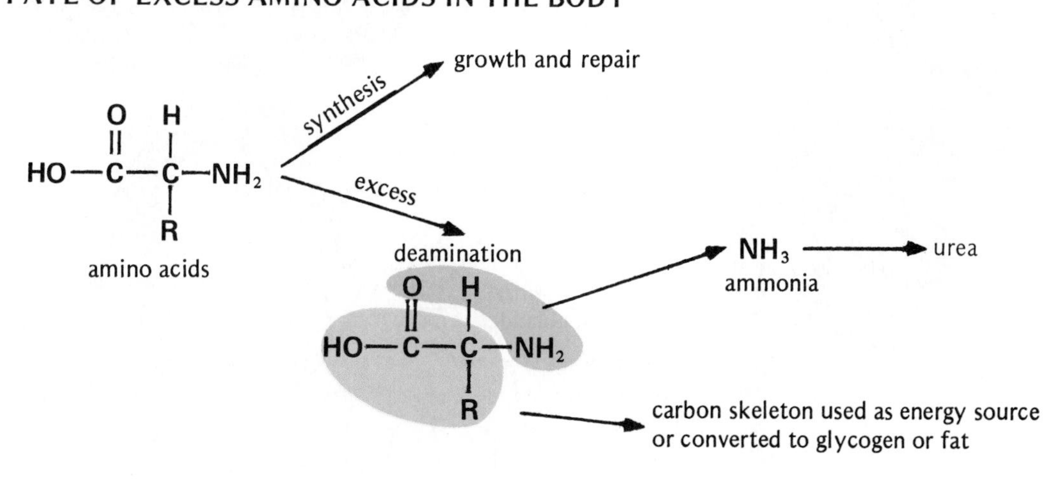

Ammonia is a highly toxic substance, and it is rapidly converted to the less toxic substance urea by a series of enzyme-catalyzed reactions. The urea diffuses from the liver into the bloodstream, which transports it to the kidneys. The kidneys filter the urea from the blood, and it is then excreted from the body in the urine.

Ammonia is converted to urea by a series of reactions called the ornithine cycle. The cycle begins when one molecule of ammonia and one molecule of carbon dioxide combine with one molecule of ornithine (a 5-carbon amino acid) to form citrulline (a 6-carbon amino acid). Citrulline combines with another molecule of ammonia to form arginine (a 6-carbon amino acid). Arginine is hydrolyzed, forming ornithine and urea. The ornithine is reused in the cycle.

12-8 The Urinary System

The **urinary** (*yur*-uh-ner-ee) **system** includes the kidneys, bladder, and associated tubes (see Figure 12-6). The **kidneys** are bean-shaped organs about 10 cm long. They lie against the muscles of the back in the abdomen just below the diaphragm. The kidneys serve two major functions. First, they remove the wastes of cellular metabolism from the blood. Second, they control the concentrations of the various substances found in the body fluids. In these ways, the kidneys are vital in maintaining homeostasis. The kidneys filter metabolic wastes and various other substances from the blood, producing urine. Two tubes, the **ureters** (*yur*-et-urz), carry the urine to the **urinary bladder,** where it is stored temporarily. Another tube, the **urethra** (yuh-*ree*-thruh), carries the urine from the bladder to the outside of the body.

Structure of the kidneys. A lengthwise section of the kidney reveals that it is divided into three distinct regions. The

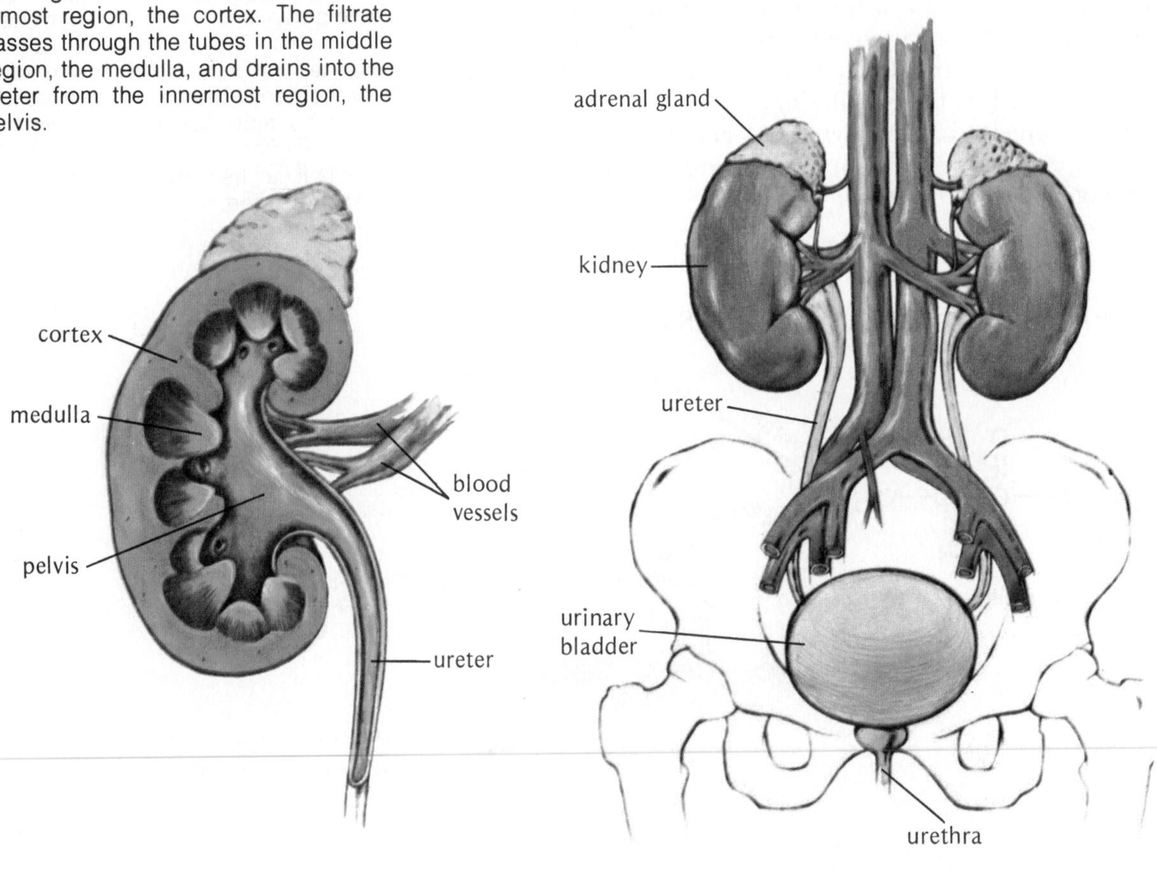

Figure 12-6. The Human Urinary System. The urinary system consists of the kidneys, ureters, bladder, and associated blood vessels. The adrenal glands rest on the kidneys, but are not part of the excretory system. The cross section of the kidney shows three distinct regions. Blood is filtered in the outermost region, the cortex. The filtrate passes through the tubes in the middle region, the medulla, and drains into the ureter from the innermost region, the pelvis.

outermost region is the *cortex* (*kor*-teks), the middle region is the *medulla* (meh-*duhl*-uh), and the inner region is the *pelvis* (*pel*-vis). The filtering of the blood occurs in the cortex; the medulla consists of collecting ducts that carry the urine; and the pelvis is a cavity connected to the ureter into which the urine drains.

The functional units of the kidneys are the **nephrons** (*nef*-rahnz). Each kidney contains about 1.25 million nephrons (see Figure 12-7). The nephron begins with a cluster of capillaries, the **glomerulus** (glah-*mer*-yuh-lus), which is surrounded by a double-walled, cup-shaped structure called *Bowman's capsule.* Coming from Bowman's capsule is a long tubule that winds and twists and then forms a long loop called the *loop of Henle* (*hen*-lee). From the loop, the tubule winds and twists again before emptying into a collecting duct. The collecting duct receives liquid waste from many nephrons.

Blood entering the kidneys passes through two sets of capillaries before it leaves the kidneys through the renal vein. The arteriole carrying blood to a nephron enters Bowman's capsule and subdivides into a capillary network, which is the glomerulus. Blood leaving the glomerulus flows into a second arteriole, which subdivides to form another capillary network that surrounds the tubules of the nephron. These capillaries merge to form a vein.

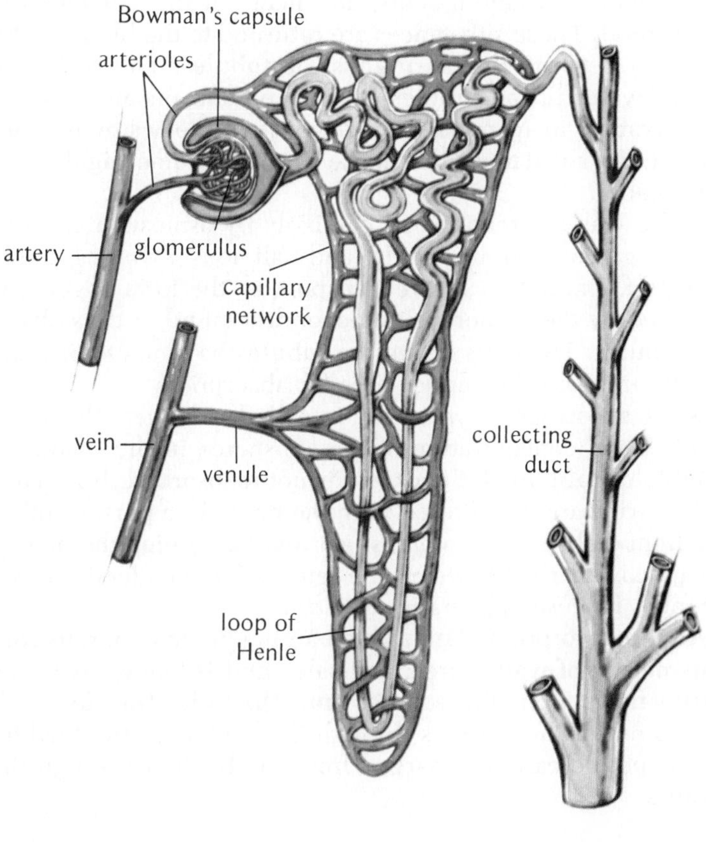

Figure 12-7. The Nephron. The nephron is the functional unit of the kidney. As blood flows through the glomerulus, water and other small molecules diffuse into the surrounding Bowman's capsule. The filtrate then passes through the tubules, where useful substances are reabsorbed into the blood. The collecting duct receives urine from many nephrons and passes it into the renal pelvis, from which it flows into the ureter.

Point out that in the glomerulus pressure forces both useful and waste substances out of the blood into the capsule, depending only on the size of the molecule.

Urine formation. The formation of urine by the nephrons takes place in two stages—filtration and reabsorption. In **filtration,** substances pass from the blood into the nephron. In **reabsorption,** substances pass out of the nephron and back into the blood.

Filtration occurs while the blood is flowing through the glomerulus within Bowman's capsule. Blood entering the glomerulus is under pressure. The pressure forces water and many small molecules, such as salts, urea, glucose, and amino acids, out through the thin walls of the glomerulus into the surrounding capsule. Blood cells and blood proteins are too large to pass through the walls of the glomerulus, and remain in the blood. The fluid in Bowman's capsule is called the *filtrate.* It is basically the same as plasma except for the absence of proteins. From Bowman's capsule, the filtrate passes through the tubules of the nephron and into the collecting duct.

About 180 liters of filtrate are formed by the kidneys during the course of 24 hours. If all the filtrate were excreted, the body would continually lose nutrients, salts, and large amounts of water. However the kidneys produce only about 1 to 1.5 liters of urine in 24 hours. The process that reduces the volume of filtrate and returns important substances to the blood is reabsorption. Normally, as the filtrate passes through the tubules of the nephrons, about 99 percent of the water, all the glucose and amino acids, and many of the salt ions are reabsorbed. These substances are returned to the blood in the capillary network that surrounds the tubules. The reabsorption of water in the tubules is an important means of water conservation in mammals. Since most of the water is reabsorbed, the substances left in the filtrate become highly concentrated.

While water is reabsorbed passively by osmosis, reabsorption of glucose, amino acids, and salt ions involves active transport. Energy for active transport, in the form of ATP, is supplied by the numerous mitochondria found in the cells of the tubules. The cells lining the tubules have microvilli that greatly increase the surface area for absorption.

Most substances have what is called a *kidney threshold level.* If the concentration of the substance in the blood exceeds a certain level, the excess is not reabsorbed. It remains in the urine and is excreted from the body. In a person suffering from diabetes, the blood sugar level is so high that not all the glucose in the filtrate can be returned to the blood. Consequently, glucose appears in the urine.

After reabsorption, the fluid remaining in the nephrons consists mostly of water, urea, and salts, and is known as urine. Urine flows from the tubules into the collecting ducts. It passes out of the kidneys through the ureters to the bladder and is periodically discharged from the bladder through the urethra.

12-9 The Lungs

Lungs are excretory organs in that they rid the body of carbon dioxide and water (in the form of water vapor). Both of these substances are end products of aerobic cellular respiration. The functioning of the lungs is discussed in Chapter 11.

12-10 The Skin

The skin is the part of the body that is in contact with the external environment. It consists of many different tissues and performs a variety of functions, including the excretion of wastes.

Structure of the skin. As shown in Figure 12-8 the skin consists of two layers, an outer epidermis and an inner dermis.

The **epidermis** (ep-uh-*der*-mis) is composed of layers of tightly packed epithelial cells. The lowermost portion of the epidermis is made up of rapidly dividing cells. As these cells are pushed farther and farther away from the dermis, they receive less nourishment and die. However, before dying, they produce large amounts of a tough, waterproofing protein called *keratin* (*ker*-uh-tin). The outer part of the epidermis consists of these hardened dead cells. It is continually wearing away and being replaced by new cells from the dividing layer. The function of the tough, waterproof epidermis is to protect the dermis.

The **dermis** lies below the epidermis and is made up of elastic connective tissue. It is a thick layer that supports the

Figure 12-8. Structure of the Skin. The epidermis protects the dermis, which contains blood and lymph vessels, glands, nerves, sense receptors, and hair follicles. Adipose tissue beneath the dermis is not shown in this drawing.

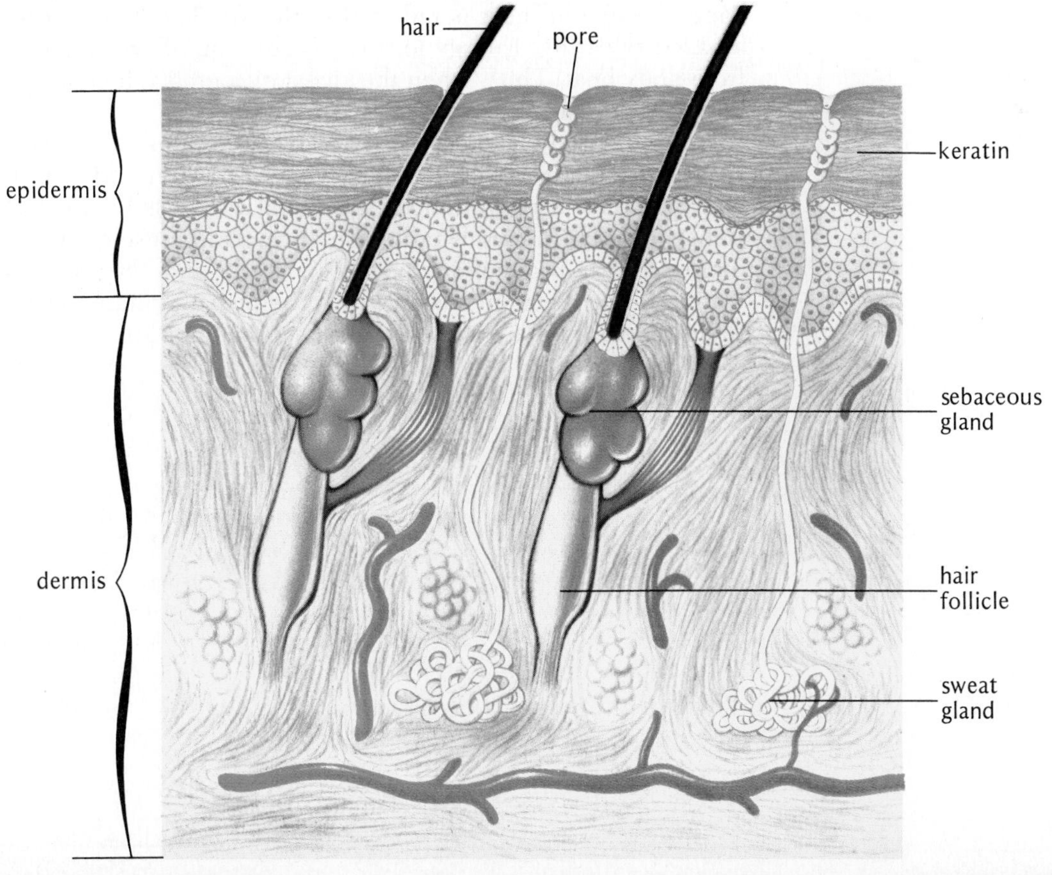

skin and binds it to the underlying muscle and bone. Within the dermis are blood vessels, lymph vessels, nerves, sense receptors, sebaceous glands, sweat glands, and hair follicles. Beneath the dermis is a layer of fat, or *adipose*, tissue. Thin people have little fat in this layer, whereas in obese people this layer is very thick.

The **sebaceous** (sih-*bay*-shus) **glands** produce oily secretions that keep the skin and hair soft and pliable and provide a protective coating. **Sweat glands** consist of tiny coiled tubes that open to the surface of the skin through pores. The perspiration, or sweat, excreted by these glands consists mainly of water (99 percent) with some salts, such as NaCl, and a trace of urea.

Functions of the skin. The skin performs several important functions.

1. The skin protects the internal tissues of the body from injury and blocks the entrance of microorganisms and other foreign materials. It also protects the body from drying out.
2. The skin excretes a small amount of urea and salt in perspiration. However, the excretory function of the skin is actually a minor one.
3. Nerve endings in the skin detect pain, touch, pressure, and temperature.
4. The skin is involved in the regulation of body temperature. When the body becomes too warm, the excess heat is lost in two ways. Blood vessels in the skin become dilated, the supply of blood to the capillaries in the skin increases (flushed appearance), and heat is radiated to the air. There is also increased sweating. Energy for the evaporation of sweat comes from body heat. Thus, when the sweat evaporates, it cools the body.

When the body is too cool, the reverse happens. Blood vessels in the skin constrict, the supply of blood to the skin capillaries decreases, perspiration is reduced, and less heat is lost from the body. In cold weather, shivering and muscle tension increase heat production by the muscles, and the body is warmed. The mechanisms by which the body maintains a constant temperature are a good example of homeostatic control.

summary

Excretion is the process by which the wastes of cellular metabolism and various excess materials are removed from the organism. The major metabolic wastes are carbon dioxide, water, nitrogen-containing compounds, and mineral salts. In protists and other very simple organisms, wastes diffuse directly from the cells into the environment. In some freshwater organisms, excess water must be excreted by active transport processes. In complex multicellular animals, excretion is accomplished by specialized excretory organs and organ systems.

Earthworms have excretory organs called nephridia. Wastes from the body fluid and blood collect in the nephridia and are excreted from the earthworm through openings called nephridiopores. Useful substances entering the nephridia are reabsorbed into the blood. Grasshoppers and other insects have excretory organs called Malpighian tubules. Wastes from the blood enter the tubules by diffusion and by active transport. From the tubules they enter the large intestine. Both in the tubules and intestine useful substances are reabsorbed. The waste product, uric acid, is eliminated from the body with digestive wastes.

In humans excretion is a complex process that involves the liver, kidneys, lungs, and skin. The activities of these organs regulate the chemical makeup of the blood and other body fluids.

The liver removes various biologically active and/or toxic materials from the blood and inactivates them or converts them to less toxic forms. These materials are returned to the blood and excreted from the body by the kidneys. The liver synthesizes bile, which consists partly of waste products. Bile passes from the liver to the small intestine. Some parts of the bile are eventually reabsorbed into the blood while the rest is eliminated from the body in the feces. The liver is also the site of deamination, the process by which amino groups are removed from excess amino acids. The amino groups are converted to ammonia, which is then converted to urea. Urea diffuses out of the liver into the blood. It is removed from the blood by the kidneys and excreted from the body.

The urinary system consists of the kidneys, ureters, urinary bladder, and urethra. There are two kidneys, each consisting of more than a million structures called nephrons. In the nephrons, wastes are filtered out of the blood, and useful substances, including water, are reabsorbed. The remaining fluid, the urine, consists of water, urea, and salts. Urine passes from the kidneys into the ureters, which carry it to the bladder. Urine, which is stored in the bladder, is periodically discharged from the body through the urethra.

The lungs excrete carbon dioxide and water from the body in the course of respiration.

The skin, which protects the internal tissues of the body, excretes small quantities of urea and salts in sweat. The skin also functions in the maintenance of a constant body temperature.

vocabulary

ammonia
dermis
epidermis
excretion
filtration
kidney
Malpighian tubule
nephridium
nephron
reabsorption
sebaceous gland
sweat gland
urea
ureter
urethra
uric acid
urinary bladder
urinary system
urine

test your learning

Section

12-1 **1.** Define the term *excretion*.

12-2 **2.** List the major metabolic wastes, and explain how each is produced.

12-3 **3.** What are the metabolic wastes of protozoa, and how are they excreted?

4. How is water balance maintained in freshwater protozoa?

12-4 **5.** How is excretion accomplished in hydra?

12-5 **6.** What are the excretory organs of the earthworm, and how do they function?

12-6 **7.** What are the excretory organs of the grasshopper, and how do they function?

8. Why is ammonia often the nitrogenous waste in aquatic organisms while uric acid is the major nitrogenous waste in many land animals?

12-7 **9.** List three functions of the liver that regulate the composition of body fluids.

10. What is deamination?

11. What happens to excess amino acids in the body?

12-8 **12.** What are the two main functions of the kidneys?

13. Name the functional units of the kidneys.

14. What is filtration and where does it occur in the kidney?

15. What is reabsorption and where does it occur in the kidney? Is it an energy-requiring process?

16. What is the fluid called that remains in the kidney tubules after reabsorption, and what substances does it contain?

17. Describe the path of the urine after it leaves the kidneys.

12-9 **18.** In what way are the lungs excretory organs?

12-10 **19.** Name the two layers of the skin.

20. What are the functions of sebaceous glands and sweat glands?

21. Briefly describe four functions of the skin.

test your understanding

1. How does each of the following organs aid in the maintenance of homeostasis: liver, kidneys, lungs, and skin?
2. Explain how the kidneys form urine.
3. How does the body get rid of excess heat?
4. How does the body conserve heat?

independent research

1. Write a report on kidney transplants or on dialysis machines.
2. Obtain a sheep or cow kidney from a butcher. Examine its external structure and then dissect it and examine its internal structure. Make drawings showing your observations and include written descriptions.
3. When a person has a physical examination, the physician usually has a sample of urine analyzed. Prepare a report explaining what information about the patient's condition can be obtained from urinalysis.

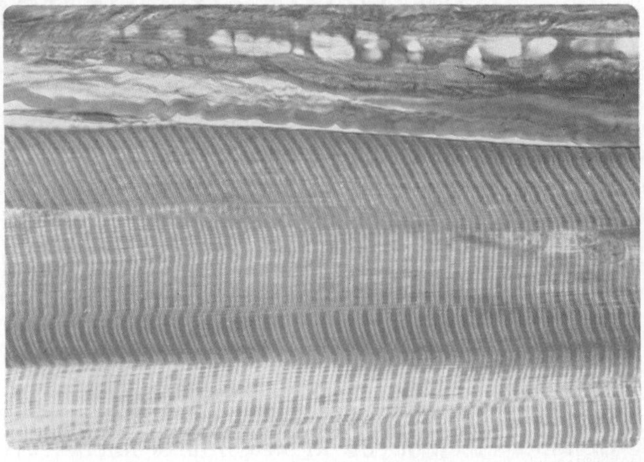

chapter 13

Support and Locomotion

CHAPTER INTRODUCTION

After completing your study of this section, you should be able to:

1. Define the terms *locomotion, motile,* and *sessile.*
2. List the advantages of locomotion.
3. Name the two types of skeletons, and describe the advantages and disadvantages of each.

13-1 Advantages of Locomotion

Many types of living things have the capacity to move on their own from one place to another. Such self-generated movement is called **locomotion.** Organisms capable of locomotion are said to be **motile** (*moh*-til). A basic characteristic of most animals and many protists is that they are motile. A basic characteristic of plants, on the other hand, is that they are not motile. Not all animals are motile either. Some aquatic animals, such as corals, barnacles, and sponges, cannot move from place to place on their own. They live attached to the ocean floor or some object. These animals are stationary, or **sessile** (*ses*-il). However, by movement of various parts of their bodies they create water currents that enable them to obtain food and oxygen and carry out their life processes.

The capacity to move from place to place offers a number of advantages for an organism.

1. Locomotion increases the opportunities for organisms to obtain food. (A cougar may hunt for food over a territory of more than 160 square kilometers.)

Figure 13-1. Exoskeleton of a Mollusk. The exoskeleton of the flame scallop is a hard double shell composed of calcium compounds.

2. Locomotion enables organisms to find suitable places to live and to move away from harmful conditions in the environment. (Fish tend to swim away from warm, oxygen-poor water to find cooler, oxygen-rich water.)

3. Locomotion enables organisms to escape from their enemies or to seek shelter. (Rabbits and deer survive because of their ability to move quickly.)

4. Locomotion enables organisms to find mates and reproduce. (Male and female salmon swim thousands of kilometers to reach their nesting grounds.)

13-2 Muscles and Skeletons

In all but the most simple animals, locomotion involves both muscles and a skeleton to which the muscles are attached. Muscles can exert force when they contract, or shorten. When muscles contract, they move the parts to which they are attached.

Most skeletons are composed of hard materials. If the skeleton is outside the body, enclosing the soft parts, it is called an **exoskeleton** (eks-oh-*skel*-uh-tun). Some protozoans and many invertebrates have exoskeletons—hard, outer coverings. Clams, oysters, and other mollusks have hard shells composed of calcium compounds (see Figure 13-1). The animal lives within the shell, and its movement is very limited. Crabs, spiders, insects, and other arthropods have exoskeletons composed of **chitin** (*kyt*-in), which is a tough material that is much lighter than the shells of mollusks. Exoskeletons serve as the site of attachment for muscles. In arthropods the exoskeleton is jointed, which makes it flexible and allows various kinds of movement (see Figure 13-2). Exoskeletons provide good protection for the soft parts of the body. However, since they are not composed of living cells, they cannot grow.

Figure 13-2. Exoskeleton of an Arthropod. The exoskeleton of the lobster is composed of tough, light-weight chitin. It protects the soft body parts and is jointed to allow movement.

Among the arthropods, the exoskeletons are periodically shed, or molted, and replaced by a new, larger covering. During the time between molting and growth of the new skeleton, the animal is in a very vulnerable, or unprotected, condition.

In vertebrates, the skeleton is composed of bone and cartilage and is located within the body walls. This type of skeleton, which is inside the body, is called an **endoskeleton** (en-doh-*skel*-uh-tun). An endoskeleton does not protect the entire animal as well as an exoskeleton. However, because bones and cartilage contain living cells and can grow, the skeleton can increase in size along with the rest of the animal. The bones of the endoskeleton serve as sites of attachment for skeletal muscles, making possible the movement of body parts. Endoskeletons are found in fish, amphibians, reptiles, birds, and mammals.

ADAPTATIONS FOR LOCOMOTION

After completing your study of this section, you should be able to describe locomotion in the ameba, paramecium, hydra, earthworm, and grasshopper.

Living things show a wide variety of adaptations for locomotion. In single-celled organisms, such as protozoa, locomotion may involve pseudopods or various cell structures. In multicellular animals, locomotion always involves specialized muscle tissue. Whatever the method of locomotion, the basis for nearly all protozoan and animal movement is contractile proteins—proteins that have the capacity to change in length.

13-3 Locomotion in Protists

Among the protists, some forms lack any means of locomotion, while others are highly motile. Among the motile forms, locomotion is generally carried out by pseudopods, cilia, or flagella.

Pseudopods. **Pseudopods** are temporary projections of the cell surfaces. The organism moves by a flowing of the cytoplasm into the projections. This type of locomotion is best known in amebas, but it is also found in slime molds and other organisms, as well as in white blood cells. Locomotion by means of pseudopods is also known as *ameboid movement.*

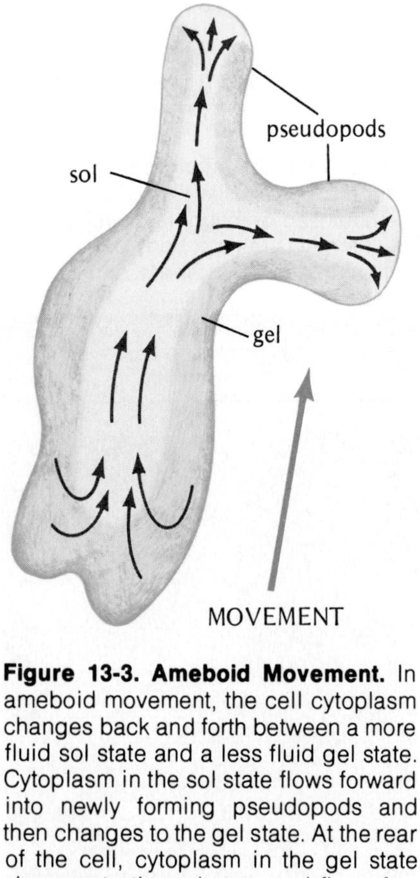

Figure 13-3. Ameboid Movement. In ameboid movement, the cell cytoplasm changes back and forth between a more fluid sol state and a less fluid gel state. Cytoplasm in the sol state flows forward into newly forming pseudopods and then changes to the gel state. At the rear of the cell, cytoplasm in the gel state changes to the sol state and flows forward. In this way the cell contents move in the direction of the new pseudopods.

Studies of the ameba show that the cytoplasm within the organism is in two states. In the central portion of the cell the cytoplasm is more fluid and is said to be a **sol** (as in *sol*ution). As the ameba moves, this sol portion of the cytoplasm flows forward through the center of the pseudopod (see Figure 13-3). At the tip, it spreads out in all directions and changes into a firmer, less fluid state. In this state the cytoplasm is said to be a **gel** (jel) (as in *gel*atin). This gel travels backward along the sides of the cell, and near the "back" end, the gel is changed back into a sol and joins the forward-flowing stream.

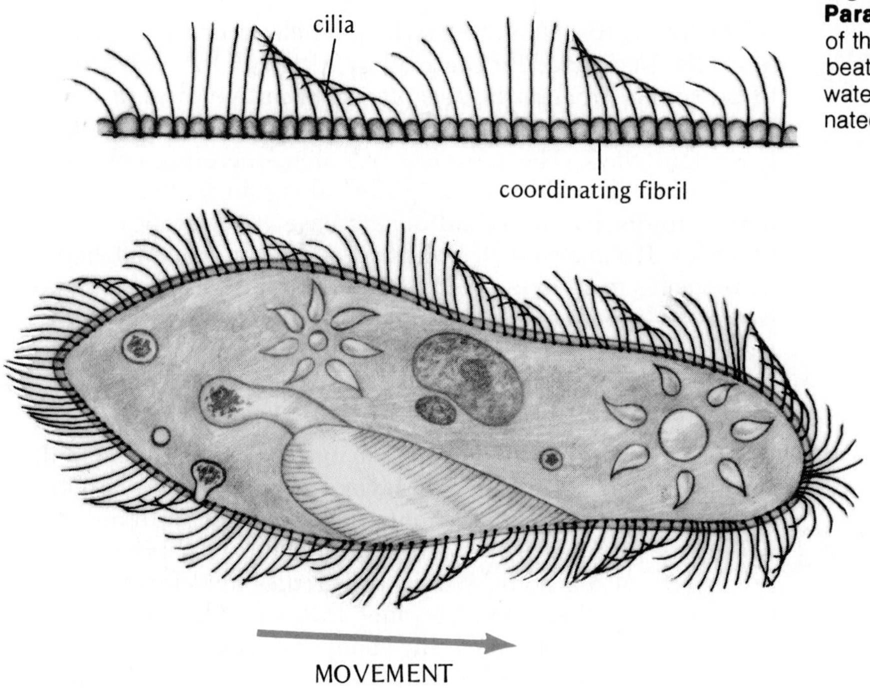

Figure 13-4. Locomotion in the Paramecium. The entire outer surface of the organism is covered by cilia that beat rhythmically to propel it through the water. The beating of the cilia is coordinated by a network of fibrils.

Energy for ameboid movement comes from the breakdown of ATP to ADP.

Cilia and flagella. Ciliated protists, such as the paramecium, move very quickly compared to the ameba. The paramecium is covered by thousands of short, hairlike cilia, whose rhythmic, oarlike beating propels the organism through the water (see Figure 13-4). The beating of the cilia is coordinated by a system of fibrils that connect the cilia at their bases.

Flagella (singular, flagellum) are similar to cilia except that they are longer and there are usually only one or two per cell. Euglena is a protist that moves by means of its long, thin flagellum (see Figure 13-5). The whiplike movements of the flagellum pull the euglena through the water.

The cilia of the paramecium push the water backwards like the oars of a boat. If the paramecium meets an obstacle, the action of the cilia is reversed, enabling it to back away. It then turns and moves forward again in a new direction.

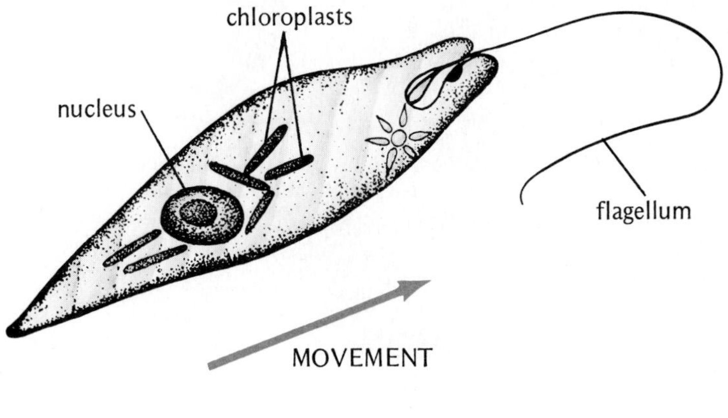

Figure 13-5. Locomotion in the Euglena. Movement of the long, whiplike flagellum pulls the organism through the water.

13-4 Locomotion in Hydra

The hydra, like all multicellular animals other than sponges, has cells specialized for contraction. Although the hydra tends to be sessile (remain in one place), primitive muscle fibers enable it to contract various parts of its body and move about in several ways. The presence of mucus-secreting cells and ameboid cells enables it to "glide" along on its base. It can move rapidly by somersaulting its base completely over its tentacles. It can also inch along by bending over and attaching its tentacles to an object and then pulling its base closer. The hydra can produce an air bubble on its base and float in the water.

13-5 Locomotion in the Earthworm

The earthworm uses muscles to burrow through the soil. Within its body wall are two layers of muscles (see Figure 13-6). An outer layer of circular muscles goes around the worm, and an inner layer of longitudinal muscles extends the full length of the body. When the circular muscles contract, the worm lengthens and becomes thinner. When the longitudinal muscles contract, the body becomes shorter and thicker. Within the earthworm, the body cavity is filled with fluid. This fluid acts as a skeleton because it cannot be compressed. When the surrounding muscle layers contract, the fluid "skeleton" stiffens the body of the worm and allows it to push through the soil.

On almost all body segments are four pairs of tiny bristles called **setae** (*see*-tee) (see Figure 13-7). In locomotion, the setae (singular, seta) in the rear of the earthworm hook

Figure 13-6. Locomotion in the Earthworm. The earthworm has both circular and longitudinal muscle layers. When the outer layer of circular muscles contracts, the worm lengthens and becomes thinner. When the inner layer of longitudinal muscles contracts, the worm becomes shorter and thicker.

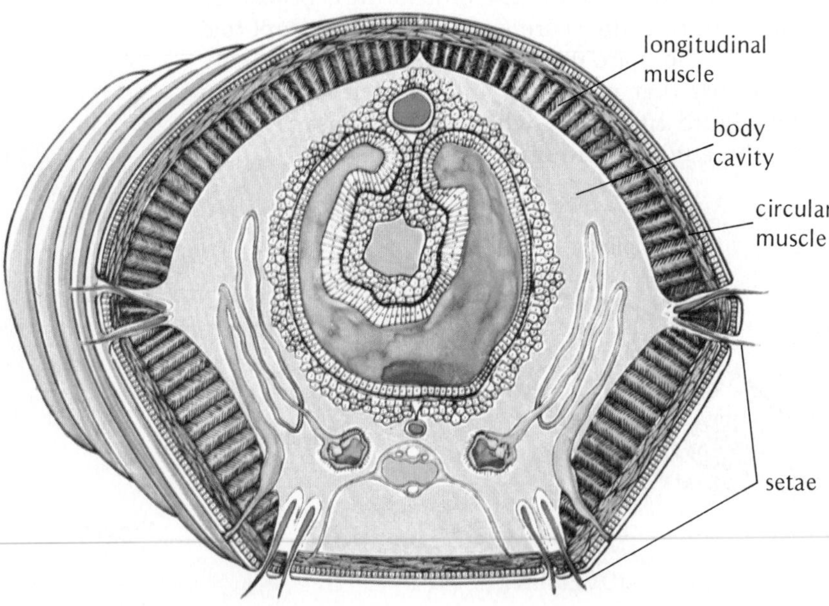

into the ground while the circular muscles contract. This lengthens the body and pushes the worm forward. Then the setae near the front of the worm anchor into the ground, and the setae in the rear relax. The longitudinal muscles contract, shortening the body and pulling forward the hind end of the worm. The earthworm moves by repeating these coordinated movements over and over again.

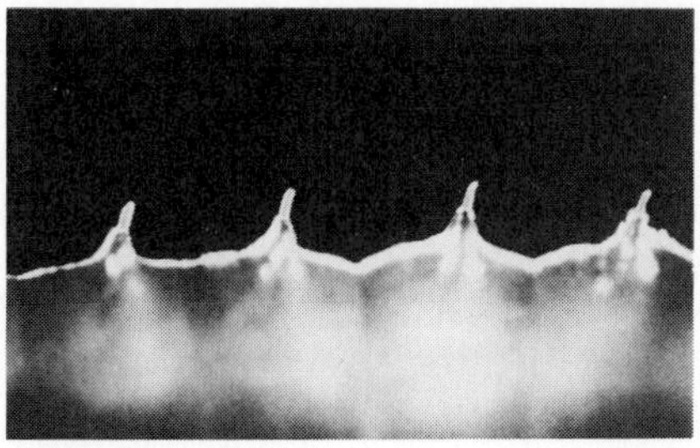

Figure 13-7. Setae of the Earthworm.

13-6 Locomotion in the Grasshopper

The body of the grasshopper is covered by an exoskeleton of chitin. The exoskeleton is divided into plates separated from each other by flexible joints. This arrangement allows the grasshopper to move freely (see Figure 13-8). Grasshoppers can walk, jump, and fly.

Like other insects, the body of the grasshopper has three major divisions—the *head, thorax* (*thor*-aks), and *abdomen* (*ab*-duh-men). Attached to the thorax are three pairs of jointed legs. The first two pairs are used for walking, while the powerful hind pair is used for jumping. A grasshopper can jump more than twenty times its body length. Also attached to the thorax are two pairs of wings. The outer pair is hard and protects the delicate inner pair, which is used in flying. The powerful vertical and longitudinal muscles involved in flight are attached to the exoskeleton of the thorax. They have no direct connection with the wings, but move the wings by changing the shape of the body wall of the thorax.

The muscles of a grasshopper work in pairs. When one muscle of a pair contracts and bends a joint, the other muscle relaxes. When the second muscle contracts, extending the joint, the first muscle relaxes.

Figure 13-8. Locomotion in the Grasshopper. The first two pairs of legs of the grasshopper are used for walking, while the powerful hind legs are used in jumping. The tough outer wings protect the delicate inner wings that are used for flying.

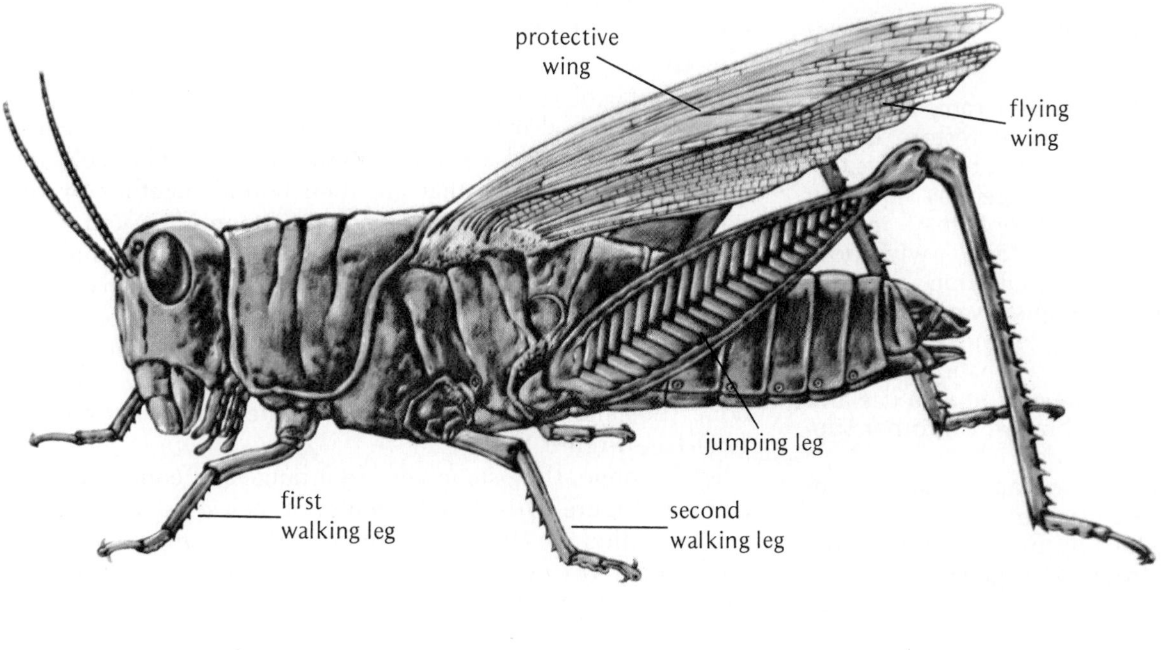

HUMAN MUSCULOSKELETAL SYSTEM

After completing your study of this section, you should be able to:

1. Describe the functions of bones.
2. Make a drawing showing the internal structure of a bone, and label its parts.
3. Define the following terms: *periosteum, marrow, cartilage,* and *ossification.*
4. Name the major parts of the human skeleton.
5. Describe the various types of joints found in the human skeleton and give an example of each.
6. Describe the structure of skeletal muscle, and explain how contraction is accomplished.
7. Explain how locomotion is accomplished in humans.

If the concentration of calcium or phosphorus in the blood falls below the normal level, these substances leave the bone and pass into the blood. They are replaced in the bone when blood levels are adequate.

Demonstrate that the mineral content of the bone can be removed by soaking a bone in vinegar (weak acetic acid) for several days.

13-7 Bones and Cartilage

The bones of the skeletal system serve a number of different functions.

1. They serve as sites of attachment for skeletal muscles, and they serve as levers that produce movement of body parts when these muscles contract.

2. They give the body its general shape and support body structures.

3. They protect delicate structures, such as the brain, spinal cord, heart, and lungs.

4. They serve as a storage site for minerals, such as calcium and phosphorus.

Bone is made up of living bone cells, connective tissue fibers, and inorganic compounds. It is a very active tissue, and there is a constant absorption of old tissue and laying down of new tissue. A basic part of the structure is **collagen** (*kahl*-uh-jen), a type of connective tissue. In bone formation, living bone cells called **osteoblasts** (*ahs*-tee-uh-blasts) secrete collagen molecules and certain polysaccharides. The collagen molecules form fibers that are then bound together by the polysaccharides, which act as cement. Bone is formed when calcium and phosphate ions from the body fluids combine, forming calcium phosphate, and precipitate as crystals in the mass of collagen fibers and cement. The hardness and heaviness of bone is due to the presence of the calcium phosphate. The osteoblasts are entrapped in small cavities within the bone substance and are then called **osteocytes** (*ahs*-tee-uh-syts) (see Figure 13-9).

In the bone, the osteocytes are arranged in concentric circles (see Figure 13-10). In the center of each series of circles is a cavity called the **Haversian** (huh-*ver*-zhun) **canal,** which contains blood vessels and nerves. Tiny canals connect the osteocytes to each other and to the Haversian canal. The blood

careers

Physical therapists carry out treatment programs to restore use of arms, legs, or other body parts that have been damaged by injury or disease. Treatment may involve exercise, massage, whirlpool baths, and application of heat. Physical therapists work with disabled people, teaching them how to overcome their handicaps. They also teach patients how to use artificial limbs, braces, and other supportive devices.

Physical therapists are state-licensed professionals with a bachelor's or master's degree from an accredited program.

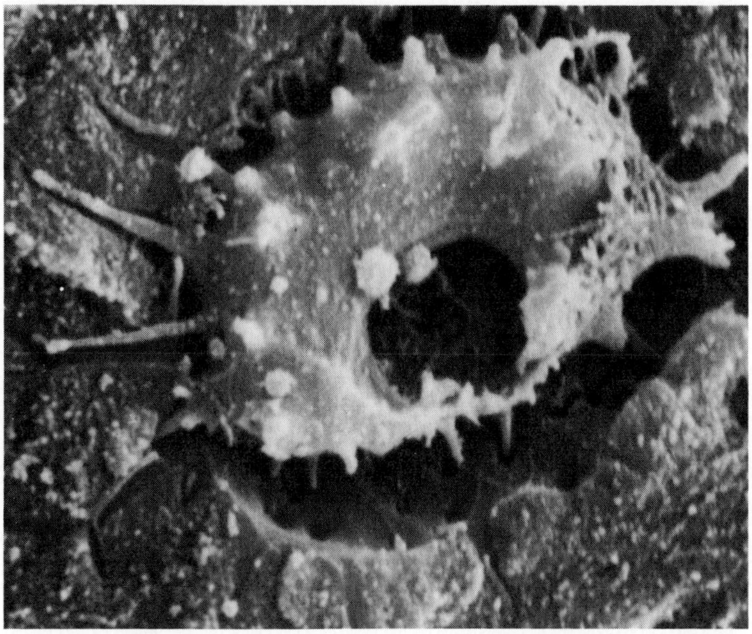

Figure 13-9. Scanning Electron Micrograph of an Osteocyte. Osteocytes are surrounded by bone. However, long, thin cytoplasmic processes extend through small canals in the bone, making contact with processes from adjacent cells.

vessels within the Haversian canals carry oxygen and nutrients to the bone cells and remove wastes. If a bone is broken, the osteocytes become active, producing new bone tissue to heal the wound.

The outside of a bone, except at its ends where it connects to other bones, is covered by a tough membrane called the **periosteum** (pehr-ee-*ahs*-tee-um). The chief function of the

Figure 13-10. Internal Structure of Bone. In the photo below, the dark spaces arranged in concentric circles around the central Haversian canal are the cavities in which osteocytes are found in living bone. The tiny canals extending from each cavity allow the osteocytes to exchange materials with each other and with the Haversian canal. The drawing at left shows the structure of a long bone.

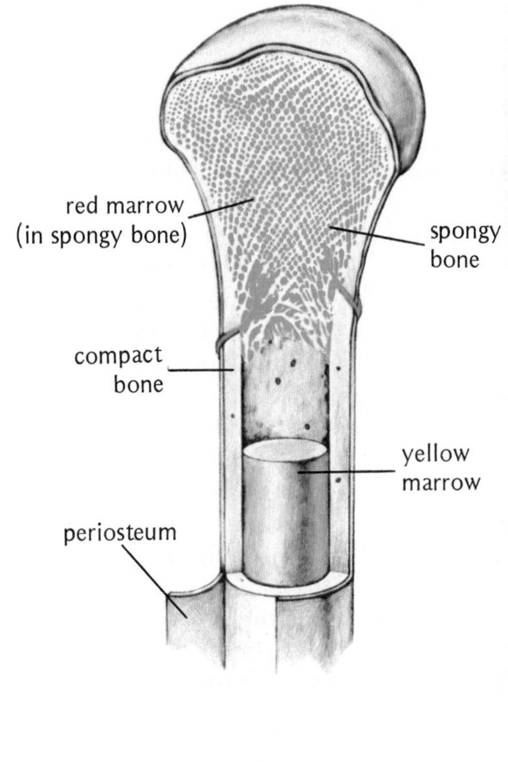

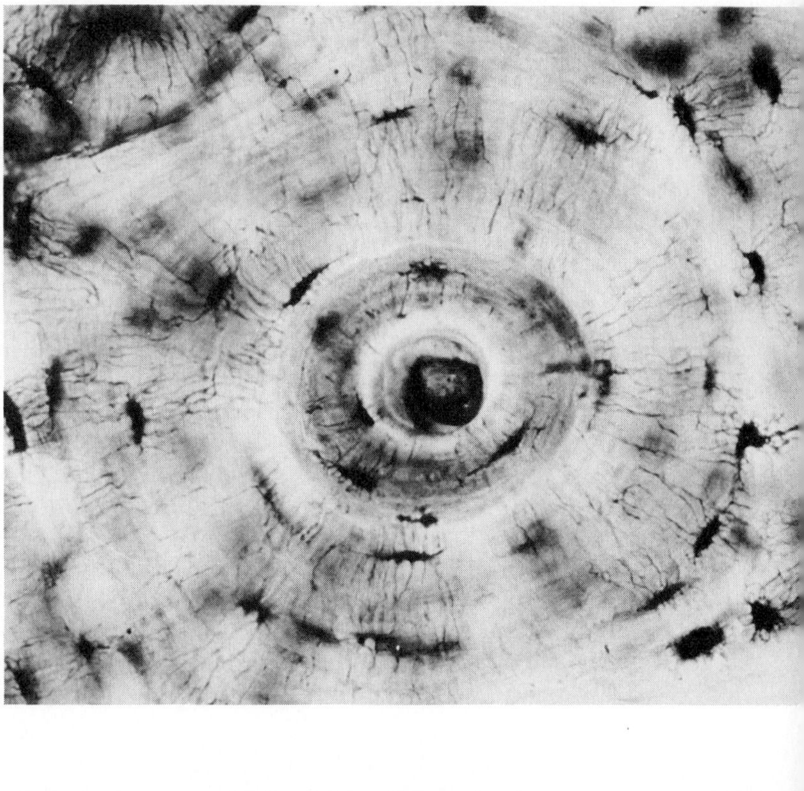

periosteum is the production of new bone for growth and repair. The periosteum also serves as the point of attachment for muscles to bones. This membrane contains blood vessels and nerves that enter the bone.

There are two types of bony tissue—**compact bone** and **spongy bone.** Their composition is the same, but compact bone is very dense, while spongy bone is comparatively porous. Most bones contain both compact and spongy bone tissue.

Some of the bones of the body are hollow, and there is also much space in spongy bone. These spaces are filled with a soft tissue called **marrow** (*mar*-oh). There are two types of marrow—red marrow and yellow marrow. Red marrow produces red blood cells, platelets, and some types of white blood cells. In adults, red marrow is found in the spongy bone of the vertebrae, ribs, breastbone, cranium, and long bones. Yellow marrow consists of fat cells. In adults it is found in the hollow central region of long bones.

Cartilage (*kart*-il-idj), like bone, is a type of connective tissue. While bone is rigid, cartilage is flexible. In the embryo, most of the skeleton is cartilage. As the embryo develops, minerals are deposited, and the cartilage is gradually changed into bone. This process, called **ossification** (ahs-ih-fih-*kay*-shun), continues into adulthood. The bones of small children contain more cartilage than the bones of adults and are therefore more elastic and not as easily broken. In adults cartilage is found at the ends of ribs, at joints, and in the nose and outer ear. Cartilage provides support, while still permitting some bending or motion. It provides flexibility at joints and cushions against impact or pressure.

13-8 The Human Skeleton

Parts of the skeleton. The human skeleton contains 206 bones (see Figure 13-11). The skeleton has two main divisions: the **axial** (*ak*-see-ul) **skeleton** and the **appendicular** (ap-en-*dik*-yuh-ler) **skeleton.**

The axial skeleton includes the skull, vertebrae, ribs, and breastbone. The upper part of the skull, the **cranium** (*kray*-nee-um), houses and protects the brain. The rest of the skull includes the facial and jaw bones. The **spinal column,** or *backbone*, consists of 33 bones called **vertebrae** (*vert*-uh-bree). The vertebrae are separated from each other by disks of cartilage. The disks act as shock absorbers and give the spine flexibility. The ribs are attached at the back to the upper vertebrae and at the front to the *breastbone*, or *sternum* (*ster*-num). The area enclosed by the sternum, ribs, and backbone is the *chest cavity*. Within the chest cavity, the heart and lungs are supported and protected by the ribs and sternum.

The appendicular skeleton includes the arms and legs and two ringlike sets of bones called the *pectoral* (*pek*-tuh-rul) *girdle* and the *pelvic girdle*. The pectoral girdle consists of the

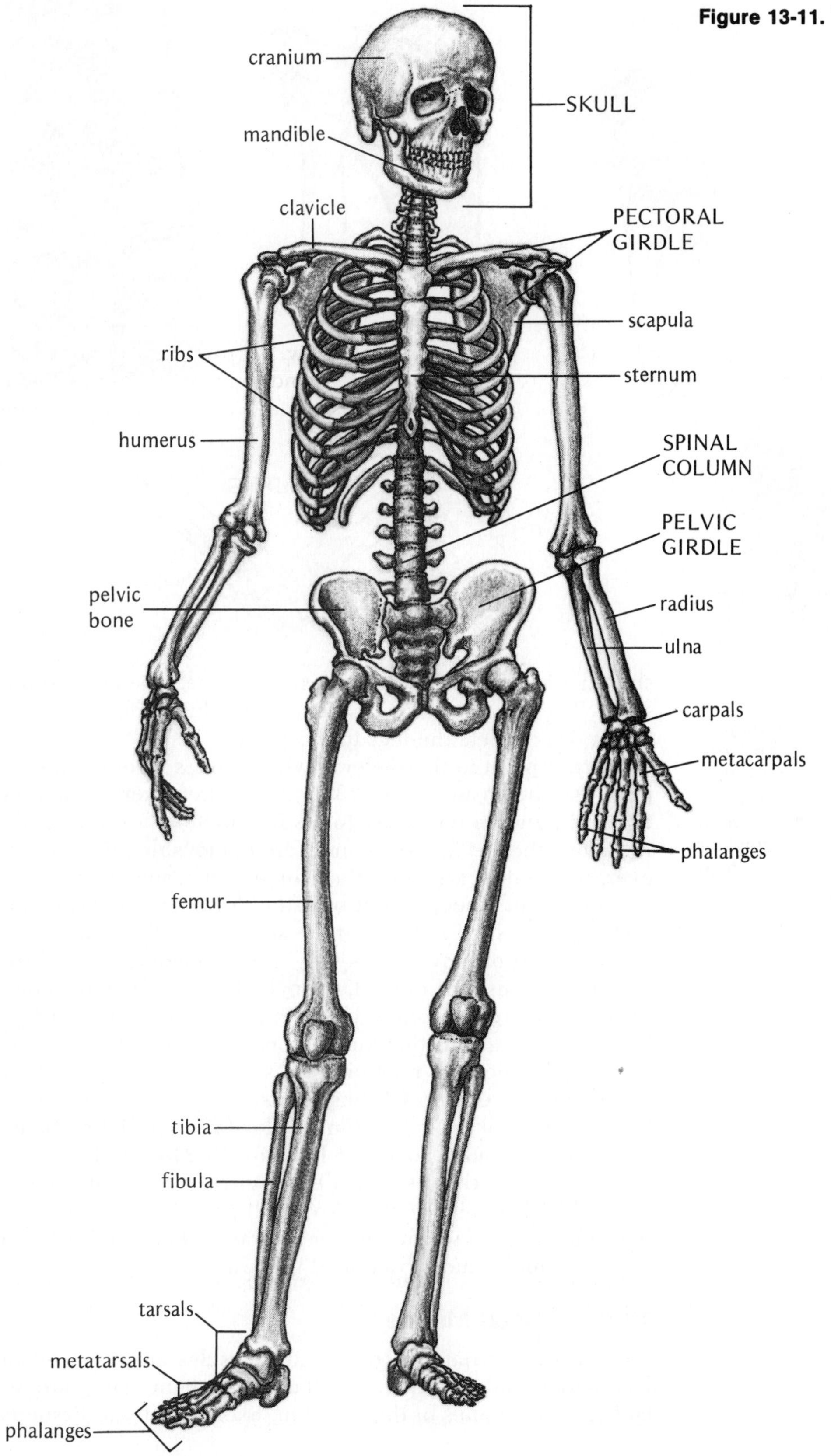

Figure 13-11. The Human Skeleton.

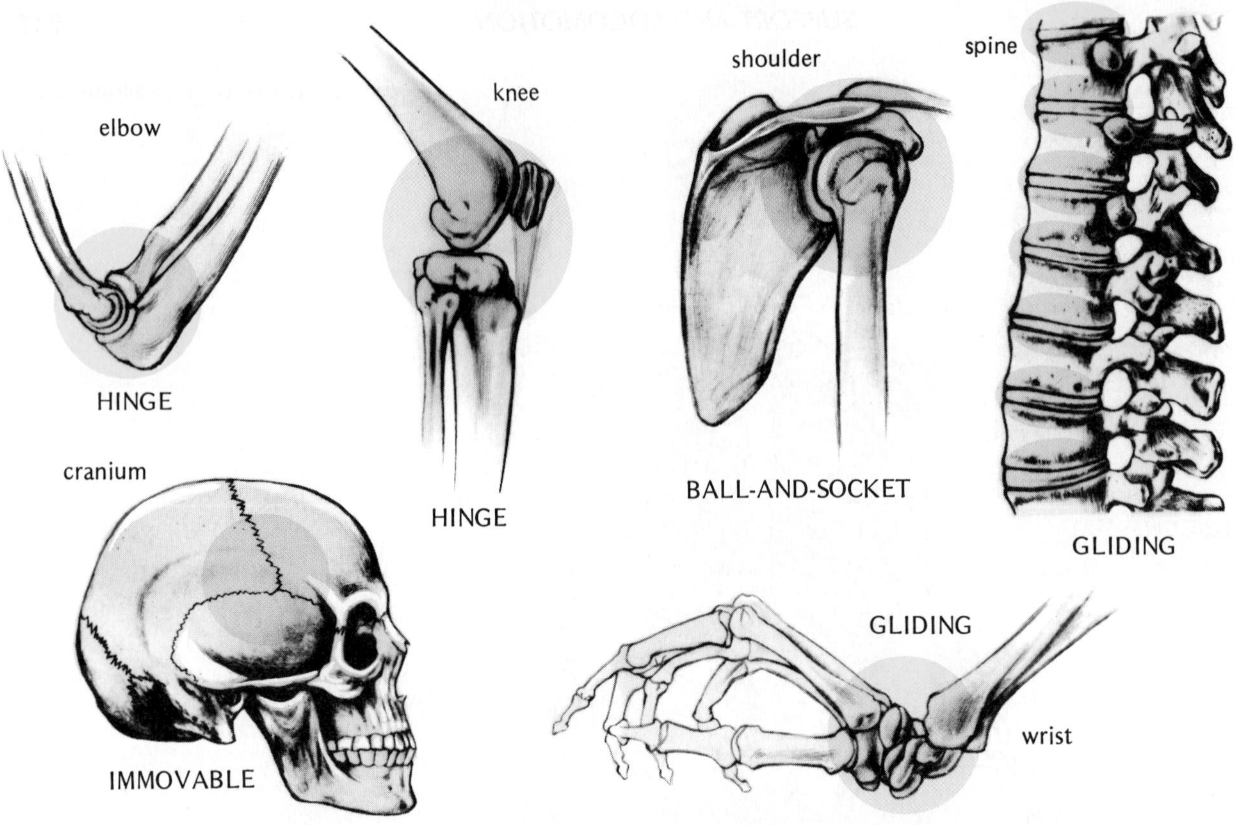

Figure 13-12. Types of Joints. Hinge joints at the knee and elbow permit back-and-forth motion. The ball-and-socket joint permits the wide range of movement of the arm at the shoulder. Gliding joints provide limited flexibility in all directions at the wrist and between the vertebrae. The bones of the cranium are joined by immovable joints in which the bones are fitted tightly together.

shoulder blades and collar bones. It connects the arms to the spine. The pelvic girdle is made up of the hip bones, or pelvic bones. It connects the legs to the spine.

Joints. A point in the skeleton where bones meet is called a **joint.** As shown in Figure 13-12, there are several different types of joints in the body. Joints in which bones are tightly fitted together, as in the cranium, are **immovable joints.** However, most joints are movable. **Hinge joints,** such as those at the elbow and knee, permit back-and-forth motion. **Ball-and-socket joints,** such as those at the shoulder and hip, offer the widest range of movement—they allow movement in all directions. In this type of joint, the ball-shaped end of one bone fits into the cuplike hollow, or socket, of another bone. A **pivot** (*piv*-it) **joint,** such as that found where the skull is connected to the spine, permits rotation from side to side as well as up and down movement. **Gliding joints,** such as those found at the wrist and ankle provide limited flexibility in all directions.

At movable joints, bones are held together by tough, fibrous bands of connective tissue called **ligaments** (*lig*-uh-ments). A fluid, called *synovial* (sih-*noh*-vee-ul) *fluid,* is secreted into movable joints by surrounding membranes. This fluid acts as a lubricant and reduces friction at the joint.

13-9 Skeletal Muscle

Skeletal, or **striated** (*stry*-ay-ted), **muscles** are involved in locomotion and all other voluntary movement. They are attached to the bones of the skeleton. Skeletal muscle tissue is not made up of clearly defined and separate cells. Instead, during development, cells fuse together, forming individual **muscle fibers.** A skeletal muscle consists of bundles of muscle fibers bound together by connective tissue.

Under a light microscope, the muscle fibers appear striped, or striated—that is, they show alternating bands of light and dark (see Figure 13-13). Electron microscope studies have shown that each fiber is actually a bundle of smaller fibers, and each of those is made up of still finer protein filaments, one thick and one thin. The thick filaments are myosin, the thin ones are actin. The two types of filaments are arranged in an overlapping pattern that gives the whole muscle fiber its striped appearance.

According to the *sliding filament theory* of muscle contraction, the muscle fibers shorten when the two types of filaments they contain slide over one another. The sliding increases the amount of overlap between the two types of filaments, and thereby shortens the fiber (see Figure 13-14). Cross bridges between the two types of filaments allow the fibers to exert a pull. Energy for the sliding of the filaments is supplied by ATP, which is produced in the numerous mitochondria of muscle fibers.

Figure 13-13. Striated Muscle. The overlapping arrangement of actin and myosin filaments gives striated muscle its striped appearance.

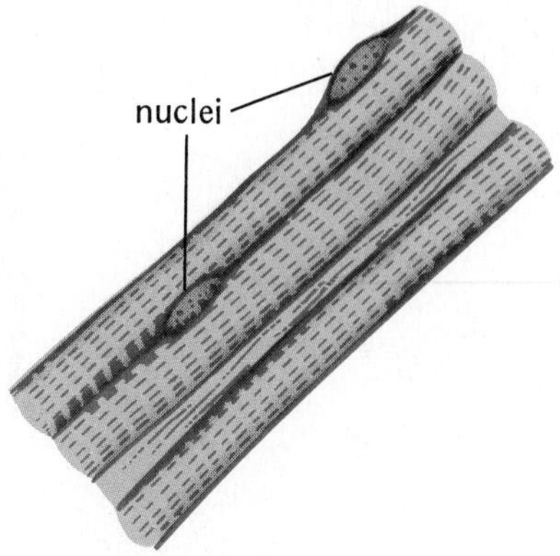

13-10 Voluntary Movement

All voluntary movement is originated and coordinated by impulses from the brain and spinal cord.

Skeletal muscles are attached to bones by strong fibers of connective tissue called **tendons.** Muscles can pull when they contract, but they cannot push when they relax. Thus, they must always work in *antagonistic* pairs. The bending and extending of the arm at the elbow illustrates how muscles and bones work together to produce movement (see Figure 13-15). When the *biceps* (*by*-seps) muscle on the front of the upper

Figure 13-14. Contraction of Striated Muscle. According to the sliding filament theory of muscle contraction, the muscle fibers shorten when the actin and myosin filaments slide over one another, increasing the amount of overlapping.

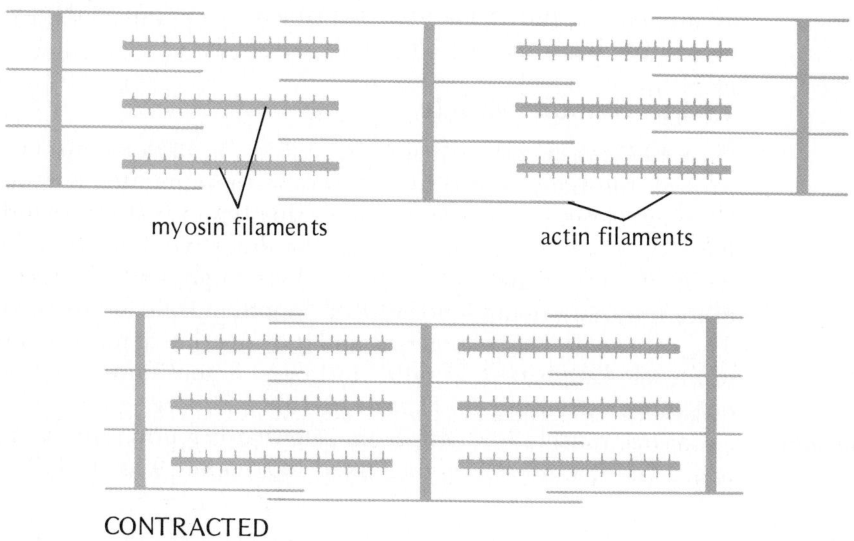

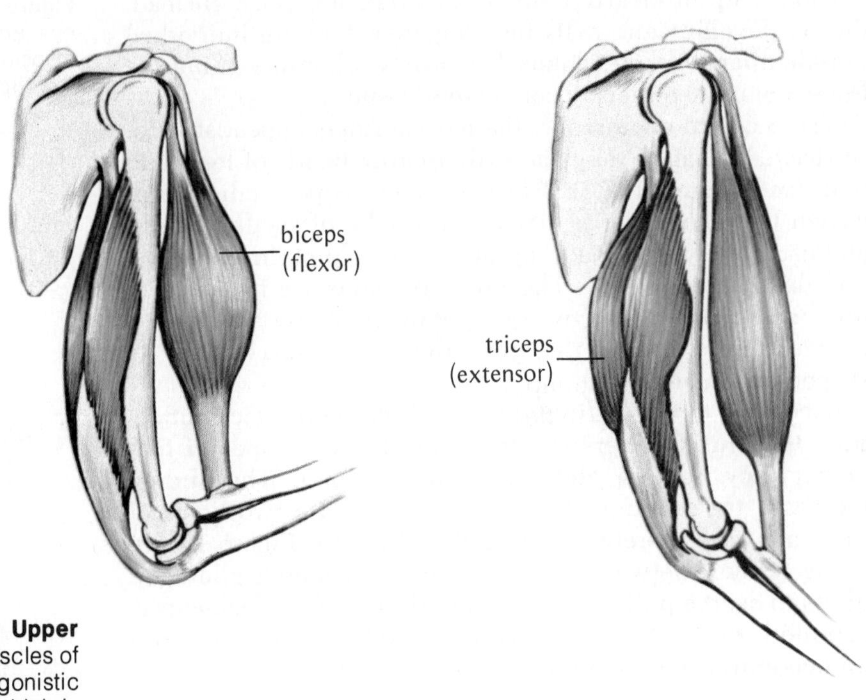

Figure 13-15. Muscles of the Upper Arm. The biceps and triceps muscles of the upper arm work as an antagonistic pair. When the biceps muscle, which is in the front of the arm, contracts, the triceps muscle in the back relaxes and the arm bends. The biceps is a flexor. When the triceps muscle contracts, the biceps muscle relaxes and the arm is straightened. The triceps is an extensor.

arm contracts, the arm bends. Because the biceps muscle bends, or flexes, the joint, it is called a **flexor** (*flek*-ser). Whenever the biceps contracts, the *triceps* (*try*-seps) muscle in the back of the arm relaxes, making it possible for the arm to bend. When the triceps muscle contracts, the biceps muscle relaxes, and the arm is extended, or straightened. Because the triceps muscle extends the joint, it is called an **extensor** (ek-*sten*-ser). Throughout the body, antagonistic pairs of muscles interact with the bones of the skeleton to produce movement.

As long as you are conscious, your skeletal muscles are never completely relaxed. Instead, all muscles are kept by the brain in a state of partial contraction called **muscle tone.** Muscle tone keeps the muscles ready for the powerful contractions of movement, and it maintains posture by keeping the muscles of the back and neck partially contracted.

13-11 Smooth Muscle

In addition to skeletal muscle, which is under conscious control, the body also contains muscle that operates without conscious control. Muscle tissue of this type is called **smooth muscle.** It is found in the walls of the digestive organs, in the walls of arteries and veins, in the diaphragm, and in various other internal organs. The cells of smooth muscle are distinct. They are somewhat elongated, and they overlap to form sheets of muscle rather than bundles of fibers. Smooth muscle does not appear striated (see Figure 13-16).

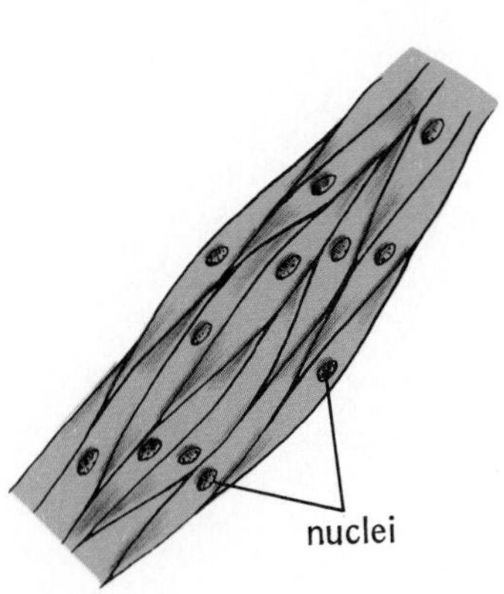

Figure 13-16. Structure of Smooth Muscle.

Cardiac muscle is a type of muscle that is found only in the heart. Cardiac muscle is discussed in Chapter 9 (page 147).

summary

Locomotion, the self-generated movement of an organism from place to place, is a basic characteristic of some microorganisms and most animals. In all but the simplest animals, locomotion involves muscles and a skeleton to which the muscles are attached. If the skeleton is on the outside of the body, it is an exoskeleton. If it is within the body walls, it is an endoskeleton.

Among the protists, locomotion is generally carried out by pseudopods, cilia, or flagella. The hydra, though often sessile, has specialized contractile cells that make movement possible. The earthworm has both longitudinal and circular muscle layers. Contraction of the circular muscles lengthens the worm, while contraction of the longitudinal muscles shortens the worm. Grasshoppers can walk, jump, and fly. They have three pairs of legs and two pairs of wings. They have a flexible, jointed exoskeleton to which the muscles of the body are attached.

The human skeleton is made up of bone and cartilage. Skeletal muscles attach to the bones, which serve as levers, moving parts of the body. The bones also give the body shape and support and protect various structures. The two divisions of the human skeleton are the axial skeleton, consisting of the skull, vertebrae, ribs, and breastbone, and the appendicular skeleton, consisting of the arms and legs and the pectoral and pelvic girdles. Joints are the points at which the bones of the skeleton meet. A few joints are immovable, but most are movable to some degree.

Skeletal muscle is made up of muscle fibers. The fibers are made up of still smaller fibers, which in turn consist of actin and myosin filaments. The arrangement of the two types of filaments gives skeletal muscle a striped appearance under a light microscope. Contraction occurs when the two types of filaments slide over one another, shortening the muscle fiber.

Skeletal muscles are attached to bones by tendons. When the muscles contract, they pull the bones. Muscles act in antagonistic pairs, one of the muscles bending the joint and the other extending the joint.

Smooth muscle, which is not under conscious control, is found in the walls of arteries and veins, as well as in the walls of various organs.

vocabulary

appendicular skeleton
axial skeleton
ball-and-socket joint
cartilage
chitin
collagen
compact bone
cranium
endoskeleton
exoskeleton
extensor
flexor
gel
sliding joint
Haversian canal
hinge joint
immovable joint
joint
ligament
locomotion
marrow
motile
muscle fiber
muscle tone
ossification
osteoblast
osteocyte
periosteum
pivot joint
sessile
setae
skeletal muscle
smooth muscle
sol
spinal column
spongy bone
striated muscle
tendon
vertebra

test your learning

Section

13-1 **1.** Define the term *locomotion*, and describe the advantages that the capacity for locomotion gives an organism.

13-2 **2.** What are the advantages and disadvantages of exoskeletons? Of endoskeletons?

13-3 **3.** Describe locomotion in the ameba.

4. Describe locomotion by means of cilia and flagella.

13-4 **5.** Briefly describe three methods of locomotion of the hydra.

13-5 **6.** Explain how locomotion is carried out in the earthworm.

13-6 **7.** Describe the structures of the grasshopper that are involved in locomotion, and explain the function of each.

13-7 **8.** What are the functions of bone?

9. Describe the function of osteoblasts.

10. What are osteocytes, and where are they found in bone?

11. What is the periosteum, and what are its functions?

12. List the functions of red marrow, and explain where it is found and in what types of bones.

13. What is ossification?

13-8 **14.** List the parts of the axial skeleton and the appendicular skeleton.

15. What is a joint?

16. Name five types of joints, and give an example of each.

17. How are bones held together at movable joints?

13-9 **18.** What is the function of striated muscle?
19. Describe the structure of striated muscle.
20. What is thought to happen to actin and myosin filaments during muscle contraction?
21. What is the source of energy for muscle contraction?
13-10 **22.** How is skeletal muscle connected to bones?
23. Why do muscles work in antagonistic pairs?
24. Define the terms *flexor* and *extensor*.
25. What is muscle tone?
13-11 **26.** Describe the structure of smooth muscle.

test your understanding

1. Compare movement of the legs of a grasshopper (with exoskeleton) with movement of the legs of a human (with endoskeleton).
2. Why is striated muscle striped in appearance?
3. How do broken bones heal?
4. Why are the bones of older people more brittle than the bones of children?

independent research

1. Prepare a report on one of the following topics:
A. hip replacement surgery
B. the role of calcium in muscle contraction
C. ameboid movement
2. Prepare a report on one of the following career opportunities:
A. physical therapist
B. orthopedic surgeon
C. chiropractor
D. biomedical engineer

If possible, interview a person who works in the field. If you have a tape recorder, record the interview. Be sure to prepare your questions in advance.

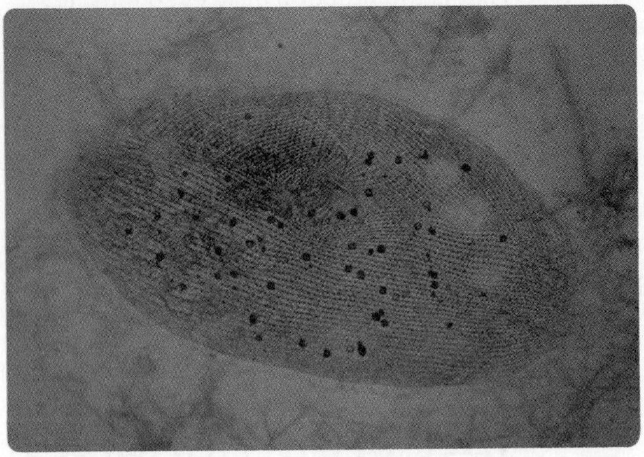

chapter 14

Regulation—Nervous Control

CHAPTER INTRODUCTION

After completing your study of this section, you should be able to:

1. Explain the functions of a nervous system.
2. Describe the roles of receptors, nerve cells, and effectors in nerve pathways.
3. Name several different types of receptors.
4. Name the two types of structures that are effectors.
5. Define the term *stimulus*.

14-1 Functions of Nervous Regulation

The environment of an organism is always changing. Some of these changes take place in the external environment—that is, outside the body. Examples of such external changes are a change in temperature; the appearance of food; the appearance of a natural enemy. Changes also occur within the organism. For example, the concentration of a waste product may increase; a disease-causing organism may enter the body; the supply of a necessary substance may decrease.

To stay alive, an organism must respond to these external and internal changes. The organism must maintain homeostasis. It must keep all the factors of its internal environment within certain limits.

Responses are seldom single, independent events. An organism is continuously responding to the wide variety of changes occurring both inside and outside its body. In fact, the various life activities of an organism are in themselves examples of complex responses. These responses must be *regulated*—that is, controlled in amount and directed to the right place. They must also be *coordinated*—that is, made to occur in the right order or relationship.

In one-celled and some simple multicellular organisms, the regulation and coordination of responses is a function of each cell as a whole, including the special activities of its organelles. This capacity of a cell to respond is often called **irritability.** In more complex multicellular animals, the regulation and coordination of responses are controlled by a nervous system and an endocrine system. In this chapter and Chapter 15 we will examine the operation of nervous systems. In Chapter 16 we will discuss the human endocrine system.

14-2 Mechanisms of Nervous Regulation

The functioning of a true nervous system involves three basic types of structures—receptors, nerve cells, and effectors. **Receptors,** or **sense organs,** are specialized structures that are sensitive to certain changes, physical forces, or chemicals in the internal and external environments. Stimulation of a receptor causes "messages," or **impulses,** to be transmitted over a pathway of nerve cells. These impulses eventually reach an **effector,** which is either a muscle or a gland. Depending on the nerve pathways involved, the effector responds to the impulses by increasing or decreasing its activity. Muscles either contract or relax; glands either increase or decrease secretion of their particular product.

Any factor that causes a receptor to trigger, or initiate, impulses in a nerve pathway is called a **stimulus** (*stim*-yuh-lus). The stimulus causes electrical and chemical changes in the receptor, and these, in turn, trigger the nerve impulses. Thus, the basic sequence of events in regulation by the nervous system involves (1) a stimulus that activates a receptor, (2) the triggering of impulses in associated nerve pathways, and finally, (3) a response by an effector (see Figure 14-1).

It should not be thought that a nerve pathway is a simple connection from a particular receptor to a particular effector. In most animals, each nerve pathway crosses and interconnects with many other pathways. Impulses arising from a single receptor are usually transmitted to a number of different nerve pathways. Impulses reaching an effector are the result of the combination and interaction of numerous impulses from many different pathways.

Multicellular animals possess several different types of receptors, each sensitive to a different type of stimulus. Among the sense organs found in animals are those sensitive to temperature, light, sound, pressure, and chemicals.

All but the simplest animals have a **brain,** a specialized group of nerve cells that controls and coordinates the activities of the nervous system. The more complex the organism, the more complex the structure and function of the brain.

Figure 14-1. Nervous Regulation. Eating a piece of pizza involves complex pathways in the nervous system. The pizza itself is a stimulus that excites impulses in sense receptors (the eyes and nose). Muscles of the hands and arms are effectors, allowing the pizza to be brought to the mouth.

NEURONS AND NERVES

After completing your study of this section, you should be able to:

1. **Describe the structure of a neuron and give the function of each of its parts.**
2. **Describe the functions of sensory neurons, motor neurons, and associative neurons.**
3. **Explain the difference between a neuron and a nerve,and name the different types of nerves.**

14-3 Structure of Neurons

In the nervous systems of all multicellular animals, the basic unit of structure and function is the **nerve cell,** or **neuron** (*noo*-rahn). Neurons are specialized for the rapid conduction of impulses, which are both electrical and chemical (electrochemical) in nature. The capacity to conduct impulses is a property of the nerve-cell membrane. The changes associated with the impulses do not enter or pass through the cytoplasm of the cell; they are transmitted only along the cell membrane.

A nerve cell usually consists of three basic parts—a cell body, dendrites, and an axon (see Figure 14-2). The **cell body,** or **cyton** (*sy*-tahn), contains the nucleus and the cell organelles. The metabolic activities common to all cells are carried out in the cell body, which also controls the growth of the nerve cell. Materials necessary for the maintenance of the nerve cell are generally synthesized in the cell body and then moved to other parts of the cell where they are needed.

The **dendrites** (*den*-dryts) are short, highly branched fibers that are specialized for receiving impulses. Dendrites generally conduct impulses toward the cell body. In some neurons, the branching of the dendrites around the cell body gives the cell a bushy appearance.

The **axon** (*ak*-sahn) is usually a long, thin fiber that extends from the cell body. Axons carry impulses away from the cell body and transmit them either to other neurons or to effectors. Axons range in length from a fraction of a centimeter to more than a meter. (The longest axons in the human body are about 1.2 meters, but in the giant squid, some axons are more than 4.5 meters in length.)

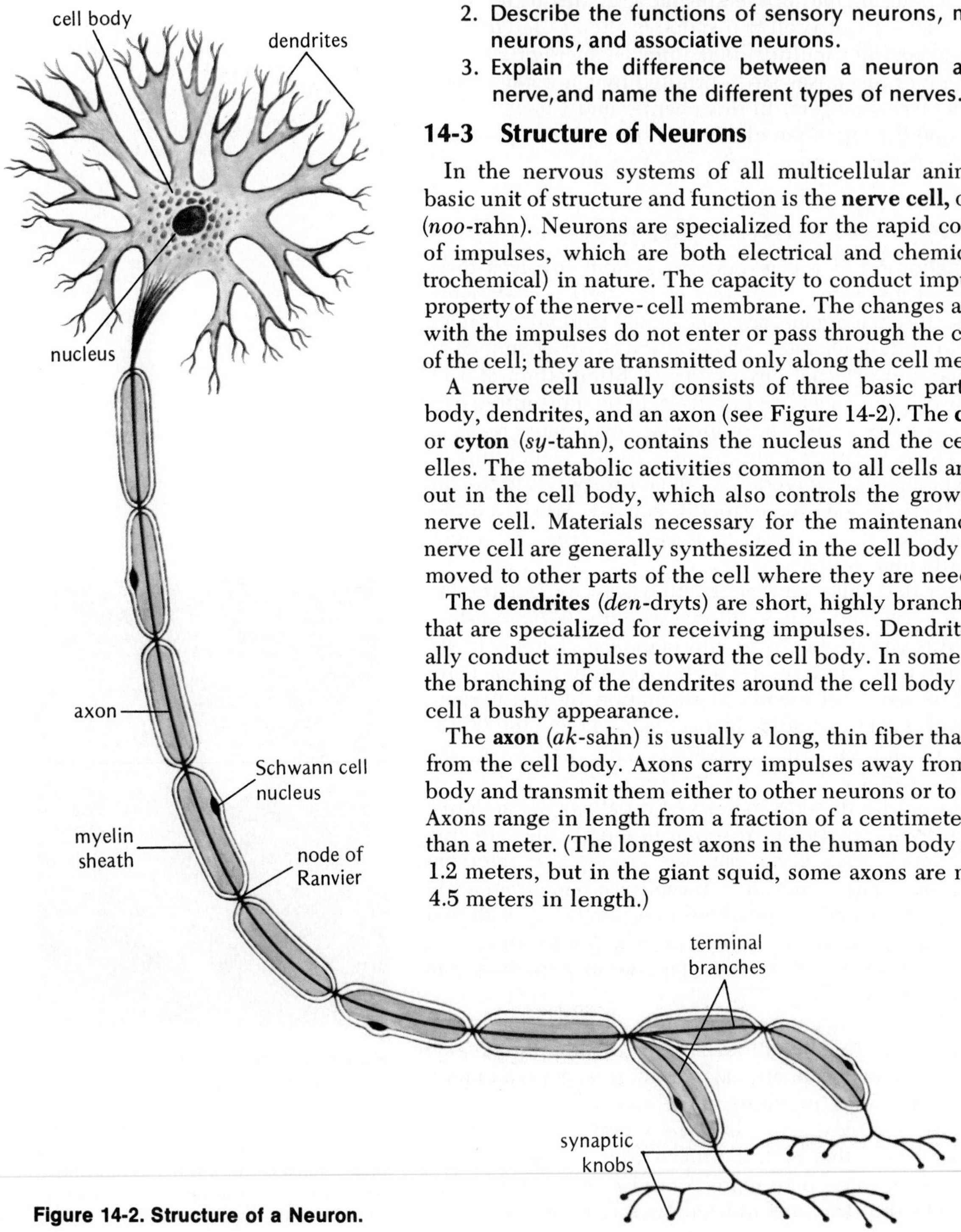

Figure 14-2. Structure of a Neuron.

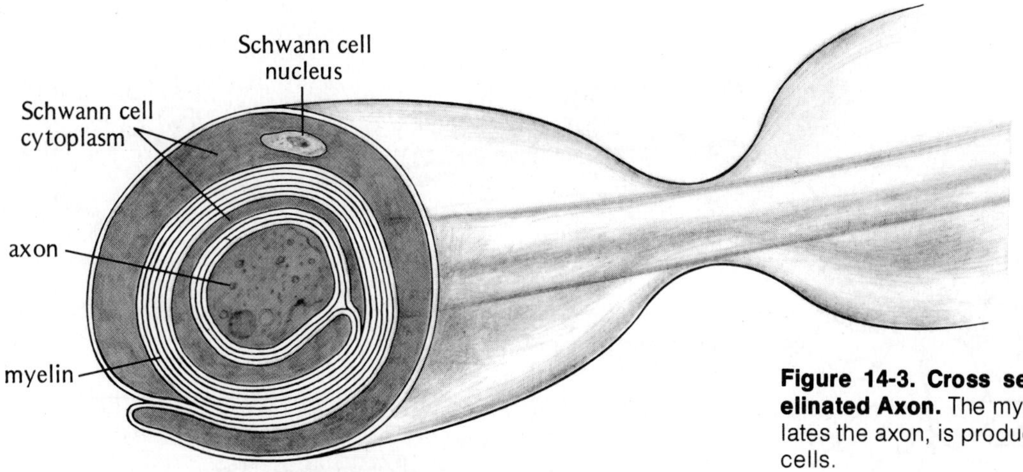

Figure 14-3. Cross section of a Myelinated Axon. The myelin, which insulates the axon, is produced by Schwann cells.

All axons are surrounded by cells called **Schwann** (shwahn) cells. On some axons the Schwann cells produce layers of a white fatty substance called **myelin** (*my*-uh-lin) (see Figure 14-3). The myelin forms a sheath around the axon, and axons having such a sheath are said to be *myelinated.* The myelin insulates the axon. At intervals along the myelinated axon, there are gaps in the myelin where the axon membrane is exposed to the surrounding medium. These gaps, which occur between adjacent Schwann cells, are called the *nodes of Ranvier* (*rahn*-vee-ay).

The nerve cells of mature animals cannot divide, so there is no periodic replacement of neurons as there is with other cells in the body. However, if the cell body is unhurt, axons and dendrites outside the brain and spinal cord can regenerate, or grow back, if they are damaged.

14-4 The Synapse

The axon of a neuron usually has no branches along its length, but it may have a great many branches at its end. Each of these *terminal branches* makes contact with another cell. The junction between the terminal branch of a neuron and the membrane of another cell is called a **synapse** (*sin*-aps). The synapse includes a microscopic gap between the end of the terminal branch and the adjoining cell. Impulses are transmitted from the axon to the adjoining cell across this gap. The structure of a synapse and the way in which impulses are transmitted across it are described in Section 14-8 (page 230). Each axon may make synaptic contact with as many as 1,000 other neurons, and it may form many synapses with each of these other cells. Axons from other neurons may also make contact with the same cells. Thus the interconnections and impulse pathways of a typical nervous system are enormously complex.

Point out that while neurons are generally microscopic, nerves look like whitish cords in a dissection.

14-5 Types of Neurons and Nerves

Neurons are generally grouped according to their function. **Sensory neurons** carry impulses from receptors toward the

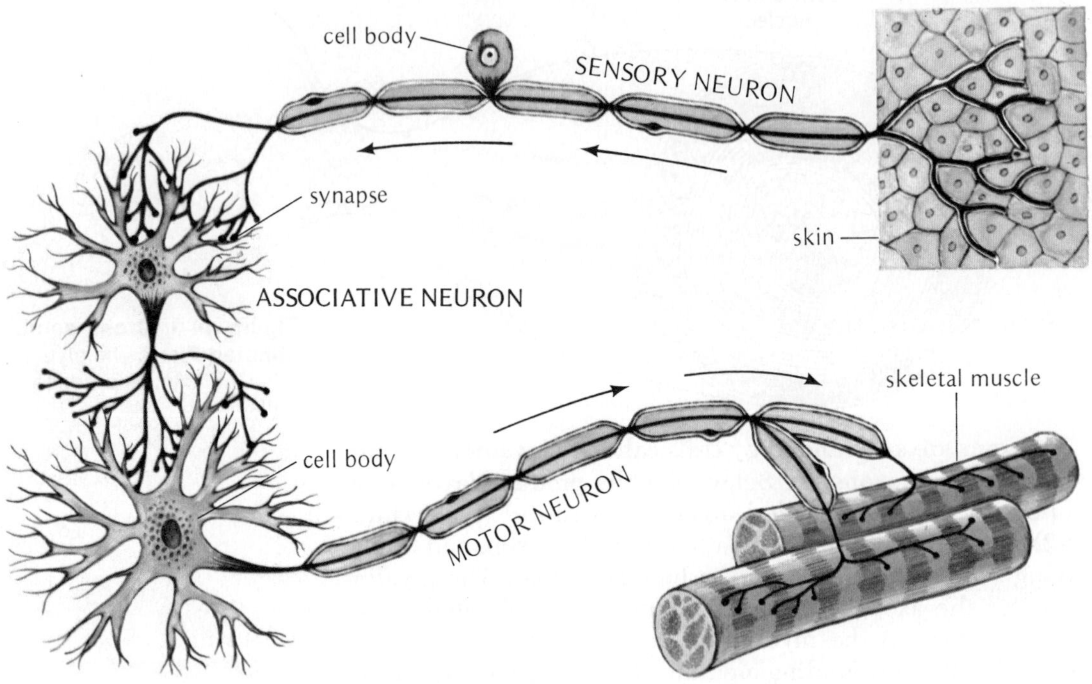

Figure 14-4. Pathway of Nerve Impulses. Sensory neurons receive stimuli and trigger impulses in other neurons. Motor neurons carry impulses toward effectors, such as skeletal muscle. Interneurons, which are found in the brain and spinal cord, relay impulses from one neuron to another.

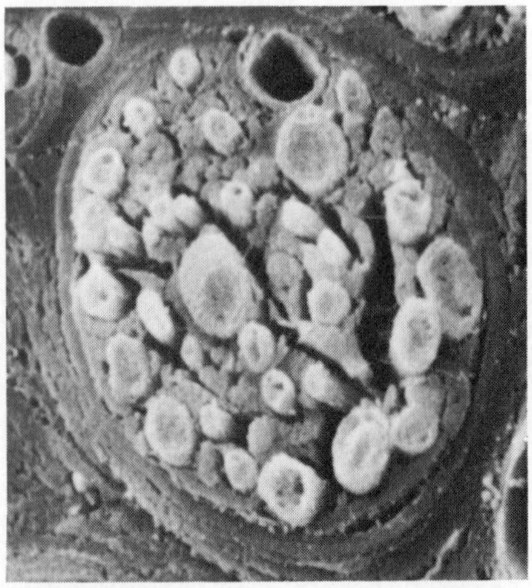

Figure 14-5. Structure of a Nerve. Nerves are made up of bundles of neurons bound together by connective tissue. Note the blood vessels that provide nutrients for the nerve fibers.

spinal cord and brain (see Figure 14-4). **Motor neurons** carry impulses from the brain and spinal cord toward effectors, usually muscles. **Associative** (uh-*soh*-shee-ay-tiv) **neurons,** or **interneurons,** relay impulses from one neuron to another in the brain and spinal cord. The great majority of neurons in the human nervous system are associative neurons.

Nerves are bundles of axons or dendrites that are bound together by connective tissue (see Figure 14-5). Nerves are called **sensory nerves** if they conduct impulses from receptors toward the spinal cord and brain; **motor nerves** if they conduct impulses from the brain and spinal cord toward effectors; and **mixed nerves** if they are composed of both sensory and motor fibers.

THE NERVE-CELL MEMBRANE AND IMPULSES

After completing your study of this section, you should be able to:

1. Describe the electrical state of the resting neuron.
2. Describe the function of the sodium-potassium pump.
3. Describe the sequence of changes associated with the passage of an impulse along an axon.
4. Name two factors that affect the rate at which impulses are transmitted along an axon.
5. Explain what is meant by the refractory period and by the nerve threshold.

6. Explain how the nervous system distinguishes between different types of stimuli.
7. Explain how the nervous system distinguishes between stimuli of the same type but different strengths.

14-6 The Resting Neuron

The transmission of a nerve impulse is made possible by a difference in electrical charge between the outer and inner surfaces of the nerve-cell membrane. When the neuron is resting (not transmitting an impulse), the outside of the membrane has a net positive charge, and the inside has a net negative charge (see Figure 14-6). The cell membrane is said to be

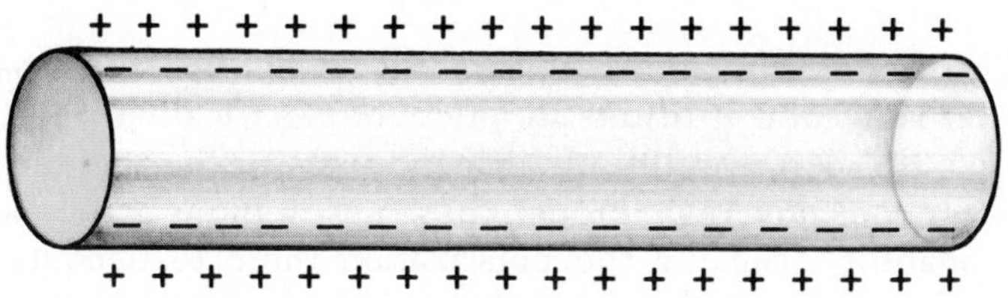

Figure 14-6. Electrical State of a Resting Neuron. As a result of the action of the sodium pump, the outside of the membrane of a resting neuron has a net positive charge and the inside of the membrane has a net negative charge.

electrically *polarized* because there is a difference in electrical charge between its outer and inner surfaces. This **polarization** is caused by different concentrations of certain ions in the mediums outside and inside the cell. The concentration differences result partly from the selective permeability of the membrane, but mainly from the active transport of these ions across the membrane. The ions involved in the polarization of the nerve-cell membrane are mainly sodium ions and potassium ions, both of which have a positive electrical charge.

The nerve-cell membrane has an active transport mechanism that pumps sodium ions out of the cell and pumps potassium ions in. This mechanism is called the **sodium-potassium pump,** or more simply, the *sodium pump*. In its resting state, the nerve-cell membrane is freely permeable to potassium ions, but not to sodium ions. As a result, the potassium ions pumped into the cell tend to diffuse back out. However, the sodium ions pumped out of the cell cannot diffuse freely through the membrane, and they accumulate outside the cell. The result is that an excess of positive charge (due to sodium ions) builds up outside the membrane. An excess of negative charge is left behind inside the membrane.

14-7 The Nerve Impulse

Membrane changes in the area of the impulse. A nerve impulse is initiated in the membrane of a neuron by the arrival of an impulse from another neuron or by a stimulus from a receptor. At the place where the impulse is initiated, the first thing that happens is that the permeability of the membrane to sodium ions suddenly increases. Recall that there is a high concentration of sodium ions outside the membrane. Under the influence of this concentration gradient, sodium ions diffuse rapidly from the outside to the inside of the membrane. This flow of positive sodium ions reverses the polarization of the membrane. In the area of the impulse the inside of the nerve cell becomes positively charged; the outside becomes negatively charged (see Figure 14-7).

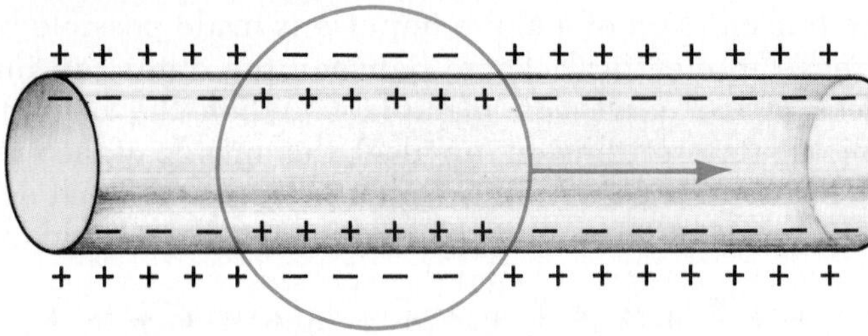

Figure 14-7. A Nerve Impulse. In the area of an impulse, the nerve cell membrane becomes permeable to sodium ions, which enter the cell. This causes a reversal of the polarity of the membrane. The area of reversed polarity is the nerve impulse, and it travels quickly down the axon membrane.

This reversal of polarity occurs in a small area of the membrane. However, it results in a flow of electrical current that affects the permeability of adjacent areas of the membrane. Sodium ions now rush through these new regions of increased permeability, causing the polarization there to become reversed. In this way the reversal of polarization travels over the entire cell membrane and down the length of the axon. The reversal of polarization is the nerve impulse. The passage of the impulse along an axon is like the burning of a firecracker fuse. The region of burning travels along the fuse by igniting the portion ahead. The big difference is that a fuse cannot be used again, while a neuron can transmit one impulse after another.

In the area of the nerve impulse, the high permeability of the cell membrane to sodium ions lasts for only a brief fraction of a second. It then returns to normal, preventing the further diffusion of sodium ions across the membrane. However, the diffusion of potassium to the outside of the membrane, together with the action of the sodium pump, soon restores the normal distribution of ions. The polarity of the membrane is thus returned to normal, with a positive charge outside and a negative charge inside.

Following the passage of an impulse, there is a brief recovery period during which the nerve cell membrane cannot be stimulated to carry impulses. This time, which lasts only a few thousandths of a second, is called the **refractory period.** When it is over, the membrane is again ready to transmit another impulse.

Rate of impulse conduction. The rate at which impulses travel depends on the size of the nerve fiber and on whether or not it is myelinated. In small unmyelinated fibers, the nerve impulse travels at a relatively slow 2 meters/second. In large myelinated fibers it may travel at over 100 meters/second.

The reason that conduction is so much faster in myelinated fibers is that the impulse travels in "jumps" from one node of Ranvier, where the axon is bare, to the next. This type of conduction is called *saltatory* (*sal*-tuh-tor-ee) *conduction*. The myelin insulates the nerve. Ions cannot flow through this substance. However, in these nerve fibers, the membrane at the nodes is highly sensitive. Saltatory conduction is not only faster than nonsaltatory conduction, but it also uses less energy because depolarization occurs only at the nodes. Thus less active transport is necessary for restoring the normal distribution of ions after the impulse has passed.

Nerve cell thresholds. For an impulse to be initiated in a given nerve cell, the stimulus must have at least a certain minimum strength. Each nerve cell has a minimum level of sensitivity, or **threshold.** A stimulus whose strength is below that threshold cannot initiate impulses in the neuron. However, any stimulus above the threshold level will trigger impulses in the neuron. The impulses transmitted by a given neuron are all alike—they are all the same "size," and they pass along the neuron at the same rate. Thus, a neuron operates on an "all-or-none" basis. That is, either an impulse is triggered or it is not triggered, depending only on whether the stimulus is above or below the threshold level. The situation is much like the firing of a gun. If enough force is exerted on the trigger, the gun fires. But the size of the explosion and speed of the bullet are always the same. Squeezing the trigger harder has no effect.

Distinguishing strength and type of stimulus. If all nerve impulses are basically alike, how does an organism know what type of stimulus caused the impulses or how strong the stimulus was? For example, why does touching a hot stove feel different from touching a merely warm surface? How do you distinguish a bright light from a loud sound?

The strength of a stimulus is measured by two effects. First of all, a stronger stimulus causes more impulses to be transmitted each second (see Figure 14-8). That is, the impulses follow each other more closely. Secondly, different neurons have dif-

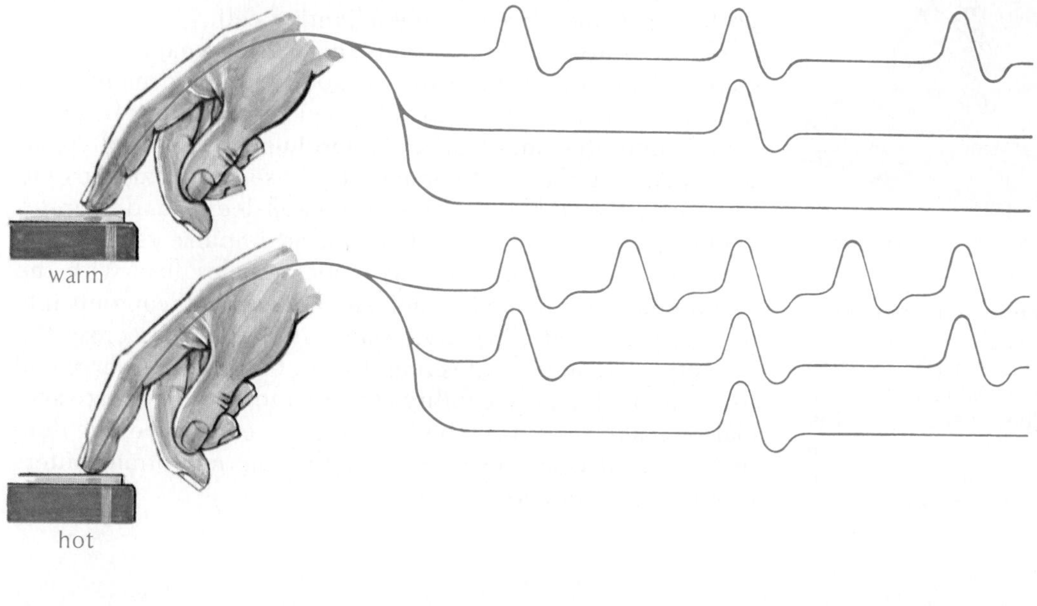

Figure 14-8. Strength of a Stimulus. A strong stimulus (hot object, bottom) triggers more impulses in more neurons than a weak stimulus (warm object, top). These differences enable the brain to determine the strength of the stimulus.

ferent thresholds. Some require a stronger stimulus than others to transmit an impulse. Therefore, a larger number of neurons will fire when a stimulus is stronger.

Recognition of the *type* of stimulus is determined by the particular pathways that carry the nerve impulses. Each type of receptor is sensitive to a particular type of stimulus. For example, receptors in the retina of the eye are sensitive to light. They trigger nerve impulses when light strikes them. Impulses from the retina travel through the optic nerve to a particular part of the brain, which interprets them as sight. Artificial stimulation of the optic nerve will cause a person to "see" flashes of light. Sound waves, on the other hand, have no effect on the eye. They trigger impulses in the auditory nerve of the ear. When these impulses reach the brain, they are interpreted as sound.

SYNAPSES

After completing your study of this section, you should be able to:

1. Identify the structures associated with the synapse.
2. Describe the transmission of an impulse across a synapse.
3. Name several neurotransmitters.
4. Describe the transmission of an impulse at a neuromuscular junction.

14-8 Transmission at the Synapse

The structure of a synapse is shown in Figure 14-9. At the synapse, the axon ends in a **synaptic knob.** The cell membrane at the knob is called the *presynaptic membrane.* The cell membrane of the adjacent cell is called the *postsynaptic membrane.* Between the pre- and postsynaptic membranes is a very narrow space called the *synaptic cleft.* When an impulse arrives at the synaptic knob, it must be transmitted from the presynaptic membrane, across the synaptic cleft, to the postsynaptic membrane of the adjoining cell.

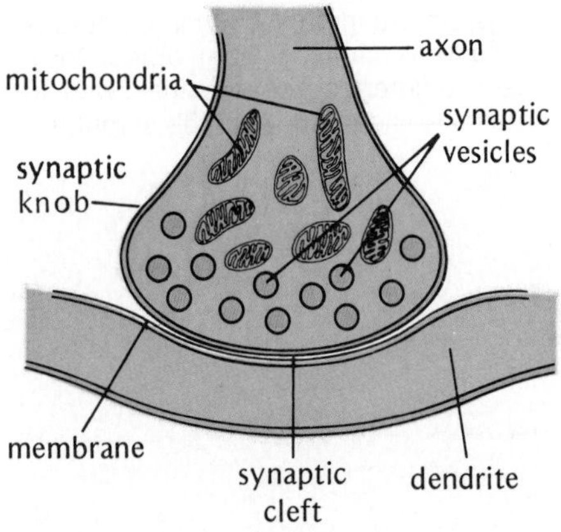

Figure 14-9. Structure of the Synapse. When a nerve impulse reaches the synaptic knob, some synaptic vesicles release their contents, which are neurotransmitters, into the synaptic cleft. The neurotransmitters diffuse across the synaptic cleft and initiate nerve impulses in the adjacent neuron.

The transmission of the impulse across the synaptic cleft is a chemical process. Within the synaptic knob are many small sacs called *synaptic vesicles.* The vesicles contain substances called **neurotransmitters,** or **neurohumors** (noor-oh-*hyoo*-merz). Among the most common of these chemical transmitters are *acetylcholine* (uh-seet-ul-*koh*-leen) and *norepinephrine* (*nor*-ep-uh-*nef*-rin). When an impulse reaches the synaptic knob, some of the synaptic vesicles fuse with the membrane of the synaptic knob and release their contents into the synaptic cleft. The neurotransmitter diffuses across the synaptic cleft and initiates impulses in the adjacent nerve cell by changing the permeability of its membrane. There are special receptor proteins embedded in the membrane of the dendrites, and it is at these receptors that the neurotransmitters produce their effects.

Note that it is not the nerve impulse that crosses the synaptic cleft from one neuron to the next. Instead, it is a chemical compound—the neurotransmitter—that is sent across the gap. Each impulse that reaches a synapse releases a certain amount of neurotransmitter. When the impulses are arriving at a faster rate (representing a stronger initial stimulus), more neurotransmitter is released into the synaptic cleft. This greater quantity of neurotransmitter acts as a stronger stimulus on the adjacent neuron, and the neuron then transmits more impulses per second. In this way, information about the strength of the original stimulus is passed across the synapse and down the nerve pathway. As soon as the neurotransmitter has done its work, it must be removed from the synaptic cleft to clear the way for new signals. This is generally accomplished by enzymes present in the synaptic cleft. These enzymes quickly break down the molecules of neurotransmitter after the neuron has responded to them.

Because neurotransmitters are released only by the ends of axons and because they exert their effects only at specialized receptor sites, impulses can travel in only one direction across synapses—from axons to dendrites or cell bodies. Thus, synapses control the direction of flow of information over nerve pathways.

Different types of neurons release different neurotransmitters. Some neurons release *excitatory neurotransmitters.* These chemicals initiate impulses in adjacent neurons. Acetylcholine, norepinephrine, and the amino acids histamine and glutamic acid are excitatory neurotransmitters. Still other neurons release neurotransmitters that do not initiate impulses in adjacent neurons. Instead, they have the opposite effect—they *inhibit* the firing of impulses. *Inhibitory neurotransmitters* include serotonin, epinephrine, and the amino acid glycine. Thus, while some synapses trasmit impulses from one neuron to the next, other synapses block the transmission of impulses.

Our discussion of the basic mechanisms of nervous regulation has been in terms of one neuron synapsing with another neuron and stimulating or inhibiting impulses in that neuron. However, this is an oversimplification of the actual arrangement. As previously mentioned, the axon of a single neuron may form a thousand or more synapses. This may include many synapses on the same neuron. The dendrites of one neuron may also have synaptic connections with a thousand or more other neurons. Thus, the dendrites of a single neuron receive impulses from many neurons. Some of these impulses may be excitatory, while others may be inhibitory. What happens is that the cell body, in effect, totals or averages these impulses. If the overall results are excitatory, impulses are transmitted down the axon to the next set of synapses. If the results are inhibitory, no impulses are transmitted. Thus, in a nerve pathway, stimulation of certain neurons results in the inhibition of other neurons. Much of the complex behavior of an organism is the result of the great number and variety of synaptic circuits formed when neurons are "switched" on and off.

14-9 Neuromuscular Junctions

The passage of impulses from motor neurons to muscles occurs at special points of contact called **neuromuscular** (noor-oh-*mus*-kyoo-ler) **junctions** (see Figure 14-10). The axons of motor neurons end in structures called **motor end plates.** Like synaptic knobs, motor end plates contain synaptic vesicles. When impulses reach the motor end plates, they cause the release of the chemical transmitter acetylcholine. The acetylcholine diffuses across the gap between the end of the axon and the muscle cell and combines with receptor molecules on the muscle cell membrane. The effect of the acetylcholine is to increase the permeability of the muscle cell membrane to sodium, causing impulses to travel along the muscle cell membrane. These impulses cause the muscle cell to contract. As in the synapses between neurons, the acetylcholine at the neuromuscular junction is quickly destroyed by enzyme action.

14-10 Drugs and the Synapse

Many poisons and drugs affect the activity of chemical transmitters at synapses. Nerve gas, *curare* (kyoo-*rah*-ree), *botulin* (*bahch*-uh-lin) *toxin* (a bacterial poison), and some insecticides are poisons that interfere with the functioning of acetylcholine at neuromuscular junctions and cause muscle paralysis. If the muscles of the respiratory system become paralyzed, death follows.

Figure 14-10. Structure of the Neuromuscular Junction. When a nerve impulse reaches the motor end plates of a motor neuron, acetylcholine is released from the synaptic vesicles. The acetylcholine diffuses across the synaptic cleft to the muscle cell membrane and initiates impulses that cause the muscle cell to contract.

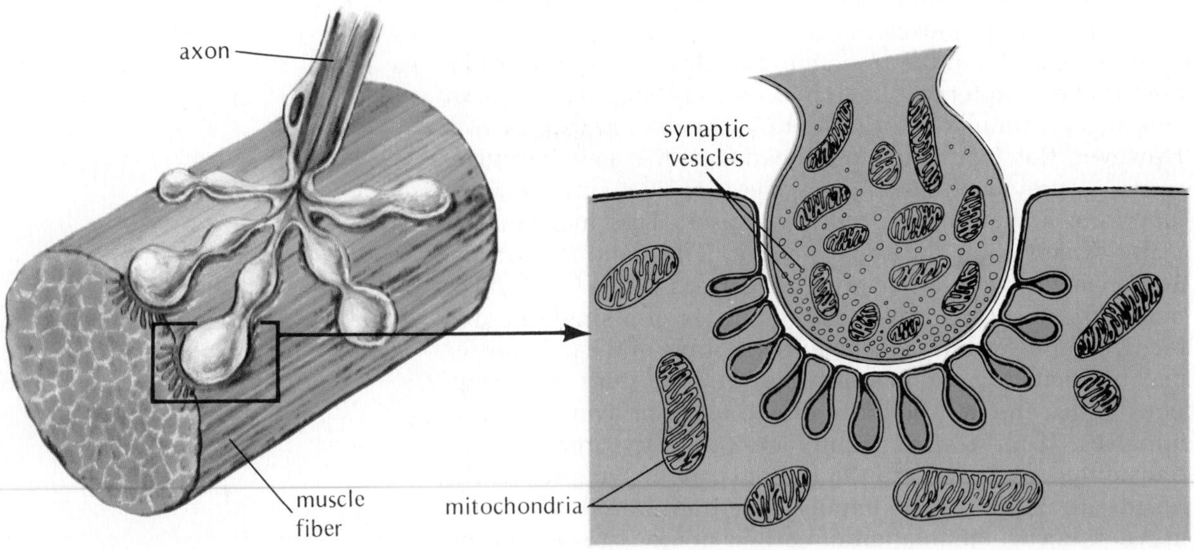

historical notes

The pioneering research of the German physiologist Otto Loewi contributed to our understanding of how nerve impulses cross synapses and how they affect muscles.

In 1921, Loewi was experimenting with the nerves that control the rate of the heartbeat in frogs. At that time, the electrical nature of the nerve impulse was known, but the role of chemicals in the transmission of impulses was not known.

In Loewi's experiments, the heart with nerves attached was dissected from the frog and placed in a saline (salt water) solution. Kept in such a solution, the heart will continue to beat for quite a while. As expected, Loewi found that electrical stimulation of the vagus nerve caused the rate of the heartbeat to decrease. Loewi then placed a second heart without a vagus nerve attached in the same sample of saline solution. Surprisingly, the rate of beating of the second heart also decreased. Evidently, a chemical was released into the saline solution by the vagus nerve endings of the first heart. This substance was later identified as acetylcholine.

In a similar experiment, Loewi demonstrated that stimulation of the accelerator nerve to the heart causes the release of a different substance, which causes the rate of the heartbeat to increase. This second substance was identified as norepinephrine. Thus, Loewi established that impulses result in the release of chemicals by nerve endings.

Otto Loewi shared the 1936 Nobel Prize in Physiology or Medicine with the English biologist Henry Dale. Dale was the investigator who showed that the substance released by the vagus nerve was acetylcholine. Dale had previously isolated acetylcholine from the fungus ergot.

Drugs that affect the mind and the emotions or that alter the activity of body systems also act on synapses. *Stimulants* are drugs that produce a feeling of well-being, alertness, and excitement. Among the stimulants, *amphetamines* (am-*fet*-uh-meenz) ("uppers") produce their effects by binding to certain receptors, thereby mimicking norepinephrine. *Caffeine* (kah-*feen*), which is found in coffee, tea, and cola drinks, aids synaptic transmission.

Depressants are drugs that slow down body activities. *Barbiturates* (bar-*bich*-uh-ritz) ("downers") produce a depressant effect by blocking the formation of norepinephrine.

Some of the mind-altering or hallucinatory drugs, such as *LSD* ("acid") and *mescaline* (*mes*-kuh-lin), interfere with the effect of the inhibitory transmitter serotonin.

ADAPTATIONS FOR NERVOUS REGULATION

After completing your study of this section, you should be able to:

1. Describe the responses of protozoans to various stimuli.
2. Compare and contrast the nervous systems of the hydra, earthworm, and grasshopper.

In the animal kingdom, all groups of organisms from the coelenterates (jellyfish, hydra) on up, have some type of nervous system. As animals become more complex, their nervous systems also become more complex and increasingly specialized. The more highly specialized nervous systems allow animals to respond to their environments with more varied behavior.

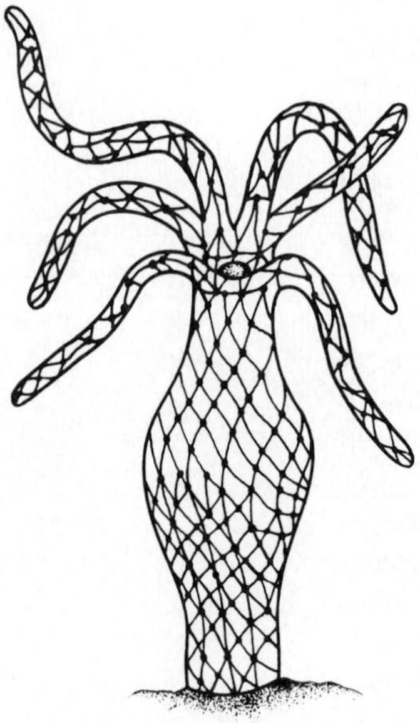

Figure 14-11. Nervous System of the Hydra. The nerve net of the hydra allows the muscles of the organism to react to stimuli in a coordinated manner. The system contains special receptor cells, but no brain or nerve cord.

14-11 Regulation in Protozoa

Protozoans do not have true nervous systems. However, they are able to respond to certain stimuli in a coordinated way. Amebas have no specialized sense receptors, but they can distinguish between food and nonfood and move away from such things as strong light and irritating chemicals. The mechanisms of these responses are not yet understood.

Some protozoa have specialized filaments that function in a manner similar to the neurons of more complex animals. In the paramecium, the beating of the cilia is controlled by an interconnected system of fibers found at the base of the cilia. The paramecium can respond to various stimuli—it can move toward food or away from strong acids and can change direction to avoid solid matter in its path. Some protozoa have organelles that are sensitive to certain stimuli and initiate responses in the organism.

14-12 Regulation in Hydra

The nervous system of the hydra is in the form of a **nerve net** (see Figure 14-11). In this system, the nerve cells form an irregular network between the two layers of the body wall. This network connects special receptor cells in the body wall with muscle and gland cells. There is no organized center, such as a brain or nerve cord, to control and coordinate the nerve impulses. Instead, when a stimulus is received by any part of the body, impulses spread slowly from the stimulated area in all directions through the nerve net. Thus all the muscle fibers in the organism respond, but the response shows coordination. For example, when a tentacle comes in contact with food, such as a daphnia, the impulses travel slowly through the entire organism. In response, the animal stretches toward the food, and the tentacles work together in a coordinated manner to capture the food and stuff it into the mouth.

14-13 Regulation in the Earthworm

The nervous system of the earthworm includes a **central nervous system** and a **peripheral nervous system** (see Figure 14-12). The central nervous system consists of a "brain" connected to a pair of solid, ventral nerve cords. The nerve cords enlarge into *ganglia* (*gang*-lee-uh) in each segment. A **ganglion** (*gang*-lee-un) is a group of cell bodies and associative neurons that switch, relay, and coordinate nerve impulses. The so-called "brain" is actually a pair of fused ganglia that is only the beginning of a brain.

Each ganglion controls the nerves in its segment. If an earthworm is cut into pieces, the pieces continue to move because the ganglia function independently of the brain. If the brain is destroyed, the worm can continue to move and live.

The peripheral nervous system includes the nerves branching from the central nervous system and passing to all parts of the body. These nerves contain sensory neurons, which carry impulses from receptors in the skin to the nerve cord, and motor neurons, which carry impulses from the nerve cord to muscles and glands (effectors). The specialized receptors in the skin are sensitive to light, vibrations, chemicals, and heat.

In the earthworm, the nerves of the peripheral nervous system connect receptors and effectors to the central nervous system. Impulses travel over definite pathways in only one direction. The nervous systems of the more complex animals are similar to the nervous system of the earthworm.

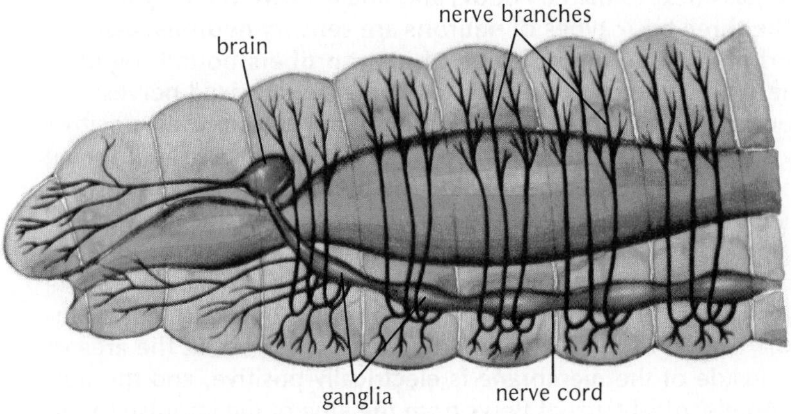

Figure 14-12. Nervous System of the Earthworm. The central nervous system of the earthworm consists of a brain connected to a pair of ventral nerve cords. The sensory and motor nerves that branch from the nerve cords make up the peripheral nervous system.

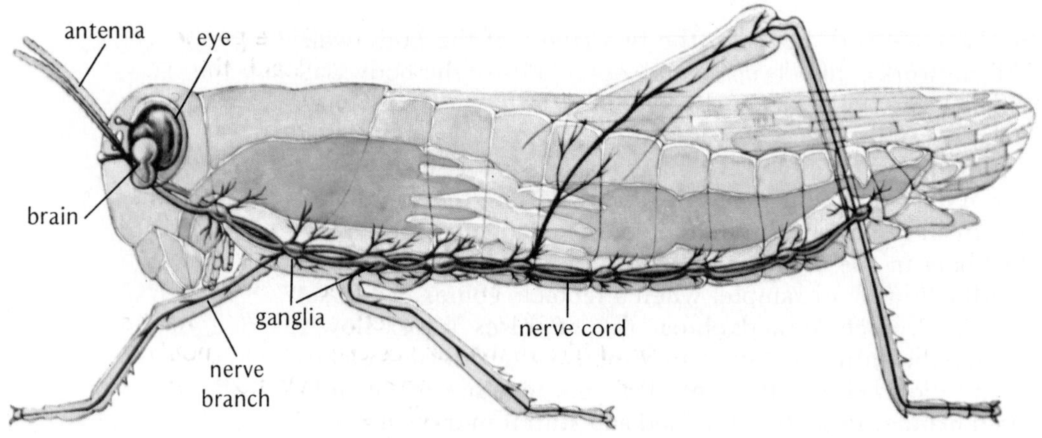

Figure 14-13. Nervous System of the Grasshopper. The nervous system of the grasshopper consists of a brain, a pair of ventral nerve cords, and branching nerves. In addition, the grasshopper has well-developed sense organs, including antennae, eyes, and taste organs.

14-14 Regulation in the Grasshopper

The nervous system of the grasshopper is basically similar to that of the earthworm (see Figure 14-13). It consists of a brain in the head region; a pair of solid, ventral nerve cords that run the length of the body, and ganglia. Nerves branch out from the ganglia to all parts of the body. The sense organs of the grasshopper are more highly developed than those of the earthworm. The grasshopper has eyes, *antennae* (an-*ten*-ee) or "feelers," and taste organs that respond to a variety of stimuli. Grasshoppers are also sensitive to sound. Because the grasshopper has a more highly developed nervous system than the earthworm, it is capable of more complex behavior.

summary

Nervous systems include receptors, nerve cells, and effectors. Various physical forces and chemical substances stimulate the receptors, which in turn trigger impulses in nerve cell pathways. These impulses eventually reach an effector, causing it either to increase or decrease its activity.

Neurons are specialized for the conduction of impulses. A neuron generally consists of dendrites, a cell body, and an axon. Impulses are usually received by the dendrites, pass next to the cell body, and finally down the long axon to adjacent cells. The three basic types of neurons are sensory neurons, associative neurons, and motor neurons. Groups of neuron fibers bound together form nerves. There are sensory nerves, motor nerves, and mixed nerves.

In a resting neuron, the outside of the cell membrane is electrically positive while the inside is negative. The membrane is polarized because of an unequal distribution of certain ions inside and outside the membrane. This, in turn, is caused by the selective permeability of the membrane and by the active transport of sodium and potassium ions by the sodium-potassium pump.

In the area of the nerve-cell impulse, the selective permeability of the membrane breaks down. Sodium ions rush into the cell in such great quantities that the polarization of the membrane becomes reversed. In the area of the impulse, the inside of the membrane is electrically positive, and the outside is negative. An electrical current flows from the area of the impulse to the adjacent area of the membrane. The current affects the membrane permeability of the adjacent area and causes the reversal of polarization that is the nerve impulse. In this way the impulse travels along the nerve-cell membrane. The breakdown in the selective permeability of the membrane associated with the nerve impulse lasts only briefly. The membrane is restored to its original electrical and chemical condition by a combination of diffusion and active transport of various ions.

At the point where impulses pass from the terminal branches of an axon to the dendrites of adjacent neurons there are specialized regions called synapses. At the ends of the axon branches are structures called synaptic knobs. These structures contain fluid-filled synaptic vesicles. When impulses reach the synaptic knobs, they cause the release of the chemicals stored in the vesicles. These chemicals, called neurotransmitters, diffuse across the synaptic cleft and bind with receptors on adjacent dendrites. Different types of neurons produce different types of neurotransmitters. Some stimulate the firing of impulses in adjacent neurons, while others inhibit the firing of impulses. At neuromuscular junctions, axons terminate in motor end plates, which also release chemical transmitters. The transmitters stimulate contraction of adjacent muscle fibers.

Protozoans do not have nervous systems. However, they can respond to various stimuli in the environment. In hydras, there is a nerve net that transmits impulses throughout the organism and allows it to respond to stimuli in a coordinated manner. The earthworm has a primitive brain and a double, ventral nerve cord that enlarges into ganglia in each segment. Sensory and motor nerves transmit impulses between the brain and nerve cord and sense receptors and effectors. The earthworm has receptors sensitive to light, vibrations, chemicals, and heat. The nervous system of the grasshopper is similar to that of the earthworm, but the sense organs are more highly developed.

vocabulary

associative neuron
axon
brain
cell body
central nervous system
cyton
dendrite
effector
ganglion
impulse
irritability
mixed nerve
motor end plate
motor nerve
motor neuron
myelin
nerve
nerve net
neurohumor
neuromuscular junction
neuron
neurotransmitter
node of Ranvier
peripheral nervous system
polarization
receptor
refractory period
Schwann cell
sense organ
sensory nerve
sensory neuron
sodium-potassium pump
stimulus
synapse
synaptic knob
threshold

test your learning

Section	
14-1	1. What two systems are involved in the regulation and coordination of responses?
	2. Define the term *irritability*.
14-2	3. What are the three basic types of structures found in a true nervous system?
	4. What is a receptor? Give three examples of receptors.
	5. What are the two types of effectors? How does each type of effector respond to nervous stimulation?
	6. Define the term *stimulus*.
	7. What is the function of the brain in a nervous system?
14-3	8. List the three basic parts of a nerve cell and describe the structure and function of each.
14-4	9. What is a synapse?
14-5	10. Explain the difference between a sensory neuron and a motor neuron. What are associative neurons?
	11. Define the following terms: *nerve, sensory nerve, motor nerve, mixed nerve*.
14-6	12. Describe the electrical state of the membrane of a resting neuron.
	13. Explain how the difference in electrical charge across the nerve-cell membrane is maintained.
14-7	14. Describe the electrical state of the nerve-cell membrane in the area of an impulse.
	15. What changes in ion distribution are found in the area of an impulse?
	16. Describe the process by which an impulse travels along a nerve-cell membrane.
	17. Why is the rate of impulse conduction much faster in myelinated than in unmyelinated nerve fibers?
	18. What is a nerve-cell threshold, and in what way does a nerve cell fire on an all-or-none basis?
	19. How does the nervous system distinguish between different types of stimuli?
	20. How does the nervous system distinguish between stimuli of the same type but of different strengths?
14-8	21. Describe the structure of a synapse.
	22. Describe how nerve impulses cross the synaptic cleft.
	23. How is stimulus strength reflected in the events at the synapse?
	24. Briefly describe how excitatory and inhibitory synaptic transmitters affect the functioning of the nervous system.
14-9	25. Describe the structure of the neuromuscular junction.
	26. How do impulses pass from a motor neuron to a muscle cell?
14-10	27. List three ways in which drugs can affect the transmission of impulses across synapses.
14-11	28. To what types of stimuli do protozoans respond? What kinds of responses do they show?
14-12	29. Describe the nervous system of the hydra. How does the hydra respond to stimuli?

14-13 **30.** Describe the structures of the central and peripheral nervous systems in the earthworm.

14-14 **31.** Compare the nervous system of the grasshopper with that of the earthworm.

test your understanding

1. Describe the electrical and chemical changes that occur as an impulse passes down an axon and crosses a synapse.
2. Name five neurotransmitters, classifying each as excitatory or inhibitory.
3. How do synapses control the transmission of information through a nerve pathway?

independent research

1. Prepare a report on one of the following topics:
   A. The effects of various drugs on synapses.
   B. Nerve regeneration.
   C. The sodium-potassium pump.
2. Demonstrate how paramecia, hydras, earthworms, or fruit flies respond to such stimuli as light and dark, acid and base, or warmth and cold.
3. Dissect a crayfish or a frog to show the major parts of the nervous system.

chapter 15

The Human Nervous System

THE CENTRAL NERVOUS SYSTEM

After completing your study of this section, you should be able to:

1. Describe the functions of the skull, meninges, spinal column, and cerebrospinal fluid.
2. Name the major parts of the brain and describe the structure and function of each.
3. Describe the structure and functions of the spinal cord.

The human nervous system, like that of other vertebrates, can be divided into two main subdivisions. One of these is the central nervous system, which consists of the brain and the spinal cord. The other is the peripheral nervous system, which is a vast network of nerves that conduct impulses between the central nervous system and the receptors and effectors of the body.

Most of the activities of the body are controlled by the central nervous system—the brain and the spinal cord. Impulses from sense receptors throughout the body bring a constant flow of information about the internal state of tissues and organs and about the external environment. In the brain and the spinal cord the information is interpreted, and impulses are sent out to muscles and glands, causing appropriate responses.

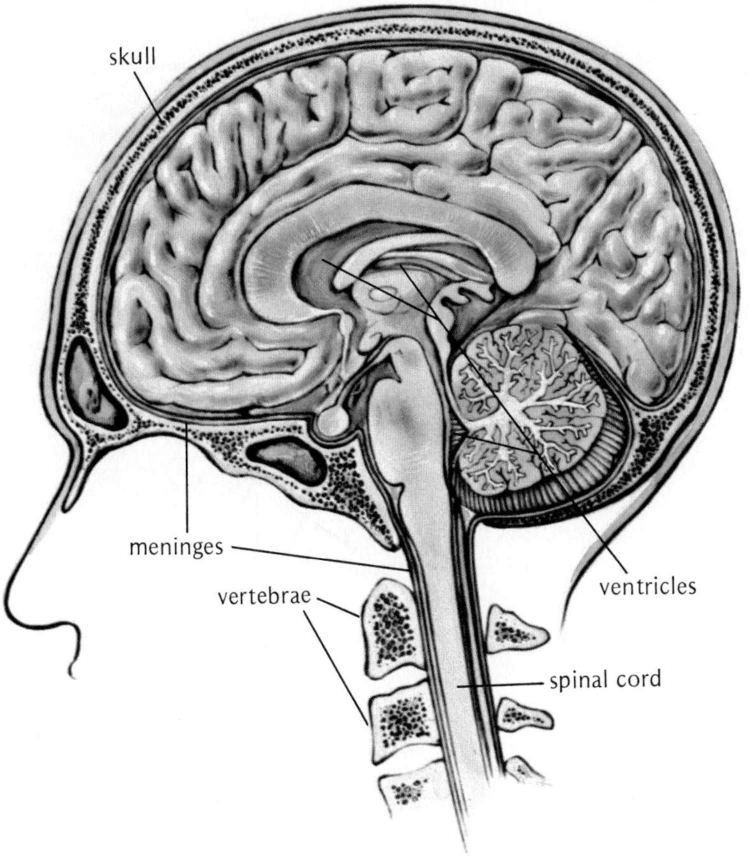

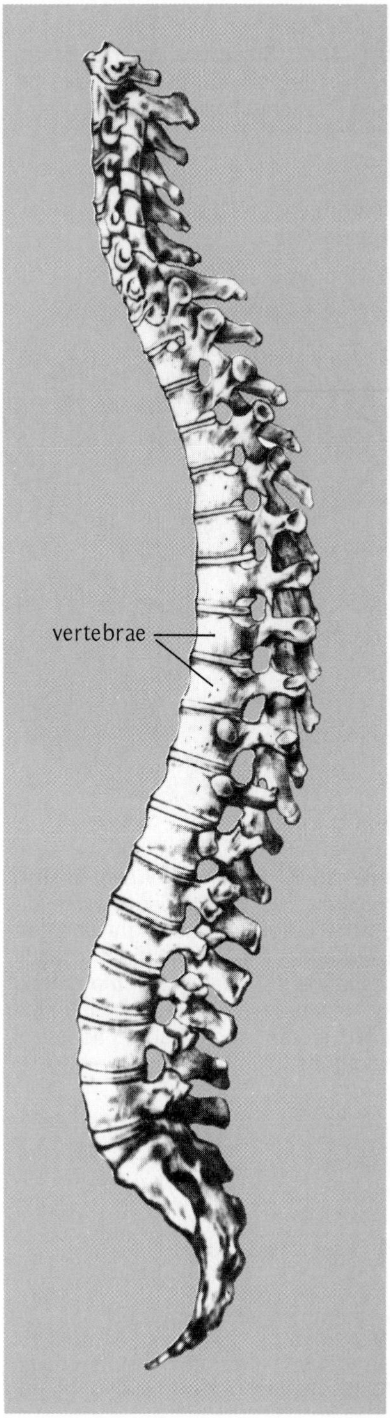

15-1 The Skull and Spinal Column

The brain and the spinal cord are protected by bone (see Figure 15-1). The brain is enclosed by the **skull,** while the spinal cord is surrounded by the vertebrae of the spinal column, or backbone. The brain and the spinal cord are also covered and protected by three tough membranes known as the **meninges** (muh-*nin*-jeez). A liquid, the **cerebrospinal** (suh-ree-broh-*spyn*-ul) **fluid,** cushions the delicate nervous tissues against shock. Within the brain are four spaces, or *ventricles,* that are filled with cerebrospinal fluid. These spaces connect with a space between the meninges and with the central canal of the spinal cord, which are also filled with fluid.

15-2 The Brain

The brain is one of the most active organs in the body. It receives 20 percent of the blood pumped from the heart, it replaces most of its protein every three weeks, and it is the major user of glucose in the body. Unlike the cells of other tissues the cells of the brain generally metabolize only glu-

Figure 15-1. The Skull and Spinal Column. The brain is protected by the skull, and the spinal cord is protected by the vertebrae of the spinal column. Added protection is provided by the meninges and by the cerebrospinal fluid, which cushions the tissues against shock.

Figure 15-2. Structure of the Brain. The major regions of the brain can be seen in this lengthwise view.

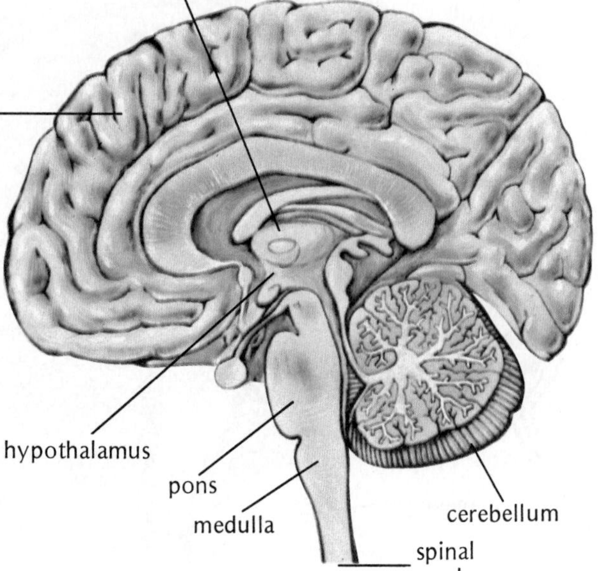

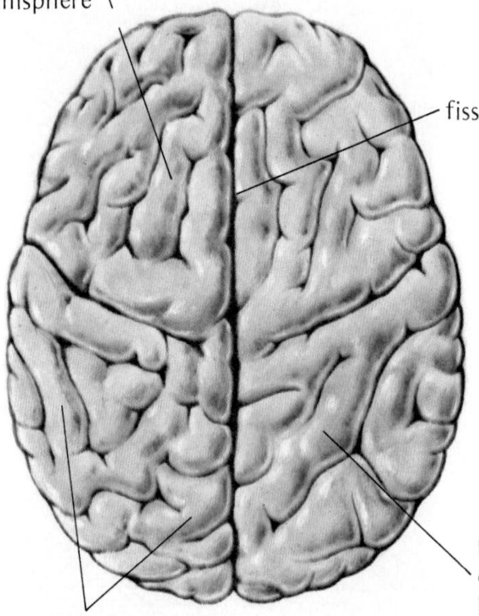

Figure 15-3. External View of the Cerebrum. The longitudinal fissure divides the cerebrum into right and left hemispheres. The convolutions greatly increase the surface area of the cortex, which is made up primarily of unmyelinated fibers and vast numbers of interneurons.

The thalamus plays a part in the mechanisms responsible for emotions by associating sensory impulses with feelings of pleasantness and unpleasantness.

cose for the release of energy. The major parts of the brain are the cerebrum, cerebellum, and medulla (see Figure 15-2).

Other parts of the brain are the thalamus, hypothalamus, and pons. The *thalamus* serves as a relay center between various parts of the brain and the spinal cord; it also receives and modifies all sensory impulses except those involved in smell before they travel to the cerebral cortex; and it may be involved in pain perception and maintenance of consciousness. The *hypothalamus* is involved in control of body temperature, blood pressure, sleep, and emotions; it is also involved in the functioning of the endocrine system (see page 269). The *pons* serves as a relay system linking the spinal cord, medulla, cerebellum, and cerebrum.

The cerebrum. The **cerebrum** (suh-*ree*-brum) is the largest part of the human brain, making up about two-thirds of the entire organ. The greatest difference between the human brain and the brains of other vertebrates is in the larger size and greater development of the human cerebrum. The cerebrum is divided in half from front to back by a deep groove, or fissure, which separates it into the right and left **cerebral hemispheres** (see Figure 15-3). Nerve fibers from each hemisphere pass to the other hemisphere and to other parts of the nervous system.

The outermost layer of the cerebrum is the **cortex,** or **gray matter,** which is made up of the cell bodies of motor neurons

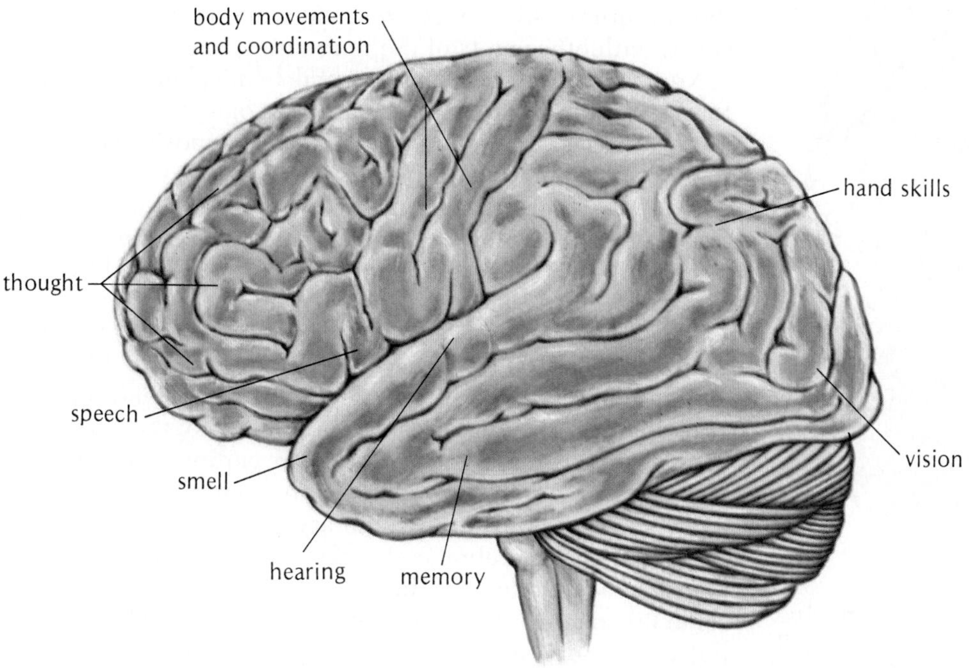

Figure 15-4. Functions of Various Areas of the Cerebral Cortex.

and a tremendous number of associative neurons, interconnected by unmyelinated fibers. The outer surface of the cortex is highly folded. These ridges, or **convolutions** (kahn-vuh-*loo*-shunz), greatly increase the surface area of the gray matter.

The cerebral cortex performs three major types of functions—sensory, motor, and associative functions. Each part of the cortex is specialized to carry out a particular function. However, some functions may involve two or more areas of the cortex as well as other parts of the brain. The functions of the various parts of the cortex are shown in Figure 15-4.

The sensory areas of the cortex receive and interpret impulses from the sense receptors, including the eyes, ears, taste buds, and nose, as well as the touch, pain, pressure, and temperature receptors in the skin and other organs. The motor areas of the cortex initiate impulses that are responsible for all voluntary movement and for the position of the movable parts of the body. Impulses from the motor cortex may be modified by other parts of the brain. The associative areas of the brain are responsible for memory, learning, and thought.

Recent research indicates that the two cerebral hemispheres do not perform identical functions. Instead, some functions are performed by the left hemisphere and others by the right hemisphere (see page 249).

Beneath the gray matter of the cerebrum is an inner area called the **white matter.** This area consists of myelinated nerve fibers. One of the bundles, or tracts, of fibers in the white matter connects the right and left hemispheres, so that

UNDERSIDE OF BRAIN

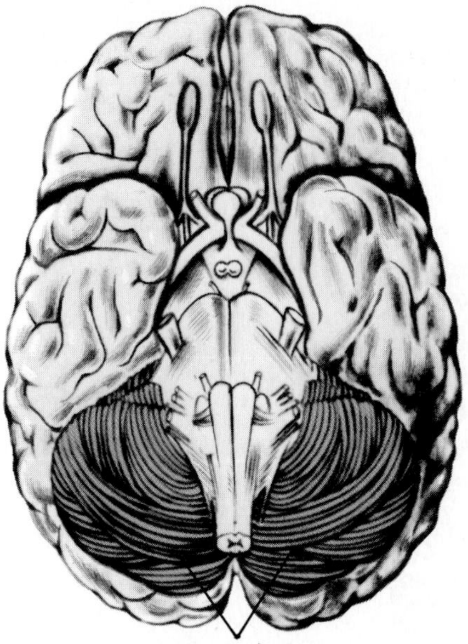

Figure 15-5. The Cerebellum. The cerebellum coordinates and controls all voluntary movements and some involuntary movements. It is also involved in the maintenance of muscle tone.

UNDERSIDE OF BRAIN

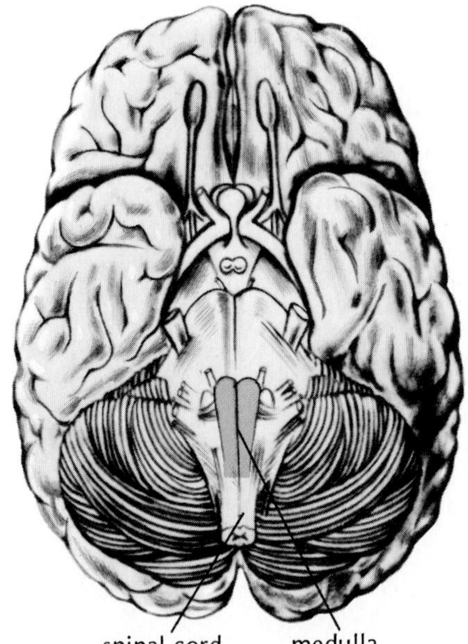

Figure 15-6. The Medulla. The medulla controls many involuntary activities, such as breathing, heartbeat, and blood pressure.

there is an exchange of information between the two halves of the cerebrum. Other tracts from the white matter connect the cortex with other parts of the nervous system.

Nerve fibers leaving the cerebral hemispheres pass down through the brain and spinal cord. At some point along their pathway, these fibers cross over to the opposite side of the brain or spinal cord and then continue to various parts of the body. Thus the left cerebral hemisphere controls the right side of the body, and the right hemisphere controls the left side of the body. Therefore, an injury to one side of the cerebrum will affect the opposite side of the body.

The cerebellum. The **cerebellum** (sehr-uh-*bel*-um) is located below the rear part of the cerebrum (see Figure 15-5). The cerebellum, like the cerebral cortex, is divided into two hemispheres. The highly folded outer layer of the cerebellum consists of gray matter, while the inner portion is white matter.

The cerebellum coordinates and controls all voluntary movements and some involuntary movements. Motor impulses from the cerebral cortex are carried by nerve pathways that send some branches directly to the muscles involved and some branches to the cerebellum. The muscles also send impulses over sensory nerve pathways to the cerebellum, providing information about their position, rate of contraction, and so on. The cerebellum then sends impulses to the cerebral cortex to correct and coordinate the movement of the muscles. Thus, the cerebral cortex and the cerebellum function together to produce smooth and orderly voluntary movement. With certain involuntary movements, the cerebellum functions in the same manner, but in cooperation with other parts of the brain. The cerebellum, using information from receptors in the inner ear, maintains balance, or equilibrium. It is also involved in the maintenance of *muscle tone* (keeping the muscles slightly tensed). Damage to the cerebellum results in jerky movements, tremor, or loss of equilibrium. Staggering and other signs of coordination loss seen with alcohol intoxication reflect a temporary loss of cerebellar function.

The medulla. Beneath the cerebellum and continuous with the spinal cord is the **medulla** (muh-*duhl*-uh) (see Figure 15-6). In this lowest part of the brain, the white matter makes up the outer layer, while the gray matter is the inner layer. The medulla consists mainly of nerve fibers connecting the spinal cord to the various other parts of the brain. Nerve centers in the medulla control many involuntary activities, including breathing, heartbeat, blood pressure, and coughing.

15-3 The Spinal Cord

The spinal cord, which is about 45 centimeters long, extends from the base of the brain down through the vertebrae of the spinal column. A cross section of the spinal cord shows an

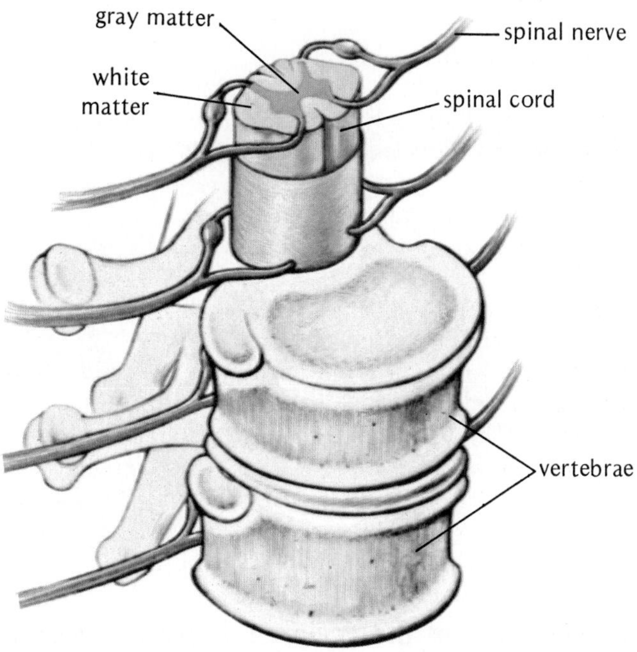

Figure 15-7. Structure of the Spinal Cord.

inner H-shaped region of gray matter surrounded by an outer layer of white matter (see Figure 15-7). The gray matter contains associative neurons as well as the cell bodies of motor neurons. The white matter contains myelinated fibers that carry impulses between all parts of the body and the spinal cord and brain. In the center of the cord is the **spinal canal,** which is filled with cerebrospinal fluid.

The spinal cord performs two main functions. First, it connects the nerves of the peripheral nervous system with the brain. Impulses reaching the spinal cord from sensory neurons travel up the cord through associative neurons to the brain. Impulses from the brain are transmitted down the spinal cord by associative neurons to motor neurons. These impulses travel through peripheral nerves to muscles and glands. Second, the spinal cord controls certain reflexes, which are automatic responses not involving the brain (see page 257).

Point out that the positions of white matter and gray matter in the spinal cord and medulla are opposite their positions in the cerebrum and cerebellum.

THE PERIPHERAL NERVOUS SYSTEM

After completing your study of this section, you should be able to:

1. Identify the nerves that make up the peripheral nervous system.
2. Compare and contrast the structures and functions of the somatic and autonomic nervous systems.
3. Identify the two divisions of the autonomic nervous system and compare and contrast their functions.
4. Define the following terms: *spinal nerve, cranial nerve, ganglion, plexus.*

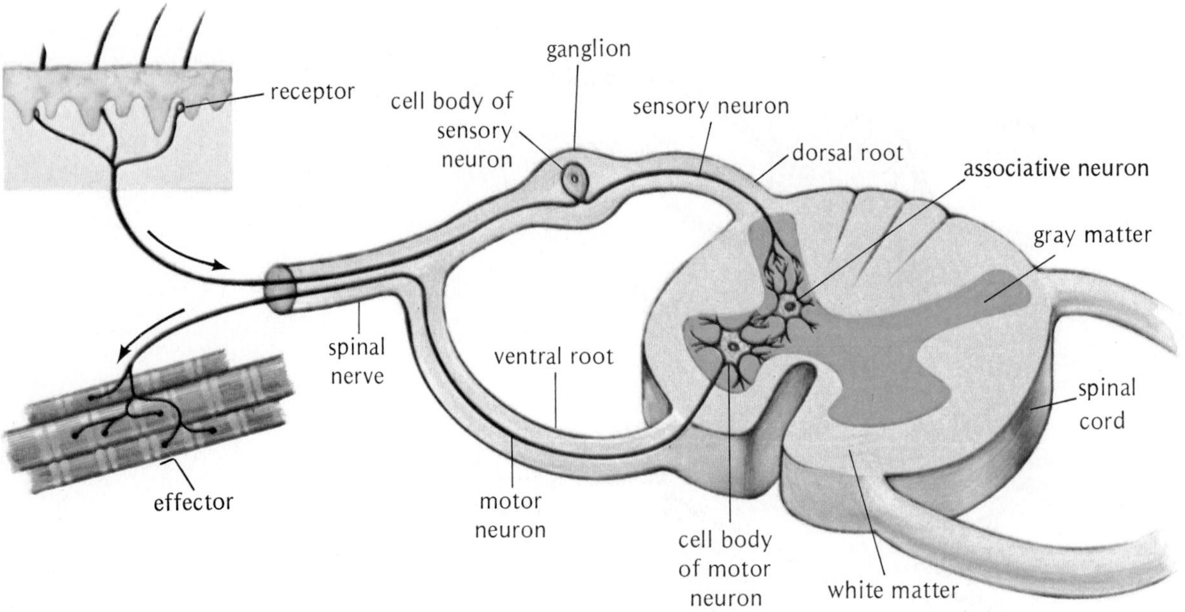

Figure 15-8. Structure of a Spinal Nerve. A spinal nerve contains both motor and sensory fibers. Sensory fibers transmit impulses into the dorsal root of the spinal cord, and motor fibers transmit impulses from the ventral root to effectors. Note that the cell bodies of sensory neurons are outside the spinal cord.

15-4 Structure of the Peripheral Nervous System

The peripheral nervous system includes all the neurons and nerve fibers outside the brain and spinal cord. The neurons of the peripheral nervous system are connected to either the brain or the spinal cord. The neurons are in bundles, forming nerves. The nerves connected to the spinal cord are called the **spinal nerves,** while those connected to the brain are called the **cranial** (*kray*-nee-ul) **nerves.**

There are thirty-one pairs of spinal nerves, each serving a particular part of the body . Each nerve contains both sensory and motor fibers (see Figure 15-8). The cell bodies of the motor fibers are found in the gray matter of the spinal cord. The cell bodies of the sensory fibers are found in ganglia outside the spinal cord. Just outside the spinal cord, the sensory and motor fibers separate. The sensory fibers enter the *dorsal root* (toward the back) of the spinal cord, while the motor fibers leave through the *ventral root* (toward the front) of the cord.

There are twelve pairs of cranial nerves. Those serving the eyes, ears, and nose are made up mostly of sensory fibers. The other cranial nerves contain more equal numbers of sensory and motor fibers. Most of the cranial nerves serve the sense organs and other structures of the head.

On the basis of function, the peripheral nervous system is divided into the somatic nervous system and the autonomic nervous system.

15-5 Somatic Nervous System

The **somatic** (soh-*mat*-ik) **nervous system** contains both sensory and motor neurons that connect the central nervous sys-

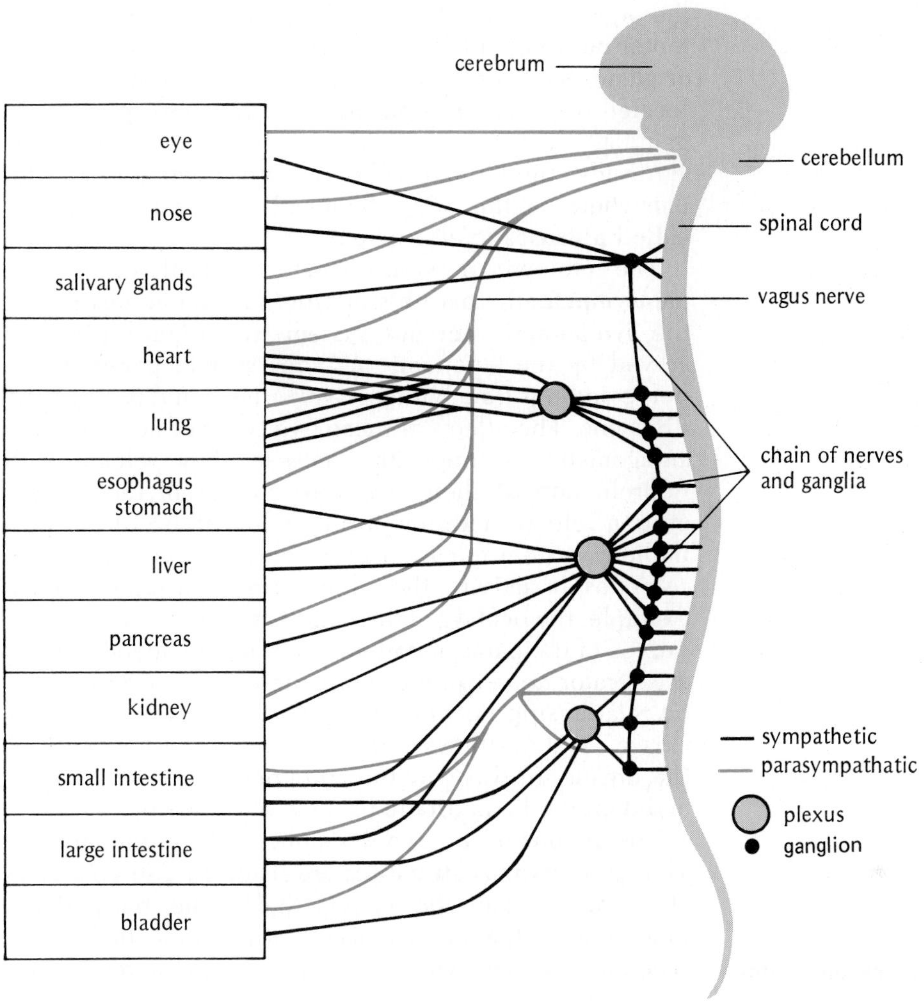

Figure 15-9. Nerve Pathways of the Sympathetic and Parasympathetic Nervous Systems.

tem to skeletal muscles, the skin, and the sense organs. This system is responsible for body movements over which there is some conscious awareness or voluntary control.

15-6 The Autonomic Nervous System

The **autonomic** (awt-uh-*nahm*-ik) **nervous system** consists of certain motor fibers from the brain and spinal cord that serve the internal organs of the body. There is no voluntary control over the activities of the autonomic system. The autonomic system controls many vital functions of the body, including the rate of heartbeat, the diameter of arteries, breathing movements, movements of the digestive system, and secretions of certain glands, such as sweat glands.

The autonomic system consists entirely of motor neurons. Sensory information for this system is provided by the same sensory nerves that serve the somatic system. Impulses in the autonomic system start in motor neurons in the brain or spinal cord. However, the axons of these neurons do not extend to the organ involved. Instead, the axon synapses with a second motor neuron, which then carries the impulses to the muscle or gland. Some of the cell bodies of these second neurons are located in ganglia just outside the brain and spinal cord. The ganglia, which are interconnected by nerves, form two chains alongside the spinal column. Other ganglia are located elsewhere in the body. Some of them form large clusters called **plexuses** (*plek*-sus-sez).

The solar plexus is near the stomach, while the cardiac plexus is near the heart.

The autonomic nervous system consists of two divisions, the **parasympathetic** (par-uh-sim-puh-*thet*-ik) **nervous system** and the **sympathetic nervous system** (see Figure 15-9). Organs served by the autonomic nervous system generally contain nerve endings from both the sympathetic and parasympathetic divisions. The effects of these two types of nerve endings are antagonistic, or opposite, because they release different neurohumors at their synapses. Nerves of the sympathetic system release norepinephrine, while those of the parasympathetic system release acetylcholine. Where one system accelerates an activity, the other retards the same activity. For example, the beating of the heart is slowed down by the vagus nerves of the parasympathetic system and speeded up by the accelerator nerves of the sympathetic system. This antagonistic relationship between the two divisions of the autonomic nervous system allows more precise and sensitive control over the organs. In this way the autonomic nervous system helps maintain the homeostatic balance of the body.

The actions of the two divisions of the autonomic nervous system on various structures are listed in Table 15-1. Generally, the sympathetic system helps the body deal with emergency situations by accelerating some body activities, whereas the parasympathetic system promotes normal, relaxed body functioning.

Table 15-1. Functions of the Autonomic Nervous System

Effects of the Autonomic Nervous System		
Organ	Sympathetic division	Parasympathetic division
Heart	speeds up and strengthens beat (stimulates)	slows and weakens beat (inhibits)
Digestive tract	slows peristalsis, slows activity (inhibits)	speeds peristalsis, increases activity (stimulates)
Blood vessels	mostly constricts	mostly dilates
Bladder	relaxes	constricts
Bronchi	dilates	constricts
Iris of eye	dilates pupil	constricts pupil

frontiers of biology

Since the mid-1800s, scientists have known that damage to a particular part of the left cerebral hemisphere interferes with speech. The part of the left hemisphere concerned with speech was discovered by the French surgeon Paul Broca, and this part of the brain is still called "Broca's area." It was also known that the left side of the brain controls the right side of the body and vice versa.

The location of the speech center in the left hemisphere was the first hint that the right and left cerebral hemispheres do not function identically, but instead, each functions alone in certain types of mental activities. The localization of different mental activities in one hemisphere or the other increases the functional capacity of the brain. In the normal brain, there are tracts of nerve fibers connecting the right and left hemispheres. The different types of information sent to the brain from the sense receptors of the body are processed in the appropriate hemisphere. Because of the connection between the two hemispheres, the information is, in effect, shared between them. Thus, the two halves of the cerebrum normally function as a unit.

The basic information on the separate functions of the right and left cerebral hemispheres has been obtained mainly from animal studies and from studies on people in whom the connection between the hemispheres has been severed. Such studies have shown that in the great majority of right-handed people, speech and verbal processes, writing, and mathematics are functions of the left hemisphere. The right hemisphere, on the other hand, is the site of nonverbal processes, including the recognition of shapes, textures, and music, spatial perceptions, and emotions.

In left-handed people, the division of labor between the two hemispheres is not always so clear-cut. In many left-handers, speech and verbal processes are functions of the left hemisphere, just as they are in right-handers. In others, both hemispheres are involved. In still others, these processes are functions of the right hemisphere, and the roles of the two hemispheres are opposite to those of right-handers.

Although each hemisphere normally controls certain specific functions, studies of people with brain injuries have shown that in many cases, after a period of time, the opposite hemisphere can develop the capacity to carry out the former functions of the damaged hemisphere. The capacity of the opposite hemisphere to take over is greater in younger people than in older people.

A new, somewhat controversial study done recently in Japan, suggests that the language learned in childhood may affect the development of the separate functions of the two cerebral hemispheres. The results of this study appear to show that in people brought up speaking Japanese, the handling of certain sounds, emotions, and some other mental activities is different from that in English-speakers, Europeans, Chinese, and various other groups. Apparently, in the Japanese, more and different types of information are processed in the left hemisphere than in other groups.

The idea that it is the language of childhood that determines this difference in cerebral function is based on several observations. For one thing, Japanese raised in the United States and other Western countries and speaking the languages of those countries from birth, appear to process information in the same way as other Westerners, not like native-born Japanese. And Americans and other Westerners raised in Japan speaking Japanese, process information in the same way as native-born Japanese. Thus, it appears that the difference is not inherited. Other results show that native Japanese blind from birth, who can neither read nor write, process information in the same way as sighted Japanese. Thus, reading and writing the language apparently is not involved.

Researchers in the United States are currently experimenting with the use of radioisotopes and scanners to trace the flow of blood to different parts of the brain during various types of mental activity. In this way, they hope to map the areas in a normal brain that handle particular mental functions.

SENSE RECEPTORS

After completing your study of this section, you should be able to:

1. Draw and label the parts of the eye.
2. Explain how vision works.
3. Draw and label the parts of the ear.
4. Explain how the ear functions in hearing and balance.
5. Identify the sense receptors of the skin.
6. Describe the structures and functions of taste buds and olfactory cells.

In animals, sense receptors provide information about both the external and internal environments. The receptors of the human nervous system range from those in the skin, which are relatively simple structures, to the eye and ear, which are highly complex organs.

15-7 The Eye

Sight is the dominant sense in humans. It provides more than 80 percent of the information received about the external environment.

Structure of the eye. The walls of the human eye are composed of three basic layers (see Figure 15-10). The outer layer of the eye is the **sclera** (*sklehr*-uh), or the "white" of the eye. It is tough and fibrous and maintains the shape and protects the inner structures of the eye. In the front, it bulges and becomes the transparent **cornea** (*kor*-nee-uh). Light enters the eye through the cornea.

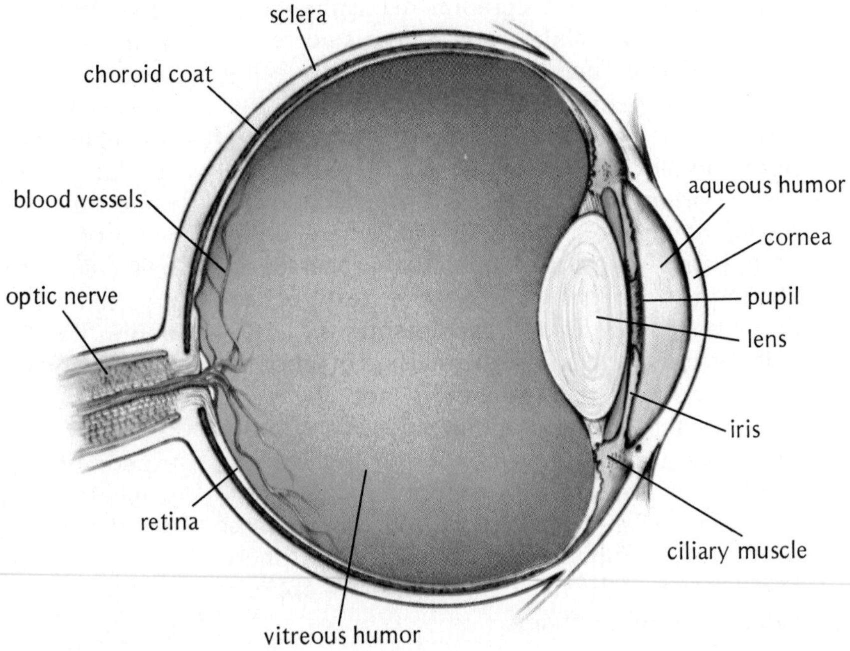

Figure 15-10. Structure of the Eye.

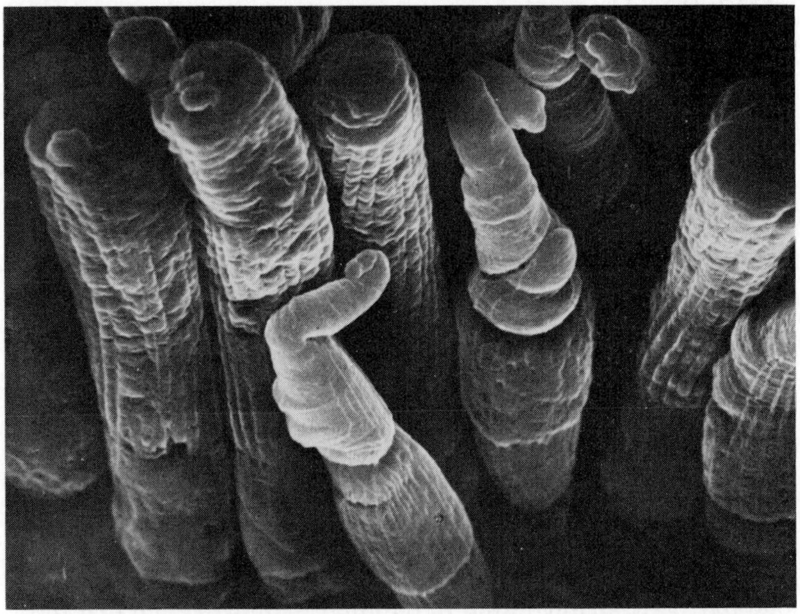

Figure 15-11. Rods and Cones. The innermost layer of the retina is made up of rods and cones. Rods are responsible for vision in dim light—black-and-white vision. Cones function in bright light and are responsible for color vision.

Just inside the sclera is the darkly pigmented middle layer, the **choroid** (*kor*-oyd) **coat.** This layer prevents the reflection of light within the eye and also contains many blood vessels. At the front of the eye the choroid layer forms the **iris** (*i*-ris), which is the colored part of the eye. In the center of the iris is an opening called the **pupil.** The iris functions like the diaphragm of a camera. It has muscles that regulate the size of the pupil. In dim light the pupil becomes larger, or dilates, allowing more light to enter the eye. In bright light the pupil becomes smaller, or constricts, reducing the amount of light that enters the eye. The size of the pupil is controlled automatically by the central nervous system.

Behind the iris is the **lens.** It focuses the light on the **retina** (*ret*-in-uh) in the rear of the eye, producing an image like that on the film in a camera. *Ciliary* (*sil*-ee-ehr-ee) *muscles* attached to the choroid layer hold the lens in place. These muscles also change the shape of the lens, which allows the eye to focus on objects whether close or far away.

The innermost layer of the eye, the retina, contains the light receptors. At the rear of the eye the retina is attached to the **optic** (*op*-tik) **nerve,** which carries impulses from the light-sensitive cells to the brain.

The eyeball is a hollow sphere that is divided into two cavities. The cavity between the cornea and the lens is filled with a transparent watery fluid called the **aqueous** (*ahk*-wee-us) **humor.** The large cavity behind the lens is filled with a colorless, jellylike liquid called the **vitreous** (*vih*-tree-us) **humor.**

Vision. Light entering the eye passes through the cornea, pupil, aqueous humor, lens, and vitreous humor, and forms an image on the retina. The retina is made up of several different layers of cells. The innermost layer contains the light-sensitive cells—the **rods** and the **cones** (see Figure 15-11). Rods are sensitive to weak light, but not to color. They are responsible for vision in dim light, which is black-and-white vision. Cones are sensitive to color, but require bright light to function. There are three different types of cones in the retina—one type is sensitive to red light, one to green light, and one to blue light. The retina contains about 125 million rods and 6.5 million cones.

Both black-and-white and color vision involve the light-sensitive pigment *retinal* (*ret*-in-al), which is synthesized from vitamin A. Retinal combines with proteins within the disks of the rods and cones. The proteins in the rods and in the three types of cones are all different, and each binds with retinal differently. It is the effect of each type of protein on the retinal that allows this pigment to respond to different colors and intensities of light.

When light strikes a rod or cone, it breaks the chemical bond between the retinal and the protein with which it was combined. This results in the initiation of impulses from that rod or cone. Nerve fibers from the rods and cones join to form the optic nerve, which carries the impulses to the brain. The brain interprets them as vision. The point where the optic nerve leaves the eye contains no rods or cones and is called the *blind spot*.

A severe deficiency of vitamin A leads to a condition called *night blindness,* which is an inability to see in dim light. In this condition the amount of retinal in both the rods and cones is decreased, and both become less sensitive to light. Thus, vision in dim light is greatly affected. However, there is enough pigment left for vision in bright light. *Color blindness,* which is an inability to see certain colors, is a hereditary condition in which the proteins of one or more of the three types of cones do not function properly.

15-8 The Ear

The human ear has two sensory functions. One of course, is hearing. The other is maintaining balance, or equilibrium, of the body.

Structure of the ear. The three parts of the ear are the **outer ear,** the **middle ear,** and the **inner ear** (see Figure 15-12). The outer ear is the visible part of the ear. It consists of the **pinna** (*pin*-uh), a flap of skin supported by cartilage, and a short **auditory** (*aw*-dih-tor-ee) **canal.** Stretched across the inner end of the auditory canal is the delicate **tympanic** (tim-*pan*-ik) **membrane,** or **eardrum.**

The middle ear is an air-filled chamber that begins at the eardrum. It contains three tiny bones—the *hammer, anvil,* and *stirrup*. These bones form a chain across the middle ear linking the eardrum to another membrane, the **oval window.** The hammer is attached to the eardrum, the anvil connects the hammer to the stirrup, and the stirrup is connected to the oval window. Extending between the middle ear and the throat is

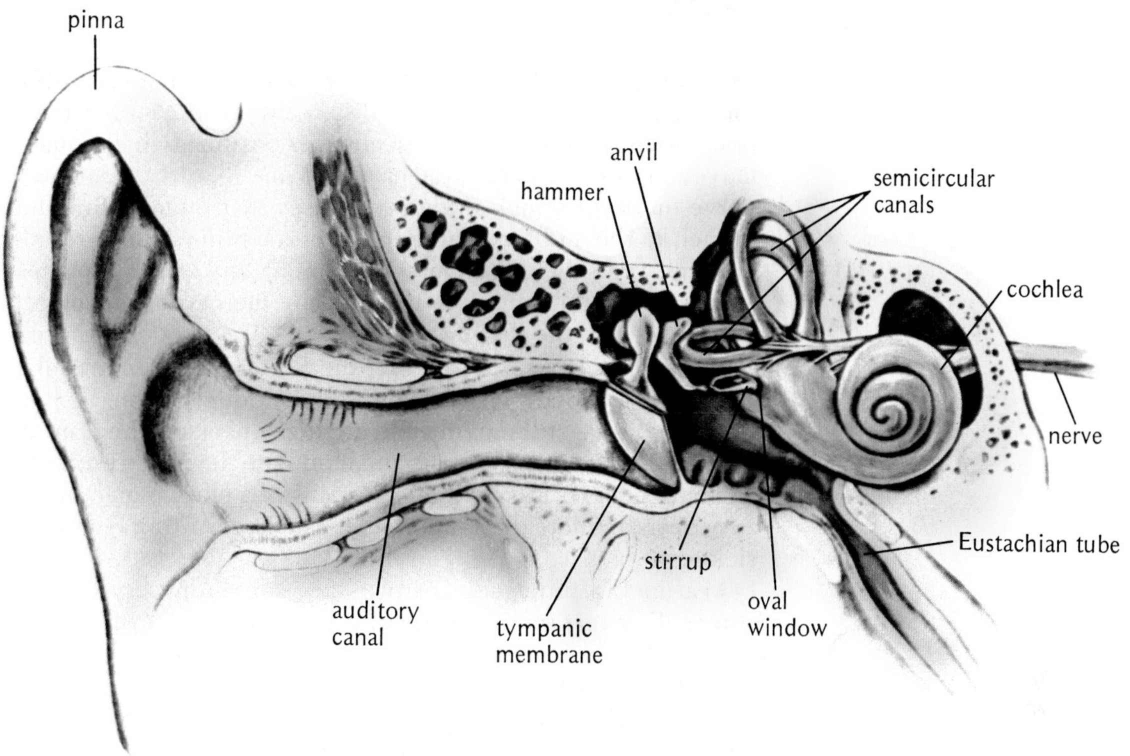

Figure 15-12. Structure of the Ear.

the **Eustachian** (yoo-*stay*-shun) **tube.** Its function is to equalize the pressure in the middle ear with that of the atmosphere outside.

The inner ear consists of the **cochlea** (*kahk*-lee-uh) and the **semicircular canals.** The cochlea is the organ of hearing. It consists of coiled, liquid-filled tubes that are separated from one another by membranes. Lining one of the membranes are specialized hair cells that are sensitive to vibration.

The semicircular canals enable the body to maintain balance. They consist of three interconnected loop-shaped tubes at right angles to one another. Like the cochlea, these canals contain fluid and hairlike projections that detect changes in body position.

Hearing. Sound waves are vibrations in air or some other medium, such as water. Hearing takes place when these vibrations are transmitted to the inner ear, where they initiate impulses that are carried to the brain by the auditory nerve.

Sound waves collected by the outer ear pass down the auditory canal to the eardrum. They cause the eardrum to vibrate, and the vibrations are transmitted across the middle ear by the hammer, anvil, and stirrup. Vibrations of the stirrup cause vibrations in the oval window, which in turn cause the fluid within the cochlea to vibrate. The movement of the fluid causes vibrations in specialized hair cells lining one of the membranes within the cochlea. This initiates impulses in nerve endings around the hair cells. These impulses are carried to the cerebral cortex, where their meaning is interpreted.

Balance. Balance, or equilibrium, is a function both of the inner ear and the cerebellum. In the inner ear, the fluid-filled semicircular canals lie at right angles to one another in the three different planes of the body. As the head changes position, the fluid in the canals also changes position, which causes movement of hairlike projections. This in turn stimulates nerve endings, which initiate impulses that travel through a branch of the auditory nerve to the cerebellum. The cerebellum interprets the direction of movement, and sends impulses to the cerebrum. Impulses initiated by the cerebrum correct the position of the body.

If you spin around for a time, the fluid in the semicircular canals also moves. When you stop suddenly, you feel as though you are still moving and are dizzy because the fluid in the canals continues to move and stimulate the nerve endings. In some people, the rhythmic motions of a ship, plane, or car may overstimulate the semicircular canals, resulting in motion sickness.

Also in the inner ear are two sacs containing crystals, or stones, that rest on sensory hairs. The pressure of the stones on the sensory hairs provides information on the body's position in relation to gravity.

15-9 Receptors of the Skin

Located in the skin are sense receptors for touch, pressure, heat, cold, and pain (see Figure 15-13). Each type of receptor differs in structure from the others and is sensitive to only one kind of stimulus. When a receptor is stimulated, it produces impulses that travel over sensory nerve pathways to the brain, where they are interpreted.

Although all types of receptors are present all over the body, the different types are not uniformly distributed. For example, receptors sensitive to touch are farthest apart on the back, much closer together on the fingertips, and closest together on the tip of the tongue. The ability to judge the size of an object you feel is partly determined by the number of touch receptors stimulated.

Pressure receptors lie deep in the skin. They are stimulated only when firm pressure is applied to the skin. Heat receptors

Figure 15-13. Sense Receptors of the Skin.

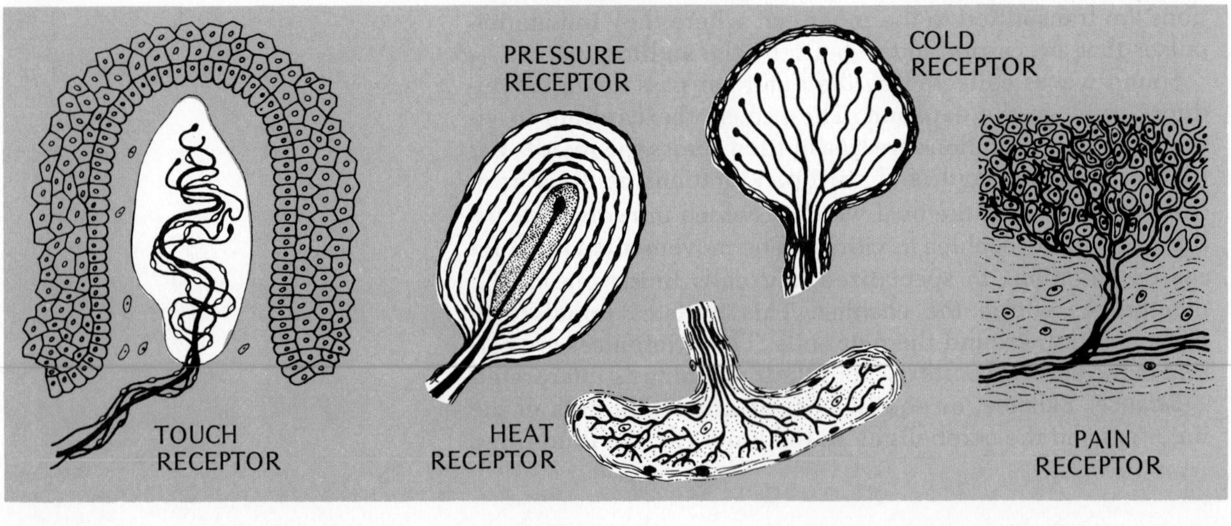

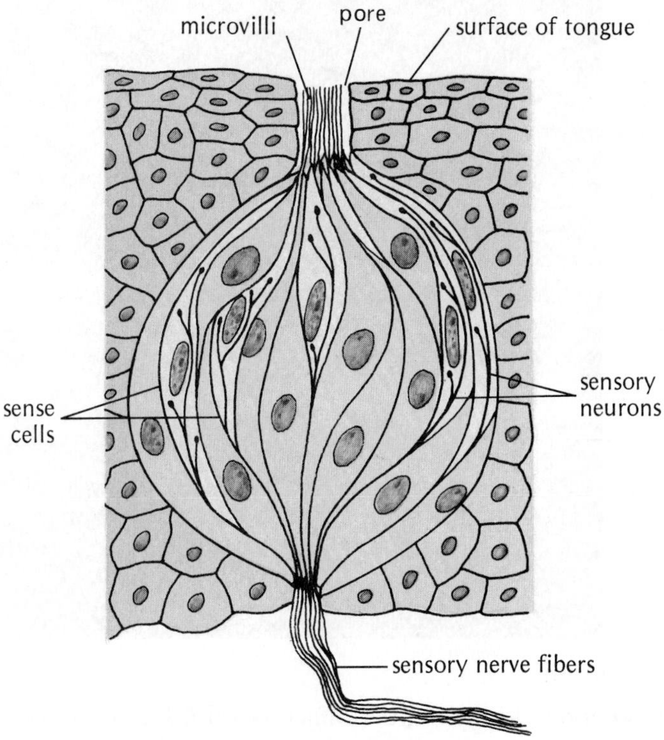

Figure 15-14. Structure of a Taste Bud.

and cold receptors respond to the direction of heat flow. The sensation of warmth is the result of heat flowing into the skin and stimulating the heat receptors. The sensation of coolness is the result of heat flowing out of the skin and stimulating the cold receptors. Pain receptors warn against injury. They respond to all types of massive stimulation. The sensation of pain is the same regardless of the stimulus.

15-10 Taste

The surface of the tongue is covered with small projections called *papillae* (puh-*pil*-ee). Within the papillae are the taste receptors, or **taste buds.** Each taste bud consists of a number of sense cells and opens to the surface of the tongue through a pore (see Figure 15-14). Microvilli from the sense cells extend through the pore. Nerve fibers branch through the cells of the taste bud, and each cell is in contact with one or more fibers.

Only substances that are in solution can stimulate the taste buds. Many substances dissolve in the saliva in the mouth. Taste buds are sensitive to only four basic tastes—sweet, sour, salt, and bitter. Each taste bud is particularly sensitive to one of these tastes, responding only slightly to the others. The taste buds for each taste tend to be localized on specific areas of the tongue: taste buds for sourness are found along the sides of the tongue, taste buds for bitterness at the back of the tongue, and taste buds for sweetness and saltiness on the tip of the tongue.

When taste buds are stimulated, impulses are initiated by the sensory cells of the structure and carried by sensory pathways to the brain, where they are interpreted. Actually, most of the flavor of food comes from its smell. This is why most food seems tasteless to a person with a stuffy nose.

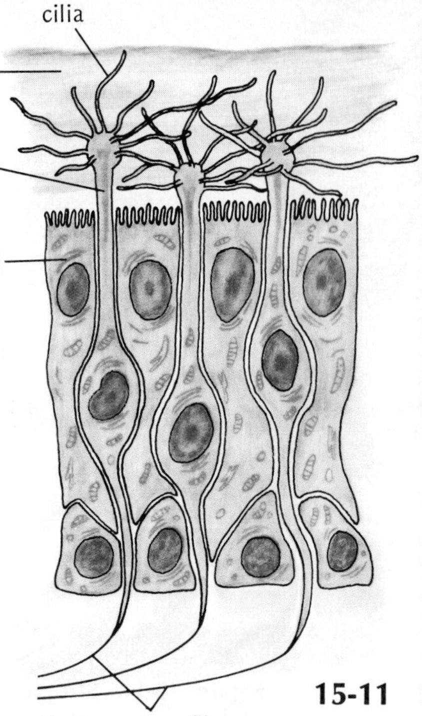

Figure 15-15. Structure of Olfactory Receptors.

Some scientists think that the olfactory receptors detect odors by responding to the shape of the molecule rather than to a chemical reaction.

15-11 Smell

The receptors for smell, the **olfactory** (ol-*fak*-tuh-ree) **cells,** are located in the mucous membrane lining the upper nasal cavity. Odor is detected when molecules of a gaseous substance enter the nose, dissolve in the mucus, and stimulate the olfactory receptors. The olfactory cells are specialized nerve cells (see Figure 15-15). When they are stimulated, impulses are carried by the olfactory nerves to the brain, where they are interpreted.

Unlike taste buds, which respond to only four basic tastes, olfactory cells appear to respond to more than fifty different basic odors. Like the taste buds, each olfactory cell appears to be more sensitive to one basic odor than to all the others. Continuous exposure to a specific odor quickly leads to an inability to detect that odor, but does not interfere with the detection of other odors. This is called *adaptation*, and is thought to be partly a response of the central nervous system.

Both taste and smell result from the chemical stimulation of receptors. However, olfactory receptors are much more sensitive than the cells of the taste buds. They are stimulated by much lower concentrations of chemicals and they are sensitive to a much greater variety of chemicals.

BEHAVIOR AND LEARNING

After completing your study of this section, you should be able to:

1. Define the term *behavior,* and explain the difference between innate behavior and acquired behavior.
2. Define the term *reflex,* and name several body functions that are controlled by reflexes.
3. Describe the operation of a reflex arc.

4. Define and give examples of the following: instincts, conditioned responses, habits, and voluntary behavior.
5. Describe the three types of memory.

15-12 Innate and Acquired Behavior

Behavior is the response of an organism to stimuli. In studying behavior scientists distinguish between inborn, or innate, behavior and acquired, or learned, behavior. **Innate behavior** is determined by heredity. Simple reflexes and instincts are examples of innate behaviors. **Acquired behavior,** on the other hand, is learned from experience and involves some choice of responses to a given stimulus. Habits are examples of acquired behaviors. Humans and other animals with highly developed nervous systems tend to exhibit very complex acquired behaviors. In addition, some patterns of behavior are partly inherited and partly learned.

15-13 Reflexes

A **reflex** is an involuntary, automatic response to a given stimulus. It involves a relatively simple pathway between a receptor, the spinal cord and/or brain, and an effector. Many normal body functions are controlled by reflexes. These include blinking, sneezing, coughing, breathing movements, heartbeat, and peristalsis. The knee-jerk reflex and the reflex constriction and dilation of the pupil of the eye in response to light are used by doctors to check the condition of the nervous system.

Reflex arcs. The pathway over which the nerve impulses travel in a reflex is called a **reflex arc.** The simplest reflex arcs involve only two neurons—one sensory and one motor. The pathway of the knee-jerk reflex is of this type. Most reflexes, however, involve three or more neurons. Withdrawal reflexes, for example, involve a three-neuron reflex arc (see Figure 15-16).

When your hand touches a hot stove, it is pulled back before you feel the sensation of heat or pain. This removal of your hand is accomplished by a withdrawal reflex. The parts of this reflex arc are as follows:

1. A receptor in the skin is stimulated by the heat.

2. The receptor initiates impulses in a sensory neuron, which carries impulses to the spinal cord.

3. Within the spinal cord, the sensory neuron synapses with an associative neuron, which synapses with a motor neuron. Impulses are also carried to the brain, but this is not part of the reflex arc.

4. The motor neuron transmits impulses to the effector. In this example impulses are carried to the various muscles of the arm. Some contract and others relax, moving the hand and arm away from the heat.

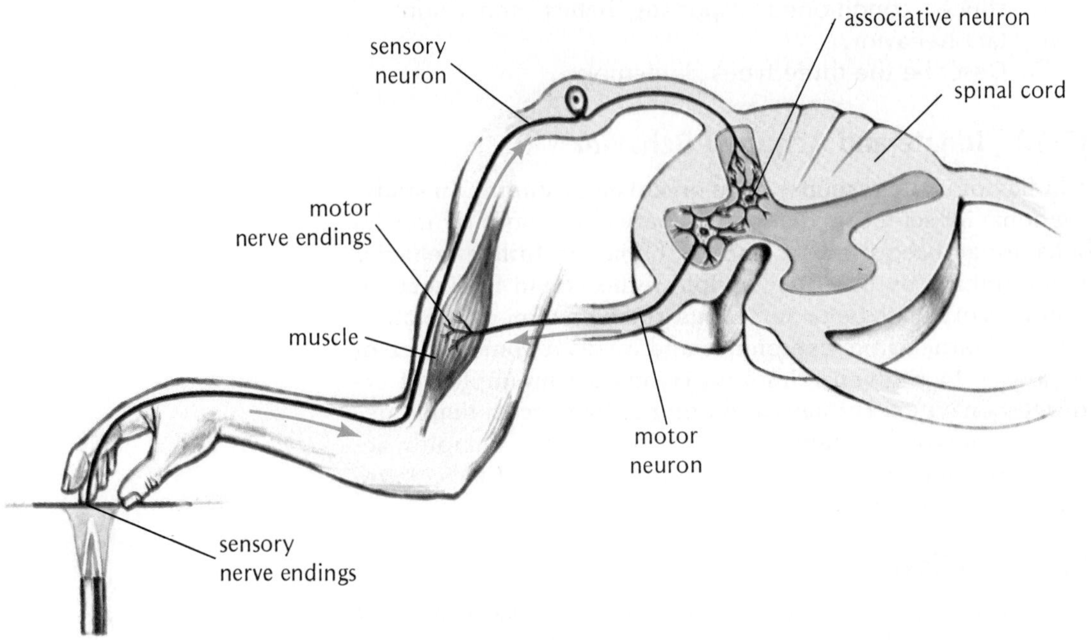

Figure 15-16. A Reflex Arc. The withdrawal reflex involves a sensory neuron, an associative neuron,and a motor neuron.

The withdrawal reflex is accomplished without the involvement of the brain. However, shortly after the hand is withdrawn from the hot object, there may be sensations of heat and pain. These result from impulses passing up the spinal cord to the brain.

15-14 Instincts

Instincts are complex inborn behavior patterns. An instinct consists of a series, or chain, of reflexes. Each reflex in the chain triggers the next reflex until the behavior pattern, or instinct, is completed. It is difficult to identify instinctive behavior in humans, but in many other animals, including insects, fish, and birds, it can be clearly observed. For example, a bird can build a nest characteristic of its species without ever seeing another bird construct one, and a spider raised in isolation spins a web with a pattern characteristic of its species. In many animals reproductive behavior is instinctive, following a highly complex pattern.

15-15 Conditioned Responses

A **conditioned response** is the simplest type of learned behavior. In one type of conditioned response a new stimulus is substituted for the original stimulus in a reflex action. The Russian physiologist Ivan Pavlov investigated this type of response in a famous series of experiments with dogs. When a dog smells food, the flow of saliva in its mouth normally increases. This is a reflex response to the stimulus of the odor of food. In his experiments, Pavlov rang a bell every time he presented food to a dog. After repeating this procedure many times, Pavlov then rang the bell without offering any food. The flow of saliva in the dog's mouth increased just as though food had been presented. The sound of the bell acted as a substitute for the original stimulus, the odor of food, and caused the same reflex response.

Other types of conditioned responses develop as the result of chance and involve a change in behavior. That is, an animal performs a particular act by accident. If it is rewarded each time it performs this act, it will learn to do it for the reward. If it is punished each time, it will learn not to do it to avoid the punishment. Much human behavior is acquired by this type of conditioning. The development of habits, likes, dislikes, prejudices, and fears involves conditioning. Animals with well-developed nervous systems, such as dogs, horses, and seals, can be trained by conditioning.

15-16 Habits

Humans can perform many routine activities with little or no conscious thought. Such an act, which is first learned and then by frequent repetition becomes automatic, is called a **habit.** Habits are a type of conditioned behavior. Dressing, writing, talking, tying shoelaces, typing, and dancing are all habits. Each of these activities begins as a slow, voluntary, and often difficult series of actions. Through repetition it eventually becomes a habit, requiring little or no conscious effort. The development of an activity into a habit makes it automatic, easier and faster to perform, and more accurate.

15-17 Voluntary Behavior

Voluntary behavior is purposeful and under a person's conscious control. It includes all the physical and mental activities that an individual wants to do, such as writing a story, memorizing a song, or cooking. All voluntary behavior is controlled by the cerebrum and involves a combination of memory of past experiences, associations, reasoning, and judgments. This most complex type of acquired behavior is more developed in humans than in other animals.

15-18 Memory

Most learning depends on the ability to store and recall memories of past experiences. Memory is thought to be a function of the cerebral cortex. Although there are several theories on how memory is stored, there is relatively little that is actually known about the process. However, scientists now recognize the existence of three kinds of memory—**momentary, short-term,** and **long-term memory.**

Momentary memory is memory that is retained for a few minutes at most. Looking up a phone number and remembering it only long enough to dial it is memory of this type.

sidelights

Some people have extraordinarily good memories for details. They can describe objects, pictures, or scenes that they have viewed in the past with great detail. This capacity, which is commonly called a "photographic memory," is known in scientific terms as *eidetic imagery*. An eidetic image is not recalled in the mind as a regular memory. Instead, people with this capacity report that the image is projected in front of them, and that they are "seeing" what they describe.

The gift of eidetic imagery is mostly limited to young children. Some researchers think that as many as half of all children under the age of ten have this ability to some extent. However, it is exceedingly rare in adults.

Short-term memory can be recalled for up to several hours. Memory lasting weeks or years is *long-term memory*. By some process as yet unknown, short-term memory is converted into long-term memory. A person can lose his momentary and short-term memories and still retain his long-term memory. This is sometimes found in older people, who may be unable to remember recent events but can recall in detail events that took place decades earlier.

At this time no one knows how memories are stored, transferred, or recalled in the human brain. There is some evidence that short-term memory is associated with patterns of impulses circulating repeatedly through particular pathways of neurons. Long-term memory may be the result of permanent changes in particular synapses, or changes within certain neurons. Memory is a field of research that is wide open for new hypotheses, experiments, and theories.

summary

The human nervous system consists of the brain and spinal cord of the central nervous system and the nerve network of the peripheral nervous system.

The major parts of the brain are the cerebrum, cerebellum, and medulla. The largest part of the brain is the cerebrum, which consists of an outer layer of gray matter, the cortex, and an inner layer of white matter. The cortex receives and interprets information from the sense receptors of the body and initiates impulses for all voluntary movement. It is also responsible for memory, learning, and thought. The white matter consists of bundles of fibers connecting the cortex with various other parts of the nervous system.

The cerebellum coordinates and controls voluntary movements. It is also responsible, along with the inner ear, for maintenance of balance. The medulla is a relay center, connecting the spinal cord with the higher parts of the brain. Nerve centers in the medulla control a number of involuntary activities, including heartbeat, breathing, blood pressure, coughing, and sneezing.

The spinal cord connects the nerve network of the peripheral nervous system with the brain. It also controls various reflexes that do not involve the brain.

The peripheral nervous system includes all neurons and nerve fibers outside the brain and spinal cord. It includes spinal nerves, which are connected to the spinal cord, and cranial nerves, which are connected to the brain. The peripheral nervous system is divided into the somatic nervous system and the autonomic nervous system.

The somatic system, which includes both sensory and motor nerves, is responsible for all body movements over which there is some conscious control. The autonomic nervous system controls many important functions over which there is no conscious control, including rate of heartbeat and breathing. The autonomic system consists entirely of motor neurons. It is divided into two separate systems whose effects are antagonistic—the sympathetic and parasympathetic nervous systems.

The sense receptors of the human nervous system include the eyes, ears, olfactory cells of the nose, taste buds of the tongue, and the receptors for touch, pressure, pain, heat, and cold in the skin.

Behavior is the response of an organism to stimuli. Innate behavior is determined by heredity, while acquired behavior is learned by experience. Reflexes and instincts are innate behaviors. Conditioned responses and habits are acquired behaviors. Voluntary behavior, which is under conscious control, is a function of the cerebral cortex.

Memory is the ability to store and recall past experiences. It is the basis of most learning.

vocabulary

acquired behavior
aqueous humor
auditory canal
autonomic nervous system
cerebellum
cerebral cortex
cerebral hemisphere
cerebrospinal fluid
cerebrum
choroid coat
cochlea
conditioned response
cone
convolution
cornea
cranial nerve
eardrum
Eustachian tube
gray matter
habit
innate behavior
inner ear
instinct
iris
lens
medulla
meninges
middle ear
olfactory cell
outer ear
oval window
parasympathetic nervous system
pinna
plexus
pupil
reflex
reflex arc
retina
rod
sclera
semicircular canal
skull
somatic nervous system
spinal canal
spinal column
spinal nerve
sympathetic nervous system
taste bud
tympanic membrane
vitreous humor
white matter

test your learning

Section		
15-1	**1.**	What are the functions of the skull, the vertebrae, and the meninges?
	2.	Where is the cerebrospinal fluid located, and what is its function?
15-2	**3.**	What is the major source of energy for brain tissue?
	4.	Describe the structure of the cerebrum.
	5.	Describe the three types of functions performed by the cerebral cortex.
	6.	Describe the structure and function of the white matter of the cerebrum.
	7.	Why does the left cerebral hemisphere control the right side of the body?
	8.	Describe the location and structure of the cerebellum.
	9.	What are the functions of the cerebellum?
	10.	Describe the location and functions of the medulla.
15-3	**11.**	Describe the structure of the spinal cord.
	12.	What are the two major functions of the spinal cord?
15-4	**13.**	Which nerves make up the peripheral nervous system?
	14.	How many cranial nerves are there?
	15.	What are the two divisions of the peripheral nervous system?
15-5	**16.**	What nerves are included in the somatic nervous system, and what do they control?
15-6	**17.**	What type of nerve fibers make up the autonomic nervous system?
	18.	What body functions does the autonomic nervous system control?
	19.	What is a plexus?
	20.	Name the two divisions of the autonomic nervous system, and explain how they function together in regulating body functions.
15-7	**21.**	Describe the structure of the eye.
	22.	Describe the path of light through the eye.
	23.	What are the functions of the rods and cones?
	24.	Explain the functioning of retinal in vision.
15-8	**25.**	Describe the path of sound waves through the outer, middle, and inner ears.
	26.	Briefly explain how hearing occurs.
	27.	How is the ear involved in the maintenance of equilibrium?
15-9	**28.**	Identify the sense receptors in the skin.
15-10	**29.**	Describe the structure and functioning of a taste bud.
15-11	**30.**	How is odor detected?
15-12	**31.**	Define behavior, and distinguish between innate and acquired behavior.
15-13	**32.**	What is a reflex? Give several examples of reflexes.
	33.	Explain the operation of a reflex arc generated by touching a hot stove.
15-14	**34.**	What is an instinct?
15-15	**35.**	What is a conditioned response?
15-16	**36.**	Define the term *habit*, and give several examples of habits.
15-17	**37.**	What part of the brain controls voluntary behavior?
15-18	**38.**	Describe the three types of memory.

test your understanding

1. List all the parts of the human nervous system that can play a role in maintaining balance and position.
2. Explain the differences between a reflex response, a conditioned response, an instinct, and a habit.
3. What types of situations can stimulate the sympathetic division of the autonomic nervous system? What changes in body functions occur when the sympathetic system is stimulated?
4. What parts of your nervous system are involved when you are reading and writing out an answer to this question?

independent research

1. Write a report on one of the following topics:
   A. use of biofeedback in medicine
   B. extrasensory perception (ESP)
   C. optical illusions
   D. headaches
2. Prepare a report on one of the following career opportunities:
   A. psychiatric nurse
   B. psychologist
   C. optometrist
   D. audiologist

   If possible, interview a person who works in the field. If you have a tape recorder, record the interview. Be sure to prepare your questions in advance.

chapter 16

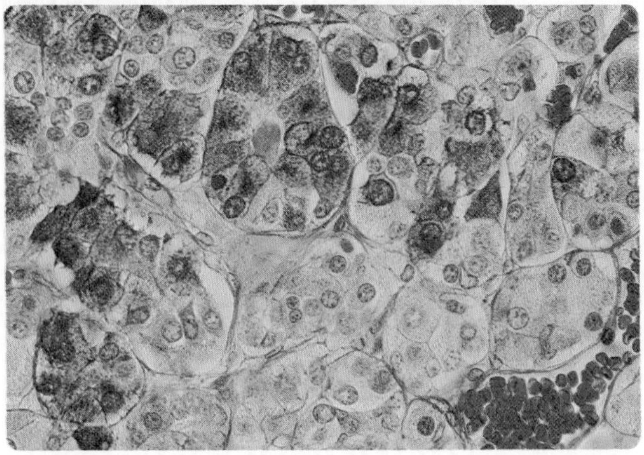

Regulation—Chemical Control

16-1 Two Systems of Control

The systems of the body are never at rest. They are continually making adjustments to changing conditions both outside and inside the body in order to maintain homeostasis. We have already seen how the nervous system takes part in this process. The body also has another system, called the **endocrine system,** that helps to regulate and coordinate its functions.

The nervous system operates by means of electrical impulses in nerve fibers and neurotransmitters that cross the tiny gaps that separate adjacent neurons. It is a system that acts quickly and directs its messages to specific parts of the body. The endocrine system, on the other hand, operates by means of chemicals released into the bloodstream, which then carries them to all tissues of the body. It takes time for these substances to reach their target organs and produce an effect. The endocrine system is therefore slower in its action than the nervous system. Its effects also tend to last longer. Generally speaking, the body uses the nervous system for making rapid responses of short duration. It uses the endocrine system for producing effects that last for hours, days, or even years.

GLANDS AND HORMONES

After completing your study of this section, you should be able to:

1. Define the following terms: *endocrine gland, exocrine gland, hormone, target tissue.*
2. List the bodily processes regulated by hormones.
3. Explain the regulation of hormone secretion by negative feedback.
4. Describe the mechanism of hormone action according to the one-messenger and two-messenger models.

16-2 Glands

Glands are organs made up of epithelial cells specialized for secretion of substances needed by the organism. Some glands, such as the digestive glands, discharge their secretions into ducts, which carry the secretions to where they are used. Such glands are called **exocrine** (*ek*-suh-krin) **glands.** Other glands release their secretions directly into the bloodstream. These glands are called **endocrine glands,** and they make up the endocrine system. (Figure 16-1 shows the glands of the human endocrine system.) Endocrine glands are also called *ductless glands,* or glands of internal secretion. The secretions of the endocrine glands are called **hormones.**

16-3 Hormones

Hormones are released into the bloodstream by cells in one part of the body, but they exert their effect somewhere else in the body. Because of this, hormones are sometimes called "chemical messengers."

Hormones are usually present in the bloodstream in very low concentrations. Each type of hormone is recognized only by specific tissues. The tissues regulated by a given hormone are called the **target tissues** of that hormone. The hormone may stimulate the target tissue and increase its activities, or it may inhibit the target tissue and decrease its activities.

Hormones affect the functioning of target tissues by changing the rates of certain biochemical reactions in those tissues. A hormone may cause a reaction to start, to speed up, to slow down, or to stop. However, hormones do not produce their effects by acting directly on the reacting substances, as enzymes do. They appear to act always through some intermediate cellular process. The processes in the body that are chiefly regulated by hormones include: (1) overall metabolism; (2) maintenance of homeostasis; (3) growth; and (4) reproduction.

In terms of their chemical makeup, most hormones fall into two classes. *Protein-type hormones* consist of chains of amino acids or related compounds. Insulin, oxytocin, and ACTH are

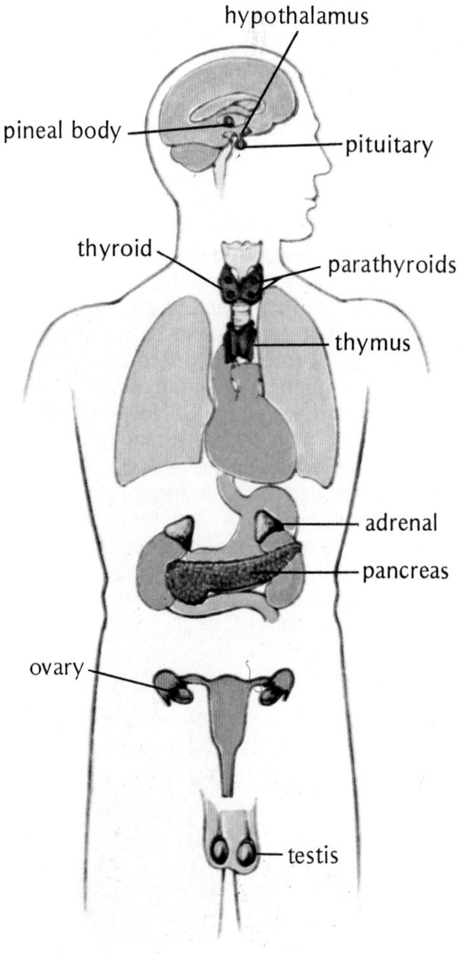

Figure 16-1. Glands of the Endocrine System.

examples of this type of hormone. *Steroid* (stihr-oyd) *hormones* are lipidlike, carbon-ring compounds that are chemically similar to cholesterol and bile. Cortisone, testosterone, and estrogen are examples of steroid hormones.

16-4 Regulation of Hormone Secretion

As a general rule, endocrine glands do not secrete their hormones at a constant rate. The rate varies with the needs of the body. The signals or messages that cause a gland to speed up, slow down, or stop its production of a hormone may be nerve impulses. However, in most cases they are chemical stimuli, including other hormones.

The mechanism that alters the activity of a gland is usually an example of **negative feedback.** Negative feedback has the effect of returning a condition toward its normal value. If the condition decreases below its normal level, negative feedback acts to increase it. If the condition rises above normal, negative feedback acts to decrease it.

A common example of a negative feedback mechanism is the thermostat that keeps an oven at a constant temperature. When the temperature rises above the set value, the thermostat turns the oven off, allowing it to cool down. When the temperature drops below the set value, the thermostat turns the oven on again. A driver who maintains a speed of 55 miles per hour by adjusting pressure on the gas pedal is also using negative feedback.

To understand negative feedback in terms of metabolic processes, consider a situation in which factor A affects factor B, and factor B affects factor C (see Figure 16-2). Any change in A will produce a change in C. If a change in C then produces a change in A, we say that there is *feedback* from C to A. If the effect of the feedback on A is to oppose its original change, the feedback is *negative*, and it prevents any great variation in A. If the feedback were positive, the change in A caused by C would be in the same direction as the original change in A.

In negative feedback in the endocrine system, the secretion of a hormone is controlled by the concentration of another substance in the blood, often another hormone. For example,

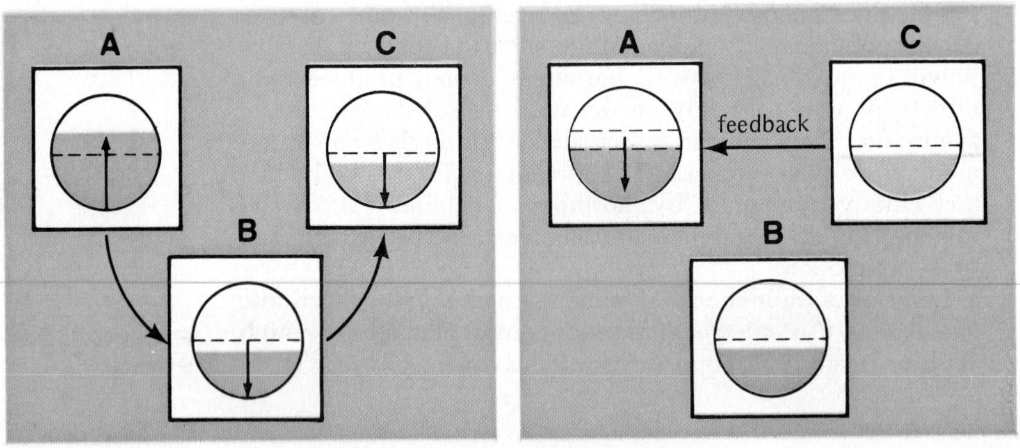

Figure 16-2. Negative Feedback. A, B, and C represent three related metabolic processes. In this example an increase in A causes a decrease in B, and a decrease in B causes a decrease in C. Thus, through this chain, the increase in A causes a decrease in C. However, the change in C also causes a change in A. This is called a feedback loop. If the change caused by C is opposite to the original change in A, the feedback is negative. Negative feedback prevents A from changing very much in either direction. It is an important factor in maintaining homeostasis.

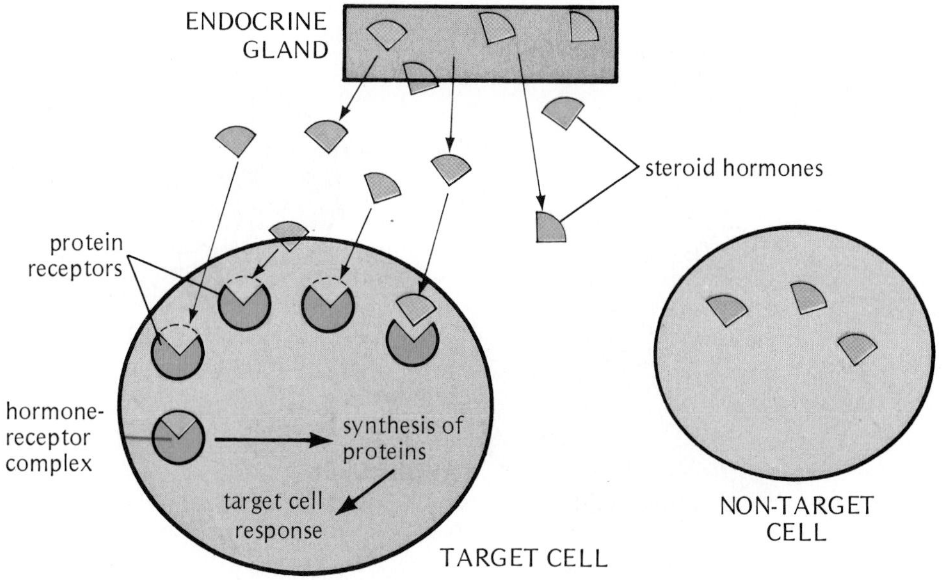

Figure 16-3. One-Messenger Model of Hormone Action. Steroid hormones produced by endocrine glands pass through the cell membranes of target cells and combine with special receptors. The hormone-receptor complexes trigger the response of the target cell. Non-target cells do not have the protein receptors and are not affected by the hormones.

the secretion of the hormone thyroxine by the thyroid gland is regulated by thyroid-stimulating hormone, or TSH, which is secreted by the pituitary gland. When the thyroxine level is low, the pituitary is stimulated to secrete TSH, which in turn stimulates the thyroid to produce thyroxine. When the thyroxine level reaches a certain point, the secretion of TSH by the pituitary is inhibited. The pituitary stops secreting TSH, and the thyroid stops secreting thyroxine. Some endocrine organs are controlled by the blood levels of simple substances, such as calcium and glucose.

16-5 Mechanisms of Hormone Action

Each hormone controls the activity of a particular target tissue. Since hormones are carried in the bloodstream and therefore reach all body tissues, each target tissue must have a way of recognizing the particular hormone intended for it. There must also be a mechanism by which the hormone produces its effect within the target cells.

Recent research indicates that there are two basic mechanisms of hormone action. One of these, called the *one-messenger model*, applies mainly to steroid hormones. The other, called the *two-messenger model*, applies to protein hormones.

One-messenger model. Steroid hormones are small molecules that are able to pass through cell membranes. These hormones therefore enter most of the cells of the body. However, it is only in the target cells that the hormones produce any effect. In these cells there are receptor proteins that recognize a particular steroid hormone and combine with it, forming an active factor (see Figure 16-3). The active factor alters the rate of some chemical reaction in the cell, thereby producing the hormonal effect. There is evidence that the ac-

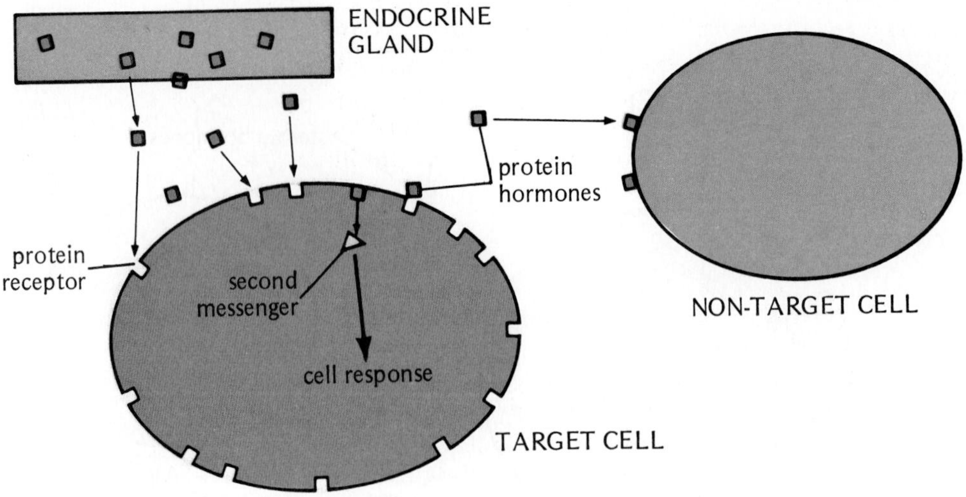

Figure 16-4. Two-Messenger Model of Hormone Action. Protein hormones produced by endocrine glands cannot pass through cell membranes. Instead, they react with receptors on target cell membranes, which then produce a second messenger. The second messenger enters the cell and produces the hormonal effect.

The most common second messenger is cyclic AMP (adenosine monophosphate). Dr. Earl W. Sutherland won the Nobel Prize in 1971 for his discovery of the role of cyclic AMP in hormone action. Other substances that can act as "second messengers" are GMP and Ca^{++}.

tive factors produce their effect by entering the cell nucleus and acting on the genetic material (DNA) that controls the cell's activities.

Two-messenger model. Protein hormones are generally not able to pass through cell membranes. They are, however, recognized by specific receptors on the outer surface of target cell membranes (see Figure 16-4). When the hormone combines with the receptor on the membrane surface, the combination causes enzymes in the membrane to produce a compound that acts as the second messenger. The second messenger diffuses throughout the cell interior and produces the hormonal effect. The hormone does not enter the cell in this model. Instead, it sends a second messenger to do its work.

Although the same second messenger may be produced in different types of target cells, it produces different effects in different cells. For example, it causes thyroid cells to produce thyroxine, adrenal cortex cells to produce cortisol, and kidney tubule cells to reabsorb more water.

HUMAN ENDOCRINE SYSTEM

After completing your study of this section, you should be able to name the major endocrine glands of the human body, list the hormones secreted by each, and briefly describe the action of the hormone in the body.

16-6 Introduction to the Human Endocrine System

The human endocrine system consists of a number of endocrine glands that regulate a wide range of activities. In addition, there are a few tissues that are not organized as separate glands, but which do secrete hormones. For example, certain cells in the lining of the stomach and small intestine function in this way. The improper functioning of an endocrine gland may result in a disease or disorder of the body. An excess, or **hypersecretion** (hy-per-suh-*kree*-shun), of a hormone may cause one type of disorder, while a deficiency, or **hyposecretion** (hy-poh-suh-*kree*-shun), of a hormone may cause another disorder. In the following sections we will describe the structure and function of the individual glands of the human endocrine system.

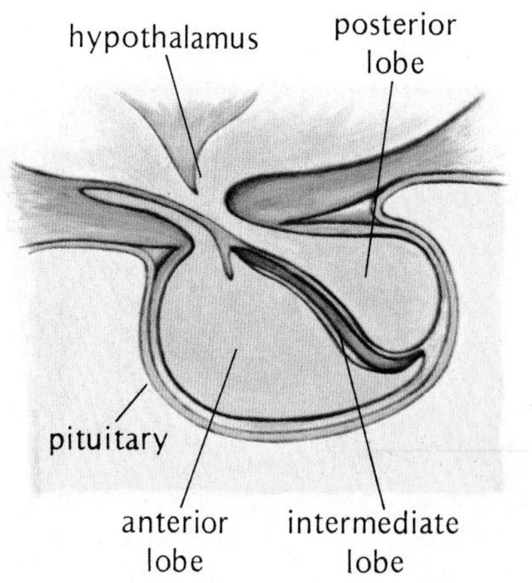

Figure 16-5. Structure of the Pituitary Gland. The pituitary gland is connected by a stalk to the hypothalamus, which regulates the release of pituitary hormones.

16-7 Pituitary Gland

The **pituitary** (pih-*too*-uh-tehr-ee) is a small gland about 1 centimeter in diameter. It consists of an anterior, or front, lobe and a posterior, or back, lobe (see Figure 16-5). Between these two lobes there is a very small intermediate zone that is not functional in humans, but which is larger and functional in other animals. The pituitary is often called the "master gland" of the body because it controls the activity of a number of other endocrine glands.

The pituitary is connected by means of a stalk to a part of the brain called the *hypothalamus* (hy-poh-*thal*-uh-mus). The hypothalamus controls the release of hormones by the pituitary and serves as a major link between the nervous system and the endocrine system. The hypothalamus receives information from many different parts of the nervous system. This information is a major factor in determining when the hypothalamus stimulates the pituitary to release its hormones. Another factor is the concentration of various hormones in the blood.

Anterior pituitary. The anterior lobe of the pituitary secretes several different hormones, many of them very important in controlling metabolic functions. The release of hormones from the anterior pituitary is controlled by hormones produced by the hypothalamus. The hormones from the hypothalamus are called **releasing hormones,** or **releasing factors.** The release of each type of hormone from the anterior pituitary is controlled by a specific releasing factor. The releasing factors are produced by the endings of specific neurons within the hypothalamus. When they are released by the neurons, the factors are absorbed directly into capillaries that carry them to the anterior pituitary.

It is thought that each different hormone of the anterior pituitary is produced by a different type of cell. The major hormones of the anterior pituitary and their functions are as follows:

1. **Thyroid-stimulating hormone,** or TSH, stimulates the production and release of thyroid hormone by the thyroid gland.

2. **Adrenocorticotropic** (uh-*dree*-noh-kort-ih-koh-troh-pik) **hormone,** or ACTH, stimulates the production and release of hormones from the cortex layer of the adrenal glands. ACTH is used in the treatment of arthritis, asthma, and allergies.

GLANDULAR DISORDERS			
Gland	Hormone	Effect of oversecretion (hypersecretion)	Effect of undersecretion (hyposecretion)
Anterior pituitary	growth hormone	*in childhood:* Oversecretion causes giantism. Individual grows very tall, but is normally proportioned. Mental development is not affected. *in adulthood:* Oversecretion causes acromegaly. Individual has abnormally large hands and feet, and enlarged facial structures. Does not affect mental processes.	*in childhood:* Undersecretion results in dwarfism. Individual is very small, but is normally proportioned. Adult sexual development often does not occur.
Adrenal cortex	aldosterone, cortisol	Oversecretion results in Cushing's disease. Individual has excess fat deposits in the upper body, a puffy face, excess growth of facial hair, and a high blood glucose level. Decreased immunity to disease also occurs.	Undersecretion results in Addison's disease. Normal blood glucose level cannot be maintained. Individual becomes sluggish, weak, loses weight, and develops increased skin pigmentation. Tolerance to stress is reduced. Without medication, the disease causes death.
Thyroid	thyroxine	Oversecretion results in hyperthyroidism. Individual is nervous, irritable, loses weight, and cannot sleep. Often eyes protrude, a condition called exophthalmos. Hyperthyroidism is often accompanied by a goiter, or enlarged thyroid.	*in infancy:* Undersecretion results in cretinism. Individual is a dwarf whose body parts are out of proportion. Mental retardation occurs. *in adulthood:* Undersecretion results in myxedema. Individual gains weight and skin becomes puffy. A slowdown of mental activity also occurs.
Pancreas (β cells, islets of Langerhans)	insulin	Oversecretion results in diabetic shock. The blood glucose level falls, and convulsions, unconsciousness, and death may occur if untreated.	Undersecretion results in diabetes. Individual has an abnormally high blood glucose level, becomes dehydrated, loses weight, and cannot resist infections. If untreated, can cause death.
Pancreas (α cells, islets of Langerhans)	glucagon	Oversecretion results in an abnormally high blood glucose level. Similar to diabetes.	Undersecretion results in an abnormally low blood glucose level.

Table 16-1. Effects of Oversecretion and Undersecretion of Hormones.

3. **Growth hormone,** or GH, controls growth of the body. It affects the growth of bone and cartilage. This is accomplished indirectly by its control of the production of another factor that acts directly on these tissues. Growth hormone directly affects protein, carbohydrate, and fat metabolism at a cellular level. (See Table 16-1 for the effects of over- and undersecretion of GH.)

4. **Follicle-stimulating hormone,** or FSH, stimulates the development of egg cells in the ovaries in females. In males, it controls the production of sperm cells in the testes.

5. **Luteinizing** (*loot*-ee-in-iz-ing) **hormone,** or LH, causes the release of egg cells from the ovaries in females, and it

controls the production of sex hormones in both males and females .

6. **Prolactin** (*proh*-lak-tin) stimulates the secretion of milk by the mammary glands of the female after she gives birth. Otherwise, it is secreted only in very small amounts. It is thought that the production of prolactin is normally inhibited by a factor secreted by the hypothalamus. Following childbirth, the secretion of this inhibitory factor is blocked, and prolactin is produced.

Posterior pituitary. The posterior lobe of the pituitary is directly connected to the hypothalamus. Two tracts of nerve fibers originating in the hypothalamus have their endings in the posterior pituitary. Two hormones, **oxytocin** (ahk-sih-*toh*-sin) and **vasopressin** (vay-zoh-*pres*-in) are produced by these nerve cells in the hypothalamus. The hormones then pass down the axons to the posterior lobe of the pituitary for storage and eventual release.

Oxytocin stimulates contraction of the smooth muscles of the uterus during childbirth. Vasopressin, which is also known as *antidiuretic* (ant-ih-dy-uh-*ret*-ik) *hormone* or ADH, controls the reabsorption of water by the nephrons of the kidneys. ADH increases the permeability of the tubules to water, so that water is reabsorbed by osmosis.

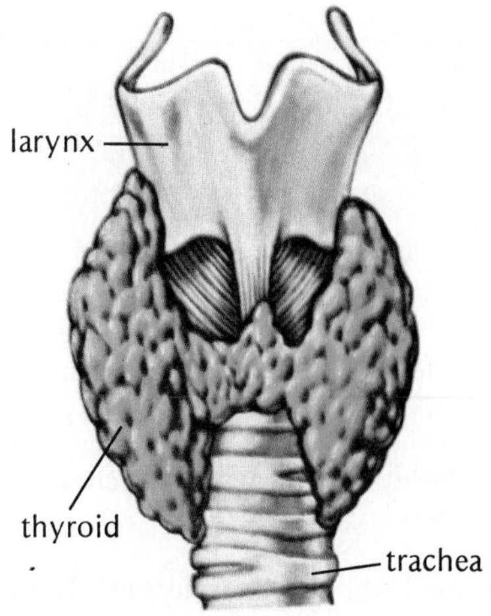

Figure 16-6. The Thyroid Gland. The hormones of the thyroid regulate the rate of metabolism in the body and the blood calcium level.

16-8 Thyroid Gland

The **thyroid** (*thy*-royd) **gland** is located in the neck just below the voice box and in front of the trachea (see Figure 16-6). This gland secretes the iodine-containing hormone **thyroxine** (thy-*rahk*-sin). Thyroxine regulates the rate of metabolism in the body. It increases the rate of protein, carbohydrate, and fat metabolism and the rate of cellular respiration. This hormone is essential for normal mental and physical development. The thyroid secretes another hormone, **calcitonin** (kal-suh-*toh*-nin), which is involved in the regulation of the blood calcium level.

The secretion of thyroxine is regulated by the interaction of several hormones (see Figure 16-7). If the concentration of

Figure 16-7. Regulation of Thyroxine Secretion.

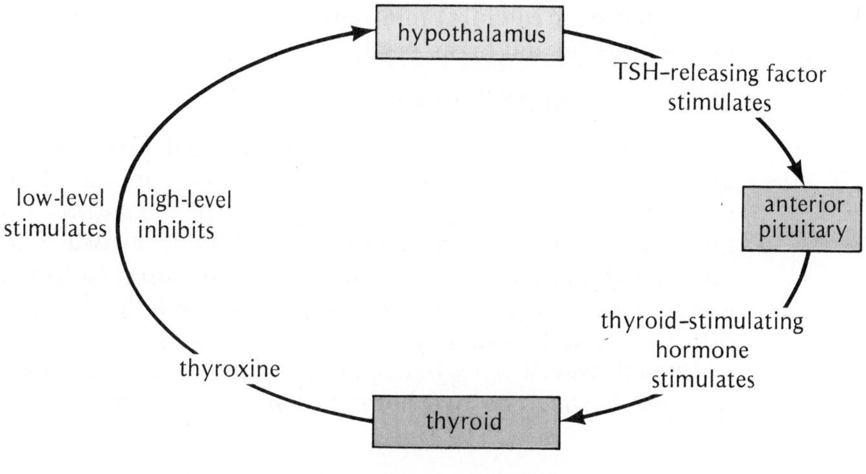

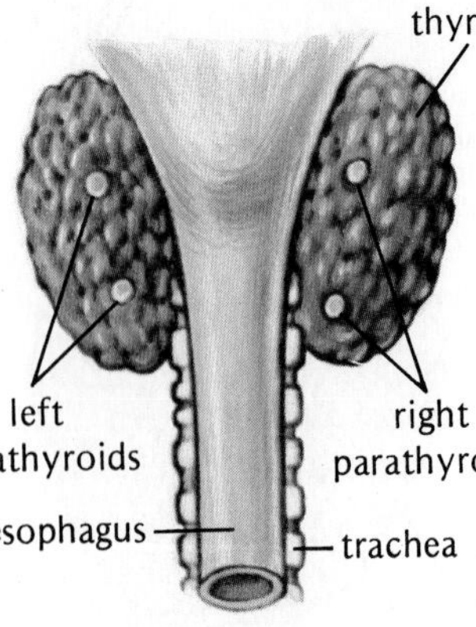

Figure 16-8. The Parathyroid Glands. The four small parathyroid glands embedded in the back of the thyroid produce hormones that regulate calcium and phosphate metabolism in the body.

thyroxine in the blood falls below a certain level, the hypothalamus is stimulated to produce TSH-releasing factor. The releasing factor stimulates the anterior pituitary to secrete thyroid-stimulating hormone (TSH). The TSH, in turn, stimulates the release of thyroxine by the thyroid. Increasing levels of thyroxine in the blood inhibit the production of releasing factor by the hypothalamus. This inhibits the production of TSH, and thereby decreases the stimulation of the thyroid. Thus, by negative feedback the concentration of thyroxine in the blood controls the system by which it is produced. (See Table 16-1 for the effects of over- and undersecretion of thyroxine.)

16-9 Parathyroid Glands

Four tiny, oval glands called the **parathyroids** (par-uh-*thy*-royds) are embedded in the back of the thyroid (see Figure 16-8). They secrete parathyroid hormone, or **parathormone** (par-uh-*thor*-mohn). This hormone regulates calcium and phosphate metabolism.

Calcium is necessary for proper growth, the health of bones and teeth, blood clotting, nerve function, and muscle contraction. Phosphate is found in bone and in many important compounds in the body, including ATP, DNA, and RNA.

The concentration of calcium ions in the blood must be kept within relatively narrow limits for the normal functioning of nerves and muscles. Calcium is stored to some extent within cells, but it is stored mainly in bones in the form of calcium phosphate compounds. When the blood calcium level drops even slightly, the parathyroids are stimulated to secrete parathormone. This hormone causes the release of calcium from bone into the plasma. When the blood calcium concentration rises above a certain level, calcium is stored in bone. Excess calcium can also be excreted by the kidneys and intestines.

A deficiency of parathormone results in low blood calcium levels. If the level is low enough, the skeletal muscles become hypersensitive and contract violently, a condition called *tetany* (*tet*-uh-nee). Oversecretion of parathormone results in the removal of calcium from bones to the point where they become brittle and break easily.

16-10 Adrenal Glands

Capping the two kidneys are the **adrenal** (uh-*dreen*-ul) **glands** (see Figure 16-9). Each gland consists of an inner layer called the *medulla* and an outer layer called the *cortex*. The hormones of the adrenal gland help the body to deal with stress. The hormones of the medulla are released to handle sudden stress, while hormones of the cortex help the body deal with long-term stress.

Adrenal medulla. The tissue of the adrenal medulla is related to nerve tissue. The two hormones secreted by the adrenal medulla are **epinephrine,** or **adrenalin** (uh-*dren*-uh-lin), and **norepinephrine,** or *noradrenalin* (nor-uh-*dren*-uh-lin). About 80 percent of the secretion is epinephrine, and 20 percent norepinephrine. Secretion of these hormones by the adrenal medulla is regulated directly by nerves of the sympathetic nervous system. In general, the effects of these hormones are the same as those produced by stimulation of the sympathetic nervous system, except that the effects of the hormones are much longer lasting.

Epinephrine and norepinephrine produce what is called the "emergency response," or "fight-or-flight" reaction. They are secreted in response to sudden stresses, such as fear, anger, pain, or physical exertion. Both hormones constrict the blood vessels of the body. Epinephrine increases the rate of metabolism. It increases the release of glucose by the liver. It increases the rate and strength of the heartbeat, blood pressure, breathing rate, blood clotting rate, and sweating.

Adrenal cortex. The hormones of the adrenal cortex are compounds called **corticosteroids** (kort-ih-koh-*stihr*-oyds). They are all synthesized from cholesterol. The major hormones of the adrenal cortex are cortisol and aldosterone, but more than thirty others are known.

Cortisol (*kort*-uh-sahl) or *hydrocortisone* (hy-druh-*kort*-uh-sohn), affects the metabolism of carbohydrates, proteins, and fats. Its major action involves the synthesis of glucose in the liver and other tissues. It is important in regulating the glucose level in the blood.

Cortisone is a compound that is closely related to cortisol. Cortisone is produced synthetically and used as a drug for the treatment of arthritis and for counteracting the symptoms of allergies.

Aldosterone and related hormones maintain the normal mineral balance in the blood. Aldosterone increases both the reabsorption of sodium by the kidney tubules and the excretion of potassium by the kidney tubules. By controlling the concentrations of these ions, aldosterone also controls the volume of the intercellular fluid and the blood.

The adrenal cortex also secretes both male and female sex hormones, although the amount of female hormones produced is very slight. The male sex hormones may play some role in regulating sexual development in males. (See Table 16-1 for the effects of over- and undersecretion of the hormones of the adrenal glands.)

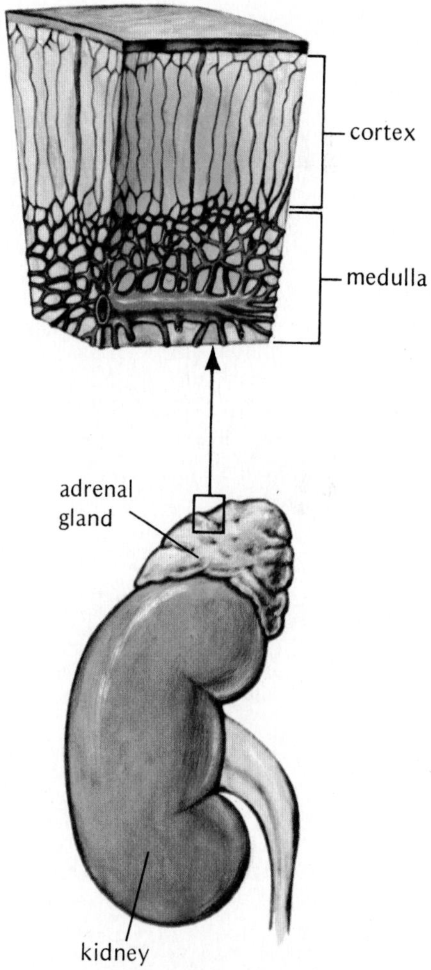

Figure 16-9. The Adrenal Glands. The adrenal glands are located on top of the kidneys. Hormones of the adrenal medulla deal with sudden stress, while hormones of the adrenal cortex deal with long-term stress.

16-11 Pancreas—Islets of Langerhans

The pancreas is both an exocrine gland and an endocrine gland. The exocrine portion secretes digestive juices into the pancreatic duct (see page 136). The endocrine portion consists of small clusters, or islands, of hormone-secreting cells—the **islets of Langerhans** (*lahng*-er-hahnz). These are scattered throughout the pancreas. There are two types of cells in the islets—*alpha cells*, which secrete the hormone glucagon, and *beta cells*, which secrete the hormone insulin. Both of these hormones function in the control of carbohydrate metabolism.

Stress that through their antagonistic effects, insulin and glucagon act to keep the blood glucose levels within normal limits.

Insulin. **Insulin** (*in*-suh-lin) affects glucose metabolism in several ways. It increases the rate of transport of glucose through cell membranes in most of the tissues of the body. When the level of glucose in the blood is high, the beta cells of the pancreas are stimulated to secrete insulin. The insulin promotes the passage of the glucose into the body cells, thereby lowering the blood glucose level. Within the cells of the liver and skeletal muscle, insulin promotes the conversion of glucose to glycogen, and in fatty tissues, it promotes the conversion of glucose to fat. It also increases the rate of oxidation of glucose within cells.

Glucagon. The effects of **glucagon** (*gloo*-kuh-gahn) on glucose metabolism are generally opposite, or antagonistic, to those of insulin. While insulin lowers the blood glucose level, glucagon raises it. When the glucose concentration in the blood falls below a certain level, the alpha cells of the pancreas are stimulated to secrete glucagon. Glucagon promotes the conversion of glycogen to glucose in the liver. This glucose quickly diffuses out of the liver into the bloodstream.

When the supply of liver glycogen is exhausted, glucagon causes the conversion of amino acids and fatty acids to glucose. Thus, when adequate carbohydrates are not available, body fat and proteins are broken down to provide glucose to meet energy requirements.

Diabetes. When the islets of Langerhans fail to produce enough insulin, the amount of glucose that can enter the body cells is greatly decreased. Instead, the concentration of glucose in the blood increases, and the excess sugar is excreted in the urine. This condition is called **diabetes** (dy-uh-*beet*-eez). Symptoms of diabetes include loss of weight despite increased appetite, thirst, and general weakness. If untreated, diabetes causes death. Proper diet and daily injections of insulin can control the disease. (See Table 16-1 for the effects of over- and undersecretion of the hormones of the islets of Langerhans.)

16-12 Gonads

The gonads, or sex glands, are the ovaries of the female and the testes of the male. The ovaries produce egg cells and the testes produce sperm cells. The gonads also secrete sex hormones, which control all aspects of sexual development and reproduction. The role of sex hormones in reproduction is discussed in Chapter 23.

The ovaries. The **ovaries** (ohv-uh-reez) produce two hormones, **estrogen** (*es*-truh-jen) and **progesterone** (proh-*jes*-tuh-rohn). During development, estrogen stimulates the development of the female reproductive system. Estrogen also promotes the development of the female secondary sex characteristics, such as broadening of the hips and development of breasts. Estrogen acts with progesterone to regulate the menstrual cycle .

The testes. The **testes** (*tes*-teez) secrete male sex hormones called androgens. The most important androgen is **testosterone** (tes-*tahs*-tuh-rohn). During fetal development, testosterone stimulates development of the male reproductive system. This hormone also promotes development of male secondary sex characteristics, such as a deep voice, beard, body hair, and the male body form.

16-13 Stomach and Small Intestine

Special cells in the lining of the stomach secrete the hormone **gastrin,** which stimulates the flow of gastric juice (see page 135). In the lining of the small intestine there are cells that secrete the hormone **secretin** (see page 136), which stimulates the flow of pancreatic juice. Secretin was the first hormone to be discovered.

16-14 Thymus

The **thymus** (*thy*-mus) is a gland located in the upper chest cavity near the heart. It is large in infants and children, but shrinks after the start of adolescence. Early in life, the thymus is involved in the processing of lymphocytes, which are part of the body's defense against infection (see page 166). Current research indicates that through childhood the thymus produces a hormone called **thymosin** (*thy*-muh-sin). Thymosin is thought to stimulate development of T lymphocytes, which are important in immunity. The thymus appears to serve no function in adults.

16-15 Pineal Gland

The **pineal** (*pin*-ee-uhl) **gland** is a pea-sized structure attached to the base of the brain. It produces a hormone called *melatonin* (mel-uh-*toh*-nin). In frogs, this hormone acts on the pigment cells, while in rats it inhibits the functioning of the ovaries and testes. Some recent research indicates that melatonin may inhibit sexual development in human males. At puberty, when sexual development begins, the secretion of melatonin decreases. Melatonin may also inhibit sexual development in human females.

16-16 Prostaglandins

Prostaglandins (prahs-tuh-*glan*-dinz) are "local hormones" that produce their effects on the cells in which they are synthesized without ever entering the bloodstream. They may act by modifying the effects of other hormones. They are thought to influence a wide variety of metabolic activities, including

historical notes

In the early 1900s, the English physiologists Ernest Starling and William Bayliss showed definitely that a substance released into the bloodstream by one organ could affect the activity of another organ elsewhere in the body.

It had previously been thought that the secretion of pancreatic juice by the pancreas was controlled by the nervous system. However, Starling and Bayliss found that the passage of acidic food from the stomach into the small intestine caused the release of pancreatic juice even when nerves to the pancreas were cut. They discovered that the acid in the food stimulated the lining of the intestine to secrete a substance into the blood that in turn stimulated the release of pancreatic juice. They named this substance "secretin." Starling later suggested the general term *hormone* for substances released into the blood that stimulated activity in a distant tissue.

heartbeat, blood pressure, excretion of urine, and contraction of the uterus at childbirth. Prostaglandins are being studied for possible use in the treatment of such diverse diseases as high blood pressure, stroke, asthma, and ulcers.

summary

The endocrine system consists of a number of specialized glands and tissues that secret substances called hormones. The hormones, which act as chemical messengers, are released directly into the bloodstream and carried throughout the body. Each hormone exerts its effects on only one type of tissue—its target tissue.

The rate at which a hormone is secreted varies with the needs of the body. The activity of most endocrine glands is controlled by a negative feedback mechanisms in which the concentration of a certain substance in the blood stimulates or inhibits gland function.

The glands of the human endocrine system and their major hormones are listed below.

1. pituitary gland: TSH, ACTH, GH, FSH, LH, prolactin, oxytocin, vasopressin
2. thyroid gland: thyroxine , calcitonin
3. parathyroid glands: parathormone
4. adrenal glands: epinephrine, norepinephrine, aldosterone , cortisol
5. islets of Langerhans (pancreas): insulin, glucagon
6. testes: testosterone
7. ovaries: estrogen, progesterone
8. thymus: thymosin
9. pineal gland: melatonin
10. stomach lining: gastrin
11. intestinal lining: secretin

vocabulary

adrenal gland
adrenocorticotropic hormone
aldosterone
androgen
calcitonin
corticosteroid
cortisol
diabetes
endocrine gland
epinephrine
estrogen
exocrine gland
follicle-stimulating hormone
gastrin
glucagon
growth hormone
hormone
hypersecretion
hyposecretion
insulin
islets of Langerhans
luteinizing hormone
negative feedback
norepinephrine
ovary
oxytocin
parathormone
parathyroid gland
pineal gland
pituitary gland

progesterone
prolactin
prostaglandin
releasing factor
secretin
target tissue
testis
testosterone
thymosin
thymus gland
thyroid gland
thyroid-stimulating hormone
thyroxine
vasopressin

test your learning

Section

16-1 1. Compare the operations of the nervous system and endocrine system in maintaining homeostasis.

16-2 2. Explain the difference between an exocrine and an endocrine gland, and give an example of each.

16-3 3. What are target tissues, and what effects do hormones have on the metabolism of target tissues?

4. Which body processes are chiefly regulated by hormones?

16-4 5. Give an example of a negative feedback mechanism.

16-5 6. Explain the one-messenger and two-messenger models of hormone action.

16-6 7. Define the terms *hypersecretion* and *hyposecretion.*

16-7 8. How is the secretion of hormones by the anterior pituitary controlled?

9. List the major hormones of the anterior pituitary and describe their functions.

10. What two hormones are released by the posterior pituitary, and where are they produced?

11. What are the functions of the two posterior pituitary hormones?

16-8 12. What two hormones are secreted by the thyroid, and what are their functions?

13. How is the secretion of thyroxine regulated?

16-9 14. Where are the parathyroid glands located?

15. What are the functions of parathormone?

16. Why must blood calcium levels be kept fairly constant?

16-10 17. Where are the adrenal glands located?

18. Name the two hormones secreted by the adrenal medulla, and describe their functions.

19. Which division of the nervous system controls the secretion of the adrenal medulla?

20. What are the major hormones secreted by the adrenal cortex, and what are their functions?

16-11 21. Is the pancreas an endocrine gland or an exocrine gland? Explain.

22. Name the two types of hormone-secreting cells in the islets of Langerhans and the hormone produced by each.

23. What is the function of insulin?

24. What is the function of glucagon?

25. Describe the cause, symptoms, and treatment of diabetes.

16-12 **26.** Name the hormones secreted by the ovary and describe the functions of each.

27. Name the major hormone secreted by the testes and describe its function.

16-13 **28.** Name the hormones secreted by the stomach and small intestine, and describe the functions of each.

16-14 **29.** Where is the thymus located?

30. Name the hormone secreted by the thymus, and describe its function.

16-15 **31.** Where is the pineal gland located?

32. What hormone does the pineal gland secrete, and what are its functions?

16-16 **33.** What are prostaglandins?

34. How are prostaglandins thought to work in the body?

test your understanding

1. Each case described below involves a hormone imbalance. Decide which hormones are probably involved and whether there is an oversecretion or undersecretion:

A. A person's bones are very brittle and break easily.

B. A child is abnormally small for his age and does not seem to be growing.

C. A person becomes nervous, irritable, and overactive.

D. A child has no natural immunity to common germs.

E. A person's urine shows an abnormally high concentration of glucose.

2. Explain how the blood glucose level is regulated.

3. Explain how the blood calcium level is regulated.

4. What causes the rate and strength of the heartbeat to increase when a person is frightened or startled?

independent research

1. Prepare a report on one of the following topics:

A. the discovery of insulin

B. diabetes

C. prostaglandins

D. Hans Selye's stress theory

2. Design an experiment that would show that a particular organ in a rat is an endocrine gland that produces a hormone that has certain effects in the rat.

UNIT 3
PLANT MAINTENANCE

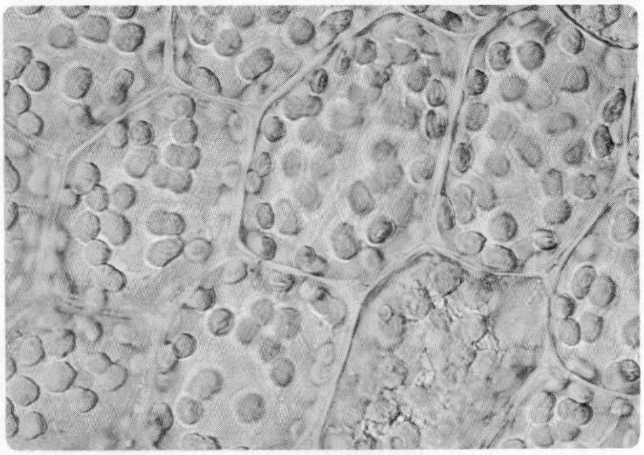

chapter 17

Plant Nutrition

PHOTOSYNTHESIS

After completing your study of this section, you should be able to:

1. Describe the early experiments that provided the basic facts about the process of photosynthesis.
2. Explain the nature of light.
3. Describe what happens when light hits a pigment.
4. Describe some of the characteristics of chlorophyll—which colors of light it absorbs, which colors it reflects, where it is found in the plant, and what happens when light strikes chlorophyll.
5. Write a balanced equation for the overall events of photosynthesis.
6. Explain what happens in the light reactions.
7. Explain what happens in the dark reactions.
8. List the environmental factors that affect the rate of photosynthesis, and describe the effects of each.

Green plants are autotrophs—they can synthesize all the organic nutrients that they require. These nutrients can then be broken down by cellular respiration for the release of energy, or they can be incorporated into the structure of the plant. The process by which organic nutrients are synthesized in plants is **photosynthesis.**

Photosynthesis requires the presence of special pigments that can absorb the energy of light. A few types of plants do not contain such pigments and obtain their nutrition by heterotrophic means.

17-1 Historical Background

"Tall oaks from little acorns grow." That simple sentence contains what was once a most puzzling scientific mystery. It is easy to see that animals live and grow by eating food. But where does the material come from that enables a tiny seed to develop into a plant millions of times as large and heavy.

One of the earliest known scientific attempts to solve this mystery was made by the Flemish physician Jan van Helmont in the early 1600s. He planted a small willow tree in a pot of soil after first weighing each the tree and the soil. The soil was watered regularly, and the tree thrived and grew. At the end of 5 years, the tree and soil were weighed again. The tree had gained 75 kilograms. There was no significant change in the weight of the soil. As far as van Helmont could see, water had been the only substance supplied to the tree. He concluded that new plant material came entirely from water.

Van Helmont was partly right. Water is one of the substances from which new plant tissues are formed. It did not occur to him that the air could have contributed anything to the growth of the plant. In fact, no one was aware that air was even necessary to the life of a plant. It was known that animals need a supply of fresh air, and that an animal placed in a closed container eventually dies. Another well-known fact was that a burning candle placed in a closed container soon went out. Something happened to the air in the container so that nothing could burn in it. It was also known that animals could not live in air that had lost its ability to support burning.

In the 1770s the English chemist Joseph Priestley was investigating these phenomena. He decided to see what would happen to a plant placed in air that had been "damaged" by a burning candle. He found that the plant survived very well. In fact, he discovered that the plant actually restored the ability of the air to support a flame and to support the life of an animal. This was the first real evidence that plants interact with air in some way.

Within a few years, the French chemist Antoine Lavoisier showed that the gas oxygen was removed from the air during burning. (Priestley had discovered oxygen, but had not recognized its true nature.) It could now be seen that animals need oxygen from the air to survive, just as a flame does. Air loses the capacity to support animal life or a flame when its oxygen has been used up. On the other hand, plants can restore this capacity to air by giving off oxygen to it.

Additional discoveries followed fairly quickly. In 1779 the Dutch physician Jan Ingenhousz found that plants can restore the air only in sunlight; in the dark, they actually "damage" it just as animals do. A Swiss pastor, Jean Senebier, found that plants take in carbon dioxide (called "fixed air" at that time) during growth in sunlight. Thus, by the beginning of the 19th century, scientists could state the basic facts of plant growth and photosynthesis: In sunlight, green plants use carbon dioxide and water for the synthesis of organic material and release oxygen in the process.

The concept of energy was not developed until later in the century. In 1842, after the idea of energy had been clearly formulated, the German surgeon Julius Robert Mayer stated that during photosynthesis, plants convert light energy into chemical energy.

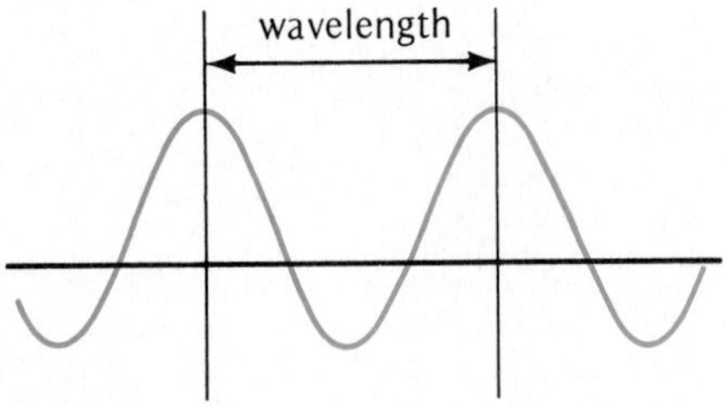

Figure 17-1. The Meaning of Wavelength. The various colors of light differ from one another in wavelength. Violet light has the shortest wavelength, red light has the longest, and green and yellow light are in between.

17-2 Light

Light is the original source of energy for almost all living things. Light is a form of radiation. It travels through space in waves. The distance between the crest of one wave and the crest of the next wave is the **wavelength** of the light (see Figure 17-1). The various colors of light differ from one another in wavelength. Visible light has wavelengths between 3,600 Å (violet light) and 7,600 Å (red light). (The Angstrom unit, Å, is defined on page 13.)

Visible light makes up only a very small portion of the electromagnetic spectrum. At increasing wavelengths there are: infrared rays, which are heat radiations; UHF waves, which are used for FM radio and television; and radio waves. At decreasing wavelengths there are ultraviolet rays, X rays, and gamma rays.

Sunlight is a mixture of all visible wavelengths. When all wavelengths of light are reflected equally by an object, the object appears white to the human eye. Sunlight is therefore called "white light." When white light is passed through a prism, the rays of different wavelengths are bent by different amounts, and the beam is spread out, forming a **spectrum** (*spek*-trum) (see Figure 17-2). In a spectrum, which is like a rainbow, the different colors of light appear in order of wavelength, from violet (shortest wavelength) to red (longest wavelength).

Although light travels through space in waves, it also acts as though it is made of particles. These particles are called **photons** (*foh*-tahnz). Each photon carries a definite amount of energy that depends on its wavelength.

When light falls on a material, some of the atoms may absorb energy from the light. Atoms absorb energy from light by capturing a photon. The energy of the photon is transferred to one of the electrons in the atom, thus raising the electron to a

Figure 17-2. Spectrum of White Light. When white light (light consisting of all visible wavelengths) is passed through a prism, the light rays of different wavelengths spread out to form a spectrum. The colors in the spectrum are arranged in order of wavelength.

higher energy level. In most cases the absorbed energy is changed to heat, which is then radiated away as radiation of a longer wavelength. However, green plants and other photosynthetic organisms are able to store some of this energy in chemical form in high-energy compounds.

17-3 Photosynthetic Pigments

A **pigment** is a substance that absorbs light of particular wavelengths. Wavelengths that are not absorbed are *transmitted* (pass through the material) or *reflected* (bounce back off the material). Thus, the material in which the pigment is found appears to have the color of the wavelengths that are not absorbed. For example, a ball that appears red reflects red light and absorbs other wavelengths.

Absorbed light energy is generally changed to heat, which is reradiated by the object.

Photosynthetic pigments are pigments that absorb light energy and make it available for conversion to chemical energy. Like other pigments, the atoms of photosynthetic pigments capture light photons, whose energy raises certain electrons to higher energy levels. In the reactions of photosynthesis, some of the energy of these electrons is used, in a stepwise fashion, to form new chemical bonds.

The most important photosynthetic pigments are the **chlorophylls** (*klor*-uh-filz). If white light is passed through a solution of chlorophyll and then through a prism, the resulting spectrum shows mainly green and yellow. Most of the violet and blue and much of the red and orange wavelengths are absorbed by the solution. A more precise measurement of which wavelengths are absorbed by a solution can be obtained with an instrument called a *spectrophotometer* (spek-troh-fuh-*tahm*-uh-ter). A beam of light of different wavelengths is passed through the solution, and the amount of each wavelength that is absorbed is measured by the instrument. The results are called an *absorption spectrum.* Figure 17-3 shows the absorption spectrum for chlorophyll. It is the

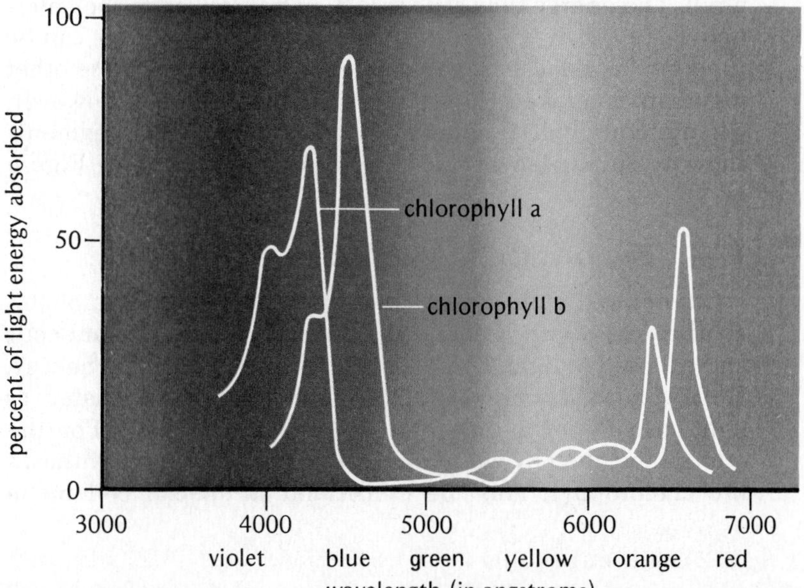

Figure 17-3. Absorption Spectrum for Chlorophyll. The peaks on this graph represent wavelengths of high absorption and little reflection. Very little energy in the green-yellow range is absorbed. Most of the light of these wavelengths is reflected. This accounts for the characteristic color of plant leaves and other structures containing chlorophyll.

Figure 17-4. Summer and Autumn Leaf Colors in the Sugar Maple.

reflection of green and yellow wavelengths that gives plants their characteristic color.

There are two major types of chlorophyll, *a* and *b*, which differ very slightly in their chemical makeup. Except for photosynthetic bacteria, all photosynthetic organisms contain chlorophyll *a*. Green plants contain both *a* and *b*. Bacteria contain a special form of chlorophyll called *bacteriochlorophyll* (bak-tihr-ee-oh-*klor*-uh-fil). In addition to chlorophyll, the leaves of many plants contain one or more other pigments, including *carotenes* (*kar*-uh-teenz) which are orange, and *xanthophylls* (*zan*-thuh-filz), which are yellow. These other pigments absorb light of wavelengths not absorbed by chlorophyll. The energy they absorb is then transferred to the chlorophyll. In this way more of the incoming light energy can be used by the plant. In many plants the presence of these other pigments is masked by the chlorophyll. In the fall, however, when chlorophyll production decreases, the other pigments show up, giving leaves their bright autumn colors (see Figure 17-4).

Carotenes and xanthophylls are also contained in the chloroplasts.

17-4 Photosynthetic Membranes

Chlorophyll molecules cannot by themselves cause photosynthesis to occur. If chlorophyll is extracted from plant cells and exposed to light, it does momentarily absorb light energy. However, this energy is almost immediately reradiated as light, usually of a different wavelength or color. For the energy absorbed by chlorophyll to be used for photosynthesis, the cholorophyll must be embedded in special cell membranes—the photosynthetic membranes. These membranes contain electron acceptors and other molecules that are needed for the conversion of the absorbed light energy to chemical-bond energy.

In chloroplasts the photosynthetic membranes are folded and stacked to form the grana. In the cells of photosynthetic bacteria and blue-green algae, which do not have chloroplasts, the photosynthetic membranes are distributed through the cytoplasm or associated with the cell membrane. Photosynthetic membranes are remarkably rapid and efficient devices for converting light energy to chemical energy, but very little is known about their chemical structure and organization. Scientists who would like to trap the energy of sunlight for their own purposes would very much like to know how these membranes are put together and how they work. This is an active area of current research.

17-5 Chemistry of Photosynthesis

Photosynthesis is, in effect, the reverse of cellular respiration. In respiration, glucose and oxygen are used to produce carbon dioxide, water, and energy. In photosynthesis, carbon dioxide and water and energy obtained from light are used to produce glucose and oxygen. In simplest terms, these processes can be represented by the following chemical equations:

$$\text{respiration: } C_6H_{12}O_6 + 6O_2 \longrightarrow 6CO_2 + 6H_2O + \text{energy}$$

$$\text{photosynthesis: } 6CO_2 + 6H_2O + \text{energy} \longrightarrow C_6H_{12}O_6 + 6O_2$$

The equation for photosynthesis gives a misleading impression of what actually occurs chemically. The right side of the equation shows 6 molecules of free oxygen (O_2), or 12 oxygen atoms, being produced. Note that there are only 6 oxygen atoms in the water on the left side of the equation. It seems that at least some of the 12 oxygen atoms in the gas on the right must come from the carbon dioxide. In fact, it was originally believed that *all* the oxygen came from the CO_2.

Then, in 1941 it was shown by Samuel Rubin and Martin Kamen that all the oxygen released during photosynthesis comes from the splitting of water molecules. How can 12 oxygen atoms come from 6 water molecules? The answer is that the reactions of photosynthesis occur in two stages. In the first stage, water is split into hydrogen and oxygen. In the second stage, some of the hydrogen combines with oxygen from the carbon dioxide to produce water again. In other words, water is both a raw material (first stage) and a product (second stage) of photosynthesis. The complete equation for photosynthesis is therefore written as follows:

$$6CO_2 + 12\ H_2O + \text{energy} \longrightarrow C_6H_{12}O_6 + 6O_2 + 6H_2O$$

Note that there are now enough oxygen atoms in the water on the left to provide the free oyxgen produced on the right.

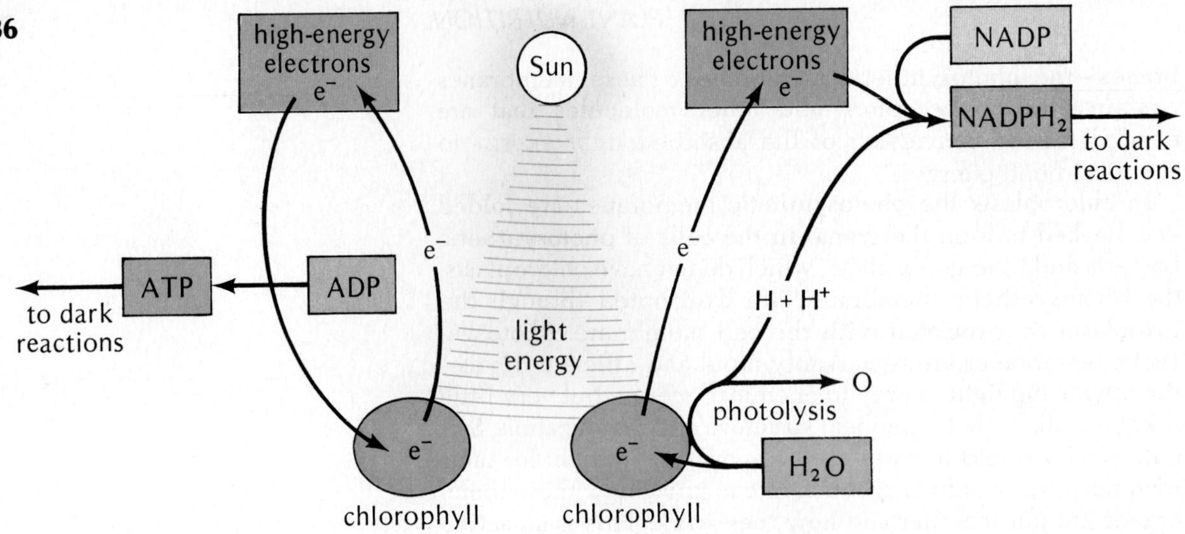

Figure 17-5. The Light Reactions. When light strikes a chlorophyll molecule, electrons are excited to a high-energy state. Some of this energy is used to make ATP from ADP (left side of diagram). In another series of reactions (right side of diagram), water is split into hydrogen and oxygen and an excited electron. The hydrogen and the electron are transferred to NADP, forming $NADPH_2$. The oxygen atoms form molecules of free oxygen (O_2).

The first set of reactions of photosynthesis, which are called the **light reactions,** require light energy. The end products of the light reactions are the energy carrier ATP and the hydrogen carrier $NADPH_2$. The second set of reactions, the **dark reactions,** can take place without light. However, they cannot proceed without the ATP and $NADPH_2$ produced by the light reactions. The end products of the dark reactions are carbohydrates.

17-6 The Light Reactions

The light reactions of photosynthesis begin with the absorption of light energy by chlorophyll (see Figure 17-5). As a result of this absorption of energy, electrons in the chlorophyll molecules are "excited"—that is, raised to higher energy levels. As the excited electrons drop back to their normal energy levels, their excess energy is used to carry on three types of chemical reactions: the splitting of water, hydrogen transfer, and ATP formation.

1. In one set of reactions, water molecules are split into hydrogen and oxygen, a process called **photolysis** (foh-*tahl*-uh-sis). The oxygen is released into the environment. All the oxygen given off during photosynthesis comes from the photolysis of water.

2. In another set of reactions, the hydrogen produced by the splitting of water is attached to the hydrogen carrier NADP, which is a coenzyme similar to the NAD of aerobic respiration. The product of this reaction is $NADPH_2$. Most of the energy used in the splitting of the water molecule is transferred to the $NADPH_2$.

3. In still other reactions, some of the energy from the excited electrons is used to form molecules of ATP.

17-7 The Dark Reactions

In the dark reactions, carbon dioxide is converted to carbohydrates, a process called **carbon fixation.** These reactions

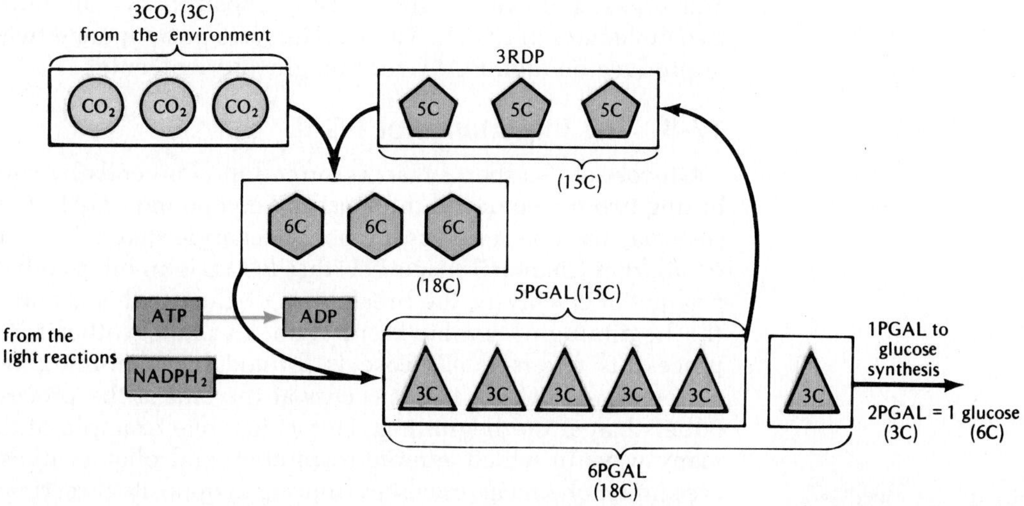

Figure 17-6. The Dark Reactions (Calvin Cycle). By means of the reactions of the Calvin cycle, carbon dioxide from the environment and hydrogen from the light reactions are combined to produce the 3-carbon compound PGAL. Glucose, as well as other nutrients, can be synthesized by plant cells from PGAL. Energy for this synthesis is provided by ATP from the light reactions.

are called dark reactions because, unlike the light reactions, they do not require light. They can proceed with or without light, but they do need the ATP and $NADPH_2$ produced by the light reactions.

In 1961, Dr. Melvin Calvin of the University of California received the Nobel Prize for his research on the sequence of events in the dark reactions of photosynthesis. These reactions are now also known as the *Calvin cycle.* In their research, Calvin and his associates used the radioactive isotope carbon-14 to "label" carbon dioxide. This labeled carbon dioxide was then taken up by green algae during photosynthesis. By stopping the dark reactions after varying periods of time, the researchers could isolate and identify the labeled compounds—those containing carbon-14. In this way, the path of the carbon from carbon dioxide to carbohydrate was traced.

The reactions of the Calvin cycle are shown in Figure 17-6. The cycle involves two compounds that are used over and over—the 5-carbon sugar ribulose and the 3-carbon compound glyceraldehyde. Both of these compounds are present in their phosphorylated forms—ribulose diphosphate (RDP) and phosphoglyceraldehyde (PGAL).

The cycle begins with the combination of a molecule of carbon dioxide (CO_2) with the 5-carbon RDP, forming a 6-carbon molecule. In a series of reactions involving $NADPH_2$ and ATP from the light reactions, this molecule is changed to two molecules of the 3-carbon PGAL. These reactions repeated three times produce six molecules of PGAL from 3 RDP and $3CO_2$.

Out of every six molecules of PGAL formed, only one is released as a product. The other five remain in the cycle. Five PGALs contain fifteen carbons. By a complex series of reactions, the five PGALs are converted to three RDP (which also contain fifteen carbons). These three RDPs are available to pick up three more CO_2 molecules, produce six more PGALs, and repeat the cycle. Glucose is synthesized by combining two molecules of PGAL. The Calvin cycle must operate twice to produce enough PGAL for one glucose molecule.

17-8 The Importance of PGAL

Glucose, a 6-carbon sugar, is formed in plant cells by combining two molecules of the 3-carbon compound PGAL. Glucose may then be stored as the polysaccharide starch. You will recall from Chapter 7 (page 111) that PGAL is an intermediate product of glycolysis, the breakdown of glucose that occurs at the beginning of aerobic respiration. In photosynthesis, the process is reversed. Glucose is formed by combining two molecules of PGAL, and it occurs at the end of the process, rather than at the beginning. This is just one example of the many ways in which aerobic respiration and photosynthesis are similar chemical processes running in opposite directions.

From the point of view of heterotrophs, the sugars and other carbohydrates that plants make and store are the products of photosynthesis. From the point of view of the plant, however, PGAL may be considered the true product. Plant cells use PGAL for the synthesis of fats and amino acids as well as glucose. They also use PGAL as the source of energy for cellular respiration. It is only the excess PGAL, produced during active photosynthesis, that is converted to glucose and stored as starch.

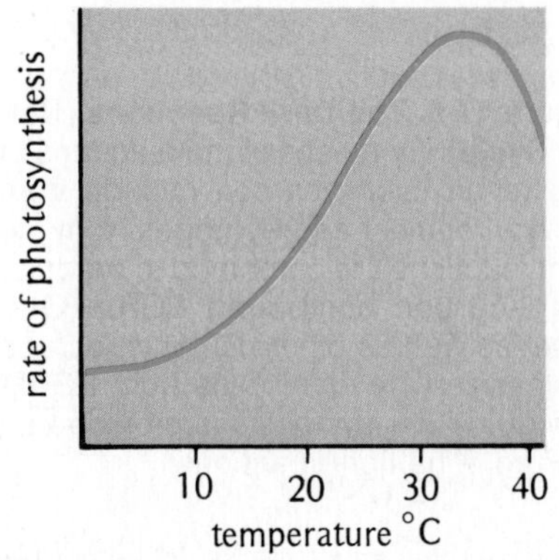

Figure 17-7. Effect of Temperature on Photosynthesis. The rate of photosynthesis is most rapid at 35°C. Above this temperature, the rate decreases sharply.

17-9 Factors Affecting the Rate of Photosynthesis

Several environmental factors influence the rate of photosynthesis. Often, it is the rate of enzyme action that is affected.

Temperature. Up to a certain point, the rate of photosynthesis increases as the temperature of the environment increases (see Figure 17-7). Photosynthesis occurs most rapidly at 35°C. As the temperature increases above this point, the rate of photosynthesis declines steeply, possibly due to the inactivation or destruction of enzymes.

Light Intensity. As the strength, or intensity, of light increases up to approximately one-third the strength of summer sunlight, the rate of photosynthesis in an individual leaf increases (see Figure 17-8). Beyond this point, the rate declines because the stomates close to cut water loss or because the pigments begin to oxidize. (Stomates are small openings in the leaves through which gases enter and leave the plant.) However, the most favorable light intensity for a whole tree is much higher than for an individual leaf because most of the leaves are at least partly shaded. Thus, with increased light intensity, the rate of photosynthesis continues to increase in the many shaded leaves.

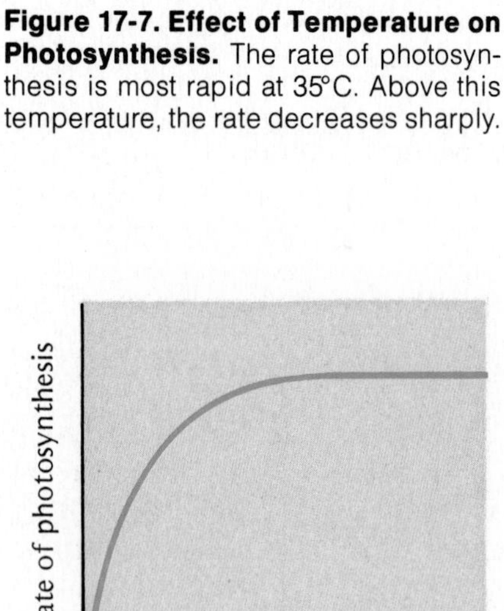

Figure 17-8. Effect of Light Intensity on Photosynthesis. The rate of photosynthesis is greatest with a light intensity of approximately one-third the strength of summer sunlight.

The intensity of sunlight varies with time of day, season, and position on the earth's surface. Water vapor, clouds, dust, and air pollutants reduce light intensity.

historical notes

The growth of plants toward light is an easily observable phenomenon. In about 1880, Charles Darwin and his son Francis conducted experiments to find out why this occurs.

In their experiments, the Darwins used grass seedlings. In the newly sprouted seedlings, the first leaves are covered by a protective sheath called the **coleoptile.** In one group of seedlings, the tip of the coleoptile was covered with a tiny paper cap. In a second group, the seedlings were left completedly uncovered. In a third group, all parts of the seedlings were covered except the coleoptile. The seedlings of all three groups were then placed near a window. Within a day, the uncovered seedlings and those with uncovered tips had grown toward the light. The seedlings with the capped coleoptiles did not bend, but grew straight up. The Darwins concluded that the coleoptile is light-sensitive, and that some stimulus passes from the coleoptile to the lower parts of the plant, and that the stimulus causes the plant to bend. They drew no conclusions about the nature of the stimulus.

In the early 1900s, Peter Boysen-Jensen continued the investigations of the Darwins. He cut off the coleoptile tips from some oat seedlings, and put agar on the bottoms of the cut tips. Boysen-Jensen then put the cut tips back on the remaining lower parts of the plants. The coleoptile tips were thereby separated from the lower parts of the plants by the agar. The seedlings grew toward light. Boysen-Jensen concluded that a chemical produced at the tip must be transmitted down to the lower part of the seedling to stimulate growth.

In another series of experiments, Boysen-Jensen inserted thin mica plates into the seedling stems, partially separating the coleoptile tip from the remainder of the plant. When the mica sheet was on the same side as the light source, the seedling continued to grow and bend toward the light. When the mica sheet was on the side away from the light source, the seedling did not bend.

Further experiments to discover the nature of the growth stimulus were performed by Frits Went. Went cut the tips of coleoptiles and placed the tips on pieces of agar. After a period of time, the tips were removed from the agar, and the agar alone was put on the remaining stumps of the plants. The plants grew as if the tips had been replaced. Pieces of agar that had not been in contact with the coleoptile tips had no effect on the growth of the stumps. When a piece of agar on which several coleoptile tips had been placed was put on a stump, they showed increased growth and bending. Went showed conclusively that a chemical that stimulates growth is produced by the coleoptile and passes downward from the tip. He named this substance **auxin,** from a Greek word meaning "to grow."

Recent experiments have shown that the auxin produced at the tip moves from the lighted side of the plant to the unlighted side. It passes downward on the unlighted side, stimulating uneven growth, which causes bending toward the light. How light is detected by the plant and how and why the auxin moves from one side to the other is not known.

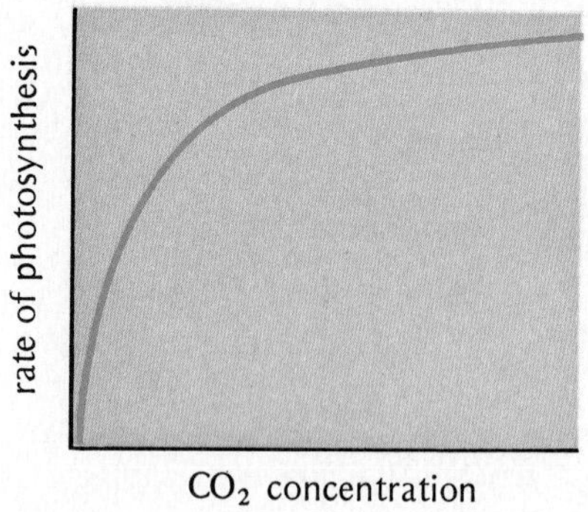

Figure 17-9. Effect of Carbon Dioxide Concentration on Photosynthesis.

Carbon dioxide level. The concentration of carbon dioxide in the atmosphere is only about 0.03 percent. It has been found under experimental conditions that, up to a certain point, increasing carbon dioxide concentration can increase the rate of photosynthesis (see Figure 17-9).

Water. Only a small amount of the water taken in by a plant is used in photosynthesis. However, a shortage of water does cause a decrease in the rate of photosynthesis. In addition, when water is in short supply, the stomates close, thereby preventing an exchange of gases between the leaf and the atmosphere. This slows or stops photosynthesis.

Minerals. Certain minerals play a role in photosynthesis. Magnesium and nitrogen are important in the formation of chlorophyll. Zinc, manganese, iron, and copper are involved in various metabolic reactions. If any of these minerals is in short supply, the whole metabolic process will eventually be affected.

HETEROTROPHIC NUTRITION IN PLANTS

After completing your study of this section, you should be able to describe the two types of heterotrophic nutrition found in plants.

17-10 Parasitic Plants

Figure 17-10. Indian Pipe.

Some plants have developed heterotrophic methods of nutrition in addition to or instead of photosynthesis. The Indian pipe, for example, completely lacks chlorophyll (see Figure 17-10). Instead, its roots contain innumerable filaments of a fungus, forming a combination of root and fungus. The fungus in the roots obtains nutrients from decaying matter in the soil. The Indian pipe is completely dependent on the fungus for nutrients and water. Dodder is a parasitic plant, which appears as a leafless, coffee-colored vine wrapped around other plants. The roots of the dodder are modified to enter the tissues of its host, from which it draws nutrients and water.

17-11 Insect-eating Plants

Some plants that are capable of photosynthesis supplement their nutrition by trapping and digesting insects. Extracellular digestion is carried out by enzymes, and nutrients are absorbed into the cells of the plant. Insect-eating plants most commonly grow in bogs or marshes where the acidic water tends to reduce the rate of decay of dead organisms. The slow rate of decay limits the amount of nitrogen available for plants to use in synthesizing proteins. Insect-eating plants capture insects to acquire needed nitrogen-containing compounds.

The pitcher plant has green, pitcher-shaped leaves lined with downward-pointing hairlike bristles that prevent escape of the prey. At the base of the leaf is a pool of water that contains digestive enzymes. Eventually, the insect falls into the pool and is digested. Venus's-flytrap has hinged leaves (see Figure 17-11). Along the leaf margins are "trigger hairs." When several trigger hairs are stimulated by an insect, the leaf snaps shut, trapping the insect. Digestion occurs within the closed leaf.

AUTOTROPHIC NUTRITION IN BACTERIA

After completing your study of this section, you should be able to describe the processes of bacterial photosynthesis and chemosynthesis.

17-12 Bacterial Photosynthesis

Photosynthesis in bacteria is similar to photosynthesis in green plants. In these organisms the photosynthetic pigment is *bacteriochlorophyll*, which is similar to chlorophyll *a*. With this pigment and cytochromes, light energy is converted to chemical energy. The chemical energy is used in carbon fixation.

A major difference between photosynthesis in bacteria and photosynthesis in plants is that in bacteria, water is not the source of hydrogen for the dark reactions. Instead, hydrogen sulfide (H_2S), gaseous hydrogen (H_2), or various organic compounds serve as hydrogen donors. Since water is not split in bacterial photosynthesis, no oxygen is released by the process. In purple and green sulfur bacteria, for example, H_2S is the hydrogen source. When this compound is broken down and hydrogen atoms and electrons removed, free sulfur is left. Thus, these bacteria accumulate sulfur crystals in their cytoplasm or expel sulfur from their cells.

$$2H_2S + CO_2 \longrightarrow H_2O + \underset{\text{(sulfur)}}{2S} + \underset{\text{(carbohydrate)}}{(CH_2O)}$$

Figure 17-11. Venus's-Flytrap.

17-13 Chemosynthesis

Chemosynthesis is a form of autotrophic nutrition carried on only by a few types of bacteria. In this process, which does not use light energy, inorganic compounds are oxidized and the energy that is released is trapped and used in the synthesis of organic compounds. For example, sulfur bacteria oxidize sulfur to sulfate.

$$2S + 3O_2 + 2H_2O \longrightarrow 2SO_4^{-2} + 4H^+ + \text{energy}$$

Other chemosynthetic bacteria play an important role in the recycling of materials in the environment.

summary

By the beginning of the nineteenth century, it was known that in photosynthesis green plants use water and carbon dioxide from the environment and in the presence of sunlight synthesize organic compounds and release oxygen.

Light is a form of radiation and travels in waves. It also acts as though it is made up of particles. Such particles are called photons. The atoms of some materials absorb energy from light by capturing photons. This energy is transferred to electrons, raising the energy levels of the electrons. Some of the light energy captured by photosynthetic pigments is transferred to chemical bonds. Thus, in photosynthetic organisms, some of the energy from sunlight can be stored in chemical form in high-energy bonds. The most important photosynthetic pigments are the chlorophylls, which give plants their characteristic green color.

In photosynthesis, carbon dioxide, water, and energy from light are used to produce glucose and oxygen. The reactions of photosynthesis occur in two stages. In the light reactions, which can occur only in the presence of light, water is split into hydrogen and oxygen. The hydrogen is picked up by NADP, forming $NADPH_2$. ATP is also formed during the light reactions. The light reactions take place mainly in the grana of the chloroplasts. In the dark reactions, ATP and $NADPH_2$ from the light reactions and carbon dioxide from the environment are used in the synthesis of organic compounds. This process is called carbon fixation.

The rate of photosynthesis depends on a number of environmental factors, including temperature, light intensity, carbon dioxide level, and the availability of water and minerals.

Some plants do not carry on photosynthesis. Instead, they are parasites, obtaining their nourishment from other living organisms. Still other plants obtain needed nitrogen by trapping and digesting insects.

In photosynthetic bacteria, water is not split in the light reactions. Other compounds, such as hydrogen sulfide, serve as hydrogen donors. Because water is not split, no oxygen is released by bacterial photosynthesis.

Chemosynthesis is a form of autotrophic nutrition found in a few types of bacteria. In chemosynthesis energy for the synthesis of organic compounds is obtained by the oxidation of inorganic compounds.

vocabulary

carbon fixation	light reactions	pigment
chemosynthesis	photolysis	spectrum
chlorophyll	photon	wavelength
dark reactions	photosynthesis	

test your learning

Section

17-1 1. Briefly describe the experiments, beginning with van Helmont and ending with Mayer, that provided the basic facts about the process of photosynthesis.

17-2 2. Explain what light is, and describe its wave and particle nature.

3. What happens when light is absorbed by a material?

17-3 4. What is a pigment?
5. What happens when light is absorbed by a photosynthetic pigment?
6. Name the most important photosynthetic pigments.
7. What gives plants their green color?
8. What function is served by the pigments other than chlorophyll found in photosynthetic plants?

17-4 9. What role do photosynthetic membranes play in photosynthesis?

17-5 10. Compare the events of photosynthesis with those of cellular respiration.
11. Write a balanced equation showing the overall reaction of photosynthesis.

17-6 12. Describe the light reactions of photosynthesis, including necessary materials and end products.

17-7 13. Describe the dark reactions of photosynthesis, including necessary materials and end products.

17-8 14. Discuss the role of PGAL in the metabolism of both plant and animal cells.

17-9 15. Explain how temperature, light intensity, carbon dioxide level, and supplies of water and minerals affect the rate of photosynthesis.

17-10 16. Explain how parasitic plants obtain nourishment.

17-11 17. Where are most insect-eating plants found, and why do such plants need this form of nourishment?

17-12 18. How does photosynthesis in bacteria differ from photosynthesis in plants?

17-13 19. What is chemosynthesis?

test your understanding

1. Why does chlorophyll make plants green? What is happening when leaves change colors in the autumn?
2. Scientists now have complete knowledge of the reactions of photosynthesis down to an atomic level. Can you think of any ways that this knowledge might eventually be used to help solve the world's energy problems?
3. Explain why photosynthesis in purple sulfur bacteria does not result in the release of oxygen.
4. Explain why green plants give off carbon dioxide as well as oxygen.

independent research

1. Prepare a written report on one of the scientists who contributed to the discovery of the nature of photosynthesis.
2. Grow one or more types of insect-eating plants in class or at home. As part of the project, obtain information from the library on the life history of the plant and on its method of getting nutrients. Your teacher will tell you where to get the plants.
3. The chemosynthetic activities of some species of bacteria play important roles in the environment, including the formation of mineral deposits. Prepare a written report on chemosynthetic bacteria and their activities.

chapter 18

Plant Structure

Figure 18-1. Organs of a Plant.

18-1 Chapter Introduction

Plants, like animals, are made up of various types of tissues that form organs. The organs of a plant are its roots, stems, leaves, and reproductive structures (see Figure 18-1). Unlike animals, however, plants contain no organ systems.

Roots anchor a plant in the soil and absorb water and minerals from the soil. **Stems** hold the leaves and expose them to the sun. They also display flowers and hold fruits and seeds. **Leaves** are the sites of photosynthesis, the process by which plants synthesize food. **Flowers** and **cones** are reproductive organs. (Plant reproduction is discussed in Chapter 24.)

PLANT TISSUES

After completing your study of this section, you should be able to:

1. Explain the functions of meristematic, protective, conducting, and fundamental tissues.
2. Describe in detail the structure and function of xylem and phloem.
3. Name three types of cells that serve in supporting the plant.

Plants have many fewer types of tissues than animals. Some plant tissues consist of only one type of cell. Others are made up of two or more different types of cells functioning together. Some tissues are found throughout the plant, while others are found only in specific structures. The basic types of plant tissues are meristematic, protective, conducting, and fundamental tissues.

18-2 Meristematic Tissues

In most animal tissues, cell division occurs continuously, replacing cells that have been damaged or died. In plants this is not the case. **Meristematic** (mer-uh-stuh-*mat*-ik) **tissues** are usually the only tissues of the mature plant that are capable of cell division. Meristematic tissue is composed of thin-walled cells with large nuclei. The cells are all about the same size. Meristematic tissues are found only in certain parts of the plant. They are present, for example, in the growing tips of roots and stems (see Figure 18-2). Growth of these tissues increases the length of the roots and stems. In some plants, including trees and shrubs, growth of a meristematic tissue called **cambium** (*kam*-bee-um) increases the diameter of stems and roots. The cells produced by the meristem develop into the various types of specialized tissues that form the plant organs.

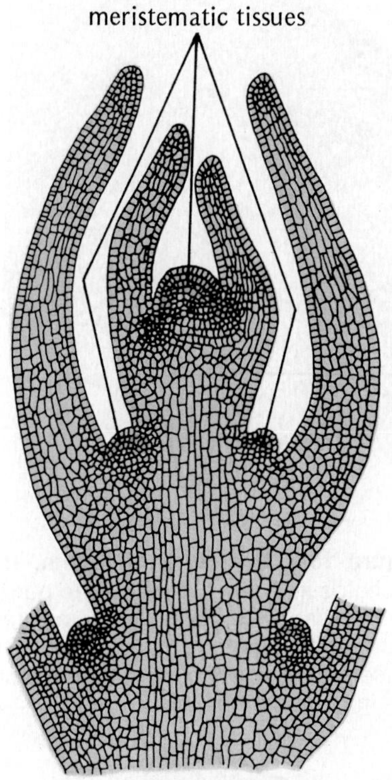

Figure 18-2. Meristematic Tissue. Meristematic tissue is found in the growing tips of mature roots and stems.

18-3 Protective Tissues

The **epidermis** is the protective tissue that forms the outer layer of leaves, green stems, and roots. The epidermal layer is generally one cell thick. The cells of the epidermis fit tightly together. In the epidermis of plant parts that are aboveground, the cell walls contain a waxy substance called **cutin** (*kyoot*-in). Cutin forms a continuous layer over the surface of the epidermis. This layer, the **cuticle** (*kyoot*-ih-kul), reduces water loss and protects against infection by microorganisms.

Cork is a protective tissue that covers the surface of woody stems and roots (see Figure 18-3). It protects the more delicate inner tissues from mechanical injury. It also waterproofs the outer surface and prevents infection. Cork is formed by a special type of meristematic tissue called *cork cambium.* The cells of the cork layer live only a short time. The functional cork cells are dead, and they contain no living cytoplasm. It is these dead cells with their waxy cell walls that provide protection.

Figure 18-3. Cork. The nonliving cork cells protect the internal tissues of woody stems and roots.

18-4 Conducting Tissues

Xylem (*zy*-lum) and **phloem** (*floh*-em) are the **vascular,** or conducting, **tissues** of the plant. Xylem conducts water and minerals from the roots upward through the stems and into the leaves of the plant. It also plays an important part in supporting the plant and holding it erect. Phloem conducts food and other dissolved materials both upward and downward throughout the plant.

Most of the cells that form mature xylem are dead—they contain no cytoplasm. They form continuous tubes from the roots up through the stems and leaves. Xylem is composed

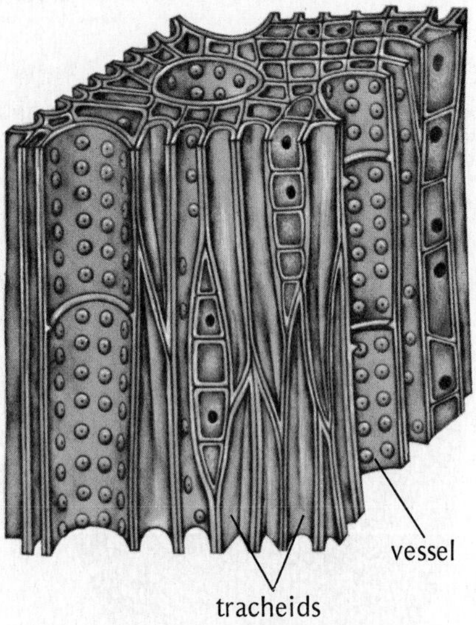

Figure 18-4. Structure of Xylem. The tracheids in xylem are aligned to permit the passage of water and minerals through the pits to adjacent cells. The vessels form conducting tubes. Mature xylem cells are nonliving.

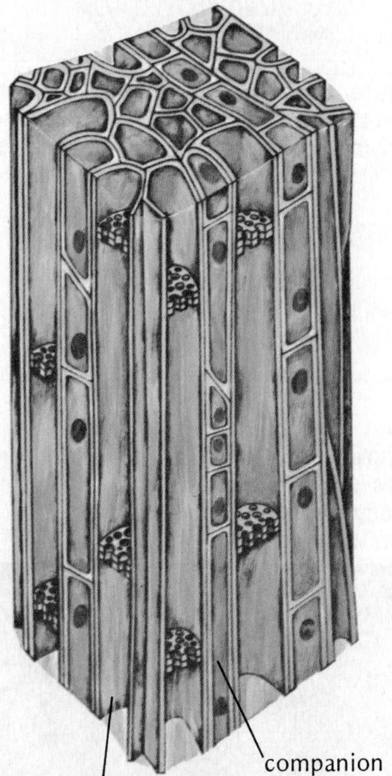

Figure 18-5. Structure of Phloem. The companion cells of phloem are thought to control the food transport activities of the sieve cells. The cells of phloem are alive and contain cytoplasm.

mainly of two types of cells—*tracheids* (*tray*-kee-idz) and *vessels* (see Figure 18-4). Tracheids contain pits, or openings, in the cell wall. The pits of adjacent tracheids are aligned, permitting the passage of water and minerals. Xylem vessels are cells that form conducting tubes. These cells, which lack end walls, are positioned end-to-end, forming long, tiny tubes. Xylem also contains thin-walled cells that serve as storage cells. What we know as wood is the xylem.

Unlike the tracheids and vessels of xylem, phloem cells are alive and contain cytoplasm. The substances transported by phloem are mainly organic compounds dissolved in water. These compounds include amino acids and sugars and other carbohydrates. Food synthesized in the leaves is transported through the phloem to other parts of the plant. Surplus food is often transported to the roots for storage. In the spring, sap containing dissolved materials is transported upward through the phloem.

Phloem is composed mainly of two types of cells (see Figure 18-5). These are *sieve cells* and *companion cells.* Sieve cells contain cytoplasm, but do not have a nucleus at maturity. The ends of the cell walls of sieve cells have many small openings. Thin strands of cytoplasm extend through the openings, connecting adjacent cells. The tubes formed by the sieve cells resemble a stack of cans with holes punched in their tops and bottoms. Companion cells, which contain both a nucleus and cytoplasm, are thought to control the transport activities of sieve cells.

18-5 Fundamental Tissues

Fundamental tissues are involved in the production and storage of food and in the support of the plant. The three types of fundamental tissues are parenchyma, collenchyma, and sclerenchyma.

Parenchyma (puh-*ren*-kuh-muh) is a tissue made up of unspecialized cells with thin cell walls. These cells are found in roots, stems, leaves, and fruits. Parenchyma cells in leaves and young stems have chloroplasts and produce food by photosynthesis. In roots, fruits, and portions of stems, parenchyma cells are used for food storage.

Collenchyma (kuh-*len*-kuh-muh) cells are similar to parenchyma, but are elongated and have thickened cell walls. They strengthen and support stems and leaves and other parts of the plant. Collenchyma cells may also contain chloroplasts.

Sclerenchyma (skluh-*ren*-kuh-muh) tissue consists of thick-walled cells that are found where support is needed. When mature, the cells usually contain no cytoplasm. Occasionally, the cell walls are so thick that the internal space of the cell is almost completely filled. *Fibers* are a type of sclerenchyma cell. They are long cells with tapered ends, and are strong and flexible. They are often found in xylem and phloem. Fibers are used to make twine, rope, and linen.

THE ROOT

After completing your study of this section, you should be able to:

1. Explain the functions of the root.
2. Describe each of the following: primary root, secondary roots, taproots, fibrous roots, and adventitious roots.
3. Name the tissues of the root, and give the functions of each.
4. Name the different zones of the root tip, beginning with the root cap, and describe what happens to the cells in each zone.

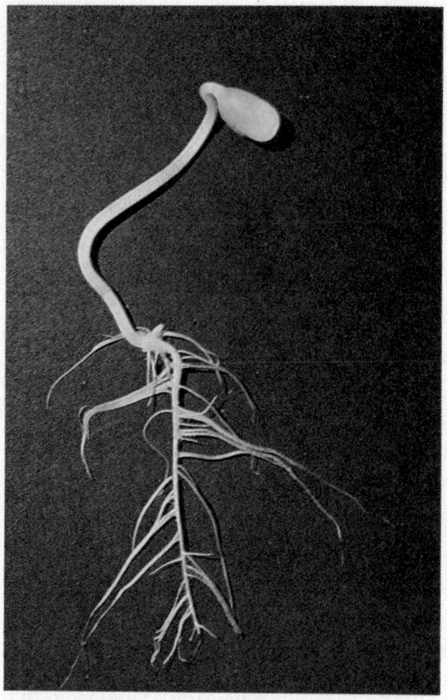

Figure 18-6. Primary and Secondary Roots. Secondary roots branch from the tissues of the primary root after it has grown from the seed.

18-6 Types of Roots

The roots of a plant are generally found underground. Roots serve several functions. They anchor the plant in the soil and absorb water and minerals from the soil. They transport water and minerals upward to the stem and dissolved food downward from the stem. In addition, the roots of some plants are specialized for the storage of food. The root system underground is generally as large as the system of stems and branches aboveground. The roots spread out, covering a large area. They usually grow no deeper than 1 meter into the soil.

The first structure to emerge from a sprouting seed is the **primary root** (see Figure 18-6). As the plant grows and matures, new roots develop from within the tissues of the primary root. These new branches of the primary root are called **secondary roots.** As roots grow, their direction of growth is influenced by obstructions, such as rocks or other roots, in the soil. Other factors, such as moisture and chemical composition of the soil, also influence growth. These factors cause the root to grow in an irregular fashion, with frequent bends and kinks.

There are two common types of root systems—taproots and fibrous roots (see Figure 18-7). A **taproot** system develops when the primary root grows most rapidly and remains the largest

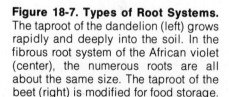

Figure 18-7. Types of Root Systems. The taproot of the dandelion (left) grows rapidly and deeply into the soil. In the fibrous root system of the African violet (center), the numerous roots are all about the same size. The taproot of the beet (right) is modified for food storage.

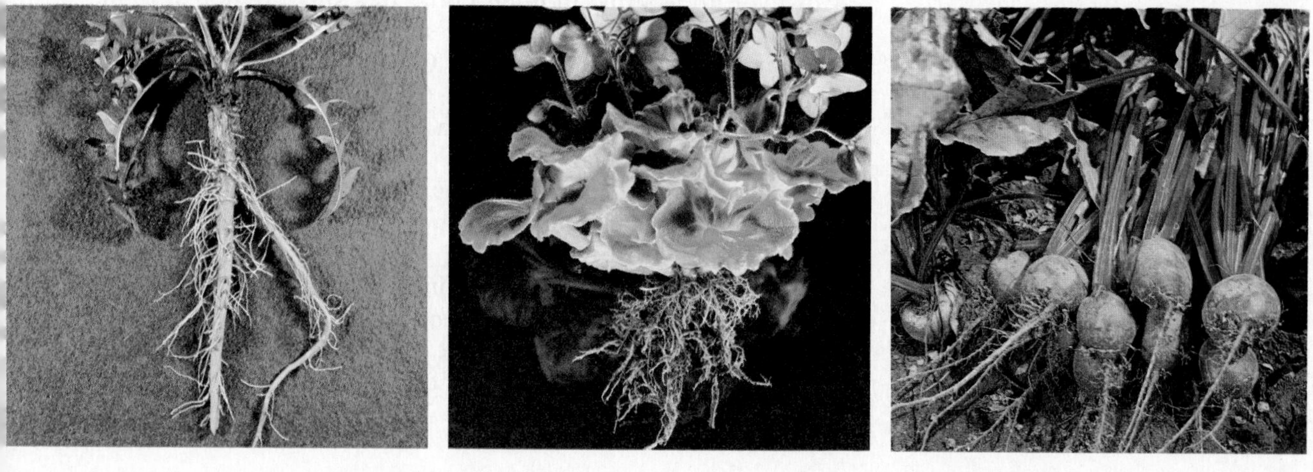

Figure 18-8. Adventitious Roots. The climbing roots of ivy (left) grow from the stem and attach the plant to a solid support. The prop roots of corn (right) help to brace the plant.

root of the root system. Taproots grow deep into the soil and become thick and fleshy. Oak trees and dandelions have taproots. A **fibrous root** system is made up of numerous roots, many of which are nearly equal in size. This type of system develops when branching secondary roots are as large as or larger than the primary root. Corn and grasses have fibrous root systems. In some plants, taproots and fibrous roots are modified for food storage. The carrot, radish, and beet are storage taproots, while the sweet potato and tapioca are fibrous storage roots.

Adventitious (ad-ven-*tish*-us) **roots** do not originate from the primary root or one of its branches. Instead, they grow from stems or leaves (see Figure 18-8). The *climbing roots* of ivy are adventitious roots that grow out from the stem and attach the plant to a solid support. The *prop roots* of corn grow from the stem down into the soil and help to brace the plant. Spanish moss, a plant that lives attached to trees, develops *aerial roots.* These roots absorb moisture from the air.

18-7 Root Tip Zones

The branches of a root system may extend for many meters. However, roots grow in length only in a small region at their tips. There may be thousands of such root tips gradually extending themselves into the soil. Other parts of the roots may be increasing in thickness, but they are not increasing in length. A mark made on the surface of a root will be found in the same location year after year.

Examination of a root tip shows that it is divided into a number of different zones, each zone containing different types of cells (see Figure 18-9).

Root cap. The **root cap** is a thimble-shaped group of cells that form a protective covering for the delicate meristematic tissues of the root tip behind it. As the root tip is pushed through the soil by the addition of cells behind it, the outer cells of the root cap are crushed. The crushed cells release a lubricating fluid that aids the passage of the root tip through the soil. New root cap cells are continuously formed by the meristematic tissue.

Meristematic zone. The **meristematic zone** is a region of actively dividing cells just behind the root cap. The cells of this region are small, thin-walled, and cubical in shape. All the other cells of the root are formed from these cells.

Elongation zone. Behind the meristematic zone is the **elongation zone.** In this zone, the cells produced in the meristematic zone grow longer. The elongation of these new cells pushes the root tip forward.

Maturation zone. In the **maturation zone,** which is behind the zone of elongation, the cells differentiate. They develop into mature, functioning cells of various types of root tissues. For example, some develop into xylem, others into phloem, and still others into parenchyma.

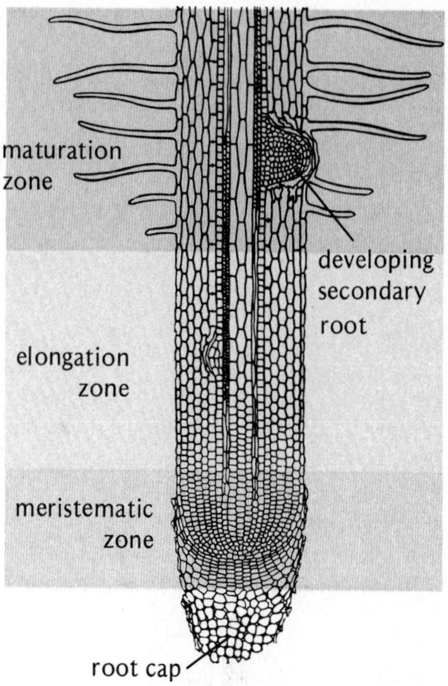

Figure 18-9. Zones of the Root Tip. The meristematic zone consists of rapidly dividing, undifferentiated cells. In the elongation zone, the newly formed cells grow in length, forcing the root tip through the soil. In the maturation zone, the cells develop into specialized tissues.

18-8 Root Structure and Function

In a cross section through the maturation zone, the root can be seen to consist of several distinct tissue layers (see Figure 18-10). The outermost layer, the epidermis, is only one cell layer thick. Absorption of water and minerals from the soil is the major function of the epidermis. Many epidermal cells have hairlike extensions called **root hairs,** which greatly increase the surface area for absorption. The delicate root hairs are short-lived. As the root tip grows, new root hairs are formed, and older ones farther back die and fall off. Note that root hairs are present only in the small zone of maturation behind the growing root tips. It is in this region at the ends of the root branches that practically all water absorption takes place.

Just beneath the epidermis is the **cortex.** The parenchyma cells of the cortex store food, mainly starch. They also transport water absorbed by the root hairs to the conducting tissues

Allow several radish seeds to germinate on wet filter paper in a Petri dish. The root hairs will be easy to see. Tape the Petri dish closed to prevent drying out.

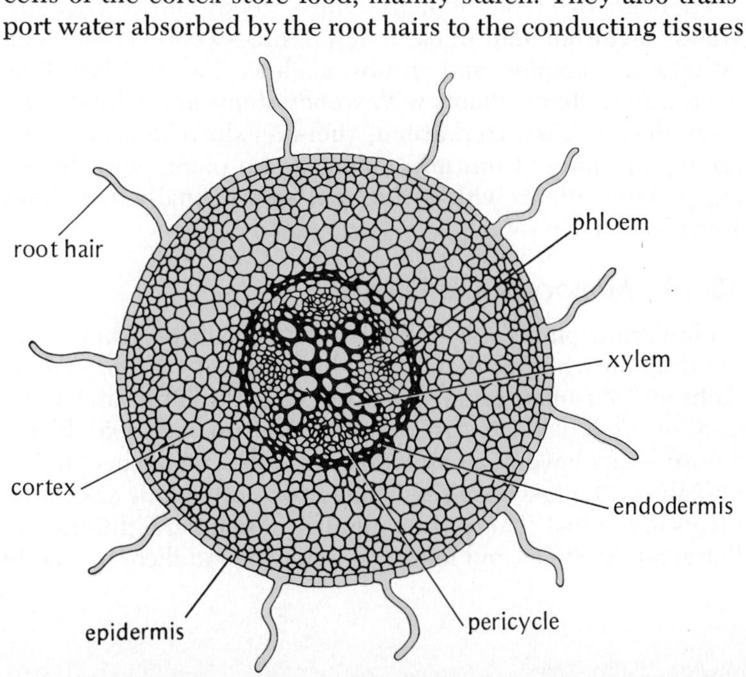

Figure 18-10. Cross Section of Root Tip.

in the center of the root. Beneath the cortex is the **endodermis** (en-duh-*der*-mis). The cells of this layer control the movement of water into the central cylinder.

The **central,** or **vascular, cylinder** is the central core of the root. It is surrounded by a ring of parenchyma cells called the **pericycle** (*per*-uh-sy-kul). The pericycle is the layer from which all secondary roots originate. These roots push their way out through the cortex and epidermis into the soil.

At the center of the vascular cylinder are the conducting tissues, the xylem and phloem. The xylem carries water and minerals up the root to the stem and leaves. The phloem carries dissolved food manufactured in the leaves throughout the plant. In some older roots a layer of cambium develops between the xylem and phloem. Growth of the cambium cells increases the diameter of the root. The cambium produces both xylem and phloem tissues.

THE STEM

After completing your study of this section, you should be able to:

1. Describe the functions of the stem.
2. Compare and contrast the internal structures of the stems of woody dicots, herbaceous dicots, woody monocots, and herbaceous monocots.
3. Describe the external structure of a woody dicot stem.

18-9 Woody and Herbaceous Stems

Most plant stems grow aboveground and serve to display the leaves, fruits, and seeds. Some underground stems are specialized for food storage.

There are two types of plant stems—woody and herbaceous. **Woody stems** contain thick, tough tissue—wood. Trees, such as oaks and maples, and shrubs, such as lilac and forsythia, have woody stems. Plants with woody stems normally live for more than 2 years. **Herbaceous** (her-*bay*-shus) **stems** are soft, green, and juicy. Corn and tomatoes are plants with herbaceous stems. Plants with herbaceous stems usually live either 1 or 2 years.

Herbaceous plants are divided into several groups based on longevity. Annuals, such as beans, corn, petunias, and peas, live for one growing season. Biennials, such as carrots, beets, cabbages, and turnips, live for two growing seasons. Perennials, such as rhubarb, asparagus, dahlias, and peonies, live for more than two years. Woody-stemmed trees, shrubs, and vines are usually perennials.

18-10 Monocots and Dicots

Flowering plants are divided into two major groups, depending on whether their seeds have one or two *cotyledons* (kaht-uh-*leed*-uns), or seed leaves. (The structure and functions of cotyledons are discussed in detail on page 395). Plants whose seeds have one cotyledon are called monocots (*mahn*-uh-kahts). Plants whose seeds have two cotyledons are called **dicots** (*dy*-kahts). There are a number of structural differences between the stems and leaves of monocot and dicot plants. In

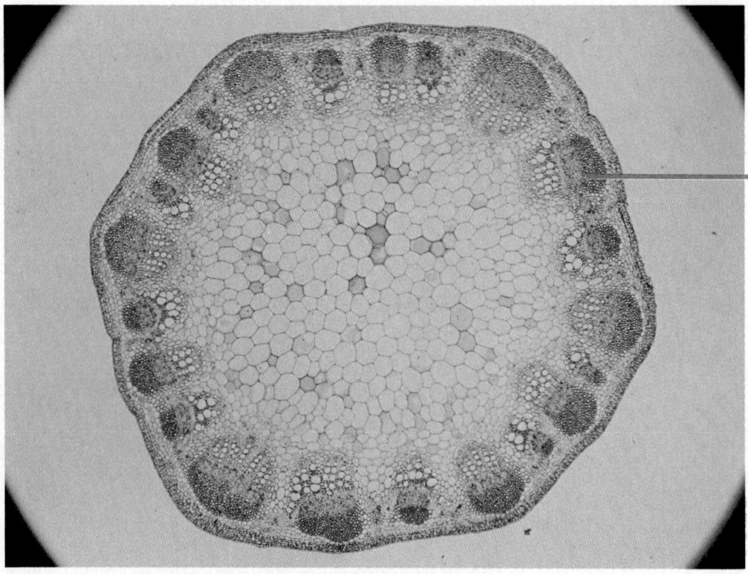

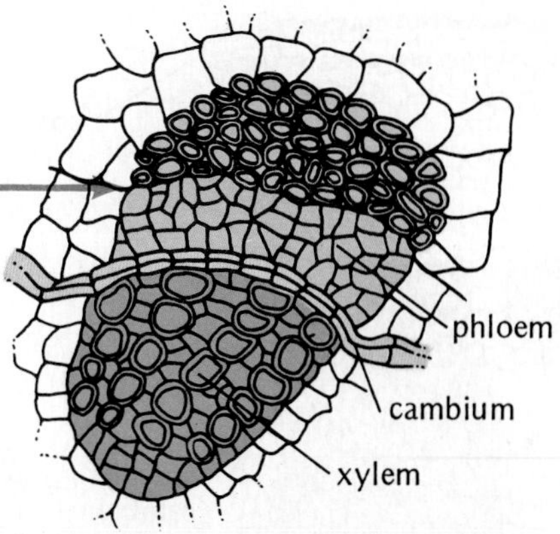

Figure 18-11. Cross Section of a Herbaceous Dicot Stem. The vascular bundles of a herbaceous dicot stem are arranged in a ring inside the cortex. Pith cells fill the center of the stem.

both groups, some plants have herbaceous stems and some have woody stems.

18-11 Dicot Stems

Herbaceous dicot stems. Herbaceous dicot stems are generally soft and green, such as those of the sunflower, geranium, buttercup, or alfalfa. Figure 18-11 shows a cross section of a herbaceous dicot stem. The stem is enclosed by a protective layer of epidermis. Inside the epidermis is the cortex, which is made up of collenchyma and parenchyma. These tissues provide support for the stem and serve for food storage. Inside the cortex is a ring of **vascular bundles.** Each bundle is made up of an outer group of phloem cells, an inner group of xylem cells, and cambium, which is between the xylem and the phloem. The outer cambium cells produce new phloem cells, and the inner cambium cells produce new xylem cells. The center of the stem is filled with **pith.** Pith consists of parenchyma cells that store food.

Woody dicot stems—external structure. Woody dicot stems are very hard but flexible. Figure 18-12 shows the external features of a dormant twig, one that has lost its leaves for the winter. At the tip of the twig is the **terminal bud.** The main function of the bud begins with the growing season. The protective **bud scales** drop off. Meristematic tissue in the bud begins active cell division, forming cells that develop into new stem tissues. New leaves are produced at intervals along the growing stem. At the place on the twig where the bud scales drop off, scars remain called **bud scale scars.** These scars mark the point at which the season's growth began. The length of stem between two sets of bud scale scars represents 1 year's growth.

Another feature of the dormant twig are the **leaf scars.** The leaf scars mark the points of attachment of leaves from previ-

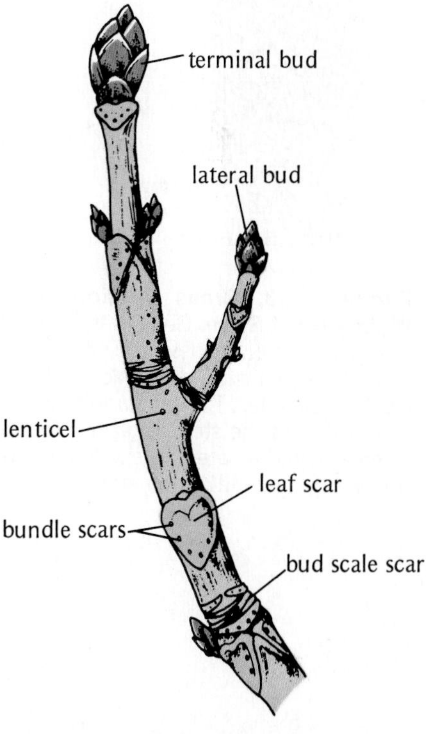

Figure 18-12. External Structure of Dormant Woody Dicot Stem.

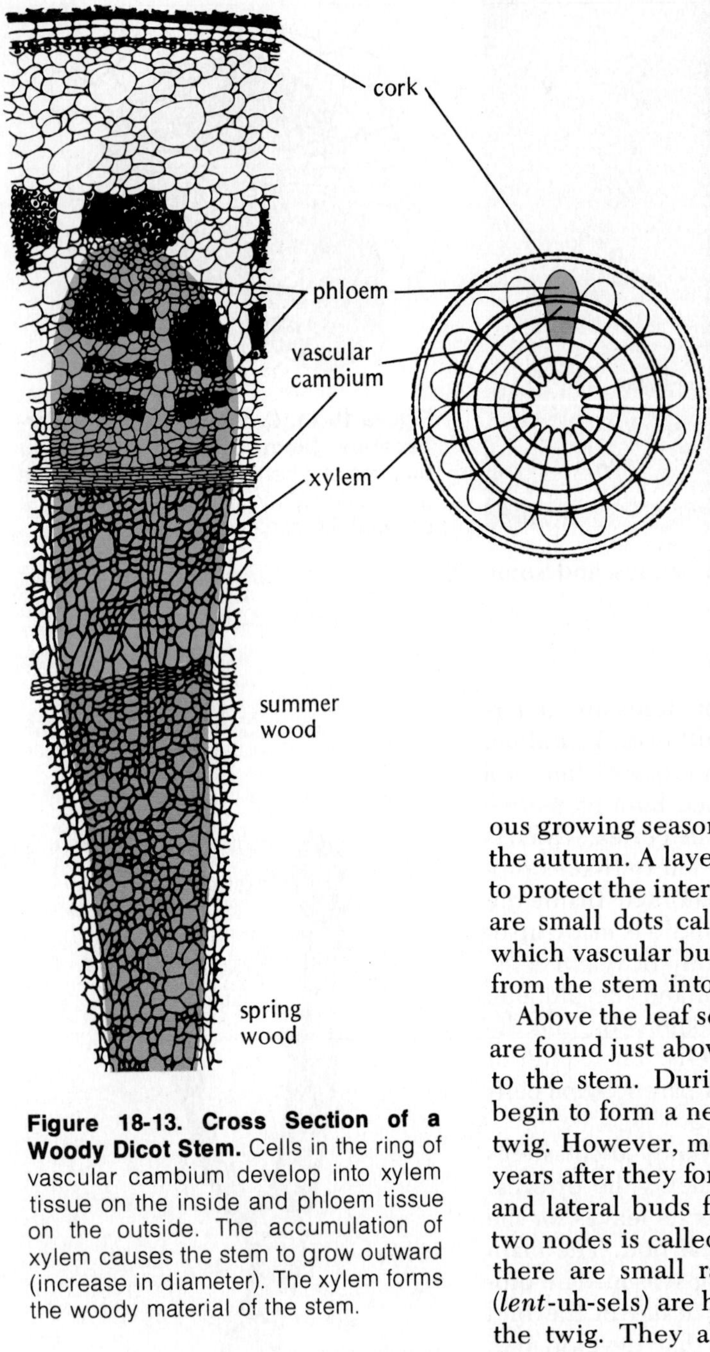

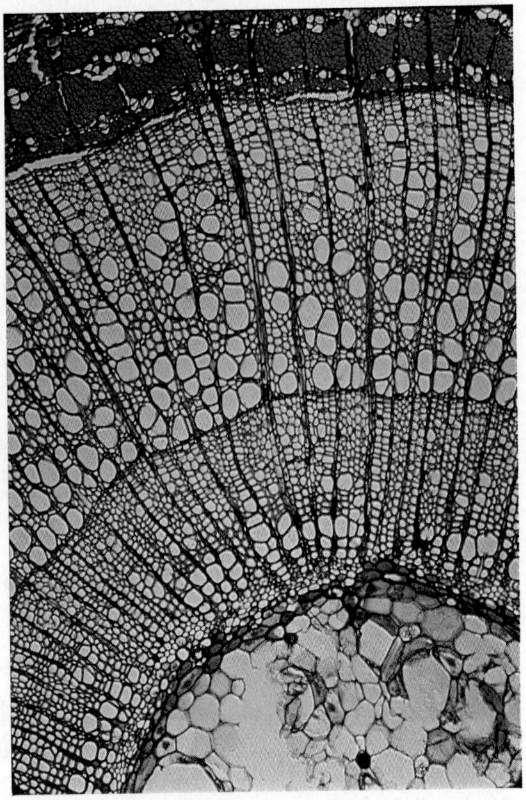

Figure 18-13. Cross Section of a Woody Dicot Stem. Cells in the ring of vascular cambium develop into xylem tissue on the inside and phloem tissue on the outside. The accumulation of xylem causes the stem to grow outward (increase in diameter). The xylem forms the woody material of the stem.

ous growing seasons. Scars are formed when leaves drop off in the autumn. A layer of protective tissue is produced at the scar to protect the internal tissues of the stem. Within the leaf scars are small dots called **bundle scars.** These are the points at which vascular bundles containing xylem and phloem passed from the stem into the leaf.

Above the leaf scar is a **lateral,** or **axillary, bud.** Lateral buds are found just above the point where a leaf is or was attached to the stem. During any growing season, a lateral bud can begin to form a new twig, becoming the terminal bud of that twig. However, most lateral buds remain dormant for several years after they form. The points along the stem where leaves and lateral buds form are called **nodes.** The space between two nodes is called an **internode.** Along the internode surface there are small raised openings called lenticels. **Lenticels** (*lent*-uh-sels) are holes that pass through the outer covering of the twig. They allow the exchange of oxygen and carbon dioxide between the atmosphere and the internal tissues of the stem.

Woody dicot stems—internal structure. In woody dicots the xylem and phloem are arranged in concentric rings (see Figure 18-13). The xylem rings are innermost; the ring of cambium is next to the outermost ring of xylem; and the phloem is just outside the cambium. When a cambium cell toward the inside of the stem divides, xylem cells are produced. When a cambium cell toward the outside of the stem divides, phloem cells are produced.

The production of new xylem during each growing season results in the formation of **annual rings** (see Figure 18-14). The age of a woody dicot stem may be determined by counting these rings. Each annual ring represents 1 year's growth. In some woody dicot stems, the cells of the xylem formed in the spring are larger and lighter in color than those formed in the summer.

In young woody dicots, the center of the stem is filled with pith, and there is a cortex layer inside the epidermis. In older woody stems, the cortex and pith are lost. The pith is replaced by xylem fibers. The inner region of xylem is called **heartwood,** and it increases in size every year. The xylem of the heartwood does not conduct water through the stem. It does serve to strengthen the stem. The functional xylem cells, which conduct water, lie next to the cambium. This functional xylem is called **sapwood.** The thickness of the sapwood remains more or less constant from year to year.

The outermost layer of a woody stem is the **bark,** a protective tissue. On young stems the bark may be relatively thin, but older stems and trunks have bark of considerable thickness. Bark consists of phloem, cork cambium, and cork cells. The cork cells are produced by the cork cambium. The inner portion of the bark is alive, while the outer portion is dead tissue. Bark is continually produced as the stem grows in diameter. As the stem size increases, the older outer bark cracks and peels off and is replaced by new bark.

Figure 18-14. Annual Rings. Each year's growth is visible as an annual ring in the cross section because of differences in spring and summer wood.

18-12 Monocot Stems

Herbaceous monocot stems. Most monocots have herbaceous stems. Corn is a typical herbaceous monocot. Enclosing the soft, green stem is a protective epidermis (see Figure 18-15).

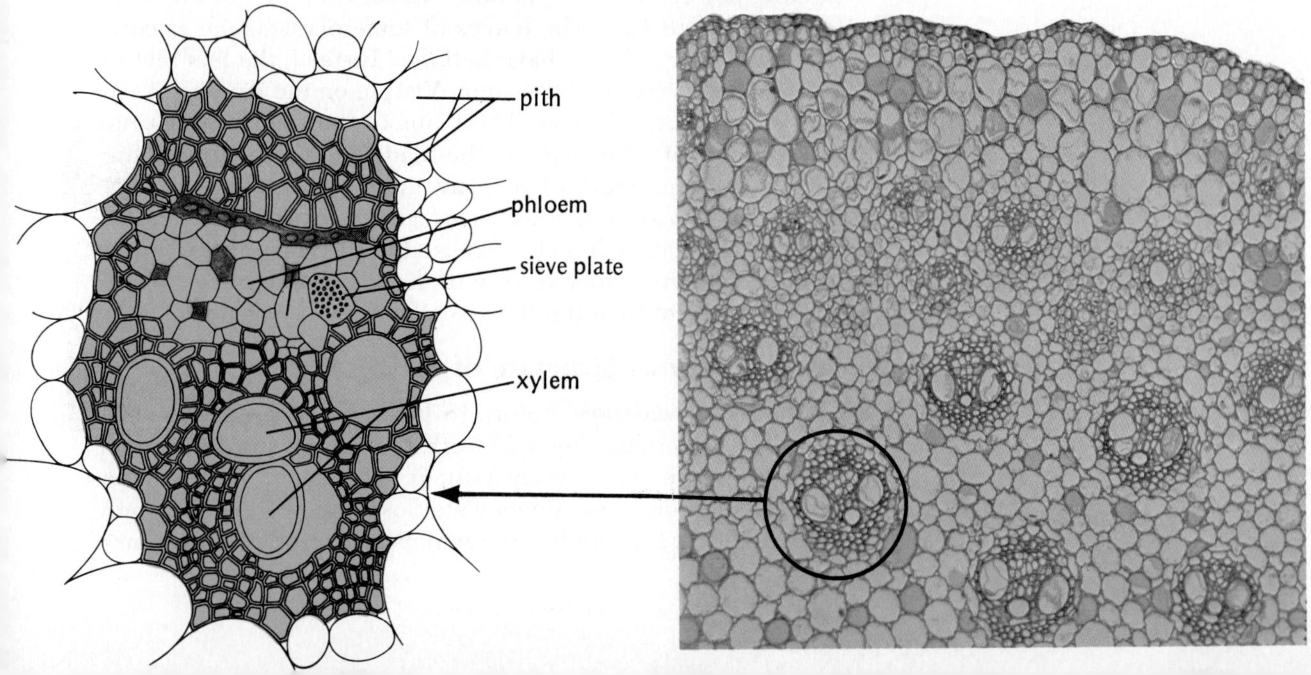

Figure 18-15. Cross Section of a Herbaceous Monocot Stem. In corn, a herbaceous monocot, the vascular bundles are scattered throughout the pith of the stem. Because no cambium is present, there is little growth in stem diameter.

The epidermis is dotted with small openings that allow an exchange of gases between the internal tissues of the stem and the atmosphere.

Under the epidermis is a layer of chloroplast-containing cells. This layer of photosynthetic cells is interrupted by fiber cells that stiffen and support the stem. The interior of the corn stem is filled with pith, which is made up of parenchyma cells. Vascular bundles are scattered throughout the pith. Each bundle contains xylem and phloem enclosed by supporting thick-walled cells. Unlike herbaceous dicots, the stems of most herbaceous monocots have no cambium. Therefore, they show very little growth in diameter.

Woody monocot stems. The stems of woody monocots are similar in structure to those of herbaceous monocots. Vascular bundles are scattered throughout the pith (parenchyma cells). The stems become woody by the thickening of the walls of the pith cells. Woody monocots, such as the palm tree, show relatively little growth in stem diameter. Growth of the terminal bud increases the length of the stem and adds new leaves, which usually surround the growing tip.

THE LEAF

After completing your study of this section, you should be able to:

1. Describe the functions of the leaf.
2. Make a drawing showing the external structure of a leaf and label the blade, petiole, and veins.
3. Draw and label a cross section of a leaf.

18-13 External Structure of the Leaf

A typical leaf consists of a thin, flat **blade,** and a **stalk,** or **petiole** (*pet*-ee-ohl). The petiole attaches the leaf to the stem (see Figure 18-16). The leaves of some plants, such as corn, lilies, and irises, do not have petioles. Instead, the leaf blades are attached directly to the stem. Visible on the surface of the leaf is a network of **veins.** The veins contain the vascular tissues of the leaf. The shape of the blade and the pattern of the veins vary from one type of plant to another and are characteristic of each species. Leaves are generally arranged around the stem so that each leaf is exposed to the maximum amount of sunlight. The upper surface of the leaf has a greater exposure to sunlight than the lower surface.

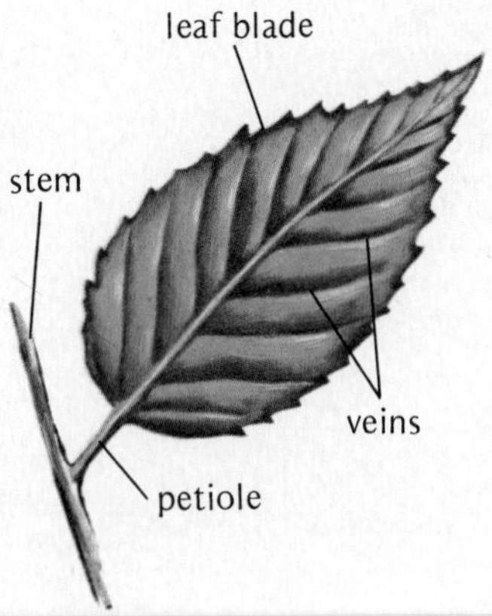

Figure 18-16. External Structure of a Leaf.

18-14 Internal Structure of the Leaf

Cuticle and epidermis. Figure 18-17 shows a cross section of a leaf. The outermost layer of both the upper and lower leaf surfaces is the clear, waxy cuticle. This layer protects the inner tissues and slows down water loss from the leaf. Beneath the cuticle is the epidermis, which also protects the inner

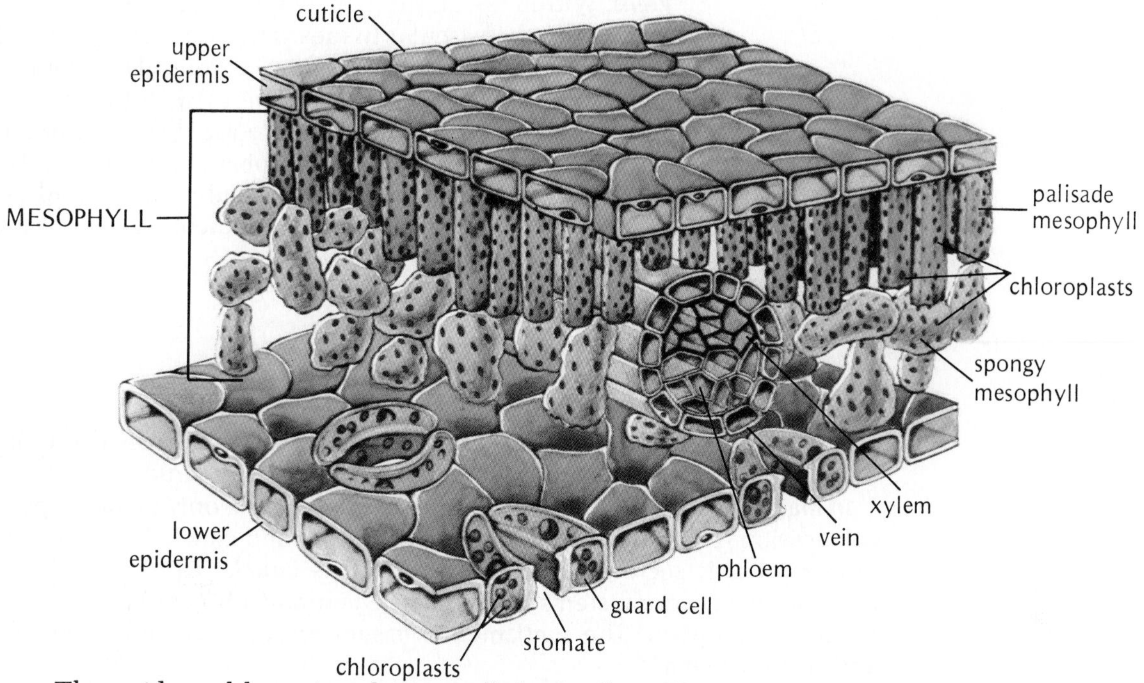

Figure 18-17. Cross Section of a Leaf.

tissues. The epidermal layer is only one cell thick. The cells are flattened and fit together like the pieces of a jigsaw puzzle. Most cells of the epidermis are clear, containing little or no pigment. This allows light to reach the photosynthetic tissues below.

Scattered through the epidermis are small openings called **stomates** (*stoh*-mayts). There are generally many more stomates on the lower surface of the leaf than on the upper surface. The stomates allow the exchange of carbon dioxide and oxygen between the internal tissues of the leaf and the environment. Water vapor also passes out of the leaf through the stomates. The stomates are not open continuously. Instead, they open and close according to the needs of the leaf. Each stomate is surrounded by a pair of specialized epidermal cells called **guard cells.** The kidney-shaped guard cells regulate the opening and closing of the stomates. The mechanisms by which this is accomplished are described in Chapter 19 (page 311).

Mesophyll. Between the upper and lower layers of epidermis is a layer of photosynthetic tissue called **mesophyll** (*mez*-uh-fil). The mesophyll contains two types of thin-walled cells. The upper portion of the mesophyll is called **palisade** (pal-uh-*sayd)* **mesophyll.** It is one or two cells in thickness. This layer consists of tall, tightly packed cells filled with chloroplasts. Below the palisade layer is the **spongy mesophyll.** This layer consists of irregularly shaped cells separated by large air spaces. The stomate openings of the lower epidermis are continuous with the intercellular air spaces of the spongy mesophyll. The cells of the spongy mesophyll contain fewer chloroplasts than the cells of the palisade layer.

Veins. Within the mesophyll layer is a network of veins. The veins contain the vascular tissues. The vein network is so fine that no mesophyll cell is far from a vein. The xylem and phloem of the leaf veins are continuous with the xylem and phloem of the stem and roots. There are distinct differences between the vein patterns of monocot and dicot leaves. In the leaves of monocots, the main veins usually run parallel to one another along the length of the leaf. In dicots, the veins form a network of branches.

summary

Plants are made up of various types of tissues that form organs. The organs of a plant are the root, stems, leaves, and reproductive structures.

In mature plants, meristematic tissues are usually the only tissues capable of cell division. The protective tissues are epidermis and cork. Aboveground, the epidermal cells secrete cutin, which forms the cuticle. Cork is found in the outer layer of woody stems and roots. Xylem and phloem are the vascular tissues of the plant. The fundamental tissues are parenchyma, collenchyma, and sclerenchyma.

The primary root is the first structure to emerge from a sprouting seed. Secondary roots grow out from the primary root. Most plants have either a tap root system or a fibrous root system. Adventitious roots usually develop from mature tissues in the stem.

In cross section, the tissues of a young root from the outside inward are the epidermis, cortex, endodermis, pericycle, and central cylinder. In some older roots, a layer of cambium develops between the xylem and phloem of the central cylinder.

The root tip can be divided into zones along its length. The root cap covers the growing tissue at the tip of the root. Behind the root cap is the meristematic zone, which contains actively dividing cells. In the elongation zone, cells increase in size. In the maturation zone, the cells differentiate and become functional.

Herbaceous dicot stems are soft and green. The central core of the stem is filled with pith. Vascular bundles are arranged in a circle around the pith. In woody dicot stems the xylem and phloem are arranged in concentric rings with cambium between them. Externally, a dormant twig of a woody dicot has a terminal bud at its end and lateral buds above the point of attachment of leaves. New twigs and leaves grow from these buds.

In both herbaceous and woody monocots, the interior of the stem is filled with pith, with the vascular bundles scattered throughout. Neither type of monocot stem contains cambium. Stem growth occurs at the terminal bud.

Leaves are the major sites of photosynthesis in the plant. They usually consist of a flat blade attached to the stem by a petiole. Vascular tissues run from the stem through the petiole and into the leaves, forming veins. The outer surface of the leaf is covered by a waxy cuticle. Beneath the cuticle is a thin, clear epidermis. Between the top and bottom epidermis are the palisade and spongy mesophyll layers. Stomates, mainly on the underside of the leaf, allow the exchange of gases between the leaf tissues and the atmosphere.

vocabulary

adventitious root
annual ring
axillary bud
bark
blade
bud scale
bud scale scar
bundle scar
cambium
central cylinder
collenchyma
cone
cork
cortex
cuticle
cutin
dicot
elongation zone
endodermis
epidermis
fibrous root
flower
fundamental tissue
guard cell
heartwood
herbaceous stem
internode
lateral bud
leaf
leaf scar
lenticel
maturation zone
meristematic tissue
meristematic zone
monocot
node
palisade mesophyll
parenchyma
pericycle
petiole
phloem
pith
primary root
protective tissue
root
root cap
root hair
sapwood
sclerenchyma
secondary root
spongy mesophyll
stem
stomate
taproot
terminal bud
vascular bundle
vascular cylinder
vascular tissue
vein
woody stem
xylem

test your learning

Section

18-1 **1.** Name the four types of organs found in plants, and give the functions of each.

18-2 **2.** What is the function of meristematic tissue, and where is it found in the plant?

18-3 **3.** Name two types of protective tissues found in plants, and describe where each is located.

18-4 **4.** Name the two types of conducting tissues found in plants, and describe the structure and function of each.

18-5 **5.** Name the three types of fundamental tissues of the plant. Briefly describe the functions of each and where it is found.

18-6 **6.** Distinguish between primary roots and secondary roots.

7. Compare and contrast taproot, fibrous root, and adventitious root systems.

18-7 **8.** List in order beginning with the root cap the different zones of cellular activity in the root tip. Describe the cellular activities within each zone.

18-8 **9.** Draw a cross section of a root, label the different tissue layers, and state the functions of each.

18-9 **10.** What are the differences between woody and herbaceous stems?

18-10 **11.** What is a cotyledon?

12. What is the basic difference between a monocot and a dicot?

18-11 **13.** Draw a cross section of a herbaceous dicot stem, and label the different tissues.

14. Draw a dormant twig of a woody dicot, and label the following parts: terminal bud, bud scale scar, leaf scar, bundle scar, lateral bud, and lenticels.

15. Where does growth occur on the woody dicot stem?

16. What is the function of the lenticels?

17. Draw a cross section of a woody dicot stem, and label the tissues.

18. What are annual rings, and how are they produced?

19. What is the difference between heartwood and sapwood? From what type of tissue are they both formed?

18-12 **20.** Draw a cross section of a herbaceous monocot stem, and label the different tissues.

21. What makes a woody monocot stem woody?

22. Where does growth occur in woody monocot stems? Does the stem increase in diameter?

18-13 **23.** What are the blade, petiole, and veins of a leaf?

18-14 **24.** Describe the structure of a leaf in cross section.

test your understanding

1. Explain how growth occurs in the roots and stems of a woody dicot. Where on the stems do new leaves grow in the spring?
2. How do the tissues of the plant obtain oxygen from the environment and get rid of carbon dioxide and water vapor?
3. Compare and contrast the structure of herbaceous and woody dicot stems.
4. In what ways are the stems of plants adaptations for life on land?

independent research

1. Prepare a report on the structural differences between monocot and dicot plants.
2. Maple syrup is made from the sap of sugar maple trees. Prepare a report on the production of maple syrup, including a description of how and when the trees are tapped.

chapter 19

Plant Maintenance

19-1 Chapter Introduction

Plants, like animals, must carry on the basic life processes to remain alive. These processes include transport, nutrition, excretion, cellular respiration, synthesis, and reproduction. In terms of the life processes, the major difference between plants and animals is the capacity of green plants to synthesize the organic nutrients they need by the process of photosynthesis. Because the plant synthesizes its nutrients, it does not need complex organ systems for locomotion, ingestion or digestion of food, circulation, or excretion of wastes. The necessary functions are carried out by specialized tissues.

In this chapter we will discuss all the life processes of plants except photosynthesis and reproduction, which are discussed in separate chapters.

TRANSPORT IN VASCULAR PLANTS

After completing your study of this section, you should be able to:

1. Describe the process of transpiration and the factors that affect it.
2. Explain the mechanism of transport of fluid in the xylem of plants, describing each of the factors involved.
3. Describe the transport of nutrients in plants.

19-2 Transpiration

Transpiration (tranz-puh-*ray*-shun) is the loss from a plant of water in the form of water vapor. Most transpiration takes place by evaporation through the stomates of the leaves, but

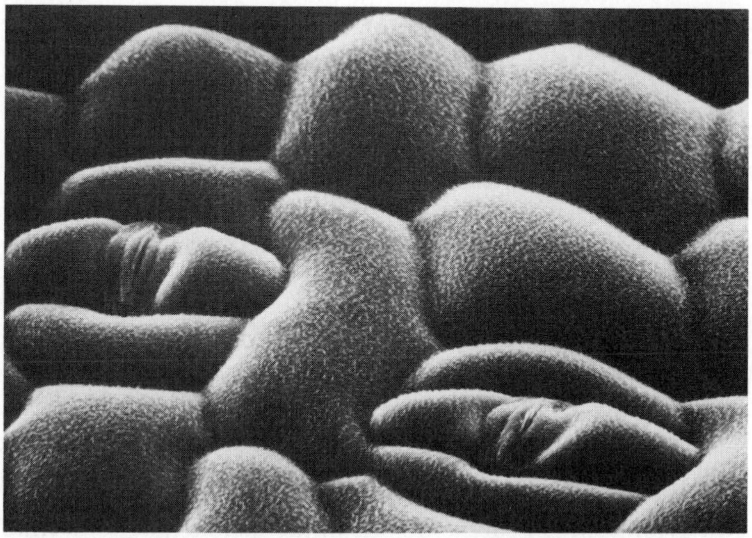

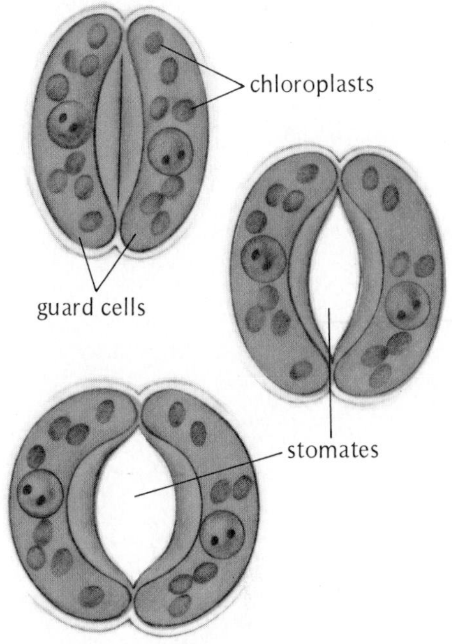

Figure 19-1. Stomates and Guard Cells. The scanning electron micrograph shows two closed stomates, each surrounded by two guard cells. The other cells are epidermal cells. The drawing shows how the stomate opens when the walls of the guard cells buckle outward.

some also occurs through the lenticels of the stem. Transpiration is closely related to the plant's need to exchange carbon dioxide and oxygen with the atmosphere. For these gases to diffuse through the plant cell membranes, the cell surfaces must be moist. The internal surfaces of leaf cells are kept moist by water drawn up from the roots. This water continuously evaporates into the intercellular spaces of the leaf and passes out through the stomates. Large quantities of water are removed from the soil and released into the atmosphere as the result of transpiration. During the summer, one large tree can give off as much as 250 liters of water each day. The evaporation of water from the leaves removes heat. Thus transpiration also has a cooling effect on the plant.

The rate of transpiration is regulated by the opening and closing of the stomates of the leaves. The stomates are generally closed when there is a shortage of water in the leaves, when the temperature is low, or when there is little light. They are open only when there is adequate water and when an exchange of gases with the environment is necessary, as during photosynthesis.

Demonstrate transpiration by tying a clear plastic bag around an entire plant. Water vapor given off by the plant will condense on the inside of the bag.

The opening and closing of each stomate is controlled by the pair of guard cells that surrounds it. The guard cells are sausage-shaped, and their inner walls are thicker than their outer walls (see Figure 19-1). When the guard cells become *turgid* (*ter*-jid) (filled with water and swollen), the uneven thicknesses of their walls causes them to buckle outward. The opening left between the two cells is the stomate. When the guard cells lose water and become less turgid, they resume their original shape, and the stomate closes.

Unlike other cells in the leaf epidermis, guard cells contain chloroplasts and carry on photosynthesis. The fact that guard cells carry on photosynthesis is related to their ability to open and close the stomates. Photosynthesis produces soluble carbohydrates, such as glucose. When these soluble substances are present in the guard cell cytoplasm, the concentration of water is reduced. Water from the surrounding epidermal cells therefore enters the guard cells by osmosis. The cells buckle outward, and the stomates open. However, through enzyme-catalyzed reactions, the guard cells can convert the soluble carbohydrates to insoluble forms, such as starch. Insoluble substances do not exert any osmotic effects. Thus, when the soluble carbohydrates are converted to insoluble forms, the osmotic balance between the guard cells and surrounding epidermal cells is reversed. Water leaves the guard cells, they become less turgid, and the stomates close. The carbohydrates in the guard cells can be changed back and forth between soluble and insoluble forms, thus opening and closing the stomates.

The concentration of dissolved carbon dioxide in the guard cell cytoplasm appears to be one of the factors that determine whether the carbohydrates of the guard cells are in the soluble or insoluble form. There is also some evidence that an active transport mechanism involving ATP and potassium ions affects the osmotic pressure in the guard cells. Furthermore, certain plant hormones have been found to affect the opening and closing of stomates.

19-3 Transport in the Xylem

Water and dissolved minerals absorbed by the roots from the soil travel upward through the xylem of the roots, stems, and leaves of the plant. In tall trees, such as redwoods and Douglas firs, water is raised to heights of more than 125 meters. The mechanism by which this is accomplished has long puzzled botanists. It cannot be a matter of active transport within the xylem, because xylem does not contain living cells. Two processes that can be easily observed are part of the answer. These are capillary action and root pressure. However, their effects are not strong enough to be the whole answer. In recent years a process called transpiration pull has been proposed to complete the picture.

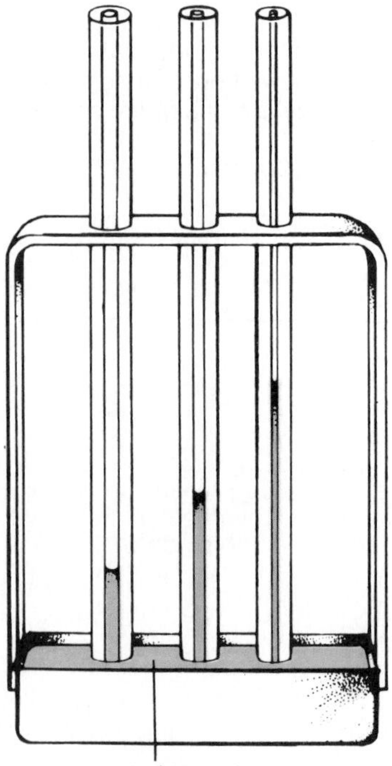

Figure 19-2. Capillary Action. The upward movement of water in tubes of small diameter involves the forces of adhesion and cohesion. The water rises highest in the narrowest tube.

Capillary action. **Capillary action,** or **capillarity** (kap-uh-*lar*-uh-tee), is the upward movement of a liquid in a tube of narrow diameter. As you can see in Figure 19-2, the water in the tubes has risen above the surface of the water in the container. How far the water rises depends on the diameter of the tube—the narrower the tube, the higher the water rises.

There are two factors involved in capillary action—adhesion and cohesion. **Adhesion** (ad-*hee*-zhun) is an attractive force between unlike molecules. Thus, there is an attractive force between the water molecules and the glass sides of the tube. Because of adhesion, water creeps up the sides of the tube. **Cohesion** (koh-*hee*-zhun) is an attractive force between like molecules. Thus, there is an attractive force between the water molecules in the tube. Water moving up the sides of the tube pulls other water molecules up with it because of cohesion.

Xylem is similar to a narrow tube. Water will rise in it as the result of capillary action. However, the most that capillary action can do is to raise water several centimeters.

Root pressure. When the stem of a well-watered plant is cut off close to the soil, sap flows from the stump. If a glass tube is attached to the cut end of the stump, sap rises in the tube to a height of 1 meter or so (see Figure 19-3). The pressure that holds up the column of water is **root pressure,** an osmotic pressure in the root cells. The situation is very much like the demonstration of osmosis in Figure 5-16 (page 81). The cytoplasm of the root cells has a higher concentration of dissolved materials than the water in the soil. Therefore, water diffuses into the cells by osmosis and produces an osmotic pressure. This pressure drives the water into and up the xylem of the central cylinder. There is also evidence that active transport plays a part in generating root pressure. Some plant physiologists believe that the cells of the endodermis, which surround the central cylinder of the root, secrete water into the xylem by active transport. In any event, root pressure cannot account for more than about a meter of the rise of the sap in stems.

Transpiration pull. In the latest theory of upward movement of water, the sap in the xylem of a tall plant is viewed as a continuous column of liquid. This column extends from the roots, through the stem, and into the leaves (see Figure 19-4). It is held together by the cohesive forces of the water molecules. As a result of transpiration in the leaves, molecules evaporate from the upper end of the column of water. As this occurs, other molecules are drawn into the leaf tissues to replace them. These molecules exert a pull on the ones below them. In this way, the entire column of water is slowly pulled up. At the base of the column (the roots), water molecules constantly move into the xylem to keep the column intact. According to this theory, water is not pushed up, but *pulled* up, through the xylem as transpiration occurs. Experiments have shown that this process, called **transpiration pull,** can account for the movement of water to the tops of the tallest trees.

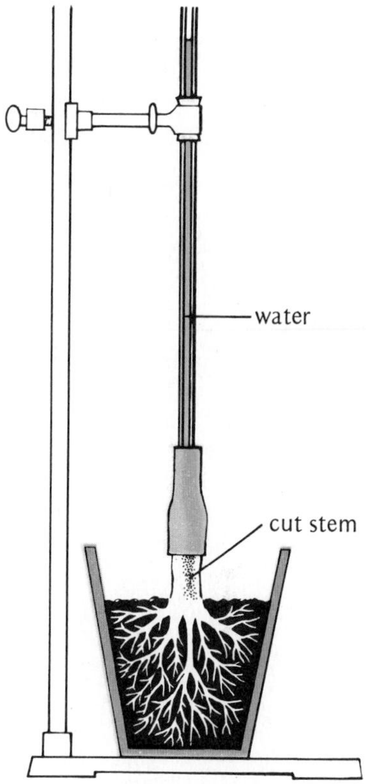

Figure 19-3. Root Pressure. Root pressure, an osmotic pressure in the root cells, can hold up a column of water about 1 meter high.

19-4 Translocation

The movement of dissolved inorganic and organic materials through a plant is called **translocation** (tranz-loh-*kay*-shun). Minerals and other inorganic substances absorbed from the soil are transported upward through the plant in the xylem. Some of these substances are absorbed and used as needed by individual cells. Others are circulated from place to place within the plant, depending on where they are needed at a particular time. Circulation of these substances takes place in the phloem.

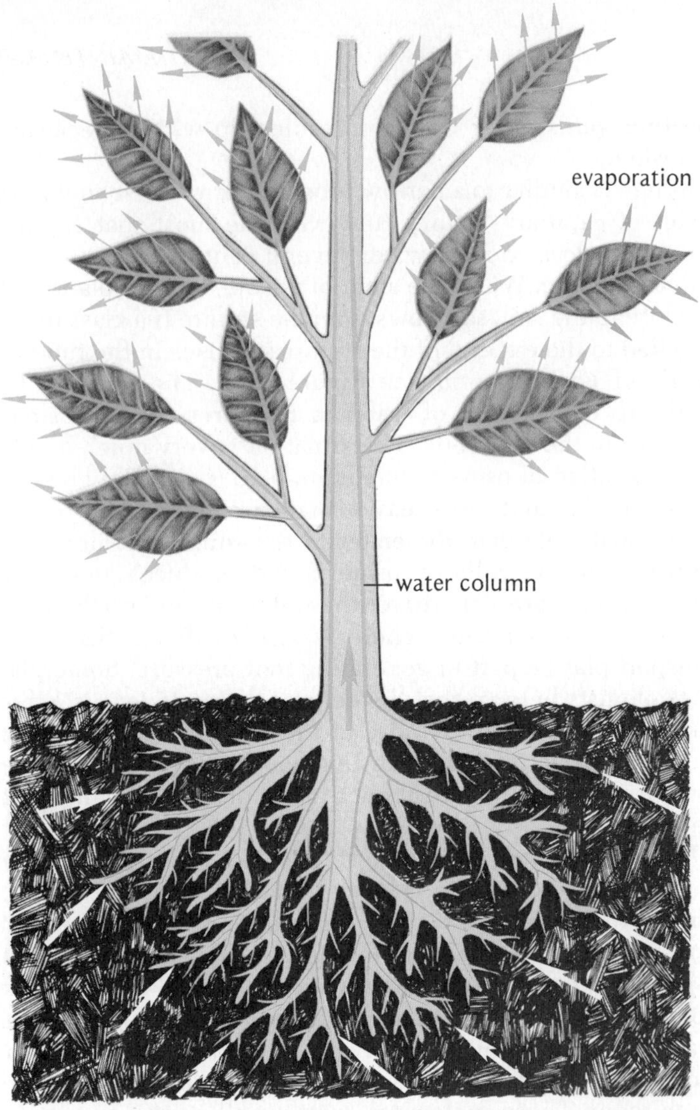

Figure 19-4. Transpiration Pull. As water molecules evaporate from the stomates of the leaves, other water molecules are drawn up the column to replace them. Transpiration pull can account for the movement of water through xylem.

Sugars and other nutrients are produced by photosynthesis in the leaves of plants. These nutrients are transported as needed to all other parts of the plant. The translocation of these dissolved organic compounds occurs in the sieve cells of the phloem. The movement of substances in the phloem can be either upward or downward. Furthermore, different substances in adjacent sieve cells can move in opposite directions, and the direction of movement can change very quickly. Although movement of materials in the phloem generally occurs in the direction of the concentration gradient, it can also occur against the concentration gradient, a process requiring active transport.

The movement of water and minerals in the xylem is a passive, mechanical process because the cells of the xylem are dead. The cells of the phloem, however, are alive. If they are killed, the movement of materials in the phloem stops. The movement of materials through the phloem is very rapid, much more rapid than can be explained by simple diffusion. Several theories have been developed to explain this rapid movement. However, none is completely satisfactory. The most widely accepted theory at this time is the *pressure flow theory*. According to this theory, the rapid movement of soluble materials occurs because of differences in osmotic pressure in different parts of the column of sieve cells. Where cells have a high concentration of dissolved substances, as in the leaves, water enters by osmosis. This produces an osmotic pressure that forces the dissolved substances into adjacent cells. The concentration of the dissolved substances therefore increases in these cells. Water now enters these cells, and the process is repeated from cell to cell. Where cells have a low concentration of dissolved substances because sugars are being used up, water will leave by osmosis. The osmotic pressure inside the cells will therefore drop, and materials will be forced in from adjacent cells.

EXCRETION

After completing your study of this section, you should be able to:

1. Describe the exchange of respiratory gases between green plants and the environment, and also the use of carbon dioxide and oxygen produced by cellular respiration and photosynthesis.
2. Describe how nitrogenous wastes and other wastes are treated in plants.

19-5 Gas Exchange

In green plants, not all metabolic wastes are excreted; some are used by the plant. This is true to some extent for oxygen and carbon dioxide. Plants carry on cellular respiration both day and night. Oxygen, which is needed for cellular respiration, is a by-product of photosynthesis. During the day, when photosynthesis is occurring, some of the oxygen produced is used for cellular respiration. The rest diffuses out of the plant through the stomates of the leaves and the lenticels of the stem. Carbon dioxide, which is an end product of cellular respiration, is used in photosynthesis. Thus, during the day, the carbon dioxide produced by cellular respiration is used in photosynthesis. At night, when there is no photosynthesis going on, carbon dioxide is excreted through the stomates and lenticels.

19-6 Nitrogenous and Other Wastes

Nitrogenous, or nitrogen-containing, wastes are normally excreted by animals, but may be used by plants. When, for example, there are excess amino acids, the amino group (NH_2) is removed, and the nitrogen is used in the synthesis of other compounds.

Other wastes may be stored within vacuoles in certain cells, and still other wastes are stored as crystals. Spinach, for example, stores oxalic acid crystals in its leaves.

Actively dividing meristematic cells grow away from their waste materials. The wastes are simply left behind in the cells produced by these tissues.

NUTRITION AND SYNTHESIS

After completing your study of this section, you should be able to:

1. Name the various types of nutrients required by plants.
2. List the basic types of nutrients that can be synthesized by plants.

19-7 Plant Nutrients

Plants are able to synthesize the carbohydrates, proteins, and other organic compounds they need. However, to do so, they need inorganic raw materials. For making carbohydrates, they need water and carbon dioxide, which provide hydrogen, oxygen, and carbon. For amino acids and proteins, they need a source of nitrogen. Some plants are supplied with usable nitrogen compounds by bacteria that live in their roots. Most, however, must obtain nitrogen compounds from the soil. Plants must also obtain various inorganic substances, called minerals, from the soil. Minerals required by plants include compounds of magnesium, iron, phosphorus, calcium, and sulfur. Magnesium and iron are needed for the synthesis of chlorophyll. Copper, zinc, and a few other mineral elements are needed in very small, or trace, amounts. A deficiency of any of these elements can have serious effects on plant growth (see Figure 19-5).

Figure 19-5. Plant Nutrients. The healthy plant (left) was grown with an adequate supply of minerals, such as magnesium, copper, and iron. The smaller, less healthy plant (right) was grown in a mineral deficient medium.

19-8 Plant Synthesis

Plants have the capacity to synthesize a wide variety of complex organic substances. They are able to synthesize amino acids, proteins, carbohydrates, lipids, nucleic acids, and vitamins. Certain plants also synthesize unusual organic compounds that humans have found useful. For example, digitalis, morphine, and quinine are plant products that are used as drugs. Other plants produce substances that are used in making beverages—for example, cocoa beans, coffee beans, tea leaves, ginger root, and cola nuts.

HORMONES AND GROWTH RESPONSES IN PLANTS

After completing your study of this section, you should be able to:

1. Describe the effects of auxins on different parts of the plant.
2. Define the term *tropism*.
3. Describe positive phototropism in a stem.

4. Describe the various effects of gibberellins on plant growth.
5. Explain how plant growth is coordinated by the interaction of various hormones.
6. Define the term *photoperiodism*.

19-9 Plant Hormones

Hormones play an important role in the regulation of plant functions. Like animal hormones, plant hormones are complex organic compounds that act as chemical messengers. They affect cell metabolism, cell division, and plant growth in general. Most hormones are synthesized by actively dividing meristematic tissues at the tips of roots and stems.

There are a number of different types of hormones in plants, but the three most important kinds are auxins, gibberellins, and cytokinins. These hormones affect the growth of various plant tissues.

Auxins. **Auxins** (*awk*-sinz) are hormones that affect the growth of all types of plant tissues. Whether growth is stimulated or inhibited by auxins depends on the type of tissue and the concentration of the hormone. The most common auxin in nature is IAA, indoleacetic acid.

In the growing tips of roots and stems, auxins stimulate the differentiation of cells in the maturation zones. These new cells are initially unspecialized and nonfunctional. Under the influence of specific concentrations of auxins, they develop the characteristics of the various types of mature tissues they will become.

Auxins produced by the terminal bud of a stem stimulate stem growth, but inhibit the growth of lateral buds for some distance along that stem. When a terminal bud has grown a sufficient distance away from a lateral bud, the lateral bud will begin to grow. It will become the terminal bud of a new stem. Snipping off the terminal buds of various types of house plants will result in the development of lateral stems and produce a bushier plant.

High auxin concentrations that stimulate the growth of stems inhibit the growth of roots. However, low auxin levels stimulate growth in the roots. The development of fruits is stimulated by auxins.

Leaves, flowers, and fruits drop off the plant when a special layer of cells, called the *abscission layer,* forms at the point of attachment to the stem. Auxins inhibit the formation of the abscission layer and thus prevent the dropping of the structures until the proper time. Another hormone, ethylene (discussed below), stimulates production of this layer when the auxin level drops. For example, leaves fall when the production of auxins by the blade decreases.

Auxins and tropisms. A **tropism** (*troh*-piz-um) is a growth response in a plant caused by an environmental stimulus that comes primarily from one direction. An easily observed

sidelights

A wide variety of plants, from orchids to pine trees, appear to require the presence of fungi that grow in association with their roots. Fungi that grow in association with the roots of other plants are called *mycorrhizae*.

The mycorrhizae actually grow into the outer, cortex layer of the root, and may form a sheath around the root. It is thought that both the fungus and the plant benefit from this relationship. The fungus supplies the plant with water and minerals taken up from the soil, while the plant supplies the fungus with organic nutrients.

The inhibition of lateral buds by auxins produced at the growing tips is called apical dominance.

Figure 19-6. Phototropism. The bending of the plant toward the light is positive phototropism.

tropism is **phototropism** (*foh*-toh-*troh*-piz-um), the bending of a plant stem toward a light source (see Figure 19-6). Growth of a plant toward the light is an example of a *positive tropism*—the plant grows toward the stimulus. In a *negative tropism*, the plant grows away from the direction of the stimulus. Roots, unlike stems, generally show negative phototropism—they grow away from the light source.

Another type of tropism is **geotropism** (*jee*-oh-*troh*-piz-um), the response of the plant to the force of gravity. Roots generally show a positive geotropism—they grow down into the earth in the direction of the force of gravity. Stems, on the other hand, generally show a negative geotropism—they grow up against the force of gravity. Other tropisms include *chemotropism*, which is a response to various chemicals; *hydrotropism*, which is a response to water; and *thigmotropism*, which is a response to touch.

The growth responses seen in tropisms result from an uneven distribution of auxins in the growing tips of roots and stems. In phototropism, for example, the concentration of auxins is higher on the shady side of the stem than on the lighted side. The stem cells are stimulated by auxins, so those with the higher auxin concentrations (the shady side) grow faster than those with the lower concentration (the lighted side). Thus, through uneven growth, the stem bends toward the light. It is not known how the auxins become unevenly distributed in the plant tissues.

Gibberellins. **Gibberellins** (jib-uh-*rel*-inz) are hormones that affect plant growth as well as the development of fruits and seeds. Unlike auxins, gibberellins are evenly distributed throughout the plant tissues. Thus they are not involved in the uneven growth responses of tropisms. Under the influence of gibberellins, plant stems begin to grow early in the spring when temperatures are still low. In dwarf plants and plants whose stems normally show little growth (for example, cabbage), the application of gibberellins stimulates rapid stem growth. In plants with normally tall stems, gibberellins have much less effect. Gibberellins have also been found to cause seeds to sprout, to increase the size of fruits, and to cause flowering in some plants.

Other hormones. **Cytokinins** (syt-uh-*ky*-ninz) are a group of plant hormones that stimulate cell division and growth. They are thought to function together with auxins in stimulating the differentiation of different plant tissues. **Ethylene** (*eth*-uh-leen), a relatively simple organic compound, stimulates flowering in some groups of plants and hastens the ripening of fruit. **Abscisic** (*ab*-sis-ik) **acid** influences the shedding of leaves and the seasonal slowing down of plant activities.

Interaction of plant hormones. In the early phases of a plant's life, gibberellins play an important role in seed sprouting. These hormones promote the secretion of an enzyme that weakens the seed coat so that the developing embryo can break out of the seed. After the seed sprouts, cytokinins stimulate cell division and may influence tissue and organ formation. Auxins generally influence the growth of plants after the early stages of development.

19-10 Photoperiodism

Plant growth is directly affected by the number of hours of light and darkness each day, as well as by temperature and hormones. The response of a plant to the changing duration of light and darkness that occurs during the year is called **photoperiodism** (foh-tuh-*pir*-ee-uhd-iz-um). Photoperiodism controls flowering and the fall of leaves in the autumn.

In many types of plants, flowering is related to the number of hours of light and darkness in the daily cycle. Although it was once thought that it was the number of hours of daylight that stimulated flowering, recent investigations indicate that flowering is induced by the number of hours of uninterrupted darkness each day. Plants are divided into three groups, depending on the influence of the daily cycle on their growth. *Long-day plants,* such as clover, potatoes, corn, beets, and gladiolus, produce flowers in summer when there are 12 to 14 hours of daylight. *Short-day plants* include forsythia, tulips, chrysanthemums, and asters. These plants flower in the early spring, late summer, or fall, when the nights are longer. *Day-neutral plants* are only slightly influenced or are unaffected by the length of day or night. Plants of this type include tomatoes, cotton, zinnias, dandelions, and snapdragons.

summary

In green plants, water is lost by evaporation from the stomates of the leaves and the lenticels of the stem, a process called transpiration. The upward movement of water from the roots through the stem and to the leaves takes place in the xylem. It is accomplished by a combination of capillary action, root pressure, and transpiration pull. The movement through the plant of nutrients and other dissolved organic and inorganic materials is called translocation. The translocation of materials takes place in the phloem.

Not all wastes are excreted in plants. Oxygen produced by photosynthesis may be used in cellular respiration, while carbon dioxide produced by cellular respiration may be used in photosynthesis. Nitrogenous wastes may be broken down and the nitrogen reused. In some plants, various wastes are stored in vacuoles.

Plants can synthesize all the complex organic nutrients that they require. However, to do this they require hydrogen, carbon, oxygen, nitrogen, and a variety of inorganic minerals from the environment.

Plant hormones are generally produced by actively dividing meristematic tissues. The three most important types of hormones are auxins, gibberellins, and cytokinins. All affect plant growth. In plants, a growth response caused by an environmental stimulus that comes primarily from one direction is called a tropism. Plant growth, flowering, and the fall of leaves are affected by the number of hours of light and dark each day. The response of a plant to changing lengths of day and night during the year is called photoperiodism.

vocabulary

abscisic acid
adhesion
auxin
capillarity
capillary action
cohesion
cytokinin
ethylene
geotropism
gibberellin
photoperiodism
phototropism
root pressure
translocation
transpiration
transpiration pull
tropism

test your learning

Section

19-1 1. What is the major difference between the life processes of a plant and an animal?

19-2 2. What is transpiration?

3. How do guard cells control the opening and closing of the stomates?

4. Explain how the conversion of carbohydrates between soluble and insoluble forms affects the rate of transpiration.

19-3 5. Why is it not possible for xylem cells to carry on active transport?

6. Define the terms *adhesion* and *cohesion,* and explain the process of capillary action.

7. What is root pressure?

8. Describe transpiration pull.

19-4 9. What is translocation?

10. What materials are transported in the phloem?

11. Compare and contrast transport of materials in the phloem and in the xylem.

19-5 12. Explain the relationship between the production and use of carbon dioxide and oxygen in plants.

19-6 13. Describe how nitrogenous and other wastes are dealt with by plants.

19-7 14. Name the most important substances that plants must obtain from the environment to carry on their life processes.

19-8 15. Name the various types of nutrients synthesized by plants.

19-9 16. Name the three major types of plant hormones and describe their effects on different plant tissues.

17. What is a positive tropism? A negative tropism?

18. Describe three types of tropisms.

19-10 19. What is photoperiodism?

test your understanding

1. Trace the path of a water molecule from the point where it enters a root hair until it evaporates from a stomate of a leaf.
2. What evidence is there that transport of material in the phloem involves active transport?
3. Explain what happens in a plant when it grows toward a light source.
4. Discuss some of the ways in which hormones enable a plant to adapt to its environment.

independent research

1. Prepare a report on the use of plants in the treatment of disease in various societies.
2. Prepare a report on the use of plant hormones in growing fruit, flowers, and ornamental plants.

UNIT 4
REPRODUCTION AND DEVELOPMENT

chapter 20

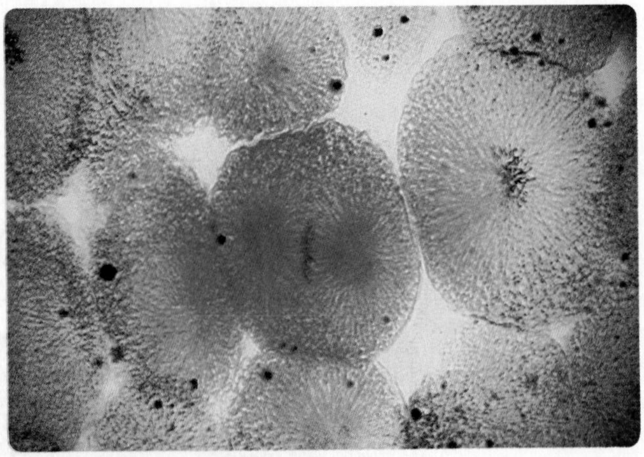

Mitosis and Asexual Reproduction

20-1 Chapter Introduction

All cells arise from other cells. This occurs by the division of the original cell into two cells. When a unicellular organism divides into two identical but separate organisms, the result of the cell division is reproduction. In a multicellular organism, the division of body cells produces daughter cells that remain part of the original organism. In this case, cell division usually results in growth in size of the organism or replacement of tissue. A new individual is not ordinarily formed. However, division of body cells may also be a method of reproduction in some multicellular organisms if the new cells separate from the parent and form a complete individual.

There are two basic types of reproduction—asexual and sexual. In **asexual** (ay-*sek*-shuh-wul) **reproduction** there is only one parent, and no special reproductive cells or organs are involved. The new individual is a separated part of the parent organism. **Sexual** (*sek*-shuh-wul) **reproduction,** on the other hand, involves the union of two nuclei from special sex cells, which are usually produced by two separate parent organisms. Some organisms reproduce only asexually, others reproduce only sexually, and still others can reproduce by either method. Reproduction is not one of the essential life processes for the individual. However, it is essential for the survival of the species.

In this chapter we will discuss the process of cell division and its role in asexual reproduction. Sexual reproduction will be discussed in Chapter 21.

MITOSIS

After completing your study of this section, you should be able to:

1. Name the two basic processes involved in cell division.
2. Explain why each cell must contain a full set of chromosomes to function properly.
3. List the stages of mitotic cell division, and briefly describe the events in each.
4. Explain how division of the cytoplasm occurs in animal cells.
5. Explain the differences in mitotic cell division between plant and animal cells.
6. Explain which types of cells divide frequently and which do not.
7. Discuss the mechanisms thought to control mitotic division in unicellular and in multicellular organisms.

20-2 Nuclear and Cytoplasmic Division

Cell division consists of two processes—the division of the nucleus and the division of the cytoplasm. The process by which the nucleus divides is called **mitosis** (my-*toh*-sis), and the division of the entire cell is called **mitotic cell division.** During mitosis, a series of changes occurs in the nucleus that results in the duplication of the hereditary material. When the nucleus divides, each daughter nucleus receives a complete copy of this material. During cytoplasmic division, the cytoplasm of the cell is divided into two parts, each containing one of the newly formed nuclei and approximately half of the other contents of the parent cell. Cytoplasmic division may occur at the same time as mitosis or after mitosis is completed.

Figure 20-1. Chromosome of Fruit Fly.

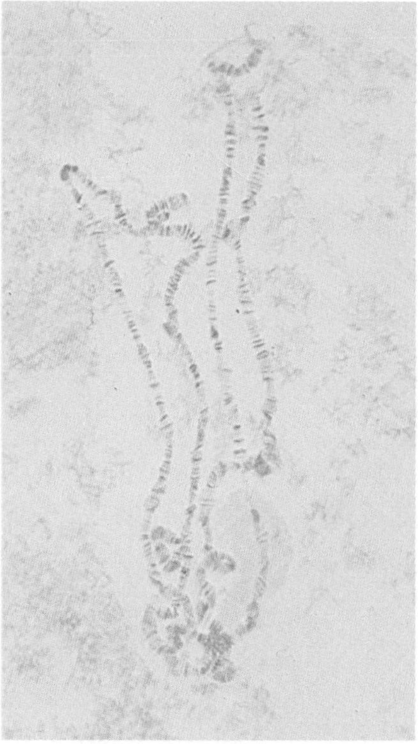

Photograph by Carolina Biological Supply Company

20-3 Structure of the Nucleus

As you learned in Chapter 5, the nucleus is the control center of the cell. Without the nucleus and the hereditary material it contains, the rest of the cell quickly dies. The nucleus also plays a major role in cell division.

The hereditary material of the nucleus is DNA (deoxyribonucleic acid). The information necessary for the synthesis of all components of each cell is stored in the structure of the DNA. The DNA also includes information that determines the makeup and functions of the organism as a whole. This information must be passed on to all cells produced. In nondividing cells, DNA is found in the dark-staining nuclear material called **chromatin** (*kroh*-muh-tin), which consists of a network of long, thin, twisting threads. During cell division, the chromatin becomes organized into the rodlike structures called **chromosomes** (*kroh*-muh-sohmz) (see Figure 20-1).

Figure 20-2. The Eight Chromosomes of the Fruit Fly. Note that the eight chromosomes consist of four pairs, which are similar in size and shape.

Each type of organism has a specific and characteristic number of chromosomes in its body cells. For example, humans have 46 chromosomes, wheat has 42, fruit flies have 8, crayfish have 20, and potatoes have 48 (see Figure 20-2). The number of chromosomes in the body cells of an organism is constant. Since each chromosome contains only part of the total hereditary information, each cell must receive an entire set of chromosomes to function properly.

20-4 Stages of Mitosis in Animal Cells

Once begun, mitosis is a continuous process. However, for convenience it is divided into stages, or phases. These stages are prophase, metaphase, anaphase, and telophase. There is no sharp distinction between these stages; each merges into the next. Figure 20-3 shows the major events of each stage of mitosis.

Interphase. When a cell is not dividing, it is in the **interphase** (*in*-ter-fayz) stage. Although interphase is also called the resting stage, the cell is never really at rest. Interphase lasts from the end of one cell division to the beginning of the next. Dur-

Figure 20-3. Stages of Mitosis in Animal Cells.

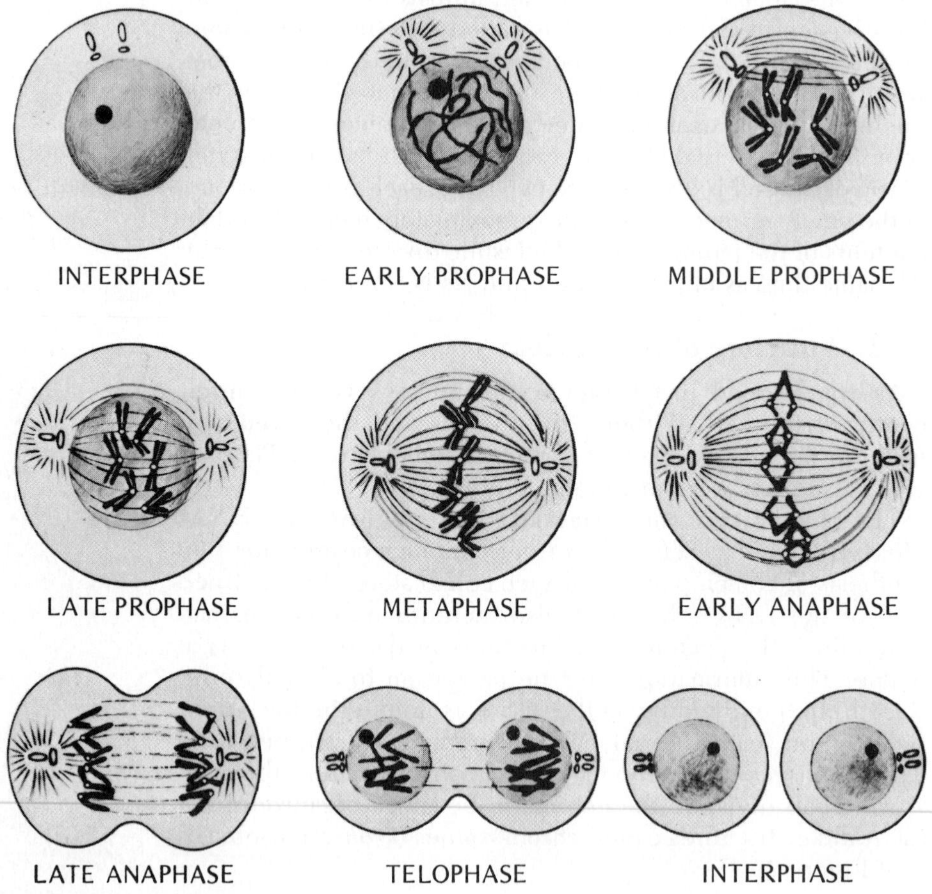

ing interphase, the nucleus is synthesizing nucleic acids, the cytoplasm is synthesizing proteins, and the cell is growing. At some point before mitosis begins, each chromosome makes a copy of itself, or *replicates* (*rep*-luh-kaytz), and is actually a double chromosome.

During interphase, the nucleus of the cell is bounded by the nuclear membrane, and one or more nucleoli are present (see Figure 20-4). The chromosomes are not distinguishable under the microscope at this time. Instead, the DNA appears as a tangled, threadlike mass of chromatin. Near the nucleus are the centrioles, two tiny bodies that lie at right angles to each other. The centrioles also replicate during interphase, forming two pairs.

Prophase. During **prophase** (*proh*-fayz) the doubled chromosomes become visible as long threads that coil and contract into thick rods. The two halves of each double chromosome are called **chromatids** (*kroh*-muh-tidz). They are connected at a region called the **centromere** (*sen*-truh-meer) (see Figure 20-5).

At the beginning of prophase, the two pairs of centrioles move toward the opposite ends, or **poles,** of the cell. The centrioles appear to be involved in the formation of protein-containing structures that were in the past thought to be fibers. Although electron microscope studies have shown them to be microtubules, they are still referred to as fibers. Fibers extending outward from the centrioles form star-shaped structures called **asters.** Other threadlike fibers extend between the poles. These fibers form a double cone-shaped structure called the **spindle.** Some of the spindle fibers become attached to the centromeres of the chromosomes. As prophase progresses, the chromosomes start moving toward the *equatorial plane,* which is the region midway between the poles (see Figure 20-6). At the end of prophase, the nuclear membrane and the nucleolus disappear.

Photograph by Carolina Biological Supply Company

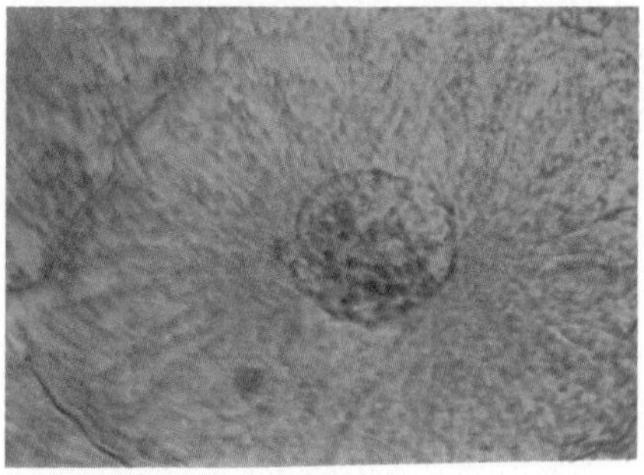

Figure 20-4. Interphase.

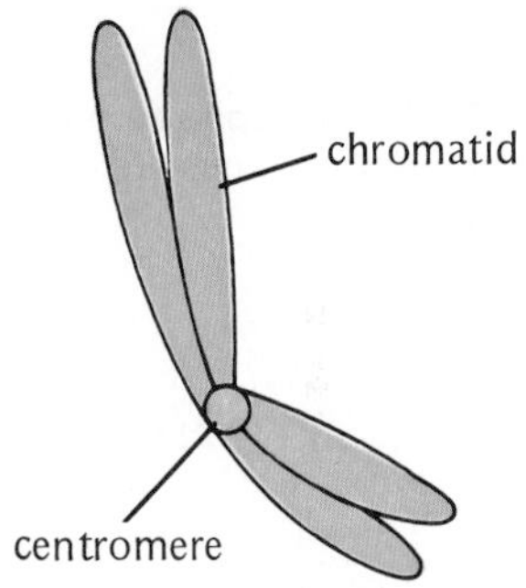

Figure 20-5. Chromatids. The two chromatids are connected at the centromere.

Figure 20-6. Prophase. In early prophase (left) the chromosomes become visible. In late prophase (right) the chromosomes begin to move toward the cell equator, and the nuclear membrane has disappeared.

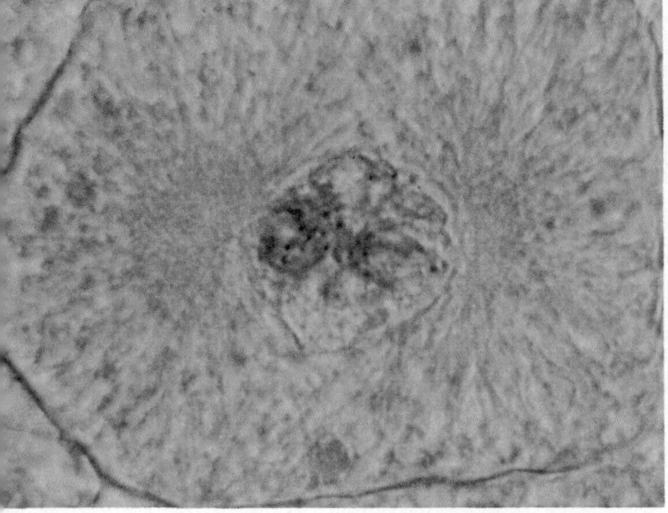

Photograph by Carolina Biological Supply Company

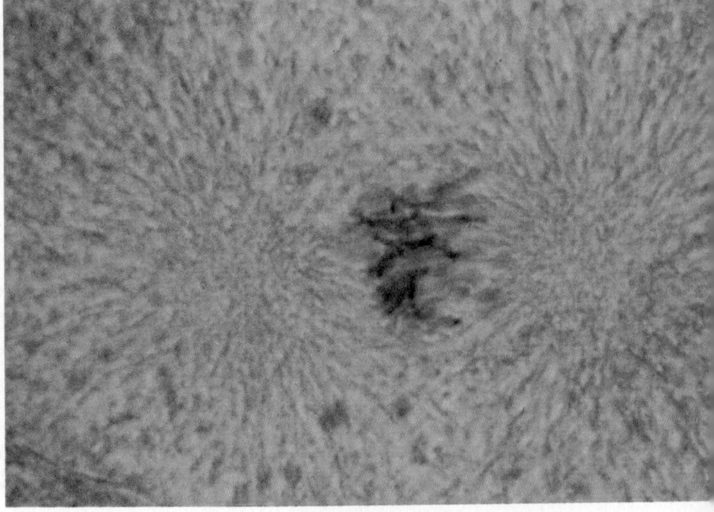

Photograph by Carolina Biological Supply Company

Photograph by Carolina Biological Supply Company

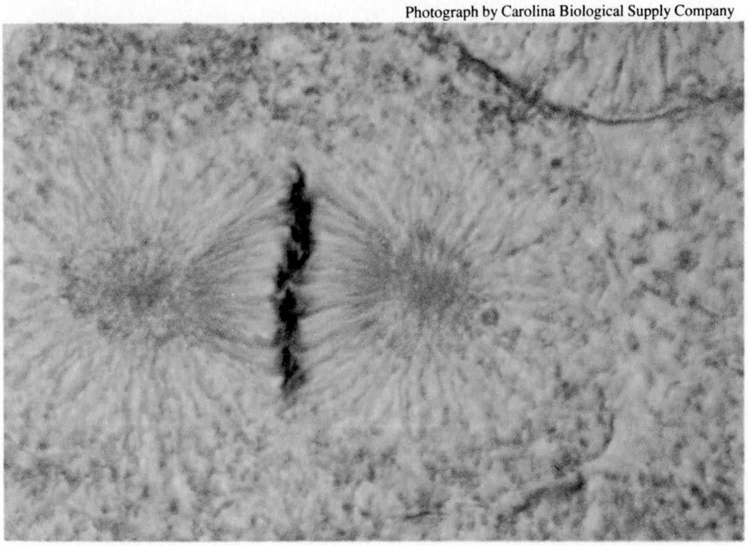

Figure 20-7. Metaphase. In metaphase, the chromosomes are lined up at the cell equator.

Metaphase. During **metaphase** (*met*-uh-fayz), the chromosomes are lined up across the equatorial plane (see Figure 20-7). At the end of metaphase, the centromeres divide, and the two chromatids of each doubled chromosome become separate daughter chromosomes. In other words, each double-stranded chromosome gives rise to two single-stranded daughter chromosomes.

Photograph by Carolina Biological Supply Company

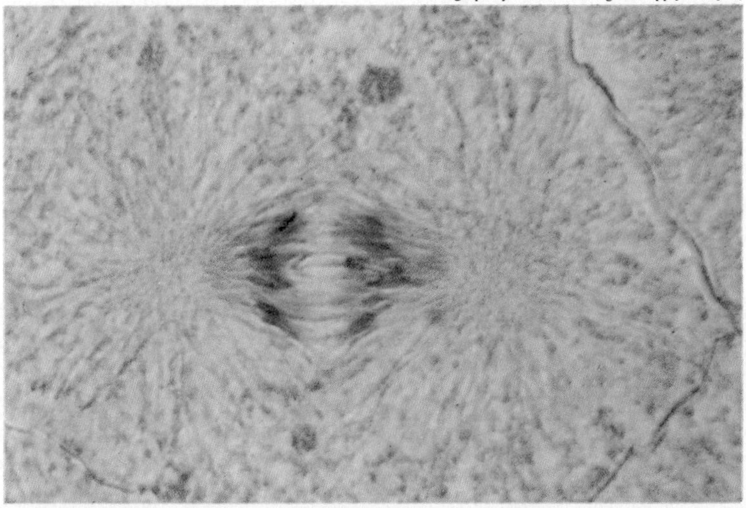

Figure 20-8. Anaphase. In anaphase, the daughter chromosomes move to opposite poles of the cell.

Anaphase. At **anaphase** (*an*-uh-fayz), the daughter chromosomes move apart to opposite poles (see Figure 20-8). The spindle fibers aid in this movement, which results in one complete set of daughter chromosomes going to one pole while the other complete set goes to the other pole.

The mechanism by which the chromosomes move is unknown. However, it is thought that ATP is involved.

Telophase. **Telophase** (*tel*-uh-fayz) begins when the chromosomes reach the poles. The chromosomes elongate, uncoil, and gradually assume the threadlike appearance of chromatin (see Figure 20-9). The spindle and asters disappear. A nuclear

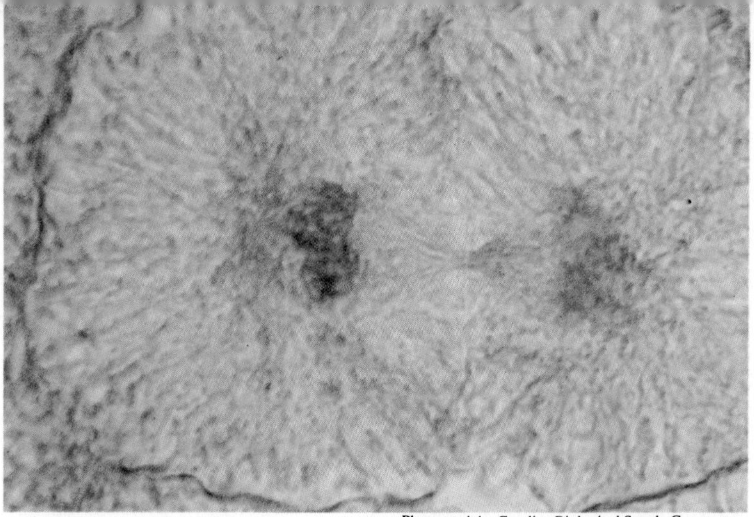

Photograph by Carolina Biological Supply Company

Figure 20-9. Telophase. In telophase, two daughter nuclei form.

membrane forms around each daughter nucleus, and the nucleoli reappear. This completes the nuclear division of an animal cell.

20-5 Cytoplasmic Division in Animal Cells

Cytoplasmic division often begins during late anaphase and is completed during telophase. In animal cells, the division of the cytoplasm is accomplished by a pinching-in of the cell membrane. This furrow occurs in the middle of the cell and results in the formation of two daughter cells of about the same size (see Figure 20-10).

Figure 20-10. Cytoplasmic Division. Division of the cytoplasm occurs by a pinching-in of the cell membrane, forming a furrow in the middle of the cell (left). The two daughter cells formed are approximately equal in size (right).

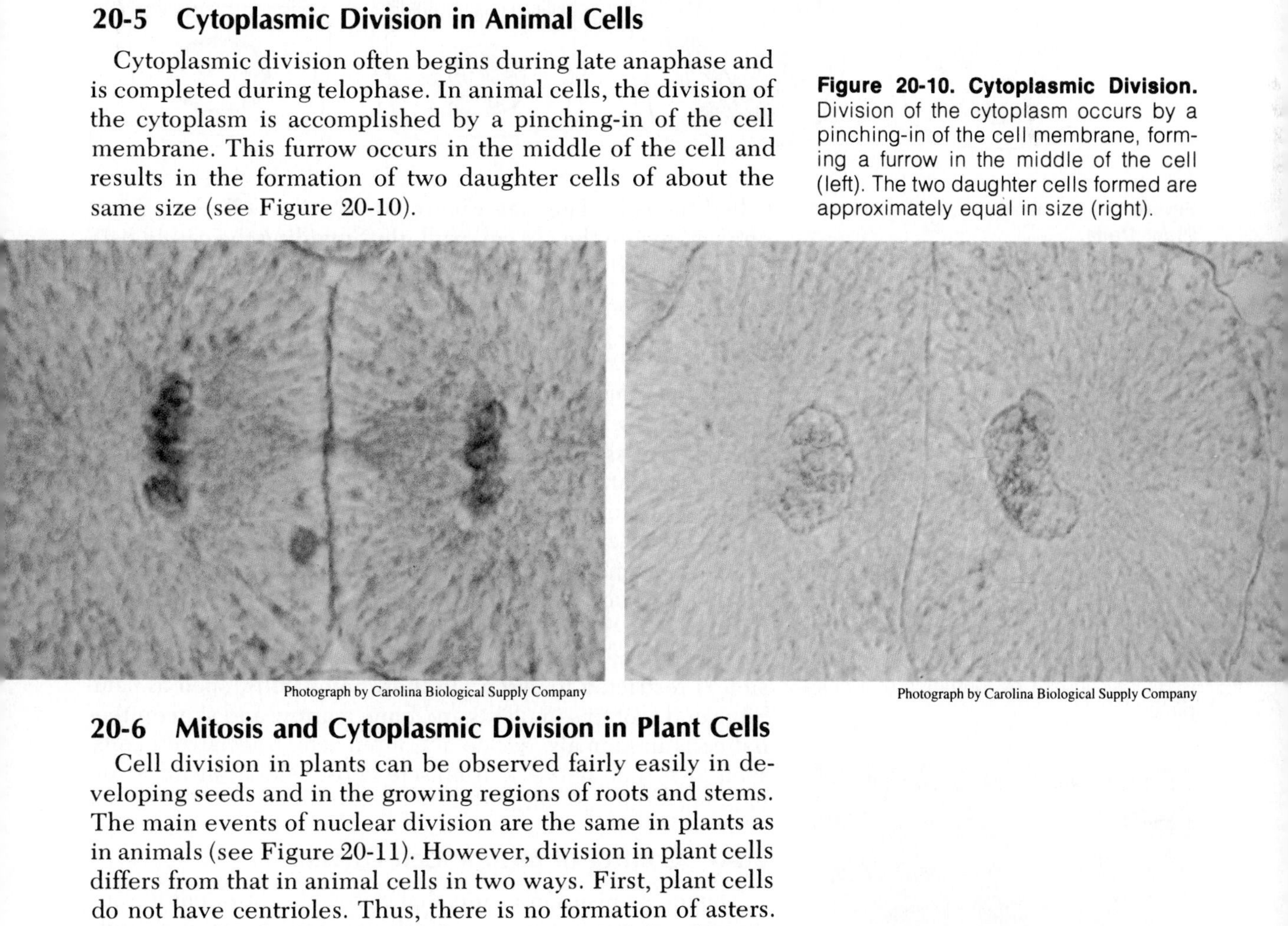

Photograph by Carolina Biological Supply Company

Photograph by Carolina Biological Supply Company

20-6 Mitosis and Cytoplasmic Division in Plant Cells

Cell division in plants can be observed fairly easily in developing seeds and in the growing regions of roots and stems. The main events of nuclear division are the same in plants as in animals (see Figure 20-11). However, division in plant cells differs from that in animal cells in two ways. First, plant cells do not have centrioles. Thus, there is no formation of asters. But a spindle does form, and the movement of the chromosomes is the same as in animal cells. Second, plant cells are surrounded by a rigid cell wall. During telophase, the spindle fibers at the equatorial plane thicken, forming a structure

Figure 20-11. Stages of Mitosis in Plant Cells.

called the **cell plate** (see Figure 20-12). The cell plate grows outward to join the old cell wall, thus dividing the cell in half. New cell wall material is secreted on each side of the cell plate.

20-7 Time Span of Cell Division

The time required for a cell to pass through all the stages of mitosis varies from one type of organism to another and from one type of tissue to another. In general, the interphase period is long compared with the other stages of mitotic division. For example, a human cell in tissue culture takes about 1 hour to divide and then remains in interphase for 16 to 20 hours.

Mitosis is most frequent in cells that are least specialized. Most cells in a developing embryo divide at a very rapid rate. However, as the embryo matures, cells become specialized, and the rate of mitosis decreases. In adults, frequent cell division is restricted to certain tissues. Some cells, such as cambium and root tips in plants and bone marrow and skin epithelial cells in animals, divide at a rapid rate. Specialized cells, such as xylem, nerve, and muscle cells, seldom or never divide once they are formed.

Figure 20-12. Cytoplasmic Division in Plant Cells. In plant cells the cytoplasm is divided in half by formation of a cell plate.

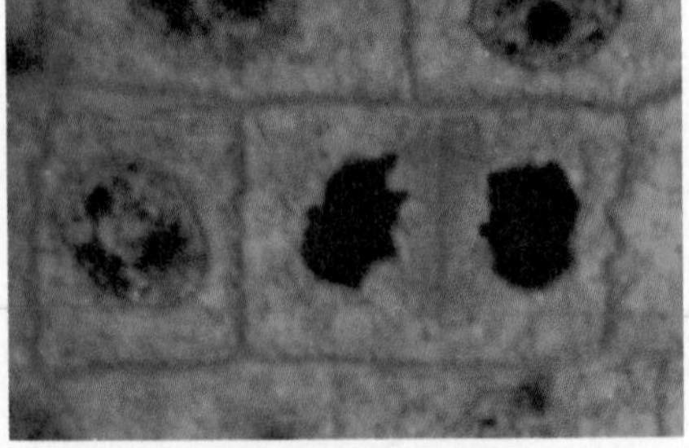

Photograph by Carolina Biological Supply Company

20-8 Control of Mitotic Cell Division

The mechanisms or factors that start and control mitotic cell division are not known. In unicellular organisms it is thought that an increase in cell size triggers mitotic division. As a cell enlarges, its volume increases faster than its surface area—in this case, the area of the cell membrane. When cell size increases above a certain point, the surface area of the membrane becomes inadequate for the necessary exchange of materials between the cell interior and the environment. Thus, for a cell to function, there is an upper limit to its size. When a cell reaches the size characteristic of its type, it either stops growing or it divides.

In complex multicellular organisms, some cells divide regularly, others divide very rarely or not at all once they are formed, and still others divide only under certain circumstances. Normally, cell division occurs only as needed for tissue repair or growth. It is possible that the cells themselves regulate their own division by secreting a control substance that acts by negative feedback. According to this hypothesis, when the number of cells is normal, they secrete enough control substance to prevent cell division. If the number of cells decreases, the concentration of control substance also decreases, thus permitting cell division to occur and restore the normal cell population.

Occasionally a group of cells begins to divide in an uncontrolled fashion, invading surrounding tissue and interfering with normal organ functions. Such uncontrolled cell division is called cancer. Understanding the factors that normally initiate and control cell division would be of great help in controlling cancer.

The repeating sequence of cell growth and division is called the *cell cycle.* The length of the cell cycle varies with cell type and environmental conditions. In the cell cycle, the interphase is divided into three stages. The first stage, called G1, follows mitotic cell division. At the end of the G1 stage, the cell enters the S stage, during which DNA replication occurs. The S stage is followed by the G2 stage. At the end of the G2 stage the cell begins mitosis. During the G1 and G2 stages, the cell is synthesizing various types of molecules and organelles.

Experimental evidence indicates that the events of the cell cycle are controlled by specific chemical factors, some of which stimulate cell division, and some of which inhibit cell division.

ASEXUAL REPRODUCTION

After completing your study of this section, you should be able to:

1. Describe the process of binary fission in bacteria, ameba, and paramecium.
2. Describe budding in yeast and hydra.
3. Describe spore formation in yeast and bread mold.
4. Explain why spore formation is an important form of reproduction for some types of organisms.
5. Define *regeneration,* and name three types of animals in which regeneration can be a form of reproduction.
6. Briefly describe each of the various types of natural and artificial vegetative reproduction.
7. Explain why farmers or gardeners might prefer to use artificial vegetative reproduction of plants rather than growing plants from seed.

Unicellular organisms, many lower animals, and many plants reproduce asexually, at least during part of their life cycles. In asexual reproduction in multicellular organisms, the offspring develop from undifferentiated, unspecialized cells of the parent.

Because asexual reproduction involves only mitotic cell division, each offspring has exactly the same hereditary information as its parent. The offspring show little variation—that is, they are all nearly identical to each other and to the parent. Thus asexual reproduction results in stable characteristics within a species from one generation to another.

Asexual reproduction is generally rapid and often results in the production of large numbers of offspring. There are several types of asexual reproduction, including binary fission, budding, spore formation, regeneration, and vegetative propagation.

20-9 Binary Fission

In the simplest form of asexual reproduction, **binary fission** (*by*-nehr-ee *fish*-un), the parent organism divides into two approximately equal parts. Each of the daughter cells becomes a separate individual and grows to normal size. No parent is left by this method of reproduction because the parent has become two individuals. Binary fission is the usual method of reproduction among one-celled organisms, including bacteria, protozoa, and many algae. In binary fission in cells that contain a distinct nucleus, the nucleus divides by mitosis.

Fission in Bacteria. Bacteria lack an organized nucleus. The hereditary material is in the form of a single circular chromosome. Prior to cell division, the chromosome replicates. A cell wall forms near the center of the parent cell, dividing it into two daughter cells, each containing one of the replicated chromosomes (see Figure 20-13). Each daughter cell grows to normal size before it divides. Sometimes the daughter cells do not separate from each other, thereby forming chains of bacteria. Under favorable conditions some bacteria can divide every 20 minutes.

Fission in Protozoa. When an ameba reaches full size, it rounds up, and the nucleus undergoes mitosis. After nuclear division, the cytoplasm in the middle of the cell pinches in, or constricts, producing two daughter cells (see Figure 20-14). The two resulting cells are both smaller than the original parent cell, but they eventually grow to full size.

The paramecium has two nuclei, a **micronucleus** (my-kroh-*noo*-klee-us) and a **macronucleus** (mak-roh-*noo*-klee-us). The small micronucleus controls the reproductive functions of the

Figure 20-13. Fission in Bacteria.

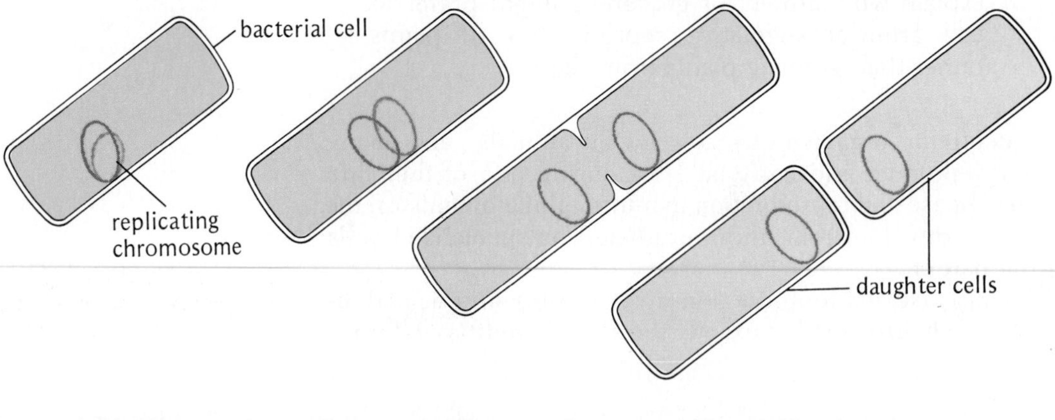

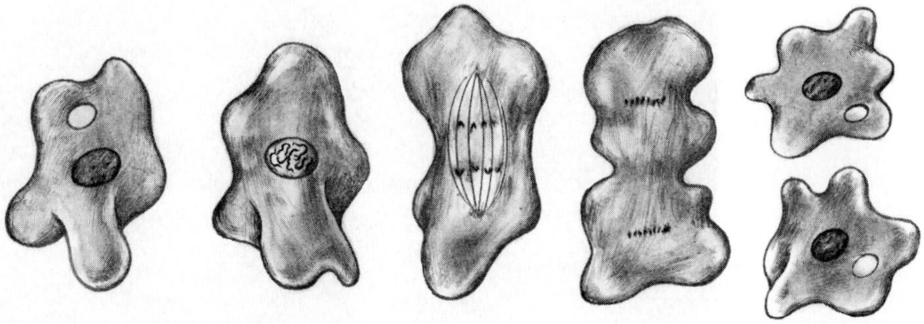

Figure 20-14. **Binary Fission in the Ameba.** In fission, the nucleus divides by mitosis and the cytoplasm divides into two approximately equal parts.

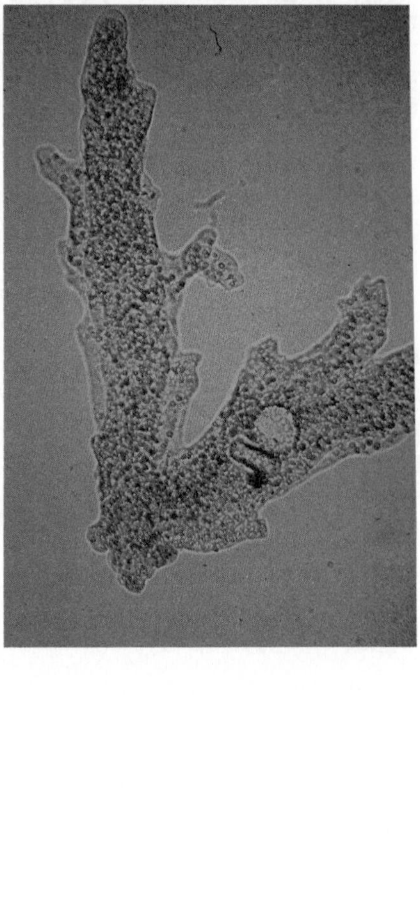

cell. During binary fission, the micronucleus divides by mitosis. The macronucleus divides by a modified mitosis. One of each kind of nucleus goes to each daughter cell. The oral groove and gullet also replicate, and two new contractile vacuoles appear. Thus, before separation occurs, the parts necessary for two complete organisms are present. Division of the cytoplasm occurs when the middle of the cell pinches in. The paramecium can also reproduce sexually.

20-10 Budding

Budding is a type of asexual reproduction in which the parent organism divides into two unequal parts. New individuals develop as small outgrowths, or buds, on the outer surface of the parent organism. The buds may break off and live independently or they may remain attached, forming a colony. Budding differs from binary fission in that the parent and offspring are not of equal size. Budding occurs in yeast and hydra, as well as in sponges and some worms.

Budding in yeast. When a yeast cell reaches a certain size, the nucleus moves toward the side of the cell. The cell wall there is softened by an enzyme so that it bulges outward, forming a small knoblike structure called a *bud* (see Figure 20-15). The nucleus then undergoes mitosis, producing two daughter nuclei. One daughter nucleus moves into the bud, while the other remains in the parent cell. A cell wall forms between the parent cell and the bud. The bud may remain attached to the parent cell or it can separate from it. In either case, the bud is an independent cell that can increase in size and eventually produce its own buds.

Figure 20-15. Budding in Yeast. Budding differs from binary fission in that the cytoplasm divides unequally.

Figure 20-16. Budding in Hydra. The bud begins as a small mound of cells on the side of the parent. The cells divide, producing a complete hydra, which eventually separates from the parent.

Budding in hydra. Budding in hydra is quite different from budding in yeast. Hydras are composed of several kinds of cells. As budding begins, undifferentiated cells on the side of the parent hydra undergo repeated mitotic divisions, producing a small mound of cells. These cells continue to divide, and in a few days a small, complete hydra with a mouth and tentacles is formed (see Figure 20-16). The hydra bud eventually separates from the parent. Hydras can also reproduce sexually.

20-11 Spore Formation

Spores are small, often microscopic, specialized cells. Each spore contains a nucleus and a small amount of cytoplasm surrounded by a thick, hard outer wall. This protective wall enables spores to withstand unfavorable environmental conditions, such as extreme cold, heat, or dryness, for long periods of time. When conditions become favorable, the spore can give rise to a new organism. Spore formation, or *sporulation* (spor-yuh-*lay*-shun), is an effective means of reproduction and occurs in bacteria, yeasts, molds, mushrooms, mosses, and ferns, as well as in certain protozoa. Spores are generally produced in large numbers in special spore-producing structures.

Spore formation in yeast. When unfavorable conditions arise, the nucleus and cytoplasm of the yeast cell undergo two cell divisions, forming four spores. These spores are enclosed within the original cell wall, which is now called a **spore case,** or **sporangium** (spuh-*ran*-jee-um). The spore case eventually bursts, releasing the spores. When conditions become favorable, each spore may develop into a yeast cell, which can reproduce by budding.

Spore formation in bread mold. Bread mold, which is a fungus, can often be seen growing as a dark, cottony mass on bread and other foods. The spores are produced in spore cases on specialized stalks that grow upward from the surface (see Figure 20-17). Thousands of black spores develop within each spore case. At maturity, the walls of the spore case break down, and the tiny, light spores are carried away by air currents. When a spore lands in an environment where there is warmth, food, and moisture, it germinates and grows to form a new mass of mold. Bread molds also reproduce sexually.

Photograph by Carolina Biological Supply Company

Figure 20-17. Spore Cases of Bread Mold.

20-12 Regeneration

Regeneration (rih-jen-uh-*ray*-shun) is the ability of an organism to regrow lost body parts. Relatively simple animals, such as the hydra, planaria, starfish, and earthworm, have the ability to regenerate lost parts. If a hydra is cut in half, each half will regenerate into a new individual. Planaria can be cut into several pieces, each of which will grow into a complete worm.

Starfish feed on oysters. Oystermen used to try to destroy the starfish they caught by chopping them into pieces and tossing the pieces back into the water. However, each part of a starfish can regenerate into a whole new organism as long as it contains a piece of the central disc. Thus the fishermen were actually helping the starfish to multiply, rather than destroying them.

The power of regeneration decreases as animals become more complex. A crab can regrow a lost claw, but cannot regenerate a whole animal from small pieces. Mammals can repair damaged tissue, but cannot regenerate a leg or even a toe. Although simple organisms have great powers of regeneration, they do not usually reproduce in this manner under natural circumstances.

20-13 Vegetative Reproduction

Although most plants reproduce sexually by means of seeds, asexual reproduction involving roots, stems, and leaves is also quite common. Roots, stems, and leaves are called *vegetative* structures. They normally function in nutrition and growth of plants. When they give rise to a new plant, the process is called **vegetative** (*vej*-uh-tay-tiv) **reproduction,** or *vegetative propagation.*

In vegetative reproduction, undifferentiated cells, such as cambium and epidermal cells, divide mitotically and then differentiate to give rise to an independent plant. The new plant has the same hereditary characteristics as its parent. Vegetative reproduction occurs naturally, and it can also be brought about artificially.

Fragmentation can be a form of asexual reproduction. In fragmentation, the body of the organism breaks into several pieces, and each piece grows into a new organism. Fragmentation occurs in flatworms, as well as in various algae.

Natural vegetative reproduction. Vegetative propagation occurs naturally in several different ways (see Figure 20-18).

1. A **bulb** is a short underground stem surrounded by thick, fleshy leaves that contain stored food. Tulips, onions, and lilies reproduce by bulbs. As the plant grows, small new bulbs

A

C

D

E

B

Figure 20-18. Some Types of Natural Vegetative Propagation. Bulbs, corms, tubers, runners, and rhizomes are specialized structures from which complete plants can develop. (A) Bulb—onion. (B) Corm—crocus. (C) Tuber—potato. (D) Runner—strawberry plant. (E) Rhizome—iris.

sprout from the old one. Each of the new bulbs can give rise to a new plant.

2. **Corms** (kormz) resemble bulbs, but they do not contain fleshy leaves. Rather, corms are short, stout underground stems containing stored food. Gladiolus, crocus, and water chestnut are plants that grow from corms.

3. A **tuber** (*too*-ber) is an enlarged portion of an underground stem that contains stored food. White potatoes are tubers. Along the surface of a tuber are indentations called "eyes." These eyes are actually tiny buds. When a farmer plants white potatoes, the tuber is cut into pieces, each piece having at least one "eye." Each eye develops into a shoot that grows upward through the soil surface and that also produces roots. The young shoot uses the stored food of the tuber until it develops sufficiently to carry on photosynthesis.

4. A **runner,** or **stolon** (*stoh*-lun), is a horizontal stem with buds. It grows along the surface of the ground. Where buds from a runner touch the soil, roots, stems, and leaves develop to form a new independent plant. Strawberry plants and many kinds of grasses reproduce quickly in this manner.

5. A **rhizome** (*ry*-zohm) is a stem that grows horizontally underground. It is usually thick and fleshy and contains stored food. Along the rhizome are enlarged portions called *nodes*. Buds produced at nodes on the upper surface of the rhizome give rise to leaf-bearing branches. The lower surface of the

A

B

Figure 20-19. Some Types of Artificial Vegetative Propagation. (A) Stem cutting. (B) Kalanchoe leaves with plantlets. (C) Grafting—joining the stock and scion.

C

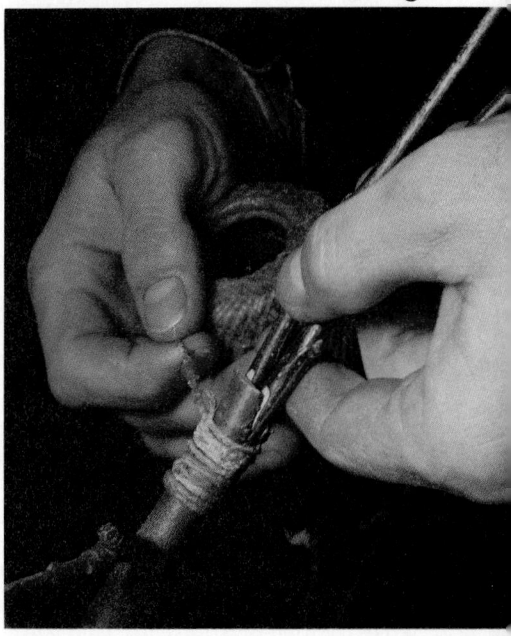

rhizome produces roots. Ferns, irises, cattails, and water lilies reproduce by rhizomes.

Artificial vegetative reproduction. Farmers and gardeners have developed several methods of artificial vegetative reproduction (see Figure 20-19). These techniques enable them to maintain plants with desirable traits.

1. A **cutting** is any vegetative part of a plant—stem, leaf, or root—used to produce a new individual. In a *stem cutting*, a branch, or slip, is cut from a plant and placed in water or moist sand. Usually the bottom of the cutting is dipped into hormones to stimulate root growth. When roots develop, the cutting becomes an independent plant and is transplanted to soil. Geraniums, roses, ivy, and grapevines are propagated in this manner.

In a *leaf cutting*, a leaf or part of a leaf is placed in water or moist soil. After a while, a new plant develops from certain cells in the leaf. African violets, snake plants, and begonias are regularly propagated by leaf cuttings.

Under natural conditions, the leaves of Kalanchoe give rise to tiny plants along their edges. These plantlets have tiny leaves, stems, and sometimes roots. When they fall from the parent plant, they take root and continue to grow in the soil. They can be separated and used to produce new plants.

The sweet potato is an enlarged root containing stored food. Farmers place it in moist sand or soil until it sprouts several new plants. Then the sprouts are removed and planted.

2. In **layering,** a stem is bent over so that part of it is covered with soil. After the covered part forms roots, the new plant may be cut from the parent plant. Layering is used to reproduce such plants as raspberries, roses, and honeysuckle. It also occurs naturally.

3. In **grafting,** a stem or bud is removed from one plant and joined permanently to the stem of a closely related plant. The

part of this combination providing the roots is called the **stock;** the added piece is called the **scion** (*sy*-en). The cambium layers (growing regions) of the scion and stock must be in close contact. Usually they are held together by tape and coated with wax to protect the growing tissue from water loss and from disease. After a time the cambiums of the two pieces form new xylem and phloem, which grow together and connect the scion and stock. The stock supports and nourishes the scion. However, the scion retains its own characteristics. For example, although scions of McIntosh apples can be grafted onto stock of any kind of apple tree, the scions will produce only McIntosh apples. Grafting is used to propagate roses, peach trees, plum trees, grapevines, and various seedless fruits, including navel oranges, grapes, and grapefruits.

Advantages of artificial vegetative propagation. Among the advantages of vegetative propagation are:

1. Plants grown from seeds do not always show the same characteristics as the parent plant. Vegetative propagation ensures the production of new plants exactly like the parent. There is little variation because all offspring have the same hereditary makeup as the parent.
2. The development of a plant by vegetative propagation often takes less time than development from seed. In the development of an improved plant variety, stem cuttings or grafts made onto mature plants will produce fruit in much less time than it takes for small plants to bear fruit.
3. Plants bearing *seedless fruit* can be grown only by vegetative propagation.
4. Grafting can be used to obtain higher yields of fruits or nuts.

summary

New cells arise from existing cells by the division of the original cell into two cells. Cell division is necessary for growth, cell replacement, and reproduction. Cell division consists of two processes—the division of the nucleus, which is called mitosis, and the division of the cytoplasm.

The nucleus contains the hereditary material, which is found in the chromosomes. Each type of organism has a specific and characteristic number of chromosomes in its body cells. In cell division, the chromosomes must be duplicated, and each new cell must receive an entire set for it to function properly.

Mitotic cell division is divided into stages, or phases. The stage between the end of one cell division and the beginning of the next is interphase. During this stage the chromosomes, which are in the form of chromatin, double.

During prophase in animal cells, the chromosomes become visible, each consisting of two chromatids connected at the centromere. The centrioles move to opposite poles of the cell, and the asters and spindle form. The chromosomes begin to move toward the equatorial plane midway between the poles, and the nuclear membrane and nucleoli disappear.

During metaphase, the chromosomes are lined up on the equatorial plane. At the end of this stage, the two chromatids of each doubled chromosome separate, forming two single-stranded daughter chromosomes.

During anaphase, the daughter chromosomes separate and move to opposite poles of the cell.

Telophase begins when the chromosomes reach the poles. Once there they gradually return to the chromatin form. The spindle and asters disappear. New nuclear membranes form around the nuclei at either end of the cell. Division of the cytoplasm may begin in anaphase. It is accomplished by a gradual pinching in of the cell membrane, eventually forming two daughter cells of equal size.

Mitosis in plant cells is similar to that in animal cells. However, plant cells do not contain centrioles. A spindle does form, but there are no asters. In the division of the cytoplasm, during telophase, the spindle fibers in the plane of the equator form a cell plate, which grows and joins the cell wall, dividing the cell in half.

Mitotic cell division occurs most frequently in unspecialized cells, such as those of the developing embryo. The actual mechanisms that control mitosis are not known. In unicellular organisms, it is thought that cell size is a controlling factor. In complex multicellular organisms, it is possible that control substances secreted by the cells regulate cell division by negative feedback.

Asexual reproduction involves mitotic cell division of only one parent. The simplest form of asexual reproduction is binary fission, where the parent divides into two daughter cells of approximately equal size. In budding, the parent organism divides into two individuals of unequal size—the new individual is smaller than the parent and grows to full size after separation from the parent. Sporulation involves the production of small cells called spores. Each spore contains a nucleus and a small amount of cytoplasm and is surrounded by a thick outer wall. Spores can withstand cold, heat, and dryness. When conditions become favorable, the spore develops into a new organism. Regeneration is the ability to regrow lost body parts. It is not generally a method of reproduction under natural circumstances.

In plants, asexual reproduction involves vegetative structures, including roots, stems, and leaves. In vegetative reproduction, undifferentiated cells undergo mitotic division, differentiate, and give rise to an independent plant. Vegetative reproduction occurs naturally with bulbs, corms, tubers, runners, and rhizomes. Vegetative reproduction can be accomplished artificially with cuttings, layering, and grafting.

vocabulary

anaphase	micronucleus
asexual reproduction	mitosis
aster	mitotic cell division
binary fission	pole
budding	prophase
bulb	regeneration
cell plate	rhizome
centriole	runner
centromere	scion
chromatid	sexual reproduction
chromatin	spindle
chromosome	spore
corm	spore case
cutting	stock
grafting	stolon
interphase	telophase
layering	tuber
macronucleus	vegetative reproduction
metaphase	

test your learning

Section

20-1 **1.** Define *reproduction.*

2. Explain the differences between asexual and sexual reproduction.

20-2 **3.** Define the terms *mitosis* and *mitotic cell division.*

20-3 **4.** What material contains the hereditary information and where is it located in the cell?

5. Why is the nucleus so important in cell division?

6. What is the difference between chromatin and chromosomes?

20-4 **7.** List the phases of mitotic cell division, and briefly describe the events of each stage in an animal cell.

20-5 **8.** When and how does cytoplasmic division occur in animal cells?

20-6 **9.** How does mitotic cell division in plant cells differ from mitotic cell division in animal cells?

20-7 **10.** Which is the longest phase of mitosis?

11. What kind of cells undergo mitosis most frequently? What kind of cells rarely undergo mitosis?

20-8 **12.** What factor is thought to trigger mitotic cell division in unicellular organisms?
13. How is mitotic cell division involved in cancer?
20-9 **14.** Briefly describe the events of binary fission in bacteria and in the ameba and paramecium.
20-10 **15.** What are the differences between budding and binary fission?
16. Briefly describe the process of budding in yeast and in hydra.
20-11 **17.** What are spores?
18. Briefly describe spore formation in yeast and bread mold.
20-12 **19.** What is regeneration?
20. What types of animals have the greatest powers of regeneration?
20-13 **21.** What is vegetative reproduction?
22. Briefly describe bulbs, corms, tubers, runners, and rhizomes. Explain how vegetative reproduction occurs in each.
23. Briefly describe three methods of artificial vegetative reproduction.

test your understanding

1. Discuss the functions of mitotic cell division in unicellular and in multicellular organisms.
2. What are the advantages of using artificial vegetative propagation instead of growing plants from seed?
3. How can a single tree produce three different varieties of apples?
4. What part of the plant would a grower use to produce each of the following plants by artificial vegetative propagation?
A. geraniums
B. African violets
C. white potatoes
D. tulips

independent research

1. Prepare a report on the use of grafting in commercial fruit-growing.
2. Try and propagate one of the following plants by means of vegetative reproduction: white potatoes, sweet potatoes, carrots, onions, African violets, or begonias.

chapter 21

Meiosis and Sexual Reproduction

CHAPTER INTRODUCTION

After completing your study of this section, you should be able to:

1. Compare and contrast asexual reproduction and sexual reproduction, and discuss the advantages and disadvantages of each.
2. Define the terms *gamete, fertilization,* and *zygote*.

21-1 Sexual Reproduction

All living things give rise to new members of their own kind by either asexual or sexual reproduction. In asexual reproduction, a single parent gives rise to new offspring by mitotic cell division. Each new individual receives a set of chromosomes identical to its parent's chromosomes. Therefore, in asexual reproduction, the hereditary information transmitted from generation to generation remains the same. Asexual reproduction does not produce differences, or variations, in the offspring. Sexual reproduction, on the other hand, does introduce hereditary variation.

In sexual reproduction there is always a fusion of nuclei from two cells. These two cells generally come from two separate parent organisms. The cells that provide the nuclear material for sexual reproduction are called **gametes** (*gam*-eets). In most species there are two physically distinct types of gametes, which are called male and female. The female gamete is generally larger and nonmotile, while the male gamete is generally smaller and motile. The fusion of the nuclei of two gametes is called **fertilization,** and the single cell formed from this fusion is called a **zygote** (*zy*-goht).

In sexual reproduction, the offspring produced are not identical to either parent. Instead, they show new combinations of characteristics. Thus, in any species in which sexual reproduction occurs, the members will show variations in structure and/or function. Increasing the amount of variation in members of a species increases the possibility that some individuals of that species will be better adapted than others to survive both short-term and long-term changes in the environment. The better-adapted individuals are more likely to survive environmental changes and to transmit the helpful variations to their offspring. Variations may also enable certain individuals in a population to move into new environments. By making a population more flexible, variations brought about by sexual reproduction help to ensure the survival of the species.

MEIOSIS

After completing your study of this section, you should be able to:

1. Explain the importance of meiosis in sexual reproduction.
2. Define the terms *somatic cell, diploid chromosome number,* and *monoploid chromosome number.*
3. Explain which cells have the diploid chromosome number and which have the monoploid number.
4. Describe the end results of the first meiotic division and the second meiotic division.

21-2 Diploid and Monoploid Chromosome Numbers

Body cells, or **somatic** (soh-*mat*-ik) **cells,** are all the cells of an organism except the sex cells. The body cells of each species contain a characteristic number of chromosomes. For example, human body cells contain 46 chromosomes, bullfrog body cells contain 26 chromosomes, and fruit fly body cells contain 8 chromosomes. However, these chromosomes are present as similar, or **homologous** (hoh-*mahl*-uh-guhs), pairs. Except for the pair of chromosomes that determines sex, the chromosomes in each homologous pair are similar in size and shape, and they control the same hereditary characteristics, or traits. Thus, the 46 chromosomes in human body cells consist of 22 pairs of homologous chromosomes and one pair of sex chromosomes (see Figure 21-1). Cells that contain the full number of chromosomes characteristic of the species are called **diploid** (*dip*-loyd), or $2n$, cells.

The gametes that fuse in sexual reproduction do *not* have the same number of chromosomes as the body cells. Gametes do not contain homologous pairs of chromosomes as the dip-

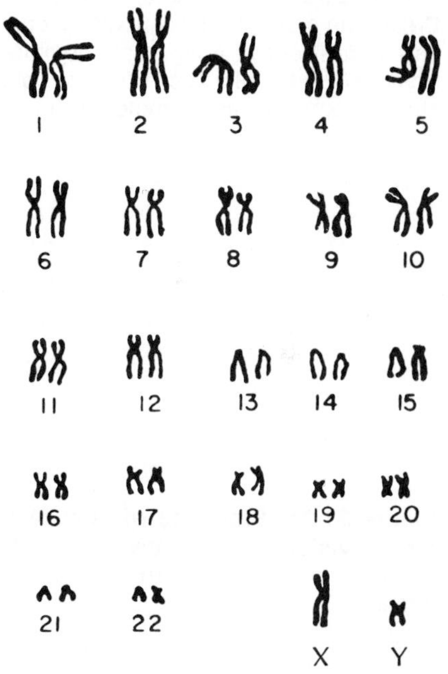

Figure 21-1. Human Chromosomes. The chromosomes were photographed during mitotic cell division, when they are visible as paired chromatids. The photographs were then cut apart and assembled into homologous pairs. These chromosomes were from a male. The pair labeled X and Y are the sex chromosomes. In a human female cell, this pair consists of two X chromosomes.

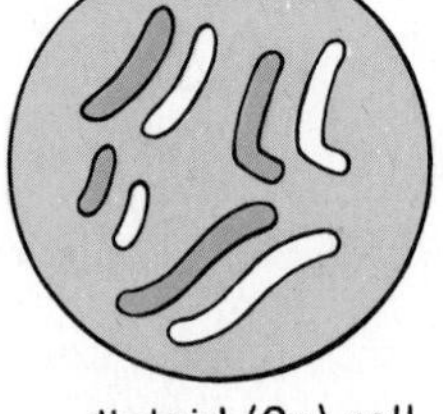

diploid (2n) cell
(4 chromosome pairs)

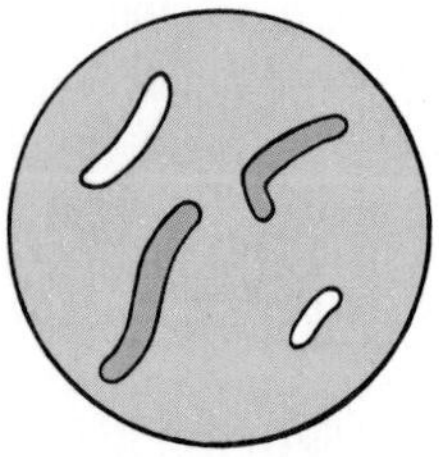

monoploid (n) cell
4 chromosomes

Figure 21-2. Diploid and Monoploid Cells. The monoploid cell contains only one chromosome from each homologous pair. The diploid cell contains both chromosomes of each homologous pair.

loid cells do. They contain only one of the chromosomes of each homologous pair. As a result, they have only half the diploid number of chromosomes. For example, human gametes contain 23 chromosomes—one from each of the 23 pairs in body cells. Such cells are said to be **monoploid** (*mahn*-uh-ployd), or **haploid** (*hap*-loyd). Monoploid cells contain *n* chromosomes, rather than 2*n* (see Figure 21-2).

If gametes were diploid cells, the chromosome number per cell would double with each generation. The doubling would occur when two gametes unite at fertilization. Because of the process of meiosis, the doubling of the chromosome number does not occur. **Meiosis** (my-*oh*-sis) is a type of cell division that occurs only in sex cells. As a result of meiosis, the daughter cells receive only half the number of chromosomes present in the body cells. They receive only one member of each homologous pair of chromosomes.

21-3 Stages of Meiosis

Meiosis, which is also known as *reduction division*, occurs in specialized sex cells. At the start of meiosis, these cells have the diploid number of chromosomes. In meiosis, each cell divides twice. However, the chromosomes replicate only once. This replication occurs before the first meiotic division. In the second meiotic division, no replication of the chromosomes occurs. As a result of the two meiotic divisions, each original sex cell produces four daughter cells, each containing the monoploid number of chromosomes.

Both the first and second meiotic divisions can be divided into stages similar to the stages of mitosis. Thus, both divisions show a prophase, metaphase, anaphase, and telophase. The events of the first and second meiotic divisions are shown in Figure 21-3A-H.

Prophase I. At the beginning of prophase of the first meiotic division, each chromosome has already replicated and consists of two chromatids, as in mitosis. However, the replicated chromosomes do not move independently to the equatorial plane. Instead, each chromosome lines up very exactly with its homologous chromosome, and they become attached at their centromeres. This pairing process is called **synapsis**

Figure 21-3A. Prophase of First Meiotic Division. (Left) Early prophase; (center) mid-prophase; (right) late prophase.

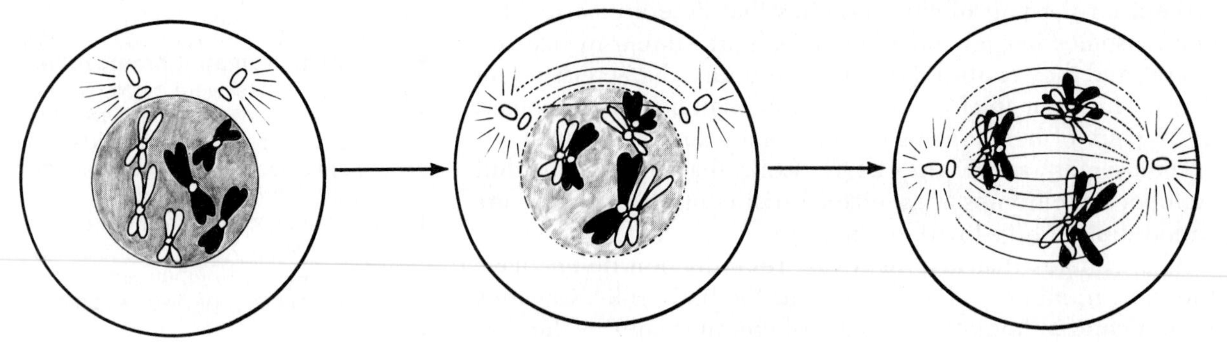

(suh-*nap*-sis), and the chromosome pairs, each consisting of four chromatids, are called **tetrads.** The strands of the tetrad sometimes twist about each other, and at this time they may exchange segments. The exchange of segments between chromatids during synapsis is called *crossing-over.*

While these chromosomal changes are occurring, the nuclear membrane disappears and the spindle fibers form. As prophase I ends, the homologous chromosome pairs move toward the equator of the cell.

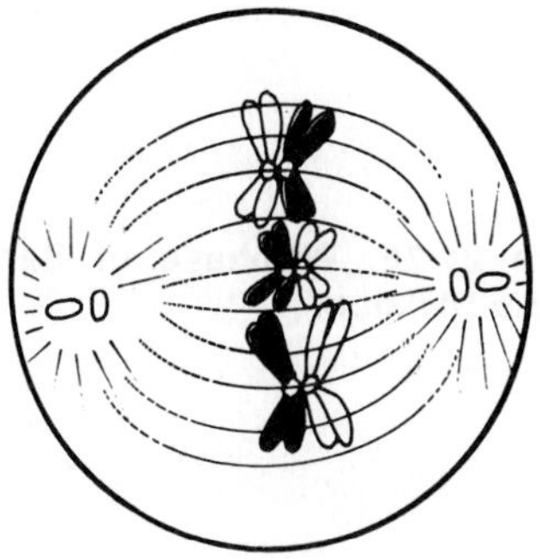

Figure 21-3B. Metaphase of First Meiotic Division.

Metaphase I. In metaphase of the first meiotic division, the chromosome pairs (tetrads) line up on the equatorial plane. The chromosomes are attached to the spindle fibers at their centromeres.

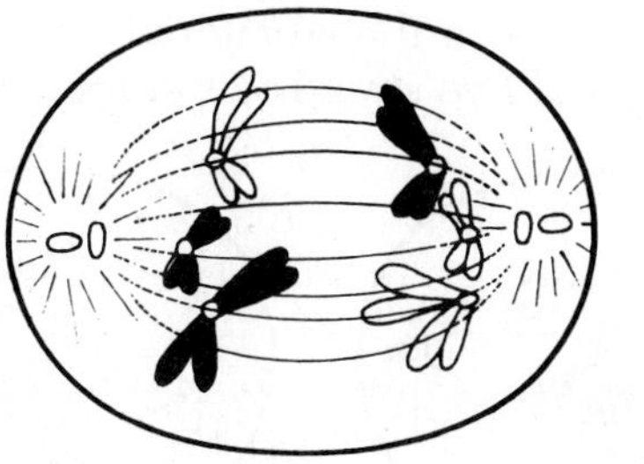

Figure 21-3C. Anaphase of First Meiotic Division.

Anaphase I. During anaphase of the first meiotic division, the homologous chromosomes of each tetrad separate from each other and move to opposite ends of the cell. This process of separation of the tetrad is called **disjunction** (dis-*junk*-shun). The cluster of chromosomes around each pole is monoploid—there are half as many chromosomes as in the original cell. However, each chromosome is double-stranded.

Telophase I. Telophase marks the end of the first meiotic division. The cytoplasm divides, forming two daughter cells. Each of the newly formed daughter cells has half the number of chromosomes of the parent cell, but each chromosome is already in replicated form.

Sometimes at the end of telophase I nuclear membranes form and a short interphase follows. However, in most cases, the cells immediately begin the second division. No further replication of the chromosomes occurs, but the remainder of the division is exactly like mitosis.

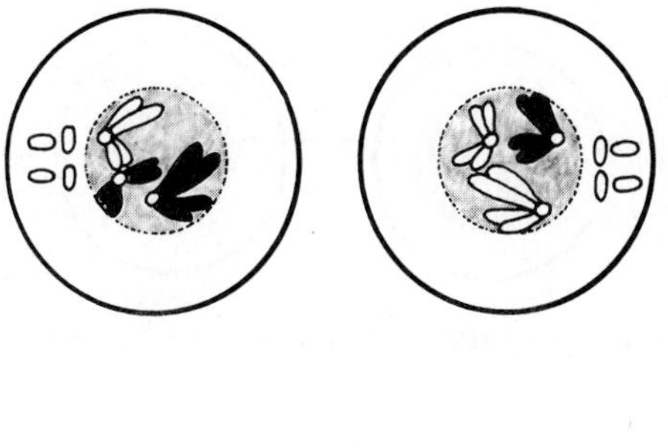

Figure 21-3D. Telophase of First Meiotic Division. The first meiotic division produces two daughter cells.

Prophase II. During prophase II, each of the daughter cells forms a spindle, and the double-stranded chromosomes move toward the middle of the spindle.

Figure 21-3E. Prophase of Second Meiotic Division.

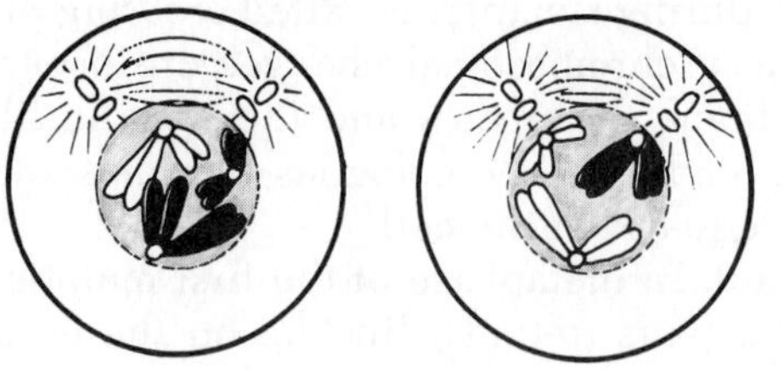

Metaphase II. During metaphase II, the chromosomes become attached to spindle fibers at their centromeres, and the chromosomes line up on the equatorial plane. Each chromosome still consists of two strands, or chromatids.

Figure 21-3F. Metaphase of Second Meiotic Division.

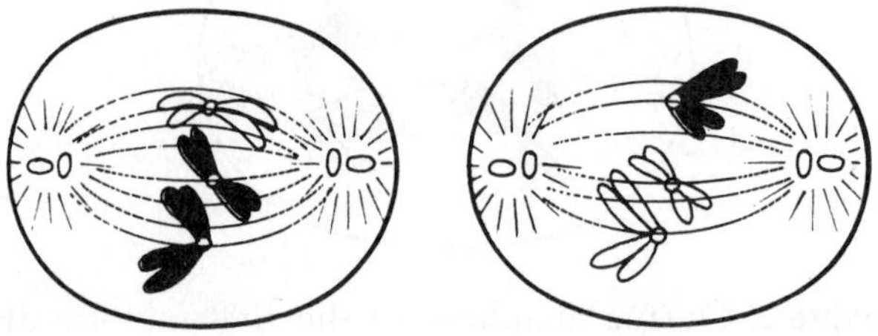

Anaphase II. During anaphase II, the centromeres divide, and the sister chromatids separate. The chromatids, which are now single-stranded chromosomes, move toward the opposite ends of the spindle.

Figure 21-3G. Anaphase of Second Meiotic Division.

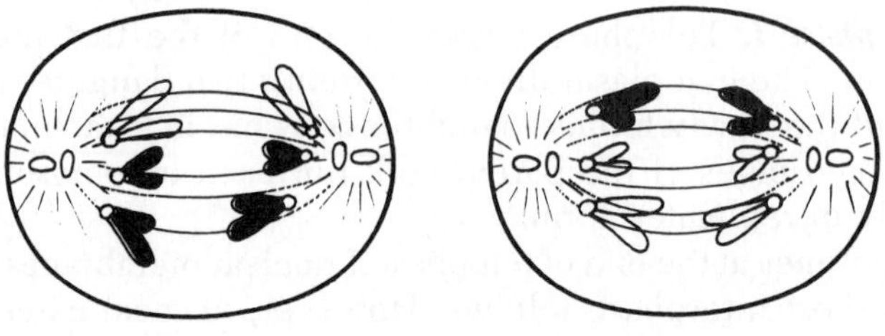

Telophase II. During telophase II, both daughter cells divide, forming four monoploid cells. In each cell, the chromosomes return to their interphase state, and the nuclear membrane reappears.

Figure 21-3H. Telophase of Second Meiotic Division. The second meiotic division produces four monoploid cells.

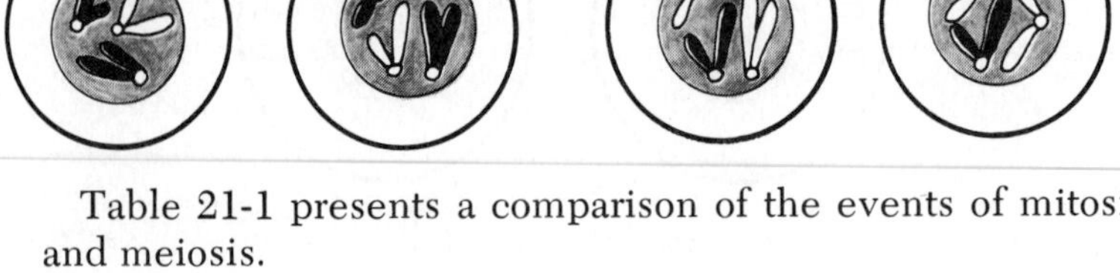

Table 21-1 presents a comparison of the events of mitosis and meiosis.

Mitosis	Meiosis
1. Occurs in growth and asexual reproduction.	1. Occurs in production of sex cells.
2. Homologous chromosomes do not pair up during prophase. There is no exchange of parts between homologous chromosomes.	2. Homologous chromosomes pair up during prophase of first division. While paired, there may be an exchange of parts between homologous chromosomes.
3. Involves one cell division. In the course of division, the two-stranded chromosomes line up at cell equator, centromeres divide, and one chromatid of each chromosome goes to each daughter cell.	3. Involves two cell divisions. During first division, pairs of two-stranded chromosomes line up at equator. The pairs separate, and one two-stranded chromosome of each homologous pair goes to each daughter cell. During second division, centromeres of two-stranded chromosomes divide, and chromatids separate, one going to each daughter cell.
4. As a result of mitosis, each daughter cell receives the same number of chromosomes as the original cell. Mitosis maintains the chromosome number.	4. As a result of meiosis, each daughter cell receives only one member of each homologous pair of chromosomes. It therefore has only one-half the number of chromosomes in the original cell. Meiosis reduces the chromosome number by one-half.

Table 21-1. Comparison of Mitosis and Meiosis.

SEXUAL REPRODUCTION IN PROTISTS

After completing your study of this section, you should be able to:

1. Explain the importance of sexual reproduction in protists.
2. Describe the basic events of conjugation.
3. Explain the importance of mating types among protists.
4. Briefly describe conjugation in spirogyra and paramecium.

21-4 Conjugation and Mating Types

The simplest type of sexual reproduction occurs in the protists. Although protists usually reproduce asexually, some also reproduce sexually. In these organisms, sexual reproduction has the effect of restoring the organism's ability to grow and reproduce. If sexual reproduction is prevented in some protists, they die. Sexual reproduction also permits a recombination of hereditary material, thereby introducing variation within the species.

The first meiotic division produces two monoploid cells containing double-stranded chromosomes. The second meiotic division produces four monoploid cells containing single-stranded chromosomes.

Among protists that reproduce sexually, there are no distinct sexes—that is, all members of a single species are almost identical in appearance. Although no male or female cells can be distinguished, there are usually two different **mating types,** or

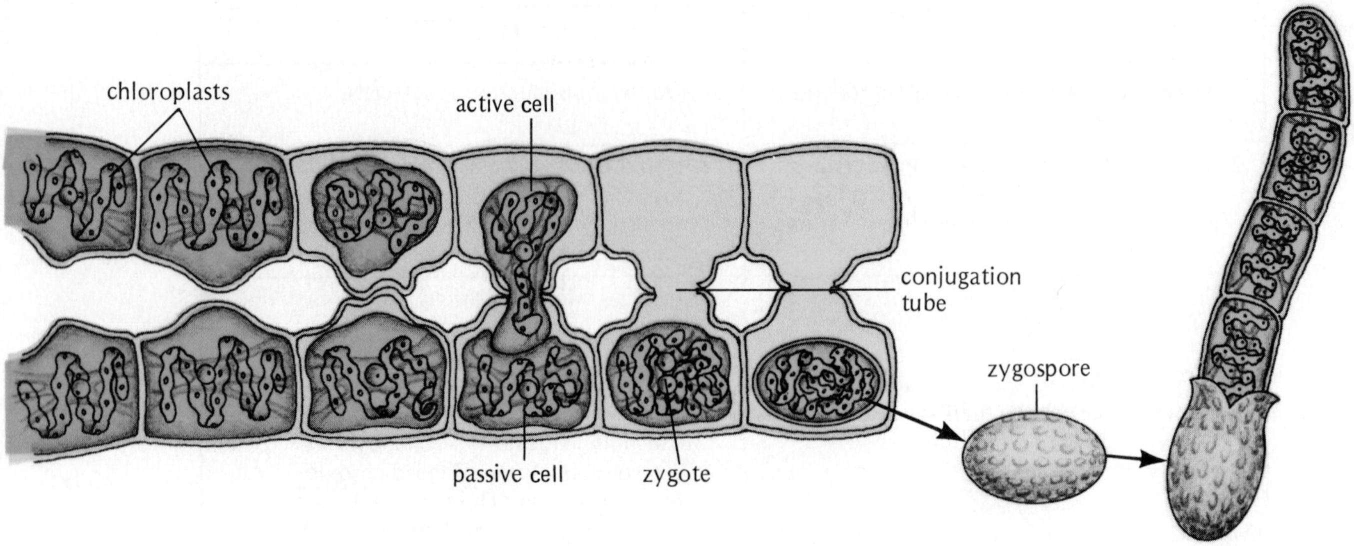

Figure 21-4. Conjugation in Spirogyra. The drawing above shows the conjugation tube, the flow of the cell contents from the active into the passive strand, and the formation of a zygospore. The zygospore undergoes meiotic division, forming a monoploid cell that gives rise to a new filament by mitotic cell division. The photograph below shows the conjugation tubes and the zygospores.

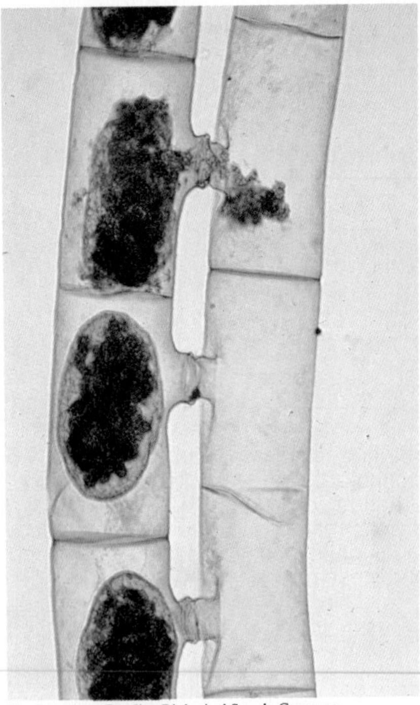

Photograph by Carolina Biological Supply Company

strains, which are commonly designated as plus (+) and minus (−). Apparently there are biochemical and chromosomal differences between different mating types.

The type of sexual reproduction most commonly found among protists is **conjugation** (kahn-juh-*gay*-shun). In conjugation, a cytoplasmic bridge forms between two cells, and an exchange or transfer of nuclear material occurs through the bridge. Conjugation occurs only between two cells of different mating types.

21-5 Conjugation in Spirogyra

Spirogyra is a type of green alga made up of a mass of filaments. The filaments consist of cells attached end to end. These organisms usually reproduce asexually by binary fission, but sometimes they reproduce sexually by conjugation.

During conjugation, two filaments of opposite mating types come to lie side by side. Projections develop on the sides of adjacent cells (see Figure 21-4). These projections meet, the walls where the projections meet break down, and a passageway called the *conjugation tube* opens between the cells of the two filaments. The two mating types of spirogyra are called *active* and *passive*. The contents of the active cells flow through the conjugation tube and fuse with the nucleus and cytoplasm of the adjacent passive cells, forming zygotes. The cells of the filaments are monoploid, while the newly formed zygotes are diploid.

Each zygote secretes a thick wall that protects it during its dormant season. This new structure is called a **zygospore** (*zy*-guh-spor). The cell walls of the original filaments decay and release the zygospores. After a period of rest, and when favorable conditions return, each zygospore undergoes meiosis, forming four monoploid cells. Only one cell survives, and it divides by mitosis, giving rise to a new monoploid filament.

21-6 Conjugation in Paramecium

Paramecia usually reproduce asexually by binary fission. However, they periodically reproduce by conjugation. Conjugation takes place between two different mating types—plus and minus. In some species, the periodic exchange of hereditary material by conjugation is necessary for the cells to reproduce asexually. If it does not occur, the cell stops dividing and eventually dies.

During conjugation, two paramecia—one plus, the other minus—stick together at the region of their oral grooves (see Figure 21-5). A protoplasmic bridge forms between them. A complex series of nuclear changes then occurs in each. Paramecia and other ciliates have two types of nuclei—macronuclei and micronuclei. Each cell may contain more than one of each. During conjugation, the macronucleus disappears. The micronucleus divides by meiosis. One of the newly formed monoploid micronuclei from each paramecium moves across the protoplasmic bridge into the opposite cell where it fuses with a micronucleus of that cell. Both cells now contain a diploid micronucleus. The conjugating paramecia now separate, and the new micronuclei undergo several mitotic divisions. These divisions result in the formation of new macronuclei and micronuclei. Both organisms then divide twice without nuclear division. Eight new organisms are produced.

Photograph by Carolina Biological Supply Company

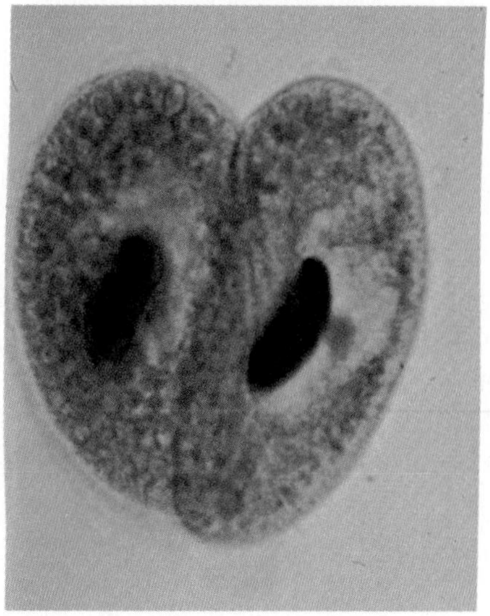

Figure 21-5. Conjugation in Paramecium.

SEXUAL REPRODUCTION IN ANIMALS

After completing your study of this section, you should be able to:

1. Define the following terms: *gonad, ovary, ovum, testis, sperm, hermaphroditism, gametogenesis.*
2. Briefly describe the processes of oogenesis and spermatogenesis.
3. Describe the structures of a sperm and an egg.
4. Explain what occurs in fertilization.
5. Contrast the processes of external fertilization and internal fertilization and discuss the problems involved in each.
6. Define the term *parthenogenesis.*

21-7 Reproductive Systems

Sexual reproduction in animals involves two sexes—male and female. In many animals, the sex of the individual can be identified by physical appearance. Even in animals where there is little or no difference in external appearance between the sexes, there are internal differences. The gametes of animals develop in specialized organs called **gonads** (*goh*-nadz). The female gonads are called **ovaries** (*oh*-vuh-reez). The ovaries produce the female gametes, which are called **egg**

Figure 21-6. Earthworms Mating.

cells, or **ova** (*oh*-vuh) (singular, ovum). The male gonads are called **testes** (*tes*-teez). The testes (singular, testis) produce male gametes, which are called **sperm cells.** For convenience, egg cells are commonly referred to as eggs, and sperm cells are referred to as sperm (either singular or plural). In addition to the gonads, most animals also have other organs that perform functions necessary for reproduction. These organs together with the gonads form the reproductive system.

21-8 Separation of Sexes and Hermaphroditism

In most types of animals the sexes are separate—that is, each individual has either testes or ovaries and is either male or female. In some animals, each individual contains both testes and ovaries. Such organisms are called **hermaphrodites** (her-*maf*-ruh-dyts). *Hermaphroditism* (her-*maf*-ruh-dit-iz-um) is generally found among slow-moving or sessile animals, such as earthworms, snails, and hydra.

Although hermaphroditic organisms can produce both eggs and sperm, self-fertilization is rare. Instead, these organisms exchange sperm with another animal of the same species. For example, during mating, two earthworms lie parallel to each other (see Figure 21-6). Each transfers sperm to the *sperm receptacle* of its partner. After they separate, each worm uses the stored sperm from the partner to fertilize its own eggs.

21-9 Gametogenesis

The process by which gametes develop in the gonads is called **gametogenesis** (guh-meet-uh-*jen*-uh-sis). More specifically, the formation of eggs in the ovaries is called **oogenesis** (oh-uh-*jen*-uh-sis), while the formation of sperm in the testes is called **spermatogenesis** (sper-mat-uh-*jen*-uh-sis). Although the same basic processes are involved in the production of both eggs and sperm, there are some differences.

Oogenesis. Oogenesis is the production of eggs in the ovary. The major steps in oogenesis are shown in Figure 21-7.

Eggs develop in the ovary from immature sex cells called **oogonia** (oh-uh-*goh*-nee-uh) (singular, oogonium). In many

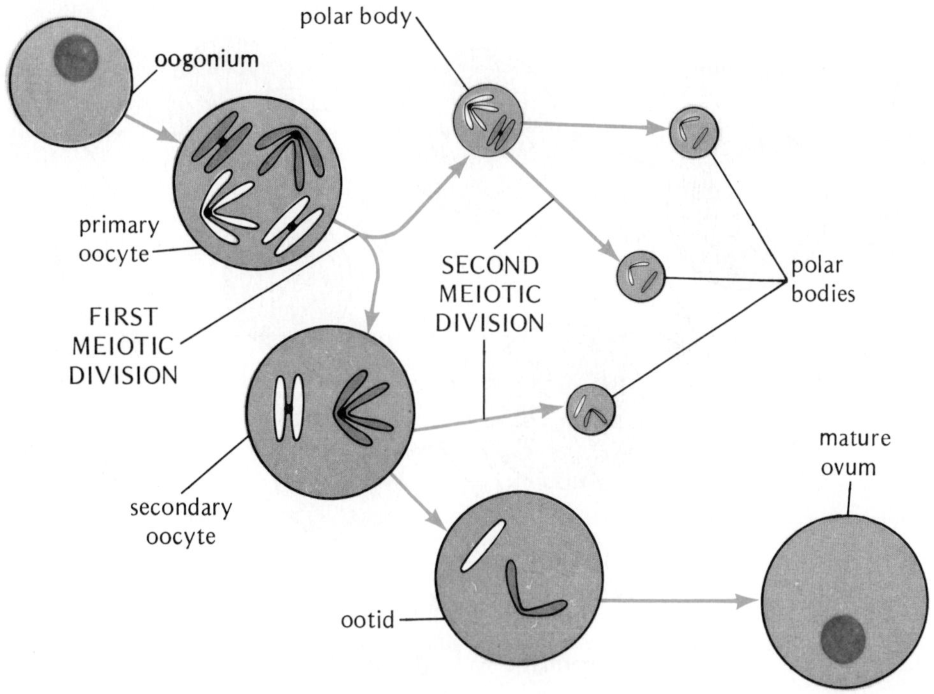

Figure 21-7. Oogenesis. A single functional egg cell is produced by meiotic division of a primary oocyte. The oocyte is diploid, the egg cell is monoploid.

animals the oogonium is surrounded by a *follicle,* which later holds the mature egg. Oogonia contain the diploid number of chromosomes. During early development of the female organism, the oogonia divide many times by mitosis to form a supply of oogonia. In human females, the production of oogonia stops at birth. Thus, each human female has a limited number of oogonia.

In the human female fetus, by the third month of development, oogonia within the ovary begin to develop into cells called **primary oocytes** (*oh*-uh-syts). By birth, the primary oocytes are in prophase of the first meiotic division. At this point, meiosis stops until the female reaches sexual maturity. Then periodically (about once a month in most women) one of these primary oocytes completes meiosis and develops into a functional egg.

When the first meiotic division occurs in the primary oocyte, the cytoplasm of the cell is divided unequally. One of the daughter cells, which is large and receives most of the cytoplasm, is called the **secondary oocyte.** The other daughter cell is very small and is called the first **polar body.** Each of these daughter cells contains the monoploid number of chromosomes.

During the second meiotic division, the secondary oocyte divides unequally into a large cell called an **ootid** (*oh*-uh-tid) and another polar body. The first polar body may also divide into two polar bodies. The ootid grows into a mature egg, which has the monoploid chromosome number. The polar bodies disintegrate and die.

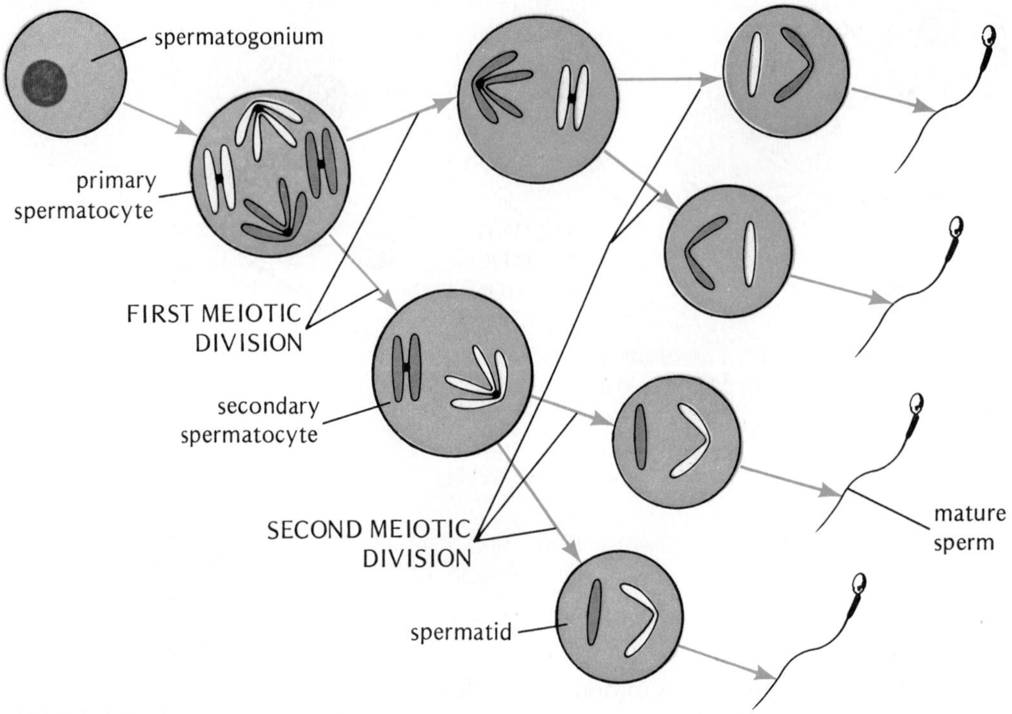

Figure 21-8. Spermatogenesis. Four functional sperm cells are produced by meiotic division of a primary spermatocyte.

Spermatogenesis. Spermatogenesis is the production of sperm in the testes. The major steps in spermatogenesis are shown in Figure 21-8.

Within the testes the sperm develop from immature sex cells called **spermatogonia** (sper-mat-uh-*goh*-nee-uh). Throughout childhood, these spermatogonia (singular, spermatogonium) divide mitotically many times to produce additional spermatogonia. The spermatogonia contain the diploid number of chromosomes. In humans, after a male matures sexually there is a continual development of some spermatogonia into functional sperm. Other spermatogonia continue to divide mitotically, producing more spermatogonia. Thus, while the number of the eggs is limited, the number of sperm is not limited.

In the course of development, a spermatogonium increases in size to become a **primary spermatocyte** (sper-*mat*-uh-syt). The primary spermatocyte undergoes the first meiotic division, forming two cells of equal size. These are **secondary spermatocytes.** Each secondary spermatocyte then undergoes the second meiotic division, forming four **spermatids** (*sper*-muh-tids), all of equal size. The spermatids contain the monoploid number of chromosomes. With no further division each spermatid develops into a mature sperm with a flagellum. Thus, each primary spermatocyte gives rise to four sperm.

21-10 Comparison of Egg and Sperm

The male and female gametes of a species differ in structure. Eggs are round in shape and nonmotile. They contain a nucleus and stored food in the form of **yolk** (yohk). The egg is always larger than the sperm of the same species. The size of the egg varies from one species to another and depends on the amount of yolk stored in it. Yolk is used as nourishment by the developing animal. The yellow center of a chicken egg is the egg cell. It contains a great deal of yolk because the developing chicken receives no other nourishment while in the egg. The eggs of humans and other mammals are usually microscopic and contain little yolk because the developing animal gets nourishment from the mother. The human egg is about 0.1 millimeter in diameter.

Most sperm cells are microscopic. A typical sperm is made up of a head, a middle piece, and a long, thin tail called a flagellum (see Figure 21-9). The head consists of the nucleus, which contains the chromosomes, and an *acrosome* (*ak*-ruh-sohm), which aids in the penetration of the egg. The middle piece is packed with mitochondria, which provide energy so the sperm can move. The long, whiplike flagellum enables the sperm to swim through liquids.

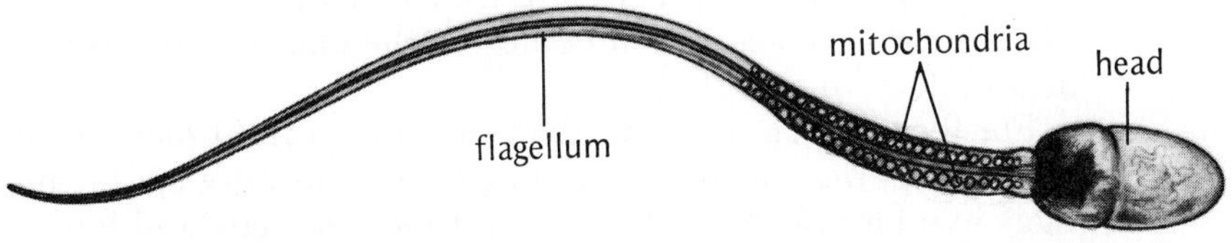

Figure 21-9. Structure of a Human Sperm Cell. The overall length of the sperm is about 0.05 millimeters, half the diameter of a human egg.

21-11 Fertilization and Zygote Formation

As previously mentioned, the union of an egg cell nucleus and a sperm cell nucleus is called fertilization, and the resulting cell is the zygote. The joining of the two monoploid gametes produces a diploid zygote. Fertilization restores the species number of chromosomes.

Eggs are nonmotile—they have no power to move by themselves. Sperm, on the other hand, are streamlined cells specialized for fast movement. When sperm are released by the male, their flagella beat rapidly, pushing them along in all directions. As they approach an egg, they encounter a chemical called *fertilizin,* which has been released by the egg. Fertilizin stimulates the sperm to move faster and aids in their attachment to the surface of the egg.

When a sperm comes in contact with an egg, the acrosome releases enzymes that dissolve an opening through the protective membranes of the egg. This allows the head of the sperm to enter the egg, while the tail remains outside. The sperm cell nucleus moves through the cytoplasm toward the egg cell nucleus. The n chromosomes of the sperm nucleus join with

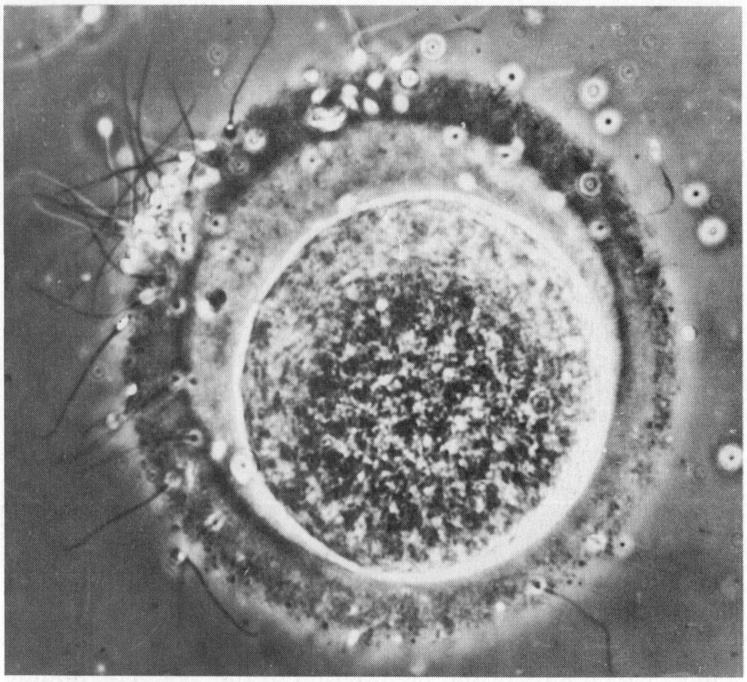

Figure 21-10. Human Egg Surrounded by Sperm.

the *n* chromosomes of the egg nucleus to form the zygote, which thus has $2n$ chromosomes.

A *fertilization membrane* is formed around the egg after a sperm penetrates it (see Figure 21-10). This membrane prevents additional sperm from entering the egg, and also serves as a protective covering.

For fertilization to occur, there must be a fluid medium so that the sperm can swim to the egg. Also, because sperm and eggs live for only a short period of time, the male and female gametes must be released together. There are two basic ways in which the gametes are brought together. One is external fertilization, in which the gametes fuse outside the body of the female. The other is internal fertilization, in which the gametes fuse inside the body of the female.

External Fertilization. In **external fertilization,** the eggs are fertilized in the environment outside the body of the female. This type of fertilization is limited to aquatic animals. In such animals, the only sex organs needed besides the gonads are the ducts that transport the gametes from the gonads to the water. Fertilization occurs directly in the water after each parent releases its gametes. The sperm swim through the water to the eggs. Although there is no problem about moist surroundings for fertilization, there are many hazards in the environment. The sperm and eggs may not meet, the eggs or developing offspring may be eaten by other animals, they may die because of variations in the temperature and/or oxygen concentration in the water, and so on. To overcome the hazards of external fertilization, large numbers of eggs and sperm are released. External fertilization occurs in almost all aquatic invertebrates, most fish (not sharks), and many amphibians.

Figure 21-11. Amplexus. The male and female frogs release their gametes into the water at the same time, thereby ensuring fertilization of some of the eggs.

To improve the chances of eggs and sperm meeting, aquatic animals do not release their gametes at random. There are many hormonally controlled behavior patterns that ensure that sperm and eggs are released at approximately the same time and place. In some fish, the female deposits thousands of eggs, and the male swims over them releasing sperm. This process is known as *spawning*. Salmon hatch in freshwater streams. The young fish then travel downstream to the ocean where they mature. When the salmon are ready to spawn, they return to the freshwater stream where they were hatched. This adaptation ensures that the males and females are in the same place and in a proper environment for spawning.

In frogs, when a female is full of eggs and ready to mate, she approaches a male. The male embraces the female with his front legs in a process called *amplexus* (see Figure 21-11). This stimulates the female to release her eggs, and at the same time, the male releases his sperm. Because they are in close contact and the gametes are released at the same time, the sperm reach many of the eggs. Amplexus coordinates the proper release of the gametes.

Internal Fertilization. **Internal fertilization,** fertilization within the body of the female, is characteristic of animals that reproduce on land. It is also found in some aquatic animals, such as sharks and lobsters. Internal fertilization requires a specialized sex organ to transfer the sperm from the body of the male into the body of the female. After the sperm are placed within the female's body, they travel to the eggs and fertilize them. The moist tissues of the female provide the watery environment required for the sperm to swim to the egg. After fertilization, the zygote is either enclosed in a protective shell and released by the female, or it remains and develops within the female's body.

Internal fertilization avoids the scattering of gametes and the hazards of the outside environment. Few eggs are produced because they are well protected and the chances of fertilization are much greater than they are when the gametes are released externally into water. However, even with internal fertilization, large numbers (often in the millions) of sperm are released by the male into the body of the female. Even within the female's body, the sperm can fertilize the egg only for a brief period of time. Because the sperm store little food, they live only a short time. Also, the egg can be penetrated by the sperm only for a brief time. In humans, the egg can be fertilized for only about 24 hours.

In animals with internal fertilization, many of the specialized adaptations involved in reproduction are concerned with the timing of the release of sperm and eggs. Since the gametes generally live only for a short time, mating must occur within certain time periods for fertilization to occur. Many of the reproductive adaptations are controlled by hormones. Reproductive adaptations include such things as singing, the display of special feathers, color patches on the skin, and the release of chemicals called *pheromones* (*fer*-uh-mohnz), which have distinctive odors. These adaptations attract males, stimulate a mating response, and trigger the release of eggs and sperm.

In many insects and in bats the problem of timing is solved in an interesting way. After mating, the sperm are stored in specialized structures in the female and then used to fertilize the eggs at some later time. In the queen honeybee, for example, enough sperm are stored from one mating to fertilize the hundreds of thousands of eggs she lays during her lifetime. In bats, mating occurs in the fall, and the sperm are stored until the following spring, when fertilization occurs. It is not known how the sperm remain alive for such long periods.

It is thought that normally, the entry of the sperm into the egg is the stimulus that causes the egg to start dividing. Apparently, however, fertilization, the union of the egg nucleus and the sperm nucleus, is not necessary to induce development. In the laboratory, eggs of various types of animals have been stimulated to develop by pricking them with a needle, exposure to various chemicals, etc. In some cases, development of the unfertilized egg has produced an adult animal.

21-12 Parthenogenesis

The development of an unfertilized egg into an adult animal without fusion with sperm is called **parthenogenesis** (par-thuh-noh-*jen*-uh-sis). In nature, it occurs in many insects, including bees, wasps, aphids (plant lice), certain ants, and in rotifers and other microscopic animals. For example, in bees, the queen bee mates only once. She can then produce either unfertilized eggs or fertilized eggs. The unfertilized eggs become male drones while the fertilized eggs become female workers or queens. Female aphids reproduce by parthenogenesis during the spring and summer. In the fall, the eggs produce both males and females. These insects mate, and the females produce fertilized eggs that hatch in the spring.

summary

Sexual reproduction involves hereditary material from two parents. Two specialized sex cells, or gametes, one from each parent, unite in a process called fertilization. The product of fertilization is a zygote, the first cell of the new individual. Unlike asexual reproduction, sexual reproduction produces offspring that are not identical to either parent, thereby introducing variation within the species.

The body cells of each organism contain a constant number of chromosomes that is characteristic of its species. This is the diploid, or $2n$, chromosome number. The chromosomes of the body cells are present in homologous pairs. The sex cells of the organism contain half the diploid chromosome number. This is the monoploid, or n, chromosome number. The sex cells contain only one of each homologous pair of chromosomes.

The formation of monoploid gametes involves a type of cell division called meiosis. In meiosis, the chromosomes replicate once and the cell divides twice. In the first meiotic division homologous pairs of chromosomes become separated. In the second meiotic division the two strands of the double-stranded chromosomes become separated. Meiosis results in the formation of four monoploid cells. Both the first and second meiotic divisions can be divided into a prophase, metaphase, anaphase, and telophase.

The most common type of sexual reproduction found among protists is conjugation. In conjugation, a protoplasmic bridge forms between two cells of opposite mating types, and there is an exchange or transfer of nuclear material. In spirogyra and paramecium, conjugation serves to rejuvenate the nuclear material.

In animals the development of gametes takes place in the ovaries of the female and in the testes of the male. The ovaries produce eggs and the testes produce sperm. The process by which eggs develop is called oogenesis, while the development of sperm is called spermatogenesis. Eggs are round and nonmotile and contain varying amounts of yolk, depending on the species. Sperm are much smaller than eggs and are specialized for rapid movement. They swim by the beating of a tail-like flagellum.

In fertilization, the sperm nucleus enters the egg and fuses with the egg nucleus. The resulting zygote develops by mitotic cell division. In many aquatic animals fertilization is external, while in land animals, fertilization is generally internal.

vocabulary

body cell
conjugation
diploid
disjunction
egg
external fertilization
fertilization
gamete
gametogenesis
gonad
haploid
hermaphrodite
homologous chromosomes
internal fertilization
mating type
meiosis
monoploid
oogenesis
oogonium
ootid
ovary
ovum
parthenogenesis
polar body
primary oocyte
primary spermatocyte
secondary oocyte
secondary spermatocyte
somatic cell
sperm
spermatid
spermatogenesis
spermatogonium
synapsis
testis
tetrad
yolk
zygospore
zygote

test your learning

Section

21-1
1. Compare the advantages of asexual and sexual reproduction.
2. Why is it desirable for members of a species to have variations in their hereditary material?

21-2
3. Which cells of an organism are usually diploid and which are usually monoploid?
4. What are homologous chromosomes?

21-3
5. What is accomplished by the process of meiosis?
6. Describe the processes of synapsis and disjunction.
7. In what way is the chromosome content of the cell changed by the first meiotic division?
8. In what way is the chromosome content of the cell changed by the second meiotic division?

21-4
9. What are mating types in protists?

21-5
10. Briefly describe conjugation in spirogyra.

21-6
11. Briefly describe conjugation in paramecium.

21-7
12. What are the functions of the ovaries and the testes?

21-8
13. What is a hermaphrodite?

21-9
14. Briefly describe the process of oogenesis.
15. How many mature eggs are produced from each oogonium?
16. Briefly describe the process of spermatogenesis.
17. How many mature sperm are produced from each spermatogonium?

21-10 **18.** Compare the structure of a sperm with that of an egg.
21-11 **19.** Describe the fertilization of an egg by a sperm.
20. In what types of organisms does external fertilization occur?
21. Why do organisms in which fertilization is external produce tremendous numbers of gametes?
22. In what types of animals does internal fertilization occur?
23. Why are relatively few eggs produced in animals in which fertilization is internal?
21-12 **24.** What is parthenogenesis?

test your understanding

1. Compare and contrast the events in mitotic and meiotic cell division.
2. Compare and contrast the processes of oogenesis and spermatogenesis.
3. Why must gametes contain the monoploid number of chromosomes rather than the diploid number?
4. Describe some of the problems of external fertilization and of internal fertilization.

independent research

1. Write a report on one of the following subjects:
A. parthenogenesis
B. reproductive behavior in birds
C. reproductive behavior in fish
2. Write a report on sexual reproduction in bacteria and yeasts.

chapter 22

Animal Development

EMBRYONIC DEVELOPMENT

After completing your study of this section, you should be able to:

1. Define the terms *development* and *embryo*.
2. Explain in general terms the events of cleavage and embryonic development through the gastrula stage.
3. Name the three germ layers and list a few of the tissues and organs formed from each.
4. Define the term *differentiation*.

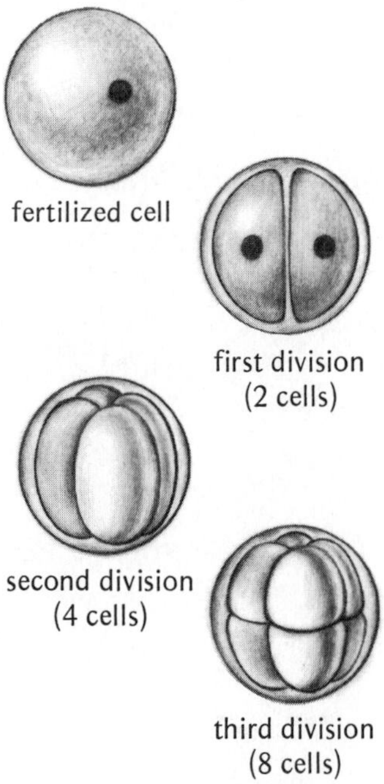

Figure 22-1. Early stages of Cleavage. Although the number of cells doubles at each division during cleavage, no growth occurs.

22-1 Cleavage

Fertilization in animals is the start of a complex series of events that eventually give rise to an adult organism. These events are referred to as **development.** In the early stages of development, the organism is called an **embryo** (*em*-bree-oh). The study of embryonic development is called **embryology** (em-bree-*ahl*-uh-jee).

Although there are many different patterns of embryonic development, the basic processes involved are always the same. These processes include cleavage, growth, and differentiation.

After fertilization, the zygote begins a series of cell divisions known as **cleavage** (*klee*-vidj). During cleavage, the fertilized egg divides by mitosis into two cells. Each of these cells divides again, producing four cells. These four produce eight, and so on (see Figure 22-1).

During cleavage, the cells do not grow, so with each division, the cells decrease in size. The eggs of a species are generally many times larger than the average cell of the adult organism. Cleavage continues until the size of the cells of the developing embryo have been reduced to the size of the cells of the adult organism. Cleavage thereby converts a single, large fertilized egg into many small cells.

The early divisions of cleavage result in the formation of a solid ball of cells. At this stage the embryo is called a **morula** (*mor*-yuh-luh) (see Figure 22-2). As cleavage continues, the cells undergo a rearrangement, forming a hollow sphere. The layer of cells in the sphere is generally only one cell thick. The cavity of the sphere is filled with fluid. At this stage the embryo is called a **blastula** (*blas*-chuh-luh), and the fluid-filled cavity is called the **blastocoel** (*blas*-tuh-seel) (see Figure 22-3).

Although the events of cleavage are generally as described above, the arrangement of cells in the developing embryo depends on the amount and distribution of yolk in the egg. Some eggs, such as those of humans and echinoderms, have very little yolk. In such eggs, cleavage results in a blastula in which all the cells are nearly equal in size. However, other eggs, such as those of amphibians, bony fish, birds, and reptiles, have a large amount of yolk concentrated in one part of the egg cell. The yolk does not divide with the cells. Therefore, in eggs with a lot of yolk, the cells undergoing cleavage are found at one pole and the yolk is found at the other.

In frog eggs, the large amount of yolk found at one pole retards cleavage in that region. This results in a blastula with larger cells at the yolk-filled, or *vegetal,* pole and more numerous, smaller cells at the yolkless, or *animal,* pole (see Figure 22-4). The blastocoel is formed only within the region of the animal pole.

In the chicken egg, the nucleus and cytoplasm are concentrated in the *germinal disk,* a platelike area on the surface of the ball of yolk (see Figure 22-5). Cleavage occurs only in the cells of the germinal disk. The blastocoel is formed when these cells separate from the yolk, leaving a space between the yolk and the cells. The developing chick eventually uses the yolk for food and completely fills the space within the egg.

Figure 22-2. Morula. At this stage, the developing embryo is a solid ball of cells.

Figure 22-3. Blastula. At this stage, the developing embryo is a hollow sphere with a fluid-filled interior.

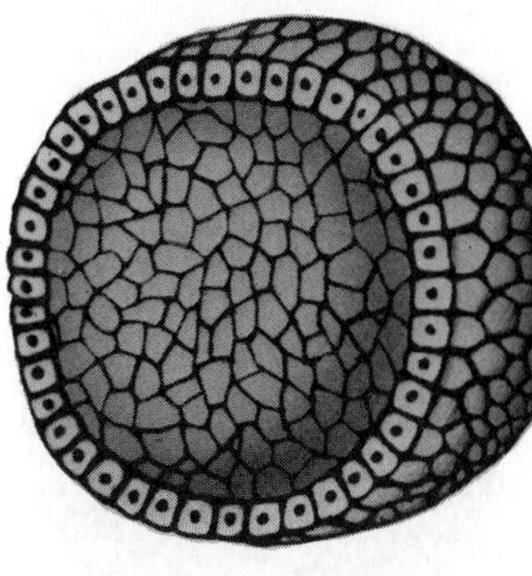

Figure 22-4. Blastula of Frog Egg.

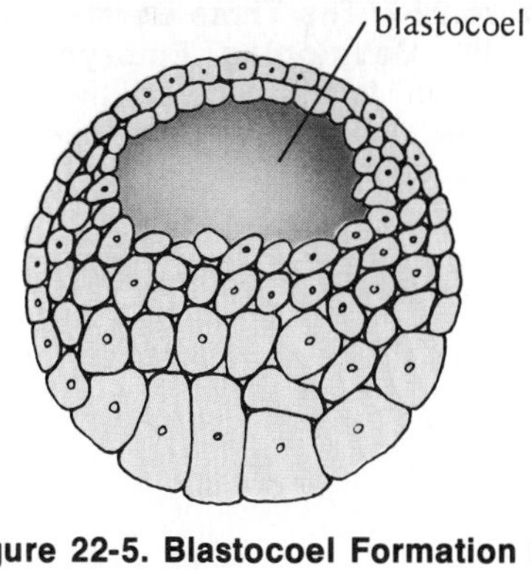

Figure 22-5. Blastocoel Formation in the Chicken Egg.

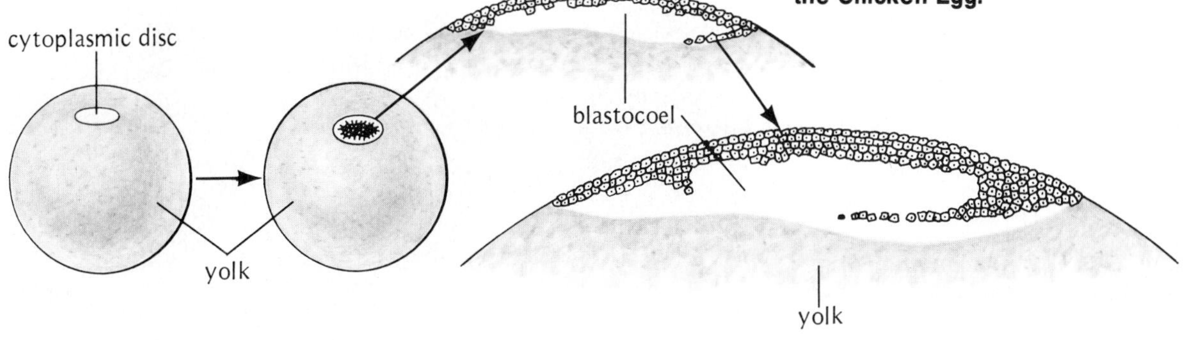

22-2 Gastrulation

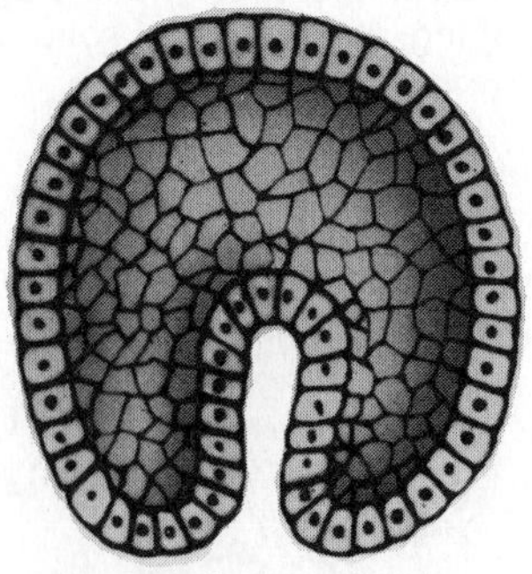

Figure 22-6. Gastrulation. In gastrulation a second cell layer is formed when the cells of one side of the embryo push inward, forming an indentation.

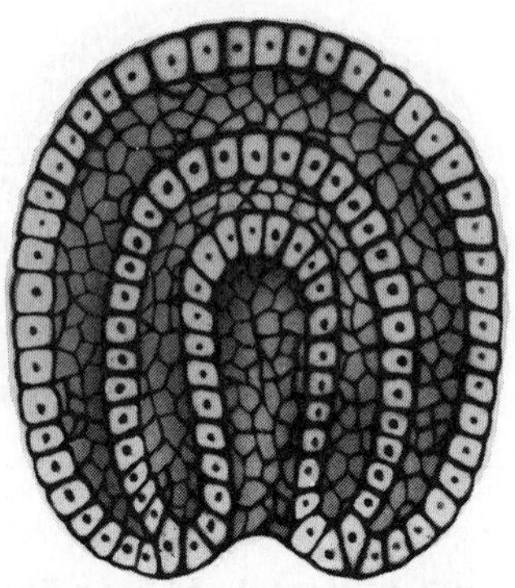

Figure 22-7. The Three Germ Layers of the Developing Embryo. The mesoderm forms between the outer layer, the ectoderm, and the inner layer, the endoderm.

As development of the blastula continues, it reaches a point at which the cells begin to grow before dividing. Mitotic division continues, but it is now accompanied by growth. In addition, various movements of the cells occur that will establish the shape of the embryo.

When the blastula reaches several hundred cells, gastrulation occurs. In **gastrulation** (gas-truh-*lay*-shun), the cells on one side of the blastula push in and form a two-layered embryo called the **gastrula** (*gas*-truh-luh) (see Figure 22-6). The opening created by the gastrulation process is called the **blastopore** (*blas*-tuh-por). It later becomes an opening to the digestive system in the adult organism, usually the anus.

The outer layer of cells in the gastrula is called the **ectoderm.** The inner layer is called the **endoderm.** The cavity within the gastrula is called the *primitive gut*, or **archenteron** (ar-*kent*-uh-rahn). It later becomes the digestive system. Eventually, the primitive gut cavity breaks through the opposite end of the developing embryo, forming the second opening of the digestive system. This usually becomes the mouth. After the endoderm and ectoderm are established, a third cell layer, the **mesoderm** (*mez*-uh-derm), forms between them (see Figure 22-7).

In the frog, the yolk-containing cells of the vegetal pole do not take part in gastrulation. The blastopore forms next to the mass of yolk cells (see Figure 22-8.) Cells from the animal pole move down and push in through the blastopore at the edge of the yolk mass.

In the chicken, the cells of the blastula separate into an outer and an inner layer. The outer layer becomes the ectoderm, and the inner layer becomes the endoderm. The space between the two layers is the blastocoel. The cells of the outer layer roll inward to produce the third cell layer, the mesoderm. This inward movement of cells gives rise to a visible line, called the *primitive streak*, on the surface of the germinal disk. The primitive streak is really an elongated blastopore.

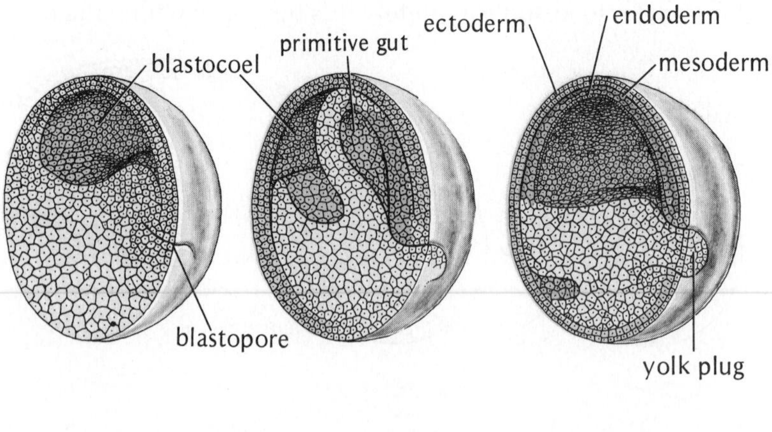

Figure 22-8. Gastrulation and Formation of Germ Layers in the Frog Egg.

Ectoderm	Mesoderm	Endoderm
Nervous system, including brain, spinal cord, nerves.	Bones and muscles.	Lining of digestive tract.
Lining of mouth, nostrils, and anus.	Blood and blood vessels.	Lining of trachea, bronchi, and lungs.
Epidermis of skin, sweat glands, hair, nails.	Reproductive and excretory systems.	Liver, pancreas.
	Inner layer (dermis) of skin.	Thyroid, parathyroid, thymus.
		Urinary bladder.

Table 22-1. Development of Organs and Organ Systems from the Germ Layers.

The three cell layers—ectoderm, mesoderm, and endoderm—are called the **germ layers** because they give rise to all the tissues and organs of multicellular animals. Table 22-1 shows some of the organs and systems that arise from each layer.

22-3 Growth and Differentiation

As the development of the gastrula proceeds, the number of cells continues to increase. Since the cells are now growing before dividing, the embryo as a whole begins to increase in size. Cell growth alone would produce only a formless mass of cells. It is necessary for the cells of the embryo to be arranged into specific structures, and within these structures, the cells must be specialized to perform particular functions. Although the cells of the gastrula are organized into distinct layers, they are all very much alike in appearance. The series of changes that transforms the unspecialized embryonic cells into the specialized cells, tissues, and organs that make up the organism is called **differentiation.**

The process by which the embryo develops its characteristic shape is called *morphogenesis.* Morphogenesis involves the movement of masses of cells and occurs early in embryonic development. Gastrulation and the formation of the three germ layers marks the beginning of morphogenesis.

Early evidence of differentiation is found on the upper surface of the gastrula. Here the ectoderm cells divide, forming a *neural plate* with two raised edges, called *neural folds* (see Figure 22-9). The neural folds unite over the center of the neural plate, forming a *neural tube.* The neural tube later forms the brain and spinal cord.

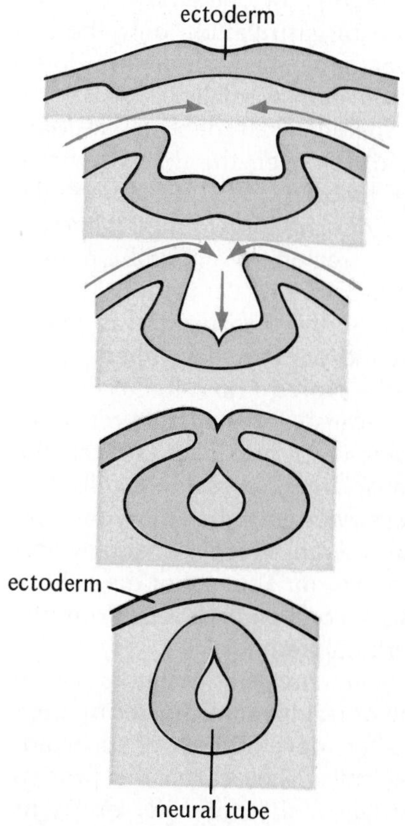

Figure 22-9. Formation of the Neural Tube.

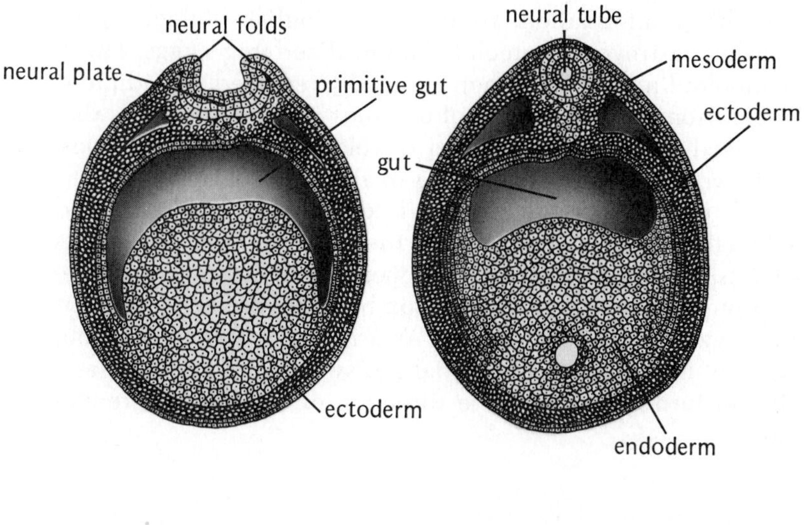

CONTROL OF DEVELOPMENT

After completing your study of this section, you should be able to:

1. Describe the roles of the nucleus and cytoplasm in controlling development.
2. Describe the process of embryonic induction and explain how this process controls development.

22-4 Role of the Nucleus and Cytoplasm in Development

Within the nucleus of the fertilized egg is the hereditary material, which contains all the information necessary for the development of the organism. The hereditary information is encoded within the chemical structure of DNA in the chromosomes. DNA controls the chemical processes of the cell and determines which proteins are synthesized by the cell. Because the cells of the embryo divide by mitosis, each cell contains the same chromosomes and DNA as the original fertilized egg cell.

If DNA controls cellular activities and all cells of an organism contain the same DNA, how are the many different kinds of cells in the organism produced? It has been found that although the DNA of all the cells of an organism is the same, different sections of the DNA molecules can be turned off and on, and this results in the formation of different types of cells. Thus, in muscle cells, for example, the part of the DNA that controls the synthesis of muscle proteins is turned on, while the part of the DNA that controls the synthesis of nerve proteins is turned off. In nerve cells, on the other hand, only the part of the DNA involved in the synthesis of nerve cell proteins is turned on. If this were not the case, then all the cells of an embryo would be the same. However, very little is known at this time about how the activity of DNA in different cells is controlled.

Experiments with frogs have demonstrated that a nucleus from a fully differentiated cell contains a complete copy of the hereditary information. In 1962, the English biologist J. G. Gurden destroyed the nuclei of unfertilized frog's eggs. These monoploid nuclei were then surgically replaced with diploid nuclei from intestinal cells of tadpoles. Some of the eggs that received the intestinal nuclei developed into normal frogs. This would indicate that some of the DNA that was inactivated, or switched off, in the intestinal cell was activated when the nucleus was placed in the egg cell. From the results of this and other research, it appears that the control of development involves an interaction between the DNA and certain cytoplasmic constituents. As a result of this interaction, parts of the hereditary material are switched on and off, and this in turn determines the direction of cellular differentiation.

historical notes

In the early 1900s, the German zoologist Hans Spemann found that before gastrulation occurs in an embryo, it can be divided in two, and each half develops into a normal organism. However, if the embryo is divided after gastrulation begins, only one normal organism develops. Spemann found that for a normal embryo to develop, the **dorsal lip** of the blastopore has to be present. (The blastopore is the opening created by gastrulation, and the dorsal lip is the group of cells on the side of the blastopore nearer the animal pole.) When the embryo is divided after the beginning of gastrulation, only the half containing the cells of the dorsal lip develop normally.

Spemann's student, Hilde Mangold, removed the dorsal lip from the embryo of a light-colored salamander and transplanted it into the belly region of an embryo of a dark-colored salamander. The result of the transplant was that a second embryo developed in the dark-colored "host."

Because of the difference in color, it was possible to see that the transplanted dorsal lip cells had developed into the embryonic spinal column, which is what they normally form. The rest of the cells of this second embryo were from the dark-colored host.

Spemann and Mangold called the dorsal lip an **organizer** because it alters development of surrounding cells. They called the process by which the organizer exerts its influence **induction.**

Other experimental evidence indicates that differentiation begins early in development. For example, if the cells of a four-celled frog embryo are carefully separated, each cell will develop into a normal tadpole. But if the cells of an older embryo are separated, the cells develop abnormally and die. In the older embryo, the cells have already begun to differentiate and can no longer produce a whole, normal organism.

22-5 Role of Neighboring Cells in Differentiation

As an embryo develops, there must be coordination and communication between its tissues. By the late blastula or early gastrula stage, the path of development of groups of cells is determined. Cells in specific regions are committed to specific lines of development. For example, there is a particular region in the frog gastrula that normally develops into an eye. If this tissue is removed from the embryo and placed in a special nutrient solution, it develops into an irregular mass of cells. On the other hand, if this tissue is transplanted into any other part of another frog embryo, it will develop into a recognizable eye, even though it is not a functioning eye. Some of the tissues in the extra, non-functioning eye did not develop from the transplanted tissue. Instead, the transplanted tissue caused some of the surrounding tissue, which would not ordinarily be part of the eye, to develop into eye structures. This experiment showed that a tissue can influence the differentiation of neighboring tissues.

It has been found that certain parts of the developing embryo act as *organizers*, influencing the development of adjacent cells. The process by which the organizer induces another structure to differentiate is called **embryonic induction.** The mechanism by which induction is accomplished is not yet known. Some chemical substances have been shown to cause induction. Cell contact may also be important. It may be that at various stages of development, tissues use different parts of their hereditary material and that organizers select which parts will be used at a given time.

EXTERNAL AND INTERNAL DEVELOPMENT

After completing your study of this section, you should be able to:

1. Compare and contrast external development in water and internal development on land.
2. Describe the adaptations of reptiles, birds, nonplacental mammals, and placental mammals for reproduction on land.

22-6 External Development in Water

Embryonic development may be either outside or inside the mother's body, depending on the type of organism. Regardless of where development occurs, the embryo has certain

Although embryos that develop externally lack parental protection, they do have adaptations that increase their chances of survival. For example, in frog eggs, the jellylike layer that forms after fertilization offers some protection from predators and provides insulation. Also, the dark upper surface and the light lower surface of the eggs provide protective coloration.

Figure 22-10. (Top) Eggs of a Red-winged Blackbird. (Bottom) Eggs of a northern Black Racer Snake.

Point out that the egg is fertilized before it is enclosed in the shell. Also mention that the shell prevents most bacteria from entering the egg and slows down the rate of evaporation of water from the embryo.

needs that must be met. It needs nourishment, proper environmental conditions, oxygen, protection, and a means of getting rid of wastes.

In most aquatic animals, the eggs are fertilized externally and development is external in the water. Nourishment for these embryos is supplied by yolk stored in the egg. The developing young are usually assured proper environmental conditions because mating and fertilization occur at specific times of the year. Oxygen from the surrounding water diffuses into the embryo, and wastes diffuse from the embryo into the water.

In most aquatic animals, there is usually little or no care of the young by the parents. Some fish, however, do provide a certain amount of care for the developing young. For example, the male stickleback guards the nest and fans the embryos with water currents to provide oxygen. Some fish are "mouth-breeders"—that is, the fertilized eggs are held in one parent's mouth until they hatch. In general, survival of species that develop in water is dependent on the production and fertilization of large numbers of eggs. Many of the eggs are eaten or destroyed in other ways, and only a small number survive from each mating.

22-7 External Development on Land

In birds and reptiles, as well as in a few mammals, fertilization is internal and development is external. In these animals the fertilized egg, which contains a large amount of yolk, is enclosed in a protective shell. The shelled egg is moist inside, providing the embryo with a self-contained aquatic environment. The shell is practically waterproof, but it is porous enough to allow oxygen from the air to diffuse into the egg and carbon dioxide from the embryo to diffuse out. Because the chances of survival are greater for embryos of animals with shelled eggs, fewer of these eggs are produced. Both the hard, calcium-containing shell of the bird egg and the tough, leathery shell of the reptile egg provide good protection for the embryo (see Figure 22-10). Reptiles lay considerably more eggs than birds. Reptile eggs are usually abandoned by the mother, whereas bird eggs and young birds are carefully tended by the parents. Thus, fewer reptile eggs survive than bird eggs.

Internal structure of the chicken egg. As the chicken embryo develops, it forms four membranes that are outside the embryo itself but inside the shell. These are the **extraembryonic membranes** (see Figure 22-11). The extraembryonic membranes perform a number of important functions.

1. The **chorion** (*kor*-ee-ahn) is the outermost membrane. It lines the inside of the shell and surrounds the embryo and the other membranes. The chorion aids in gas exchange.

2. The **allantois** (uh-*lan*-tuh-wuhs) is a saclike structure that grows out of the digestive tract of the embryo. It is through the

blood vessels of the allantois that the exchange of oxygen and carbon dioxide occurs. The metabolic wastes of the embryo also collect in the allantois.

3. The **amnion** (*am*-nee-ahn) is a fluid-filled sac that surrounds the embryo. The amniotic fluid within the sac provides a watery environment for the embryo and acts as a cushion to protect it from shocks.

4. The **yolk sac** surrounds the yolk, the source of food for the embryo. Blood vessels in the yolk sac transport the food to the embryo.

The shelled egg with its extraembryonic membranes is an important adaptation that allows bird embryos to develop on land. When the young bird hatches, the extraembryonic membranes are discarded along with the shell. The eggs of reptiles have similar features.

Figure 22-12 shows various stages of development in the chicken.

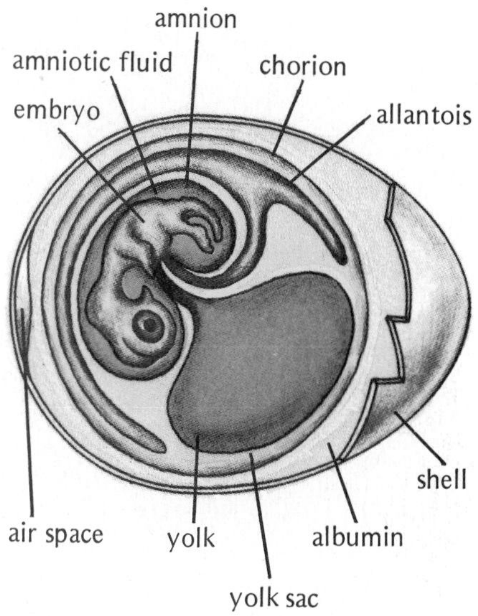

Figure 22-11. Internal Structure of the Chicken Egg.

22-8 Internal Development

In some sharks and in some reptiles, such as garter snakes, fertilization and development are internal. However, in these animals, the young do not receive nourishment directly from

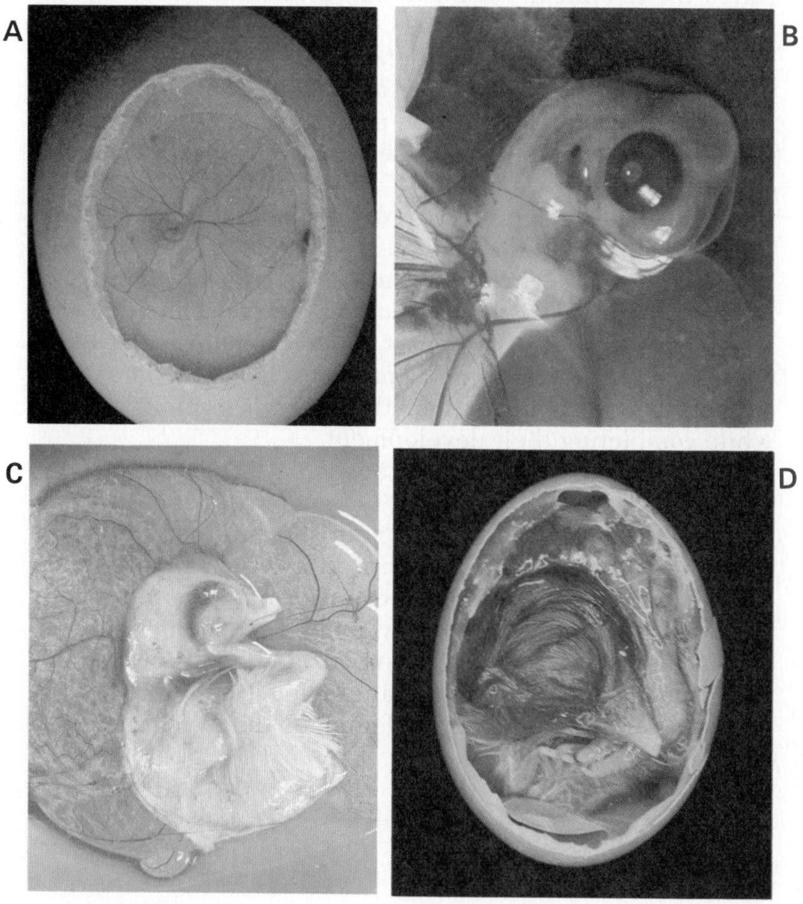

Figure 22-12. Stages of Development of Chicken Egg. (A) 3 days (B) 7 days (C) 14 days (D) 19 days.

the mother. Instead, the source of their food is yolk stored in the egg. When the offspring reach a stage at which they can maintain themselves, they are born.

Among mammals, fertilization is internal and the embryos typically develop internally within a structure called the **uterus** (*yoo*-tuh-rus). They are born in a relatively undeveloped condition and for a period feed on milk produced by the mother's mammary glands. The young are well-protected both during development and after birth, and most survive. Therefore, in animals in which the young develop internally, few eggs are produced.

Placental mammals. Most mammals, including humans, are **placental** (pluh-*sent*-ul) **mammals.** In these mammals, blood vessels of the embryo's circulatory system are in close contact with vessels of the mother's circulatory system. This contact occurs in a specialized structure called the **placenta** (pluh-*sent*-uh), which is in the wall of the uterus. In the placenta, nutrients and oxygen diffuse from the mother's blood into the embryo's blood, and carbon dioxide and other wastes diffuse from the embryo's blood into the mother's blood. However, there is no direct connection between the two circulatory systems. The embryo is attached to the placenta by a structure called the **umbilical** (um-*bil*-ih-kul) **cord.** This structure contains blood vessels that connect the embryo's circulatory system to capillaries in the placenta.

Nonplacental mammals. There are two types of **nonplacental mammals**—mammals in which no placenta forms during development of the embryo. These are the **egg-laying mammals** and the **pouched mammals.**

The duckbill platypus is an example of an egg-laying mammal. The embryo of the platypus is encased in a leathery egg resembling that of a reptile. Unlike the eggs of other mammals, the eggs of the platypus contain a large amount of yolk. The female lays the egg in a nest. When the young hatch out of the eggs, the female gathers them against her body. The young animals then feed on milk from the mother's mammary glands while completing their development.

In the pouched mammals, or marsupials, some internal development of the embryo occurs in the uterus, but no placenta is formed. The embryo obtains nourishment from the yolk of the egg. The young animal is born in a very immature condition. It crawls into a pouch on the outside of the mother's body and attaches itself to a mammary gland. Development is completed in the pouch. Most marsupials are found in Australia. The kangaroo is the most familiar example (see Figure 22-13). The opossum is a marsupial found in the Western Hemisphere.

Figure 22-13. Mother Kangaroo and Baby.

summary

Following fertilization, the zygote undergoes a series of cell divisions called cleavage. The early divisions of cleavage lead to the morula stage, where the embryo is in the form of a solid ball of cells. After further divisions and rearrangements of the cells, the embryo reaches the blastula stage. The blastula is a hollow sphere with a central cavity filled with fluid.

At the end of the blastula stage, gastrulation occurs. Gastrulation results in the formation of two cell layers—the ectoderm, which is the outer layer, and the endoderm, which is the inner layer. After these two layers are established, the third layer, the mesoderm, forms between them. During the gastrula stage the two openings of the digestive system form.

Embryonic development involves growth and cellular differentiation. Patterns of development are controlled by the DNA of the chromosomes. Furthermore, certain embryonic cells specifically influence the development of neighboring cells by a process known as embryonic induction.

Development may be external or internal. In most aquatic animals, development is external, with the embryos receiving nourishment from yolk in the eggs. Birds, reptiles, and a few mammals produce shelled eggs that develop externally on land. The shell protects the eggs and makes possible an internal environment in which the embryo can develop. Stored yolk within the egg provides nourishment for the embryo. Among placental mammals, development is internal. The embryo develops within the uterus of the mother. A special structure, the placenta, is the site of the exchange of substances between the circulatory systems of the mother and developing young. Pouched mammals have no placenta and the young, after a short period of development in the uterus, develop in an external pouch.

vocabulary

allantois
amnion
archenteron
blastula
chorion
cleavage
development
differentiation
ectoderm
egg-laying mammal
embryo
embryology
embryonic induction
endoderm
extraembryonic membrane
gastrula
gastrulation
germ layer
mesoderm
morula
nonplacental mammal
placenta
placental mammal
pouched mammal
umbilical cord
uterus
yolk sac

test your learning

Section

22-1 **1.** What is cleavage?
2. Describe the structure of the embryo at the morula and blastula stages.
3. How does the amount of yolk in the eggs of frogs and chickens affect cleavage?

22-2 **4.** Describe the process of gastrulation, and explain how the three germ layers are formed.
5. Name the three germ layers and give examples of structures formed from each.
6. How are the two openings of the digestive system formed?

22-3 **7.** Define the term *differentiation*, and explain the role of differentiation in development.

22-4 **8.** Discuss the role of DNA in controlling development.

22-5 **9.** What is embryonic induction?

22-6 **10.** How do eggs that develop in water obtain nourishment and oxygen and get rid of wastes?
11. What are the advantages and disadvantages of external development in water?

22-7 **12.** Briefly describe the structure of a bird's egg.
13. What are the functions of the four extraembryonic membranes of the bird's egg?
14. What are the advantages of a shelled egg for external development on land?

22-8 **15.** What is the placenta?
16. Where does embryonic development occur in placental mammals?
17. Where does embryonic development occur in pouched mammals?

test your understanding

1. Describe how each of the following stages in embryonic development is formed from the fertilized egg: morula, blastula, and gastrula.
2. How are the sites of fertilization and development and amount of parental care related to the number of gametes and young produced by a species?
3. Discuss the roles of DNA and the cytoplasm and embryonic induction in controlling embryonic development.
4. Compare and contrast external development in water and on land and internal development on land. Discuss the major problems of each, as well as the adaptations that overcome the problems.

independent research

1. Prepare a report on one of the following topics:
   A. The role of the blastopore in embryonic induction.
   B. Embryonic development in marsupials (pouched mammals).
2. Prepare a report on the importance of the shelled egg in the early success of the reptile phylum.

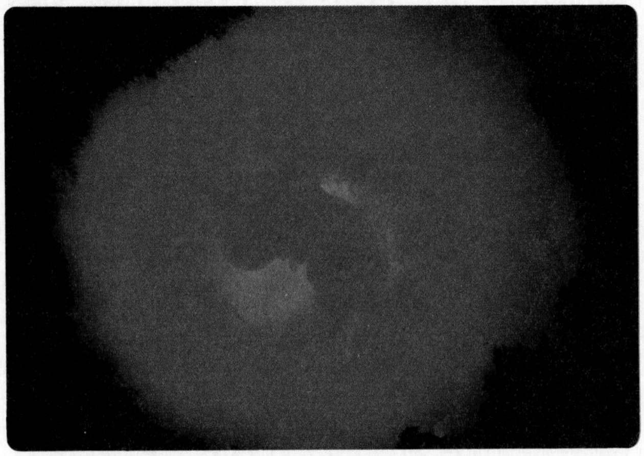

chapter 23

Human Reproduction

HUMAN REPRODUCTIVE SYSTEMS

After completing your study of this section, you should be able to:
1. List the major structures of the male reproductive system and briefly describe the functions of each.
2. List the major structures of the female reproductive system and briefly describe the functions of each.
3. Describe the male and female secondary sex characteristics, and name the two hormones involved in the development of these characteristics.

Interestingly, both sexes produce female and male sex hormones. However, the dominant hormone—testosterone in males and estrogen in females—neutralizes the effects of the opposite hormone, which is normally produced in only small quantities.

23-1 The Male Reproductive System

The male gonads are the testes. The testes produce sperm cells, which are the male gametes, and the male sex hormone, testosterone. Testosterone is responsible for the **secondary sex characteristics** of males, such as body hair, muscle development, and deep voice. These characteristics usually appear during adolescence.

The structure of the male reproductive system is shown in Figure 23-1. There are two testes, which are located in a sac of skin that is outside the body wall. This sac, which is called the **scrotum** (*skroht*-um), keeps the temperature of the testes slightly lower than that of the rest of the body. The lower temperature is best for the production and storage of sperm.

The temperature in the scrotum is about 2°C lower than the rest of the body.

Each testis consists of small, coiled tubes called the **seminiferous** (sem-uh-*nif*-uh-rus) **tubules.** There are 300 to 600 tubules in each testis. Immature sperm are produced in

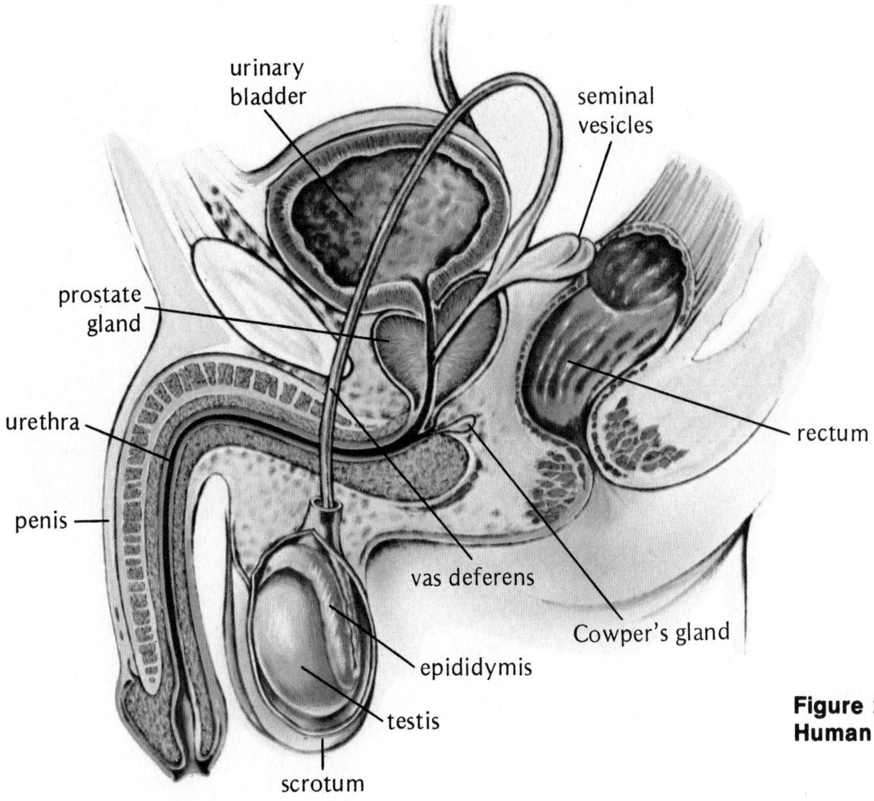

Figure 23-1. Reproductive System of Human Male.

the seminiferous tubules. From there, the sperm pass to the **epididymis** (ep-uh-*did*-uh-mis), a storage area on the upper, rear part of the testis. The sperm remain in the epididymis until they are mature. They leave the epididymis through the **vas deferens** (*def*-uh-renz), a tube that leads upward from each testis into the lower part of the abdomen.

The two vas deferens join at the urethra, the passageway for the elimination of urine (see page 198). In the human male, the urethra passes through the penis to the outside of the body. It is also the passageway through which sperm leave the body. As sperm enter the urethra, the **seminal vesicles Cowper's glands,** and the **prostate** (*prahs*-tayt) **gland** all secrete fluids into the urethra. The mixture of these fluids and the sperm is called **semen** (*see*-men). The passage of semen through the urethra occurs by a process called **ejaculation** (ih-jak-yuh-*lay*-shun). For a short time before, during, and after ejaculation, reflex actions keep the outlet of the urinary bladder closed, thereby preventing urine from entering the urethra.

The liquid transport medium for sperm—semen—is an adaptation for life on land.

23-2 The Female Reproductive System

The female gonads are the ovaries. The ovaries produce eggs, which are the female gametes, and also secrete the female sex hormone estrogen. Estrogen is responsible for the female secondary sex characteristics, such as development of the breasts, broadened pelvis, and pattern of fat distribution.

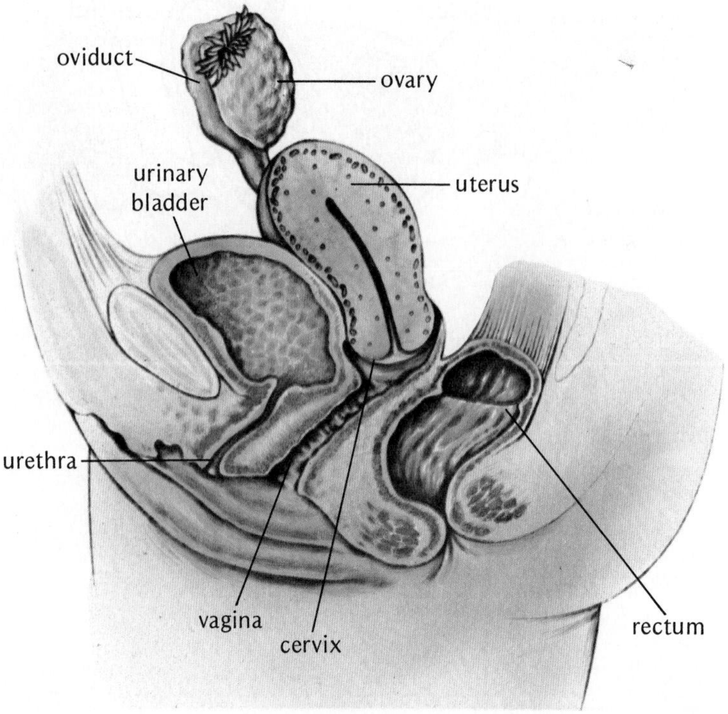

Figure 23-2. Reproductive System of Human Female.

These characteristics usually appear during adolescence. Estrogen also plays a large role in the menstrual cycle, which we will study in the next section.

The structure of the female reproductive system is shown in Figure 23-2. The female has two ovaries, located deep in the lower part of the abdomen. They are about 4 centimeters long and 2 centimeters wide. Each ovary contains about 200,000 tiny egg sacs called **follicles.** Each follicle contains an immature egg. These immature eggs are already present at the time of birth (see page 351). During the life of a female, no more than about 500 mature eggs are produced.

When an egg matures, the follicle surrounding it ruptures, or bursts, and the egg is released at the surface of the ovary (see Figure 23-3). This process is called **ovulation** (ahv-yuh-*lay*-shun). Ovulation first occurs at puberty, when the individual becomes sexually mature and capable of reproduction. Thereafter ovulation occurs about once a month.

Mention that puberty occurs earlier in girls than in boys.

Near each ovary, but not connected to it, is an **oviduct** (*oh*-vuh-duhkt), or **Fallopian** (fuh-*loh*-pee-un) **tube.** The oviduct is a tube with a funnel-like opening. Ciliated cells lining the oviduct create a current that draws the released egg into the tube. The egg passes through the oviduct to the **uterus,** (*yoot*-uh-rus), a thick-walled, muscular, pear-shaped organ. If sperm are present in the oviduct, the egg may be fertilized. If the egg is fertilized, it completes its development in the uterus. The narrow neck of the uterus is called the **cervix** (*ser*-viks). The cervix opens into the **vagina** (vuh-*jy*-nuh), or *birth canal,*

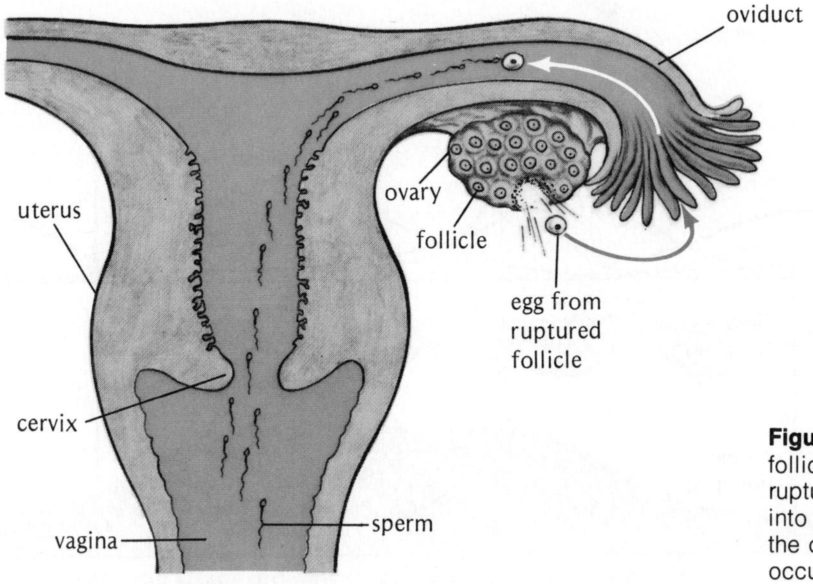

Figure 23-3. Ovulation. Eggs mature in follicles in the ovaries. When a follicle ruptures, the egg is released and drawn into the oviduct. If sperm are present in the oviduct, fertilization of the egg may occur.

which leads to the outside of the body. At birth, the child leaves the mother's body through this passageway. In the human female, the urethra has its own opening and is completely separate from the reproductive system.

THE MENSTRUAL CYCLE

After completing your study of this section, you should be able to:

1. Describe the events of the menstrual cycle.
2. Name the hormones involved in the menstrual cycle and describe the functions of each.

23-3 Characteristics of the Menstrual Cycle

In the human female, a mature egg develops and is released from one of the ovaries approximately every 28 days. At this time, the wall of the uterus has undergone a build-up and is prepared to accept a fertilized egg for development. If the egg is not fertilized, the newly built-up portion of the uterine wall breaks down, and this material, along with the unfertilized egg, is discharged from the body. The cycle then begins again with the maturing of another egg and the build-up of the uterine wall. This cycle is known as the **menstrual** (*men*-struhl) **cycle.** The changes that take place during the cycle involve the interaction of hormones produced by the hypothalamus, pituitary gland, and ovary.

The menstrual cycle begins at puberty, which usually occurs in human females sometime between the ages of 12 and 15. The cycle ceases temporarily during pregnancy. It ceases permanently sometime in middle age, usually between the

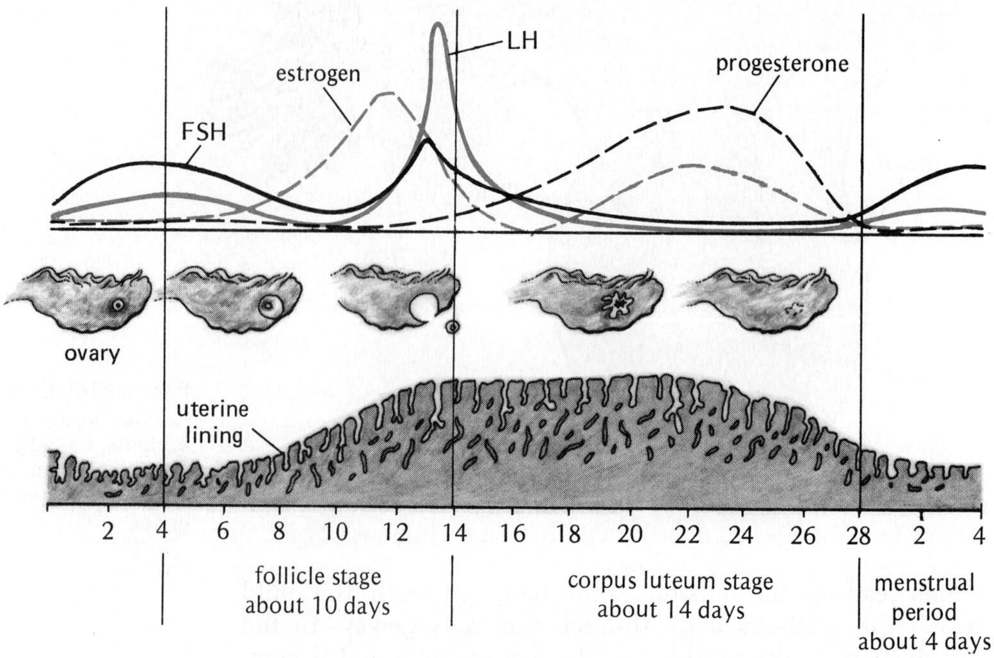

Figure 23-4. The Menstrual Cycle. This cycle of changes results in the release of an egg, the preparation of the uterine lining for a possible implantation and pregnancy, and the return to the initial state if no implantation occurs. The cycle is controlled by four interacting hormones and repeats about every 28 days.

ages of 45 and 50. The permanent cessation of the menstrual cycle is called *menopause* (*men*-uh-pawz).

23-4 Stages of the Menstrual Cycle

The menstrual cycle can be divided into four stages (see Figure 23-4).

Follicle stage. Follicle-stimulating hormone (FSH) is secreted by the pituitary gland (see page 270). FSH causes several follicles in the ovary to begin developing. Usually, only one matures. As the follicle develops, it secretes estrogen. The estrogen stimulates the uterine lining to thicken with mucus and a rich supply of blood vessels. These changes prepare the uterus for a possible pregnancy. This stage lasts 10 to 14 days.

Eggs can be released from either or both ovaries.

Ovulation. A high level of estrogen in the blood causes the pituitary to decrease secretion of FSH and begin secretion of luteinizing hormone (LH). When the concentration of LH in the blood reaches a certain level, ovulation occurs—that is, the follicle ruptures, releasing a mature egg. Ovulation usually takes place in about the middle of the menstrual cycle.

Corpus luteum stage. After ovulation, LH causes the ruptured follicle to fill with cells, forming a yellow body called the **corpus luteum** (*kor*-pus *loot*-ee-um). The corpus luteum begins to secrete the hormone progesterone, which maintains the continued growth of the uterine lining. Because of its role in maintaining the uterine wall, progesterone is often called the hormone of pregnancy. It also prevents the development of new follicles in the ovary by inhibiting the release of FSH. The corpus luteum stage lasts 10 to 14 days.

Menstruation. If fertilization does not occur, secretion of LH decreases, and the corpus luteum breaks down. This results in a decrease in the level of progesterone. With a drop in the progesterone level, the thickened lining of the uterus can no longer be maintained, and it breaks down. The extra layers of the lining, the unfertilized egg, and a small amount of blood pass out of the body through the vagina. This is called **menstruation** (men-*stray*-shun). It lasts from about 3 to 5 days. While menstruation is occurring, the amount of estrogen in the blood is dropping. The pituitary increases its output of FSH, and a new follicle starts to mature.

FERTILIZATION, IMPLANTATION, AND DEVELOPMENT

After completing your study of this section, you should be able to:

1. Describe fertilization and implantation in humans.
2. Explain the role of the placenta and umbilical cord in pregnancy.
3. List the extraembryonic membranes of human pregnancy, and explain the functions of each.
4. Define the following terms: *gestation period, labor, navel, afterbirth.*
5. Explain the difference between fraternal and identical twins.

23-5 Fertilization

In human mating, or sexual intercourse, hundreds of millions of sperm are ejaculated into the vagina. The sperm then travel through the cervix, across the uterus, and into the oviducts. If an egg is passing through one of the oviducts at this time, fertilization—the fusion of a sperm nucleus and an egg nucleus—may occur. The egg secretes a chemical that attracts the sperm. One of the sperm breaks through the membranes surrounding the egg, and the nucleus of the sperm cell enters the cytoplasm of the egg cell. As soon as this happens, the membranes around the egg change, preventing penetration by any other sperm. The sperm nucleus moves to the egg nucleus and the two nuclei fuse. The cell formed by fertilization is the zygote.

23-6 Implantation and Development

After fertilization, the zygote undergoes cleavage and dedevelops into a blastula (see page 360). Meanwhile, it is moving down the oviduct toward the uterus. About 5 to 10 days after fertilization, the embryo enters the uterus. Within the uterus, the outer layer of cells of the embryo secrete enzymes that digest part of the thick lining of the uterus, and the embryo attaches itself at this spot. The attachment of the embryo to the wall of the uterus is called **implantation** (im-plan-*tay*-shun). Implantation marks the beginning of **pregnancy,** the period during which the developing baby is carried in the uterus.

After implantation, the embryo undergoes gastrulation. The three germ layers are formed, and all the tissues and organs of the body develop from these layers by growth and differentiation.

The developing human is called an embryo from the time of fertilization up to about 8 weeks. After this time, it is usually called a **fetus** (*feet*-us).

During pregnancy, the menstrual cycle is suppressed by a hormone secreted by the chorion, one of the membranes that surrounds the embryo. This hormone prevents the breakdown of the corpus luteum. The corpus luteum continues to secrete high levels of progesterone, which in turn maintains the thickened wall of the uterus.

23-7 Nourishment of the Embryo

From the time of fertilization until implantation in the uterus, the embryo is nourished by food stored in the egg. After implantation, the embryo receives food and oxygen from the mother's body through the temporary organ called the placenta.

In humans, the outer cell layer of the blastula becomes the **chorion,** which is the membrane that surrounds the embryo. Small fingerlike projections called *chorionic* (kor-ee-*ahn*-ik) *villi* form on the outer surface of the chorion. The villi extend into the uterine lining. The chorionic villi and the uterine lining form the placenta. The placenta provides for the exchange of nutrients and wastes between the embryo and the mother. It also secretes hormones necessary for the maintenance of pregnancy.

The placenta has a fetal side, where fetal blood circulates, and a maternal side, where the mother's blood circulates (see Figure 23-5). The blood of the fetus and mother never mix. In the placenta, nutrients and oxygen diffuse from the mother's blood into the fetus' blood, and wastes diffuse from the fetus' blood into the mother's blood. The fetus and the placenta are connected by the umbilical cord, which contains fetal blood vessels. These vessels carry blood rich in nutrients and oxygen from the placenta to the fetus and blood containing fetal wastes from the fetus to the placenta.

The placenta acts as a barrier that protects the fetus from some harmful substances in the mother's blood. However, many dangerous substances can pass through the placenta from the mother's blood to the fetus' blood. The German measles virus, as well as nicotine, alcohol, and many drugs, can pass through the placenta and harm the fetus.

23-8 Extraembryonic Membranes

The human embryo develops the same extraembryonic membranes as birds and reptiles (see page 366). However,

sidelights

Humans and other primates (apes and monkeys) are the only mammals in which there is a menstrual cycle. In other types of mammals, there is an *estrous cycle.* The estrous cycle is marked by periodic changes in the sex organs and in the sex urge. During most of the cycle, the female is not fertile and will not mate with a male. This part of the cycle is called *anestrus.*

The female will mate with a male only during the short periods in the estrous cycle when she is fertile. During this time, the uterus and associated structures increase in size in preparation for pregnancy. In some species, ovulation does not occur until after mating has taken place. In others, ovulation occurs spontaneously during the fertile period. During fertile periods, the female is said to be "in heat," or in estrus. If fertilization does not occur, the sex organs gradually regress to their anestrus state, and there is little or no bleeding at the end of the cycle.

Wild mammals, such as foxes, coyotes, and wolves, have only one estrous cycle a year. Cats and dogs have two estrous cycles a year.

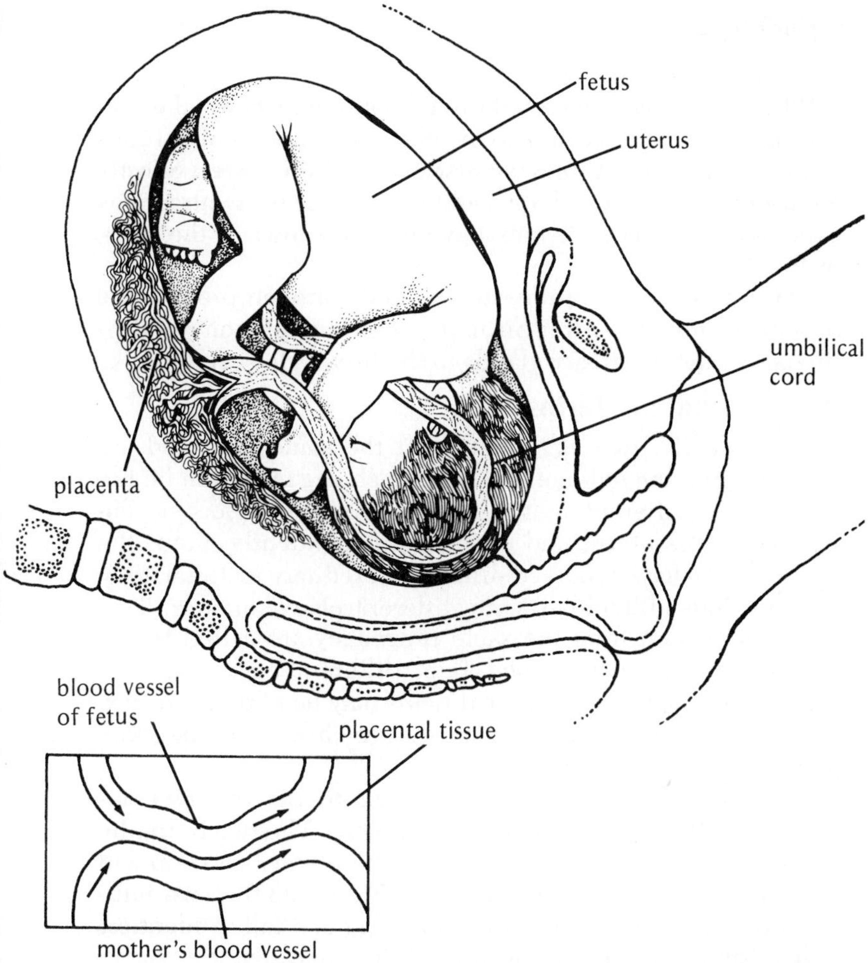

Figure 23-5. Nourishment of the Fetus. Nutrients and oxygen needed by the developing embryo are obtained by diffusion between blood vessels of the mother and the fetus in the placenta. Wastes from the fetus also pass into the mother's blood in the placenta. Materials are transported to and from the fetus through the fetal blood vessels in the umbilical cord. There is no direct connection between the circulatory systems of the fetus and the mother.

these membranes serve different functions in human development. The chorion, as discussed above, is involved in implantation and the formation of the placenta. The amnion, which is filled with **amniotic fluid,** surrounds the fetus. The fluid protects the fetus, providing it with a stable environment and absorbing shocks. The allantois is a membrane that grows out of the fetal digestive tract. Along with the yolk sac it forms the umbilical cord.

23-9 Birth

The length of a pregnancy is called the **gestation** (jes-*tay*-shun) **period.** The human gestation period is a little over nine months.

When the fetus is ready to be born, the uterine muscles begin slow, rhythmic contractions. This is called **labor.** At this time the opening of the cervix begins to enlarge. Its diameter must expand from 1 or 2 centimeters to 11 or 12 centimeters before the baby can pass out of the uterus and into the birth canal. When the cervix is expanded, the contractions force the baby, head first, from the uterus into the vagina and out of the mother's body. During labor, the amniotic membrane bursts, releasing the amniotic fluid. This fluid eases the passage of the baby through the birth canal.

careers

Until the early years of the twentieth century, women gave birth to their children at home, generally with the aid of another woman known as a midwife. Doctors were called only if the delivery showed signs of complications. Today some women are again choosing to use midwives to help them through delivery rather than physicians. A midwife can often provide a warm, supportive environment that makes the birth process more comfortable and relaxed for the expectant parents.

The midwife is now a nurse, specially trained to preside at a normal delivery. Prior to delivery, she works with the parents, teaching them about the birth process. Working either in the home or at a hospital, the midwife sees the mother and child safely through delivery, calling on a medical team if the delivery is not normal.

Figure 23-6. Identical Twins. Identical twins develop from the same egg. They are always of the same sex and look very much alike.

When the baby is expelled from the mother's body, the umbilical cord is still attached to the placenta. The umbilical cord is then tied and cut, leaving a scar called the **navel.** Shortly after the birth of the baby, additional uterine contractions expel the placenta and amnion, which are known as the **afterbirth.**

During pregnancy, progesterone and estrogen prepare the breasts for nursing. After birth, the pituitary hormone prolactin causes the mammary glands in the breasts to secrete milk.

23-10 Multiple Births

Occasionally, two eggs mature at the same time and are released into the oviduct together. Each egg may then be fertilized by a different sperm. Both embryos may become implanted in the uterus and develop independently. Since the two embryos have received different hereditary material, they develop into individuals with different characteristics. Two individuals born from the same pregnancy are called *twins.* When they have developed from different eggs, they are called **fraternal twins.** Fraternal twins may be of opposite sex, and they are no more alike than any two children of the same parents.

In other cases, a single fertilized egg divides into two embryos at a very early stage of development. The two individuals that then develop have the same hereditary makeup and are physically very much alike (see Figure 23-6). Two individuals that develop from the same egg are called **identical twins.** Identical twins are always of the same sex.

Twins are the most common type of multiple birth. However, in rare cases, three or more embryos may form during the same pregnancy. Such multiple births may be fraternal, identical, or a combination of both types.

summary

The male gonads, the testes, produce sperm and secrete testosterone, the hormone responsible for male secondary sex characteristics. The secretions of several glands together with the sperm are called semen.

The female gonads, the ovaries, produce eggs and secrete estrogen, the hormone responsible for the female secondary sex characteristics. Estrogen is also involved in the menstrual cycle. The ovaries are filled with follicles, each containing one egg. Once a month a follicle bursts, releasing a mature egg at the surface of the ovary. The release of the egg from the ovary is called ovulation. Once released, the egg enters an oviduct, which is connected to the uterus. The cervix of the uterus leads into the vagina, which opens to the outside of the body.

Ovulation occurs about every 28 days. Prior to the release of the mature egg, the wall of the uterus becomes thickened in preparation for the receipt of a fertilized egg. If the egg is not fertilized, the wall of the uterus breaks down, and the layers of tissue and the unfertilized egg pass out of the body, along with a small quantity of blood. Another egg then begins to mature, and the wall of the uterus again begins to thicken. This is the menstrual cycle. The menstrual cycle is regulated by estrogen and progesterone from the ovaries and FSH and LH from the pituitary.

Fertilization generally occurs while the egg is in the oviducts. Once a sperm penetrates the egg, the outer membrane around the egg changes, preventing the entry of any other sperm. The fertilized egg undergoes cleavage as it passes down the oviduct into the uterus. The outer layer of the embryo is responsible for implantation of the embryo in the uterine wall. It also forms the chorion. Chorionic villi and uterine lining together form the placenta. The fetus is attached to the placenta by the umbilical cord. Nourishment and wastes pass between mother and fetus through the blood vessels of the umbilical cord.

In addition to the chorion, the other extraembryonic membranes are the amnion, which serves to protect the fetus, and the allantois and yolk sac, which form the umbilical cord.

The human gestation period is about nine months. At the end of pregnancy, rhythmic uterine contractions push the baby out of the uterus into the birth canal and then out of the mother's body.

vocabulary

afterbirth
cervix
corpus luteum
Cowper's gland
ejaculation
epididymis
Fallopian tube
fetus
follicle
fraternal twins
gestation period
identical twins
implantation
labor
menstrual cycle
menstruation
navel
oviduct
ovulation
placenta
pregnancy
prostate gland
scrotum
secondary sex characteristic
seminal vesicle
seminiferous tubule
umbilical cord
urethra
uterus
vagina
vas deferens

test your learning

Section

23-1
1. What are the functions of the testes?
2. What is the function of testosterone?
3. Where are the testes located in the human male? Why?
4. Trace the path of sperm from their site of formation to the urethra.
5. Name the three glands whose secretions are added to the sperm.
6. What does semen consist of?

23-2
7. What are the functions of the ovaries?
8. What are the functions of estrogen?
9. Where are the ovaries located in the human female?
10. Describe the path of an unfertilized egg from the ovarian follicle until it leaves the body.

23-3
11. Describe briefly what happens during the menstrual cycle.
12. What is menopause?

23-4
13. Describe the events of each stage of the menstrual cycle. Approximately how long is each stage?

23-5
14. In what part of the female's reproductive system does fertilization actually occur?
15. What happens when sperm reach the egg?

23-6
16. Describe the development of a zygote from fertilization through implantation.
17. Define the terms *pregnancy*, *embryo*, and *fetus*.
18. How is the menstrual cycle suppressed during pregnancy?

23-7 **19.** What tissues form the placenta?
20. What functions are performed by the placenta?
21. What are the functions of the umbilical cord?
23-8 **22.** Name the extraembryonic membranes of human development, and describe the functions of each.
23-9 **23.** Describe what happens during the birth of a baby.
24. What is the afterbirth?
23-10 **25.** What is the difference between fraternal and identical twins?

test your understanding

1. Describe the hormonal regulation of the menstrual cycle.
2. Why does only one sperm enter the egg in fertilization?
3. How would an underactive pituitary gland affect the menstrual cycle?
4. Describe the hormonal regulation of pregnancy.

independent research

1. Prepare a report on one of the following topics:
   A. Effects of coffee, smoking, alcohol, and drugs on the development of the fetus.
   B. Natural childbirth.
   C. The importance of prenatal care for the mother.
2. Prepare a report on one of the following career opportunities:
   A. Pediatric nurse.
   B. Pediatrician.
   C. Physician's assistant.
   If possible, interview a person who works in the field. A tape recorder is very helpful in doing the interview. Be sure to prepare your questions in advance.

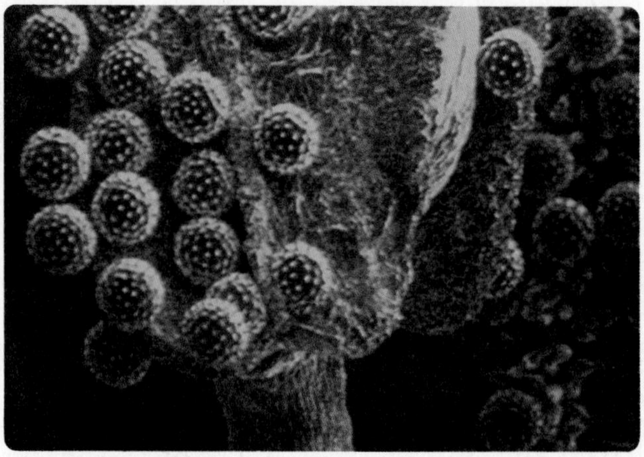

chapter 24

Sexual Reproduction in Plants

CHAPTER INTRODUCTION

After completing your study of this section, you should be able to:

1. Name the major plant groups.
2. Explain alternation of generations.

Sexual reproduction in plants, as in animals, involves the fusion of a male and a female gamete. Special structures in plants produce sperm cells and egg cells, and there are various adaptations in the different kinds of plants for bringing the sperm nucleus and the egg nucleus together.

The major plant groups are the mosses, ferns, and seed plants. The seed plants include the **gymnosperms** (*jim*-nuh-spermz), which are the cone-bearing plants, and the **angiosperms** (*an*-jee-uh-spermz), which are the flowering plants. For fertilization to occur in mosses and ferns, the sperm must swim to the egg. Moisture, in the form of dew or rain, must be present. Gymnosperms and angiosperms have special adaptations for transferring sperm without water. Thus, they are better adapted for life on land.

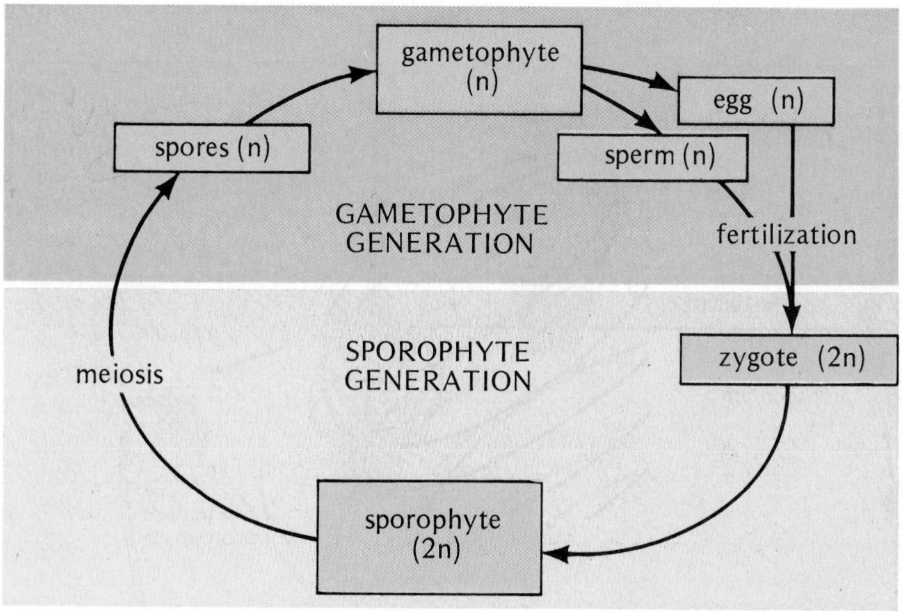

Figure 24-1. Alteration of Generations in Land Plants. In land-dwelling plants there is a sexual, gamete-producing stage and an asexual, spore-producing stage.

24-1 Alternation of Generations

The life cycles of land-dwelling plants show an alternation between two stages—a sexual, gamete-producing stage and an asexual, spore-producing stage. Often, each stage of the life cycle consists of a separate and different form of the plant. Life cycles having these two different stages are said to show an **alternation of generations.**

In the gamete-producing, or **gametophyte** (guh-*meet*-uh-fyt), **generation,** all the cells of the plant are monoploid (n) (see Figure 24-1). The plant produces reproductive cells, the gametes, by ordinary mitosis. The gametes, therefore, are also monoploid. When fertilization occurs, a male and a female gamete fuse to form a diploid ($2n$) zygote. The spore-producing, or **sporophyte** (*spor*-uh-fyt), **generation** develops from the zygote and is a diploid organism. Meiosis, or reduction division, occurs during the formation of spores by the sporophyte. Spores therefore contain monoploid nuclei. When the spores are released and germinate, they develop into the monoploid gametophyte plants.

Usually one generation is more conspicuous than the other. The more obvious generation is said to be the **dominant generation.** The plant of the dominant generation is larger and lives longer than the plant of the other generation.

LIFE CYCLES OF LOWER PLANTS

After completing your study of this section, you should be able to:

1. Describe the life cycle of mosses.
2. Describe the life cycle of ferns.
3. Explain which generation is dominant in mosses and in ferns.

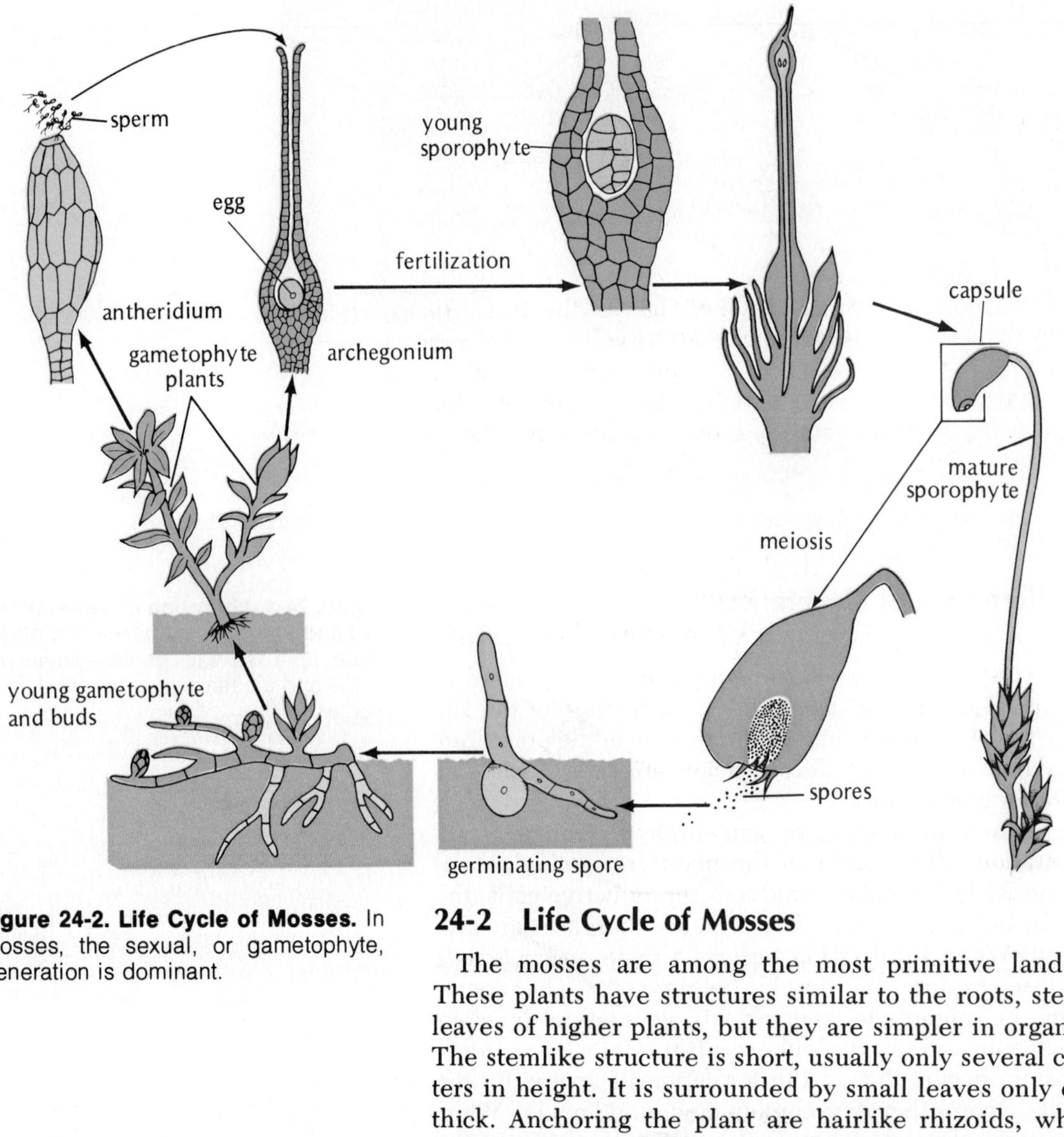

Figure 24-2. Life Cycle of Mosses. In mosses, the sexual, or gametophyte, generation is dominant.

24-2 Life Cycle of Mosses

The mosses are among the most primitive land plants. These plants have structures similar to the roots, stems, and leaves of higher plants, but they are simpler in organization. The stemlike structure is short, usually only several centimeters in height. It is surrounded by small leaves only one cell thick. Anchoring the plant are hairlike rhizoids, which are composed of only one type of cell. Mosses lack the specialized conducting tissues of higher plants, so that transport of materials through the plant is relatively inefficient. Mosses, therefore, are small in size. They require a moist environment for reproduction and are found on the damp floor of the forest, on shady rocks, and in swamps.

Mosses show an alternation of generations in which the gametophyte generation is dominant (see Figure 24-2). The gametophyte plant is much larger than the sporophyte. The monoploid gametophyte generation is what we recognize as the moss plant. The sporophyte plant grows from the gametophyte and cannot live independently.

In mosses, there are separate male and female gametophytes. The male reproductive organ is called the **antheridium** (an-thuh-*rid*-ee-um); the female reproductive organ is called the **archegonium** (ar-kuh-*goh*-nee-um). Each produces monoploid gametes. Sperm released from the antheridium of a male plant swim through rain or dew to reach the egg in the archegonium of the female plant.

Fertilization of the egg produces a diploid sporophyte that grows directly out of the archegonium. The sporophyte is a single leafless stalk that is dependent on the leafy green gametophyte for nourishment. The sporophyte obtains its nourishment by means of a structure called a *foot,* which grows down into the gametophyte tissue. At the tip of the mature sporophyte, a cylindrical *capsule* develops. Within the capsule many monoploid spores are produced by meiosis. These spores are released, and when they germinate, they form new monoploid gametophyte plants,completing the life cycle.

24-3 Life Cycle of Ferns

In **ferns,** unlike mosses, the leafy green dominant generation is the sporophyte (see Figure 24-3). The diploid sporophyte consists of an underground stem called a rhizome,

Figure 24-3. Life Cycle of Ferns. In ferns, the asexual, or sporophyte, generation is dominant.

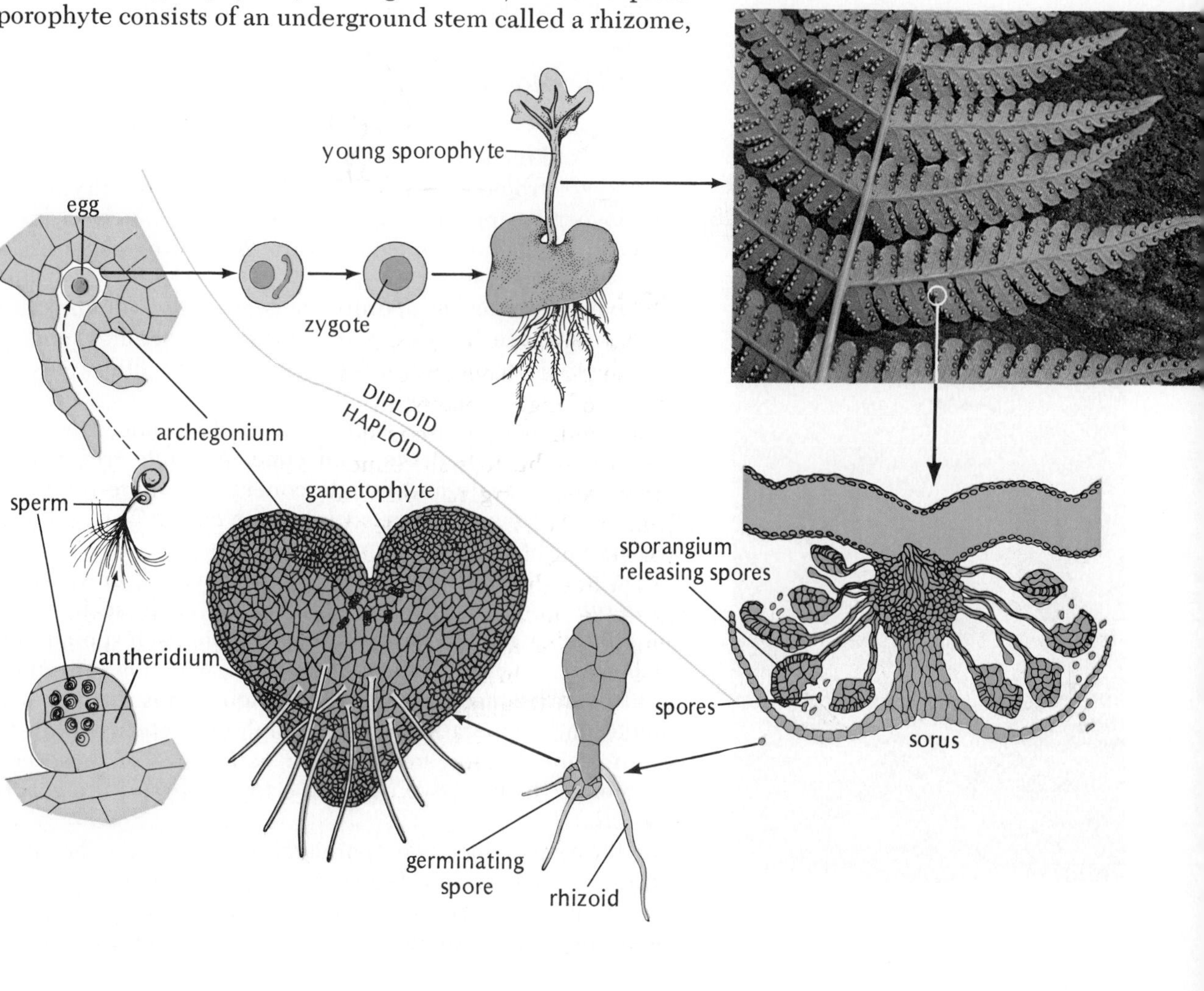

which grows just beneath the surface of the soil. From the lower surface of the rhizome, true roots develop, which anchor the plant and absorb water and minerals. From its upper surface the rhizome bears large leaves called **fronds.**

On the underside of some fronds are rows of small dots called **sori** (*sor*-ee). Within the sori, monoploid spores are produced by meiosis. The spores are eventually released, and under favorable conditions they germinate. The germinating spore forms a small, heart-shaped structure called a **prothallus** (proh-*thal*-us), which is the monoploid gametophyte plant. A prothallus contains both antheridia and archegonia in which gametes develop. The sperm can fertilize an egg in the same plant or it can swim (in rain or dew) to a different plant. The fertilized egg then grows into the mature sporophyte, the fern plant. The gametophyte withers and dies.

Because the prothallus is so small, it is very hard to find.

LIFE CYCLE OF GYMNOSPERMS

After completing your study of this section, you should be able to describe the life cycle of a pine tree.

24-4 Development of Gametes

Seed plants are the most abundant land-dwelling plants. The seeds of the plant contain the plant embryo. They protect the embryo from extreme temperatures and from drying out. Gymnosperms are cone-bearing seed plants, such as pines, spruces, and hemlocks (see Figure 24-4). Angiosperms are flowering seed plants.

Figure 24-4. A Gymnosperm.

In gymnosperms, the sporophyte generation is dominant. In these plants, the leaves are in the form of needles, and the reproductive organs are in the form of cones. Pine trees and other gymnosperms produce two types of cones (see Figure 24-5). The male cone is called the **pollen cone;** the larger female cone is called the **seed cone.** A single tree usually produces both male and female cones. The spore-producing structures are found on the *scales* of the cones. The scales are actually modified leaves.

In a pollen cone there are two spore cases, or **sporangia** (spuh-*ran*-jee-uh) on the underside of each scale. Many monoploid spores are formed by meiosis in each sporangium. Each spore develops into a pollen grain, which is surrounded by a tough protective coat. The **pollen grains** are the male gametophyte generation. The monoploid nucleus within the pollen grain divides, forming four cells. Two of these cells degenerate, leaving two cells—the *tube cell* and the *generative cell.*

In the seed cone, two sporangia are found on the upper surface of each scale. Meiosis within each sporangium produces four monoploid spores, three of which degenerate. The remaining spore divides by mitosis, forming the female

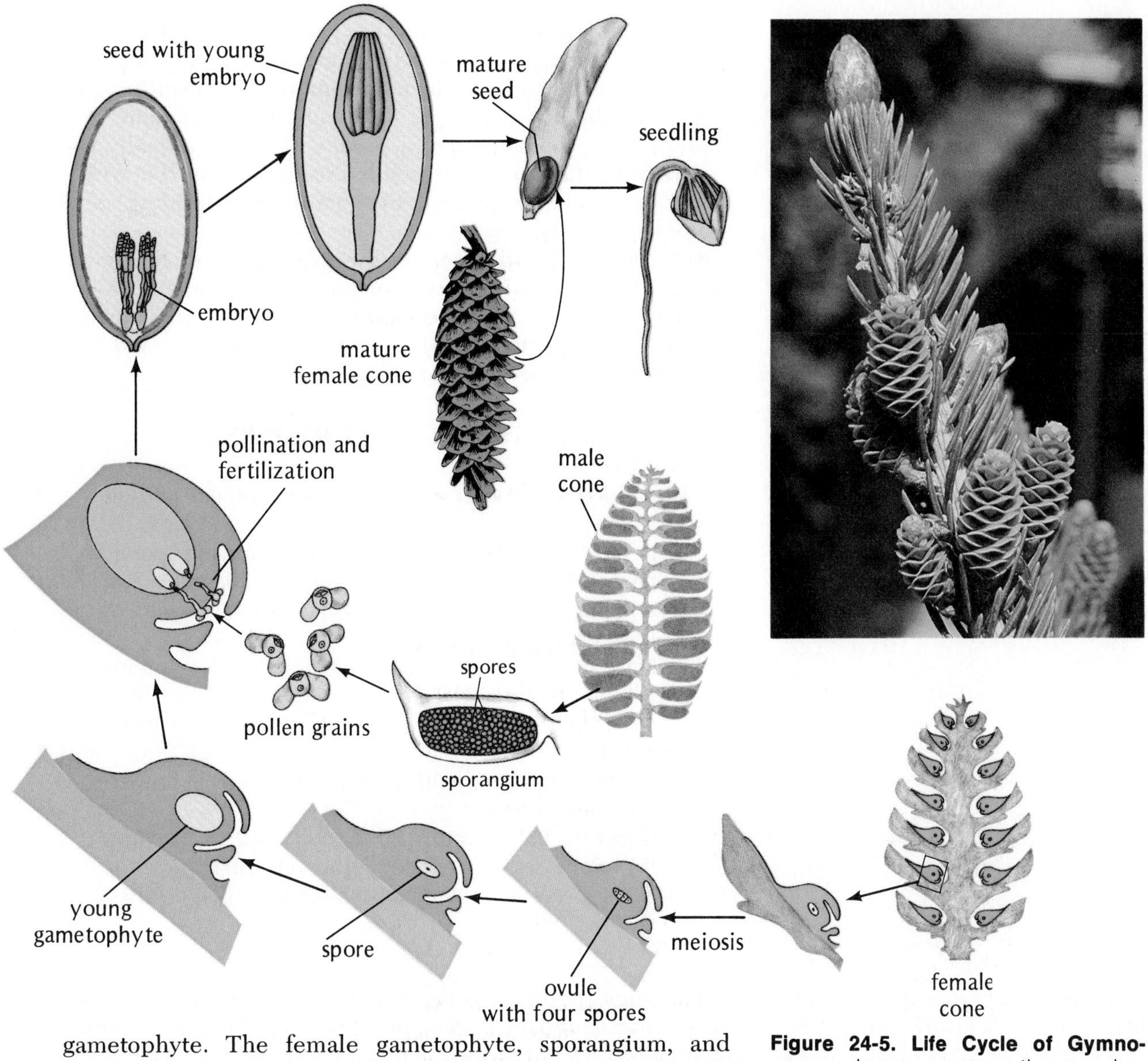

Figure 24-5. Life Cycle of Gymnosperms. In gymnosperms, the reproductive organs are in the form of cones and the leaves are in the form of needles.

gametophyte. The female gametophyte, sporangium, and associated structures form the **ovule** (*ohv*-yool). The female gametophyte forms two or three archegonia, and within each archegonium an egg cell develops.

24-5 Fertilization and Seed Development

When the pollen cones are mature, the sporangia burst, releasing millions of pollen grains. The pollen grains are carried by the wind. Some of the pollen grains land on a sticky material near a small opening on the ovule, the **micropyle** (*my*-kruh-pyl). A tube grows from a pollen grain through the micropyle and into the ovule and archegonium. This is the **pollen tube,** and it serves as a bridge between the pollen grain and the egg. The activities of the pollen tube are controlled by the tube cell of the pollen grain. The generative cell of the pollen grain forms two sperm cells. The tube cell and the two sperm pass through the pollen tube into the ovule. One of the sperm fertilizes an egg in the archegonium. The resulting zygote forms the plant embryo. The ovule, which contains the plant embryo, develops into a **seed,** which is eventually released from the cone. The seeds are carried by the wind. Under favorable conditions, they germinate, forming new sporophyte plants, such as pine trees.

Note that in the life cycle of the gymnosperms, the small gametophyte is totally dependent on the sporophyte. Also, water is not necessary for fertilization because wind carries the male gametophyte to the female gametophyte and the sperm travels to the egg through the pollen tube.

LIFE CYCLE OF ANGIOSPERMS

After completing your study of this section, you should be able to:

1. Draw a flower and label the following parts: pedicel; receptacle; sepals; petals; filament and anther of the stamen; and stigma, style, and ovary of the pistil.
2. Describe the formation of male and female gametes in flowering plants.
3. Describe pollination and fertilization in flowering plants.
4. Describe the formation of fruits and seeds in flowering plants.
5. Describe the structure of a seed, and explain the functions of the cotyledon, epicotyl, and hypocotyl.
6. Describe several mechanisms for seed dispersal.

24-6 Structure of a Flower

The angiosperms, the flowering plants, are the most successful and abundant land plants. The reproductive structures of angiosperms are within the flowers. In these plants the seeds are enclosed within a fruit. As in the gymnosperms, the sporophyte generation is dominant.

The flower develops from tissues that resemble those from which stems and leaves grow. It is made up of rings of modified leaves on a specialized stem (see Figure 24-6). In the center are the reproductive organs. The parts of the flower are described below.

1. The **pedicel** (*ped*-uh-sel) supports the flower and connects it to the stem of the plant.

2. The **receptacle** (ruh-*sep*-tuh-kul) is the expanded end of the pedicel to which the other flower parts are attached.

3. The **sepals** (*seep*-ulz) are leaflike structures that form a ring around the base of the flower. They enclose and protect the flower bud before it blossoms. The sepals may be small

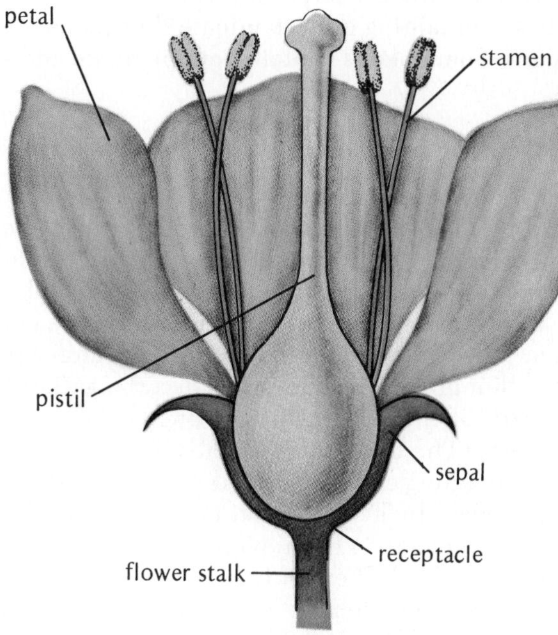

Figure 24-6. Structure of a Flower.

and green, or they may be large and brightly colored like the petals. The complete circle of sepals is called the **calyx** (*kay*-liks).

4. The **petals** are found within the sepals. In some flowers the petals are white, in others they are brightly colored. The complete circle of petals forms the **corolla** (kuh-*rohl*-uh). The petals surround the reproductive organs of the flower, the stamens and pistils.

5. The **stamens** (*stay*-menz) are generally called the male reproductive organs of the angiosperms. They are located inside the corolla. A stamen is made up of two parts—a saclike structure called the **anther** (*an*-ther), and a stalklike **filament,** which supports the anther. Pollen grains are produced within the anthers. A flower may contain several stamens.

6. The **pistil** (*pis*-tul) is generally called the female reproductive organ of the angiosperms. It is located in the center of the flower. The pistil is made up of three parts. The top of the pistil is the **stigma** (*stig*-muh), which consists of an enlarged sticky knob that receives the pollen. Supporting the stigma is the **style.** At the base of the pistil is the expanded **ovary,** which contains the ovules. The ovary and other associated flower parts develop into the **fruit,** while the ovules develop into seeds.

Stamens and pistils are the *essential organs* of the flower. The corolla and calyx are *accessory organs*. Some flowers contain stamens, pistil, corolla, and calyx, while others are missing one or more of these structures. *Pistillate* (*pis*-tuh-layt) *flowers* contain pistils but no stamens, and *staminate* (*stay*-muh-nayt) *flowers* contain stamens but no pistils. Plants con-

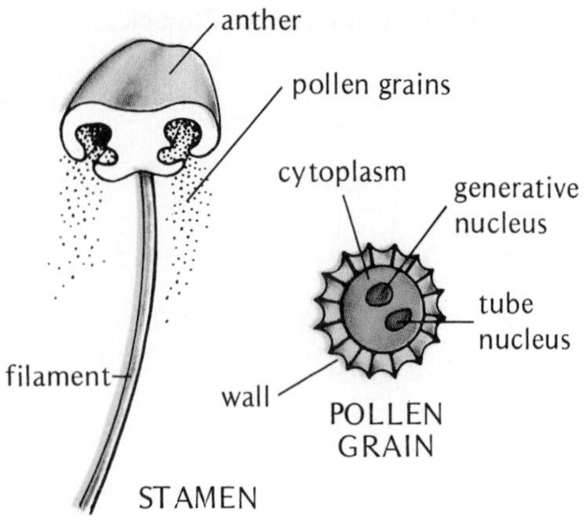

Figure 24-7. The Stamen. When the anther bursts, pollen grains are released.

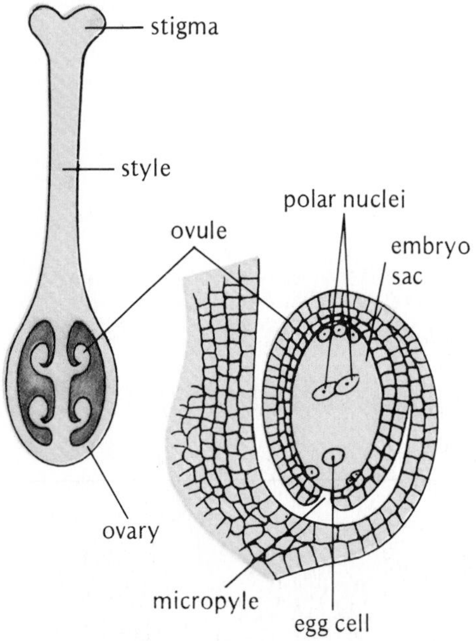

Figure 24-8. The Pistil. After fertilization, the ovary develops into a fruit and each ovule develops into a seed.

The pollen tube is actually a specialized cell that digests a path to the ovule.

taining only pistillate flowers are considered female plants, while those containing only staminate flowers are considered male plants. Some plants contain both pistillate and staminate flowers.

24-7 Development of Gametes

Within the anthers of the stamen, monoploid spores are produced by meiosis. The spores develop into pollen grains, which consist of a thick, protective wall that encloses cytoplasm containing two monoploid nuclei—the tube nucleus and the generative nucleus (see Figure 24-7). The pollen grain is the male gametophyte generation of the angiosperm. The mature pollen grains are released when the anther bursts.

The ovary of the pistil contains one or more ovules (see Figures 24-8). The ovules are actually sporangia. Each ovule has a small opening called the micropyle and is attached to the wall of the ovary by a short stalk. Four monoploid spores are produced by meiosis in each ovule. Three of the four spores degenerate, while the remaining cell divides three times by mitosis, forming the female gametophyte, the **embryo sac.** The embryo sac contains eight monoploid nuclei. Two of the nuclei, called the **polar nuclei,** move to the center of the embryo sac and fuse, forming a single cell. A nucleus near the micropyle becomes the egg cell, or female gamete.

24-8 Pollination

Pollination (pahl-uh-*nay*-shun) is the transfer of pollen from an anther to a stigma. In some plants, **self-pollination** occurs. In this case pollen grains either fall or are transferred from an anther to a stigma on the same plant. Where the pollen grains fall onto the stigma, the anthers are generally located above the stigmas. **Cross-pollination** occurs when pollen from an anther on one plant is transferred to a stigma on another plant. The transfer of pollen carried out by humans is called artificial pollination. This is done in plant breeding, where specific characteristics are desired.

In cross pollination, pollen grains are most commonly transferred by the wind or by insects or birds. Pollination is not generally a haphazard event. Pollen grains that are carried by the wind may show structural adaptations that aid in dispersal. Flowers pollinated by animals that are active at night frequently have white petals, which make them more visible. Flowers pollinated by animals that are active during the day have brightly colored petals and also distinctive odors, which make them easy to identify.

24-9 Fertilization

When a pollen grain reaches the stigma of a flower, it germinates (see Figure 24-9). Its protective coat breaks open. A pollen tube grows down through the stigma and style and into

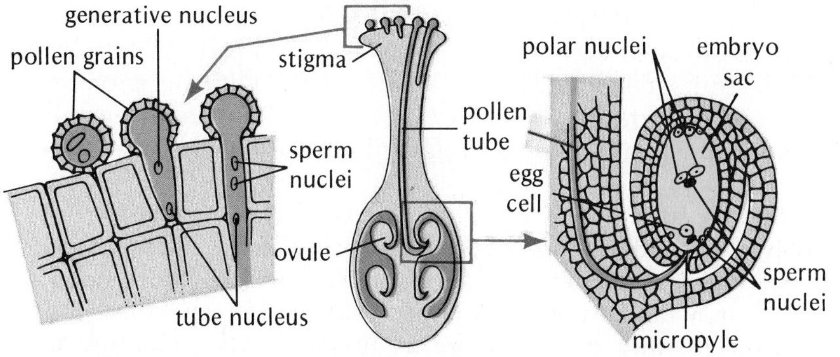

Figure 24-9. Fertilization in a Flower. When a pollen grain lands on a stigma and germinates, a pollen tube grows from the pollen grain down through the style of the pistil to an ovule. The generative nucleus divides into two sperm nuclei. The tube nucleus directs the growth of the pollen tube. The sperm nuclei enter the ovule through the micropyle. One sperm nucleus fuses with the egg cell nucleus to form a diploid zygote. The other sperm nucleus fuses with the two polar nuclei, forming a triploid ($3n$) cell that develops into endosperm tissue.

the ovary. It then enters the ovule through the micropyle. The tube nucleus, which controls the activities of the pollen tube, and the generative nucleus pass from the pollen grain down the pollen tube. As the generative nucleus moves down the pollen tube, it divides to form two monoploid sperm nuclei. The two sperm nuclei enter the embryo sac. One fertilizes the egg cell to form a diploid zygote that develops into the sporophyte plant embryo. The other fuses with the two polar nuclei to form a triploid ($3n$) **endosperm nucleus.** The endosperm nucleus divides by mitosis to form endosperm cells, which store food for the plant embryo. This **double fertilization** of the egg and the two polar nuclei is characteristic of flowering plants.

Flowers often have more than one ovule. Each ovule is fertilized by the contents of one pollen grain.

24-10 Fruits

After fertilization, each ovule develops into a seed, and the ovary develops into a fruit (see Figure 24-10). In angiosperms,

Figure 24-10. Stages in the Formation of a Bitter Lemon Fruit.

the seeds are always enclosed within the fruit. Other structures associated with the ovary may also form part of the fruit. Most fruits develop from a single pistil, with or without associated parts. However, some fruits develop from several pistils of a single flower, while still others develop from the pistils of a number of different flowers.

Shortly after fertilization, the parts of the flower not involved in the formation of the fruit wither and die. The ovary grows larger, and its wall thickens. The wall of the ripened ovary may be hard or soft, dry or fleshy, and it may consist of several distinct layers. Figure 24-11 shows the structures of various types of fruits. To a botanist, string beans, olives, and milkweed pods are as much fruits as apples and peaches. The term "vegetable" is not used by botanists. Tomatoes and cucumbers are actually fruits. On the other hand, radishes, beets, and carrots are roots, lettuce and spinach are leaves, and rhubarb and celery are stems.

24-11 Structure of the Seed and Embryo

The seed, which is the ripened ovule, consists of the seed coat, the embryo, and endosperm. The tough, protective **seed coat** develops from the wall of the ovule. On the outside of the

Figure 24-11. Various Types of Fruits. (A) Strawberries. (B) Green pepper. (C) Orange. (D) Green pea. (E) Lotus. (F) Tomato.

A

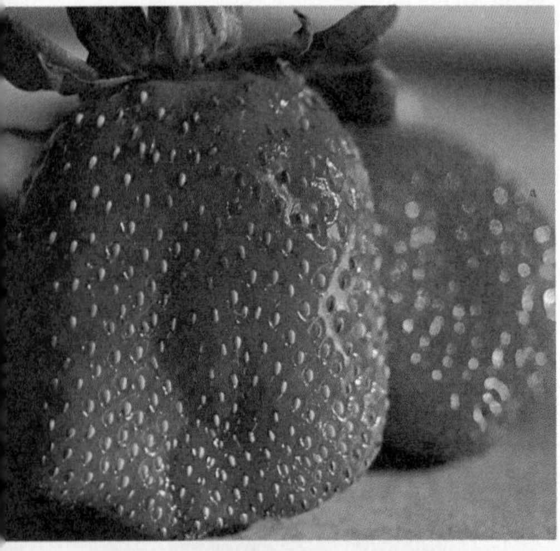

seed there is a scar called the **hilum** (*hy*-lum), which marks the attachment of the ovule to the ovary. The embryo develops by mitosis from the fertilized egg. The *endosperm* is a food storage tissue that develops by mitosis from the endosperm nucleus. The nutrients stored in the endosperm cells are obtained from the parent plant.

The plant embryo consists of one or two cotyledons, the epicotyl, the hypocotyl, and the radicle. **Cotyledons** (kaht-uh-*leed*-unz) are modified leaves. In some plants, nutrients from the endosperm are incorporated into the cotyledons. In this case, the cotyledons are greatly thickened and do not look like leaves. Depending on the species, the endosperm of the seed may degenerate after the cotyledons develop, or it may remain. Until it can synthesize its own nutrients, the developing seedling obtains nourishment from the cotyledons and also from the endosperm, if it is present. Cotyledons that do not contain stored nutrients are much thinner and more leaflike in appearance. In such plants the developing seedling obtains nourishment from the endosperm. Plants with one cotyledon are called **monocots,** and those with two cotyledons are called **dicots.**

The part of the embryo above the point of attachment of the cotyledons is called the **epicotyl** (*ep*-uh-kaht-ul). It generally gives rise to the terminal bud, leaves, and the upper part of the stem of the young plant. The **hypocotyl** (*hy*-puh-kaht-ul) is the part of the embryo below the point of attachment of the cotyledons, and the **radicle** (*rad*-uh-kul) is the lowermost part of the hypocotyl. In some plants the hypocotyl gives rise to the lower part of the stem, while the radicle gives rise to the roots. In other plants, the stem forms entirely from the epicotyl, and the roots arise from both the hypocotyl and radicle.

Beans are dicots, and in the bean seed, the two large cotyledons enclose the rest of the embryo between them (see Figure 24-12). In the bean seed the endosperm degenerates, and nu-

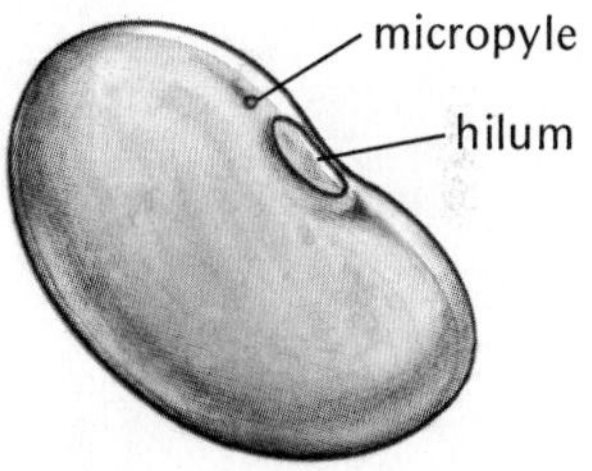

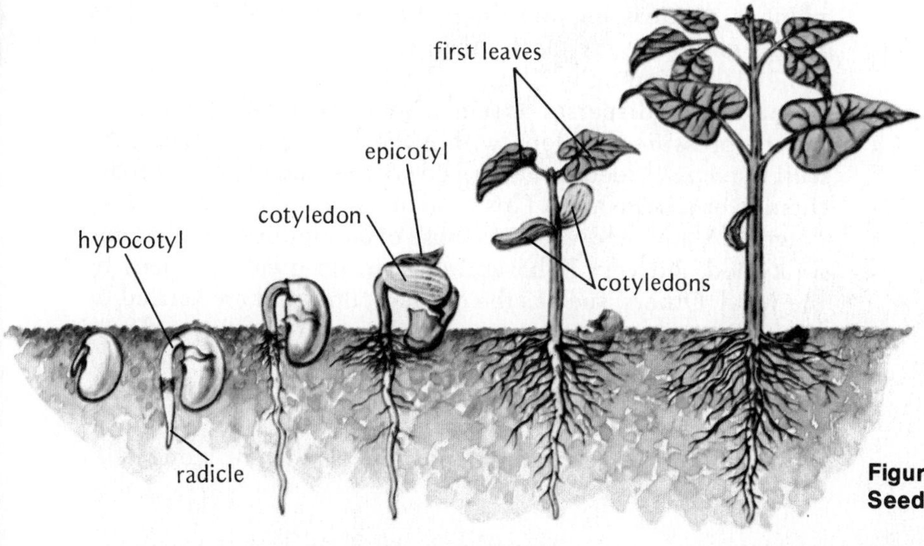

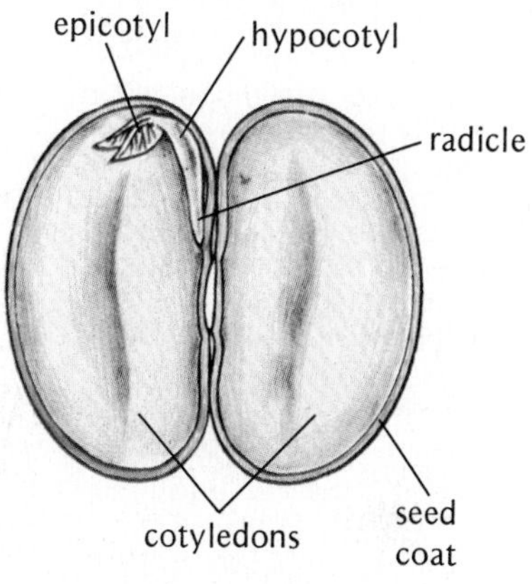

Figure 24-12. Development of a Bean Seed.

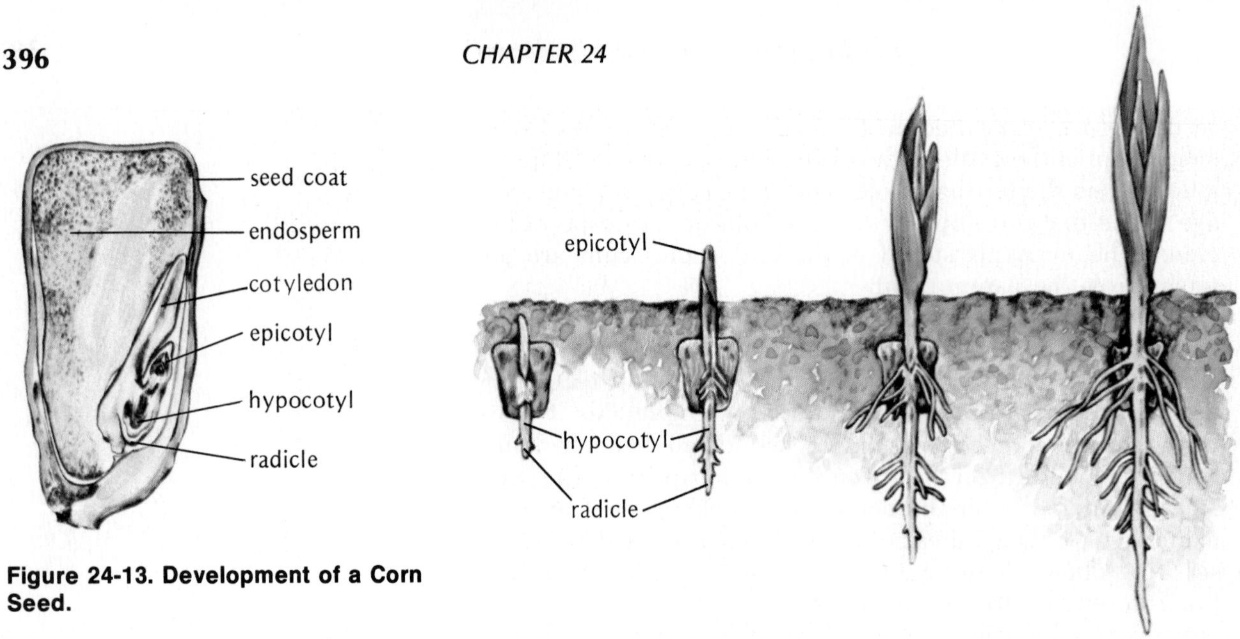

Figure 24-13. Development of a Corn Seed.

trients are stored only in the cotyledons. In the developing bean seedling, the epicotyl gives rise to the terminal bud, the leaves, and the upper part of the stem. The hypocotyl gives rise to the lower part of the stem, and the radicle gives rise to the roots.

Corn is a monocot. Each kernel of corn is a complete fruit and contains one seed. The embryo is partially surrounded by endosperm. In the sweet corn that we eat, the endosperm contains sugar and starch as food storage products. The cotyledon also stores nutrients in the form of oils and proteins. In the developing corn seedling, the epicotyl gives rises to the stem and leaves, while the hypocotyl and radicle give rise to the roots (see Figure 24-13).

24-12 Seed Dispersal

Seeds that are dispersed by the wind usually have a sail or some other structural adaptation to catch the wind, so that the seed is lifted and carried away. Ask students to contribute to a class collection of different types of seeds, emphasizing various adaptations for dispersal.

The scattering, or dispersal, of seeds away from the parent plant is of great importance in the survival of the species. Plants growing very close together must compete for water, minerals and sunlight. Thus, many different adaptations have arisen for the dispersal of seeds (see Figure 24-14). In some plants, pressure develops within the drying fruit. When the fruit bursts, the seeds are released with enough force to scatter them over a large area. This type of dispersal occurs in snapdragons. Many seeds, such as those of dandelions, maples, and milkweed, are very light, and are carried great distances by the wind. Others, such as the coconut, float and are carried by water. Some seeds or fruits, such as those of sandbur and wild carrot, have burs or hooks. They become attached to the fur of animals and are dispersed in that way. Sweet, fleshy fruits are often eaten by birds and mammals. The seeds, which are usually indigestible, are later deposited elsewhere along with other digestive wastes.

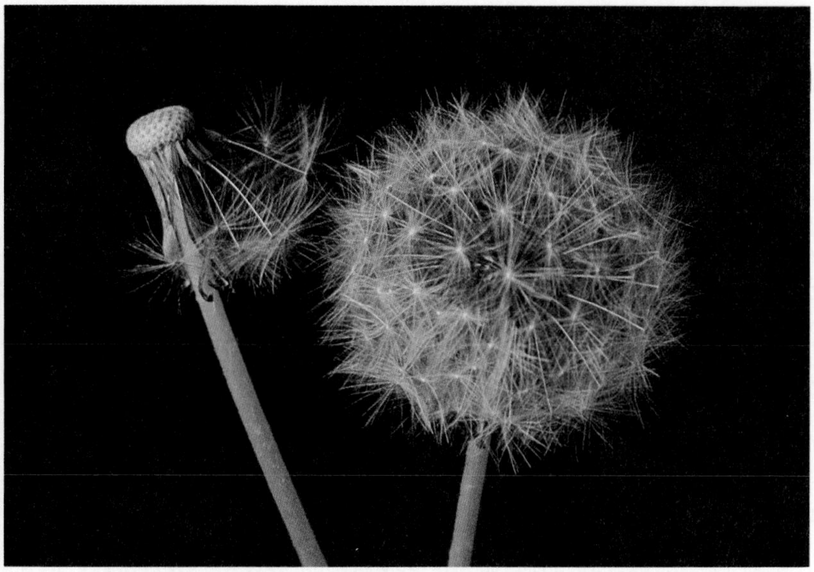

Figure 24-14. Some Adaptations for Seed Dispersal. Dandelion seeds (left) are dispersed by the wind. The burdock fruit (right) has hooks that cling to the fur of passing animals.

24-13 Seed Dormancy and Germination

For a seed to begin to sprout, or germinate, it needs water and oxygen and the proper temperature. Some seeds also require light. Many seeds go through a dormant, or resting, period before they begin to grow. During the dormant phase, the seed will not sprout even if all necessary conditions are present. The length of the dormant period varies with the type of plant. Even within a single species individual seeds show different lengths of dormancy. Some seeds might begin to grow after 1 year, some after 2 years, some after 3 years, and so on. This characteristic is useful for the survival of the species because not all seeds would be killed by unusually harsh conditions during a given year.

There are several ways in which **dormancy** (*dor*-mun-see) is brought about. In some species, dormancy occurs because the seed coat does not permit water and/or oxygen to reach the embryo. In others, the seed coat is so strong that the embryo cannot break through it. In still others, the embryo must undergo further development before growth can occur, or chemical inhibitors are present that prevent germination. Where dormancy is caused by the toughness of the seed coat, it lasts until the seed coat decays or is broken down sufficiently for germination to occur. With immature embryos and chemical inhibitors, a certain amount of time must pass either for the embryo to mature or for the chemicals to disappear.

summary

The major plant groups are the mosses, ferns, and seed plants (gymnosperms and angiosperms). The life cycles of terrestrial plants show an alternation of generations, with a sexual, gamete-producing stage and an asexual, spore-producing stage. The gametophyte generation produces monoploid reproductive cells, the gametes. The male and female gametes fuse to form a diploid zygote, which is the beginning of the sporophyte generation. The sporophyte plant produces monoploid spores by meiosis, and these spores form the monoploid gametophyte plant.

In mosses the gametophyte generation is dominant. There are separate male and female gametophytes. The antheridium of the male and the archegonium of the female each produces monoploid gametes. Fertilization produces a diploid sporophyte that grows out of the archegonium. Spores released by the mature sporophyte germinate and form new gametophytes.

In ferns the sporophyte is dominant. The sporophyte produces monoploid spores. When the spores germinate, they form a prothallus, which is the monoploid gametophyte. Gametes develop in the antheridia and archegonia of the prothallus. When fertilization occurs, the resulting zygote develops into the mature sporophyte fern plant.

In gymnosperms, the sporophyte generation is dominant. Gymnosperms produce separate male and female cones. In the male cones, sporangia produce monoploid spores that develop into pollen grains. In the female cones, spores develop into female gametophyte structures containing archegonia, within which eggs are produced. The female gametophyte is encased in an ovule.

When a pollen grain lands on the female cone near the ovule, a tube grows from the pollen grain through the ovule and into the archegonium. The generative cell from the pollen grain forms two sperm cells, which pass through the tube into the ovule. One sperm cell fertilizes an egg in the archegonium. The resulting zygote forms the plant embryo. The ovule, which contains the plant embryo, develops into the seed.

In flowering plants, the sporophyte generation is dominant. The male reproductive organs are the stamens, and the female reproductive organs are the pistils. Within the anther of the stamen, monoploid spores are produced by meiosis. The spores develop into pollen grains. In the ovary of the pistil are one or more ovules, which are sporangia. The ovules produce monoploid spores by meiosis, one of which develops into the female gametophyte, the embryo sac. One of the cells of the embryo sac is the egg, while another, larger cell contains two polar nuclei.

When a pollen grain lands on a stigma of a pistil, it germinates. A pollen tube grows down through the stigma, style, and ovary, and into the ovule. As the generative nucleus moves down the pollen tube, it divides to form two monoploid sperm cells. The two sperm cells enter the embryo sac, where one fuses with the egg and the other fuses with the two polar nuclei to form a triploid endosperm nucleus. The fertilized egg develops into the plant embryo, while the endosperm nucleus divides to form food storage tissue. After fertilization, the ovule develops into a seed, and the ovary develops into a fruit.

vocabulary

alternation of generations
angiosperm
anther
antheridium
archegonium
calyx
corolla
cotyledon
cross-pollination
dicot
dominant generation
dormancy
double fertilization
embryo sac
endosperm nucleus
epicotyl
fern
filament
frond
fruit
gametophyte generation
gymnosperm
hypocotyl
micropyle
monocot
moss
ovary
ovule
pedicel
petal
pistil
polar nuclei
pollen cone
pollen grain
pollen tube
pollination
prothallus
radicle
receptacle
seed
seed coat
seed cone
seed plant
self-pollination
sepal
sorus
sporangium
sporophyte generation
stamen
stigma
style

test your learning

Section

24-1 **1.** Define the terms *gametophyte* and *sporophyte*.
2. Explain alternation of generations.

24-2 **3.** Which is the dominant generation in mosses?
4. Describe the life cycle of mosses.

24-3 **5.** Which is the dominant generation in ferns?
6. Describe the structures of the fern sporophyte and gametophyte.
7. Describe the life cycle of a fern.
8. Why do mosses and ferns need a moist environment for reproduction?

24-4 **9.** Give three examples of gymnosperms.
10. Where are the reproductive organs of gymnosperms located?
11. Which is the dominant generation in gymnosperms?

24-5 **12.** Describe the life cycle of a gymnosperm.

24-6 **13.** Which is the dominant generation in angiosperms?
14. Draw a flower and label the following parts: pedicel, receptacle, sepals, petals, stamens, and pistil. Label the anther and filament of the stamen and the stigma, style, and ovary of the pistil.
15. Briefly describe the function of each part of the flower.

24-7 **16.** Describe the development of the male and female gametes.
24-8 **17.** Define the term *pollination,* and explain what is meant by self-pollination and cross-pollination.
24-9 **18.** Explain how the double fertilization characteristic of flowering plants occurs, beginning with the germination of the pollen grain.
24-10 **19.** What parts of the flower develop into the fruit?
24-11 **20.** What are the basic parts of the seed and how are they formed?
21. Name the parts of the plant embryo, and describe what part of the plant each develops into.
22. Define the term *cotyledon.*
24-12 **23.** What are some of the methods of seed dispersal?
24. Why is the dispersal of seeds important in plant reproduction?
24-13 **25.** What environmental factors affect seed germination?
26. What is *seed dormancy,* and what is the advantage of a dormant period?

test your understanding

1. Discuss some of the ways in which the life cycles of seed plants differ from those of the lower plants.
2. Compare the location of seeds in gymnosperms and angiosperms.
3. Name the major plant groups, and state the dominant generation in each—sporophyte or gametophyte.
4. Compare the popular and scientific meanings of the terms *fruits* and *vegetables.*
5. Compare the structures and development of a bean seed and a corn kernel.

independent research

1. Prepare a report on the importance of insects in plant pollination.
2. Prepare a report on the microscopic structure of pollen grains.
3. Using a field guide, learn to identify the common spring and summer wildflowers in your area. Keep a list of the flowers you have actually seen.

UNIT 5
GENETICS

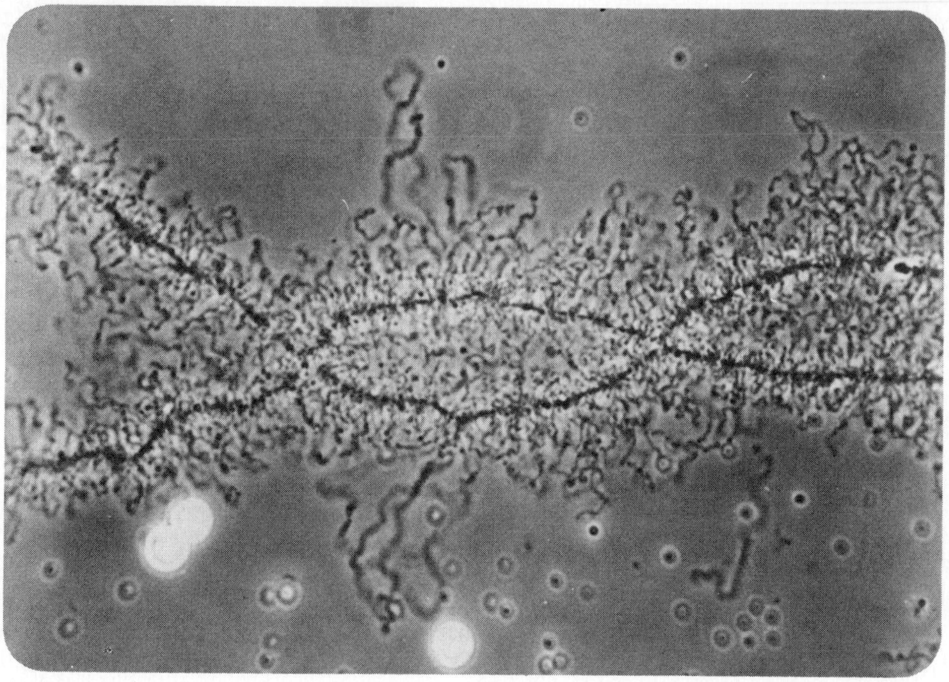

chapter 25

Mendelian Genetics

25-1 Chapter Introduction

In sexual reproduction, the new individual develops from a single cell—the zygote—that was formed by the union of two gametes, one from each parent. The chromosomes of each gamete bring hereditary material to the new cell. This material controls the development and characteristics of the embryo as it grows and matures. Since the hereditary material comes from two parents, the offspring resembles both parents in some ways, but it also differs from both parents in other ways. The offspring has all the characteristics of its species, but it also has its own individual characteristics that distinguish it from all other members of the species.

Genetics (juh-*net*-iks) is the branch of biology that is concerned with the ways in which hereditary information is transmitted from parents to offspring. Modern genetics started with the scientific work done in the nineteenth century by an Austrian monk, Gregor Mendel.

MENDEL'S PRINCIPLES OF HEREDITY

After completing your study of this section, you should be able to:

1. Describe the basic nature of Mendel's experiments—the type of plant he used and how he experimented with it.
2. Define the term *hybrid*.
3. State and give an example of Mendel's principle of dominance.

4. State and give an example of Mendel's principle of segregation.
5. Explain the relationship between the modern gene-chromosome theory and Mendel's principles of heredity.

25-2 Mendel's Experiments

The first scientific study of heredity was conducted by **Gregor Mendel** (*men*-dul), a monk who was interested in mathematics and science (see Figure 25-1). Mendel lived at the Abbey of St. Thomas, a monastery in the town of Brünn in what is now Czechoslovakia. He also taught science at the local high school. For 8 years—from 1857 to 1865—Mendel investigated the inheritance of certain traits in pea plants that he grew in the monastery garden. Through a series of experiments, Mendel arrived at the basic principles of heredity that we accept today.

Figure 25-1. Gregor Mendel.

Pea plants were an excellent choice for the investigations that Mendel wished to make. They are fairly easy to grow, and they mature quickly. Pea plants have several pairs of sharply contrasting traits, such as tallness or shortness, green or yellow pods, and smooth or wrinkled seeds, which are readily observable. Furthermore, the structure of the pea flower and its natural method of pollination make it easy to use in controlled experiments. Pea flowers normally self-pollinate because the stigma and anthers are enclosed by the petals. This effectively prevents cross-pollination in nature. However, by removing the stamens from a flower before they ripened, Mendel could cross-pollinate the flower by dusting pollen from another plant onto the stigma. If he wanted certain plants to self-pollinate in the normal way, he left them alone.

Mendel kept careful records of his treatment of each generation of plants. He collected the seeds from each experimental cross and planted them in a definite place so he could observe the results. Mendel made a careful count of the offspring of each type and analyzed his results mathematically. It was this use of mathematics that enabled him to draw the important conclusions he did.

Mendel wrote a paper about his discoveries. It was published in the journal of his local scientific society and distributed to other scientific organizations and libraries. However, no other scientists seem to have noticed its importance at the time. Mendel died in 1882, never knowing the real significance of his work. In 1900, however, Hugo De Vries in Holland, Karl Correns in Germany, and Erich von Tschermak in Austria, all working independently, reached the same conclusions about heredity that Mendel had. Before they published their works, they researched past scientific literature and found Mendel's papers. They gave him credit for his original discoveries. Mendel finally obtained the recognition he deserved.

Using traits found in pea plants, assign several crosses with contrasting traits to be completed in class. Students should find the phenotypes of the F_1 and F_2 generations. Emphasize that the phenotypes of the F_1 generation illustrate the principle of dominance.

1. pure tall (TT) × pure short (tt)
2. pure yellow seeds (YY) × pure green seeds (yy)

25-3 The Principle of Dominance

Mendel had observed that pea plants have certain traits that come in two forms. For example, plants are either tall or short; seeds are either yellow or green; and so on. In his experiments, Mendel studied seven such pairs of contrasting traits.

Mendel discovered that some plants "bred true" for a particular trait. For example, when short plants were allowed to self-pollinate through several generations, the offspring were always short. Mendel considered these plants to be pure for shortness. In his experiments, Mendel started with plants that he knew were pure for the particular trait he was interested in.

Mendel then proceeded to find out what would happen if he cross-pollinated pure plants that had contrasting traits. To do this, he removed the stamens from a plant that was pure for one trait, to prevent self-pollination. He then pollinated that plant with pollen from a plant that was pure for the contrasting trait. For example, he pollinated short plants with pollen from tall ones, and he pollinated tall plants with pollen from short ones. In these experiments, the pure plants made up the parent, or P, generation. Mendel collected the seeds produced by this cross-pollination, planted them, and allowed them to grow. Mendel found that all the offspring of this cross were tall (see Figure 25-2*a*). The short trait disappeared in this *first filial*, or F_1, generation. Similar results were obtained for all seven of the pairs of contrasting traits that Mendel investigated. The offspring of crosses between pure parents showing contrasting traits are called **hybrids.** In Mendel's experiments, the hybrids showed only one of the contrasting traits and not the other.

Mendel was curious to find out whether the trait of shortness had been permanently lost as a result of the cross. To investigate this question he allowed the hybrid plants of the F_1 generation to self-pollinate (see Figure 25-2*b*). When their seeds were planted and grown, only three-fourths of the offspring were tall. One-fourth were short. These plants made up the F_2 generation. The presence of short plants in the F_2 gen-

Figure 25-2*a*. A Cross of Pure Tall and Pure Short Pea Plants. All offspring in the first filial (F_1) generation are tall. Tallness is dominant. Shortness is recessive.

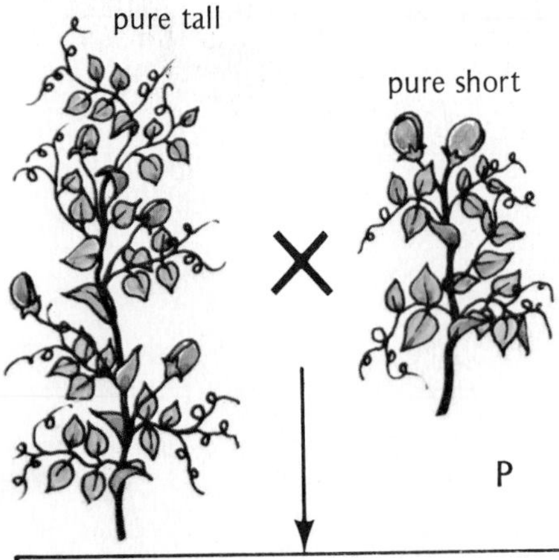

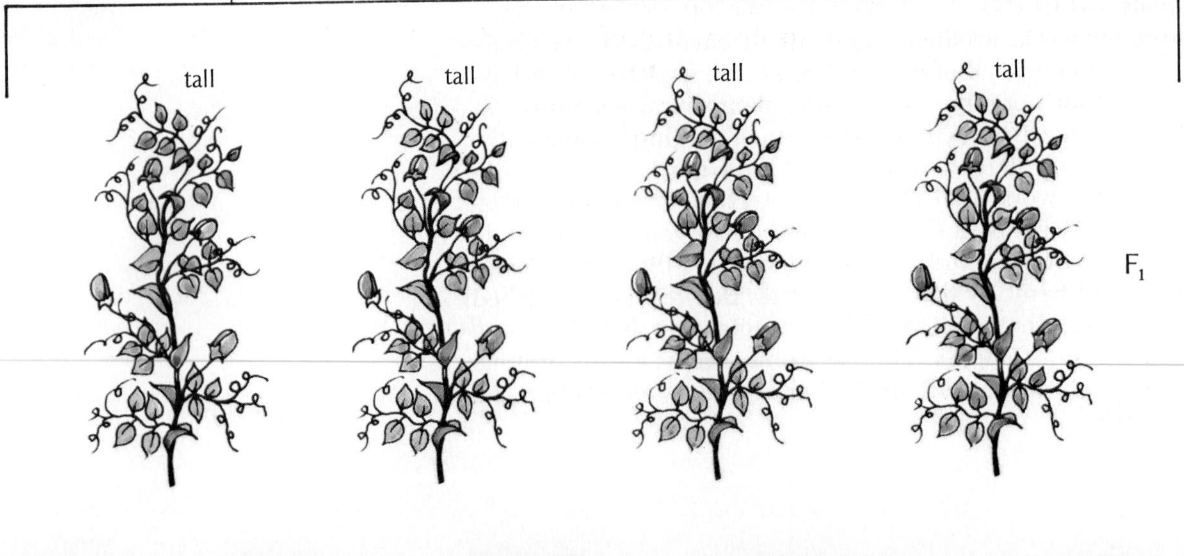

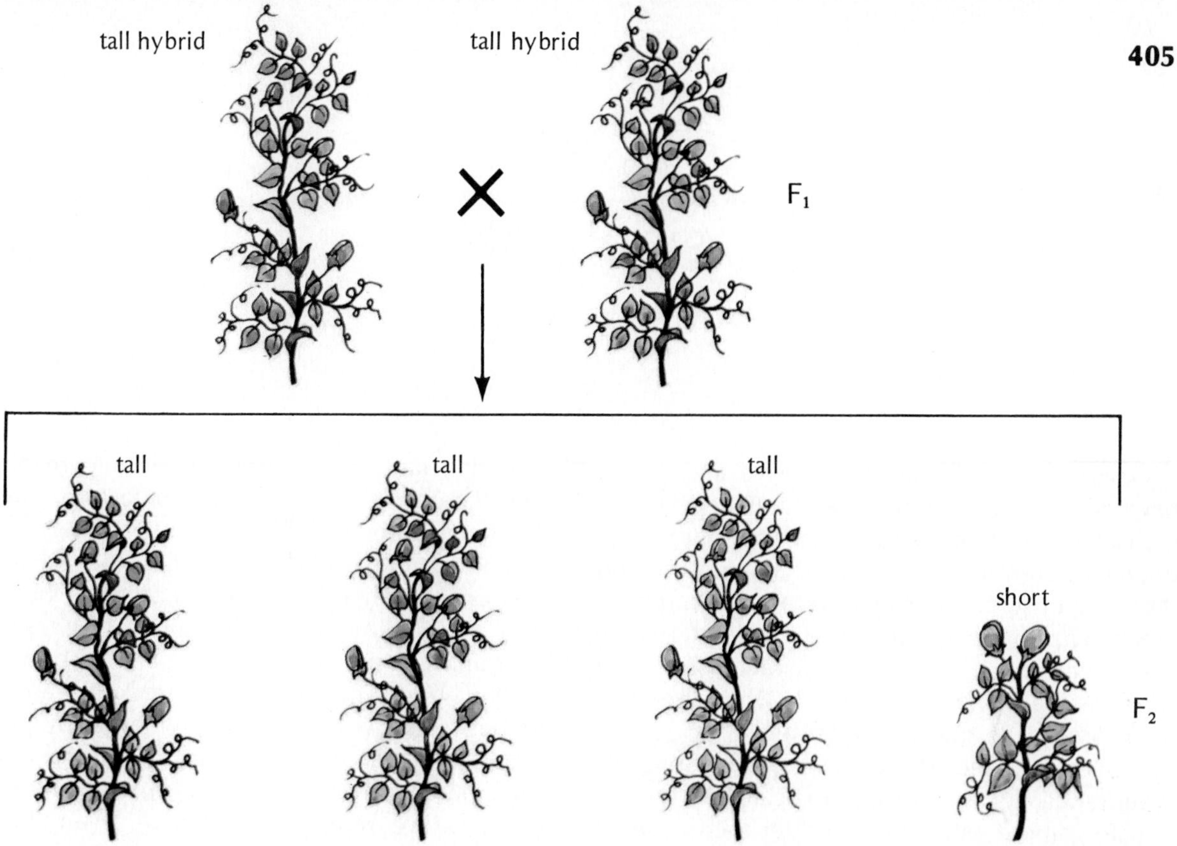

Figure 25-2b. A Cross of the Hybrid Plants of the F_1 Generation. Only three-fourths of the offspring are tall. One-fourth are short.

eration demonstrated that the shortness trait had somehow still been present in the F_1 generation.

Mendel described the traits that were expressed in the F_1 generation as **dominant,** and the traits that were hidden in the F_1 as **recessive.** He concluded that *when organisms that are pure for contrasting traits are crossed, all their offspring will show the dominant trait.* This is called the principle of **dominance.**

25-4 The Principle of Segregation

Mendel tried to explain the disappearance and reappearance of the recessive trait in successive generations. He formed the hypothesis that each trait was controlled by a pair of factors. There was, for example, a factor for tallness and another factor for shortness. In a cross, the offspring received one factor from each parent. Thus, in a cross between a tall plant and a short plant, the offspring received both factors. However, only the dominant factor was expressed. The recessive factor was suppressed or hidden.

Since the factor for shortness was still present in these tall plants, it was possible for this factor to show itself in the later generations. This would happen when fertilization brought two shortness factors together in the same seed. The idea that *recessive factors could be separated from the dominant factors during gamete formation and recombined at fertilization to produce the recessive trait is called Mendel's principle of* **segregation.**

Assign several more crosses, stressing that the reappearance of the recessive trait in the F_2 generation illustrates the principle of segregation.

1. pure round peas (RR) × pure wrinkled peas (rr)
2. pure axial flowers (AA) × pure terminal flowers (aa)
3. pure green pods (GG) × pure yellow pods (gg)

sidelights

Experiments with microorganisms and plants have shown that not all of the genetic material is located on the chromosomes. The inheritance of traits determined by genetic material not on the chromosomes is called **cytoplasmic inheritance.** The existence of cytoplasmic interitance was revealed in studies of characteristics that were passed on to offspring only when they had been present in the female gamete.

It is easy to see why evidence of cytoplasmic inheritance appears to be associated with the female gamete when you consider the events of fertilization. In fertilization, the relatively large egg cell unites with the much smaller sperm. The cytoplasm of the zygote formed by the fusion of the egg nucleus and sperm nucleus comes almost entirely from the egg cell, the female gamete. Thus, hereditary information present in the cytoplasm of the egg cell is passed on to the offspring.

An example of cytoplasmic inheritance can be seen in leaf color of plants called four-o'clocks. The leaves of this plant may be either light green or dark green. When two plants with contrasting leaf color are crossed, the offspring all show the leaf color of the plant that produced the egg cell. Further research has shown that the color is determined by genetic material in the chloroplasts, which are passed to the offspring from the cytoplasm of the egg cell.

Cytoplasmic inheritance has also been observed in some strains of paramecia. In the paramecium, sexual reproduction is by conjugation, and involves the exchange of micronuclei between two organisms (see page 349). This exchange results in the production of two cells in which the nuclei contain identical hereditary material but in which the cytoplasms are different. Paramecia can also reproduce asexually by a form of binary fission.

Some strains of paramecium contain a factor that enables them to kill other strains when the two are put into the same culture. The strains containing this factor are said to show the "killer" trait. The strains that are killed are said to be "sensitive." Normally, when conjugation occurs between a killer paramecium and a sensitive paramecium, the killer remains a killer and the sensitive remains a sensitive, even though the two now contain identical nuclei. However, occasionally after conjugation, the sensitive is transformed into a killer.

It is now known that for a paramecium to exhibit the killer trait, it must contain both a cytoplasmic factor and a nuclear gene for this trait. In the cases where conjugation results in the transformation of a sensitive into a killer, the nuclear gene for the trait is transferred to the sensitive cell by the exchange of micronuclei. The cytoplasmic factor is transferred in the cytoplasm that flows from the killer paramecium into the sensitive paramecium through the bridge formed between them in conjugation. Apparently, in most conjugations, the cytoplasmic bridge exists only for a short time, and there is little flow of cytoplasm between the two organisms. Thus, the cytoplasmic factor is not transferred. The presence of the nuclear gene alone cannot make the organism a killer. The cytoplasmic factor must also be present. For this reason, after conjugation with a killer, the sensitive cell, which now contains the nuclear gene for the killer trait, remains sensitive unless the cytoplasmic factor is also transferred.

25-5 The Concept of the Gene

The importance of Mendel's work may have been overlooked in the mid-1800s because little was known about chromosomes, mitosis, and meiosis at that time. But when Mendel's research was rediscovered in 1900, chromosomes had been stained and observed in cells, and the process of mitosis and meiosis had been described in detail. It soon became clear that Mendel's results could be explained by assuming that the chromosomes carry the hereditary factors. If so, the separation of homologous chromosomes pairs during meiosis and their recombination during fertilization would account for the separation and recombination of the Mendelian factors. During the early 1900s, numerous experiments confirmed this hypothesis. At that time, the term *gene* was adopted to replace Mendel's "factor." Research provided evidence not only that chromosomes carry genes, but that the genes are arranged in a definite sequence along each chromosome. This work led to the establishment of the modern gene-chromosome theory of heredity.

BASIC CONCEPTS IN GENETICS

After completing your study of this section, you should be able to:

1. Define the following terms: *alleles, genotype, phenotype, homozygous,* and *heterozygous.*
2. Explain Mendel's principle of segregation in terms of genes and meiosis.
3. State the basic law of probability, and explain how it applies to Mendel's experimental results.
4. Use a Punnett square to work out the probable results of various types of genetic crosses.
5. Explain Mendel's principle of independent assortment in terms of genes and chromosomes.
6. Describe the procedure for a test cross, and explain the significance of the results.
7. Define the terms *incomplete dominance* and *multiple alleles.*

25-6 Alleles

According to Mendelian principles, each body cell of an organism has two genes for each trait. For example, a pea plant has two genes for plant height. From modern genetics we know that a gene for height is found at the same position on each chromosome of a homologous pair. In an individual organism, the two genes for a particular trait may be alike, or they may be different. A pea plant may have two genes for tallness, two genes for shortness, or one gene of each kind. Different genes that control the same trait are called **alleles** (uh-*leelz*). Thus in pea plants the gene for tallness and the gene for shortness are alleles of the gene that controls plant height.

An organism in which both alleles for a particular trait are the same is said to be **homozygous** (hoh-muh-*zy*-gus) for that trait. If the alleles are different, the organism is said to be **heterozygous** (het-uh-roh-*zy*-gus). "Homozygous" and "heterozygous" are synonyms for "pure" and "hybrid" respectively.

25-7 Genotypes and Phenotypes

By general agreement, the allele for a dominant trait is represented by a capital letter. For example, the allele for tallness is represented by the symbol T. It is customary to represent the contrasting recessive allele by the lowercase form of the letter used for the dominant allele. Therefore, the allele for shortness is represented by the symbol t.

A pure tall pea plant has two alleles for tallness. Its genetic makeup is represented as TT. The genetic makeup of a pure short plant is tt, while that of a hybrid is Tt. The genetic makeup of an organism is called its **genotype** (*jee*-nuh-typ). The traits that an organism develops as the result of its genotype are called its **phenotype** (*fee*-nuh-typ). Two different organisms may have the same phenotype but different genotypes. A pure tall plant and a hybrid tall plant have the same phenotype (both are tall), but they have different genotypes (TT for the pure plant and Tt for the hybrid).

25-8 The Law of Probability

To explain the *numerical* results of Mendel's experiments, we must apply the laws of chance, or probability, to the separation and recombination of alleles. If you toss a coin, you know that the chance of its turning up heads is 1 out of 2, or ½. If you toss the coin 100 times, you expect to get about 50 heads and 50 tails; that is, you expect the ratio of heads to tails to be about 1:1. In any actual trial, the ratio of heads to tails is seldom exactly 1:1. In a short trial, say, 4 tosses, you might even get a run of 4 heads or 4 tails. However, if you made a large number of tosses, say, 1000, you would expect the ratio of heads to tails to be quite close to 1:1. Experiments have shown that the larger the number of trials, the closer the ratio comes to the expected value. This assumes, of course, that there is nothing special about the coin or the way it is tossed to make one side *more likely* to turn up than the other.

Consider another example—the rolling of a die. A die is a cube with six faces numbered from 1 to 6. When the die is rolled, each face is as likely as any other to turn up. If you roll the die 600 times, you would expect to get about 100 of each face: 100 1's, 100 2's, 100 3's, etc.

These examples illustrate the basic law of chance, or probability: If there are several possible events that might occur, and no one of them is more likely to occur than any other, then they will all occur in equal numbers over a large number of trials. This law enables us to predict the results of breeding

Figure 25-3. Genetic Explanation of the Formation of Hybrids.

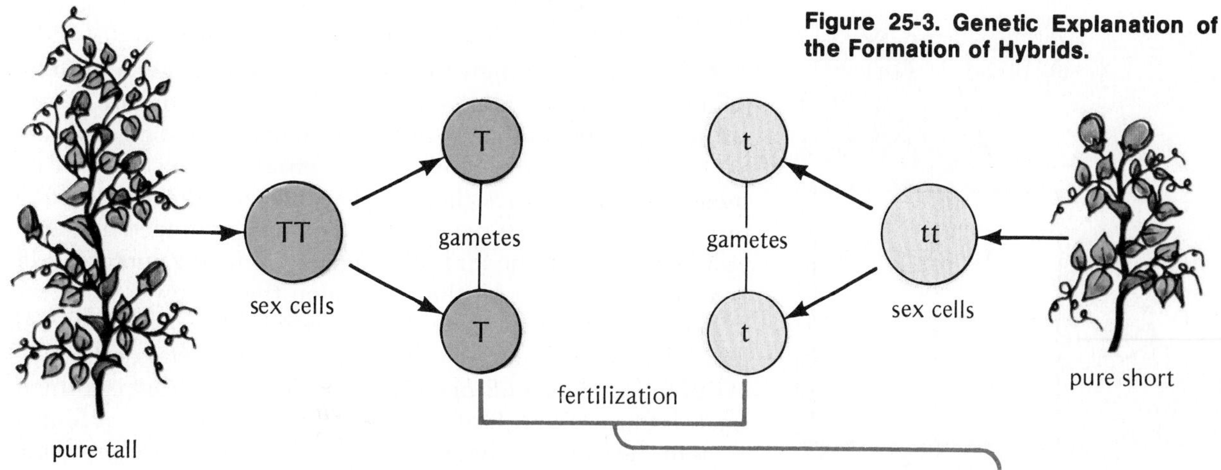

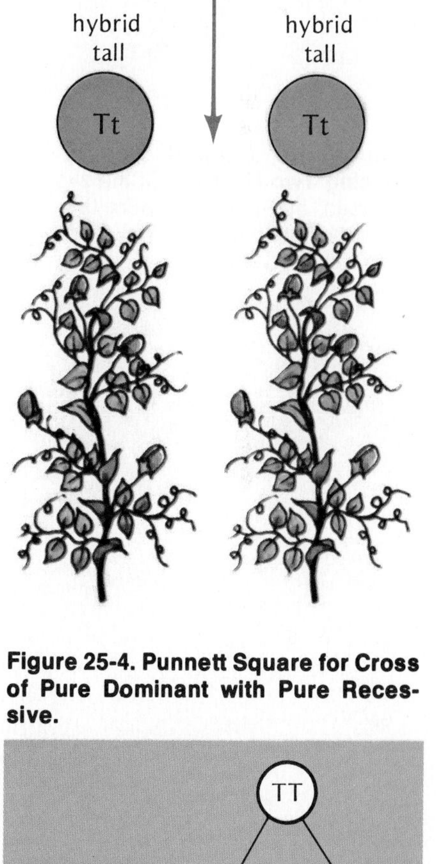

experiments like those of Mendel. Bear in mind that these predictions apply only when large numbers of individuals are involved.

25-9 The Punnett Square

Let us consider what happens when a pure tall pea plant is crossed with a pure short plant. The body cells of the tall plant have two genes for tallness. Their genotype is TT. When gametes form in this plant, each gamete receives one T gene. Its genetic composition can be shown by the single letter T (see Figure 25-3). The cells of the short plant have two genes for the recessive trait of shortness. The genotype is tt, and the gametes are t.

Suppose that we transfer pollen from the tall plant to the pistil of a short plant. Each sperm cell nucleus will be carrying one T gene. Each egg cell nucleus in the ovules of the short plant will have one t gene. When fertilization occurs, the zygotes will all receive one T gene and one t gene, and their genotype will be Tt. The plants that develop from these zygotes will be hybrid tall.

A diagram called a **Punnett square** is a convenient way to show the results of any genetic cross. The Punnett square for the cross we have just discussed is shown in Figure 25-4. In this diagram, the genes of the male gametes are written at the head of the columns of boxes. The genes of the female gametes are written at the side of the rows of boxes. (The positions of the male and female gametes can be interchanged.) In each box we then write the gene combination of the zygote that forms when the gene at the top of the column and the gene at the left of the row are brought together.

In this simple case, where there is only one possible combination and all the zygotes are alike, the diagram seems an unnecessary complication. The results are 100 percent hybrid tall (Tt). However, the method is very useful in more complicated cases.

Figure 25-4. Punnett Square for Cross of Pure Dominant with Pure Recessive.

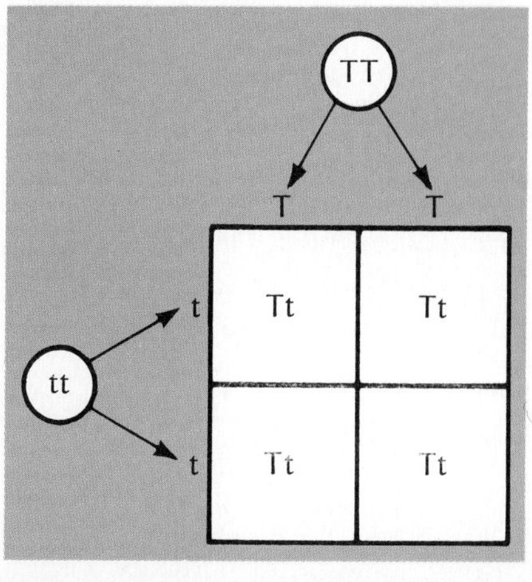

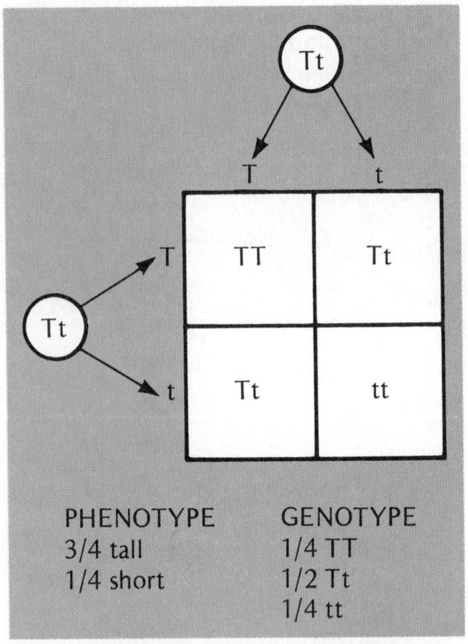

Figure 25-5. Punnett Square for Crossing Two Hybrids. Of the zygotes produced, one-fourth are pure tall (TT), two-fourths are hybrid tall (Tt), and one-fourth are short (tt).

25-10 Punnett Square for a Hybrid Cross

We will use a Punnett square for a cross in which hybrid tall plants are either allowed to self-pollinate or are cross-pollinated. The genotype of these plants is Tt. Because they contain two different alleles, they produce two types of gametes—T and t. Since the T and t genes are present in equal numbers, the two types of gametes are produced in equal numbers. This is true for both male and female gametes, and it is an important fact for the discussion that follows.

The Punnett square for the fertilizations that occur between these gametes is shown in Figure 25-5. Each letter at the head of a column represents one type of male gamete that is formed. Each letter at the left of a row represents one type of female gamete. Remember that these types of gametes are produced in equal numbers.

We now come to the key idea of this analysis. Each box in the diagram represents a possible union of a male gamete with a female gamete. Since the types of gametes are present in equal numbers, each combination is just as likely to occur as any other. The laws of probability tell us that if a large number of pollinations and fertilizations occur, all these possible combinations will occur in approximately equal numbers.

The Punnett square shows four possible combinations. All four will occur in equal numbers. Among a large number of offspring, 1/4 will be TT, 2/4 (or 1/2) will be Tt, and 1/4 will be tt. In terms of physical appearance, or phenotype, 3/4 will be tall and 1/4 will be short. With respect to phenotypes, the ratio of the offspring of this cross is 3:1 (3 tall to 1 short). In terms of genetic makeup, or genotype, 1/4 of the offspring are TT (pure tall), 2/4 are Tt (hybrid tall), and 1/4 are tt (pure short). With respect to genotype, the offspring ratio is 1:2:1.

We see that the laws of probability, combined with a Punnett square, have enabled us to account for the results that Mendel obtained.

25-11 Independent Assortment

The hybrid cross discussed above is more correctly called a **monohybrid cross** because only one pair of contrasting traits is being studied. Mendel's first experiments involved only monohybrid crosses. In experiments on tallness and shortness, for example, he did not record the other traits of the plants involved. After a time, however, Mendel decided to follow two pairs of contrasting traits at the same time. From his previous experiments he knew that yellow color was dominant over green color in pea seeds, and that round seed shape was dominant over wrinkled seeds. Mendel proceeded to make crosses in which he kept track of both seed color and seed shape.

As before, he started with plants that were pure for these traits. For one parent he used plants that were pure for both dominant traits: they produced yellow, round seeds. The other parent was pure for both recessive traits: they produced green, wrinkled seeds. He artificially pollinated one type of plant with pollen from the other type, and then observed the seeds that were produced. The results were as expected. All the seeds of the F_1 generation showed only the two dominant traits—that is, they were yellow and smooth. No green or wrinkled seeds appeared.

The next step was to plant these seeds and let the plants that grew from them self-pollinate. This would produce an F_2 generation of seeds. As expected, recessive traits reappeared in some of these seeds. Many seeds still showed both dominant traits. But some were yellow and wrinkled (dominant-recessive), some were green and smooth (recessive-dominant), and a few were green and wrinkled (recessive-recessive). A breeding experiment like this one, involving two traits, is called a **dihybrid cross.**

The actual numbers from one of these experiments are revealing. They are given in Table 25-1. Each trait considered by itself shows the 3:1 ratio expected in a single hybrid cross. There are 416 yellow seeds and 140 green seeds. The ratio of 416 to 140 is 2.97:1. There are 423 round seeds and 133 wrinkled seeds. This ratio is 3.18:1. Note also that there are about the same number of yellow, wrinkled seeds (dominant of one trait, recessive of the other) as green, smooth seeds (recessive of one, dominant of the other).

From data of this kind Mendel concluded that different traits were inherited independently of one another. This principle is known as the principle of **independent assortment.** In modern terms, this means that *genes for different traits are separated and distributed to gametes independently of one another.* Today we know that this is not always true. The reasons why the principle of independent assortment does not always apply are discussed in Chapter 26.

yellow round seeds = 315

yellow wrinkled seeds = 101

green round seeds = 108

green wrinkled seeds = 32

Table 25-1. Mendel's Results of a Dihybrid Cross.

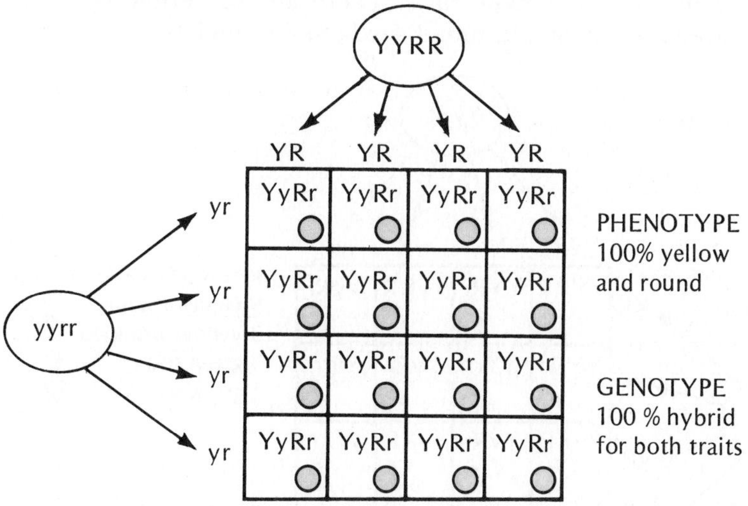

Figure 25-6. Cross of Parents Pure for Two Contrasting Traits. All offspring are hybrid dominant for both traits.

25-12 Phenotype Ratios in a Dihybrid Cross

With a Punnett square we can predict the phenotype ratios to be expected in a dihybrid cross. We first construct the diagram for the cross between the pure dominant for both traits and the pure recessive for both traits (see Figure 25-6). Note that there are spaces for four gametes from each parent. The reason for this is that there are two pairs of alleles in the parent cells. There are four ways in which the two pairs of alleles can combine when the gametes are formed. In this case, all four possible gametes have the same genetic makeup, but they are the result of four different pairings. In the second cross, this point will be important.

Illustrate several dihybrid crosses in class, completing the F_1 and F_2 generations. Students often have trouble forming the gametes for dihybrid crosses. Provide several examples.

1. Cross pure tall plant with yellow seeds with pure short with green seeds (TTYY × ttyy).
2. Cross pure round seeds with axial flowers with pure wrinkled seeds with terminal flowers (RRAA × rraa).

In their results, students should state the F_2 phenotype ratio.

As we expect, the phenotype of the offspring in the F_1 generation is 100 percent dominant for both traits (yellow and smooth). The genotype is 100 percent hybrid for both traits (YyRr).

Let us now construct the Punnett square for a cross between these dihybrids. This time the four possible gametes will be different: YR, Yr, yR, and yr. By the laws of probability, there will be equal numbers of the four types of gametes. The zygotes produced by this cross are shown in Figure 25-7.

Again by the laws of probability, all 16 of the possible zygotes will occur in equal numbers. The Punnett square shows ratios of the types of offspring produced when large numbers are involved. Considering the phenotypes, we see the following breakdown:

9 yellow-round (dominant-dominant)
3 yellow-wrinkled (dominant-recessive)
3 green-round (recessive-dominant)
1 green-wrinkled (recessive-recessive)

This phenotype ratio of 9:3:3:1 is the ratio that is observed in dihybrid crosses when the numbers of individuals are sufficiently large. Note that each trait considered by itself has the usual 3:1 phenotype ratio. There are 12 yellow seeds to 4 green; there are 12 round seeds to 4 wrinkled.

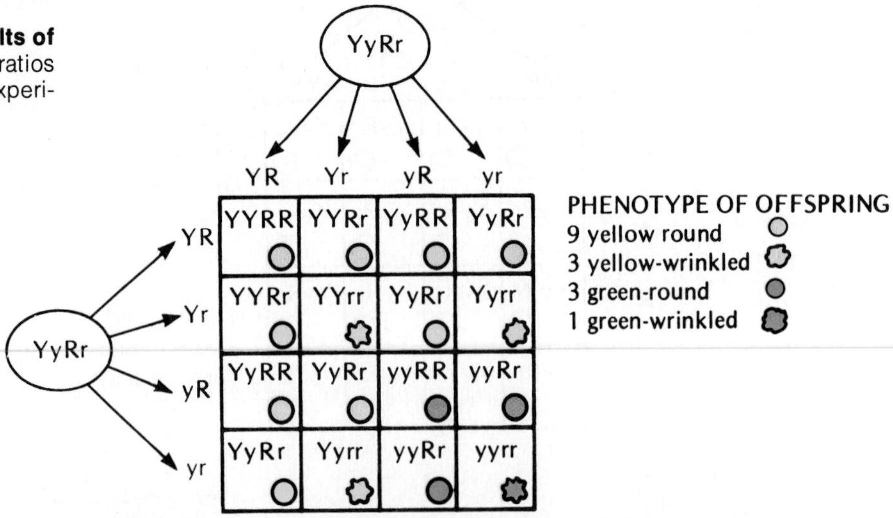

Figure 25-7. Predicting the Results of a Dihybrid Cross. The phenotype ratios agree fairly well with Mendel's experimental results.

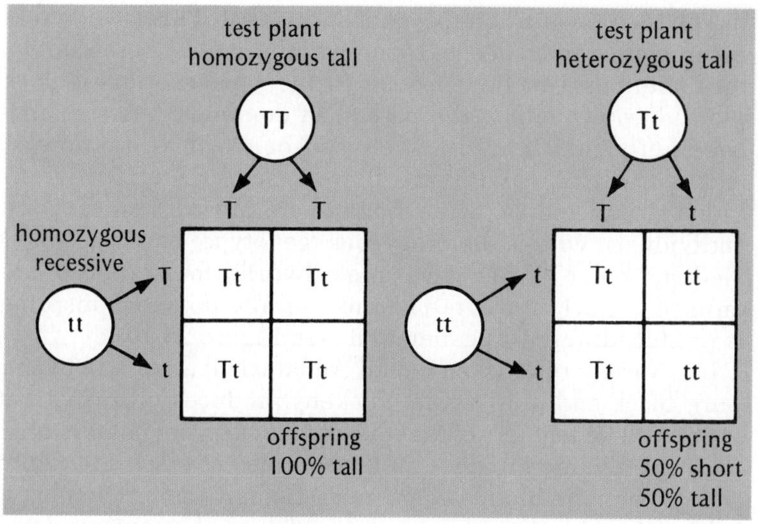

Figure 25-8. A Test Cross. An individual showing a dominant trait is crossed with a recessive. If any offspring show the recessive trait, the test individual must be hybrid.

25-13 The Test Cross

It is not possible to tell from appearance alone whether an individual showing a dominant trait is pure for the trait (homozygous) or hybrid (heterozygous). Breeders of plants and animals often need this information about parent stock. A procedure called a **test cross** can be used for this purpose.

In a test cross, the individual of unknown genotype is mated with an individual showing the contrasting recessive trait. The genotype of the latter individual is known—since it shows the recessive trait, it must be homozygous for it. The genotype of the unknown individual may be homozygous or heterozygous. The test cross will show which is the case.

To understand how the test cross works, let us take a tall pea plant as an example. A breeder wants to know whether the plant is homozygous (TT), or heterozygous (Tt). The unknown plant is crossed, by artificial pollination, with a short plant, which must be homozygous (tt). The Punnett squares in Figure 25-8 show the results of the two possible cases.

We see that if the unknown plant is pure tall, all offspring of the cross are tall. If the plant is heterozygous tall, half the offspring, on the average, will be short. That is, the test cross shows the presence of the recessive gene in the tall parent. The advantage of this method is that it does not require extensive testing and counting of phenotypes. Even a single short offspring will mark the tall parent as carrying the shortness gene. Thus, by crossing an individual of unknown genotype with a recessive individual and examining the offspring, it is possible to determine whether the unknown individual is homozygous or heterozygous.

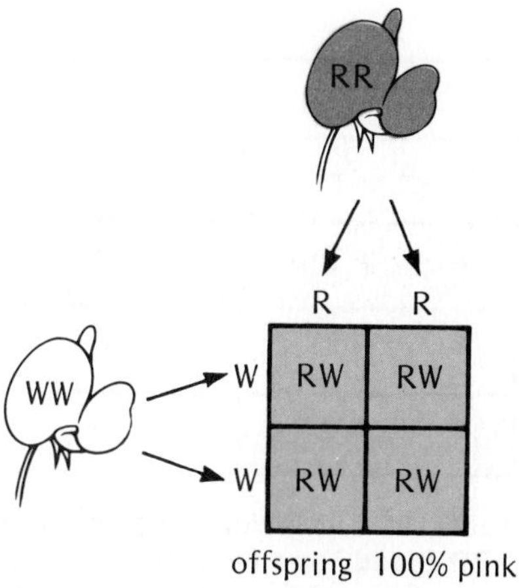

Figure 25-9. Incomplete Dominance. The hybrids of the F_1 generation show a trait intermediate between the pure traits.

25-14 Incomplete Dominance

Many genes follow the patterns outlined by Mendel's laws, but many do not. In some organisms, both alleles contribute to

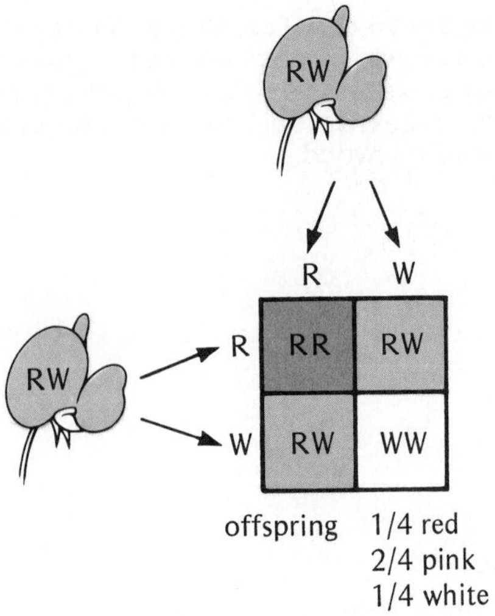

Figure 25-10. Incomplete Dominance in a Hybrid Cross. One-fourth of the offspring are pure dominant, one-fourth are pure recessive, and two-fourths are hybrid intermediate.

the phenotype of a heterozygous individual. This is known as **incomplete dominance,** or blending inheritance. For example, the inheritance of flower color in the Japanese four-o'clock plant does not follow the pattern of dominance. A cross between a plant with red flowers and one with white flowers results in offspring with pink flowers (see Figure 25-9). Individuals with red or white flowers are always homozygous. Individuals with a heterozygous genotype have an intermediate color. When two pink hybrid four-o-clocks are crossed, a 1:2:1 ratio of red to pink to white-flowered offspring is produced in the F_2 generation (see Figure 25-10).

In a variety of chicken called Andalusian, a cross between pure black and pure white chickens produces offspring that are blue. The feathers of the blue chickens do not possess blue pigment, but are arranged in tiny patches of black and white areas. When the blue fowl are crossed, the F_2 generation has a 1:2:1 ratio of black to blue to white chickens. Incomplete dominance is characterized by an F_1 generation with a phenotype different from either of the parents. The F_2 generation shows a phenotypic ratio of 1:2:1 rather than the 3:1 ratio seen in normal Mendelian inheritance. Other examples of incomplete dominance are seen in flower color in snapdragons and roan coat color in horses.

25-15 Multiple Alleles

For some traits more than two alleles exist in the species. They are referred to as **multiple alleles.** Although a single individual cannot have more than two alleles for each trait, different individuals can have different pairs of alleles when multiple alleles exist.

The alleles for human blood type are an example of multiple alleles for a trait. The ABO blood type system is described in Chapter 10, page 170. The existence of multiple alleles explains why there are four different blood types in this system. There are three alleles that control blood type, called A, B, and O. O is recessive. A and B are both dominant over O, but neither is dominant over the other. When A and B are both present in the genotype of an individual, both alleles are expressed.

The usual way to represent alleles in a multiple allele system is to use the capital letter I to represent a dominant allele and the lower case i to represent a recessive allele. A superscript letter then identifies each particular dominant allele. Thus I^A represents the dominant allele A; I^B represents the dominant allele B; and i is understood to represent the recessive allele O.

Since there are three alleles, there are six possible genotypes: I^AI^A, I^AI^B, I^Ai, I^BI^B, I^Bi, and ii. Table 25-2 shows the blood types produced by each of these genotypes.

Rh blood factors are also an example of multiple alleles in human genetics (see page 172).

GENOTYPE	BLOOD TYPE
I^AI^A or I^Ai	A
I^BI^B or I^Bi	B
I^AI^B	AB
ii	O

Table 25-2. Multiple Alleles in the ABO Blood Type System. I^A and I^B are each dominant over i, but not over each other. When both dominant alleles are present, the blood type is AB. Type O blood is produced only when neither dominant allele is present (genotype ii).

summary

Genetics is the branch of biology concerned with how genes are transmitted from parent to offspring and how they control the characteristics of an individual. Modern genetics developed from the scientific work of Gregor Mendel in the mid-1800s. From his experiments with heredity in pea plants, Mendel developed three principles of heredity—the principle of dominance, the principle of segregation, and the principle of independent assortment.

Genes are located on the chromosomes of the cell nucleus. The two chromosomes of a homologous pair both carry genes for the same traits. The different forms of a particular gene are called alleles. An individual who has two identical alleles for a trait is homozygous for that trait. An individual who has two different alleles for a trait is heterozygous, or hybrid, for that trait. The genetic makeup of an individual is called the genotype. The appearance of the individual due to the expression of the genotype is called the phenotype.

A test cross can be used to determine whether an individual is homozygous dominant or heterozygous. The individual of unknown genotype is crossed with an individual known to be homozygous recessive for the trait. The offspring are observed, and if any show the recessive trait, the individual being tested was heterozygous.

Some traits do not follow the Mendelian patterns of inheritance. Incomplete dominance occurs when both alleles contribute to the phenotype of a heterozygous individual. Other traits, such as human blood type, are controlled by multiple alleles.

vocabulary

allele
dihybrid cross
dominance
dominant
gene
genetics
genotype
heterozygous
homozygous
hybrid
incomplete dominance
independent assortment
monohybrid cross
multiple alleles
phenotype
Punnett square
recessive
segregation
test cross

test your learning

Section		
25-1	**1.**	What branch of biology deals with the study of genes and hereditary characteristics?
	2.	Where are genes found in the cell, and what are they composed of?
25-2	**3.**	Who conducted the first scientific studies of heredity, and when were they done?
	4.	Give several reasons why pea plants were an excellent choice for investigations of heredity.
25-3	**5.**	Describe Mendel's crosses of pure plants with contrasting traits and his observations.
	6.	What is the F_1 generation?
	7.	Describe the appearance of the F_1 generation in Mendel's crosses of pure plants with contrasting traits.
	8.	Define the term *hybrid*.
	9.	Define the *principle of dominance.*
25-4	**10.**	Define the *principle of segregation.*
25-5	**11.**	How were Mendel's results explained in terms of chromosomes and genes in the early 1900s?
25-6	**12.**	Define the following terms: *allele, homozygous,* and *heterozygous.*
25-7	**13.**	Define the terms *genotype* and *phenotype.*
25-8	**14.**	State the basic law of probability.
25-9	**15.**	What is a Punnett square used for?
25-10	**16.**	What phenotype and genotype ratios are observed in the offspring of a hybrid cross?
25-11	**17.**	State the principle of independent assortment, and describe the experiments that led Mendel to formulate this law.
25-12	**18.**	What is the phenotype ratio in the offspring of a dihybrid cross?
25-13	**19.**	What is the purpose of a test cross?
	20.	How is a test cross carried out?
25-14	**21.**	What is incomplete dominance?
	22.	Give examples of incomplete dominance in plants and animals.
25-15	**23.**	What are multiple alleles? Name a trait controlled by multiple alleles.
	24.	How many alleles for one trait can an individual have?

test your understanding

1. In guinea pigs, black fur and short hair are both dominant, while brown fur and long hair are recessive.
   A. Make a Punnett square showing a cross between a homozygous black guinea pig and a brown guinea pig. What are the phenotypes of the offspring?
   B. Make a Punnett square showing a cross between two dihybrid black, short-haired guinea pigs. Give the phenotype and genotype ratios of the offspring.
2. In humans, brown eyes are dominant and blue eyes are recessive.
   A. Make a Punnett square showing the possible eye colors of the children of a heterozygous, brown-eyed father and a blue-eyed mother. Give the phenotype and genotype ratios of the children.
   B. Two brown-eyed parents have two children with blue eyes. Give the genotypes of each member of the family.
3. Two newborn infants in a hospital lost their identification tags. One baby had type O blood, while the other baby had type AB blood. The two possible sets of parents of these infants had the following blood types: one set was type AB and type A, while the second set was type A and type B. Use Punnett squares to determine which set of parents could have had a child with type O blood. Could blood type have been used to match the babies and parents if both babies had had type AB blood?
4. A farmer wants to know whether a pea plant with round, yellow seeds is homozygous or heterozygous for these traits. Use Punnett squares to show the test crosses necessary to determine the genotype of this plant.

independent research

1. Prepare a report on Luther Burbank and his work in plant breeding.
2. Prepare a report on Rh blood factors in humans.

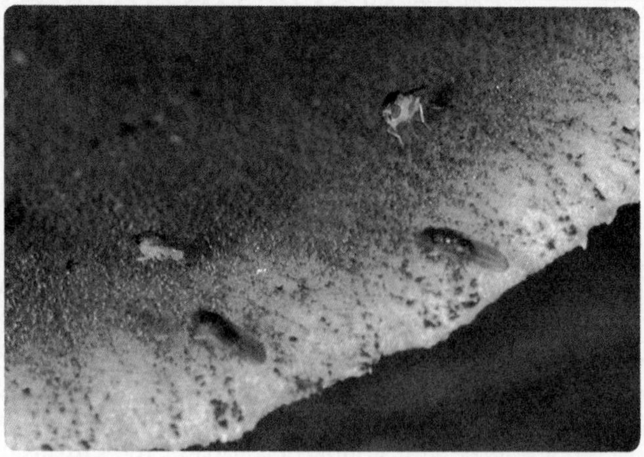

chapter 26

Modern Genetics

DEVELOPMENT OF THE GENE-CHROMOSOME THEORY

After completing your study of this section, you should be able to:

1. State the chromosome theory.
2. Explain how sex is determined in humans.
3. Define the following terms: *sex-linked trait, gene linkage, crossing-over,* and *multiple-gene inheritance.*

26-1 The Chromosome Theory

In 1902 W. S. Sutton, a graduate student at Columbia University, was studying the formation of sperm in the grasshopper. He observed the homologous pairs of chromosomes in diploid cells and the separation of the chromosome pairs during spermatogenesis. He realized that the chromosomes that separated during meiosis were the same as the chromosomes that had united during the fertilization process that originally produced the animal.

After reviewing Mendel's work, Sutton began to think that the factors, or genes, of Mendel's theory were carried on the chromosomes. Sutton explained Mendel's dihybrid experiment with pea plants by saying that the genes for yellow or green seeds are on one chromosome and the genes for wrinkled or round seeds are on another. In this way independent assortment could take place. He published his research in a paper called "The Chromosomes in Heredity."

Although Sutton's work did not prove that the genes are carried on the chromosomes, it was a very important hypothesis in the understanding of genetics. The final proof that the genes are carried on the chromosomes was obtained through the work of the geneticist Thomas Hunt Morgan, also at Columbia University.

26-2 Sex Determination and Chromosomes

Around 1890 it was observed that the chromosomes in cells from males and females were identical except for one pair. Scientists suspected that these different chromosomes determined the sex of the organism. This hypothesis is now well confirmed. These two unmatched chromosomes are known as the **sex chromosomes;** the other chromosomes are called **autosomes** (*aw*-tuh-sohmz). The discovery of the sex chromosomes was important in the study of genetics because it linked a genetic property to the chromosomes.

There are 23 pairs of chromosomes in human body cells: 22 pairs of autosomes and 1 pair of sex chromosomes. The sex chromosomes are called X and Y. The cells of human females contain two X chromosomes. The cells of males contain one X chromosome and one Y chromosome. As human egg cells are produced in the female by meiosis, each egg cell receives one X chromosome (see Figure 26-1). There are, however, two types of sperm cells produced in the male—those that receive an X chromosome, and those that receive a Y. When fertilization occurs in humans, the zygote will be either XX or XY, depending on which type of sperm fertilized the egg. An XX zygote develops into a female; an XY zygote develops into a male. In humans, it is the sperm of the male that determines the sex of the offspring.

Prior to 1956 it was thought that human cells had 48 chromosomes. The biologists Albert Levair and Joe Tjio developed a new method of counting chromosomes and discovered that the actual number was 46.

Not all animals have the same system of sex chromosomes as humans. In birds, butterflies, and some fish, the male has the two identical sex chromosomes, and the female produces two different types of gametes. In these animals, it is the egg of the female that determines the sex of the offspring.

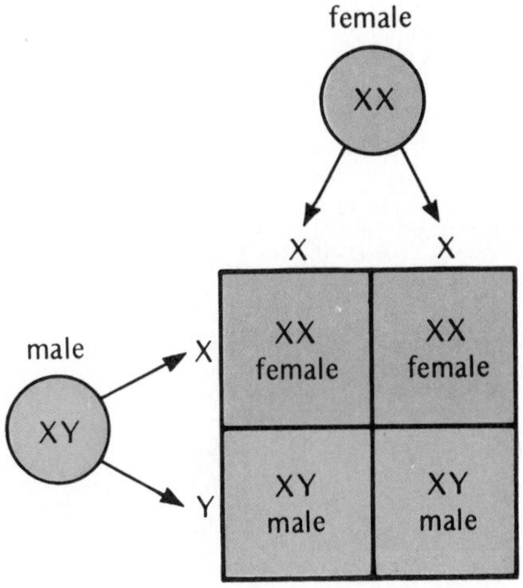

Figure 26-1. Sex Determination in Humans.

26-3 T. H. Morgan and *Drosophila*

In the early 1900s Thomas Hunt Morgan began a study of genetics at Columbia University. He made great contributions to the understanding of genes and won a Nobel prize in 1933 for his work. One reason that Morgan's research was so successful was his choice of the fruit fly, *Drosophila* (droh-*sahf*-uh-luh), as his experimental animal.

The fruit fly is so called because it is often found around ripening fruits. It is a very useful organism for genetic experiments. It is only about 2 millimeters in length so that large numbers can be kept in a relatively small space. It is easy to raise in laboratory cultures. The fruit fly produces many offspring. A mating pair can produce more than 300 young. It also has a complete life cycle of about 14 days. So a geneticist is able to study many generations of flies in a short period of time.

Another advantage to studying *Drosophila* is that it has only eight chromosomes. The cells in its salivary glands contain giant chromosomes, which can be easily observed under the microscope.

26-4 Sex-Linked Traits

Morgan examined thousands of fruit flies under the microscope to find interesting traits to study. The normal eye color of *Drosophila* is bright red. One day a white-eyed male fly appeared in the culture. Since he had never seen this trait before, he decided to investigate it. His first step was to mate the white-eyed male with a normal red-eyed female. All offspring of this mating showed red eyes, so Morgan concluded that the gene for white eyes is recessive.

If this cross obeyed the usual rules of Mendelian genetics, all the red-eyed flies of the F_1 generation would be heterozygous for eye color. If R represents the dominant gene for red eyes, and r the recessive gene for white eyes, the genotype of this generation should be Rr. To test this assumption, Morgan mated males and females of the F_1 generation. The F_2 generation did show the expected ratio of red eyes to white—three-fourths of the flies had red eyes, and one-fourth had white eyes. However, there was one peculiarity in the results—all the white-eyed flies were male. The females were all red-eyed. The inheritance of eye color seemed to have something to do with the sex of the offspring.

To find out more about what was happening, Morgan performed a kind of test cross. He mated the original white-eyed male with a red-eyed female from the F_1 generation. This time half the females had white eyes, and half had red. The males were also divided half white and half red.

After thinking about these results, Morgan concluded that the gene for eye color is carried on the X chromosome of the fruit fly and that there is no corresponding gene on the Y chromosome. Remember that the Y chromosome is shorter than the X. It is therefore reasonable to assume that some of the genes found on the X chromosome are missing from the Y chromosome. By this reasoning, a male fly will show the recessive white-eyed trait if its single X chromosome has the recessive gene for that trait. A female fly would have to have the recessive allele on both of its X chromosomes to show the trait.

By means of Punnett squares, we can show that Morgan's hypothesis accounts for the results of the crosses described above (see Figure 26-2). In these diagrams, X^R represents an X chromosome carrying the dominant gene for red eyes; X^r is an X chromosome with the recessive gene for white eyes; and Y is a Y chromosome, which has no gene for eye color.

Once a white-eyed female had been obtained, it was possible to make a further confirming test. Morgan crossed a white-eyed female with a red-eyed male. All the female

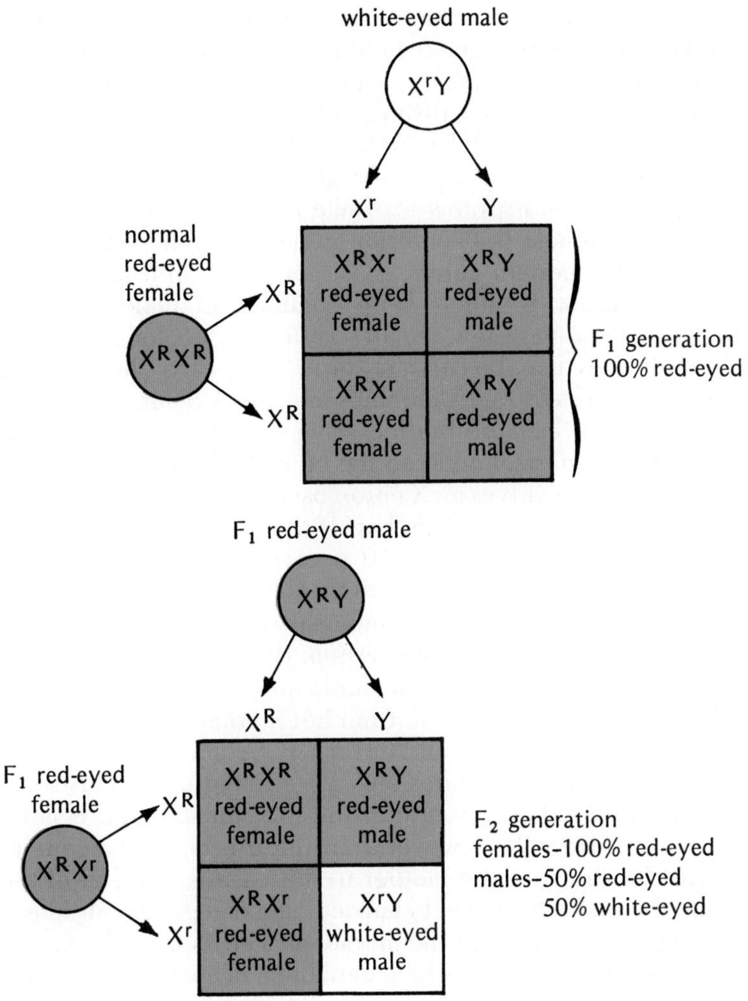

Figure 26-2. Inheritance of the White-Eye Trait in Drosophila. The gene for white eyes is recessive and is carried only on the X chromosome. *(Top)* A white-eyed male is crossed with a homozygous red-eyed female. Since all the offspring inherit the dominant red-eye gene from the female parent, all have red eyes. However, the females are heterozygous for eye color. *(Bottom)* A red-eyed male is crossed with a heterozygous red-eyed female. Since all the female offspring receive the dominant gene from the male parent, they are all red-eyed. However, the male offspring do not receive a gene for eye color from the male parent, but only from the female parent. Half the males receive the recessive gene and are white-eyed.

offspring were red-eyed; all the males were white-eyed. You may want to construct a Punnett square that will explain this result.

A trait that is controlled by a gene found on the sex chromosomes is a **sex-linked trait.** The chance of showing the trait is affected by the sex of the individual. Most sex-linked traits are determined by genes found on the X chromosome but not on the Y chromosome. Morgan's discovery of sex-linked traits was a strong confirmation of Sutton's hypothesis that genes are located on the chromosomes. It was also an important discovery in its own right, as it relates to the occurrence of several human diseases.

26-5 Sex-Linked Traits in Humans

Many human conditions and diseases are caused by abnormal recessive alleles of particular genes. The normal allele enables the body to perform some function that the abnormal allele does not. The term *defective gene* is often used to refer to the abnormal alleles that cause genetic diseases. Several of the known defective genes in human genetics are sex-linked. Among the human diseases caused by defective sex-linked genes are hemophilia, a disorder of the blood-clotting system, and muscular dystrophy, which results in the gradual destruction of muscle cells. A form of night blindness and also color blindness are less serious sex-linked hereditary disorders.

Color blindness is a condition in which the individual cannot perceive certain colors, most commonly red and green. This condition is much more common in males than in females. Relatively few females suffer from color blindness, although they may be *carriers* for it. They carry the gene for color blindness on one X chromosome, but are not affected by that condition because the recessive defective gene is counteracted by a normal gene on the other X chromosome.

Every male receives an X chromosome from his mother and a Y chromosome from his father. If the mother is a carrier for color blindness, there is a 50 percent chance that she will transmit the X chromosome with the defective gene to any son she has (see Figure 26-3). Since the Y chromosome has no corresponding gene for color vision, that son will suffer from color blindness. A daughter would be only a carrier if she received the defective gene from her mother. The X chromosome from her father would ordinarily be normal.

Since a father contributes only a Y chromosome to his sons, a color-blind father cannot transmit the color-blindness gene to his sons. He will, however, transmit this defective gene to all his daughters. If the mother in this case is a carrier of the gene, there is a 50 percent chance that a daughter will inherit the defective gene from the mother as well as from the father. Thus, on the average, half the daughters of such a mating will be color blind, and the other half will be carriers. Half the sons will also be color blind, but this result does not depend on the father's genotype. If both parents are color blind, all their offspring will be color blind, since neither parent is carrying a normal gene.

26-6 Gene Linkage

Every organism has thousands of pairs of genes. Every organism also has a certain small number of chromosomes in each body cell. Therefore many genes must be present on each chromosome. Genes located on the same chromosome are said to be *linked*.

If genes are linked on the same chromosome, they cannot be distributed independently during meiosis, and therefore they should not obey Mendel's principle of independent assortment. Mendel arrived at that principle only because the traits he studied happened to be controlled by genes located on different chromosomes.

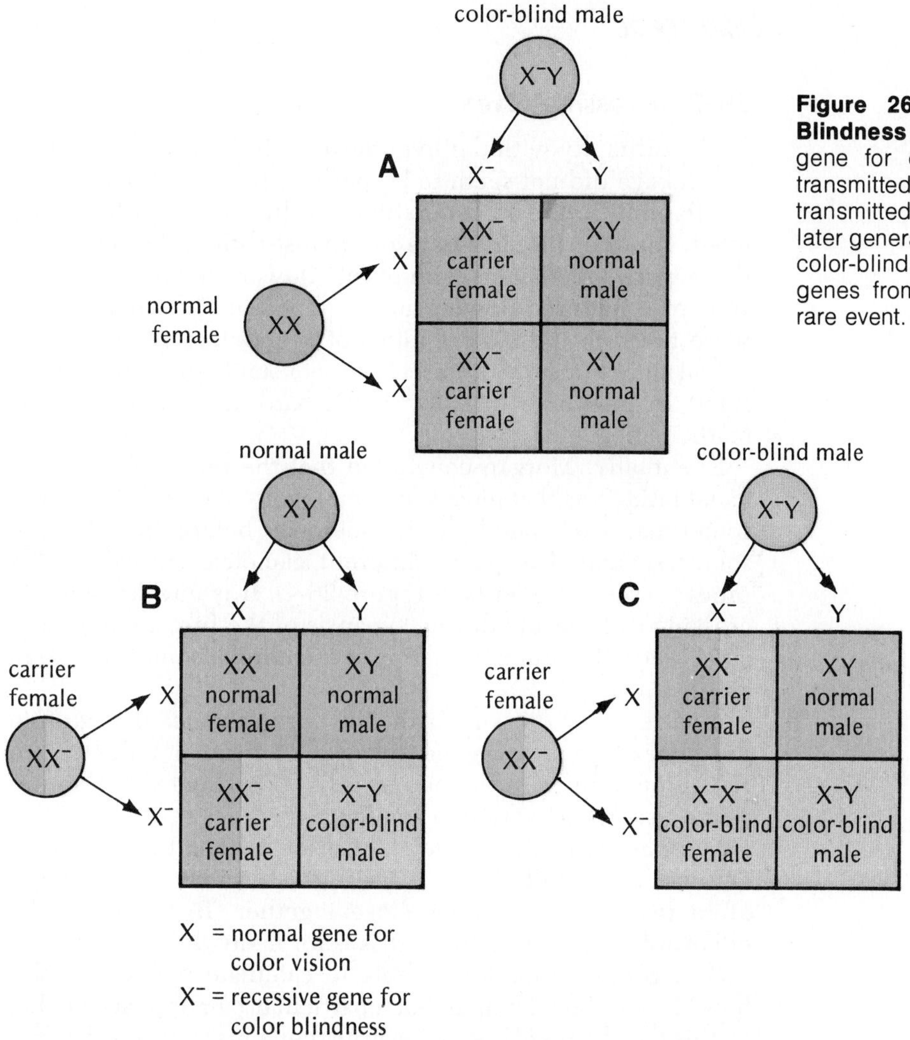

Figure 26-3. Inheritance of Color Blindness in Humans. (A and B) The gene for color blindness cannot be transmitted from father to son. It can be transmitted only through the female to later generations. (C) For a female to be color-blind, she must inherit defective genes from both parents, a relatively rare event.

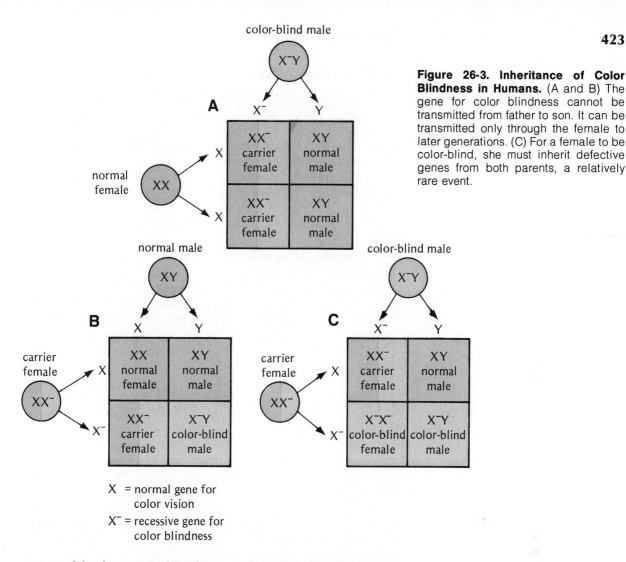

One of the first examples of **gene linkage** was found by R. C. Punnett and William Bateson in investigations at Cambridge University in 1906. They were studying the inheritance of two pairs of traits in pea plants: purple (dominant) and red (recessive) flowers, and long (dominant) and round (recessive) pollen grains. Plants pure for both dominant traits were crossed with plants pure for both recessives. The expected phenotype of 100 percent dominant for both traits in the F_1 generation was observed. However, when these dihybrids were crossed, they did not show the expected 9:3:3:1 phenotype ratios in the F_2 generation (see page 412). The results were much closer to the 3:1 ratio obtained from a single hybrid cross. The two dominant traits seemed to be staying together, as were the two recessive traits. They were not being distributed independently.

T. H. Morgan had obtained similar results with *Drosophila.* Certain traits seemed to be inherited together. Morgan took this to be further evidence that genes were carried on chromosomes, and that genes carried on the same chromosome were inherited together.

26-7 Crossing-Over

The difficulty with the hypothesis of linked genes was that the linkage did not seem to be perfect. In a small percentage of offspring in the F_2 generation, the linked genes had separated. In the Punnett-Bateson investigation, for example, there were some plants with purple flowers and round pollen, and some with red flowers and long pollen. But the numbers were far from the 9:3:3:1 ratios of Mendelian genetics. The actual ratios observed were fairly constant from one experiment to another, but they were hard to explain by any mathematical analysis.

Eventually, Morgan concluded that the reason for the unusual ratios was that pieces of homologous chromosomes were sometimes exchanged during meiosis, before the chromosomes separated to go to different gametes. He called this process **crossing-over** (see Figure 26-4). It is now known that crossing-over occurs during synapsis of the first meiotic division, when the four chromatids of the chromosome pair are in close contact.

As a result of crossing-over, the chromosomes that go into the gametes have new gene linkages. They are not identical to the chromosomes in the parent cells. Crossing-over is an important source of variation in offspring.

Morgan reasoned that genes that are far apart on the same chromosome should become separated by crossing-over more often than genes that are close together. By studying the offspring ratios of dihybrid crosses for many different pairs of linked genes, Morgan was able to calculate mathematically how close or how far apart each particular pair appeared to be. In this way he was able to construct gene maps of the chromosomes in *Drosophila.* Each gene map showed the sequence of genes on the chromosome, based on inferences from the frequency with which the genes became separated by crossing-over.

26-8 Multiple-Gene Inheritance

Unlike the traits studied by Mendel, many traits in both plants and animals do not appear in two contrasting forms. For example, humans are not either tall or short. Instead human height shows continuous variation over a wide range from very short to very tall. The same is true of human skin color and the size of fruits and vegetables. Traits that vary in a continuous manner between two extremes are not controlled

Figure 26-4. Crossing-Over. During synapsis, segments of homologous chromatids may be interchanged. If the exchanged segments carry different alleles for certain traits, new gene combinations result.

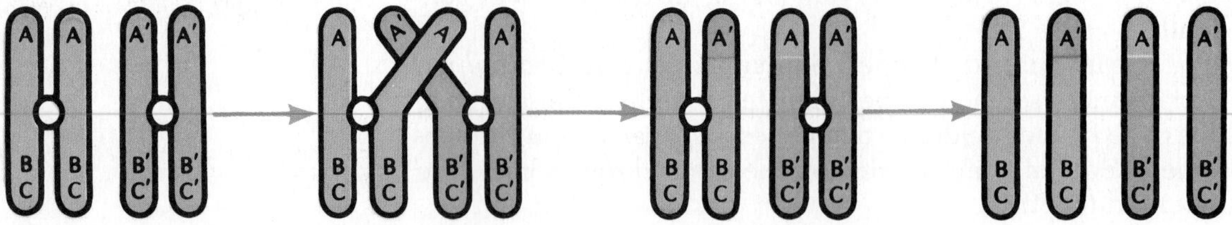

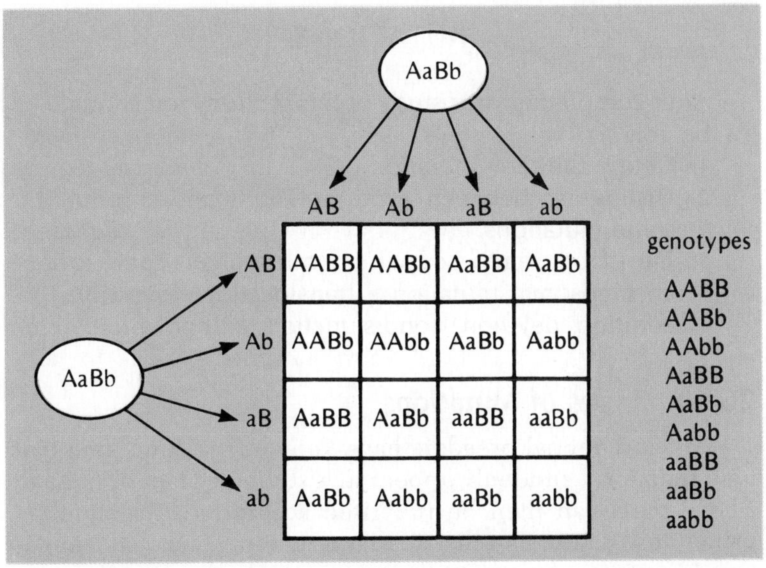

Figure 26-5. Multiple-Gene Inheritance. In multiple-gene inheritance in which there are two pairs of genes controlling a trait, there are nine different possible genotypes. There is a range of phenotypes between the pure dominant and pure recessive extremes.

Fruit flies with the curly-wing trait will grow straight wings if kept at a temperature of 16°C during development and curly wings if kept at 25°C.

by a single pair of genes alone. Instead, they are affected by two or more different pairs of genes. When two or more independent pairs of genes affect the same characteristic, it is known as **multiple-gene,** or *polygenic,* **inheritance.**

The simplest case of multiple-gene inheritance would involve two pairs of genes. The length of the ears in corn and the color of the kernels in wheat are both controlled by two pairs of genes. Using either one as an example, we can refer to the two pairs of genes as Aa and Bb. With these two pairs of genes there can be four different possible gametes and nine different genotypes (see Figure 26-5). We can say that the greater the number of capital letters in the genotype, the larger the corn ear or the darker the wheat kernel. Thus, the largest corn ears or darkest wheat kernels would have the genotype AABB. The smallest ears and lightest kernels would have the genotype aabb. All other genotypes would show traits between these two extremes.

26-9 Environment and Heredity

Genes carry all the information for the development, structure, and metabolic processes of an organism. But the environment also plays a role in determining how the genes are expressed. For example, the Himalayan rabbit has white fur over most of the body, with black fur on the ears, nose, feet, and tail (see Figure 26-6). This pattern is produced by differences in temperature in various parts of the body. A gene causes the deposition of black pigment in the fur over parts of the body in which the temperature falls below 33°C. This can be illustrated by placing an ice pack on a shaved area on the back of a Himalayan rabbit. The new growth of fur is black. Genes carry the basic information for all traits, but the phenotypes of organisms can often be modified by environmental factors.

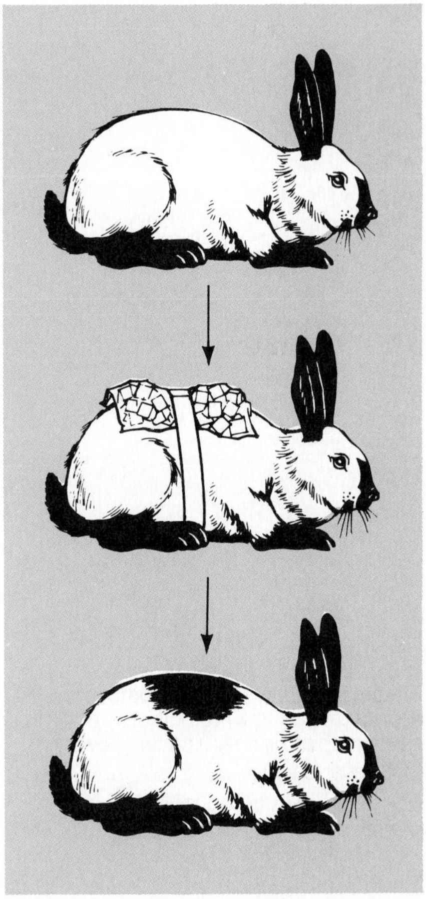

Figure 26-6. Effect of Body Temperature on Fur Color of the Himalayan Rabbit.

MUTATIONS

After completing your study of this section, you should be able to:
1. Define the term *mutation*.
2. Distinguish between gene mutations and chromosome mutations.
3. Describe each of the following types of chromosomal mutation: translocation, inversion, addition, deletion, nondisjunction, and polyploidy.

26-10 Types of Mutations

Plant and animal breeders have known for a long time that new traits may suddenly appear in a strain of plant or animal. These traits can then be inherited according to Mendelian principles. A new trait that appears suddenly is called a **mutation** (myoo-*tay*-shun). The first individuals showing the new trait are called **mutants** (*myoot*-unts). Credit for the concept of mutation is given to the Dutch botanist Hugo De Vries, one of the scientists who rediscovered Mendel's work. De Vries' first observation of a mutation in living organisms was in a plant known as the evening primrose.

It is now known that there are two different types of mutation. One type is a **gene mutation,** where a new allele for an existing trait suddenly appears on the chromosome that carries the gene. The white-eyed male fruit fly that T. H. Morgan discovered was the result of a mutation of the gene for eye color. The nature of gene mutations is discussed in Chapter 27. The other type of mutation is a chromosomal mutation. **Chromosomal mutations** involve a change in the structure of an entire chromosome or a change in the chromosome number within the cells of the organism. The mutations observed by De Vries were chromosomal mutations.

For a mutation to be inherited, it must occur in a gamete or in the primary sex cells from which gametes develop. Mutations that occur in body cells cannot be transmitted to future generations.

26-11 Chromosomal Mutations

These various types of chromosomal rearrangements occur much less frequently than normal crossing-over.

Changes in chromosome structure. Permanent changes in chromosome structure sometimes occur during cell division. As the tetrad is lined up during meiosis, the chromatids can become entangled and chromosome segments may be rearranged in several ways. **Translocation** is the transfer of a chromosome segment to a nonhomologous chromosome. An **inversion** occurs when a piece of a chromosome is rotated so that the order of genes in the segment is reversed. **Addition** involves the breaking off of a chromosome segment and its attachment to its homologue. The homologue then has some genes repeated. **Deletion** occurs when a chromosome segment simply breaks off, resulting in the loss of some genes.

Nondisjunction. The misplacement of a whole chromosome can occur during meiosis. Thus an extra chromosome may be present in the new organism ($2n + 1$) or an entire chromosome may be omitted ($2n - 1$). This variation takes place when chromosomes that normally separate during meiosis remain together. This is referred to as **nondisjunction** (non-dis-*junk*-shun).

Nondisjunction causes several serious genetic defects in humans. *Down's syndrome,* commonly known as *mongolism* (*mahn*-guh-liz-um), is the result of an extra chromosome. A person afflicted with this condition has three number 21 chromosomes in each cell; he or she is mentally retarded and has physical abnormalities. Sexual development can be affected by nondisjunction of the sex chromosomes. One condition, called Turner's syndrome, is caused by the presence of only one X chromosome in the cells and it results in a female with underdeveloped sexual characteristics. In Klinefelter's syndrome, a male has two X's and a Y in each cell, which results in a normal male appearance, but underdeveloped sex organs.

The presence of three chromosomes of one type in a cell is called *trisomy.* Down's syndrome is also called trisomy 21. Trisomy of chromosomes 13 or 18 results in severe malformation and death within several weeks after birth.

Polyploidy. **Polyploidy** (*pahl*-ee-ployd-ee) is a condition found in plants in which the cells have some multiple of the normal chromosome number. For example, they may have a $3n$, $4n$, or even $5n$ number of chromosomes. Polyploidy occurs when the chromosomes fail to separate normally during mitosis or meiosis. Polyploid plants and their fruits are often larger than normal, and plant breeders sometimes use chemicals to develop polyploid plants.

HUMAN GENETIC DISEASES

After completing your study of this section, you should be able to:

1. Describe some of the difficulties that arise in studying human genetics.
2. Name three genetic diseases, and describe the cause and symptoms of each.
3. Describe how amniocentesis and karyotyping are used in the diagnosis of genetic diseases.

26-12 Difficulty of Studying Human Heredity

Although much is known about human genetics, the transmission of traits from one generation to another in humans cannot be studied in the same way it is in plants and other animals. The time between generations is too long, the number of offspring produced is too small, and no controlled experiments are possible.

Scientists have learned about some genetic traits in humans by tracing the appearance of these traits in families over sev-

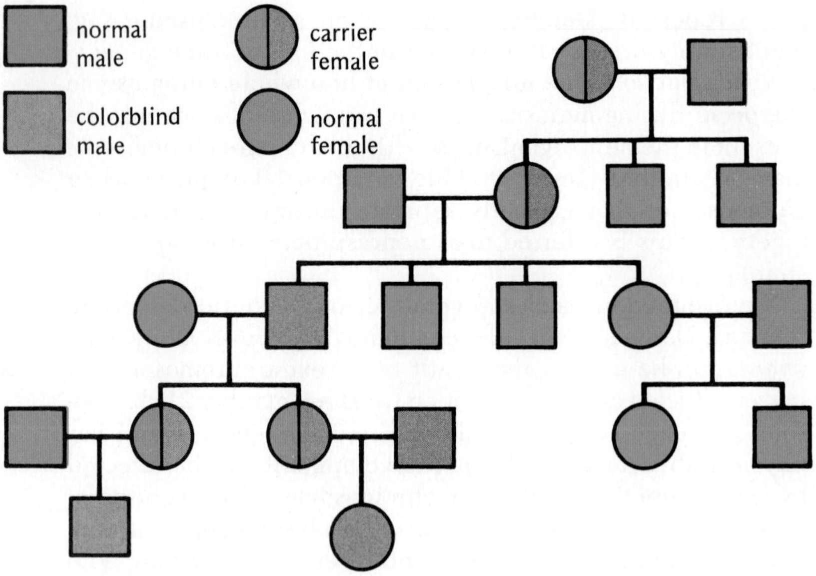

Figure 26-7. A Pedigree Chart Tracing Color Blindness in a Family.

eral generations. A pedigree chart shows the presence or absence of a particular trait in each member of each generation. Figure 26-7 shows a pedigree chart tracing the inheritance of color blindness in five generations of a family. The existence of female carriers of color blindness can be definitely shown only when the condition is found in her descendants.

26-13 Genetic Diseases

A number of human diseases are known to be caused by recessive, defective genes. These genes rarely cause symptoms in people who are carriers because there is also a normal gene present. Some sex-linked diseases were discussed on page 420. Among the other genetic diseases of humans are sickle-cell anemia, phenylketonuria, and Tay-Sachs disease.

Sickle-cell anemia is a disease in which the red blood cells have an abnormal hemoglobin molecule (see page 448). This in turn gives the cells an abnormal shape, which causes them to clump and block small blood vessels. The oxygen-carrying capacity of these cells is also decreased. A person with sickle-cell anemia suffers from oxygen deficiency, and also experiences pain and weakness. Sickle-cell anemia is found primarily in people of African descent. It has been found that carriers of the trait—those with one normal and one sickle-cell gene—are more resistant to malaria than people without the gene. Because it offers some protection from malaria, the gene has been maintained in African populations. Although carriers of the trait are not generally troubled by symptoms of the disease, such symptoms may arise occasionally as a result of severe stress. Screening for sickle-cell anemia is done by examination of the red blood cells.

Phenylketonuria, or PKU, is a disease in which an enzyme necessary for the normal breakdown of the amino acid phenylalanine is missing. Because of the missing enzyme, products of phenylalanine metabolism accumulate in the body, damaging the brain and causing mental retardation. In the past, it was not possible to diagnose PKU until the brain damage had occurred. Now, however, PKU can be diagnosed at birth by a simple test of the infant's urine. This is done routinely in most hospitals. Brain damage can then be avoided by a special diet low in phenylalanine.

Tay-Sachs disease, like PKU, results from the lack of a particular enzyme. In this case, it is an enzyme necessary for the breakdown of lipids in the brain. Without the enzyme, the lipids accumulate in the brain cells and destroy them. Tay-Sachs is a rare disease, but it is found with an unusually high frequency among Jews of Central European descent. The gene for Tay-Sachs disease is recessive, and symptoms occur only in the homozygous condition. This disease appears before the age of 1 year and death occurs within several years. There is no treatment for Tay-Sachs disease at this time.

26-14 Genetic Counseling

Although no treatment is possible for many of the known genetic diseases, modern medical knowledge makes it possible to examine and counsel prospective parents and to give them an accurate idea about the risks they carry of having a child with a genetic disease. In some cases it is possible to perform tests that show whether or not the parents are carriers of genetic diseases.

26-15 Amniocentesis

Amniocentesis (am-nee-oh-sen-*tee*-sis) is a technique in which a long needle is inserted into the amniotic sac of a pregnant woman. A small sample of amniotic fluid, which contains some fetal cells, is withdrawn. The cells are then cultured and subjected to various tests. Cell metabolism can be checked for the presence or lack of a particular enzyme. If the fetus has Tay-Sachs disease, it can be detected in this way. The chromosomes of the fetus can be examined by a process known as **karyotyping** (kar-ee-oh-*typ*-ing). In karyotyping, a photograph is taken of a fetal cell undergoing mitosis. The photograph is then enlarged, and the chromosomes are checked. The presence of an extra chromosome number 21 shows that the fetus has Down's syndrome. The sex of the fetus, as well as any abnormalities of the sex chromosomes, can also be determined by karyotyping.

GENETICS IN PLANT AND ANIMAL BREEDING

After completing your study of this section, you should be able to describe the genetic techniques used by plant and animal breeders to improve their crops and animals.

Humans have always tried to improve their crops and animals. They have tried to increase yields, upgrade quality, make both plants and animals more disease-resistant, and expand growing and breeding areas. Now modern genetic principles are used to produce plants and animals with desirable traits.

26-16 Breeding Methods

The goal of a breeder is to shift the characteristics in a population in order to improve yield and quality. Organisms with pure homozygous genes are necessary to establish a pure breeding line. A breeder has several methods to choose from.

Selection. **Selection** is the choosing of only animals and plants with the most desirable traits for mating. The breeder hopes to change the population by accumulating the desired characteristics. After mating occurs, the breeder must then select only the offspring with the desired traits for further reproduction.

Inbreeding. **Inbreeding** is the mating of closely related individuals to obtain desired results. The degree of closeness can vary. Self-pollination by plants is the closest possible hereditary relationship. In organisms that require cross-fertilization, the closest relationship would be brother-sister, mother-son, and father-daughter. More remote inbreeding would include cousins, aunt-nephew, and uncle-niece. Inbreeding is employed in raising domestic animals, such as fowl, sheep, cattle, and swine. It decreases variation for a particular trait in a population, and thus tends to increase the number of homozygous genes. Continued inbreeding and selection will eventually produce a line of animals that breeds nearly pure.

Inbreeding, because it tends to increase the number of homozygous genes, can also result in unwanted effects. Harmful, recessive genes may be brought together by inbreeding and thus be expressed. This is why close relatives are prohibited from marrying in most states.

Outbreeding. In **outbreeding,** individuals not closely related are mated. The purpose is to introduce new beneficial genes into the population. Special traits are often found in hybrid crosses of two close species. These superior characteristics are called **hybrid vigor,** or *heterosis* (het-uh-*roh*-sis). One example of hybrid vigor is the mule, the offspring of a male donkey and a female horse. The mule is superior to its parents in physical endurance, strength, and resistance to disease. Mules, however, are usually sterile.

Another type of outbreeding is the mating of pure breeding lines within a species. White short-horned cattle and black Angus cattle have been crossed to produce offspring with superior beef and rapid growth.

Successful outbreeding followed by inbreeding may produce valuable new pure lines of plants and animals.

Mutations. Mutations are used by plant and animal breeders to improve their stock. Many fruits, such as the navel orange, pink grapefruit, McIntosh apple, and seedless grape, started as plant mutations. Once discovered, a plant mutation may be reproduced by vegetative propagation. This avoids the segregation of traits that would occur in sexual reproduction. Mutations are also valuable in animal breeding. For example, in mink ranching, the most valuable fur colors, platinum and black cross, originated as mutations.

summary

W. S. Sutton proposed the idea that genes are carried on the chromosomes. T. H. Morgan, who discovered sex-linked genes, proved that Sutton was right. A sex-linked gene is a gene that is carried on a sex chromosome. Humans have 22 pairs of autosomes and 1 pair of sex chromosomes. Several human diseases are controlled by sex-linked genes.

Genes located on the same chromosome are linked and do not show independent assortment during meiosis. However, linked genes may be separated by crossing-over during synapsis. Crossing-over is an important source of genetic variation.

Some traits, such as human skin color and height, are controlled by multiple genes, not just a single pair of genes.

Various types of changes in chromosome structure can arise, generally as a result of abnormal meiosis. These changes include translocation, inversion, addition, or deletion. Nondisjunction is an abnormality in which a pair of chromosomes does not separate normally during meiosis and remains together. Thus, the new organism may be missing a chromosome or an extra chromosome may be present. In polyploidy, the cells have some multiple of the normal chromosome number.

Among the genetic diseases of humans are sickle-cell anemia, phenylketonuria, and Tay-Sachs disease. These diseases are caused by defective recessive genes. Symptoms of the diseases are found only in homozygous recessive individuals. Amniocentesis and karyotyping are techniques used to detect genetic diseases in developing fetuses.

Plant and animal breeders use genetics to try and improve their stock. The methods used to obtain desired traits include selection, inbreeding, and outbreeding. Mutations can also be valuable in plant and animal breeding.

vocabulary

addition
amniocentesis
autosome
chromosomal mutation
color blindness
crossing-over
deletion
gene linkage
gene mutation
hybrid vigor
inbreeding
inversion
karyotyping
multiple-gene inheritance
mutant
mutation
nondisjunction
outbreeding
polyploidy
selection
sex chromosome
sex-linked trait
sickle-cell anemia
translocation

test your learning

Section		
26-1	**1.**	How did Sutton explain the results of Mendel's dihybrid cross?
26-2	**2.**	Define the term *autosome*.
	3.	Explain sex inheritance in humans.
26-3	**4.**	Give several reasons why *Drosophila* is useful for genetic experiments.
26-4	**5.**	What are sex-linked genes, and how were they discovered?
26-5	**6.**	Explain why hemophilia and color blindness occur much more frequently in men than in women.
26-6	**7.**	What are linked genes?
26-7	**8.**	What is crossing-over, and during what stage of meiosis does it occur?
	9.	Why is crossing-over important?
	10.	What is a gene map and how is a gene map constructed?
26-8	**11.**	What is multiple-gene inheritance? Name two human traits controlled by multiple genes.
26-9	**12.**	Describe the effects of temperature on gene expression in the Himalayan rabbit.
26-10	**13.**	Define the terms *mutation* and *mutant*.
	14.	Explain the difference between a gene mutation and a chromosomal mutation.
26-11	**15.**	Define the following terms: *translocation, inversion, addition*, and *deletion*.
	16.	Explain what happens in nondisjunction, and name several defects caused by nondisjunction.
	17.	What is polyploidy?
26-12	**18.**	Describe some of the difficulties encountered in scientific studies of human heredity.
26-13	**19.**	Name three genetic diseases of humans, and describe the symptoms of each.
26-14	**20.**	What is the purpose of genetic counseling?
26-15	**21.**	Describe the techniques of amniocentesis and karyotyping.

26-16 **22.** Explain the processes of selection, inbreeding, and outbreeding.
23. Why is marriage between close relatives usually prohibited?
24. How are mutations used by plant and animal breeders?

test your understanding

1. Using Punnett squares, show the genotypes of the possible offspring of the following marriages:
A. A color-blind male and a normal female.
B. A normal male and a color-blind female.
2. In Mendel's studies of dihybrid crosses, he by chance chose traits whose genes were located on separate chromosomes. What would his results have been if the genes for these traits were located on the same chromosome?
3. Discuss the contributions of W. S. Sutton and T. H. Morgan to our knowledge of the roles of genes and chromosomes in heredity.
4. Distinguish between the heredity of traits involving multiple alleles and those involving multiple genes.

independent research

1. Prepare a report on the functions of genetic counseling. Include a list of the genetic diseases and conditions that can actually be detected in the developing fetus as well as those for which counseling is generally advised.
2. Prepare a report on the inheritance of height in humans.

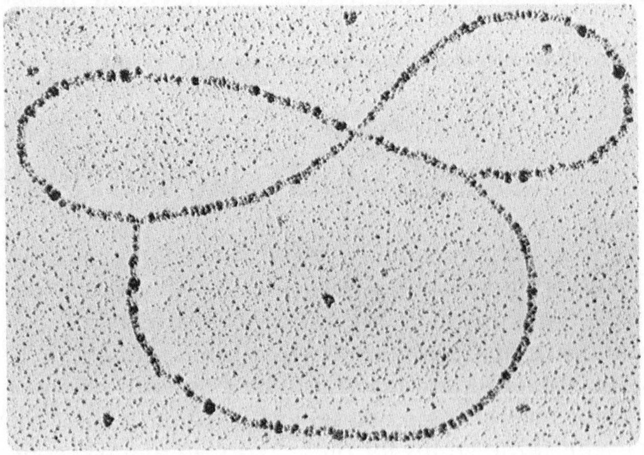

chapter 27

Molecular Genetics

As a result of the work of Mendel, Morgan, and many other researchers in genetics, it became clear that the chromosomes carry the hereditary information. It was also certain that the information is present in distinct units, and that these units, called genes, are arranged along the chromosomes like beads on a string. Still, no one knew what a gene was or how it worked. Without that knowledge, it could not be said that heredity and genetics were truly understood. This understanding did not come until the 1950s, when the chemical nature of the gene was discovered.

IDENTIFICATION OF THE GENETIC MATERIAL

After completing your study of this section, you should be able to:

1. Describe the experimental evidence proving that DNA carries the hereditary information.
2. Name the three components of a DNA nucleotide.
3. List the ways in which the chemical composition of RNA differs from that of DNA.
4. Describe the Watson-Crick model of the structure of DNA.
5. Describe the replication of a DNA molecule.

27-1 Protein vs. Nucleic Acids

Analysis of the material in the cell nucleus started in 1869 with the experiments of Friedrich Miescher, a Swiss biochemist. He isolated a material from the nuclei of fish sperm that he called *nuclein* (*noo*-klee-un). Work by other scientists showed that nuclein contained the usual elements of organic compounds—carbon, hydrogen, oxygen, and nitrogen—but it was also especially rich in phosphorus. When nuclein was shown to have an acidic nature, its name was changed to nucleic acid. Later research found two types of nucleic acid—deoxyribonucleic acid, or DNA, and ribonucleic acid, or RNA. DNA occurs only in the nuclei of cells. RNA is found mainly in the cytoplasm.

In 1914, the German chemist Robert Feulgen developed a method for staining DNA. This enabled biologists to localize DNA in various types of cells and during cell division.

In the 1920s it was shown that the chromosomes contained DNA. It was already known that chromosomes contained proteins. The chemical structure of proteins was well understood. Although a few scientists suggested that DNA was the hereditary material, most scientists believed that only proteins were complex enough to carry genetic information. It was not until the 1950s that it became clear that the hereditary material of the chromosomes must be the DNA, not the protein. To understand how this came about, we must first consider experiments performed in 1928 by Frederick Griffith, an English bacteriologist.

Griffith's experiments. Frederick Griffith was trying to find a vaccine against pneumonia. Pneumonia is a disease caused by a type of bacteria called *pneumococcus* (noo-muh-*kahk*-us). Griffith knew that there are two types of pneumococcus (see Figure 27-1). One type, called Type S, is surrounded by an

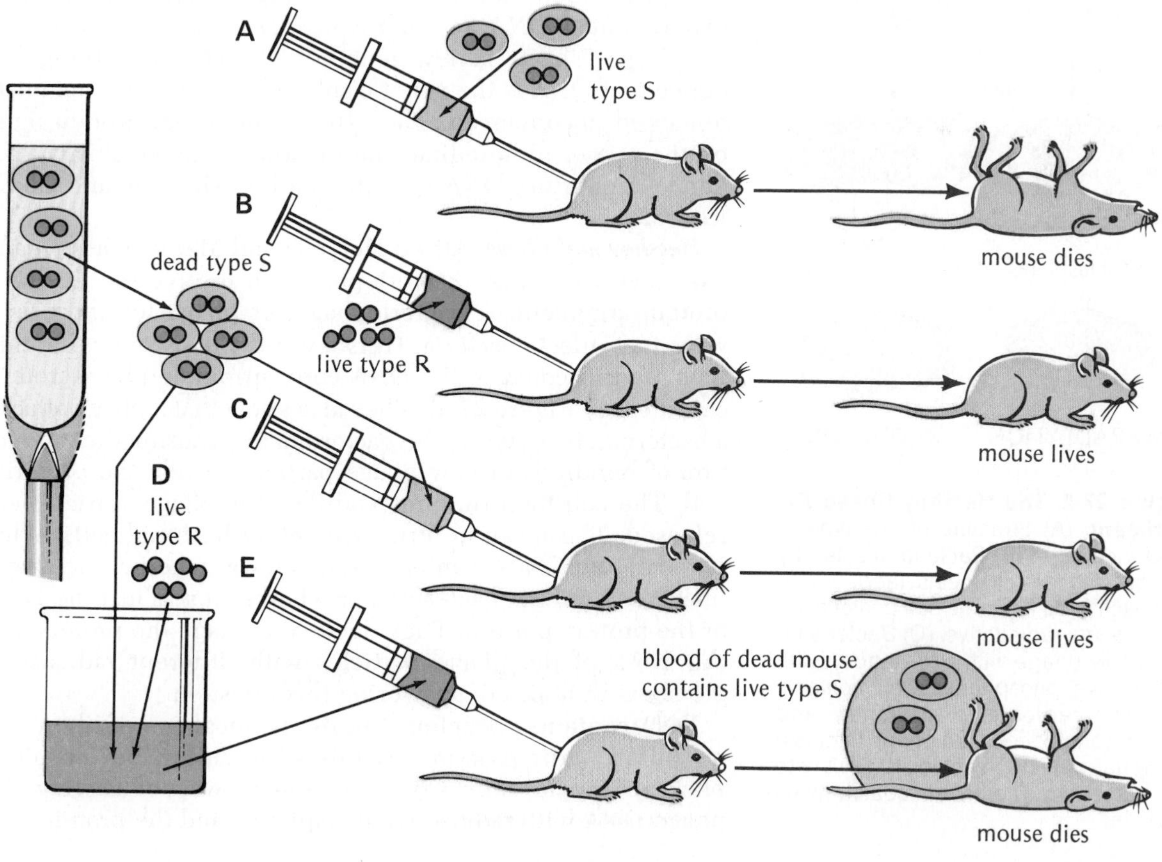

Figure 27-1. Griffith's Experiment. (A) Live type S bacteria kill the mouse. (B) Live type R bacteria are harmless. (C) Dead type S bacteria are harmless. (D) Dead type S are mixed with live type R. (E) The mixture kills the mouse, and live type S bacteria are present in the mouse's tissues. Griffith concluded that the type R bacteria had been transformed into type S.

outer covering called a *capsule*. Type S bacteria cause a severe case of pneumonia. The other type, called Type R, is not surrounded by a capsule. Type R bacteria do not cause pneumonia. If mice are injected with Type S bacteria, they develop pneumonia and die. Mice injected with Type R bacteria show no ill effects.

Dead Type S bacteria do not cause pneumonia when injected into mice. In Griffith's key experiment, he mixed dead Type S bacteria with live Type R. When he injected the mixture into mice, the mice developed pneumonia and died. Furthermore, the tissues of the dead mice were found to contain live Type S bacteria.

Remember that dead Type S bacteria alone do not cause pneumonia. Neither do live Type R alone. But when brought together, they do cause disease, and living Type S bacteria appear. Griffith concluded that some factor from dead Type S bacteria had transformed Type R bacteria into Type S. The transformed bacteria had acquired the ability to make smooth capsules and to cause pneumonia in mice.

Other researchers verified Griffith's results. They also succeeded in extracting material from the dead Type S bacteria that could transform Type R to Type S in a test tube.

Avery, MacLeod, and McCarty. In 1944, Oswald Avery, Colin MacLeod, and Maclyn McCarty of the Rockefeller Institute in New York identified the transforming material in Griffith's experiment as DNA. In other words, DNA had the capacity to give Type R bacteria new genetic traits. This was strong evidence that DNA is the genetic substance, but many scientists remained unconvinced. They still thought that protein must be the carrier of hereditary information. The conclusive evidence supporting DNA was obtained by Hershey and Chase in 1952.

Hershey and Chase. Alfred Hershey and Martha Chase made use of viruses called bacteriophages to resolve the DNA vs. protein argument. A bacteriophage, or phage for short, is a virus that infects bacteria. Hershey and Chase knew that this type of virus consists of a DNA core surrounded by a protein capsule (see Figure 27-2). They also knew that a phage attacks a bacterium by entering the bacterium and causing the production of hundreds of new phage particles inside the bacterial cell. The cell then ruptures and the new phage particles are released. These can in turn attack other bacterial cells. What Hershey and Chase wanted to find out was whether the whole phage entered the bacterium, or whether it was just the DNA or the protein portion. They decided to "tag" the protein and the DNA of the phage particles with different radioactive elements in hopes of answering this question.

DNA contains phosphorus in its chemical composition, but no sulfur. Virus protein contains some sulfur, but no phosphorus. Hershey and Chase devised a way of tagging the phage DNA with radioactive phosphorus and the protein coat

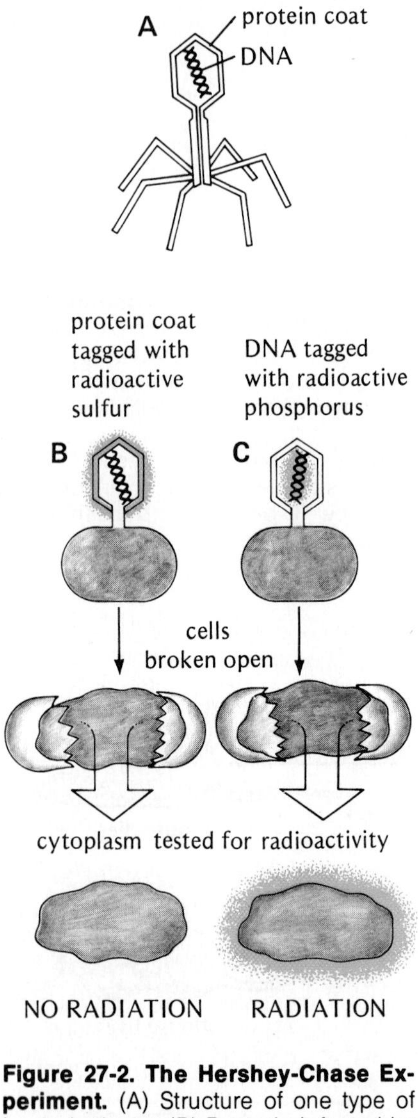

Figure 27-2. The Hershey-Chase Experiment. (A) Structure of one type of bacteriophage. (B) Bacteria infected by phage with protein coats tagged with radioactive sulfure. The cell contents do not become radioactive. (C) Bacteria infected by phage with DNA tagged with radioactive phosphorus. Cell contents become radioactive. Hershey and Chase concluded that a phage infects a bacterial cell by injected its DNA into the bacterium. The protein coat remains outside.

with radioactive sulfur. One bacterial culture was then exposed to phages with radioactive DNA and another culture exposed to phages with radioactive protein. After large numbers of bacteria had become infected with phages, the cells were separated from the medium and their contents tested for radioactivity. The cells that had been infected by phages with radioactive DNA showed a large amount of radioactivity. The cells infected by phages with radioactive protein showed almost no radioactivity. This experiment proved that when phages infect bacteria, the phage DNA enters the cells, but the phage protein remains outside.

If phage DNA can cause bacteria to manufacture more phages, without the presence of phage protein, it must be the DNA that carries the genetic instructions for making phage. This experiment finally established DNA as the hereditary material. The problem now became that of working out the chemical structure of DNA to find out how it functions.

27-2 Composition of DNA

Most organic compounds have molecules made up of chemical groups of various kinds. For example, starch molecules are chains of sugar units bonded together; fats consist of fatty acids and glycerol; proteins are chains of amino acids. The first stage in analyzing an unknown organic compound is to find out what chemical groups it is made of. The second stage is to work out the structural arrangement of these groups in the molecule.

The chemical analysis of DNA was carried out in the 1920s by the biochemist P. A. Levene. Levene found that the very large DNA molecule is made up of the following chemical groups: (1) the 5-carbon sugar **deoxyribose** (dee-ahk-see-*ry*-bohs); (2) a phosphate group; and (3) four kinds of nitrogenous (nitrogen-containing) bases. Two of the four bases, **adenine** and **guanine,** are a type of compound called **purines** (*pyoor*-eenz); the other two, **cytosine** and **thymine,** are compounds called **pyrimidines** (pih-*rim*-uh-deenz).

Levene found that for each sugar unit there is one phosphate group and one nitrogenous base. He therefore concluded that the basic unit of DNA is a sugar, a phosphate, and one of the four nitrogenous bases. He called this unit a **nucleotide** (*noo*-klee-uh-tyd). Since there are four different bases, there are four different kinds of nucleotides.

Nucleotides are precursors of DNA and RNA. They are also intermediate products in the synthetic pathways of glycogen and other substances. ATP is an adenine nucleotide, and NAD and FAD also contain adenine nucleotides. Nucleotides regulate various metabolic reactions, including the activities of certain hormones.

27-3 Structure of DNA

After the chemical composition of DNA was known, the structure of the molecule remained to be worked out. This was accomplished in 1953 by James Watson, an American biochemist, and Francis Crick, an English physicist, working together at the Cavendish Laboratory in Cambridge, England. In arriving at their model of DNA, Watson and Crick made use of everything that was known about DNA. An important piece of information came from Maurice Wilkins and Rosalind Franklin of Oxford University. They had made X-ray studies of crystals of DNA. These X-ray photographs showed that the repeating units in the crystal are arranged in the form of a helix. (A helix is the shape of a coiled spring.)

After trying many different arrangements of the chemical groups of DNA, Watson and Crick arrived at a model DNA molecule in which there are two chains of sugar-phosphate groups running parallel. Pairs of bases link the chains together like the rungs of a ladder (see Figure 27-3). The helix of the molecule is formed by twisting or coiling the ladder. Thus, the DNA molecule is a double helix.

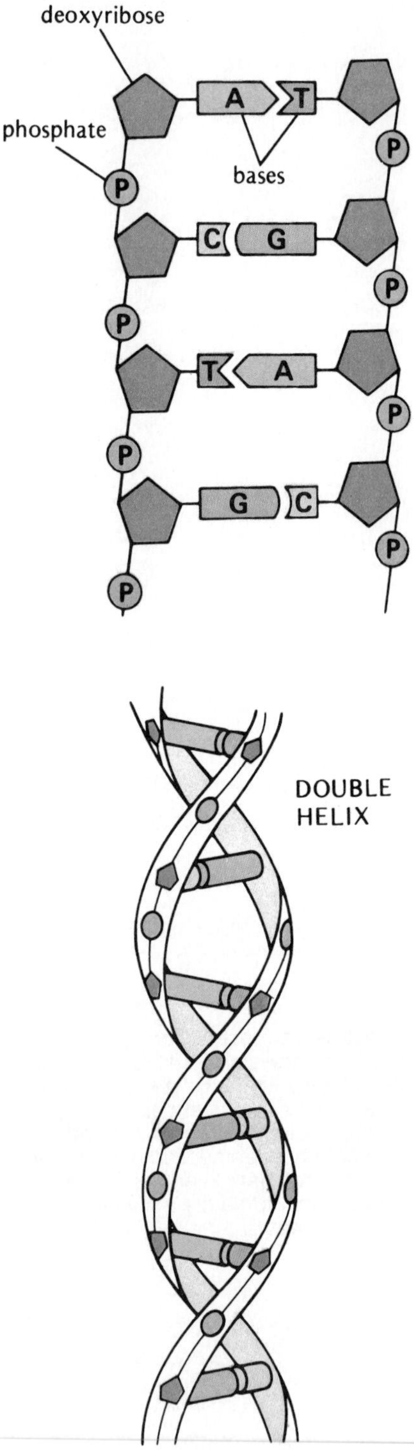

Figure 27-3. Watson-Crick Model of DNA.

Watson and Crick found that this model could be made to work only if the pairs of bases making each "rung" of the ladder is an adenine unit connected to a thymine, or a guanine connected to a cytosine. This model agreed with all the data for the DNA molecule. Besides, it explained a fact that other researchers had discovered—that the amount of adenine in DNA is always the same as the amount of thymine, and the amount of guanine is the same as the amount of cytosine. Furthermore, since the sequence of bases along the chain could vary, the sequence could be a code for genetic information.

Another important fact about this model is that the sequence of bases along one strand automatically determines the matching bases on the other strand. If we use capital letters A, T, G, and C to stand for the four bases, adenine, thymine, guanine, and cytosine, every A must be joined to a T and every G must be joined to a C. No other pairings are possible. Suppose, for example, that a sequence along one strand is AGGTTAC. The matching sequence along the second strand must be TCCAATG. The two strands are said to be *complementary*. Each strand is the complement of the other according to the A-T and G-C base pairing rule.

The double helix model of DNA was a great breakthrough in the science of genetics. Watson, Crick, and Wilkins received the Nobel prize in 1962 for this work.

27-4 Replication of DNA

One of the great questions of the gene-chromosome theory was, How can an exact copy of each chromosome be made during cell division? The double-helix model gave a simple answer. The base pairs that form the "rungs" of the model are held together by a weak type of bond called a *hydrogen bond*. If these bonds are broken, the two strands of the DNA molecule can separate like the halves of a zipper. The bases along each strand would then be exposed like the teeth of an opened zipper. If there are free nucleotides in the nucleus of the cell, their bases could be attracted to the complementary bases on each exposed strand. They could then join together to make a complete complementary strand exactly like the one

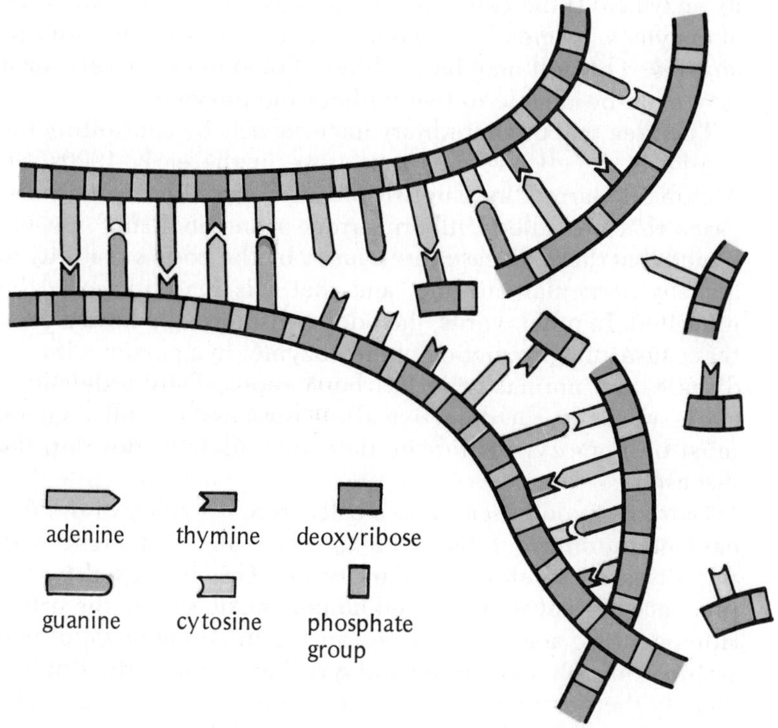

Figure 27-4. DNA Replication. DNA replication results in the formation of two double-stranded molecules exactly like the original DNA molecule.

that had been peeled away. Two double-stranded molecules of DNA exactly like the original molecule could be made in this way (see Figure 27-4). Experiments of many kinds have demonstrated that, under the action of special enzymes, this is exactly what happens in the living cell.

Recent evidence obtained with the electron microscope indicates that replication does not begin at the ends of a DNA molecule. Instead, the nitrogen bases separate at an internal point in the molecule, forming a loop. Replication then proceeds in both directions, expanding the loop.

27-5 Composition and Structure of RNA

The composition of ribonucleic acid, RNA, is very similar to that of DNA, with two differences. The 5-carbon sugar in RNA is ribose, and in RNA the pyrimidine **uracil** is substituted for thymine. So the four bases found in RNA are adenine, guanine, cytosine, and uracil. Unlike DNA, which is double-stranded, RNA consists of only a single strand of nucleotides.

PROTEINS AND CELLULAR ACTIVITY

After completing your study of this section, you should be able to:

1. Describe the experiments of Beadle and Tatum with *Neurospora*.
2. Explain the one gene—one polypeptide hypothesis.

27-6 Genes and Enzymes

Every chemical reaction in the living cell requires the presence of a specific enzyme. The enzymes that an organism needs are not present in its food. The organism must make all its enzymes. If the cell is unable to make one of its thousands of enzymes, its metabolism will be affected by the lack of this enzyme. The cell may be unable to function effectively, or it may even be unable to live without the enzyme.

The idea that the hereditary material acts by controlling the synthesis of cell enzymes first arose in the early 1900s. Sir Archibald Garrod, an English physician, studied certain diseases that he called "inborn errors of metabolism." He believed that these diseases are caused by the body's inability to make a particular enzyme, and that this inability could be inherited. In other words, the body cells normally have a gene that causes the production of the enzyme. In a person with the disease, the normal gene has been replaced by a defective allele. (Usually, the defective allele is recessive, and a person must be homozygous for the defective allele to develop the disease.)

Garrod's hypotheses came mostly from his study of the disease *alkaptonuria* (al-kap-tuh-*nyoor*-ee-uh). A patient with this disease excretes very dark urine. This is caused by the presence of a substance called homogentisic acid in the urine. Homogentisic acid is produced during the breakdown of two amino acids, phenylalanine and tyrosine, in the body. But it is usually then oxidized into another compound. A person who lacks an enyzyme necessary for the breakdown of homogentisic acid will excrete it, because the metabolic pathway is stopped after its production. Such a person is lacking the gene that controls the production of the necessary enzyme. Phenylketonuria (PKU) also results from a defective recessive gene and a missing enzyme (see page 428).

Garrod published his ideas in 1909, but they were largely ignored at the time. It was not until the 1930s and 1940s that their importance was realized.

27-7 The One Gene—One Enzyme Hypothesis

The best evidence that genes control the production of enzymes came from the experiments of George Beadle and Edward Tatum, two American scientists, in 1941. In their investigations, Beadle and Tatum used the red bread mold *Neurospora crassa*. This mold can normally grow and reproduce in a medium containing just a few nutrients—sugar, a nitrogen compound, some mineral salts, and the vitamin biotin. This is called a *minimal medium*. From the medium, the mold can synthesize all the amino acids it needs to form its enzymes and other proteins.

Beadle and Tatum knew that irradiation with X rays could produce mutations in genes. When they exposed cultures of *Neurospora* to X rays, they found that many of the mold organisms could no longer grow in the minimal medium (see Figure 27-5). If amino acids were added to the medium, some of there organisms were able to survive. By adding amino acids, one at a time, to cultures of the irradiated mold, they

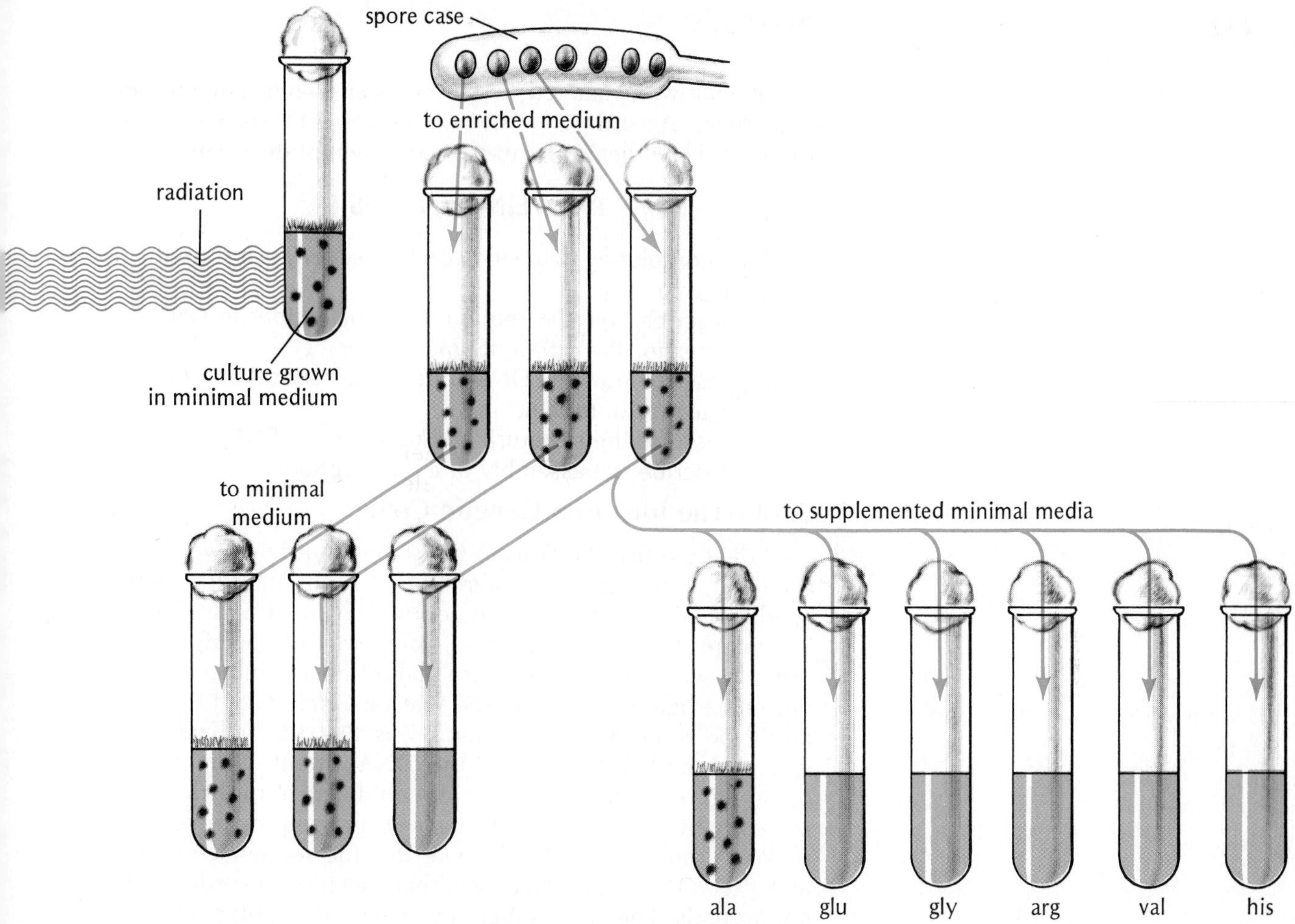

Figure 27-5. The Beadle-Tatum Experiment. (A) A spore case of Neurospora known to grow in a minimal medium was exposed to X rays. (B) Each spore was then removed from the case and placed in an enriched medium containing all basic nutrients and amino acids. Each spore produced a culture of mold. (C) Samples of each culture were tested in a minimal medium. Some samples did not grow in the minimal medium. (D) Samples of mold that would not grow in a minimal medium were then tested in other minimal media, each supplemented by a different amino acid. The mold grew in the medium that contained the amino acid it was no longer able to synthesize.

were able to separate out groups of organisms that needed one particular amino acid. The inability of the mold to produce a particular amino acid meant that the mold was not synthesizing an enzyme needed to make that amino acid. This meant, in turn, that the organism had lost the gene that directed the synthesis of that enzyme. The X rays had caused a mutation in the gene that normally causes the synthesis of the enzyme. From the results of these experiments, it was concluded that each gene produces its effects by controlling the synthesis of a particular enzyme. This is known as the *one gene—one enzyme hypothesis.*

All enzymes are proteins, but not all proteins are enzymes. Some proteins are hormones, some are materials needed for structural parts of the cell, some are needed for other special purposes. It was shown that genes control the synthesis of all proteins, not just enzymes. Proteins are made up of polypeptides—long chains of amino acids (see page 55). Some proteins consist of two or more polypeptides linked and entwined to form the protein molecule. Hemoglobin, for example, is a protein made from two different kinds of polypeptide chains. The synthesis of each polypeptide is controlled by a different gene. Because of these facts, the one gene—one enzyme hypothesis was changed to the **one gene—one polypeptide hypothesis.** According to this modified hypothesis, each gene directs the synthesis of a particular polypeptide chain.

PROTEIN SYNTHESIS

After completing your study of this section, you should be able to:

1. Describe how the sequence of nucleotides in DNA codes for the different amino acids.
2. Describe how the DNA code is transcribed into the structure of mRNA.
3. Describe the structure and function of tRNA.
4. Describe the assembly of a polypeptide.

27-8 The Idea of a Genetic Code

At the time that the Watson-Crick model of DNA was being accepted, it was generally agreed that each gene directs the synthesis of a particular polypeptide chain of amino acids. Therefore, the gene must have some way of specifying the order in which the amino acids should be assembled. It was not immediately clear from the Watson-Crick model how this might be done. One suggestion was that the polypeptides were assembled directly on the DNA strands. But no one could figure out how amino acids could match up with nucleotides, which is what would have to happen for direct synthesis. A more workable idea was that the sequence of bases along the DNA strands is a code that specifies the order of the amino acids. The code is then translated into a polypeptide by some intermediate mechanism. The second hypothesis was eventually shown to be correct, and the way it works is now fairly well understood.

Only twenty amino acids are involved in the genetic code. However, in some cell types, other amino acids are produced from these twenty by subsequent reactions.

What might the DNA code be? There are 20 amino acids in the proteins of humans and most other organisms. There must therefore be at least 20 different code "words" to specify these amino acids. There are only 4 different bases in DNA. How many base "letters" are needed to form the code words for 20 amino acids? From 4 bases, only 16 different 2-letter sequences can be made: AA, AT, AG, AC, TT, TA, TG, TC, etc. Therefore, the code words must be at least 3 letters long. From 4 bases, 64 different 3-letter sequences can be made. This is, of course, more than are needed. Research has shown that the code for specifying amino acids does consist of 3-base words, and that most of the amino acids are specified by more than one code word.

27-9 Messenger RNA

We know today that a gene is a long string of bases along the DNA molecule. Each successive group of three bases is a code that specifies a particular amino acid to be added to a polypeptide chain. The code also contains "punctuation"—code words that indicate where a polypeptide starts and

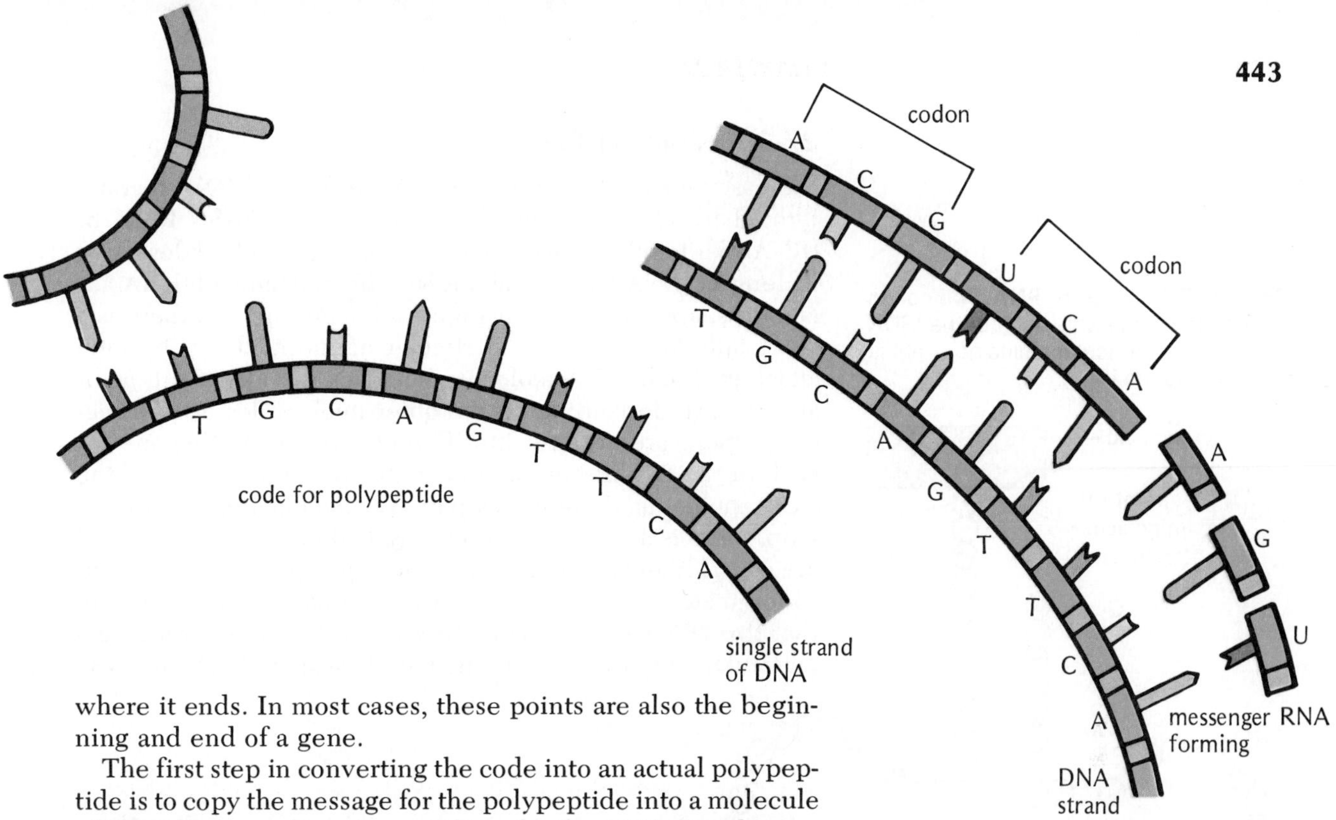

where it ends. In most cases, these points are also the beginning and end of a gene.

The first step in converting the code into an actual polypeptide is to copy the message for the polypeptide into a molecule of RNA. To copy the polypeptide code, the DNA strands temporarily separate (see Figure 27-6). Complementary RNA nucleotides then take their places along one of the exposed strands, in the same way that DNA is replicated during cell division. When the assembled RNA sequence reaches the end of the polypeptide message, it is detached from the DNA strand. The RNA strand is now a separate molecule carrying the complete message for a single polypeptide, although in complementary form; that is, each A of the DNA is represented by a U, each T by an A, each G by a C, and each C by a G. A strand of RNA of this type is called **messenger RNA,** or mRNA. The copying of a genetic message into a molecule of mRNA is called **transcription** (trans-*krip*-shun). Each group of three bases that specifies an amino acid is called a **codon** (*koh*-dahn). The complete genetic code is given in Table 27-1.

Figure 27-6. Transcription of a Gene. The code for each polypeptide is copied from one of the DNA strands into a strand of messenger RNA. The copying process is similar to DNA replication, except that uracil replaces thymine as a complement for adenine.

Table 27-1. The Genetic Code. Most of the amino acids are specified by more than one codon. For example, GCU, GCC, and GCA all code for the amino acid alanine.

Amino acid	Genetic code	Amino acid	Genetic code
phenylalanine	UUU, UUC	methionine	AUG
leucine	UUA, UUG, CUU, CUC, CUA, CUG	threonine	ACU, ACC, ACA, ACG
serine	UCU, UCC, UCA, UCG, AGU, AGC	asparagine	AAU, AAC
tyrosine	UAU, UAC	lysine	AAA, AAG
cysteine	UGU, UGC	valine	GUU, GUC, GUA, GUG
tryptophan	UGG	alanine	GCU, GCC, GCA, GCG
proline	CCU, CCC, CCA, CCG	aspartic acid	GAU, GAC
histidine	CAU, CAC	glutamic acid	GAA, GAG
glutamine	CAA, CAG	glycine	GGU, GGC, GGA, GGG
arginine	CGU, CGC, CGA, CGG, AGA, AGG	stop	UAA, UAG, UGA
isoleucine	AUU, AUC, AUA		

27-10 Transfer RNA

Messenger RNA is only one of three types of RNA that are formed by DNA. A second type is called **transfer RNA,** or tRNA. While mRNA may have thousands of nucleotides along its length, tRNA has only about 80. The molecule of tRNA has an odd shape, as shown in Figure 27-7. At one end there is a short tail. At this end, a particular amino acid can become attached. Each tRNA molecule will pick up only one type of amino acid, depending on the other nucleotides of its structure. There are at least 20 different forms of tRNA, one for each of the 20 different amino acids. At the other end of the tRNA molecule, there is a loop of exposed nucleotides. In this loop, there is a sequence of 3 bases, called an **anticodon,** that are complements of a mRNA codon. The codon that this anticodon matches is one that specifies the particular amino acid that this tRNA carries. Thus tRNA is a device for bringing a particular amino acid to a particular place specified by mRNA.

Figure 27-7. Transfer RNA. The codon that matches the anticodon of the tRNA calls for the particular amino acid that is attached to the tRNA.

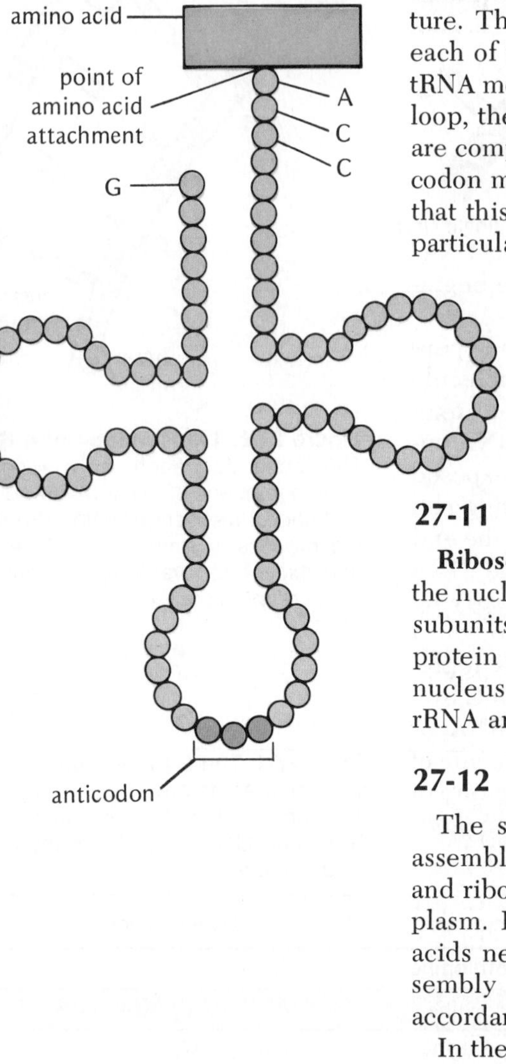

27-11 Ribosomal RNA

Ribosomal RNA, or rRNA, is RNA that is formed by DNA in the nucleoli of the cell. A ribosome consists of protein and two subunits of rRNA, one larger than the other. The ribosomal protein is made in the cytoplasm and then migrates into the nucleus. In the nucleoli, the protein and the two subunits of rRNA are combined to form complete ribosomes.

27-12 Assembly of a Polypeptide

The synthesis of the three kinds of RNA, as well as the assembly of ribosomes, occurs in the cell nucleus. The RNA and ribosomes migrate through the nuclear pores to the cytoplasm. In the cytoplasm, there is a supply of all the amino acids needed to synthesize the cell's proteins. Here, the assembly of polypeptides for those proteins is carried out in accordance with the instructions carried by mRNA.

In the cytoplasm, amino acid molecules become attached to their specific varieties of tRNA (see Figure 27-8). Ribosomes become attached to each strand of mRNA at intervals along its length. Where a ribosome is attached to mRNA, a molecule of tRNA with the right anticodon temporarily becomes attached to the corresponding codon on the mRNA. The amino acid brought into position by the tRNA joins the last amino acid in the forming chain and separates from tRNA. The ribosome then moves along to the next codon. A new tRNA takes its place

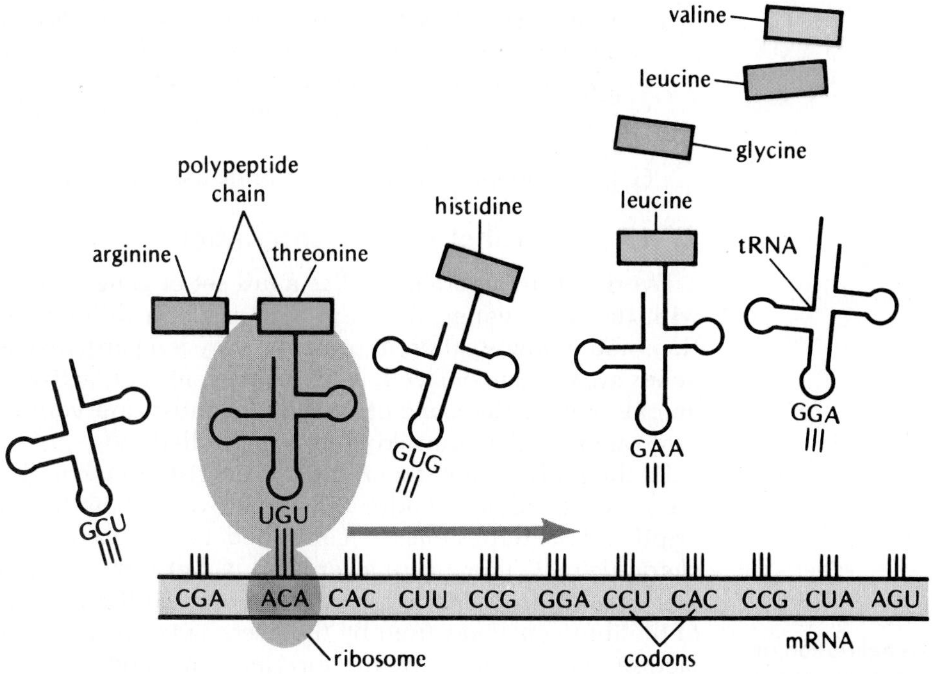

Figure 27-8. Protein Synthesis. As a ribosome moves into position at a codon of a messenger RNA, a transfer RNA with the complementary anticodon temporarily bonds to the codon. The tRNA adds its amino acid to the polypeptide chain, then detaches and moves away.

on the mRNA strand, and its amino acid joins the polypeptide chain. As the ribosome moves along, the tRNA that has served its purpose is released. It is now free to pick up another amino acid molecule and repeat its function. Amino acids continue to be added to the growing polypeptide chain until the ribosome reaches a "stop" codon. The polypeptide is then released and assembles itself into a complete protein molecule. By this remarkable system, all the cell's proteins are synthesized in the cytoplasm, while the chromosomes carrying the hereditary instructions for this synthesis remain in the nucleus.

Every step in the process of translating the genetic message into a polypeptide chain is assisted by a specific enzyme. There are enzymes that attach amino acids to tRNA. There are enzymes that attach tRNA to mRNA. There are enzymes that join the amino acids to the polypeptide chain. There are also enzymes in the nucleus that open up the DNA molecule for transcription, and others that assist in the assembly of RNA. All of these enzymes must themselves be specified by genes.

Transcription is the process by which the base sequence of a DNA segment is used for the production of RNA, thereby transferring genetic information to RNA. *Translation* is the process by which the information coded in the RNA molecule is used for the assembly of a particular sequence of amino acids, forming a polypeptide.

THE GENE

After completing your study of this section, you should be able to:

1. Define the following terms: *operator, repressor, gene mutation,* and *mutagenic agent.*

2. Discuss the gene mutation that causes sickle-cell anemia.
3. Name two cytoplasmic organelles that can replicate.
4. Define the following terms: *recombinant DNA, plasmid, transformation,* and *transduction*.
5. Explain how plasmids are used in transferring new genes to bacteria.
6. Describe the techniques currently used for cloning.

27-13 Control of Gene Transcription

Every cell in an organism has a full set of genes. But even with the same genes, different cells perform different functions and produce different proteins. Why is a particular set of genes activated in one cell, while a different set is activated in another cell of the same organism? Scientists are very interested in how gene transcription is controlled.

In the early 1960s, the French biologists Francois Jacob, Jacques Monod, and André Lwoff discovered how the transcription of certain genes is controlled in the bacterium *Escherichia coli*. They were awarded a Nobel prize in 1965 for their work. Jacob, Monod, and Lwoff studied the production of the three enzymes used by the bacteria to digest the sugar lactose. They found that the enzymes are produced by the bacteria only when they are needed—that is, when lactose is present. Thus, enzyme production is turned on and off, depending on the needs of the cell.

Jacob, Monod, and Lwoff determined that production of the lactose-digesting enzymes is regulated by a cluster of genes (see Figure 27-9). The amino acid sequences of the enzymes are determined by three structural genes. A *structural gene* is

Figure 27-9. Gene Transcription in Bacteria. In *E. coli* the synthesis of lactose-digesting enzymes is controlled by a cluster of genes. The enzymes themselves are synthesized by structural genes. The activity of the structural genes is controlled by an operator gene, which in turn is controlled by a protein repressor synthesized by a regulator gene.

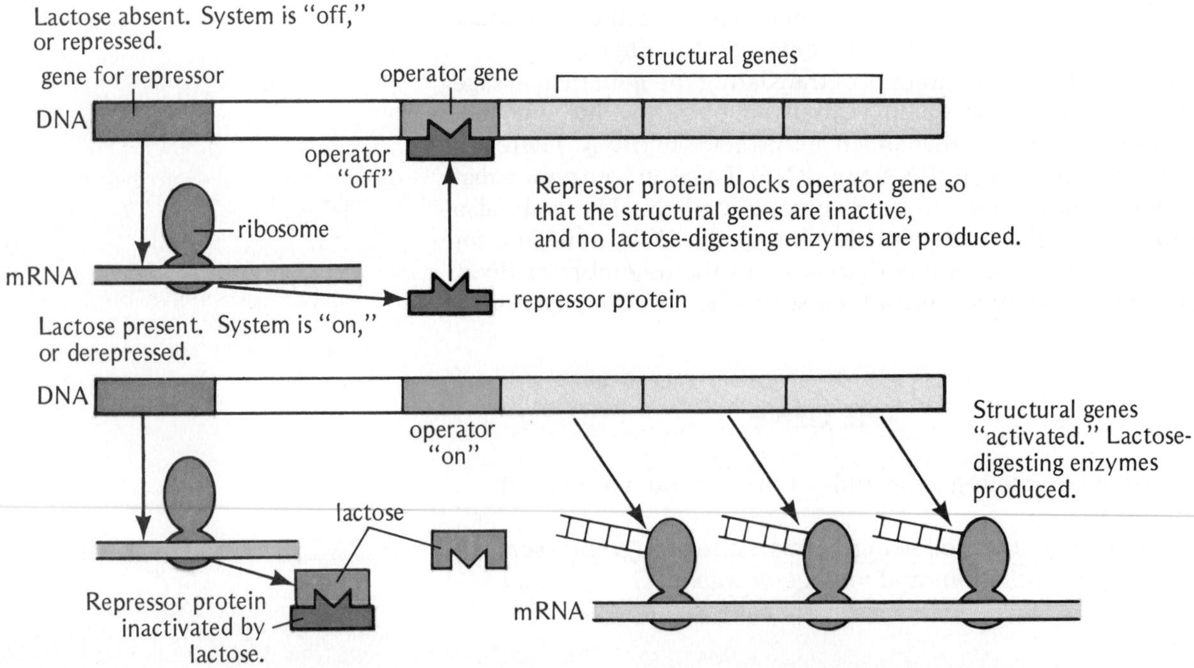

a DNA segment that codes for the production of a particular polypeptide.

The investigators found that the activity of the structural genes is controlled by an *operator gene,* a sequence of nucleotides found next to the structural genes. The structural genes cannot be transcribed unless the operator gene is in an active state. We can think of the operator as being switched "on" to cause transcription, or switched "off" to prevent transcription.

The activity of the operator is controlled by a protein called a *repressor.* The repressor is the product of yet another gene, called a *regulator gene.* When the repressor binds to the operator gene, transcription of the structural genes cannot start. The repressor protein is always present in the cell, and it is normally bound to the operator gene so that the operator is off. Lactose binds to the repressor protein, making it unable to bind to the operator gene. Therefore, when lactose is present, the operator gene is turned on, transcription of the structural genes proceeds, and the lactose-digesting enzymes are produced.

The digestion of the lactose reduces the amount present in the cell. When the amount of lactose becomes too small to inactivate the repressor, the repressor once again binds to the operator and switches it off. Transcription of the genes stops and the cell stops making the digestive enzymes. Thus the synthesis of the digestive enzymes is switched on when they are needed to digest lactose, and switched off when the lactose is gone and they are no longer needed. This is a clear example of control by negative feedback.

Remember that all the genes of a bacterial cell are on a single chromosome in direct contact with the cytoplasm, since there is no nucleus. The genetic control mechanisms in bacteria are probably much simpler than in cells with nuclei and many chromosomes. Very little is known as yet about the ways in which genes are switched on and off in eucaryotic cells.

27-14 Gene Mutations

Genes function by specifying the order of amino acids in a polypeptide chain for a certain protein. These instructions are coded into the sequence of bases along a DNA strand. Any change in this sequence is likely to change the message transcribed into mRNA and change the structure of a protein that the cell is to make. Such changes are called **gene mutations.** Once a mutation occurs in a DNA molecule, it is copied through all the later replications of the DNA. A mutation in a sex cell can be passed to future generations.

It is believed that gene mutations occur from time to time at random in all cells. Mutations in individual body cells are usually of no importance, since they are not likely to affect other cells or the functions of the organism as a whole. If a single cell loses the ability to make a certain protein, the cell may die, or it may obtain the protein from the intercellular fluid. In either case, nothing noticeable happens. Mutations in sex cells are another matter. If a mutation is present in a gamete at the time of fertilization, all the cells of the embryo and the developed organism will have the mutation in at least half of their DNA.

Inherited mutations are usually recessive. Only about 1 in 100 gene mutations is dominant. Most mutations are harmful to the organism. The genes of a normal individual already meet the needs of the organism. Any change is likely to result in the production of a useless protein, or none at all, in place of one that is useful and necessary.

Causes of mutations. Mutations that produce observable changes in traits have been studied in *Drosophila* and in other organisms. Each type of mutation seems to occur at a definite, low rate in large populations. All the causes of natural mutation are not known. They may simply be the result of random errors in replication of the DNA.

Factors in the environment that cause mutations are called **mutagenic agents.** Hermann Muller, a student of T. H. Morgan, found that he could greatly increase the rate of mutation in fruit flies by exposing them to X rays. Other forms of radiation, and chemicals such as chloroform and mustard gas, are also known to be mutagenic agents. Natural mutations may be partly the result of mutagenic agents in the environment.

Figure 27-10. Sickle and Normal Red Blood Cells. The normal red cells are round and thinner in the center than around the outside. The elongated, crescent-shaped cells are the sickle cells.

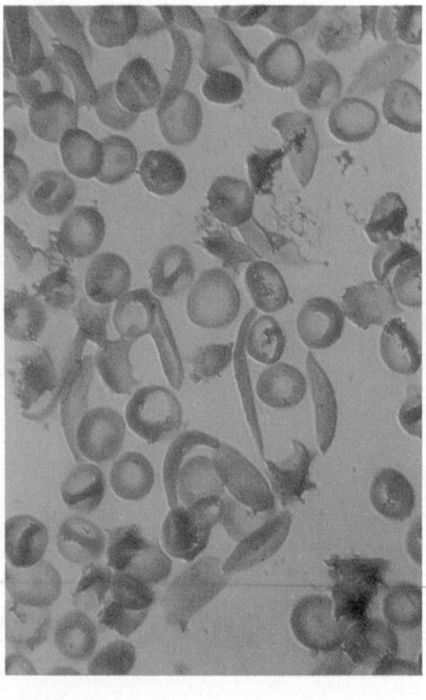

Types of gene mutations. There are various ways in which the base sequence of a gene may change and thus result in a mutation. An entire nucleotide may be added or removed at some point. Such a change would be quite drastic, since all the triplet codons beyond that point would be changed. The gene would probably be completely useless and the organism would be missing the protein it specifies. Alkaptonuria, PKU, and many other inherited diseases may be the result of gene mutations of this kind.

In other cases, one base could be substituted for another. This changes just one codon, and changes just one amino acid in the protein specified. Changing one amino acid may result in a protein that is only partially effective for its function.

Sickle cell anemia. Sickle cell anemia is caused by the change of one base in the gene that controls the production of one of the polypeptide chains in the hemoglobin molecule. There are about 300 amino acids in this chain. The change in one base changes the codon for one amino acid at a particular point in the chain. The normal codon is GAA, which places the amino acid glutamic acid in the chain. The mutant codon is GUA, which puts valine in place of glutamic acid. Hemoglobin made from the altered polypeptide does not carry oxygen as well as normal hemoglobin. The shape of the molecule is also different. It causes the red blood cells to have a distorted form that tends to make them catch and clump together in the small blood vessels (see Figure 27-10).

27-15 DNA Outside the Nucleus

Figure 27-11. A Chloroplast Dividing.

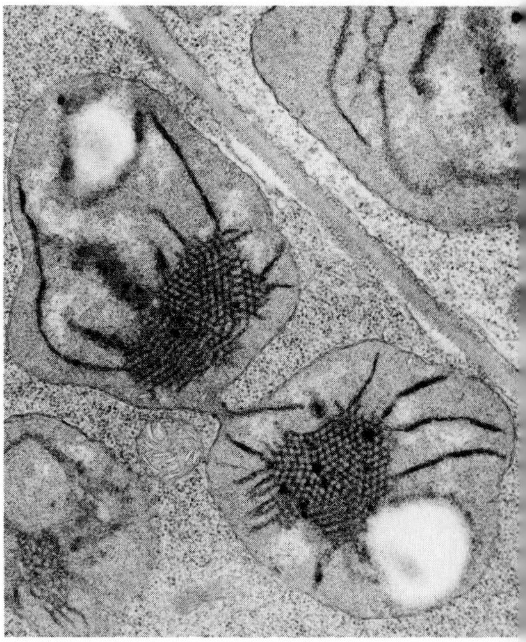

While most hereditary material is located in the nucleus of a cell, biologists have found that certain cell organelles carry genetic information. This is called *cytoplasmic DNA*. The DNA-containing organelles are chloroplasts and mitochondria. The nucleic acids in these organelles seem to code for the synthesis of materials needed for their functions—for photosynthesis and cellular respiration. The DNA in the nucleus still influences the organelles, however.

When a cell divides by mitotic division, each daughter cell receives about half the organelles in the parent cell. As the daughter cells grow, the mitochondria and chloroplasts reproduce themselves (see Figures 27-11). The DNA of these organelles also replicates to keep the new organelles supplied with their own DNA.

In the fusion of gametes in sexual reproduction, all the organelles of the zygote come from the egg cell, because of its much greater size. Thus while both parents contribute equally to the nuclear DNA of the offspring, all the cytoplasmic DNA comes from the female parent.

Because mitochondria and chloroplasts have their own DNA and are able to reproduce, some biologists speculate that these organelles were once free-living. At some early stage in the development of cells, they may have become incorporated into cells. They then became specialized for their functions inside cells, lost the DNA they no longer needed, and lost the capacity to survive outside cells.

27-16 Transformation and Transduction

Transformation and transduction are processes by which DNA is transferred from one bacterial cell to another. In **transformation,** living bacteria take in DNA from dead bacteria. The DNA causes traits of the dead bacteria to show in the living bacterial cells. In Griffith's experiments, type R bacteria were transformed by DNA from dead Type S bacteria. Transformation occurs in nature as well as in laboratory experiments. Pieces of DNA can also be transferred from one bacterial cell to another by viruses. This process is called **transduction.** Transduction occurs when a piece of bacterial DNA becomes incorporated into the virus particle. When the virus infects a new cell, it carries the piece of the DNA from its previous host cell.

27-17 Genetic Engineering

One of the most remarkable outcomes of the understanding of the gene has been the development of methods for changing the DNA of a cell. The altered DNA is called **recombinant DNA**, and the procedures for producing the altered DNA are often referred to as **genetic engineering,** or more popularly as **gene splicing.** The latter term is quite descriptive of the methods being used at this time. They involve breaking a DNA molecule and inserting or attaching a new gene by means of a chemical "splice."

One of the long-range goals of genetic engineering is to correct genetic defects by transferring normal genes to cells that lack them. Hereditary diseases could possibly be treated in this way. Another goal is to give desired properties to plants and animals that are raised for food or other human purposes. However, at this time the techniques are limited to gene transplants in bacteria and other simple organisms.

Plasmids. Some of the methods of transferring genes to bacteria make use of transformation and transduction. Another important method involves small, ring-shaped segments of DNA called **plasmids.** Many bacteria either contain plasmids or will take plasmids into their cytoplasm from a surrounding medium. Inside the bacteria, the plasmids remain separate from the bacterial chromosome. However, the plasmids include genes that affect the metabolism and traits of the organism. For example, some plasmids have a gene for producing an enzyme that destroys penicillin. Bacteria containing these plasmids are resistant to penicillin; they are not killed by it. Plasmids are replicated along with the chromosomes at every cell division. Thus a single bacterium with a particular plasmid can produce large colonies of cells with the properties conferred by that plasmid.

To transfer a new gene to bacteria, plasmids are first obtained from bacterial cells. This can be accomplished by crushing the bacteria and sorting out the contents by centrifugation or other methods. The plasmids are placed in a solution containing the gene (DNA fragment) to be transplanted (see Figure 27-12). The genes are usually obtained from animals, although in some cases the genes have actually been made by chemically assembling nucleotides in the proper sequence. An enzyme called a *restriction enzyme* is then used to break open the plasmid ring. The free genes in the solution tend to attach themselves to the open ends of the plasmid, thus closing the ring again. The plasmid now includes the new gene.

Bacteria are then exposed to the altered plasmids, and many of the bacteria will take them in. Once inside the bacterial cells, the transplanted genes begin to be expressed. The bacteria produce the protein specified by the gene. This protein may be any one of a number of desirable products that are difficult or expensive to obtain by other means. Among the proteins that are currently the object of research efforts are insulin, human growth hormone, and human interferon. Interferon is a substance produced by the body tissues that provides defense against virus infections and possibly against some forms of cancer. Several companies have formed in recent years to develop recombinant DNA technology on a commercial scale. Some of the new forms of bacteria produced

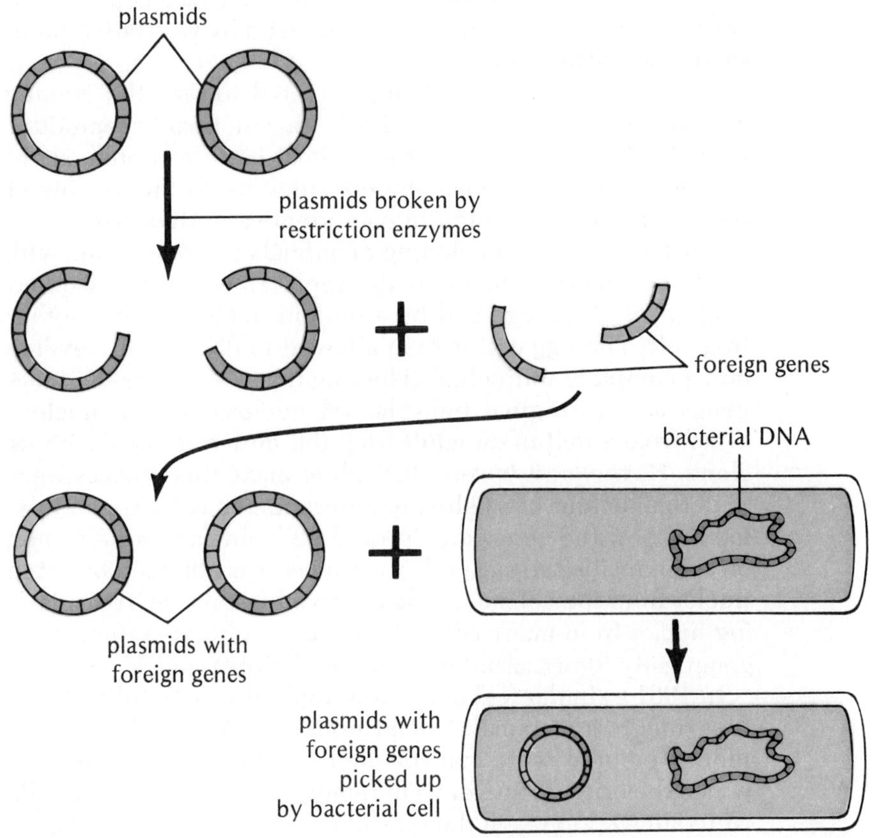

Figure 27-12. Using Plasmids to Transfer Foreign Genes to Bacterial Cells.

by this research have even been patented.

Dangers of recombinant DNA. Many scientists, including those working in the field, are aware of possible danger from research with recombinant DNA. In these experiments, new forms of microorganisms are produced. It is possible that an organism will be accidentally produced with the ability to cause an entirely new kind of human disease, against which the body will have no natural defenses. The escape of such an organism into the environment could lead to a massive, uncontrollable epidemic. To prevent this type of accident, the federal government and the scientists involved in recombinant DNA research have established rules and safeguards that must be observed. These rules are under constant study, and it is considered extremely unlikely that the accidental release of a harmful organism will ever occur. Still, the risk, however slight, does exist. Most informed people agree today that the potential benefits of genetic engineering far outweigh the risks, and this research is likely to continue.

27-18 Cloning

A **clone** is a group of individual organisms that have exactly the same genes. Organisms that reproduce asexually produce clones, since each offspring receives an exact copy of the genes of the parent. New plants produced by vegetative propagation are also clones.

Much research is now being directed toward the cloning (production of clones) in animals that normally reproduce sexually. Every body cell of an animal has a complete set of the genes that the animal started life with. In theory, any of these cells could develop into an identical individual.

Most of the work on cloning of animals has been done with frogs. The method involves the replacement of the haploid nucleus of a frog egg cell by a diploid nucleus from another frog cell. The egg cell is then allowed to divide and develop into a complete individual. The frog that results has the same genes as the original transplanted nucleus. If that nucleus came from a cell of an adult frog, the new frog would be its clone. However, it is very difficult to make this process work with the nucleus of an already differentiated cell. Apparently, too many of the genes are "turned off" and cannot be turned on again inside the egg cell. Most success is obtained by using nuclei from the cells of a frog embryo blastula. By transplanting nuclei from many cells of the same blastula, a number of genetically identical individuals can be obtained.

In 1981 a similar technique was applied successfully for the first time to a mammal. Nuclei from cells of the blastula of a mouse embryo were transplanted to mouse egg cells from which the original nuclei were removed. The altered egg cells were allowed to reach the blastula stage in a culture medium and were then transferred to the uteruses of female mice to complete their development.

The objective of these cloning experiments is not what some science fiction writers describe—the cloning of humans with certain special traits. The true purpose is to produce large numbers of genetically identical laboratory animals for research. Such animals with known and controlled heredity would be useful in the study of cancer, aging, birth defects, and the regeneration of damaged body parts, as well as in adding to our understanding of development.

summary

The hereditary information is carried by the DNA of the chromosomes. DNA, which is made up of nucleotides, is in the form of a double helix. The two parallel chains of sugar-phosphate groups are linked by pairs of nitrogen bases. In replication of DNA, the bonds between the base pairs are broken, and the two DNA strands separate. Free nucleotides join with complementary bases on the exposed strands, thereby forming two double-stranded molecules identical to the original.

According to the one gene—one polypeptide hypothesis, each gene directs the synthesis of a particular polypeptide chain. This information is encoded in the sequence of bases in the DNA molecule. Each type of amino acid is specified by a particular sequence of three bases—a codon. By transcription, the genetic information of the DNA is copied into mRNA. The mRNA passes from the nucleus into the cytoplasm.

In the cytoplasm, ribosomes become attached to different parts of the mRNA. Molecules of tRNA carry amino acids to the mRNA. The amino acids are aligned in a sequence determined by the base sequence of the mRNA. Enzymes from the ribosomes join the amino acid molecules together to form polypeptides.

Any change in the sequence of bases in a DNA strand is a gene mutation. A mutation may involve the addition, deletion, or substitution of bases in the DNA.

Genetic engineering involves the deliberate altering of the DNA of living cells. Through the use of plasmids, bacteria have been induced to synthesize proteins from nonbacterial cells. It is hoped that in the future, this method can be used to produce specific proteins for medical use or even for the treatment of certain diseases.

A clone is a group of organisms that have identical genetic makeup. Successful cloning of frogs and mice has been done using nuclei from blastulas transplanted into egg cells from which the nuclei have been removed. However, no experiments so far have been able to produce clones from the body cells of adult animals.

vocabulary

adenine
anticodon
clone
codon
cytosine
deoxyribose
gene splicing
genetic engineering
guanine
helix
messenger RNA
mutagenic agent
nucleotide
one gene—one polypeptide hypothesis
plasmid
purine
pyrimidine
recombinant DNA
ribose
ribosomal RNA
thymine
transcription
transduction
transfer RNA
transformation
uracil

test your learning

Section
27-1

1. Briefly describe the experiments of Frederick Griffith with pneumococcus.
2. What evidence did Avery, MacLeod, and McCarty provide for the idea that DNA carries the hereditary information?
3. How did Hershey and Chase use viruses and bacteria to show definitely that DNA carries the hereditary information?

27-2 **4.** Name the component parts of the DNA molecule.
27-3 **5.** Describe the Watson-Crick model of the DNA molecule.
6. Why are the two strands of a DNA molecule said to be *complementary?*
27-4 **7.** Describe how a DNA molecule replicates.
27-5 **8.** Compare the chemical composition and structure of RNA with that of DNA.
27-6 **9.** What controls the production of enzymes by the cell?
27-7 **10.** Describe the experiments of Beadle and Tatum.
11. What is the one gene—one polypeptide hypothesis?
27-8 **12.** In what form is the hereditary information encoded in the DNA molecule?
13. What is a codon?
27-9 **14.** Describe the synthesis of messenger RNA.
15. What is accomplished by the process of transcription?
27-10 **16.** Where is transfer RNA located in the cell, and what is its function?
27-11 **17.** Describe the assembly of a ribosome.
27-12 **18.** Describe how messenger RNA, transfer RNA, and ribosomes function in the synthesis of a polypeptide.
27-13 **19.** Describe how the operator and repressor function in controlling the synthesis of lactose-digesting enzymes in *E. coli.*
27-14 **20.** What is a gene mutation?
21. What are some causes of gene mutations?
22. What types of changes can occur in the DNA in gene mutations?
23. What type of gene mutation occurs in sickle-cell anemia?
27-15 **24.** Which two types of cell organelles contain DNA?
25. In what way do the DNA-containing organelles differ from other types of cell organelles?
27-16 **26.** Describe the processes of transformation and transduction.
27-17 **27.** What is recombinant DNA?
28. What are plasmids, and how are they being used in genetic engineering?
27-18 **29.** What is a clone?

test your understanding

1. How do the genes control cell metabolism?
2. List the three types of RNA found in the cell. For each, state where it is synthesized and describe its function.
3. Describe each of the processes in cell metabolism in which the pairing of complementary bases occurs.
4. Discuss the experimental evidence that led to the understanding that the DNA of the chromosomes contains the hereditary information.

independent research

1. Prepare a report on the use of gene-splicing techniques for the commercial production of insulin and other drugs.
2. Prepare a report on the cloning of frogs and mice.

UNIT 6
EVOLUTION

chapter 28

Evidence of Organic Change

28-1 Chapter Introduction

The term *evolution* means a gradual change from one state to another. Since its formation about 4½ billion years ago, the earth itself has undergone continual change, a process called **geologic evolution.** Much evidence indicates that living things have also undergone continuous change since they first appeared on the earth, a process called **organic evolution.** This chapter is concerned with the various types of evidence of organic evolution and the theories that have been proposed to account for it.

THE EVIDENCE OF FOSSILS

After completing your study of this section, you should be able to:

1. Define the term *fossil.*
2. Describe at least five different processes by which fossils may be formed.
3. Explain how sedimentary rocks are formed and what the age relationships are among the layers of such rocks.

4. Explain what is meant by relative dating of rocks and fossils.
5. State the characteristics of an index fossil and explain how index fossils are used for relative dating of rocks.
6. State two important conclusions that can be drawn from the fossil record.
7. Name the chief method used to determine the actual age of rocks.

28-2 The Formation of Fossils

A **fossil** is the actual remains or any trace of an organism that lived at some time in the past. The study of fossils provided the first, and still the strongest, evidence of organic evolution. Fossils have been formed in many different ways. In some cases, an entire organism has been preserved with almost no decay, but in the great majority of cases, the soft tissues of the fossil organism have completely disappeared, and only the hard parts, such as bones or shells, have been preserved.

Preservation in amber. Some trees produce a sticky, gumlike resin that hardens into a transparent yellow material called **amber.** Insects often become trapped and embedded in the resin, and they are found preserved in the amber (see Figure 28-1).

Preservation in ice. In very cold Arctic regions, the frozen remains of various animals have been preserved nearly intact for thousands of years. The 25,000-year-old remains of woolly mammoths are so well preserved that their flesh, skin, and hair are present.

Preserved hard parts. Although the soft tissues of animals quickly decay if exposed to bacteria, the hard parts made mostly of mineral substances can remain unchanged for millions of years. Dinosaur bones estimated to be more than 100 million years old have been found (see Figure 28-2).

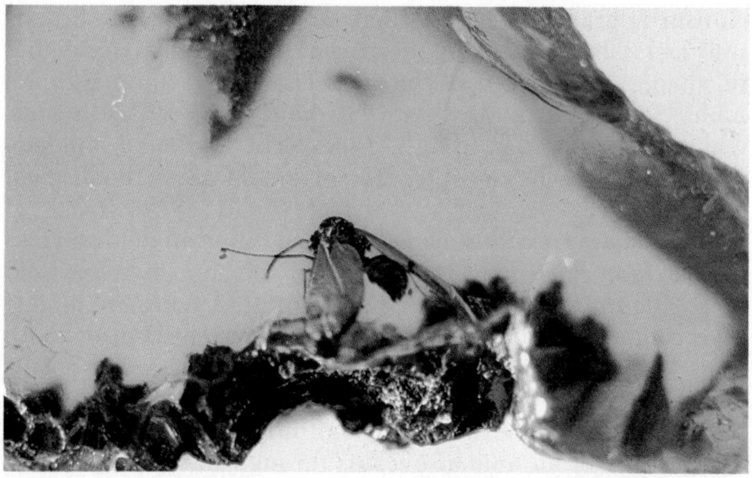

Photograph by Carolina Biological Supply Company

Figure 28-1. Insect Fossil Preserved in Amber.

Figure 28-2. Dinosaur Bones.

Many animal skeletons have also been preserved in pools of tar in which the animals had been trapped. Thousands of such fossils have been found in the **La Brea tar pits** in Los Angeles. Although most of these animals lived less than 25,000 years ago, they include many now extinct species, such as the saber-toothed tiger and the mammoth.

Petrifaction. In some cases, a dead organism lies in a body of water containing a high mineral content. Gradually, the original substances of the organism are dissolved away and replaced by minerals from the water. By this process, which is called **petrifaction** (peh-truh-*fak*-shun), the remains of the organism are turned to stone. Sometimes only the exterior form of the structures of the organism are preserved in stone. In other cases, fine details of internal structure can be seen in the petrified fossil. Whole trees estimated to be 150 million years old have been preserved as stone fossils in the Petrified Forest in Arizona (see Figure 28-3). Many fossil bones are petrified—stone replicas of the original bones.

Figure 28-3. Petrified Trees.

Molds and casts. By far the greatest number of fossils form on the bottoms of lakes and seas. The dead organism sinks and comes to rest in the sandy or muddy bottom. As additional particles of sand or mud accumulate on the bottom, the organism is gradually buried. The sand or mud later hardens into rock. Meanwhile, the remains of the organism decay, but its shape is preserved in the rock as a hollow form called a **mold.** Sometimes a mold later becomes filled with minerals, which in turn harden to form a rock. The hardened minerals form a **cast,** which is a copy of the external form of the original organism.

Imprints. Impressions made by living things in mud, such as animal footprints, may remain when the mud hardens into rock. The impression is called an **imprint.** Among the largest known imprints are dinosaur footprints (see Figure 28-4). Many imprints have also been left by thin structures, such as leaves.

Other traces. Some fossils are nothing more than traces of the passage of an animal over or through the rock material.

Worms, for example, have left fossils in the form of tubes in rock that hardened after the worms had burrowed through mud or soil.

28-3 Sedimentary Rocks

A very large fraction of all known fossils have been found in the kind of rock called **sedimentary** (sed-uh-*ment*-uh-ree) **rock.** To understand the importance of this fact, it is necessary to know how sedimentary rocks are formed. Most sedimentary rocks form on the bottom of shallow seas or on ocean bottoms along the shorelines of continents. Rivers flowing into these bodies of water carry fine particles of rock called *sediments.* These sediments have been eroded, or worn away, from the land over which the rivers flow. When the river waters enter the sea, the sediments slowly settle to the bottom. This "rain" of sediments gradually builds up a deposit on the sea bottom, sometimes to very great depths. By various chemical processes, combined with the pressure exerted by the weight of the sediments, the material slowly hardens into rock.

This process may continue for tens of millions of years at any particular location. The size and mineral composition of the sediments being deposited by the rivers will usually change from time to time. Therefore, the sedimentary rock acquires a layered structure. Some layers may be formed from fine clay or silt. Others will be made of coarse sand particles. Different mineral content will give different colors or chemical properties to the various layers. Whatever the sequence of the layers may be, one statement can be made about them. The oldest layers, that is, those laid down first, are at the bottom. The youngest, or most recent, are at the top. The layers in between are arranged in a time sequence from older below to younger above (see Figure 28-5).

Geologists have concluded that the crust of the earth is constantly changing and shifting. Portions of the crust that are

Figure 28-4. Dinosaur Footprints.

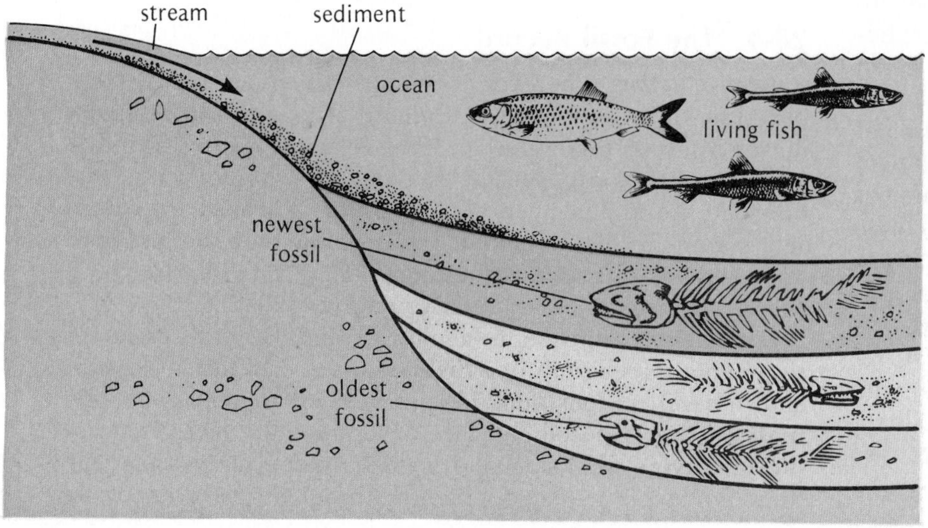

Figure 28-5. Deposition of Sediments. Streams flowing into a body of water carry fine rock particles called sediments. These sediments settle to the bottom and may gradually build up to a great thickness. The bodies of dead organisms that settle to the bottom may become fossils embedded in the sediments. The oldest fossils will be in the lowest layers and the youngest will be in the upper layers.

Figure 28-6. Sedimentary Rock. The layers of this rock formation were formed from sediments deposited under water. Shifts in the earth's crust then raised the rock layers without disturbing their order. Each layer is older than those above it.

under the seas at one time are later pushed up to form mountains and plateaus. Layers of sedimentary rock formed at some past time are thus exposed to view at many places on the earth (see Figure 28-6). Sometimes this exposure is simply the side of a mountain or plateau. In other cases the exposure occurs where a river has cut its way down through the layers. If the exposed sedimentary layers have not been greatly disturbed by the motions of the crust, they remain in their original sequence. The oldest are at the bottom, and the youngest are at the top. If these sedimentary layers contain fossils (as they usually do), they present a history of life that existed at a particular place during a particular time. This history of life is usually called the **fossil record.**

28-4 The Fossil Record

Relative dating. Wherever layers of sedimentary rock are exposed to view, they present a record of events that occurred during a certain time interval. If the rock layers are still in the original order of deposit, the lower layers were deposited earlier than the upper layers. Fossils in the lower layers represent organisms that lived at an earlier time than the fossils in upper layers. Any method of determining the order in which events occurred is called **relative dating.**

Correlation. Suppose a geologist finds a cliff made of sedimentary rock with five distinct layers of different texture and mineral composition. Then, a few kilometers away, she finds another exposed cliff face of sedimentary rock. Examining the layers of this second formation, she notices that the three top layers are exactly like the three bottom layers of the

careers

Paleontologists locate, identify, and classify fossil organisms. Through the study of fossils, paleontologists learn about the life of the past and also about changes in the earth itself. In the course of their work, paleontologists spend time in the field, locating and very slowly and carefully unearthing the fossils. Other work is done in the laboratory, arranging the fossils, comparing them with other fossils, and classifying them.

Paleontologists work at universities and for museums. Some are employed by oil companies because oil deposits are most often located in rocks that contain particular types of fossils. Many paleontologists have a specialized field of interest, such as invertebrate paleontology (study of invertebrate fossils), vertebrate paleontology (study of vertebrate fossils), or paleobotany (study of plant fossils).

Work as a paleontologist requires a bachelor's degree with courses in geology and paleontology. Most paleontologists also have advanced degrees.

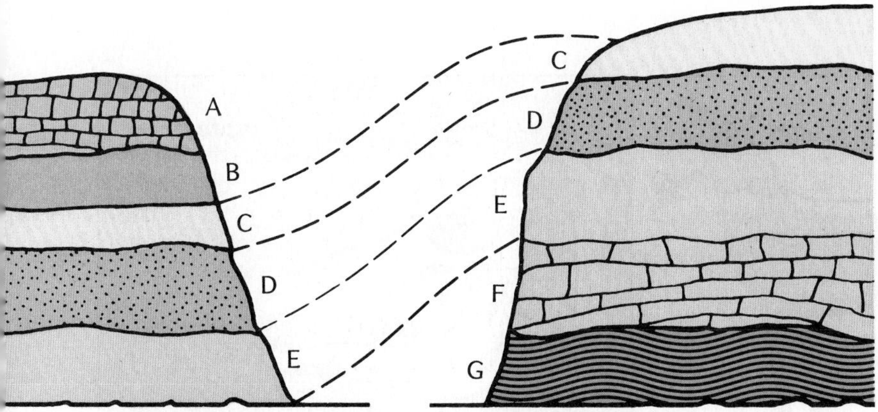

Figure 28-7. Correlation of Separate Rock Formations. Layers C, D, and E on the left have the same composition and thickness as layers C, D, and E on the right. They were probably laid down at the same time. Layers F and G on the right are therefore older than layers A and B on the left.

first formation (see Figure 28-7). They have the same makeup and the same thickness in both places. It is reasonable to conclude that the layers were originally continuous and were deposited at the same time.

Suppose, now, that two more layers are visible below these three in the second cliffside. Those two layers must have been deposited before the other three. They must be older. In fact, they must be older than the bottom three layers of the first cliffside. By this process of matching, or **correlation,** we can show that certain rock layers in one place are older than certain rock layers in another place. It also follows that the fossils in the older layers are older than fossils in the younger layers.

Correlation of sedimentary rocks enables us to establish the relative dating of rocks and fossils in different places. Correlation by comparison of rock layers is, however, limited to a particular local region. The method runs up against a boundary where there are no nearby rocks to continue the correlation. The method can produce a fairly extended relative dating of the rocks and fossils of a region, but cannot provide a correlation with rocks in another section of the continent or another part of the world.

Index fossils. A study of fossils from many regions has shown that certain types of organisms seem to have appeared, flourished for a time over wide regions of the earth, and then disappeared. Rock layers containing fossils of such organisms must therefore have been formed during the period these organisms were in existence. By means of such fossils, it is possible to match the relative ages of sedimentary rocks at widely separated parts of the world. Fossils that permit the relative dating of rocks within a fairly narrow time span are called **index fossils.** Index fossils have enabled scientists to find rock sequences with overlapping time periods from the time of the first fossils up to the very recent past.

Point out that geologists use index fossils to help find oil.

Characteristics of the fossil record. When the entire fossil record is studied, two kinds of important observations can be made. One is that the earliest organisms were relatively simple. As we travel up through the fossil record in time, we find

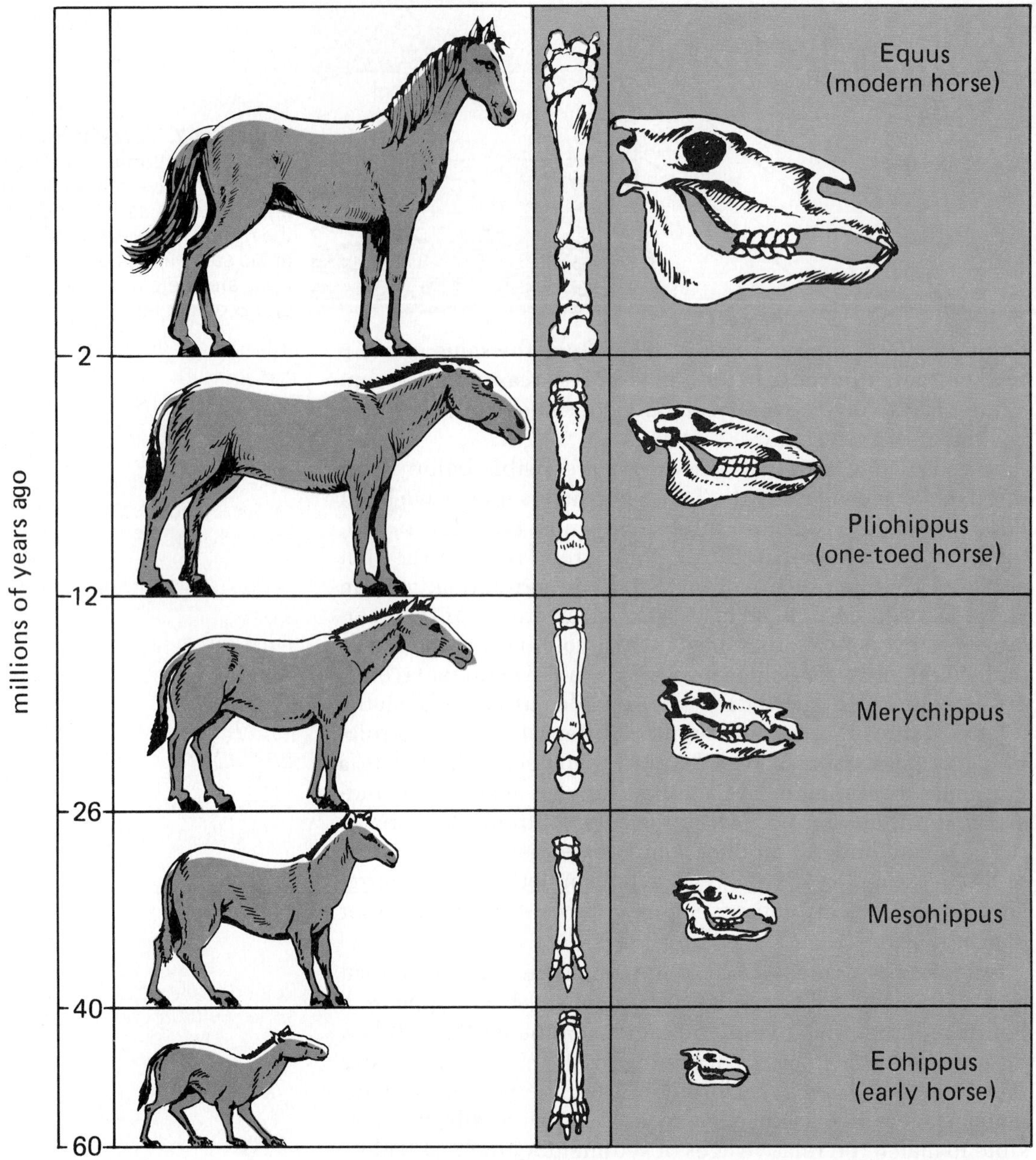

Figure 28-8. Changes in the Horse as Indicated by Fossils of Different Ages.

From the fossil record, it appears that the evolution of the horse proceeded in a definite direction. However, there were many side branches that died out.

the organisms becoming more and more complex. Another observation is that there seems to be a gradual transition from earlier forms to later ones. For example, changes in the structure of the horse have been traced from the first appearance of a horselike mammal through various modifications ending with the modern horse (see Figure 28-8). Many sequences of this kind in the fossil record indicate that later forms developed from earlier forms by a series of changes passed on from generation to generation. The fossil record is thus considered to be strong evidence of organic evolution—the gradual change of species by inherited variations.

28-5 Absolute Dating

Relative dating allows us to say that one type of organism lived earlier than another, but it does not tell us how much earlier. In other words, relative dating does not tell us the actual age of a rock or a fossil in years. Any method that does enable us to find out how long ago an event occurred is called **absolute dating.** Many methods of absolute dating have been tried, but scientists today consider radioactive dating to be the most accurate and reliable method.

Radioactive dating is based on the fact that certain elements have unstable atoms. The nuclei of these atoms tend to break down, or decay, changing to atoms of a different element. During this process, energy is given off in the form of radiation. This process is called **radioactivity.**

The rate at which a radioactive element decays is fixed and unchangeable. The time required for half the atoms of a sample of an element to decay is called the **half-life** of that element. For example, the half-life of uranium-238 is 4.5 billion years. If a rock containing uranium had been formed 4.5 billion years ago, only half the original amount of uranium would be left in the rock today. The other half would have changed to the final decay product of uranium, which is lead. By comparing the amount of lead in a rock with the amount of uranium, it is possible to calculate when that rock formed. Other radioactive elements and their decay products can also be used to date rocks by this method. The existence of different elements that can be used often provides a cross-check on the accuracy of the calculation.

Radioactive dating methods cannot be applied to sedimentary rocks. The only types of rock they can be used on are *igneous* (*ig*-nee-us) rocks—rocks that formed when molten material in the crust cooled and hardened. However, the absolute age of sedimentary rocks can often be estimated by the age of igneous rocks that formed above, below, or within the sedimentary layers.

28-6 The Geologic Time Scale

Through a combination of absolute and relative dating of rocks, geologists have constructed a timetable of the earth's history, which is known as the **geologic time scale.** In this time scale, the earth's history is divided into major divisions called *eras.* Each era is subdivided into *periods* and *epochs.* Table 28-1 shows the main subdivisions of the geologic time scale, along with a brief summary of the types of organisms that appeared, flourished, or disappeared during each time interval.

sidelights

Fossils up to about 40,000 years old can be dated by the carbon-14 method. This method uses the radioisotope carbon-14, which has a half-life of about 5,700 years. Most carbon atoms are the stable isotope carbon-12. However, a small but constant amount of carbon-14 is found in the atmosphere, and it is taken into the tissues of plants in the form of carbon dioxide. Since plants are eaten by animals, animal tissues also contain carbon-14.

As long as the plants and animals are alive, the amount of carbon-14 in their tissues remains constant. When the organisms die, no more carbon-14 is incorporated into their tissues. Instead, the carbon-14 in their remains decays at a steady rate, forming the stable isotope nitrogen-14. The amount of carbon-12 atoms in the remains stays the same. After the death of the organism, the ratio of carbon-14 to carbon-12 becomes smaller and smaller. By determining the relative amounts of carbon-14 and carbon-12 in a fossil, scientists can calculate its age.

Another isotope used to date rocks is potassium-40, which decays into argon-40. Potassium-40 has a half-life of about 1.3 billion years. The oldest rocks that have been dated by the potassium-argon method are about 3.6 billion years old.

Table 28-1. The Geologic Time Scale.

Era		Period (or Epoch)		Millions of years ago	Plant life	Animal life
CENOZOIC ERA	Age of Humans	Quaternary	Recent Epoch	.01	Herbs dominant	Modern humans and modern animals
CENOZOIC ERA	Age of Humans	Quaternary	Pleistocene Epoch	2.5	Trees decrease; herbs increase	Early humans; large mammals become extinct
CENOZOIC ERA	Age of Mammals	Tertiary Period	Pliocene Epoch	12	Grasses increase; herbs appear	Mammals abundant; earliest humans appear
CENOZOIC ERA	Age of Mammals	Tertiary Period	Miocene Epoch	26	Forests decrease; grasses develop	Mammals increase; prehumans appear
CENOZOIC ERA	Age of Mammals	Tertiary Period	Oligocene Epoch	37	Worldwide tropical forests	Modern mammals appear
CENOZOIC ERA	Age of Mammals	Tertiary Period	Eocene Epoch	53	Angiosperms increase	Early mammals at peak
CENOZOIC ERA	Age of Mammals	Tertiary Period	Paleocene Epoch	65	Modern angiosperms appear	Early placental mammals appear; modern birds
MESOZOIC ERA	Age of Reptiles	Cretaceous Period		136	Conifers decrease; flowering plants increase	Large reptiles (dinosaurs) at peak, then disappear; small marsupials; toothed birds; modern fishes
MESOZOIC ERA	Age of Reptiles	Jurassic Period		190	Conifers, cycads dominant; flowering plants appear	Large reptiles spread; first birds; modern sharks and bony fishes; many bivalves
MESOZOIC ERA	Age of Reptiles	Triassic Period		225	Conifers increase; cycads appear	Reptiles increase; first mammals; bony fishes
PALEOZOIC ERA	Age of Amphibians	Permian Period		280	Seed ferns disappear	Amphibians decline; reptiles increase; modern insects
PALEOZOIC ERA	Age of Amphibians	Carboniferous Period		345	Tropical coal forests; seed ferns, conifers	Amphibians dominant; reptiles appear; rise of insects
PALEOZOIC ERA	Age of Fishes	Devonian Period		395	First forests; horsetails, ferns	Early fishes spread; amphibians appear; many mollusks, crabs
PALEOZOIC ERA	Age of Invertebrates	Silurian Period		430	First land plants	Scorpions and spiders (first air-breathers on land)
PALEOZOIC ERA	Age of Invertebrates	Ordovician Period		500	Algae dominant	First vertebrates; worms; some mollusks and echinoderms
PALEOZOIC ERA	Age of Invertebrates	Cambrian Period		570	Algae, fungi; first plant spores	Most invertebrate phyla; trilobites dominant
PRECAMBRIAN				?	Probably bacteria, fungi	A few fossils; sponge spicules; soft-bodied invertebrates

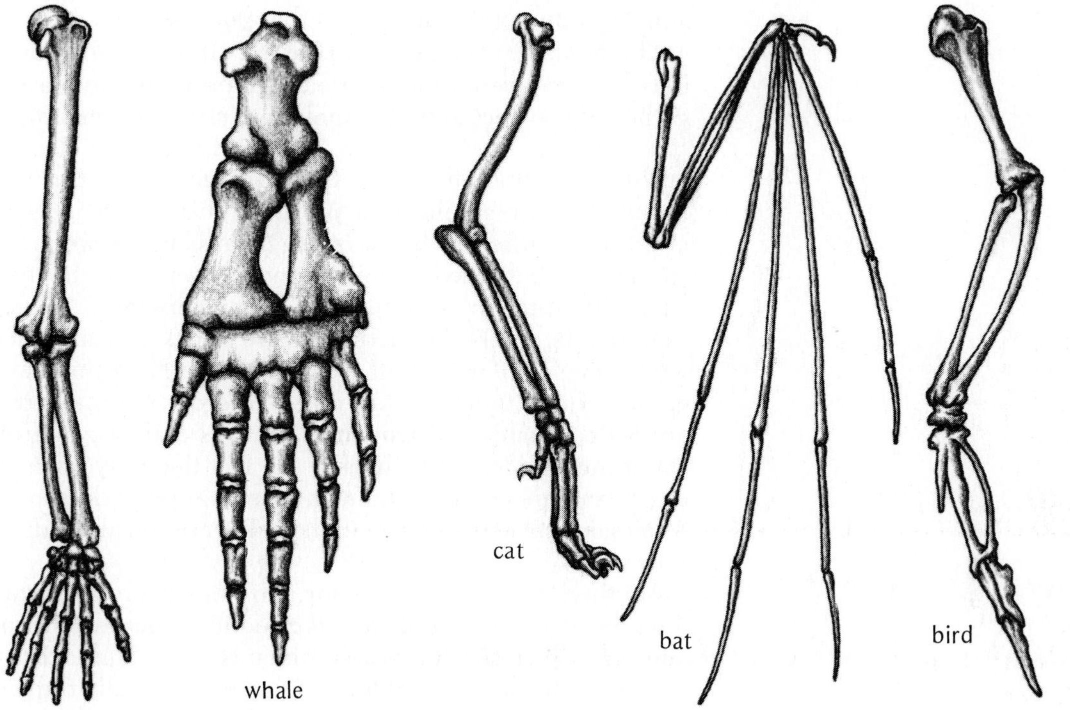

Figure 28-9. Homologous Structures. Although these organs function in different ways, they appear to have developed from the same original structure.

OTHER EVIDENCES OF EVOLUTION

After completing your study of this section, you should be able to explain how studies of comparative anatomy, embryology, and biochemistry provide evidence for evolution.

28-7 Evidence from Comparative Anatomy

Comparative anatomy is the study of structural similarities and differences among living things. The presence of certain types of similarities provides evidence about evolutionary relationships between organisms.

Figure 28-9 shows the structure of the arm and hand of a human, the flipper of a whale, the front leg of a cat, the wing of a bat, and the wing of a bird. These structures are quite different in external form. They are adapted to perform their functions in different ways. The human hand is adapted for grasping and the whale's flipper for swimming. The wings of bats and birds are both adapted for flying. Yet internally, the structures of these organs are surprisingly similar. They have the same number of bones arranged in a similar way. During embryonic development, these structures also form in similar ways. Parts of different organisms that have similar structures and similar embryonic development, but different forms and functions, are called **homologous structures.** Homologous structures are considered to be evidence of evolutionary relationships among the organisms that possess them.

The human, whale, cat, and bat are all mammals. For many reasons they seem to be related and are therefore classed together. We expect to find homologous structures among them. Homologous structures are evidence of evolution along similar lines. On the other hand, there are animals that have similar organs with similar functions, but that otherwise seem to be entirely different kinds of organisms. For example, birds and insects both have wings. In most other respects, they are very different in structure and development. When we examine the internal structure of bird wings and insect wings, we find no similarity at all. Structures that have similar external forms and functions but quite different internal structure are called **analogous structures.** If birds and insects evolved along quite different pathways, the fact that they have analogous structures, but not homologous ones, is understandable. Analogous structures are evidence of evolution along different lines.

Another type of evidence for evolutionary relationships is the presence of **vestigial** (ves-*tihd*-jee-ul) **structures** in modern animals. These structures are remnants of structures that were functional in an ancestral form. They are generally reduced in size and serve little or no function. In the human body, there are more than 100 vestigial structures, including the coccyx, the appendix, the wisdom teeth, and the muscles that move the nose and ears. The human coccyx is made up of fused vertebrae at the end of the spine. It is believed to be an evolutionary remnant of an ancestral reptilian tail. The appendix is believed to be the remnant of a large digestive sac from a vegetarian ancestor. Whales and pythons have vestigial hind leg bones embedded in the flesh of the body wall. Apparently, whales and snakes evolved from four-legged ancestors.

28-8 Evidence from Comparative Embryology

Comparison of the patterns of development of the embryos of different types of organisms can provide evidence of evolutionary relationships. Embryos of organisms believed to be closely related show similar patterns of development. Figure 28-10 shows various stages in the development of the fish, chicken, pig, and human. Note that in these vertebrates, there are many similarities during the early stages of embryonic development. For example, all the embryos have gill slits, two-chambered hearts, and tails. This similarity supports the idea that they have a common evolutionary origin. As development continues, the embryos begin to resemble the adults of their type. The more closely related the animals, the longer they resemble each other during development.

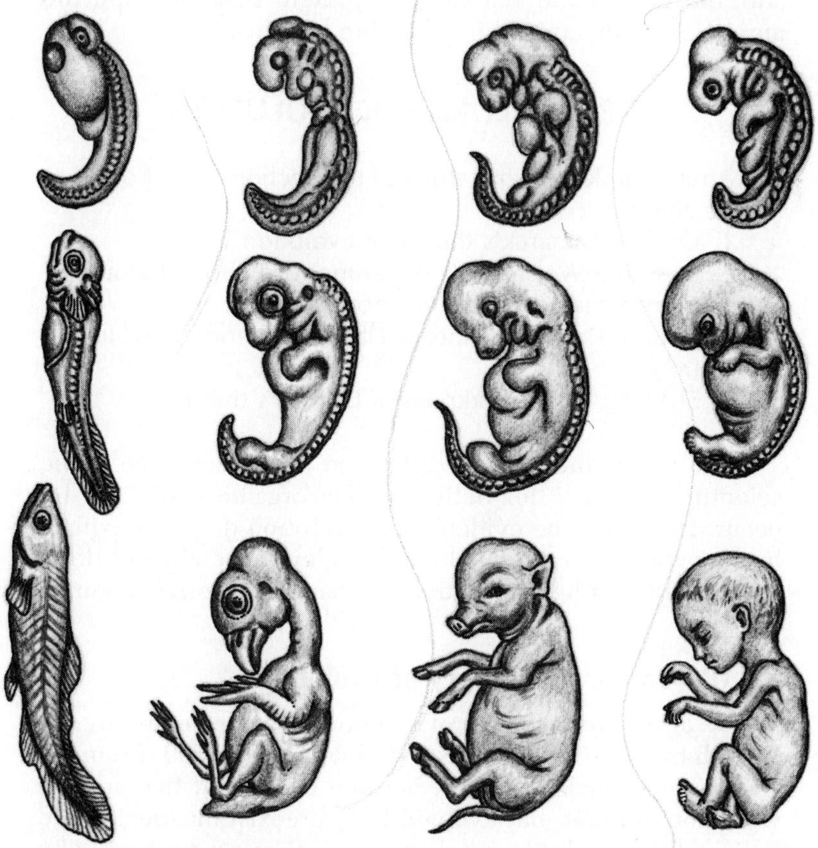

Figure 28-10. Patterns of Development of Four Vertebrate Embryos. The similarities in the early stages of embryonic development suggest a common ancestor for the vertebrates.

28-9 Evidence from Comparative Biochemistry and Immunology

Scientists have discovered that the closer the evolutionary relationship between organisms, the more alike the structure of their DNA and protein molecules. For example, the sequences of amino acids in the hemoglobin of closely related species are almost identical. The hemoglobins of humans and gorillas are the same except for one amino acid.

Among plants, chemical similarities in pigments can be used to determine the closeness of relationships.

The degree of evolutionary relationship between different types of organisms can also be determined with the Nuttall test, which is based on antigen-antibody reactions (see page 166.) For example, if human blood serum is injected into a rabbit, the rabbit produces antibodies against the proteins in the human blood. If serum from this sensitized rabbit is then mixed with human blood serum, a heavy, cloudy precipitate forms, showing an antigen-antibody reaction. The amount of the precipitate can be measured. Next, if serums from a chimpanzee, a baboon, and a pig are each tested individually with serum from the sensitized rabbit, the amount of precipitation will be found to vary. The amount of precipitation is an indica-

Related organisms may have very similar hormones and enzymes. For example, insulin and thyroxin from the pig, cow, and sheep can all be used to treat human endocrine disorders.

Figure 28-11. **Lamarck's Theory of Acquired Characteristics.** According to Lamarck, the giraffe's neck became longer as a result of stretching to reach higher branches. This acquired characteristic was then passed on to offspring.

tion of the similarity in protein structure between each of these animals and humans. The greater the amount of precipitate, the greater the similarity in protein structure, and the more closely the animal is related to humans.

EARLY THEORIES OF EVOLUTION

After completing your study of this section, you should be able to:

1. Outline Lamarck's theory of evolution.
2. Describe Weismann's experiment to show that acquired characteristics are not inherited.
3. List the six main points of Darwin's theory of evolution.
4. State the chief weakness of Darwin's theory.

Up to this point in the chapter you have read some of the scientific evidence for believing that organic evolution did occur. However, the evidence for evolution does not explain how or why it occurred. The remainder of the chapter deals with theories of how evolutionary change is brought about.

28-10 Lamarck's Theory of Evolution

One of the first theories of evolution was presented by the French biologist Jean Baptiste de Lamarck in 1809. From his studies of animals, Lamarck became convinced that species were not constant, but evolved from preexisting species. He believed that evolutionary changes in animals were caused by their need to adapt to changes in the environment.

According to Lamarck's theory, evolution involved two principles. The first was his *law of use and disuse.* According to this principle, the more an animal uses a particular part of its body, the stronger and better developed that part becomes. Also, the less a part is used, the weaker and less developed it becomes. An athlete, for example, develops the strength of certain muscles by constant use. On the other hand, muscles that are not used tend to become smaller and weaker by disuse. The second part of Lamarck's theory was the *inheritance of acquired characteristics.* Lamarck made the assumption that the characteristics an organism developed through use and disuse of various parts of its body could be passed on to its offspring.

According to Lamarck, the long neck of the giraffe would have evolved in the following way (see Figure 28-11). The ancestors of modern giraffes had short necks and fed on grasses and shrubs close to the ground. As the supply of food near the ground decreased, the giraffes had to stretch their necks to reach leaves higher off the ground. Their necks then became longer from stretching, and these longer necks were then passed on to their offspring. In the course of generations, the giraffe's neck became longer and longer, thus giving rise to the modern giraffe.

28-11 Weismann's Experiment

From modern genetics, it is known that traits are passed from one generation to the next by genes in an individual's sex cells. There is no way that these genes could be affected by the individual's life experiences or activities. Many experiments have been performed to look for evidence of such an effect, and all have failed. A famous example is the series of experiments performed by the German biologist August Weismann in the 1870s. Weismann cut the tails off mice for 22 generations. In each generation, the mice were born with tails of normal length. The acquired characteristic of shortened tails was not inherited.

28-12 Darwin

The name most closely connected with the theory of evolution is that of Charles Darwin (see Figure 28-12). Darwin was the son of a prosperous physician. At his father's urging he began to study medicine, but he found the subject very unappealing, and he gave it up. He then began to prepare for a career as a minister in the Church, but his real interest was in nature study—in observing the natural environment and collecting specimens.

In 1831 the British naval vessel H.M.S. Beagle was about to set out on a scientific expedition to chart the coastline of South America and some of the islands of the Pacific Ocean. Another purpose of the voyage was to collect specimens of wildlife from the lesser-known regions of this part of the world. Darwin learned that the captain of the Beagle was looking for someone to serve as a ship's naturalist. He applied for the position and was accepted. He was 22 years old when he sailed from England on a voyage that was expected to take 2 years, but actually lasted 5 years.

During those years, Darwin collected large numbers of specimens and made detailed observations of the regions through which he traveled. He left the ship several times and made inland journeys, rejoining it later. Darwin had plenty of time for thinking about what he saw. He also read *The Principles of Geology*, by Charles Lyell, the first volume of which was published shortly before Darwin left England. This book proposed that the earth was very old, that it had been slowly changing for millions of years, and that it was still changing. This idea led Darwin to think that perhaps living things also changed slowly over long periods of time.

There were several types of observations that particularly impressed Darwin as fitting in with this idea. One was that there was a gradual change in each species as he traveled

Figure 28-12. Charles Darwin.

down the coast of South America. For example, the ostrichlike rheas that live in the latitudes around Buenos Aires are different from those found at the tip of South America. A second class of observations concerned the fossils that Darwin found. They were not the same as any of the living animals he observed. On the other hand, they had many similarities that suggested they might be related to modern forms.

The most significant of Darwin's observations, however, were those he made on the Galapagos Islands, which are in the Pacific Ocean about 1,000 kilometers from the coast of Ecuador. He found that there were many different species of finches living on these islands. These birds were very much alike, yet each species was slightly different from those on the next island or in another part of the same island.

Darwin made similar observations about many plants, insects, and other organisms. Species on the Galapagos Islands resembled species on the mainland, but were always different in certain characteristics. He speculated that these organisms had originally reached the islands from the mainland. However, because of their isolation on the islands, the species had opportunities to develop special adaptations to each different region.

Darwin returned to England in 1836, convinced that evolution had occurred. He had a vast amount of detailed material that supported such a hypothesis, but he could offer no explanation of how evolution occurred. For that reason, he did not publish his ideas on evolution at once. Instead, he continued to collect and organize his data and to search for a reasonable theory of how evolution was brought about.

28-13 Natural Selection

Shortly after he returned to England, Darwin read *An Essay on the Principle of Population*, by Thomas Malthus. This essay greatly influenced Darwin's thinking and was to serve as the basis for his explanation of evolution. Malthus, a minister, mathematician, and economist, was concerned about the social problems of an increasing human population. Malthus reasoned that the human population tends to increase geometrically (2, 4, 8, 16, . . .). For example, if each pair of parents produced four children, the new generation would have 4 individuals to replace the two that had produced them. The next generation would have 8, the next 16, and so on. On the other hand, food production could at best be increased arithmetically (1, 2, 3, 4, . . .), by gradually increasing the amount of land under cultivation. According to this reasoning, the food supply could not keep up with the increase in population. The result was that millions of individuals had to die by disease, starvation, or war to keep a balance between the need for food and the supply.

Darwin realized that all organisms have the same potential for excess population growth. He was also familiar with the competition and struggle for existence that occurs everywhere in nature. In 1838 the idea came to him that organisms with favorable variations would be better able to survive and reproduce than organisms with unfavorable variations. He called this process **natural selection.** The result would be evolution, the formation of new species.

Darwin now had an explanation for evolution. Many of his friends in the scientific world urged him to publish a book on the subject before someone else reached the same conclusions and got all the credit. But Darwin would not be rushed. He insisted on building a strong case for his theory first. Then, in 1858, Darwin received an essay written by Alfred Russel Wallace, an English naturalist then working in Indonesia. Wallace had arrived at exactly the same conclusions as Darwin. Not knowing that Darwin had been thinking for years along the same lines, Wallace had simply sent the paper to Darwin for his opinion.

Darwin and Wallace agreed that Wallace's essay should be published along with a summary of Darwin's theory. Darwin then put his book into final shape and published it the next year, 1859, under the title *On the Origin of Species by Means of Natural Selection.* Darwin's book was well thought out and fully supported by examples. His theory of evolution was eventually accepted by most of the leading scientists of his time.

28-14 Darwin's Theory of Evolution

The main points of Darwin's theory can be summarized as follows:

1. ***Overproduction.*** Most species produce far more offspring than are needed to maintain the population. If all offspring lived long enough to reproduce, any one of the species would cover the earth in a fairly short time. This, of course, does not happen. Species populations remain more or less constant.

2. ***Struggle for existence.*** Since living space and food are limited, the offspring in each generation must compete among themselves, and with other species too, for the necessities of life. Only a small fraction can possibly survive long enough to reproduce.

3. ***Variation.*** In any species, the characteristics of the individuals are not exactly alike. They may differ in the exact size or shape of a body part, in strength or running speed, in resistance to a particular disease, and so on. These differences are called **variations.** Some variations may not be important. Others may affect the individual's chances of getting food, escaping enemies, or finding a mate. These are of vital importance.

4. ***Survival of the fittest.*** Because of variations, some individuals will be better equipped to survive and reproduce than others. In the competition for existence, the individuals that are better adapted to their environment will have a greater

frontiers of biology

There is at present a disagreement among scientists as to the way in which evolution occurs. A basic assumption of Darwin's theory is that changes in living species are gradual, taking place over many millions of years, and that new species arise through the gradual accumulation of small variations.

It was recognized, even in Darwin's time, that there is very little evidence of gradual change in the fossil record. Most species appear suddenly in the record, remain unchanged for a few million years, and then disappear. Until recently, most scientists assumed that transitional forms were simply less abundant than the most common forms and therefore less likely to leave fossils or to be discovered.

Because transitional forms in most cases are still missing from the fossil record, some biologists and paleontologists have proposed a different view of evolutionary change. This new idea is called "punctuated equilibrium." According to this view, new species do not arise by a gradual accumulation of small variations, but by the development of major variations in a relatively short period of time. As a result, the record is marked by long periods of equilibrium, or stability, punctuated by occasional, major changes.

Scientists who favor this concept of punctuated equilibrium argue that the accumulation of small variations by natural selection can result only in minor changes within a species, such as the evolution of the different varieties, or breeds, of dogs. They claim that large changes leading to new major groups of organisms require a more drastic process. Although the fossil record seems to support this new theory, the possible mechanisms that could produce large-scale variations over a short time interval are a subject of speculation.

chance of living long enough to reproduce. The phrase "**survival of the fittest**" is used to summarize this idea.

5. ***Natural selection.*** People who propagate plants and breed animals select individuals with desirable traits to be the parents of the next generation. Experience has shown that these desirable traits are usually passed on to the offspring. Further selection can then be used to produce additional improvements in the next generation. Darwin realized that survival of the fittest can act as a kind of **natural selection,** similar to the artificial selection of plant and animal breeders. Individuals with variations that make them better adapted to their environment survive and reproduce in greater numbers than those less fit. The offspring of the better adapted individuals inherit these favorable variations.

6. ***Evolution of new species.*** Over many generations, favorable variations gradually accumulate in the species and unfavorable ones disappear. Eventually the accumulated changes become so great that the net result is a new species.

28-15 Applying Darwin's Theory

Let us see how Darwin's theory would account for the evolution of the modern giraffe (see Figure 28-13). The original giraffe population had short necks and ate grass. However, some giraffes had longer necks than others. Those with longer necks could eat the lower leaves of trees as well as the grass. In times when grass was scarce, the longer-necked animals could obtain more food than the other and would therefore be more likely to survive and reproduce. Their offspring would inherit the favorable variation of a longer neck. The longer the neck of a giraffe, the higher it could reach for leaves on the trees. Therefore, as a result of natural selection, giraffe necks were slightly longer on the average in each succeeding generation. The modern long-necked animal is the result of this gradual process of evolution.

28-16 Weaknesses in Darwin's Theory

In general, Darwin's theory of natural selection gives a satisfactory explanation of evolution. However, there are weaknesses in his theory. One of these is that it does not explain the origin and transmissions of variations. Also, it does not distinguish between variations caused by hereditary differences and those caused by the environment, which are, of course, not inherited. For example, a plant growing in poor soil may be smaller than a plant of the same species growing in rich, fertile soil. Here, the differences in height are environmentally caused, and not a change that can be inherited.

In Darwin's time little was known about heredity and nothing about genetics. It remained for modern biologists to modify Darwin's theory of natural selection by combining it with the principles of genetics. The modern form of Darwin's theory is presented in Chapter 29.

Figure 28-13. Darwin's Theory of Natural Selection. According to Darwin, giraffes' necks naturally vary in length. Animals with long necks are more likely to survive and reproduce. By natural selection, giraffes with longer necks gradually increase in numbers and those with shorter necks die out.

summary

Much evidence of organic evolution comes from the study of fossils. Fossils are found most commonly in sedimentary rock. Correlation of rock layers and the presence of index fossils may be used for the relative dating of fossils. Absolute dating of fossils is done by radioactive dating methods. Evidence of evolutionary relationships is provided by studies of comparative anatomy, comparative embryology, and comparative biochemistry and immunology.

One of the first theories of evolution was that of Lamarck. Lamarck's theory was based on the law of use and disuse and the inheritance of acquired characteristics. The modern theory of evolution is based on the work of Darwin, which involved the process of natural selection. In natural selection, organisms with desirable traits survive and reproduce more successfully than organisms not showing these traits.

vocabulary

absolute dating
analogous structures
cast
correlation
fossil
geologic evolution
geologic time scale
half-life
homologous structures
imprint
index fossil
mold
natural selection
organic evolution
petrifaction
radioactive dating
radioactivity
relative dating
sedimentary rock
vestigial structures

test your learning

Section		
28-1	1.	Define the terms *geologic evolution* and *organic evolution*.
28-2	2.	What is a fossil?
	3.	List five ways in which fossils can be formed, and give a brief description of each.
28-3	4.	Describe the formation of sedimentary rock.
28-4	5.	Describe how correlation of rock layers and index fossils are used for the relative dating of fossils.
28-5	6.	Explain how radioactive dating is used for the absolute dating of fossils.
28-6	7.	What information is shown in the geologic time scale?
	8.	What are the major eras of the geologic time scale?
	9.	During what era and approximately how long ago did the fossil record become abundant?
28-7	10.	What are homologous and analogous structures, and what type of information about evolutionary relationships can be obtained from each?
	11.	What are vestigial structures, and what type of information about evolutionary relationships can be obtained from such structures?
28-8	12.	What information about evolutionary relationships can be obtained from similarities or differences in patterns of embryological development?
28-9	13.	How can comparative biochemistry and immunology be used in the study of evolutionary relationships?
28-10	14.	Explain Lamarck's theory of evolution, including his law of use and disuse and the inheritance of acquired characteristics.
28-11	15.	How did August Weismann's experiments with mice help to disprove the idea of the inheritance of acquired characteristics?
28-12	16.	Describe three basic types of observations that Darwin made during his voyage on the *Beagle* that supported the idea of evolution.
28-13	17.	According to Thomas Malthus, how does population growth compare to growth in food production?
	18.	Explain what Darwin meant by the process of natural selection.
	19.	Name the English naturalist who developed a theory of evolution very similar to Darwin's.
28-14	20.	Describe the main points of Darwin's theory of evolution.
28-15	21.	How would natural selection explain the evolution of long-necked giraffes from a population of short-necked giraffes?
28-16	22.	What were the weaknesses in Darwin's theory of evolution?

test your understanding

1. List the various types of evidence that support the theory of organic evolution.
2. Briefly state the main points of Darwin's theory of evolution.
3. Discuss the importance of homologous structures, analogous structures, and vestigial structures in determining a possible evolutionary relationship between two types of organisms.
4. Compare Lamarck's and Darwin's explanations of the cause of evolution.

independent research

1. Visit a natural history museum and prepare a report on one of the types of fossils you find on display there.
2. Prepare a report on career opportunities in the field of paleontology.

chapter 29

Theories of Evolution

VARIATION

After completing your study of this section, you should be able to:

1. Describe de Vries' contribution to Darwin's theory of evolution.
2. List the causes of variation in a species according to modern genetic theory.
3. Define the term *population genetics,* and explain its importance in modern evolutionary theory.
4. Define evolution in terms of gene frequencies.
5. Define the terms *gene pool* and *differential reproduction.*
6. State the Hardy-Weinberg law, and list the conditions necessary for this law to hold true.

Figure 29-1. The Evening Primrose.

29-1 De Vries and the Mutation Theory

The Dutch botanist Hugo de Vries introduced the concept of mutation at the beginning of this century (see page 426). De Vries based his theory of mutation on research that he conducted over several years with the evening primrose (see Figure 29-1). In the course of this research, de Vries observed that occasionally a plant appeared with a totally new structure or form, which then bred true in later generations. De Vries considered each of these sudden changes in the hereditary material to be a mutation.

De Vries added the idea of mutation to Darwin's theory of evolution. This overcame one of the main weaknesses of Darwin's theory, which was a lack of explanation of how new traits could arise. De Vries claimed that the important changes leading to new species did not occur slowly over many generations. They occurred as sudden, large changes in heredity resulting from mutation. According to de Vries, a giraffe with a longer-than-normal neck would have been produced by a mutation. Since when grass was scarce, the long-necked giraffe and its offspring had an advantage over giraffes with necks of normal length, they survived and multiplied in greater numbers. Eventually, only the long-necked variety was left.

29-2 Sources of Variation

It is now known that mutations are only one of the sources of genetic variation. Crossing-over, recombination, and immigration and emigration are also involved.

Gene mutations. In the modern theory of evolution, gene mutations are a major source of variation. The mutation of any particular gene is a rare event. Out of 10,000 gametes, only one may have a mutation of a particular gene. The mutation rate for that gene is said to be 1 per 10,000. On the other hand, each gamete has thousands of genes. Among those thousands of genes, it is very likely that at least one has mutated. Thus a few mutations are likely to be present in every zygote.

Most mutations are recessive. As a result, the mutant trait is usually hidden by the normal dominant trait. Because of the low frequency of gene mutations, it is very rare for mutant genes to be brought together in the homozygous state. When this does occasionally happen, the effect is usually harmful to the individual. However, if environmental conditions change, mutant genes may suddenly acquire usefulness to the species. Natural selection will then tend to gradually increase the frequency of this gene in the population.

Chromosomal mutations. Chromosomal mutations were described in Chapter 25 (page 426). Although these mutations do not produce new genes, they result in new combinations of genes in the organism. Since most physical traits are controlled by several genes, new gene combinations can give rise to new traits. Chromosomal mutations are another source of variation.

Crossing-over. Crossing-over, the exchange of chromosome segments that often occurs during meiosis, results in new gene linkages (see page 424). Like chromosomal mutations, crossing-over is also a source of variation.

Recombination. Mutations supply new genes and new gene combinations to a species. Recombination during sexual reproduction spreads them around and distributes them throughout the population.

Immigration and emigration. Another source of variation may result from immigration into and emigration out of a population. As individuals move into a population, they may bring in genes not already present. When individuals leave a population, they may remove some genes from the population. Migration, the movement of organisms from one area to another, tends to have its greatest effect on variations in small populations.

29-3 Population Genetics

The modern theory of evolution stresses the importance of populations. A **population** is a group of organisms of the same species living together in a given region and capable of interbreeding. According to the modern view of evolution, *individuals* do not evolve. Their genetic makeup remains the same throughout their lives. However, *populations* do evolve. Each population is made up of many individuals, each with its own unique assortment of genes. As these individuals reproduce and die, the genetic makeup of the population as a whole may change. As its genetic makeup changes from generation to generation, the population evolves. The study of the changes in the genetic makeup of populations is called **population genetics.**

29-4 Gene Frequencies

Each individual of a population has a set of genes that is not exactly the same as that of any other individual. Still, these individuals do have many of the same genes. In the population as a whole, there are a certain number of genes of each kind. Some genes may be more common than others. For example, every individual in the population may have genes for producing a particular enzyme. The **frequency** of that gene in the population is thus 100 percent. On the other hand, only one in a hundred individuals may have a certain mutant gene. Its frequency in the population is then 1/100, or 1 percent.

The total of all the genes in a population is called the **gene pool.** At any given time, each gene occurs in the gene pool with a certain frequency. This frequency may be anywhere from 100 percent down to extremely low frequencies, such as 1 per 10,000 or 1 per 1,000,000. As time goes on, the gene frequencies in the gene pool may change as the result of natural selection. Evolution may be thought of as a gradual change of gene frequencies in a population.

29-5 Differential Reproduction

As the result of mutations, new genes are constantly appearing in every gene pool, resulting in variation among individuals. As variations appear, the environment acts as a screen that selects certain variations to be preserved and rejects others. Those individuals with favorable variations will survive longer and produce more offspring than those with unfavorable variations. Thus variation leads to **differential reproduc-**

tion. As a result of differential reproduction, certain gene frequencies will gradually increase and others will decline.

If the environment in which a population is living changes, the screening effect of natural selection will change. The frequency of genes that give individuals an advantage under the new conditions will increase. The frequency of genes that are disadvantageous will decrease.

The evolution of long-necked giraffes can be described in terms of differential reproduction and changes in gene frequencies. In the original giraffe population, genes for longer neck length were present, but at a low frequency. A change in the environment may then have reduced the amount of grass available and increased the number of trees. Individuals with the genes for longer necks would be able to obtain more food, would live longer, and would produce more offspring. In later generations, their offspring would be a larger fraction of the population. Therefore, the genes they carried for long necks would be present at a greater frequency. Eventually, this frequency approached 100 percent, and only long-necked giraffes appeared in the population.

29-6 The Hardy-Weinberg Law

In Mendel's experiments with hybrid pea plants, there were two alleles for each trait that he studied. For example, there was the allele T that produced tall plants and the allele t that produced short plants. The gene frequencies for T and t in the hybrid plants were equal: 50 percent T and 50 percent t. When the hybrids reproduced, the offspring had a genotype ratio of 1:2:1 and a phenotype ratio of 3:1, but the gene frequencies in the offspring remained the same—50:50. You can check this statement by counting the T and t genes in the Punnett squares on page 410.

However, it is not necessary that two alleles in a population have the same frequency. One may be much more common than the other. Suppose, for example, that there are two alleles for a particular trait, such as eye color, in a certain species. Let us say that one allele produces white eyes; the other, red eyes. Let us not be concerned about dominance, or about the eye color of a hybrid. Let us just assume that the gene for white eyes is much more common in the population than the gene for red eyes—that 90 percent of the genes are for white eyes, 10 percent for red. As these organisms mate and reproduce, what will happen to the gene frequencies for eye color as generation follows generation? It might seem logical that the much more common white-eye gene would eventually replace the red-eye gene altogether, and the gene frequency would become 100 percent white-eye.

In 1908, G. H. Hardy, an English mathematician, and W. H. Weinberg, a German physician, both considered this question and came to the same conclusion. They showed that the segregation and recombination of genes in sexual reproduc-

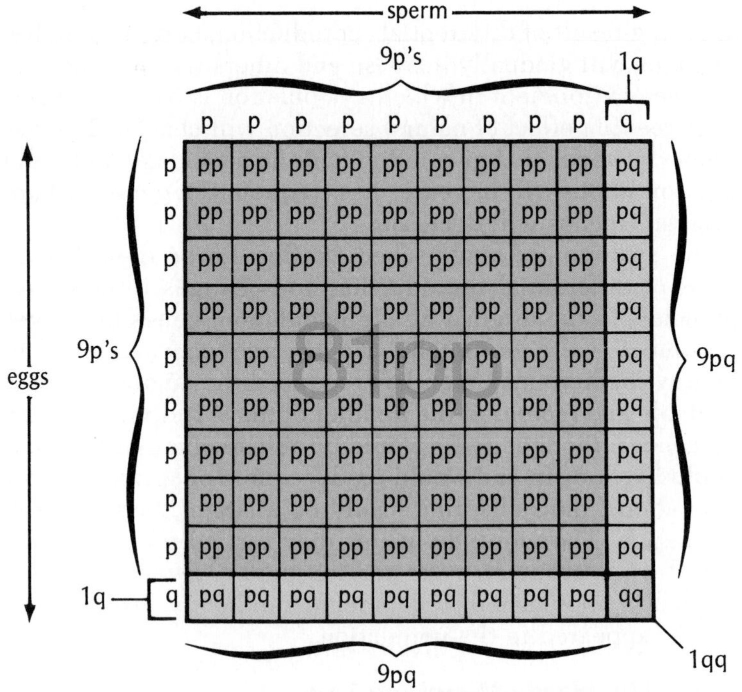

Assume that the frequency of allele p in a population is 90% and that of allele q is 10%. Then, out of every 10 sperm cells produced by the population, 9 will carry the p allele and 1 will carry the q. Likewise, of every 10 egg cells, 9 will carry p and 1 will carry q. The Punnett square shows the results of random fertilizations between these sperm and eggs. Of every 100 gametes formed, 81 are pp, 18 are pq, and 1 is qq. Let us find the total number of p's and q's in these 100 gametes:

81 pp = 162 p's	
18 pq = 18 p's and 18 q's	
1 qq =	2 q's
Totals: 180 p's and 20 q's	

We see that the ratio of p to q in the offspring generation is 180 to 20, or 9 to 1. This is the same as the ratio in the parent generation.

Figure 29-2. Illustrating the Hardy-Weinberg Law.

tion could not by itself change gene frequencies. If the frequency of gene p was 90 percent, and the frequency of its allele q was 10 percent, ordinary random mating would always produce a new generation with the same ratio of 90 percent p and 10 percent q. This is called the **Hardy-Weinberg law** (see Figure 29-2).

For the Hardy-Weinberg law to hold true, the following conditions must be met:

1. The population must be large. In a small population, genes of low frequency might be lost, or the frequency changed, by the accidental death of a few individuals possessing those genes.
2. Individuals must not migrate into or out of the population. Any individuals that did so might change the gene frequencies of the population.
3. Mutations must not occur. Mutations obviously change the frequencies of existing genes.
4. Reproduction must be completely random. This means that every individual, whatever its genetic makeup, should have an equal chance of producing offspring.

29-7 The Hardy-Weinberg Law and Evolution

The preceding section lists four conditions necessary for the Hardy-Weinberg law to hold true. The first two of these might actually exist. Populations can be large enough, and migration can be practically zero under certain circumstances. However, the last two conditions almost never exist. Mutations are always occurring at fixed rates, thus changing gene frequencies.

But more important, reproduction is not random. Differential reproduction is the rule, leading to natural selection and a resulting change in gene frequencies.

You may be wondering about the usefulness of a "law" that doesn't apply to any situation in the real world. The importance of the Hardy-Weinberg principle is that it enables us to demonstrate that evolution is occurring in a population. The law tells us that under certain conditions, gene frequencies would remain constant, and there would be no evolution. The simple fact that gene frequencies in a population are changing tells us that there are external factors causing them to change. In other words, the failure of the Hardy-Weinberg law in any given instance is a sign that evolution is occurring. The extent of the variation from the Hardy-Weinberg prediction is a measure of how rapid the evolutionary change is.

ADAPTATIONS

After completing your study of this section, you should be able to:

1. Define the term *adaptation,* and name some different kinds of adaptations.
2. Define the terms *camouflage, warning coloration,* and *mimicry.*

29-8 Types of Adaptations

An **adaptation** is any kind of inherited trait that improves the chance of survival and reproduction of an organism in a given environment. The selecting force that chooses the best and most useful inherited variations is the environment itself. For example, in a population of plants, there may be a genetic variation in the amount of waxy cutin covering the leaves. Some plants may be heavily covered with this protective layer, while others are only thinly covered. Cutin is waterproof and protects the plant from drying out. If the climate becomes drier, then plants with a thicker cutin layer will be better able to survive and produce seeds, and differential reproduction will occur. The cutin in this case is an adaptation that has been "selected" by the environment. After many generations, genes for this adaptation will accumulate in the gene pool. Eventually, only plants with a heavy cutin layer will remain in the population.

Structural adaptations are those that involve the body of the organism. The wings of birds and insects are structural adaptations for flight. The fins of fish and the webbed feet of ducks are structural adaptations for swimming. Leaves, by providing a large surface area, are an adaptation for photosynthesis. **Physiological adaptations** involve the metabolism of organisms. The protein web made by spiders and the poison venom made by snakes are examples of physiological adaptations. Still others adaptations involve particular behavior pat-

Figure 29-3. **Male and Female Frigate Birds.** The bright red pouch of the male frigate bird is in adaptation related to mating behavior.

terns. Of course, many adaptations are combinations of various types of adaptations. For example, the mating behavior and migration of birds, the spawning of fish, and the hibernation of animals involve several types of adaptations (see Figure 29-3).

Many adaptations provide effective means of protection. In **camouflage,** the organism blends into the environment (see Figure 29-4). Flounders can become practically invisible against a variety of backgrounds. Striped tigers are hard to see among the shadows of grasses in their customary environment. In **warning coloration,** the colors of the animal actually make it easier to see. This is an advantage to certain insects that birds and other enemies find unpleasant to eat. If a young bird happens to eat one of these insects, it quickly learns to avoid that species in the future. The brightly colored monarch butterfly is an example of this kind of warning coloration (see Figure 29-5). In **mimicry,** one organism is protected against enemies by resembling another, unrelated species. Birds can eat the viceroy butterfly without unpleasant effects, but they tend to avoid it because it looks like the monarch butterfly, which they do find unpleasant. In another type of mimicry, the organism resembles some part of the environment and is ignored by its enemies (see Figure 29-6).

SPECIATION

After completing your study of this section, you should be able to:

1. Define the terms *range* and *speciation*.
2. Describe the various ways in which speciation may occur.

29-9 Speciation and Geographic Separation

Each species is found in a particular region of the earth, which is called its **range.** The characteristics of a species are

Figure 29-4. **Camouflage.** (Left) A flounder against the ocean floor. (Right) A fawn half hidden in bushes.

Figure 29-5. Mimicry. (Left) A monarch butterfly. (Right) A viceroy butterfly.

Figure 29-6. Mimicry of Natural Environment. (Left) A grizzled mantis. (Below) A stick caterpillar on a cypress branch.

often different in different parts of its range. Differences in environmental conditions have exerted different selective pressures, leading to different adaptive characteristics. The leopard frog, *Rana pipiens*, for example, has a wide range extending over most of North America. Across this range the frogs gradually differ in such characteristics as body size, patterns of coloration, and the temperatures at which their embryos will develop. The species actually consists of separate populations with different gene pools. However, adjacent populations can mate and produce normal offspring. They are therefore called subspecies, or varieties, of the same species.

Leopard frogs at opposite ends of the range show the greatest differences in characteristics and in gene pools. In fact, frogs from widely separated regions cannot mate successfully. They are still considered to be the same species because there is continuous interbreeding among adjacent subspecies throughout the range. If, however, a population varies so much from its neighbors that it loses the ability to interbreed with them, a new species has developed. Under certain circumstances, one species can give rise to two or more species. This formation of new species is called **speciation** (spee-shee-*ay*-shun).

29-10 Types of Speciation

Isolation. Although a variety of factors are involved in speciation, one of the most important is isolation. *Isolation* refers to anything that prevents two groups within a species from interbreeding. Isolating a group of organisms has the effect of separating its gene pool from the gene pool of the rest of the species. It is generally believed that speciation is a two-step process involving first geographic isolation, followed later by reproductive isolation.

Geographic isolation occurs when a population is divided by some natural barrier, such as a mountain, desert, river or other body of water, or a landslide caused by an earthquake. As a result, the gene pool of each group becomes isolated and the two can no longer intermix. Over a period of time, each group will become adapted to its particular environment. Through mutation, genetic recombination, and natural selection, a different gene pool will evolve in each group. When the differences between the isolated groups become sufficiently great, they will no longer be able to interbreed, even if they could get together. Now geographic isolation has been replaced by reproductive isolation.

Reproductive isolation can be produced by several mechanisms. Differences may arise between the two groups in courtship behavior, times of mating, or structure of the sex organs. Such changes make it unlikely that mating will occur. Other changes affect events after mating and involve the inability of sperm to fertilize eggs, the death of the embryo early in development, or the development of offspring that are sterile. According to most biologists, if two groups of organisms cannot interbreed successfully, they can be considered to be two different species.

Speciation by geographic and reproductive isolation is believed to have occurred in the case of the Kaibab squirrel and Abert squirrel. The Kaibab squirrel inhabits the north side of the Grand Canyon, and the Abert squirrel inhabits the south side (see Figure 29-7). It is believed that these two squirrels evolved from a common ancestor. The Grand Canyon, acting as a geographical barrier, divided the ancestral population, which once occupied the entire area. After a long period of

Figure 29-7. **Speciation through Geographic Isolation.** (Left) A Kaibab squirrel. (Right) An Abert squirrel.

geographical isolation, the Kaibab and Abert squirrels evolved. The two squirrels are similar in appearance, but are different species because they cannot interbreed.

Polyploidy. Speciation can also occur suddenly, when abnormal cell division results in polyploidy. Polyploids are organisms, usually plants, that contain more than the usual number of chromosome sets, for example, $3n$, $4n$, or more. When the offspring can interbreed only among themselves, they are considered to be a new species.

Adaptive radiation. The process by which an ancestral species evolves into a number of different species, each occupying a different habitat, is called **adaptive radiation.** This spreading, or radiation, of the organisms into different environments is accompanied by adaptive changes to the new way of life.

For example, a single ancestral species may have migrated—radiated—into several different environments. If the descendants are successful, then through isolation, genetic variation, and natural selection, they will evolve a variety of adaptations to their new environments. After many generations, they will have evolved into several new species, each having certain adaptive traits. However, their common ancestry is indicated by the traits they share in common.

Darwin's finches are an example of adaptive radiation. In that case an ancestral type of finch probably arrived in the Galapagos Islands and then radiated into a variety of habitats and ways of life. The initial radiation involved living on the ground and living in trees. Further radiation occurred on the basis of food: some finches live on the ground and feed on seeds of varying size; some live in forests and feed on insects in trees; others feed mainly on cactus or berries; and one species lives in low bushes and feeds on insects. Without competition from other birds, the finches slowly radiated into and adapted to the various types of environment that were present.

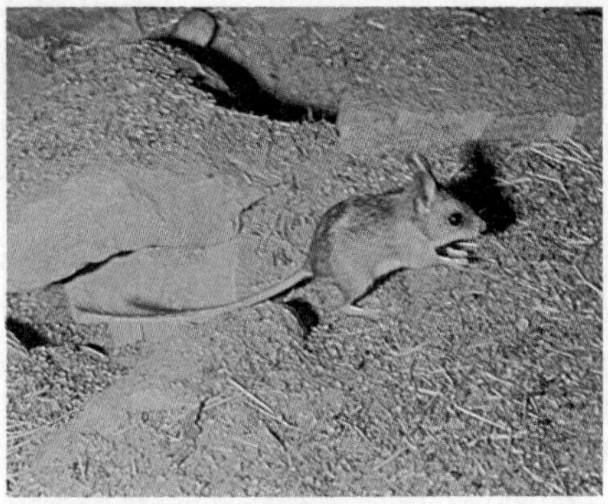

Figure 29-8. Convergent Evolution. The marsupial mouse looks very much like a placental rodent.

Marsupial mammals evolved by adaptive radiation in Australia because there were no placental mammals to compete with them for food and living space. On the other land masses of the world, where placental mammals did develop, almost all the marsupials became extinct. The placental mammals became dominant by natural selection and became varied by adaptive radiation.

Convergent evolution. One result of geographic isolation is that organisms that are not closely related may develop similar adaptations and come to resemble each other. The marsupial mouse looks very much like a placental rodent (see Figure 29-8). There is also a marsupial that resembles a wolf (the Tasmanian wolf) and one that resembles a bear (the koala). These resemblances are only "skin deep." They evolved because of similar needs in similar environments, leading to the natural selection of similar structural adaptations. Natural selection that causes unrelated species to resemble one another is called **convergent evolution.**

OBSERVED NATURAL SELECTION

After completing your study of this section, you should be able to:

1. Discuss industrial melanism and the information gained from the study of the peppered moth in England.
2. Describe how populations of antibiotic-resistant bacteria and DDT-resistant insects have arisen.

29-11 Industrial Melanism

Natural selection may take many thousands of years to produce a change in a population. However, in recent years some excellent examples of natural selection have given scientists an opportunity to study evolution in action. One of these illustrates the kind of adaptation called industrial melanism.

The peppered moth, *Biston betularia,* is found in wooded areas in England. Before the 1850s, most peppered moths were light in color. Black-colored moths, with a pigment called *melanin,* occurred but were very rare. During the years from 1850 to 1900, England became heavily industrialized. Where there was much industry, heavy smoke darkened the tree trunks and killed the light lichens growing on them. In these regions, by the 1890s, 99 percent of the peppered moths were black in color, while the light-colored variety were very rare. In the cleaner, nonindustrial areas of southern England, the light-colored moth continued to predominate.

An explanation for the change from light-colored to dark-colored moths can be found in natural selection. The light and dark color of the moth is genetically controlled. The dark color is a mutation that occurs at a constant low frequency. During daylight, peppered moths rest on tree trunks. Before England

Figure 29-9. Industrial Melanism. On the light tree (left) the lighter colored peppered moth is better camouflaged. On the dark tree (right) the darker moth is better camouflaged.

became industrialized, the light-colored moths blended in well with the lichens that covered the tree bark (see Figure 29-9). As a result of this camouflage, birds that feed upon the peppered moth could not easily find the light-colored moths. Of course, any dark-colored moths were easily seen and eaten. In this situation, the light-colored moths had a reproductive advantage. When the fumes and soot killed the lichens and blackened the trees, the light-colored moths lost their protective coloration. They no longer blended in with the trees and became easy prey for birds. Now the dark-colored moths had a distinct advantage. The blackened trees offered them good camouflage. Through natural selection, more dark moths survived and reproduced than light-colored moths. During the years from 1850 to 1900, a period of 50 generations for peppered moths, the dark-colored moths became the more frequent color in the population.

In the 1950s, H. B. D. Kettlewell of Oxford University performed experiments that supported the above explanation. He released light- and dark-colored moths in a polluted industrial area and in an unpolluted nonindustrial area. In the polluted area, where the trees were blackened with soot, more light-colored moths were eaten than dark-colored moths. In the unpolluted area, birds ate more dark-colored moths than light-colored moths.

This research on the color change in peppered moths shows that over a period of time a species can change gradually from one form to another. Two details of the evolutionary process are clearly illustrated. One is the presence of variability in the population. Both light-color and dark-color genes are in the gene pool. The second detail illustrated is the effect of the changing environment in selecting one color trait over another. In nature, it is the trait that makes the moth best adapted to the environment that is preserved.

Industrial melanism is the name used for the development of dark-colored organisms in a population exposed to industrial air pollution. In the United States, the insects around many major cities are darker in color than the ones in the unpolluted countryside. Interestingly, since the 1950s air pollution control in England has resulted in an increase in the number of light-colored peppered moths.

29-12 Bacterial Resistance to Antibiotics

Antibiotics usually kill bacteria. However, once the use of antibiotics became common, resistant strains of bacteria began to appear. Antibiotics were no longer effective in killing those strains.

Scientists wanted to know how this resistance to antibiotics developed. One possibility was that exposure to an antibiotic caused certain bacterial cells to develop resistance to it. This would be similar to the immunity an individual acquires to a disease organism after recovery from the disease. Another possibility was that in a large population of bacteria, there are always a few individuals with resistance to the antibiotic. In an environment containing the antibiotic, only the resistant individuals will grow and reproduce. By natural selection, the strain with resistance becomes the common type.

In the early 1950s, Esther and Joshua Lederberg carried out a series of experiments that showed that the second explanation, natural selection, was the correct one. The Lederbergs worked with the common intestinal bacterium *Escherichia coli*, which is normally killed by the antibiotic streptomycin. The first step of their experiment was to spread a culture of the bacteria very thinly on an agar nutrient medium in a petri dish (see Figure 29-10). This had the effect of separating the culture into individual bacteria. Each bacterial cell then multiplied on the agar, forming a distinct colony. In each colony, all the cells were genetically alike since they had developed from a single original cell.

The Lederbergs now set out to look for cells resistant to streptomycin. It would have taken too much time to investigate each colony separately. Instead, they used a velveteen cloth to pick up bacteria from all the colonies at once. The cloth was then touched to a second agar plate that contained streptomycin, thus transferring bacteria from all the colonies to the agar. Usually, none of the transferred bacteria formed a colony; they could not survive and multiply in the streptomycin environment. Occasionally, however, a colony did grow on the streptomycin plate. When this happened, the Lederbergs knew which original colony the transferred cells had come from. They knew this because the velveteen cloth placed the bacteria in the same relative positions on the new agar as the colonies from which they were picked up. It was then a simple matter to test the original colony for streptomycin resistance.

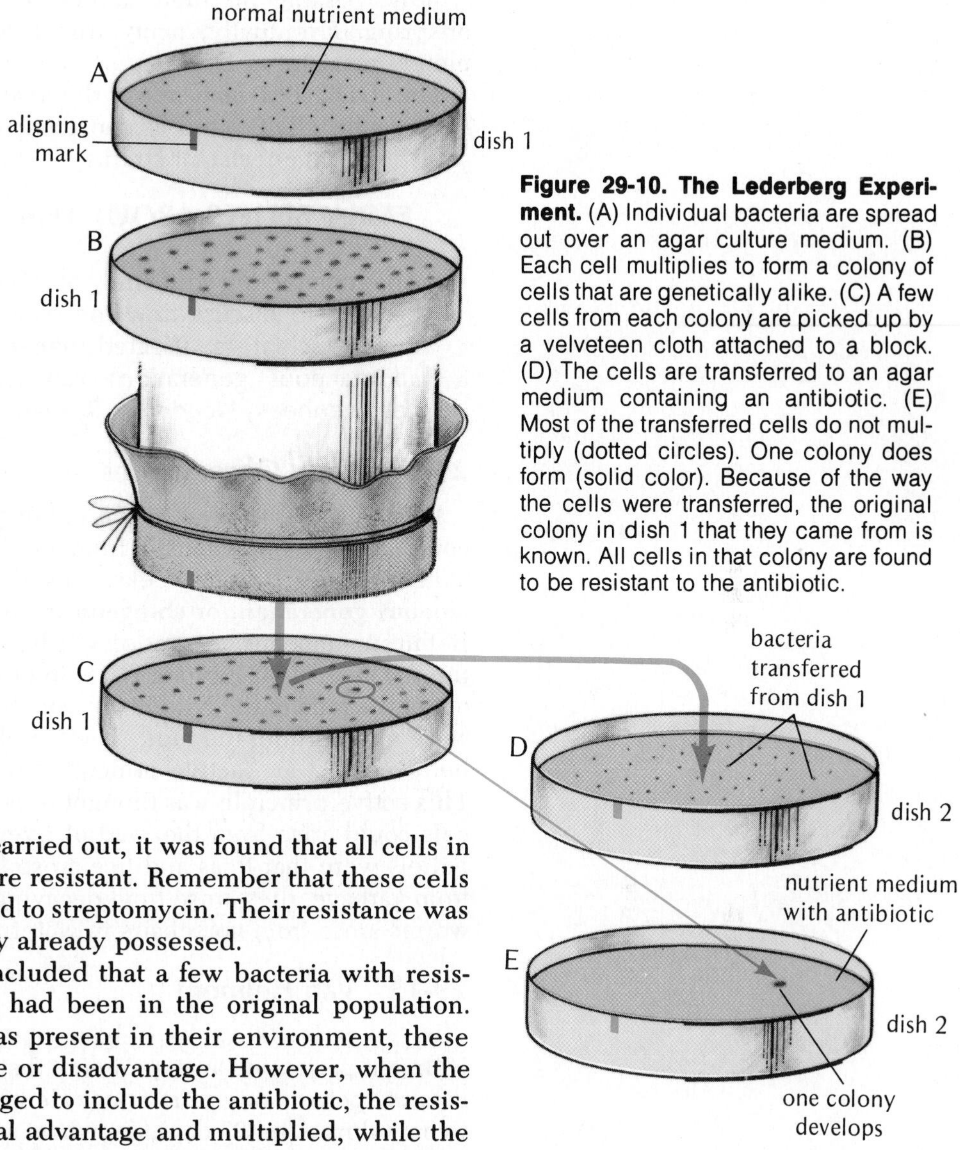

Figure 29-10. The Lederberg Experiment. (A) Individual bacteria are spread out over an agar culture medium. (B) Each cell multiplies to form a colony of cells that are genetically alike. (C) A few cells from each colony are picked up by a velveteen cloth attached to a block. (D) The cells are transferred to an agar medium containing an antibiotic. (E) Most of the transferred cells do not multiply (dotted circles). One colony does form (solid color). Because of the way the cells were transferred, the original colony in dish 1 that they came from is known. All cells in that colony are found to be resistant to the antibiotic.

When this test was carried out, it was found that all cells in the original colony were resistant. Remember that these cells had never been exposed to streptomycin. Their resistance was a genetic trait that they already possessed.

The Lederbergs concluded that a few bacteria with resistance to streptomycin had been in the original population. When no antibiotic was present in their environment, these cells had no advantage or disadvantage. However, when the environment was changed to include the antibiotic, the resistant cells had a survival advantage and multiplied, while the normal type died out. The population became 100 percent streptomycin-resistant.

This experiment showed that the change in the environment had not caused the resistance to develop. It had acted only as a selector for organisms that already had the gene for resistance to streptomycin.

29-13 Insect Resistance to DDT

When DDT was first introduced, it was a very effective killer of insects, including serious pests such as mosquitos. Apparently, however, a small proportion of insects in various insect populations possessed a natural resistance to DDT. When the DDT-sensitive members of a population were killed by spraying, the DDT-resistant insects multiplied rapidly, passing on their natural DDT-resistance to their offspring. Eventually, many insect populations were completely resistant to DDT.

The DDT did *not* create the resistance of the insects. Rather, the DDT acted as the environmental agent for the selection of the resistant strains.

EARLY BELIEFS ABOUT THE ORIGIN OF LIFE

After completing your study of this section, you should be able to discuss how the experiments of the following scientists affected belief in the theory of spontaneous generation: van Helmont, Redi, van Leeuwenhoek, Needham, Spallanzani, and Pasteur.

29-14 Early Observations

For thousands of years, it was believed that living organisms could arise spontaneously from nonliving matter over the course of a few days or weeks. This idea is the theory of **spontaneous generation,** or **abiogenesis** (ay-by-oh-*jen*-uh-sis). Belief in spontaneous generation was based on common observations. The ancient Egyptians, seeing frogs and snakes coming out of the mud of the Nile River, concluded that these animals were formed from the mud. The Greek philosopher Aristotle believed that an "active principle" was responsible for life. This active principle was thought to be present in mud. Thus eels could arise from the mud of rivers. Some other popular beliefs were that fleas and lice arose from sweat, mice arose from garbage, flies arose from decaying meat, and snakes and worms arose from horsehairs in water.

29-15 Van Helmont

In the early 1600s, the Belgian physician Jan Baptista van Helmont performed an experiment that seemed to support the idea of spontaneous generation. He placed wheat grains in a sweaty shirt. After 21 days, the wheat was gone and mice were present. Van Helmont reasoned that human sweat was the active principle that changed wheat grains into mice. Even though this was an uncontrolled experiment, his experimental "proof" gained wide acceptance among the scientists of his time.

29-16 Redi

In the mid-1600s the Italian physician Francesco Redi struck the first great blow against the idea of spontaneous generation. It was a matter of common observation that whenever meat was left exposed to the air, maggots would soon appear on it. Maggots are the larvae of flies, but they were thought to be a kind of worm because of their shape and method of movement. It was widely believed at that time that the maggots developed by spontaneous generation from the decaying meat.

Redi doubted the truth of this common belief, and he decided to subject it to a scientific test. In reporting his results, he wrote:

> It being . . . the popular belief that the putrescence of a dead body, or the filth of any sort of decayed matter, engenders worms; and being desirous of tracing the truth in the case, I made the following experiment.

Redi's account of his experiments is a perfect example of the scientific method. He began with a series of careful observations. On the basis of his observations, he made certain hypotheses. He then tested his hypotheses by controlled experiments. The following is a brief summary of Redi's investigation.

He began by placing many different kinds of meat in open containers, and he closely observed the maggots that appeared on them (see Figure 29-11). He watched the maggots consume the decaying meat, and he continued to observe them even after the meat was gone. He discovered that the maggots formed pupas, which then developed into flies of various kinds. Redi was apparently the first person to realize that maggots developed into flies.

This observation led Redi to recall that flies always gathered around the decaying meat. Everybody knew this, of course, but nobody had ever connected this observation with the maggots. Redi formed a hypothesis that the maggots developed from eggs laid on the meat by the flies. He then proceeded to test this hypothesis.

He placed some meat in open jars and other samples of the same meat in tightly sealed jars. This was a controlled experiment: The only variable was whether the jar was closed or open. Redi observed that flies entered the open jars and that maggots appeared on the meat. No maggots appeared on the meat in the closed jars.

This experiment proved only that the meat had to be exposed to develop maggots. It did not prove that the flies were the source of the maggots. Many scientists of the time claimed that fresh air was necessary for spontaneous generation, and by sealing the jars, Redi had prevented the needed air from reaching the meat.

Redi therefore performed another set of experiments in which the containers were covered by fine gauze (see Figure 29-12). The gauze allowed free circulation of air into the containers, but prevented flies from entering. Redi observed that the flies attempted to reach the meat by landing frequently on the gauze. The flies also deposited eggs on the gauze, which developed into maggots. But no maggots appeared inside the jars.

Figure 29-11. Redi's First Experiment. This experiment showed that meat had to be exposed to the environment to develop maggots.

A
Flies attracted by odor.
meat
rotting meat
Flies lay eggs on meat.
maggots on meat
meat gone
Maggots form pupas that develop into flies.
B
sealed jar
meat
rotting meat
No flies attracted to jar.
No flies or maggots in jar.

Figure 29-12. Redi's Second Experiment. This experiment showed that maggots arise in decaying meat from eggs laid by flies.

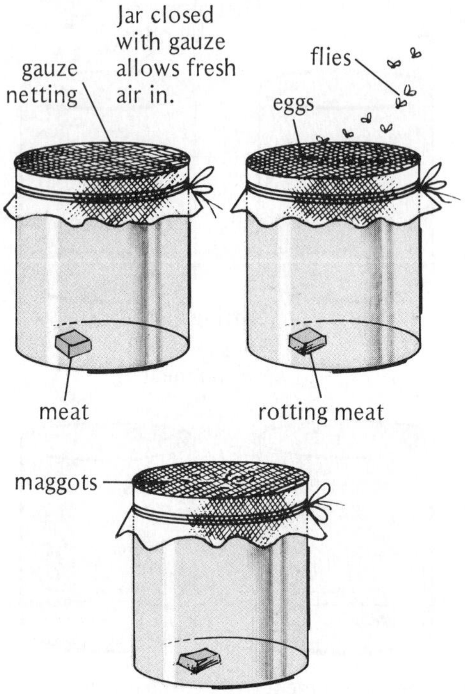

Redi had shown conclusively that maggots did not arise spontaneously from decaying meat, but from eggs laid by flies. Scientists accepted this conclusion, but with the discovery of microorganisms, the whole question of spontaneous generation was thrown open again.

29-17 Van Leeuwenhoek

At about the time that Redi was performing his experiments, Anton van Leeuwenhoek was making his simple microscopes and examining everything he could put under them. In 1677 he made the startling discovery of living things in a drop of water. Soon it was found that when hay or soil was placed in water that had no life in it to start with, millions of microorganisms appeared just a few hours later. Here, surely, was a clearcut case of spontaneous generation! Many scientists concluded that although larger animals might not be able to arise from nonliving matter, microscopic ones could. The controversy that Redi had almost put to rest flared up again and raged for the next 200 years.

29-18 Needham

In 1745, John Needham, an English scientist, performed some experiments that reinforced belief in spontaneous generation of microorganisms. He boiled flasks of chicken, lamb, and corn broth for a few minutes to kill any microorganisms in them. Then he sealed the flasks. After several days he opened and examined the flasks and found them teeming with microorganisms. He repeated the experiment several times and always obtained the same results. Needham and other biologists concluded that the microorganisms developed by spontaneous generation.

29-19 Spallanzani

About 20 years after Needham did his work, Lorenzo Spallanzani, an Italian scientist, challenged the concept of spontaneous generation of microorganisms. Like Needham, he set up flasks of chicken, lamb, and corn broth. However, he boiled the contents of the flasks for a much longer time. No living organisms appeared in the flasks.

Spallanzani claimed that Needham obtained organisms in his heated flasks because he had not heated them long enough to kill all the organisms originally present. Needham argued that Spallanzani had heated his flasks so long that he had destroyed the "vital principle" in the air that was necessary to bring about the generation of new organisms. The debate remained unsettled for almost another 100 years.

29-20 Pasteur

In 1860, the French chemist Louis Pasteur set out to disprove the theory of spontaneous generation. In his experi-

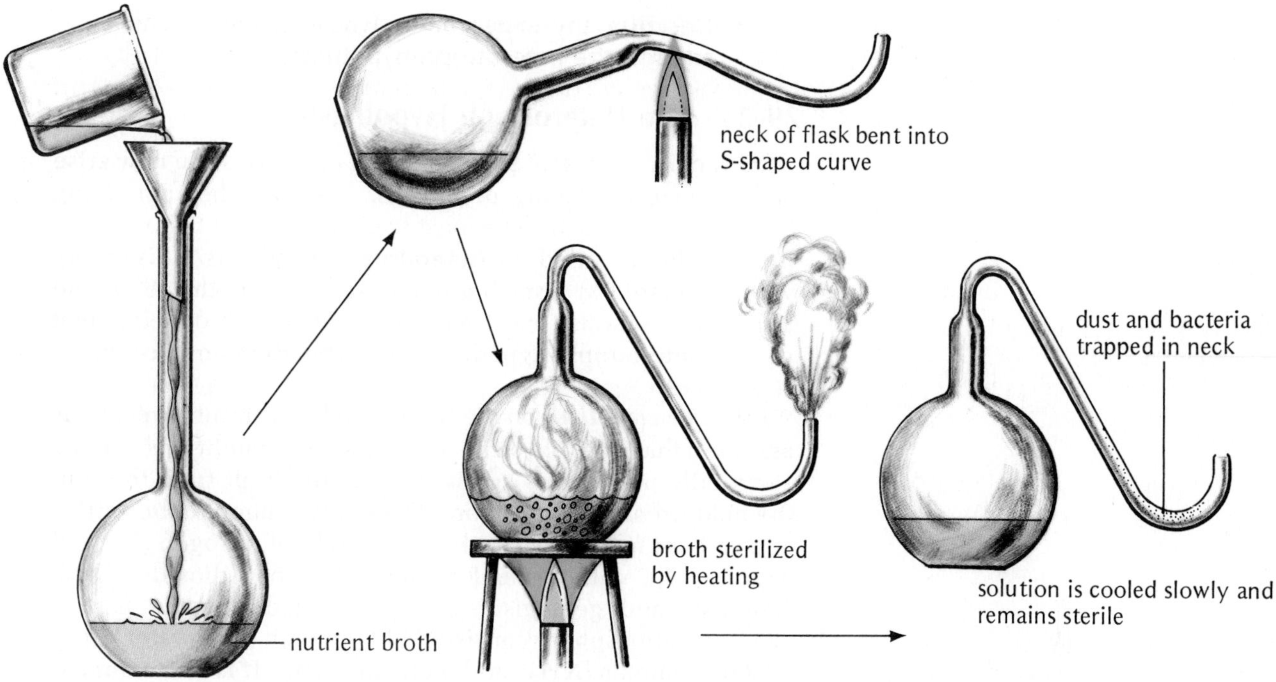

Figure 29-13. Pasteur's Experiment. This experiment showed that microorganisms that developed in a nutrient broth came from spores and microorganisms in the air.

ments he had to take into account the complaints about Spallanzani's experiments—that boiling destroyed the "force" needed for spontaneous generation and that the process required fresh air.

Pasteur thought that microorganisms and their spores were present in the air and that they became active and reproduced when they entered the nutrient broth. He claimed that the presence of air alone could not produce microorganisms in the broth. To test this theory, Pasteur filled flasks with nutrient broth and then heated the necks of the flasks and drew them out into a long S shape, leaving the ends open (see Figure 29-13). The contents of the flasks were then sterilized by boiling. Fresh air could reach the broth, but microorganisms and their spores were trapped in the long necks of the flasks. As long as the flasks were not disturbed, the contents remained sterile. Only when the flasks were tipped and some of the broth ran into the neck and became contaminated did microorganisms grow in the flasks. Pasteur's experiment finally put an end to the idea of spontaneous generation.

MODERN THEORY OF THE ORIGIN OF LIFE

After completing your study of this section, you should be able to:

1. Describe the conditions thought to exist on the primitive earth according to the heterotroph hypothesis.
2. Describe the sequence of development of living things according to the heterotroph hypothesis.

3. Describe any experiments whose results seem to support the heterotroph hypothesis.

29-21 The Heterotroph Hypothesis

If, as most scientists believe, living organisms can now arise only from other living organisms, how did the first living things arise on earth? The most widely accepted theory of the origin of life is called the **heterotroph hypothesis.** This theory was formulated by a small group of scientists in the 1920s and 1930s. The scientist most widely credited with development of the heterotroph hypothesis was the Russian biochemist A. I. Oparin.

Primitive conditions on the earth. The heterotroph hypothesis assumes that the physical and chemical conditions on the earth billions of years ago were very different from those of the modern earth (see Figure 29-14). For example, the earth's atmosphere now consists almost entirely of nitrogen (N_2) and oxygen (O_2), with a small amount of carbon dioxide (CO_2). Chemists and geologists have concluded that the earth's primitive atmosphere consisted of hydrogen (H_2), water vapor (H_2O), ammonia (NH_3), and methane (CH_4). It is also assumed that the temperatures on the earth were much higher than at present. The oceans, when they first formed, were probably not much below the boiling point of water. The oceans of this period have been described as a "hot, thin soup," in which chemical reactions were likely to occur more rapidly than in the cooler waters of the modern earth.

Natural synthesis of organic compounds. Under the primitive conditions just described, the simple compounds in the atmosphere and dissolved in the oceans could have reacted to form

Figure 29-14. Early Conditions on the Earth Compared with Modern Conditions. On the primitive earth, the composition of the atmosphere was different from the modern atmosphere, the temperature was higher, and there were more sources of energy for producing chemical change.

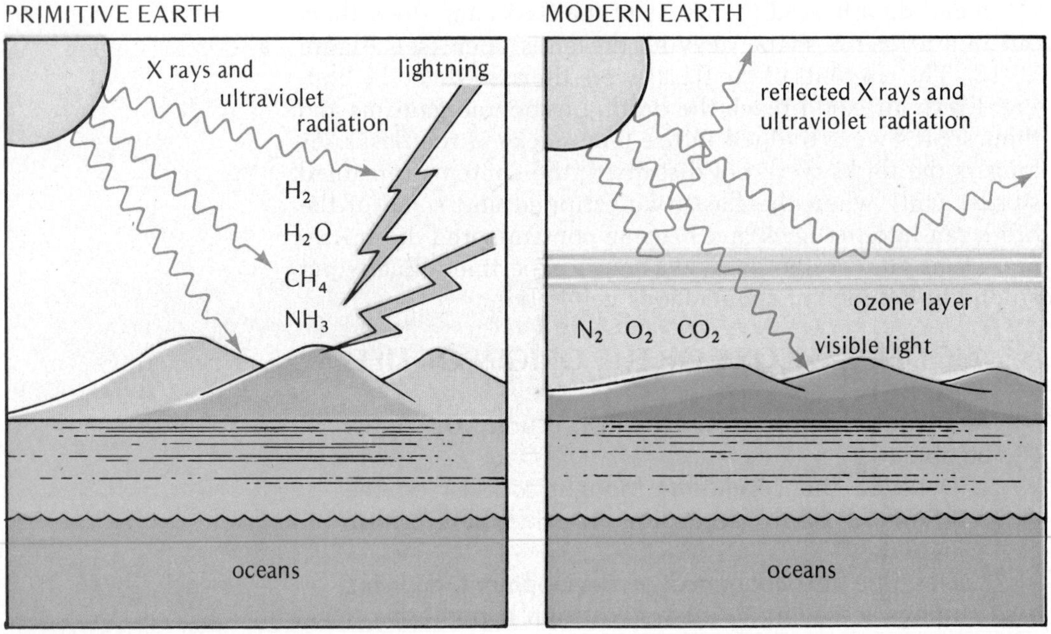

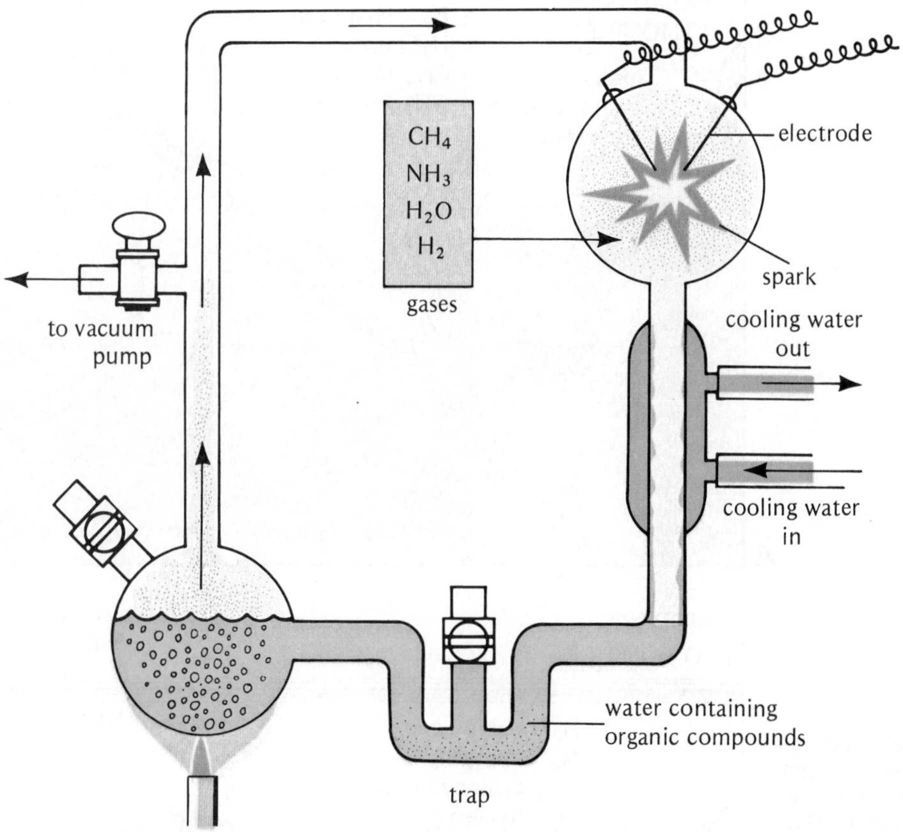

Figure 29-15. Miller's Experiment Imitating Early Conditions on the Earth. A mixture of gases like the theoretical atmosphere was continuously passed through an electric spark. Water in the apparatus dissolved the new substances produced. After a time, the solution was found to contain many organic compounds.

more complex organic compounds. The synthesis of organic compounds from inorganic raw materials requires energy. Many sources of energy are thought to have been present on the primitive earth. There was heat given off by the earth itself; radiation from the decay of radioactive elements in the earth's crust; electrical energy from lightning; and ultraviolet light, visible light, and X rays from the sun. Under such conditions, there would have been adequate energy available for the breakdown and formation of chemical bonds. The first nucleotides, amino acids, and sugars could have been formed during this period. There are experimental results that support this hypothesis.

In 1953, Stanley Miller, a graduate student at the University of Chicago, designed an experiment simulating the conditions thought to be present on the primitive earth. His specially designed experimental apparatus contained four gases—hydrogen, water vapor, ammonia, and methane (see Figure 29-15). Boiling water in the apparatus forced these gases to circulate past sparking electrodes. Miller allowed the experiment to run for a week. At the end of that time, he analyzed the contents of the apparatus and found that it now contained urea, various amino acids, hydrogen cyanide, and organic acids, such as lactic and acetic acids. This experiment clearly demonstrated that organic substances, including amino acids,

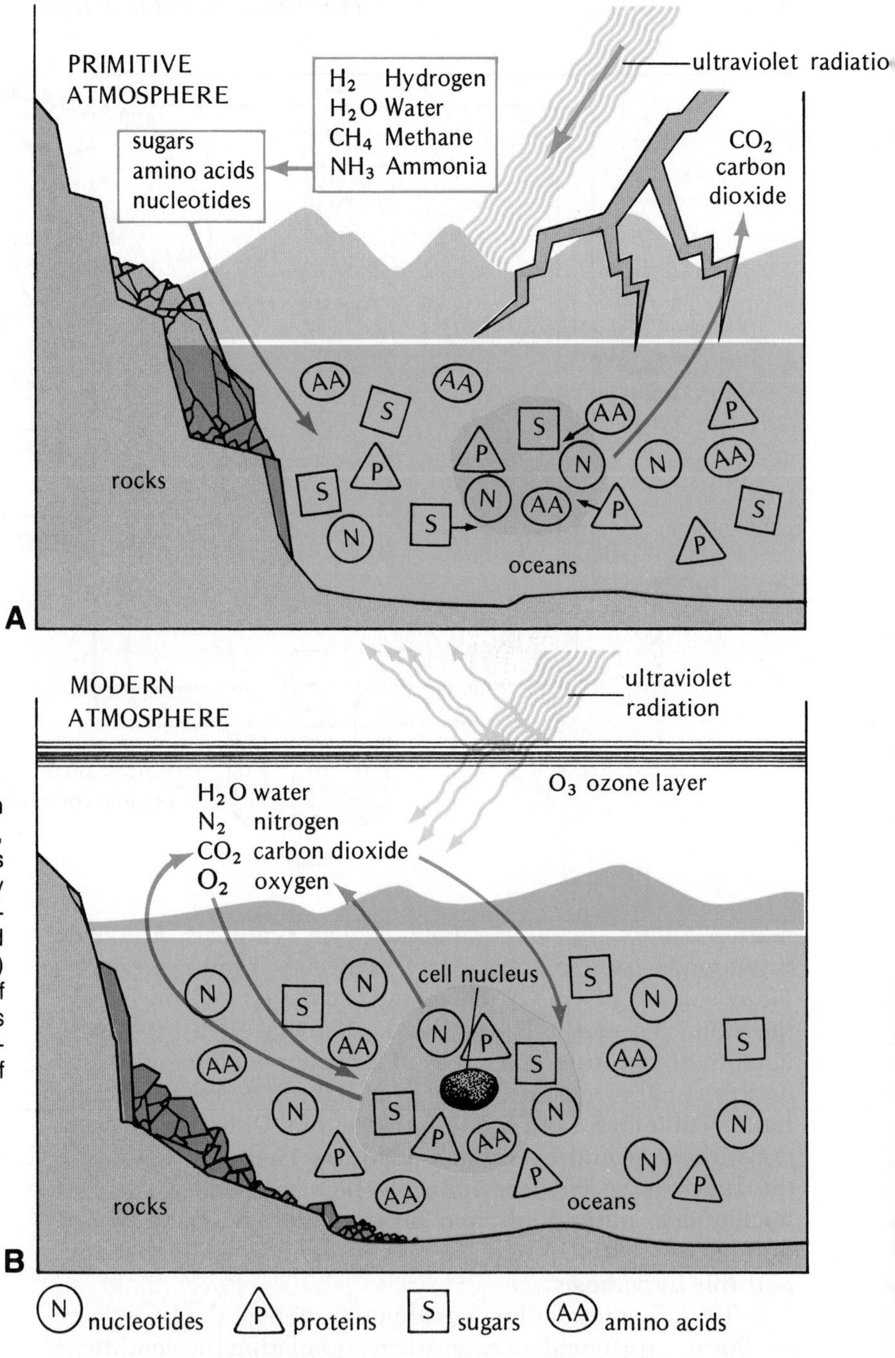

Figure 29-16. The Heterotroph Hypothesis. (A) In the early stages, coacervates obtained organic nutrients from the physical environment. They obtained energy by anaerobic respiration, or fermentation. This released carbon dioxide into the atmosphere. (B) In later stages, autotrophs capable of producing nutrients by photosynthesis appeared. This added oxygen to the atmosphere and led to the development of aerobic respiration.

could have been produced in nature under the conditions assumed for the primitive earth.

The work of an American biochemist, Sidney Fox, showed that, given a supply of amino acids, proteins could also be formed by nonbiological processes. Fox heated a mixture of amino acids at temperatures above 100°C for different lengths of time. Analysis of the resulting compounds revealed the presence of proteins.

Aggregates of organic compounds. Oparin's heterotroph hypothesis suggests that protein complexes could develop into nonliving structures having some of the characteristics of life. Oparin proposed that proteinlike substances in the prehistoric oceans may have formed aggregates, or clusters, of large molecules (see Figure 29-16). He called such aggregates **coacervates** (koh-*as*-er-vayts). These complex structures were surrounded by a "shell" of water molecules, forming a sort of bounding membrane. The development of a limiting membrane made it easier for the internal contents of the structure to be chemically different from the external environment. It also kept various types of molecules in closer contact so that chemical reactions occurred more readily. Coacervates have been formed in the laboratory from proteins and other organic molecules.

Growth and reproduction. Oparin believed that within the coacervates, numerous chemical reactions occurred. As coacervates became more complex, they developed biochemical systems with the capacity to release energy from various types of organic (nutrient) molecules, which were absorbed from the environment. Coacervates, by absorbing material from the environment, grew in size. Eventually, they split in half, and each half would again grow. Such structures would be primitive living things. Oparin called them heterotrophs because they obtained nutrients from the environment.

Anaerobic respiration. Since the atmosphere of the primitive earth contained no free oxygen, it is assumed that these first organisms carried on some form of fermentation for the release of energy. This process resulted in the release of carbon dioxide into the oceans and atmosphere. As the number of heterotrophs increased, the supply of available nutrients in the environment decreased. Thus competition arose between existing heterotrophs. Any organism with biochemical machinery that enabled it to use different or more complex nutrients than most other heterotrophs had a distinct advantage. In this way, organisms containing more and more complex biochemical systems gradually developed.

Photosynthesis and aerobic respiration. Eventually, organisms developed that could use light energy directly for the synthesis of ATP. These were the first photosynthetic organisms. In these organisms, the use of light energy for the synthesis of ATP became coupled with reactions in which carbon dioxide and water were used in the synthesis of carbohydrates. These photosynthetic autotrophs further changed the environment by adding oxygen to the atmosphere.

The presence of oxygen led to the development of organisms with the capacity to carry on aerobic respiration. Aerobic respiration is much more efficient than fermentation in releasing energy from nutrients, so that aerobic organisms became dominant.

The activities of living organisms eventually altered the earth's environment so completely that the conditions that had allowed the development of life were destroyed.

summary

The modern theory of evolution is based on the work of Darwin, which involved the process of natural selection. De Vries added the idea that the appearance of new traits within a species is caused by mutations.

According to modern genetic theory, variations and the appearance of new traits results from gene and chromosome mutations, crossing-over, recombination, and migration of organisms into and out of the population. According to the Hardy-Weinberg law, the frequency of genes within a population remains constant if the population is large, mating is random, there are no mutations, and there is no immigration or emigration. That gene frequencies in populations do change is evidence of evolution.

Adaptations are inherited traits that improve an organism's chance of survival and reproduction. Studies of industrial melanism in the peppered moth show that over short periods of time natural selection can act in favor of certain adaptations. Studies of resistance of bacteria to antibiotics and resistance of insects to DDT show that the resistance does not arise as a result of exposure to antibiotics or DDT. Instead, a small portion of the population had genes for resistance, and when the population was exposed to the antibiotic or DDT, it was the organisms with these genes that survived.

Speciation, the development of new species, can result from geographic and reproductive isolation, polyploidy, and adaptive radiation.

Early theories of the origin of life often included the idea of spontaneous generation. The idea of spontaneous generation was tested by scientists for hundreds of years, and was finally disproved by the experiments of Louis Pasteur in the mid-1800s. The most widely accepted modern theory of the origin of life is the heterotroph hypothesis, which involves the evolution of all forms of living things from the first primitive living cells. According to this theory, the conditions of the primitive earth were much different from those of the modern earth in terms of the makeup of the atmosphere, energy sources, and temperature. It is thought that under those conditions primitive heterotrophic organisms that used some form of fermentation for energy arose by natural processes. From these first organisms all other forms of life developed.

vocabulary

abiogenesis
adaptation
adaptive radiation
behavioral adaptation
camouflage
coacervate
convergent evolution
differential reproduction
gene frequency
gene pool
geographic isolation
Hardy-Weinberg law
heterotroph hypothesis
industrial melanism
mimicry
physiological adaptation
population
population genetics
range
reproductive isolation
speciation
spontaneous generation
structural adaptation
warning coloration

test your learning

Section	
29-1	**1.** How did de Vries explain the appearance of new traits within a species and also the appearance of new species?
29-2	**2.** Describe the sources of variation within a species according to modern genetic theory.
29-3	**3.** Define the terms *population* and *population genetics*.
	4. Why do modern studies of evolution concentrate on populations rather than individual organisms?
29-4	**5.** What is meant by the statement that the frequency of a particular gene in a population is 75 percent?
	6. What is the gene pool of a population?
29-5	**7.** Define the term *differential reproduction*.
	8. Does differential reproduction affect gene frequencies in a population? If so, why?
29-6	**9.** What is the Hardy-Weinberg law?
	10. What conditions must exist for the Hardy-Weinberg law to hold true?
29-7	**11.** In what way is the Hardy-Weinberg law useful?
29-8	**12.** Define the term *adaptation*, and give examples of different types of adaptations.
	13. Explain how camouflage, warning coloration, and mimicry each serves as a means of protection.
29-9	**14.** Explain how geographic separation of different populations results in the development of different subspecies.
	15. Define the term *speciation*.
29-10	**16.** Discuss the importance of geographic and reproductive isolation in the formation of new species.
	17. What is polyploidy, and how does polyploidy result in speciation?
	18. What is adaptive radiation? What example of adaptive radiation did Darwin observe during his voyage on the *Beagle*?
29-11	**19.** What is industrial melanism?
	20. Discuss the study of the color of the peppered moth in industrial and rural England. What was shown about natural selection as a result of this study?
29-12	**21.** Describe the experiments of the Lederbergs on bacterial resistance to antibiotics. What was learned as a result of these experiments?
29-13	**22.** How did insect populations become resistant to DDT?
29-14	**23.** Define the term *abiogenesis*.
	24. What were some common beliefs among the ancient Egyptians and Greeks about the origin of living things?
29-15	**25.** Did van Helmont's experiment support or disprove the theory of spontaneous generation?
29-16	**26.** Briefly describe Redi's experiments on the origin of maggots in decaying meat. Did these experiments support or disprove the theory of spontaneous generation?
29-17	**27.** How did van Leeuwenhoek's discovery of microorganisms affect the belief of scientists in spontaneous generation?

29-18 **28.** Describe Needham's experiments, and explain whether his results supported or disproved the theory of spontaneous generation.
29-19 **29.** Describe Spallanzani's experiments, and explain whether his results supported or disproved the theory of spontaneous generation.
29-20 **30.** Describe the experiment by which Pasteur finally put an end to the idea of spontaneous generation.
29-21 **31.** List the components of the atmosphere of the primitive earth according to the heterotroph hypothesis.
32. List the sources of energy thought to have been present on the primitive earth.
33. Describe Stanley Miller's experiment simulating possible conditions on the primitive earth, and discuss the meaning of its results.
34. Describe the possible course of development of living things from inorganic compounds as proposed by the heterotroph hypothesis.

test your understanding

1. List some of the factors that can change the gene frequencies in a population.
2. Discuss the factors that can be involved in the evolution of a new species.
3. List the proposed order of development of various types of organisms (autotrophic, heterotrophic, aerobic, anaerobic) according to the heterotroph hypothesis.
4. Can you think of any major questions about the development of life that are not answered by the heterotroph hypothesis?

independent research

1. Prepare a report on one of the following topics:
A. Protective coloration in animals.
B. Animals of the Galapagos Islands.
C. Bacterial resistance to antibiotics.
2. Prepare a report on the evolution of marsupials and placental mammals.

UNIT 7
DIVERSITY OF LIVING THINGS

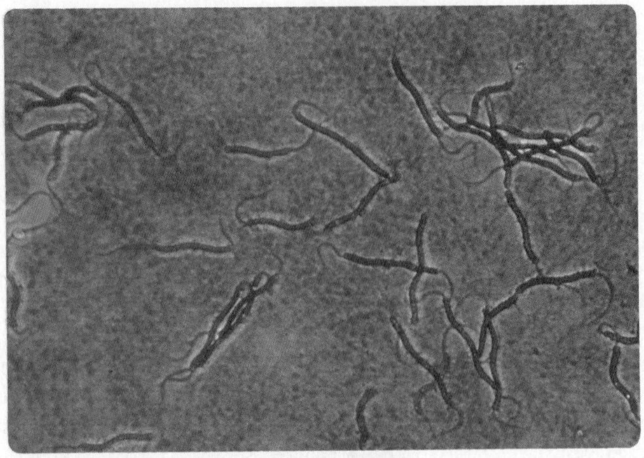

chapter 30

Monera, Protista, and Viruses

KINGDOM MONERA

After completing your study of this section, you should be able to:

1. Name the two types of organisms found in the kingdom Monera.
2. Describe the general characteristics of procaryotic cells.
3. Describe the general characteristics of the blue-green algae.
4. Name the three major groups of bacteria and describe the shape of the members of each group.
5. Describe the general structure of a bacterial cell.
6. Describe the different ways that bacteria obtain energy for their life processes.
7. Describe heterotrophic and autotrophic nutrition in bacteria.
8. Explain what is happening during the different phases of growth of a bacterial culture.
9. Briefly describe how a scientist determines whether a particular microorganism causes a particular disease.
10. List some of the beneficial activities of bacteria.

The **Monera** (muh-*ner*-uh) and **Protista** (proh-*tist*-uh) are kingdoms that include organisms that cannot be classified definitely either as plants or as animals. The viruses are an even more troublesome group. Biologists have not yet decided whether they should be considered to be living organisms. It is also unclear how the viruses are related in terms of evolution to living organisms. Whether viruses appeared before or after living cells is an unanswered question. For these reasons the viruses are studied as a separate group outside the kingdoms of the classification system.

30-1 Procaryotic Cells

The kingdom Monera includes only two different types of organisms—blue-green algae and bacteria. The main difference between moneran cells and the cells of all other organisms is the absence of a distinct, membrane-bounded nucleus. Cells that lack such a nucleus are called **procaryotic** (proh-kar-ee-*aht*-ik), and monerans are called **procaryotes** (proh-*kar*-ee-ohts). Cells that do contain a membrane-bounded nucleus are called **eucaryotic** (yoo-kar-ee-*aht*-ik).

Moneran cells also lack the other membrane-bounded organelles that are usually present in eucaryotic cells. They do not have mitochondria, endoplasmic reticulum, Golgi bodies, lysosomes, or chloroplasts. They do contain ribosomes, but these are smaller than the ribosomes of eucaryotic cells. Although there is no distinct nucleus, procaryotic cells do contain DNA. The DNA is usually concentrated in one region of the cytoplasm. However, unlike the DNA in the nuclei of eucaryotic cells, there is no protein associated with moneran DNA. The major differences between procaryotic and eucaryotic cells are summarized in Table 30-1.

Some of the enzyme-controlled reactions that ordinarily take place in or on the organelles of eucaryotic cells take place on the inner surface of the cell membrane of procaryotes. Often, the cell membrane folds into the cytoplasm. In photosynthetic procaryotes, infoldings of the cell membrane may fill the cytoplasm. These infoldings carry the photosynthetic pigments.

Table 30-1. Comparison of Procaryotic and Eucaryotic Cells.

Cell structure	Procaryotic cells	Eucaryotic cells
Nuclear membrane	Absent	Present
Chromosomes	Contain DNA only	Contain DNA and protein
Endoplasmic reticulum	Absent	Present
Mitochondria	Absent	Present
Golgi apparatus	Absent	Present
Lysosomes	Absent	Present
Chlorophyll	When present, not in chloroplasts	When present, in chloroplasts
Flagella	Twisted strands of protein	Microtubules in 9 + 2 pattern
Cell membrane	Present	Present
Ribosomes	Present but smaller	Present

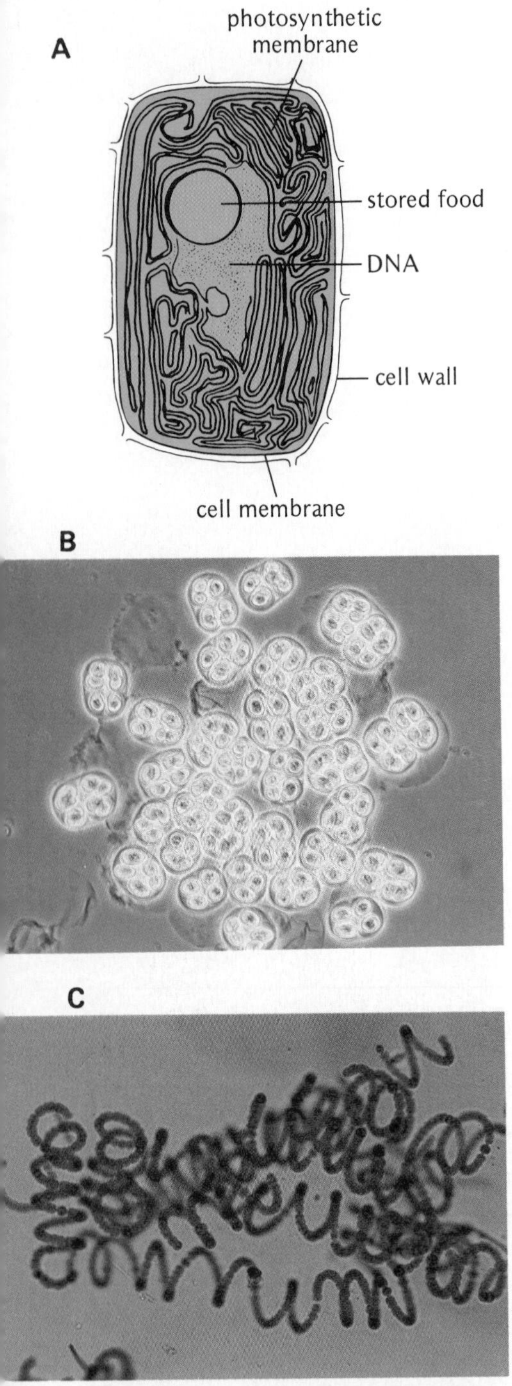

Figure 30-1. Blue-Green Algae. (A) Structure of typical cell of blue-green alga. (B) Cells of *Chroococcus*, which are surrounded by thickened cell walls. (C) *Anabaena*, a type of filamentous blue-green algae.

Procaryotes and eucaryotes differ in other ways. The cell walls of procaryotes do not have the same chemical composition as the cell walls of plants. The flagella of procaryotes do not contain the 9+2 arrangement of microtubules found in the flagella of eucaryotic cells. Instead, they consist of parallel strands of protein twisted around one another like the strands of a rope.

30-2 Blue-Green Algae

The **blue-green algae,** phylum **Cyanophyta** (sy-uh-*nah*-fuh-tuh), are the simplest of all photosynthetic organisms (see Figure 30-1). Members of this phylum contain a blue pigment, *phycocyanin* (fy-koh-*sy*-uh-nin), and the green pigment chlorophyll. About half the species are actually blue-green in color. The cells of the other species contain a number of additional pigments that make them red, yellow, brown, black, or green.

Blue-green algae are found in both fresh and salt water, as well as in soil and on rocks. A few species are found in natural hot springs where few other organisms can survive. Other species are found in icy Arctic waters. The Red Sea owes its name to the occasional appearance of huge populations of red-colored blue-green algae. Ponds or lakes that contain a rich supply of organic matter often develop large populations of blue-green algae. Because these algae thrive in polluted water, they are frequently an indication of the presence of organic pollutants.

The cytoplasm of the cells of blue-green algae generally contains storage granules filled with proteins and carbohydrates. The carbohydrates are stored as *polyglucan,* a compound similar to the glycogen of animal cells. The cells of the blue-greens do not contain the large, fluid-filled vacuoles characteristic of many plant cells. They also have no flagella. The cell walls are strengthened by a complex polysaccharide not found in eucaryotic cells. The outside of the cell walls is often surrounded by a protective jellylike layer, or **slime sheath.**

A few species of blue greens are found as single cells, but most form chains of cells attached to form threadlike filaments. Some blue-green algae live together with fungi to form mixed organisms known as **lichens** (*ly*-kinz).

Filamentous blue-green algae take nitrogen from the atmosphere. Within the filaments are thick-walled, colorless cells called *heterocysts.* Research has demonstrated that the transformation of atmospheric nitrogen into a form usable by the organism takes place in these cells. The capacity of blue-green algae to use atmospheric nitrogen plays an important role in maintaining the fertility of certain soils. For example, blue-green algae provide rice crops with a source of nitrogen, thereby reducing the need for artificial fertilizers.

Among the blue-green algae, reproduction is strictly asexual, taking place by binary fission. As the filaments or colonies grow, they break into smaller parts, often at the heterocysts. Each part can grow into a new colony. Some blue-green algae develop spores that can withstand harsh conditions.

30-3 Bacteria

Bacteria, phylum **Schizomycetes** (skit-suh-my-*seet*-eez), are found almost everywhere—in both fresh and salt water, in soil, in the air, and in and on plants and animals. Bacterial cells are much smaller than the individual cells of plants and animals. In fact, they are among the smallest known living cells. About 2,000 different kinds of bacteria have been identified.

Like the blue-green algae, bacteria are procaryotes—their cells do not contain a distinct nucleus surrounded by a membrane, and they have no mitochondria, Golgi bodies, endoplasmic reticulum, or lysosomes. They do contain ribosomes. The hereditary material, DNA, is present in the cytoplasm in the form of one circular molecule.

Types of bacteria. Bacteria are divided into three major groups according to shape (see Figure 30-2). A spherical bacterium is called a **coccus** *(kahk*-us); a rod-shaped bacterium is called a **bacillus** (buh-*sil*-us); and a spiral or coiled bacterium is called a **spirillum** (spy-*ril*-um). In some species, chains or clumps of bacteria are formed when daughter cells do not separate after cell division. Cocci are found as single cells *(monococci),* in pairs *(diplococci),* in chains *(streptococci),* and in grapelike clusters *(staphylococci).* Bacilli are also found as single cells, pairs *(diplobacilli),* and chains *(streptobacilli).* Spirilla exist only as single cells.

Structure of bacteria. Bacterial cells, like plant cells, are surrounded by a cell wall (see Figure 30-3). However, bacterial cell walls are made up of polysaccharide chains linked to amino acids, while plant cell walls are made up of cellulose, which contains no amino acids. (The antibiotic drug penicillin kills bacteria by inhibiting the formation of cell walls during cell division.) Many bacteria secrete a slimy **capsule** around the outside of the cell wall. The capsule provides additional protection for the cell. Many of the bacteria that cause diseases in animals are surrounded by a capsule. The capsule prevents white blood cells and antibodies from destroying the invading bacterium. Inside the capsule and cell wall is the cell membrane. In aerobic bacteria, the reactions of cellular respiration take place on fingerlike infoldings of the cell membrane. Ribosomes are scattered throughout the cytoplasm, and the DNA is generally found in the center of the cell. Many bacilli and spirilla have flagella, which are used for locomotion in water. A few types of bacteria that lack flagella move by gliding on a surface. However, the mechanism of this gliding motion is unknown.

Figure 30-2. Types of Bacteria.

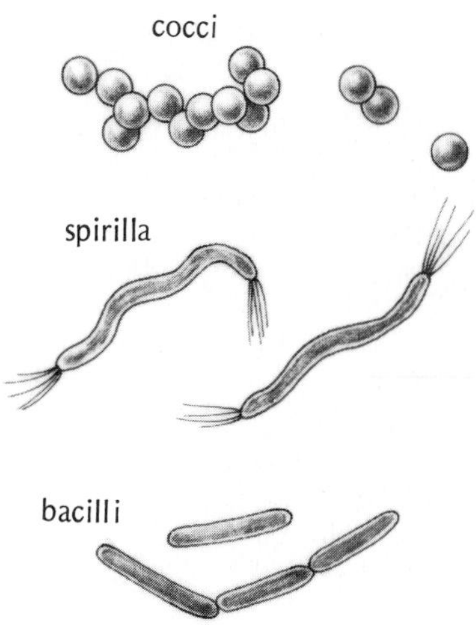

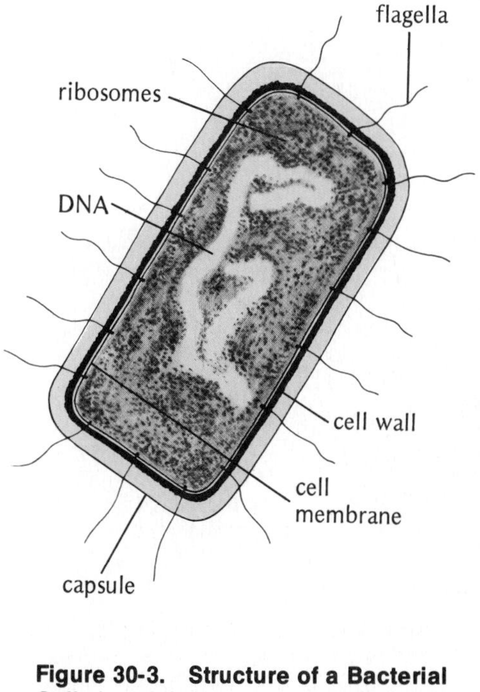

Figure 30-3. Structure of a Bacterial Cell. In addition to a cell wall, many types of bacteria are surrounded by a slimy capsule.

Life functions of bacteria. Most bacteria are aerobic—they require free oxygen to carry on cellular respiration. Some bacteria, called *facultative anaerobes* (*fak*-ul-tayt-iv *an*-uh-rohbz) can live in either the presence or absence of free oxygen. They obtain energy either by aerobic respiration when oxygen is present or by fermentation when oxygen is absent. Still other bacteria cannot live in the presence of oxygen. These are called *obligate* (*ob*-lih-get) *anaerobes.* Such bacteria obtain energy only by fermentation. *Clostridium botulinum,* a member of this group, causes *botulism* (bahch-uh-liz-um), the most dangerous kind of food poisoning. *C. botulinum* grows well in canned foods that have not been properly sterilized. Botulism is caused by the toxin produced by these bacteria.

Through fermentation, different groups of bacteria produce a wide variety of organic compounds. Besides ethyl alcohol and lactic acid, bacterial fermentation can produce acetic acid, acetone, butyl alcohol, glycol, butyric acid, propionic acid, and methane, the main component of natural gas.

Most bacteria are heterotrophic—they must obtain ready-made food from the environment. Heterotrophic bacteria are either saprophytes or parasites. Saprophytes feed on the remains of dead plants and animals, and ordinarily do not cause disease. They release digestive enzymes onto the organic matter. The enzymes break down the large food molecules into smaller molecules, which are absorbed by the bacterial cells. Parasites live on or in living organisms, and may cause disease.

A few types of bacteria are autotrophic—they can synthesize the organic nutrients they require from inorganic substances. Autotrophic bacteria are either photosynthetic or chemosynthetic. The photosynthetic bacteria contain chlorophylls (called *bacteriochlorophylls*) that are different from the plant chlorophylls. In bacterial photosynthesis, hydrogen is obtained by the splitting of compounds other than water. Therefore, oxygen is not released by bacterial photosynthesis. One type of photosynthetic bacteria splits hydrogen sulfide, releasing pure sulfur. Chemosynthetic bacteria obtain energy by oxidizing inorganic substances, such as compounds of iron or sulfur, nitrites, and ammonia. The energy is used for the synthesis of organic compounds. The nitrifying bacteria in the nitrogen cycle oxidize ammonia or nitrites to nitrates, which can be used by plants as a source of nitrogen.

Bacteria generally reproduce asexually by binary fission. The genetic material replicates, and the parent cell divides into two equal daughter cells. Under ideal conditions of food, temperature, and space, bacteria can divide about every 20 minutes. At this rate, in 24 hours one bacterial cell could theoretically produce a mass weighing about 2 million kilograms. However, such growth never occurs. Instead, the reproductive rate always slows because the food supply becomes used up and waste products accumulate.

Figure 30-4 shows a typical growth curve for a bacterial culture. It shows the number of bacteria in the culture plotted against time. The growth curve can be divided into four phases. In the *lag phase*, the bacteria are adjusting to their environment, and growth is slow. In the *exponential phase*, the bacteria are dividing very rapidly. In the *stationary phase*, the reproductive rate equals the death rate. In the *death phase*, the bacteria are dying off faster than they are reproducing.

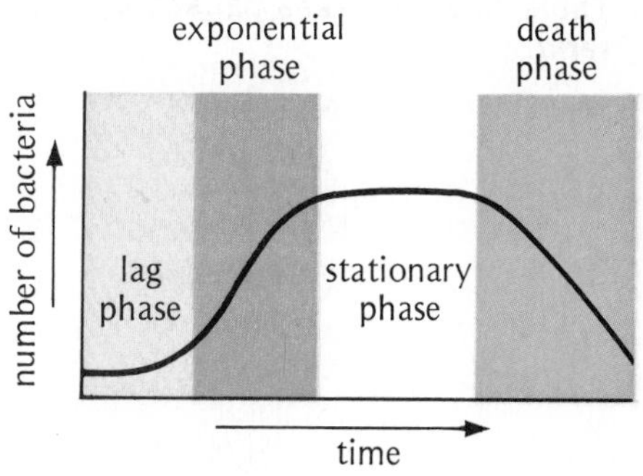

Figure 30-4. Growth Curve of a Bacterial Culture.

Although bacteria usually reproduce asexually, sexual reproduction involving the transfer of chromosomes or chromosomal parts does occur occasionally. The three mechanisms of chromosome transfer are conjugation, transformation, and transduction.

Bacteria and disease. The idea that bacteria can cause disease—the **germ theory of disease**—was developed by the French scientist **Louis Pasteur** in the mid-1880s. Bacteria can cause disease in several ways. (1) The bacteria can become so numerous that they interfere with the normal functioning of the body. (2) In some diseases, bacteria destroy body cells and tissues. (3) Some bacteria produce toxins, or poisons, that interfere with the normal functioning of the body.

Robert Koch, a German physician who studied the causes of tuberculosis and anthrax, developed a set of rules to determine whether a specific organism is the cause of a specific disease. His rules are:

1. The suspected disease microorganism should always be found in animals with the disease and should not be found in healthy animals.
2. The microorganism must be isolated from the diseased animal and grown in pure culture (a culture containing only one kind of microorganism).
3. When microorganisms from the culture are injected into a healthy, susceptible animal, they must produce the disease.
4. The microorganism must be isolated from the experimentally infected animal, grown in pure culture again, and should be the same as the original microorganism isolated in step 2.

These rules are still used today. They have helped to establish which bacteria cause the diseases listed in Table 30-2.

Bacteria and decay. For every natural organic product, there is some variety of bacteria that can use it as a source of food and energy. Bacteria thus bring about the breakdown of organic materials, a process called *decay*. While decay is necessary for the recycling of materials in nature, it is often undesirable for human purposes. The decay of food by bacterial action causes it to rot or spoil and become unfit or harmful to eat.

In order to grow and reproduce, bacteria need food, moderate temperature, moisture, darkness, and if aerobic, oxygen. Bacteria cannot grow if any of these conditions are absent.

Table 30-2. Diseases Caused by Bacteria.

Disease	Bacterium
	COCCI
Boils, carbuncles	*Staphylococcus pyrogenes*
Gonorrhea	*Neisseria gonorrhoeae*
Meningitis	*Neisseria meningitidis*
Pneumonia	*Diplococcus pneumoniae*
Scarlet fever	*Streptococcus scarlatinae*
Strep throat	*Streptococcus pyrogenes*
	BACILLI
Botulism	*Clostridium botulinum*
Diphtheria	*Corynebacterium diphtheriae*
Plague	*Yersinia pestis*
Tetanus	*Clostridium tetani*
Typhoid fever	*Salmonella typhi*
	SPIRILLA
Cholera	*Vibrio comma*
Syphilis	*Treponema pallidum*

This information is used in protecting human foods against spoilage by bacteria. Table 30-3 summarizes some of the methods for doing this.

Beneficial activities of bacteria. Most bacteria are harmless, and, in fact, are necessary for the continuance of life. The bacteria of decay break down the tissues of dead animals and plants, and return oxygen, carbon, nitrogen, phosphorus, and sulfur to the air, soil, and water. These elements can then be used by other living things. The role of bacteria in the recycling of materials is discussed in Chapter 36.

Bacteria are very important in the preparation of certain foods, such as cheeses, sauerkraut, and pickles. They are also used in industry and agriculture. One group of bacteria, the actinomycetes, is responsible for the production of many useful antibiotics, including streptomycin.

KINGDOM PROTISTA

After completing your study of this section, you should be able to:

1. Compare and contrast the general characteristics of the euglenoids, the chrysophytes, and the dinoflagellates.
2. Describe the structure of diatoms and explain their importance in nature.

Method	Food preserved	Why effective
Freezing	Meat, vegetables, desserts	Stops growth and reproduction of bacteria
Refrigeration	Meat, eggs, butter, milk	Slows growth and reproduction of bacteria
Pasteurization (heating to moderate temperature followed by rapid cooling)	Milk, egg products, apple juice, and other beverages	Almost all the bacteria are killed by the heat. Cooling slows the growth of remaining bacteria
Drying	Meats, grains, flour, starch, fruits, sugar, powdered milk, powdered eggs	Bacteria require moisture for growth
Canning	Vegetables, fruits, meats	Food is sterilized by heat; sealed container prevents entrance of new bacteria
Preservatives:		Kill bacteria or remove moisture
Salt	Meats	
Sugar	Fruits	
Lactic acid (from fermentation)	Cucumbers (pickles) and cabbage (sauerkraut)	
Vinegar	Vegetables	

Table 30-3. Methods of Food Preservation.

3. Describe the structure and life processes of the euglena.
4. Describe the general characteristics of each of the four phyla of protozoa—the sarcodines, ciliates, zooflagellates, and sporozoans.
5. Describe the structure of foraminiferans and radiolarians, and explain their importance in nature.
6. Describe the life cycle of *Plasmodium,* the organism that causes malaria.
7. Describe the general characteristics and life cycles of the slime molds.

Members of the kingdom Protista are all either unicellular or very simple multicellular organisms. Protists are eucaryotes—their cells contain a distinct, membrane-bounded nucleus and many different types of cytoplasmic organelles. The organisms included in this kingdom are extremely varied. There are both autotrophic and heterotrophic forms. Some are

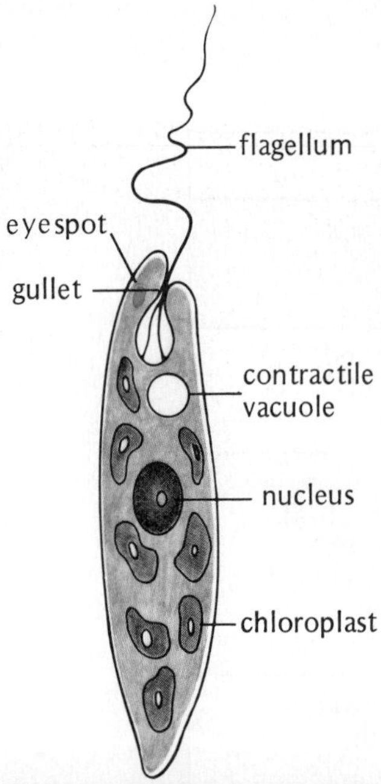

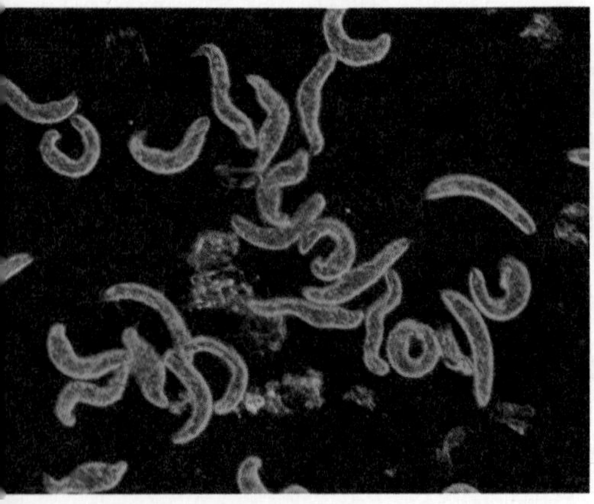

Figure 30-5. Euglena. The green color of euglenas is caused by the presence of chlorophyll.

motile and some are nonmotile. In some, reproduction is asexual, and in others it is sexual. Some protists are plantlike, some are animal-like, and still others are funguslike.

30-4 Phylum Euglenophyta—The Euglenoids

The **euglenoids** (yoo-*glee*-noyds) of the phylum **Euglenophyta** (yoo-gleen-*ah*-fuh-tuh) show both plantlike and animal-like characteristics. Like plants, they contain chloroplasts and can carry on photosynthesis. Like animals, the cells have one or two flagella that are used in locomotion. Also like animals, they lack cell walls. However, inside the cell membrane there is a grooved, flexible **pellicle** (*pel*-uh-kul) made up of protein. The pellicle gives the organism a definite shape. Euglenoids are found mainly in freshwater lakes, streams, and ponds.

The best-known euglenoids are the bright green *euglenas* (see Figure 30-5). The euglena is an oval-shaped, unicellular organism. The cell has a large, central nucleus and numerous small chloroplasts. The chloroplasts contain chlorophylls a and b, as well as several other pigments. When light is available, euglenas carry on photosynthesis. However, in the absence of light, they live as heterotrophs, absorbing dissolved nutrients from the environment. Food, in the form of starchlike *paramylum* (par-*am*-uh-lum), is stored in an organelle called the *pyrenoid* (*py*-ruh-noyd).

Euglenas have one large flagellum that is used in movement and one short flagellum that is inactive. The bases of the flagella are within an inpocketing called the *reservoir*. Next to the reservoir within the cell is a contractile vacuole, which excretes excess water into the reservoir and out of the cell. Near the reservoir is the red-orange eyespot, or *stigma*, which is sensitive to light. The stigma makes it possible for the euglena to place itself to obtain maximum light for photosynthesis.

30-5 Phylum Chrysophyta—Yellow-Green and Golden-Brown Algae and Diatoms

The **chrysophytes** (*kris*-uh-fyts), phylum **Chrysophyta** (kris-*ah*-fuh-tuh), are mostly unicellular organisms that contain large amounts of the yellow-brown carotenoids and fucoxanthins. These pigments give the cells their characteristic colors. Chlorophyll is also present. **Yellow-green** and **golden-brown algae** are mostly freshwater organisms, while **diatoms** (*dy*-uh-tahmz) are found in both fresh and salt water. Members of this phylum store food as oils or as a starchlike carbohydrate called *chrysolaminaran* (kris-uh-lam-uh-*nar*-in). The cell walls, or shells, of these organisms contain compounds of silicon that make them rigid. Yellow-green and golden-brown algae have one or two flagella. Diatoms lack flagella, but move by cytoplasmic streaming.

The diatoms are the most numerous members of this phylum. They are tremendously abundant in the oceans, where they serve as a source of food for fish and other aquatic animals. The cell cytoplasm of diatoms contains a nucleus and one or more chloroplasts. These organisms usually reproduce asexually, but sexual reproduction does occur.

The shells of diatoms are made up of two halves that fit together like the top and bottom of a box (see Figure 30-6). Microscopic examination of these shells shows an amazing variety of forms. When diatoms die, their shells sink to the ocean floor. In some places, the shells have accumulated in layers hundreds of meters thick, forming rocklike deposits known as *diatomaceous* (dy-uh-tuh-*may*-shus) *earth*. Some of the deposits formed millions of years ago are now on land. Diatomaceous earth is mined and used in metal polishes, toothpaste, insulation, and filters.

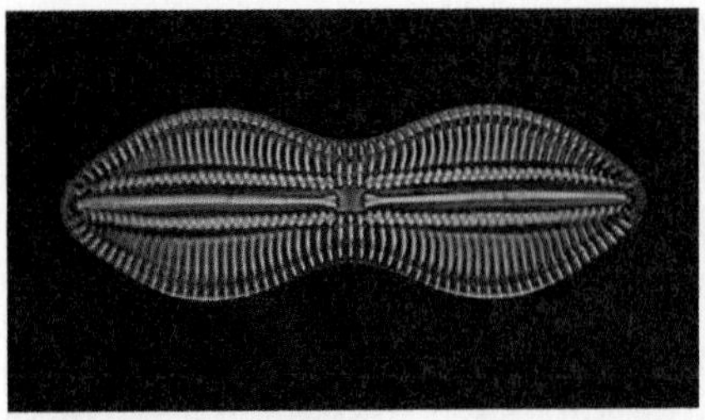

Figure 30-6. Diatom.

30-6 Phylum Pyrrophyta—The Dinoflagellates

The **dinoflagellates** (dy-noh-*flaj*-uh-luhts), phylum **Pyrrophyta** (py-*rah*-fuh-tuh), are a group of unicellular algae found mainly in the oceans. Some types are photosynthetic, while others are heterotrophic. The photosynthetic dinoflagellates, along with diatoms, serve as the major source of food for many aquatic animals. Many dinoflagellates have a cellulose shell made up of armorlike plates (see Figure 30-7). They all have two flagella—one running in a beltlike groove around the middle of the organism and the other extending from one end of the organism. Dinoflagellates have a twirling or rolling motion in the water. In these organisms food is stored as oil or starch. Reproduction is asexual.

The photosynthetic dinoflagellates contain chlorophyll, and some contain other pigments as well. They therefore vary in color from yellow-green to brown and red. Some of the red dinoflagellates produce poisonous substances. Occasionally, these organisms undergo a population explosion, producing a "red tide" that kills many fish.

Figure 30-7. Dinoflagellates.

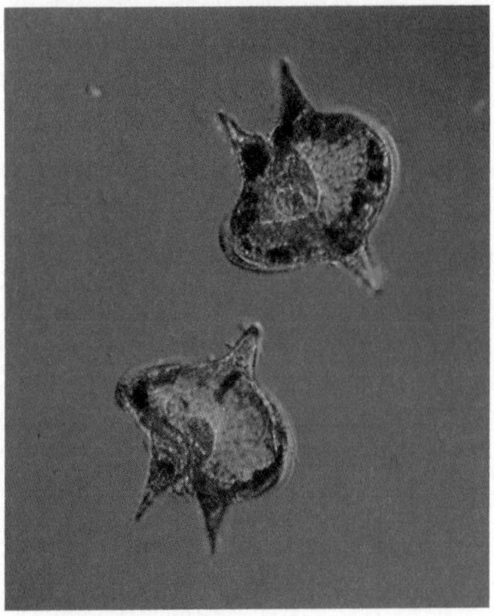

30-7 The Protozoa

Protozoa are animal-like microscopic organisms. Most are unicellular, but there are a few simple colonial forms. Protozoa are found in fresh and salt water, in the soil, and in the bodies of other organisms. Most are motile, moving by means of pseudopods, flagella, or cilia. All protozoa are heterotrophic—they must obtain food from the environment.

The life processes of two common protozoans—ameba and paramecium—were discussed in Unit 2.

On the basis of their method of locomotion, protozoa are divided into four phyla: the Sarcodina, the Ciliata, the Mastigophora, and the Sporozoa.

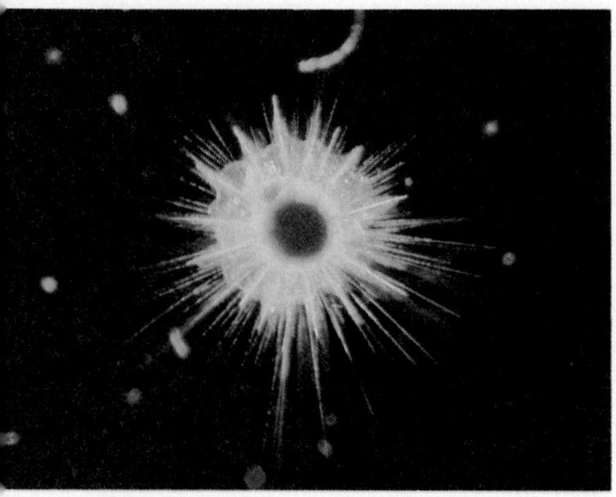

Figure 30-8. A Radiolarian. The pseudopods of the radiolarian are thin and pointed.

30-8 Phylum Sarcodina—Ameboid Protozoans

The **sarcodines,** phylum **Sarcodina** (sar-kuh-*dy*-nuh), are protozoans that move and capture prey by means of "false feet," or pseudopods. Members of this group are found in both fresh and salt water. A few are disease-causing parasites. The best known of the sarcodines are the amebas, unicellular organisms that constantly change shape.

Amebic dysentery is a disease caused by a parasitic type of ameba. This species is common in tropical areas. It lives in the human large intestine and feeds on the intestinal walls, causing bleeding ulcers. The disease is spread when some of the amebas form cysts, which pass out of the body with the digestive wastes. A person becomes infected by drinking or eating contaminated water or food. Amebic dysentery can be treated with drugs. It can be eliminated only by proper sewage disposal.

Unlike amebas, which are surrounded only by a cell membrane, some sarcodines are surrounded by shells. Among these are *foraminiferans* (fuh-ram-uh-*nif*-un-runz), which have calcium-containing shells, and *radiolarians* (rayd-ee-oh-*lehr*-ee-unz), which have silicon-containing shells (see Figure 30-8). Both are abundant in the oceans. When these organisms die, their shells drop into the mud of the ocean bottom. In some places, the accumulation of tremendous numbers of foraminiferan shells has formed huge chalk deposits. The white cliffs of Dover on the English coast were formed in this way. Radiolarian shells make up much of the bottom ooze in some parts of the oceans, and they are also an important part of certain silicon-containing rocks.

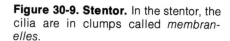

Figure 30-9. Stentor. In the stentor, the cilia are in clumps called *membranelles.*

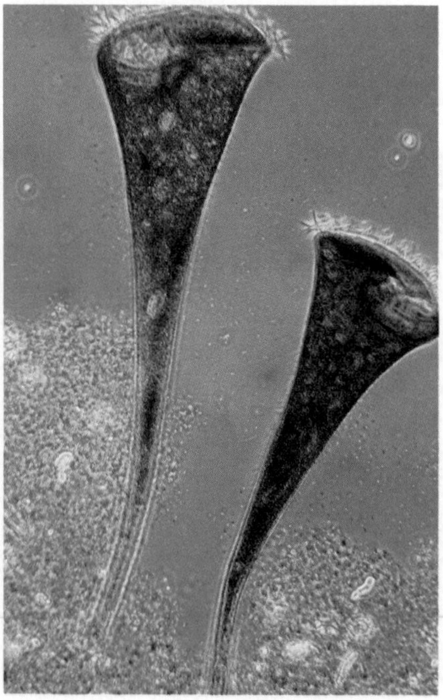

30-9 Phylum Ciliata—the Ciliates

The ciliates, phylum **Ciliata** (sil-ee-*ah*-tuh), are found in both fresh and salt water. They are the most complex protozoans. In addition to the paramecium, the ciliates include vorticella, stentor, and didinium (see Figure 30-9). The cells of ciliates are highly structured, showing a wide variety of organelles. Members of this group have many hairlike cilia. In some ciliates, the cilia are attached together in rows, forming structures called *cirri* (*sihr*-ry). In others, the cilia are in clumps, forming structures called *membranelles.* The coordinated beating of the cilia, cirri, or membranelles, enables the organism to move through the water.

Ciliates have a protective outer covering called a pellicle. Some ciliates have structures called *trichocysts* (*trik*-uh-sists) beneath the pellicle. Trichocysts are barbed structures that are discharged for defense or to aid in capturing prey. Also beneath the pellicle is a system of contractile fibers, similar to muscle fibers.

Ciliates have an oral groove through which food particles enter the organism. The movement of food into the oral groove is aided by the beating of the cilia. At the base of the oral groove, the food is enclosed in a vacuole, where it is digested. Some ciliates have contractile vacuoles, which collect and excrete excess water from the cell. Most reproduction in ciliates is asexual by binary fission. However, sexual reproduction by conjugation also occurs .

Ciliates differ from other protozoa in having two nuclei. The large macronucleus controls normal cell metabolism. The smaller micronucleus functions only in sexual reproduction. Ciliates can live without the micronucleus, but not without the macronucleus.

30-10 Phylum Mastigophora—The Zooflagellates

The **zooflagellates** (zoh-uh-*flaj*-uh-luhts), phylum **Mastigophora** (mas-tuh-*gahf*-uh-ruh), are thought to be the most primitive of the protozoans. Although some zooflagellates are free living, most live in the bodies of animals and plants. Members of this group move by the beating of long, whiplike flagella. Some have only one flagellum, while others have many. The flagella have the typical 9+2 arrangement of microtubules (see page 76). Zooflagellates reproduce both asexually and sexually.

Among the zooflagellates is *Trypanosoma gambiense* (try-pan-uh-*sohm*-uh *gam*-bee-enz), which causes African sleeping sickness (see Figure 30-10). The parasite multiplies in the blood, releasing toxins. The symptoms of the disease include weakness, sleepiness, and fever. If left untreated, the victim eventually dies. Although the protozoan lives in the blood of wild African mammals, it does not harm them. It is spread to humans and domestic animals by the bite of the tsetse fly.

Another zooflagellate is *Trichonympha* (trik-uh-*nim*-fuh), which lives in the digestive tract of the termite. Termites do not have the enzymes necessary to break down wood, but *Trichonympha* does. Thus, the zooflagellate breaks down the wood eaten by the termite, and both organisms absorb and use the nutrients.

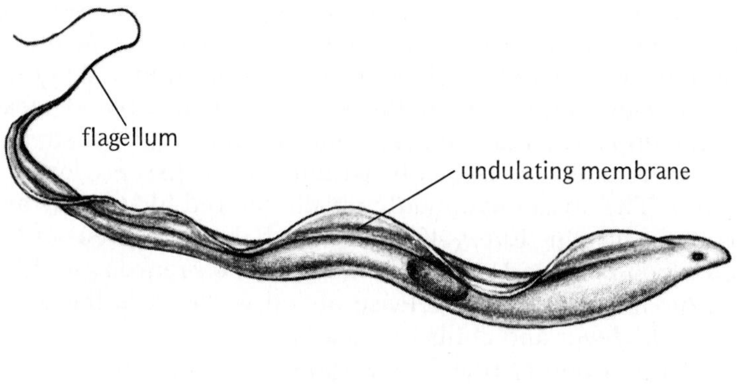

Figure 30-10. *Trypanosoma gambiense.* This zooflagellate causes African sleeping sickness.

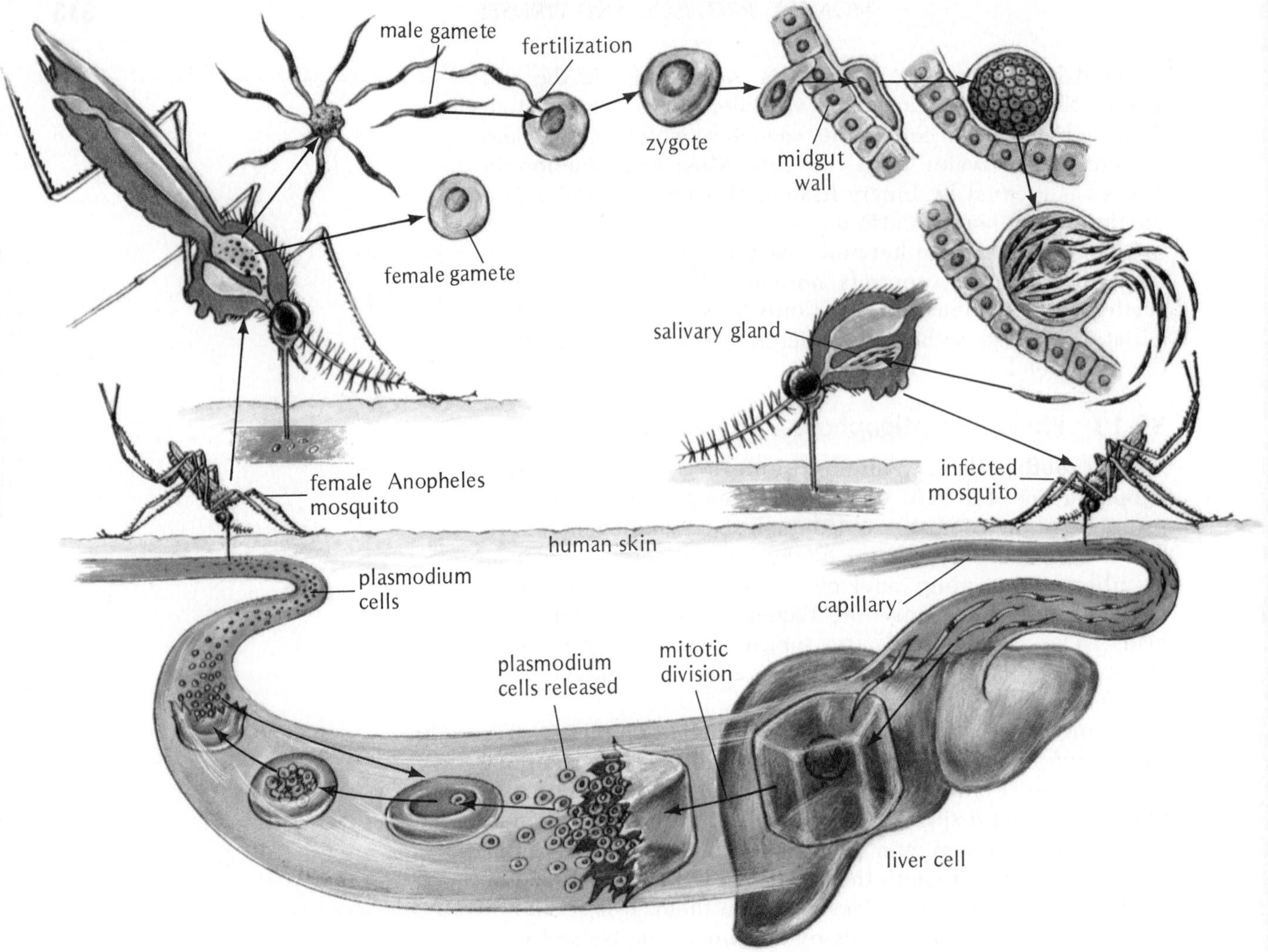

Figure 30-11. Life Cycle of the Malarial Parasite.

30-11 Phylum Sporozoa—The Sporozoans

Members of the phylum **Sporozoa** are nonmotile. All are parasitic protozoans. They obtain nutrients from the bodies of their hosts. All members of this phylum produce spores during the asexual phase of their complicated life cycles. The best known sporozoans are the members of the genus *Plasmodium* (plaz-*mohd*-ee-um), which cause malaria in humans (see Figure 30-11). The parasite is transmitted to humans by the bite of the female *Anopheles* (uh-*nahf*-uh-leez) mosquito. When an infected mosquito pierces the skin to obtain a blood meal, *Plasmodium* cells are injected into the human bloodstream. The cells multiply asexually within human tissues, forming spores. The spores eventually invade the red blood cells and multiply further. Every 48 to 72 hours they break out of the red blood cells and invade new ones. The breakdown of the red blood cells and the release of cell wastes into the blood cause the fever and chills of malaria.

After a period of time, some spores develops into gametocytes. When the infected person is bitten by a mosquito, the gametocytes pass into the mosquito with the blood. If it is a female *Anopheles* mosquito, the gametocytes develop into gametes in the mosquito's stomach. Fertilization occurs, forming a zygote. The zygote divides, forming thousands of infective cells. These cells migrate into the tissues of the mosquito, including the salivary glands, where they are ready to infect the next victim. Malaria can be treated with drugs such as quinine and chloroquine, but the most effective way to prevent malaria is to destroy the *Anopheles* mosquito.

30-12 The Slime Molds

The **slime molds** are an unusual group of organisms that show both protozoa-like and fungus-like stages in their life cycle. They are most commonly found on decaying matter in cool, damp places in forests.

The *true slime molds* belong to the phylum **Myxomycota** (*mix*-uh-my-*kaht*-uh). In the most commonly observed stage of their life cycle, they look like giant amebas, or slimy masses, generally white, yellow, or red in color (see Figure 30-12). This stage is called the *plasmodium*. The cytoplasm of the plasmodium contains many nuclei not separated by cell membranes. The plasmodium is ameboid, and feeds by engulfing bits of organic matter with pseudopods as it creeps along the forest floor. When conditions for growth become unfavorable, the plasmodium stops moving around and develops stalked, spore-producing structures called *fruiting bodies* (see Figure 30-13). Within the fruiting bodies, haploid spores are produced by meiosis. The spores are eventually released, and if they land in a moist, suitable environment, they germinate to form flagellated gametes. Two gametes join to form a diploid

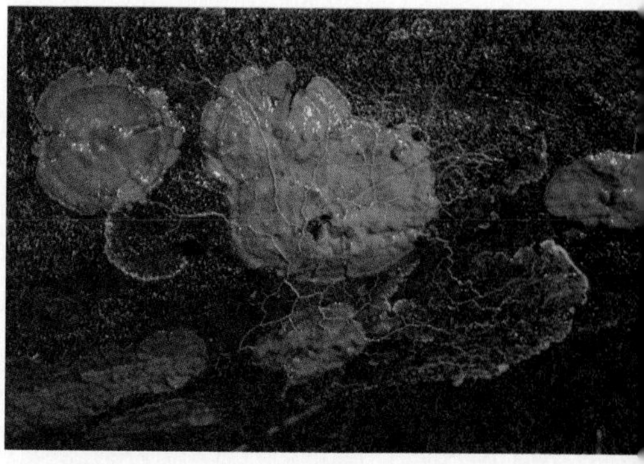

Figure 30-12. Plasmodium of a Slime Mold.

Figure 30-13. Life Cycle of a Slime Mold.

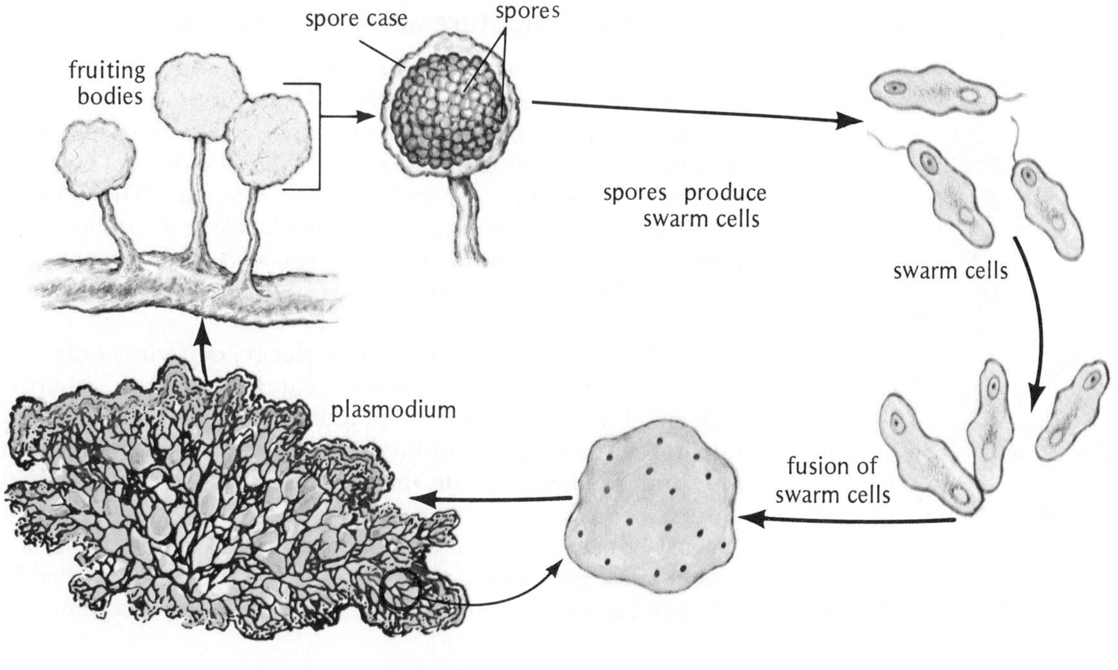

zygote, which becomes ameboid. The nucleus of the zygote undergoes repeated mitotic divisions, and becomes a new plasmodium.

Slime molds of the phylum **Acrasiomycota** (uh-*krayz*-ee-oh-my-*kaht*-uh) are called the *cellular slime molds.* In this group, the spores give rise to separate, haploid, ameboid cells. The individual ameboid cells move about and feed. They also divide repeatedly, producing new, daughter haploid cells. When food becomes scarce, these individual cells come together to form a *pseudoplasmodium.* Within the pseudoplasmodium, unlike the true plasmodium, the individual, membrane-bounded cells are distinguishable. The pseudoplasmodium forms fruiting bodies that produce spores. Apparently there is no diploid phase in the life cycle of the cellular slime molds.

VIRUSES

After completing your study of this section, you should be able to:

1. Describe the basic structure of a virus.
2. Explain how viruses replicate within a host cell.
3. Define the term *bacteriophage.*
4. Describe the body's defenses against viral infections.

Viruses are unique. They do not fit with any other group in the classification of living organisms. Although much is known about their structure and their method of replication, scientists still cannot decide if viruses are living or nonliving. Viruses are not made up of cells. They cannot reproduce, or replicate, unless they are inside a host cell.

30-13 Viral Structure and Reproduction

Viruses range in size from 0.01 to 0.3 microns. A virus consists of a nucleic acid core surrounded by a protein coat (see Figure 30-14). The virus shown in the diagram is one that infects bacteria. Other viruses have different shapes, but still consist of a protein coat and a nucleic acid core. The nucleic acid may be single- or double-stranded DNA, or it may be RNA. Viruses do not contain any internal structures or enzyme systems. Outside a host cell, viruses appear to be completely nonliving.

A cell can be infected by a particular type of virus only if it has receptors for the virus protein coat. In some types of virus infections, the entire virus, including both protein coat and nucleic acid, enter the host cell. In others, the protein coat of the virus remains outside the cell and only the nucleic acid enters.

Most viruses, upon entering a host cell, take over the cell's biochemical machinery and use it to produce more viruses. In DNA-containing viruses, the viral DNA serves as a template

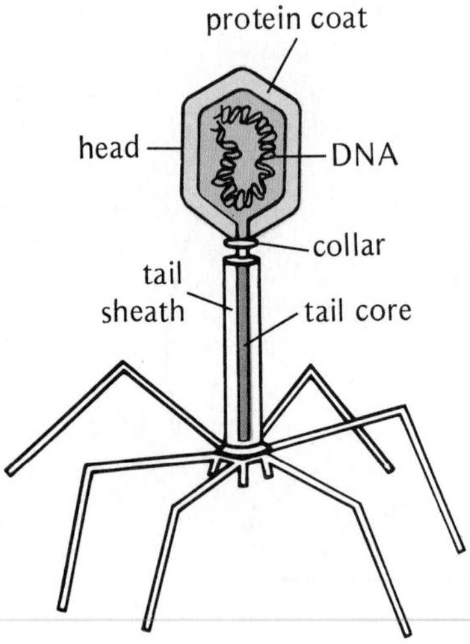

Figure 30-14. Structure of a Virus.

for producing more viral DNA. It also produces viral mRNA to direct the synthesis of viral proteins. If the viral genetic material is RNA, this RNA directs the production of more viral RNA and acts as its own mRNA. Among the proteins synthesized by the viral mRNA are enzymes that can lyse, or break down, the cell membrane of the host cell. After a number of new viruses have been assembled in the host cell, the cell membrane (and cell wall, if any) is broken, or lysed, and the viruses are released. Each new virus can infect another cell.

A virus that infects bacteria is called a **bacteriophage** (bak-*teer*-ee-uh-fayj). Some bacteriophages behave like the viruses described above. They take over the machinery of the bacterial cell, replicate themselves, and lyse the bacterial cell wall. Other bacterial viruses behave differently. When the viral DNA enters the cell, it becomes part of the bacterial chromosome. When the bacterial chromosome replicates during cell division, the viral DNA replicates too. When the bacterial cell divides, the two resulting daughter cells each contain a copy of the viral DNA along with the bacterial chromosome. The viral DNA may remain harmless through many generations, but eventually it replicates, producing new viruses that lyse and destroy the cell.

30-14 Viruses and Disease

Many human diseases are caused by viruses, including the common cold, polio, chicken pox, measles, and influenza. The human body can protect itself from viruses in several ways. The immune response to a virus occurs when lymphocytes in the blood produce antibodies that destroy the virus (see page 166). Some lymphocytes also react with virus-infected cells and destroy them. In this way no new viruses can be transmitted to healthy cells. The body also produces a substance called *interferon* when infected by a virus (see page 168). Interferon provides protection against all types of viruses. Much scientific research is now being done on interferon in search of a cure for diseases such as cancer and multiple sclerosis. Doctors also use vaccines to prevent certain virus-caused diseases, such as polio and measles (see page 168). The vaccine stimulates the production of antibodies against the disease without causing the disease. If the disease-causing virus enters the body, it is immediately attacked and destroyed by the antibodies.

sidelights

In searching for the organisms that cause certain plant diseases, scientists have discovered a disease-causing agent that is much smaller that a virus. These agents are called **viroids.** Using an assortment of laboratory techniques, it was found that viroids consist of a small piece of single-stranded RNA.

In viruses, the molecular weight of the DNA or RNA is at least 1 million. By comparison, the molecular weight of viroid RNA is only about 130,000. Thus, the amount of nucleic acid in a viroid is only about one-eighth the amount in a small virus. A nucleic acid molecule of this size is not even large enough to code for one small enzyme. Scientists could not understand how such a small molecule could replicate within a host cell. Although some possible mechanisms by which viroids might replicate have been worked out, this problem has not actually been solved. Another unsolved problem is how viroids cause disease symptoms.

So far, viroids have been found only in plants. However, there are various human and animal diseases that are contagious, but for which no infectious agent has been found. It is possible that scientists will eventually discover that these diseases are caused by viroids. There is already some evidence that one animal disease, scrapie, may be caused by a small DNA molecule with no protein coat.

summary

The kingdom Monera includes the blue-green algae and the bacteria. All members of these groups are procaryotic. The blue-green algae are the simplest photosynthetic organisms. The bacteria are divided into three groups based on shape. These are cocci, bacilli, and spirilla. Some bacteria require oxygen for respiration, some can live with or without oxygen, and some cannot live in the presence of free oxygen. Most bacteria are heterotrophs. They are either saprophytes or parasites. Among the autotrophic bacteria there are both photosynthetic and chemosynthetic forms. Although reproduction is usually asexual, sexual reproduction can occur.

Bacteria cause many diseases in humans. The germ theory of disease was developed by Louis Pasteur. Robert Koch developed four rules for determining whether a specific organism causes a specific disease. Bacteria also cause decay and are involved in the recycling of materials in nature.

The kingdom Protista includes unicellular and multicellular algae, protozoa, and slime molds. Members of this kingdom are eucaryotic. The plant-like protists are photosynthetic. The animal-like protists, the protozoa, are heterotrophs. The slime molds are fungus-like protists with complex life cycles.

Viruses have no real place in the classification scheme. They are smaller than bacteria and consist of DNA or RNA surrounded by a protein coat. Outside of living cells viruses are dormant. Within a host cell, the virus can replicate itself. Many human diseases are caused by viruses.

vocabulary

Acrasiomycota
bacillus
bacteria
bacteriophage
blue-green algae
capsule
Chrysophyta
chrysophyte
Ciliata
coccus
Cyanophyta
diatom
dinoflagellate
eucaryote
eucaryotic
euglenoid
Euglenophyta
germ theory of disease
golden-brown algae
lichen
Mastigophora
Monera
Myxomycota
procaryote
procaryotic
Protista
protozoa
Pyrrophyta
Sarcodina
sarcodine
Schizomycetes
slime mold
slime sheath
spirillum
Sporozoa
yellow-green algae
virus
zooflagellate

test your learning

Section

30-1
1. What two types of organisms belong to the kingdom Monera?
2. Describe the general structure of procaryotic cells.

30-2
3. Describe the structure and life processes of the blue-green algae.

30-3
4. Describe the structure of a bacterial cell.
5. Name the three basic types of bacteria, and describe the shape of each.

6. Define the terms *facultative anaerobe* and *obligate anaerobe.*
7. Describe both heterotrophic and autotrophic nutrition in bacteria.
8. What rules did Robert Koch establish for determining whether a particular disease is caused by a particular microorganism?
9. What important function do bacteria have in nature?

30-4 10. In what ways do euglenoids resemble plant cells, and in what ways do they resemble animal cells?
11. Describe the structure of euglena.

30-5 12. List the major characteristics of yellow-green and golden-brown algae.
13. Describe the structure of a diatom, and explain what happens to the shells of dead diatoms.

30-6 14. List the major characteristics of dinoflagellates.

30-7 15. Name the four phyla of protozoans, and list the method of locomotion in each.

30-8 16. Name three types of sarcodines.
17. How is amebic dysentery transmitted?

30-9 18. Describe the structure of a typical ciliate.
19. Name the two types of nuclei found in ciliates, and state the functions of each.

30-10 20. Describe the general characteristics of the zooflagellates.

30-11 21. How do sporozoans obtain nutrients?
22. Describe the life cycle of the malarial parasite, *Plasmodium.*

30-12 23. Describe the structure and life cycle of the true slime molds.
24. Describe the structure and life cycle of the cellular slime molds.

30-13 25. Describe the structure of a virus.
26. Describe what happens when a virus enters a host cell.

30-14 27. How does the human body combat viral infections?

test your understanding

1. Why are the blue-green algae and bacteria placed in a separate kingdom from other simple organisms?
2. How do bacteria differ from blue-green algae in structure and life functions?
3. Should viruses be considered living or nonliving? Explain your answer.
4. Discuss the importance of bacteria both in nature and in terms of human uses.

independent research

1. Prepare a report comparing the events of replication in viruses containing DNA as the genetic material and in viruses containing RNA as the genetic material.
2. Prepare a report on one of the following scientists:
   A. Walter Reed
   B. William Gorgas
   C. Charles Laveran
   D. Robert Koch

chapter 31

Plants and Fungi

KINGDOM PLANTAE—THE PLANTS

After completing your study of this section, you should be able to:

1. Describe the basic characteristics of the green algae.
2. Discuss the evolutionary relationship thought to exist between green algae and land plants.
3. Describe the general characteristics of the brown algae, and list some of the specialized structures found in large brown algae.
4. Describe the general characteristics of the red algae.
5. Name two useful substances obtained from red algae.
6. Name three types of plants found in the phylum Bryophyta.
7. Describe the general characteristics of the bryophytes.
8. Name five types of plants found in the phylum Tracheophyta.

9. Briefly describe the general characteristics of the whisk ferns, club mosses, and horsetails.
10. Describe the general structure of a fern.
11. Describe the general characteristics of the gymnosperms, and name four members of this group.
12. Describe the general characteristics of the angiosperms.

31-1 Introduction to the Plant Kingdom

Members of the plant kingdom, most of which are land dwelling, are thought to have arisen from aquatic green algae. Like the plants, the green algae contain chlorophyll enclosed in chloroplasts and their cell walls are made up of cellulose. Because of the relationship between plants and green algae, the green algae are classified in the plant kingdom, even though many show the characteristics of protists. Red and brown algae are multicellular and show some specialization of structure. Thus, they are also included in the plant kingdom instead of with the protists. The other members of the plant kingdom are divided into two groups—the *bryophytes* and the *tracheophytes*. The bryophytes include mosses, liverworts, and hornworts. These plants do not have vascular, or conducting, tissues. The tracheophytes include horsetails, ferns, evergreens, and flowering plants. Members of this group have well-developed vascular tissues for transport .

Ask students to research the volvocine series. This sequence of motile organisms shows a gradual progression from the unicellular chlamydomonas to the complex colonial organization of volvox. The sequence suggests evolutionary tendencies leading to multicellular organization.

Life on land presents a number of problems that do not exist for aquatic organisms. The most immediate problems are obtaining and conserving water. In many locations, the only water present is well below the earth's surface. The plant must be able to reach the water and to transport it to all its cells. The plant also needs adaptive mechanisms to control the evaporation of water from its tissues. Land plants also need supporting tissues to enable them to stand upright against the force of gravity, and they need special reproductive mechanisms that enable the sperm to reach the egg without swimming through water.

31-2 Phylum Chlorophyta—The Green Algae

The **green algae**, phylum **Chlorophyta** (klor-*ah*-fuh-tuh), are found in salt and fresh water and in moist places on land. This group includes unicellular, colonial, and multicellular forms. Most green algae have a cell wall composed of cellulose and contain chlorophylls a and b in chloroplasts. Some green algae have flagella, which are used in movement.

Chlamydomonas (klam-uh-duh-*moh*-nus) is a typical unicellular green algae (see Figure 31-1). This freshwater organism has two flagella of equal length, which are used in locomotion. There is one chloroplast and a pyrenoid body for starch synthesis. There are two contractile vacuoles near the bases of the flagella. Unlike other green algae, the cell wall of

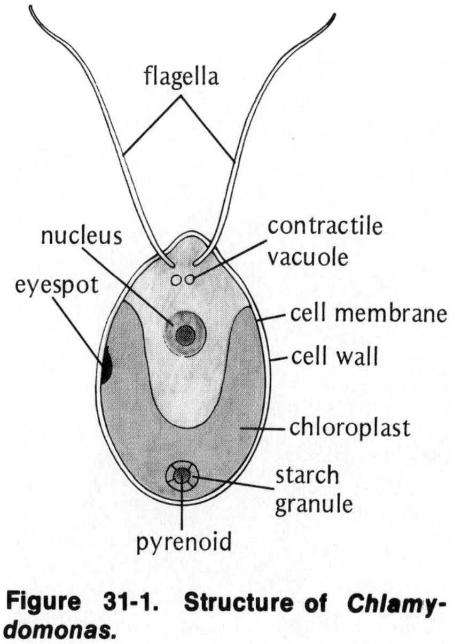

Figure 31-1. Structure of *Chlamydomonas.*

A

B

C

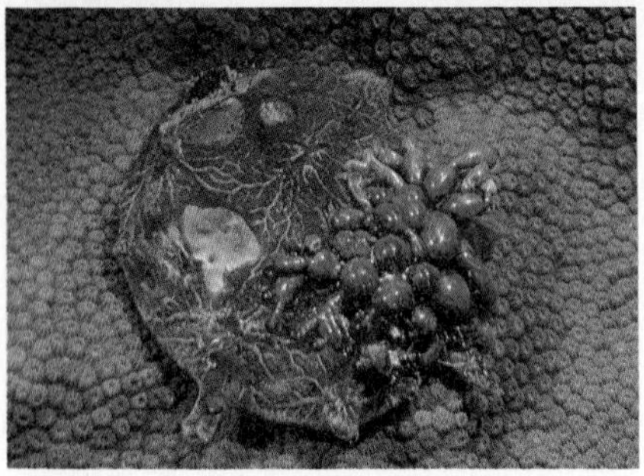

Figure 31-2. Green Algae. (A) *Acetabularia.* (B) *Halimeda.* (C) *Valonia.*

Chlamydomonas is made up of a compound containing carbohydrate and protein, instead of cellulose. Reproduction is usually asexual.

Multicellular green algae include ribbonlike forms, such as spirogyra (see page 348), and other, more complex forms (see Figure 31-2).

31-3 Phylum Phaeophyta—The Brown Algae

The **brown algae,** phylum **Phaeophyta** (fee-*ah*-fuh-tuh), include many of the common seaweeds. Members of this group are all multicellular, and range in size from microscopic to more than 50 meters in length. They are found mainly in cold ocean waters. The brown algae contain chlorophyll, which functions in photosynthesis, as well as other pigments that give them their brown color. Brown algae have cellulose in their cell walls, and they store food in the form of a polysaccharide or as oil. Their life cycles show an alternation of generations.

Some brown algae that live along the shoreline have rootlike structures that anchor them to rocks, while others found on the ocean surface have gas-filled structures that function as floats (see Figure 31-3). The surface of the so-called Sargasso Sea, which is an area stretching across the Atlantic Ocean from

Figure 31-3. Brown Algae. The giant kelp (left) has gas-filled bladders that function as floats. *Fucus* (right) is a common seaweed.

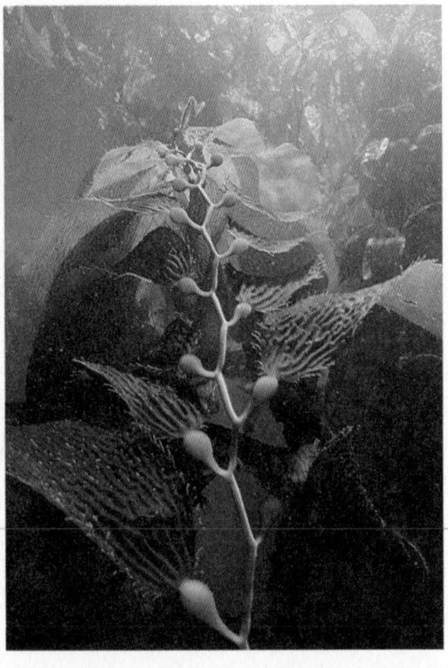

the West Indies to the coast of Africa, is densely covered by several types of floating brown algae.

31-4 Phylum Rhodophyta—The Red Algae

The **red algae,** phylum **Rhodophyta** (roh-*dah*-fuh-tuh), like the brown algae, include many common seaweeds (see Figure 31-4). Red algae are found in warmer waters and at greater depths than brown algae. They generally grow attached to rocks or some other surface. Most red algae are multicellular, but they are never as large as the largest brown algae. The chloroplasts of red algae contain chlorophyll and several other pigments. Many red algae are reddish in color, but others are black, green, yellow, or purple. Red algae have complex life cycles, including an alternation of generations. The cell walls of the red algae contain cellulose and other substances, including *agar,* which has a number of industrial uses. Agar is used as a thickener in foods, including ice cream, and it is used as a medium on which bacteria and fungi are grown in laboratories. *Carrageenan* (kar-uh-*jee*-nun), another product of red algae, is used as a stabilizing agent to prevent separation of food mixtures. It is used, for example, in chocolate milk to prevent separation of the milk and the chocolate.

Figure 31-4. Red Algae. (Top) Coralline algae. (Bottom) Irish moss.

31-5 Phylum Bryophyta—Mosses, Liverworts, and Hornworts

The phylum **Bryophyta** (bry-*ah*-fuh-tuh) includes mosses, liverworts, and hornworts (see Figure 31-5). These are nonvascular land plants. Bryophytes have no specialized conducting tissues. Transport of materials through the plant takes place by diffusion, which is relatively slow and inefficient. Therefore, members of this group must live where water is plentiful. They are found on the forest floor, on damp rocks, in swamps and bogs, and near streams. Without xylem, bryophytes also have little in the way of supporting tissues. For this reason, most are very short, ranging from 1 to 5 centimeters in height.

In many bryophytes, some branches of the young plant grow downward and enter the soil, where they function as roots. They anchor the plant and absorb minerals and water. These structures are called **rhizoids.** Other branches grow upward, forming stemlike shoots and leaves. However, the cells in the rhizoids, shoots, and leaves are all similar. Thus, these structures are not true organs.

In the bryophyte life cycle the haploid gametophyte is the prominent form. The diploid sporophyte generation is small, short-lived, and dependent on the gametophyte for its nutrition. The life cycle of mosses is shown in Figure 24-2 (page 386). In mosses and other bryophytes, the sperm must swim to the egg through water. Thus these plants are not completely adapted to life on land.

Figure 31-5. Liverworts. Liverworts and other bryophytes have no specialized conducting tissues and must live where water is abundant.

Figure 31-6. **Whisk Fern.** Whisk ferns are the oldest known vascular plants, but they are lacking both true leaves and true roots.

31-6 Phylum Tracheophyta—The Vascular Plants

The vascular plants, phylum **Tracheophyta** (tray-kee-*ah*-fuh-tuh), are a diverse group that includes most of the dominant modern land plants. Vascular plants include the whisk ferns, club mosses, and horsetails, as well as the ferns, conifers, and flowering plants. All tracheophytes contain the vascular tissues xylem and phloem in the sporophyte generation. In the tracheophytes, the sporophyte generation is prominent, and the gametophyte is small and short-lived.

The vascular plants are divided into two groups—the spore-bearing plants and the seed plants. The spore-bearing plants include the whisk ferns, club mosses, horsetails, and ferns. The seed plants include the gymnosperms and the angiosperms.

31-7 The Whisk Ferns

The **whisk ferns** are the oldest known vascular plants. Fossil evidence indicates that this group was widespread about 400 million years ago, but there are only a few modern living species. These species, which live only in warm climates, are found from South Carolina to Florida. Members of this group are not really ferns. They do not have either true leaves or true roots. The plant body consists of an underground stem anchored by rhizoids, which absorb water and minerals. Aboveground, the stems are green and carry on photosynthesis (see Figure 31-6). As the stems grow, they split into two branches, so that the ends of the stems are Y-shaped. Sporangia form at the tips of some branches. Within the sporangia, haploid spores are produced by meiosis. Upon release, some of the spores germinate, giving rise to gametophyte plants that bear both male and female reproductive organs. When fertilization occurs, the resulting zygote develops into a new sporophyte plant.

Figure 31-7. **Club Moss.** Living club mosses are generally small, but prehistoric members of this group were the size of trees.

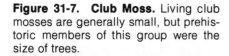

31-8 The Club Mosses

The **club mosses** were one of the dominant forms of plant life during the Carboniferous, or coal-forming, period of the earth about 300 million years ago. However, there are only a few remaining small genera of club mosses. Some of the prehistoric forms were as large as trees and formed forests. Living club mosses are mostly small, reaching about 20 centimeters in height (see Figure 31-7). However, a few tropical species may reach heights of 90 centimeters and look like bushes.

Club mosses have true roots, stems, and leaves. Like the whisk ferns, the stems branch so that the ends are Y-shaped. At the tips of some branches, groups of spore-producing structures form conelike *strobili* (stroh-bil-ly). Spores released from the strobili give rise to gametophyte plants, which bear the reproductive organs. Fertilization results in a zygote that develops into the sporophyte plant.

Some club mosses are evergreens and are used for Christmas decorations. Ground pine and ground cedar are club mosses found in forests in the United States. One species from the dry regions of Mexico is known as the "resurrection plant." When dry, this club moss curls into a gray ball. However, when water is added, it opens, forming an attractive green plant.

Figure 31-8. Horsetails.

31-9 The Horsetails

The **horsetails** include only about 20 species of plants. They represent the remains of a group of plants that flourished during the Carboniferous period. Some ancient horsetails were the size of trees, reaching 30 meters in height. The remains of these plants were eventually transformed into coal. Modern horsetails are generally less than 1 meter in height.

Horsetails are common in shaded woods and around streams, swamps, and ponds (see Figure 31-8). They have true roots and leaves. The stems are green and hollow. The leaves grow only at specific points along the stem, forming "collars" of leaves. Cone-shaped strobili form at the ends of some stems. Haploid spores produced in the strobili are released and give rise to small, inconspicuous gametophytes, which bear the reproductive organs. Following fertilization, the zygote gives rise to the sporophyte plant.

The stems of horsetails contain crystals of silicon, which made them useful to early settlers for scouring pots and pans. For this reason they are also known as *scouring rushes.*

31-10 The Ferns

The **ferns** were most abundant during the Carboniferous period, as were the other spore-bearing plants. There are now about 9,000 living species of ferns. They are particularly abundant in tropical rain forests, but are also found in cooler

Figure 31-9. Ferns. When the leaves of ferns first emerge from the soil, they are curled into the form of a fiddlehead (left). The tiny leaflets of a mature fern give it a feathery appearance (right).

climates. Some tropical tree ferns have a woody, unbranched trunk and may reach heights of more than 15 meters. Such trees may have leaves 4 meters long. The ferns of cooler climates are much smaller. They have horizontal stems called rhizomes that grow just beneath the surface of the soil. Hair-like roots grow from the rhizomes deeper into the soil. The only visible parts of these ferns are the leaves, or fronds, that grow up from the rhizome. When the leaves first emerge from the soil, they are coiled in a bud called a *fiddlehead* (see Figure 31-9). The fiddlehead gradually uncoils and develops into a mature frond. The fronds are generally divided into tiny "leaflets" that give them a feathery appearance.

The internal structure of ferns is similar to that of seed plants. Ferns contain xylem and phloem. Their roots have a root cap and show the growth zones found in the roots of higher plants. Fern stems have no cambium, so they show little or no growth in diameter.

Ferns reproduce both sexually and asexually. Sexual reproduction in ferns is discussed in Chapter 24 (page 387). In asexual, or vegetative, reproduction, the rhizome grows through the soil, producing new fronds along its length. The fronds die in the winter, but the rhizomes live and give rise to new fronds in the spring.

31-11 The Seed Plants

Figure 31-10. Redwood Tree. Some redwood trees are more than 3,000 years old.

The **seed plants** have become the dominant and most successful group of land plants. There are more than 25,000 existing species, ranging in size from the giant redwood tree to the tiny duckweed, a water plant with leaves only a few millimeters wide. There are two major groups of seed plants—the gymnosperms and the angiosperms. The gymnosperms are a diverse group in which the seeds are naked, or unprotected. The angiosperms are the flowering plants, and their seeds are enclosed within fruits. In both groups, the seeds are surrounded by a protective seed coat, and the seed contains stored food that serves to nourish the developing plant embryo until it can function independently.

31-12 The Gymnosperms

The gymnosperms are nonflowering seed plants. Their seeds are found on the inside surface of scales, which usually form a cone-shaped structure. The gymnosperms have true roots, stems, and leaves. The stems contain cambium, which produces growth in stem diameter. The gymnosperm plant is the sporophyte generation. The life cycle of gymnosperms is discussed in Chapter 24 (page 388).

Fossil evidence shows the presence of gymnosperms as much as 350 million years ago. By about 250 million years ago they were the dominant form of plant life. There are now about 700 living species of gymnosperms. The conifers are the most important group of gymnosperms. Two other gymnosperm groups are the cycads and the ginkgoes.

Conifers. The **conifers,** or evergreens, are the the best known of the gymnosperms. Members of this group are cone-bearing plants with leaves in the form of needles. In most conifers, the leaves remain green throughout the year. The conifers include pine, spruce, fir, hemlock, redwood, sequoia, cedar, and cypress trees. These trees show wide geographic distribution. In colder regions they are the dominant trees of the forest. At high altitudes, pine and spruce are most abundant.

Sequoias and redwoods include the oldest and largest trees in the world (see Figure 31-10). Some are between 3,000 and 4,000 years old and are more than 90 meters tall. Pine, spruce, and fir trees are widely used as Christmas trees, and they and other conifers are used for lumber.

Figure 31-11. A Cycad.

Cycads. The **cycads** (*sy*-kuds) look like palm trees except that they have cones. Members of this group are generally slow growing and may live to be more than 1,000 years old. Several species may reach heights of 15 meters. In some, the ovules are the size of large eggs and the cones weigh as much as 45 kilograms. Cycads grow in tropical and semitropical regions. The only cycad found in the United States is *Zamia,* which is found in Florida (see Figure 31-11).

Ginkgoes. **Ginkgo,** or maidenhair, trees are the only living representatives of a once numerous group. This species has survived primarily because the trees were cultivated as ornamental and shade trees. Few survive in the wild. Ginkgo trees, which may reach heights of more than 30 meters, are very hardy. They can survive with limited water supplies and in the presence of pollution.

31-13 The Angiosperms

The angiosperms, the flowering plants, are the most common of all land plants. This group includes about 250,000 species, many of which are used for food. Flowering plants are found in all types of climates and environments. Some live in the desert where there is almost no water, and others live completely underwater.

In the angiosperms, the reproductive structures are the flowers, which contain the male and female reproductive organs. The angiosperm plant is the sporophyte, while the gametophyte is reduced to only a few cells. Fertilization is followed by the development of a seed, which is enclosed in a fruit. The life cycle of angiosperms is discussed in Chapter 24 (page 390).

The angiosperms are divided into two major groups—the dicots and the monocots. The seeds of dicots contain two seed leaves, or cotyledons, whereas the seeds of monocots have only one (see page 395). The monocots include the grasses, palms, lilies, sedges, irises, orchids, and various aquatic plants. Most other angiosperms are dicots, which are much

	Family	Representative species
Dicots	Magnolia	magnolia and tulip trees
	Rose	roses, hawthorns, flowering quince, flowering almond, apples, pears, strawberries, blackberries, raspberries, apricots, cherries, peaches, plums
	Beech	beech, oak, and chestnut trees
	Parsley	parsley, carrots, celery, parsnips, dill, caraway, fennel, poison hemlock, anise
	Mustard	mustard, cabbage, broccoli, kale, cauliflower, brussels sprouts, turnips, horseradish, rutabaga
	Heath	heaths, heather, rhododendrons, mountain laurel, blueberries, huckleberries, cranberries, wintergreen
	Pea	peas, soybeans, lima beans, peanuts, clover, alfalfa, wisteria, sweet peas, black locust, rosewood
	Composite	sunflowers, dandelions, asters, dahlias, marigolds, zinnias, lettuce, artichoke, endive
	Nightshade	potato, tomato, tobacco, eggplant, red pepper, petunia
	Mallow	hollyhock, okra, cotton
	Mint	spearmint, peppermint, lavender, rosemary, thyme, sage
Monocots	Lily	tiger lily, easter lily, lily of the valley, day lily, onion, leek, chive, garlic, asparagus, tulip, crocus
	Grass	rice, wheat, corn, rye, barley, oats, sugar cane, bamboo, buffalo grass, Kentucky bluegrass
	Palm	coconut palm, date palm

Table 31-1. Major Families of Dicots and Monocots.

more numerous than monocots. Table 31-1 lists some of the major families of dicots and monocots and representative members of each.

KINGDOM FUNGI

After completing your study of this section, you should be able to:

1. Describe the general characteristics of fungi.
2. List the common names of the fungi phyla. State the distinguishing characteristics of each phylum, and name two or three of its members.
3. Describe both asexual and sexual reproduction in the bread mold *Rhizopus*.
4. Describe the structure and growth of a mushroom.
5. Describe the structure of a lichen.

The kingdom Fungi includes familiar organisms, such as yeasts, molds, and mushrooms, as well as rusts, smuts, and other less familiar organisms. Fungi are nongreen organisms that absorb needed nutrients from the environment. Most fungi are saprophytic and obtain their nutrients from the remains of dead plants and animals. In many cases they secrete digestive enzymes onto the food and then absorb the digested nutrients. The fungi, along with the bacteria, play a key role in decomposing dead organisms and releasing the minerals and other substances they contain for reuse by other organisms. Some fungi are parasitic and obtain nutrients from the organisms they live on.

31-14 General Characteristics of Fungi

Fungi vary greatly in size. Some are microscopic, while others weigh several kilograms. The bodies of most fungi consist of threadlike filaments called **hyphae** (*hy*-fee). As the hyphae grow, they branch and twist, eventually forming a tangled mass called a **mycelium** (my-*see*-lee-um). In some fungi, the cytoplasm within the hyphae is not divided by any cell walls. The continuous cytoplasm contains several nuclei. Such hyphae are said to be *multinucleate.* In other fungi, the hyphae are divided by incomplete septa, or cross walls, so that the hyphae are partly compartmentalized, but the cytoplasm is still continuous. Each compartment may contain more than one nucleus. The cell walls of most fungi are composed of chitin, not cellulose. Fungi reproduce both asexually and sexually. Asexual reproduction always involves the formation of some kind of microscopic spores.

Based more or less on the pattern of sexual reproduction present, the 80,000 species of fungi are grouped into four phyla. These are the conjugation fungi, the water molds, the sac fungi, and the club fungi. There is also a fifth group, called the *Fungi Imperfecti,* which includes thousands of fungi whose pattern of sexual reproduction is unknown so that they cannot be properly classified. On the basis of their pattern of asexual reproduction, it is thought that most members of this group are sac fungi.

31-15 Phylum Zygomycota—The Conjugation Fungi

The **conjugation fungi,** phylum **Zygomycota** (*zy*-goh-my-*kaht*-uh), all produce a special type of thick-walled spores that develop from a zygote during sexual reproduction. Another type of spore is produced asexually. Most of the conjugation fungi are saprophytes, but some are parasites on plants, insects, or other fungi. The hyphae of the conjugation fungi lack cross walls, but cross walls do form during the production of gametes. The common bread mold *Rhizopus* is a typical member of this group.

Rhizopus grows on the surface of bread and fruit as a cottonlike mass of filaments (see Figure 31-12). The whitish or grayish mycelium consists of several kinds of hyphae. Rootlike hyphae called rhizoids anchor the fungus, secrete digestive enzymes, and absorb nutrients. Other hyphae, called **stolons,** grow in a network over the surface of the food. The stolons give rise to still another type of hyphae that grow upward from the surface of the food. These reproductive hyphae are called **sporangiophores.** At the tip of each sporangiophore, a round, black, spore case, or sporangium, develops. Numerous spores form within each sporangium. At maturity, when the cases open, the spores are released. Those that land in favorable environments germinate and form new mycelia.

Reproduction in bread mold is usually asexual by spore formation. However, under certain conditions, bread molds reproduce sexually by conjugation. The pattern of conjugation is similar to that found in spirogyra, an alga (see page 348).

Conjugation occurs when hyphae of different strains touch. Following contact, the tips of both hyphae enlarge, and cross walls form behind the tips. These partitioned-off ends are now the gamete-producing structures. The two strains of bread mold are called "plus" and "minus." One tip contains several plus nuclei, while the other contains several minus nuclei. At the point of contact, the end walls of the two touching hyphae disintegrate, and the nuclei of opposite strains fuse to form a number of diploid nuclei. A hard wall forms around the nuclei and their associated cytoplasm to form a thick-walled zygospore, which is resistant to harsh environmental conditions. When conditions become favorable, the zygospore geminates. Only one diploid nucleus remains, and this nucleus undergoes meiosis. Meiosis produces four nuclei, but all but one disappear. This zygospore gives rise to a sporangiophore, which in turn produces spores asexually.

Figure 31-12. Life Cycle of Bread Mold. The bread mold *Rhizopus* can be found growing on the surfaces of bread and fruit.

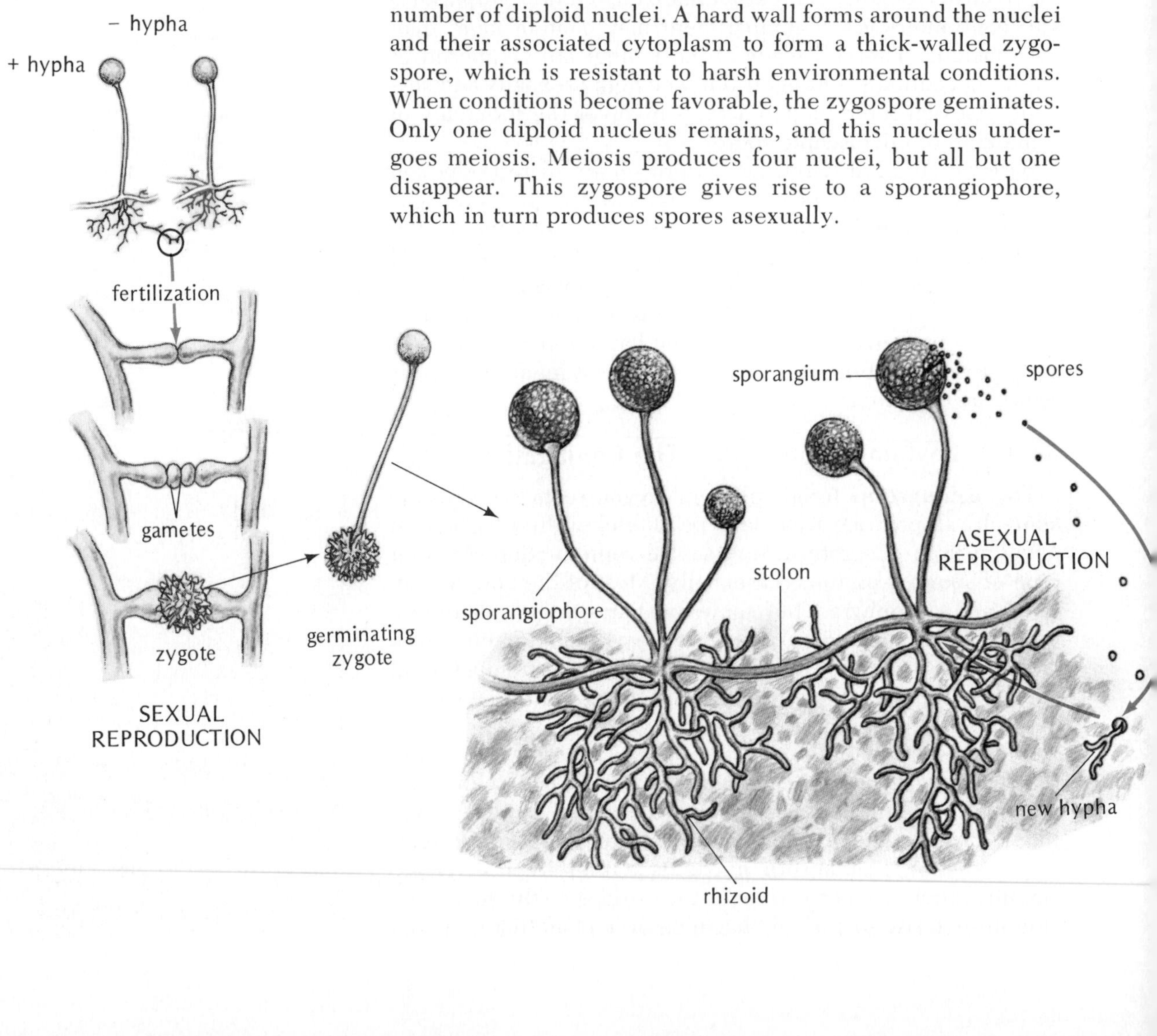

31-16 Phylum Oomycota—The Water Molds

The **water molds,** members of the phylum **Oomycota** (*oh*-uh-my-*kaht*-uh), are mostly aquatic saprophytes, but a few are parasites of fish. Also, a few species are parasites of land plants and cause severe economic damage. The most damaging of the water molds has been the *late blight fungus,* which destroyed the potato crops of Ireland from 1845 to 1847. The resulting famine caused about 750,000 deaths and the emigration of about half the population of the country. Downy mildew of grapes and beets is also caused by water molds.

The water molds differ from other fungi in several basic ways. They are the only group with motile, flagellated spores. They are the only group in which the male and female gametes are structurally different. The male gametes are sperm, and the female gametes are eggs. Unlike the other fungi, the cell walls of the water molds contain cellulose, not chitin. In most species, the hyphae have no cellular partitions. And finally, in the life cycle of water molds, it is the diploid stage that is prominent.

31-17 Phylum Ascomycota—The Sac Fungi

The **sac fungi,** phylum **Ascomycota** (*as*-koh-my-*kaht*-uh), are the largest group of fungi. Included in the sac fungi are cup fungi, powdery mildews, morels, truffles, blue and green molds, and yeasts.

Sac fungi produce two kinds of spores, each of which can give rise to new organisms under the proper conditions. Spores produced as a result of sexual reproduction are called *ascospores.* Usually eight, but occasionally four, ascospores develop inside a saclike *ascus*, which serves as a sporangium. Spores produced asexually are called *conidia.* Conidia are formed in chains at the tips of specialized reproductive hyphae called *conidiophores.*

Except for the yeasts, which are unicellular, the sac fungi are multicellular. Hyphae of multicellular sac fungi are divided by cross walls. Holes in the cross walls permit cytoplasm and nuclei to move from one compartment of the hypha to the next. Each compartment has one to several nuclei.

The cup fungi are saprophytic and grow on decaying organic matter (see Figure 31-13). The visible portion of the fungus is the cup-shaped *fruiting body,* which contains the spore-bearing sacs, or *asci.* However, beneath the surface of the soil is a large mycelium made up of many hyphae.

Figure 31-13. Cup Fungi. Cup fungi grow on decaying organic matter.

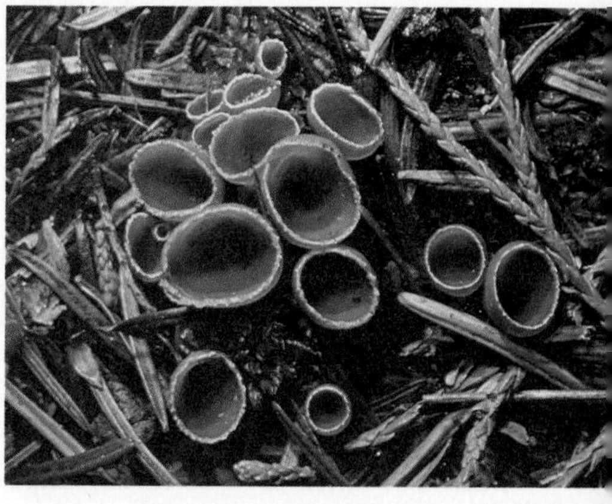

The unicellular yeasts are not typical of the Ascomycota. Yeasts reproduce by budding and also by spore formation (see page 333). In spore formation, the yeast cell itself functions as an ascus. Yeasts are economically important because they are used in the manufacture of alcohol, alcoholic beverages, and breads.

Some Ascomycota cause plant diseases, including Dutch

Figure 31-14. A Morel.

elm disease, chestnut blight, and ergot. Ergot is a disease of wheat and rye caused by a parasitic species. Ergot poisoning results from eating flour made from infected plants. Modern methods of flour production have eliminated this problem.

Truffles and morels are ascomycetes that are edible and are considered great delicacies. Truffles grow several centimeters below the surface of the soil. They are spherical, brown fruiting bodies that range from about 1 to 7 centimeters in diameter. In France, where truffles have been used in cooking for many hundreds of years, pigs and dogs are trained to locate them by their odor. Morels, which are also known as sponge or honeycomb fungi, are common in many areas of the United States. The stem and distinctive cap are the fruiting body (see Figure 31-14). The asci are located within the folds of the cap.

31-18 Phylum Basidiomycota—The Club Fungi

The **club fungi,** phylum **Basidiomycota** (buh-*sid*-ee-uh-my-*kaht*-uh), include most of the large and prominent fungi seen in fields and woods. Mushrooms, toadstools, bracket fungi, puffballs, and various parasites, such as rusts and smuts, are club fungi (see Figure 31-15).

In the club fungi, sexual reproduction involves the production of a special type of spores, *basidiospores*. These spores are formed in an enlarged, club-shaped reproductive structure, the *basidium,* at the end of a specialized hypha. Other kinds of spores are also produced by the club fungi. As in the Ascomycota, the hyphae of the Basidiomycota are divided by incomplete cross walls. The cells of the hyphae may contain one or two nuclei.

The most familiar of the club fungi are the mushrooms. The mushroom is actually a fruiting body, the spore-producing part of the fungus. The main part of the mycelium grows beneath the surface of the ground, living as a saprophyte on the remains of plant and animal matter. The mycelium may live for many years, slowly growing through the soil. Only when growing conditions are favorable do mushrooms grow up above the surface.

Figure 31-15. A Mushroom of the Genus *Russula.*

A mushroom consists of a stalk, or **stipe,** and a **cap** (see Figure 31-16). Mushrooms begin to develop on the underground mycelium as small knobs. As the cap pushes up through the soil, it is kept closed and protected by a thin membrane that connects the edges of the cap to the stalk. Once above ground, the membrane breaks, and the cap expands. The part of the membrane that remains attached to the stalk is called the **annulus.**

The undersurface of the cap contains many **gills,** which radiate out from the center of the stalk like wheel spokes. Each gill consists of many hyphae that are pressed closely together. On the sides of the gills are the basidia, each bearing four basidiospores. One mushroom can produce over one billion spores.

Many types of mushrooms are edible, but others are extremely poisonous. It takes an expert to distinguish between the edible and poisonous species. Never eat mushrooms that you find growing in the wild.

Rusts are club fungi that produce rust-colored spores during one phase of their life cycle. Rusts are parasites on wheat, barley, oats, and other crop plants. Each year they cause millions of dollars worth of damage to these crops. Smuts are similar to rusts. Their name refers to the black and dusty-looking mass of spores that they form within the tissues of the host plant. Smuts attack corn, wheat, oats, barley, and rye.

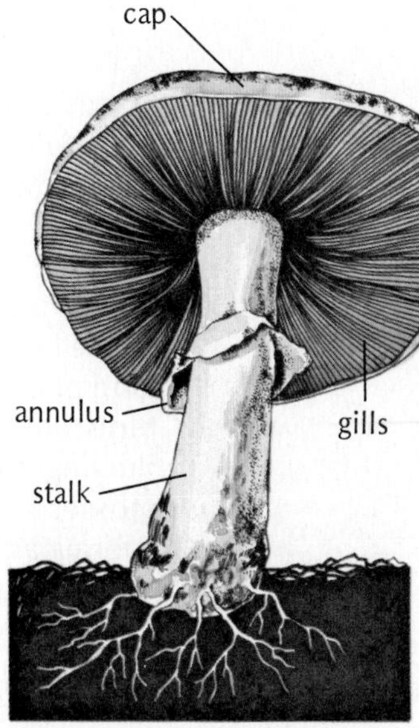

Figure 31-16. Structure of a Mushroom.

31-19 Lichens

A **lichen** (*ly*-ken) is made up of two types of organisms—an alga and a fungus—living together. The algal cells are embedded within the mycelium of the fungus. The fungus is usually a sac fungus, while the alga may be a green alga or a blue-green alga. Through photosynthesis, the alga provides nutrients for the fungus. The fungus provides the alga with water, essential elements, and protection from intense light and dryness. Lichens reproduce when fragments of existing lichens break off, blow away, and start growing independently at a new location.

Some lichens are crustlike and resemble spots of paint; some are flat, but curled at the edges like leaves; and some are shrublike and have branches (see Figure 31-17). Lichens grow on the bark of trees, on rocks, and on soil. They are very hardy organisms and can exist for months without water. In Arctic regions they serve as food for caribou, musk ox, and other animals. Lichens are usually the first organisms to grow on bare rock. They gradually break it down, beginning the process of soil formation.

Figure 31-17. Lichens.

summary

The green algae include both unicellular and multicellular forms. Members of this group contain chlorophyll in chloroplasts and have cell walls composed of cellulose. It is thought that the higher plants evolved from the green algae. The brown algae are multicellular and contain other pigments in addition to chlorophyll. Some brown algae are very large and show various specialized structures. Most common seaweeds are either brown algae or red algae. Red algae, like brown algae, are all multicellular.

The bryophytes include mosses, liverworts, and hornworts. These are mainly land plants that lack vascular tissues. They are generally small and grow where moisture is abundant. Tracheophytes are vascular plants—they contain conducting tissues. The spore-bearing tracheophytes include whisk ferns, club mosses, horsetails, and ferns. The seed-bearing plants include the gymnosperms and angiosperms.

Most fungi consist of a tangled mass of hyphae that form a mycelium. In most, the cell walls are composed of chitin. The conjugation fungi can reproduce both asexually and sexually. Sexual reproduction includes conjugation and the formation of zygospores. This group, which includes bread mold, consists mainly of saprophytes. The water molds are mostly aquatic, but a few are parasites of land plants, including potatoes, grapes, and beets. The water molds produce motile, flagellated spores; they have structurally distinct male and female gametes; and their cell walls contain cellulose. The sac fungi include cup fungi, morels, truffles, and yeasts. In sexual reproduction they form ascospores, while in asexual reproduction they form conidia. Yeasts are unicellular, but the other sac fungi are multicellular. The club fungi include mushrooms, bracket fungi, puffballs, rusts, and smuts. In sexual reproduction the club fungi form basidiospores.

vocabulary

annulus
Ascomycota
Basidiomycota
brown algae
Bryophyta
cap
Chlorophyta
club fungus
club moss
conifer
conjugation fungus
cycad
fern
gill
gingko
green algae
horsetail
hypha
lichen
mycelium
Oomycota
Phaeophyta
red algae
rhizoid
Rhodophyta
sac fungus
sporangiophore
stipe
stolon
Tracheophyta
water mold
whisk fern
Zygomycota

test your learning

Section

31-1 **1.** Discuss some of the problems that exist for land plants that do not exist for aquatic plants.

31-2 **2.** Name three types of green algae.

3. Describe the structure of *Chlamydomonas*.

31-3 **4.** Describe the general characteristics of brown algae.
31-4 **5.** Describe the general characteristics of red algae.
31-5 **6.** Name three members of the phylum Bryophyta.
7. Describe the general characteristics of bryophytes.
31-6 **8.** Name the members of the phylum Tracheophyta.
9. List the general characteristics of the tracheophytes.
31-7 **10.** Describe the general characteristics of the whisk ferns.
31-8 **11.** What are the spore-producing structures of the club mosses called?
31-9 **12.** Describe the general characteristics of horsetails.
31-10 **13.** Describe the general characteristics of ferns.
31-11 **14.** Name the two types of seed plants.
31-12 **15.** Name three groups of gymnosperms.
16. Describe the basic characteristics of the conifers.
31-13 **17.** Name the two major groups of angiosperms, and describe the general characteristics of each.
31-14 **18.** Describe the general structure of a fungus.
31-15 **19.** Describe nutrition and reproduction in the bread mold *Rhizopus*.
31-16 **20.** In what ways do the water molds differ from other types of fungi?
31-17 **21.** Name three types of sac fungi.
31-18 **22.** Name three types of club fungi.
23. Describe the structure of a mushroom.
31-19 **24.** Describe the structure of a lichen.
25. What important role do lichens play in nature?

test your understanding

1. In the past, the fungi were generally classified as part of the plant kingdom. Now, however, they are often assigned to a separate kingdom by themselves.
   A. What are the major structural differences between plants and fungi?
   B. What are the major differences between life functions in plants and fungi?
   C. In what ways are plants and fungi similar?
   D. Do you think that plants and fungi should be classified in the same or separate kingdoms? Support your answer.

2. In what ways are ferns and seed plants better adapted for life on land than bryophytes.

3. Why are green, brown, and red algae classified as members of the plant kingdom while most other algae are considered protists?

4. Name three types of plants that were abundant during the Carboniferous period.

independent research

1. Prepare a report on one of the following topics:
   A. Plants of the Carboniferous period.
   B. The possible evolutionary relationship between green algae and modern land plants.
   C. The Sargasso Sea.

2. Collect, identify, and catalogue the dormant twigs of local trees (not evergreens) after the leaves have fallen. Use a local field guide for reference.

chapter 32

Invertebrates— Sponges to Mollusks

CHAPTER INTRODUCTION

After completing your study of this section, you should be able to:

1. Describe the basic characteristics of animals.
2. Explain the difference between vertebrates and invertebrates.
3. Define each of the following terms: *radial symmetry, bilateral symmetry, dorsal, ventral, anterior,* and *posterior*.

32-1 The Animal Kingdom

The animal kingdom is the largest of the five kingdoms. Animals are multicellular organisms that must obtain food from the environment. Most have nervous and muscular systems that enable them to move. Most animals reproduce sexually, but some of the simpler forms also reproduce asexually. In some animals the young have the same basic features as the adult, but in others, the young are very different from the adult. In such cases, the young forms are known as **larvae** (*lar*-vee). The larvae undergo a series of developmental changes that produce the adult form.

The branch of biology that deals with the study of animals is called **zoology** (zoh-*ahl*-uh-jee), and scientists that study animals are called **zoologists** (zoh-*ahl*-uh-jists). Zoologists divide the animal kingdom into about 30 major groups, or phyla. The nine largest phyla contain the majority of species, and it is these phyla that we will study. On the basis of the presence

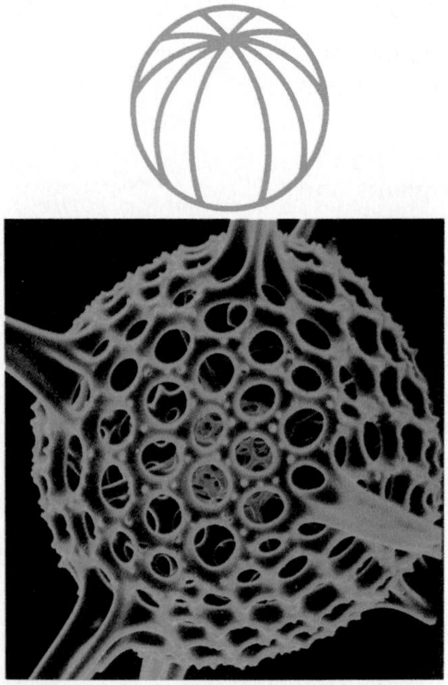

Figure 32-1. Spherical Symmetry. In spherical symmetry, any cut passing through the center of the sphere divides the organism into two equal parts. A radiolarian skeleton (bottom) shows spherical symmetry.

or absence of a backbone, animals are divided into two groups—**vertebrates,** animals with backbones, and **invertebrates,** animals without backbones.

32-2 Symmetry

The bodies of most animals show **symmetry** (*sim*-uh-tree). This means that the body can be cut into two halves that have matching shapes. A few organisms, including amebas and most sponges, are *asymmetrical* (ay-suh-*meh*-trih-kul)—that is, there is no way that the organism can be cut into two matching halves.

There are different kinds of symmetry. **Spherical symmetry** is found in a few protists. These organisms are in the shape of a sphere, and any cut passing through the center of the sphere divides the organism into matching halves (see Figure 32-1).

In **radial** (*rayd*-ee-ul) **symmetry,** there is a central line, or axis, running the length of the animal from top to bottom or from front to rear. Any cross section at right angles to the central axis shows repeating structures arranged around the center like spokes in a wheel (see Figure 32-2). Cross sections at different levels are not alike, but any lengthwise cut down the center divides the animal into matching halves. The hydra shows radial symmetry. One end of the animal has a mouth and tentacles. The other end is closed and rounded. But any lengthwise cut down the center divides the animal into matching halves, like the halves of a vase. Animals showing radial symmetry are generally either sessile or they drift with the water currents.

Figure 32-2. Radial Symmetry. An adult starfish shows radial symmetry.

In **bilateral** (by-*lat*-uh-rul) **symmetry,** the organism varies both along its length (top to bottom) and also from front to back (see Figure 32-3). The human body shows bilateral symmetry. In this type of symmetry, there is only one way to cut the body into two symmetrical halves. Each half is a mirror image of the other. Bilaterally symmetrical animals have fixed right and left sides. There are special terms that describe other positions on bilaterally symmetrical animals. **Dorsal** (*dor*-sul) refers to the upper side or the back of the animal; **ventral** (*ven*-trul) is the lower or belly side of the animal. The front or head end of the animal is **anterior,** while the rear or tail end is **posterior.**

Figure 32-3. Bilateral Symmetry. Frogs, like humans, show bilateral symmetry. There is only one way to cut the organism into two symmetrical halves.

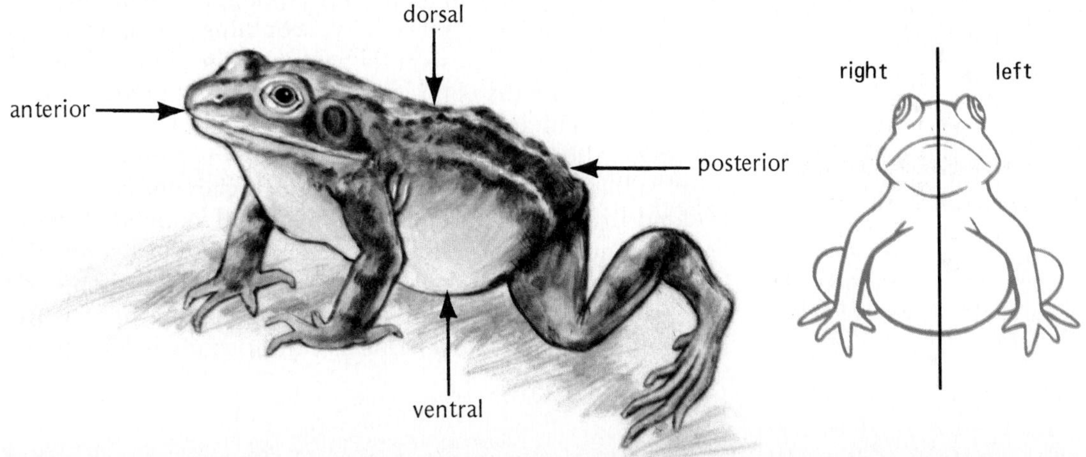

Figure 32-4. Sponges. Sponges are the simplest multicellular animals.

PHYLUM PORIFERA—THE SPONGES

After completing your study of this section, you should be able to:

1. Name the phylum to which sponges belong.
2. Describe the general structure of a sponge.
3. Explain how the following life processes are carried out in the sponge: nutrition, respiration, excretion, and reproduction.

32-3 General Characteristics

The **sponges,** phylum **Porifera** (puh-*rif*-uh-ruh), are the simplest multicellular animals. Porifera means "pore bearing." Sponges are pierced by many **pores,** or holes, through which water moves continuously. All sponges are aquatic. Most are found in salt water, but a few live in fresh water. Although the larvae are free swimming, adult sponges are sessile—that is, they live attached to something, usually shells or rocks on the ocean floor. Some sponges are found in clusters, or colonies. Some colonies look like plants, with individuals branching from a common stem. Other sponges live singly.

Members of this group vary widely in size and shape. Most are asymmetrical. Some are the size of a pearl, while others are the size of a bathtub. Simple sponges are shaped like a hollow, upright cylinder or vase. More complex sponges have folds in the body walls, while still others have complex systems of canals and chambers within the body walls. Many sponges are gray or black, but others are bright red, yellow, orange, or blue (see Figure 32-4).

32-4 Structure and Life Functions

Sponges have a low level of organization. Although their cells show specialization and are present in layers, they do not form true tissues. The sponge body is composed of three layers (see Figure 32-5). The outer layer, which consists of thin, flat cells, is pierced by numerous pores. These pores allow water, dissolved oxygen, and food particles (microscopic plants and animals) to enter the sponge. The inner layer, which lines the central cavity, contains specialized cells called **collar cells.** These cells have a collar of cytoplasm that extends out from the cell into the central cavity. Extending out through the collar of each cell is a flagellum.

Between the outer and inner cell layers is a middle layer of jellylike material that contains wandering ameboid cells. Embedded in the jellylike material are small skeletal structures called **spicules** (*spik*-yoolz), which are secreted by some of the ameboid cells. Spicules provide support and give shape to the sponge. Sponges are classified according to the chemical makeup of their spicules. One group of sponges has spicules

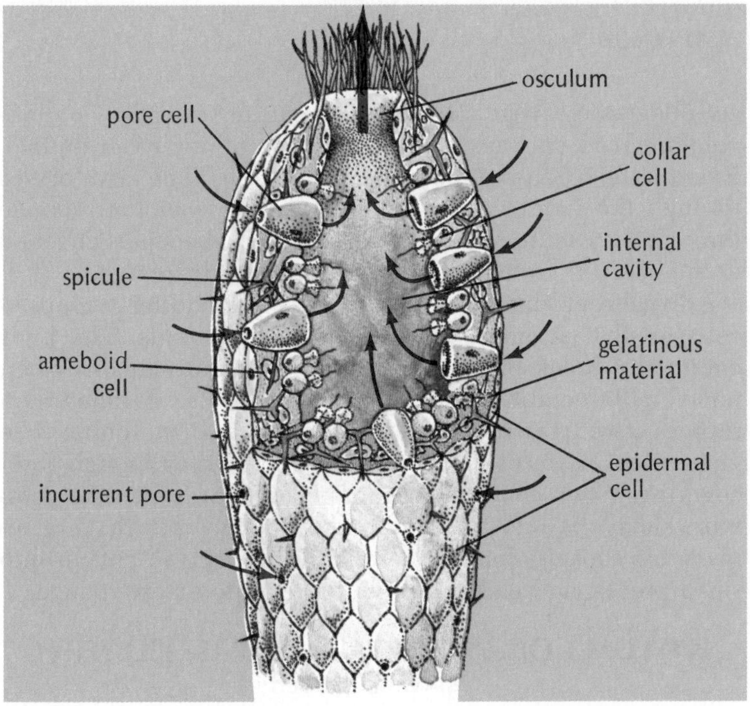

Figure 32-5. Structure of a Sponge. There is a constant flow of water through the body of the sponge. It enters through the pores and leaves through the osculum.

composed of calcium compounds; another group has spicules composed of silica. The third group has spicules composed of tough, flexible fibers made up of a protein-containing substance called *spongin.* In the past, sponges with spongin skeletons were widely used for household cleaning and as bath sponges.

The pores of the sponge serve as *incurrent openings,* allowing water to enter the body of the sponge. Water is drawn into the sponge and circulated in the central cavity by the beating of the flagella of the collar cells. From the central cavity, water passes out of the sponge through the osculum. The **osculum** (*ahs*-kyoo-lum) is a large opening at the top (unattached end) of the sponge, which serves as the *excurrent opening.*

As water passes through the sponge, food particles are captured, ingested, and digested by the collar cells. Some partly digested food is picked up from the collar cells by the ameboid cells of the middle layer. Digestion is completed in the ameboid cells, which then carry the nutrients to other parts of the sponge.

Wastes diffuse out of the cells into the central cavity of the sponge and leave with the water through the osculum. Gases are exchanged by diffusion between the cells and the water. Although sponges have no specialized nerve or muscle cells, some the cells surrounding the incurrent pores respond to harmful substances in the water by closing the pores.

Sponges can reproduce sexually or asexually. In sexual reproduction, both male and female gametes are formed in the same sponge. However, self-fertilization does not occur. Mature sperm leave the sponge through the osculum, and are drawn into other sponges through their pores. The eggs are found in the jellylike middle layer. After fertilization, the zy-

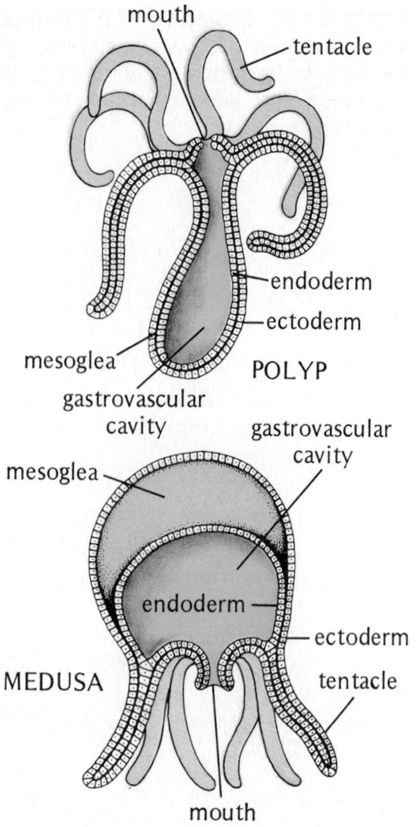

Figure 32-6. Body Forms of Coelenterates. The polyp form (top) is found in hydra. The medusa form (bottom) is commonly seen in jellyfish.

gote begins cleavage. However, the stages of embryonic development in sponges are unlike those of any other animal. Eventually, a free-swimming larva develops. The larva passes through the inner cell layer and leaves the mother sponge through the osculum. After a time the larva becomes attached to the ocean floor and develops into an adult sponge.

Asexual reproduction usually occurs by budding. Groups of cells on the parent sponge divide to form buds. The buds eventually break off and grow into new individuals. When unfavorable conditions arise, some freshwater sponges form reproductive structures called *gemmules* (*jem*-yoolz). The gemmule consists of a group of cells enclosed by a tough outer covering. When conditions again become favorable, the gemmule develops into a new sponge. Sponges also have a remarkable capacity for regeneration. They can be cut up into small pieces, and each piece will grow into a new sponge.

PHYLUM COELENTERATA—HYDRAS, JELLYFISH, AND CORALS

After completing your study of this section, you should be able to:

1. Name some representative animals of the phylum Coelenterata.
2. Describe the general characteristics of the coelenterates.
3. Describe the structure of the two body forms found among coelenterates.
4. Name two coelenterates showing the polyp body form.
5. Describe the life cycle of *Aurelia*.

32-5 General Characteristics

The **coelenterates** (suh-*lent*-uh-rayts), phylum **Coelenterata** (suh-*lent*-uh-rah-tuh), show a more complex level of organization than the sponges. This phylum includes hydras, jellyfish, corals, and sea anemones (uh-*nem*-uh-neez). Coelenterates are aquatic. Hydras live in fresh water, but most other coelenterates are marine. There are two general body forms found among the coelenterates (see Figure 32-6). The **polyp** (*pahl*-ip) form is sessile and has a cylindrical body with a mouth and tentacles at the upper free end. Corals and hydras are examples of polyps. The other form, the **medusa** (muh-*doo*-suh), is shaped like an upside-down bowl, with the mouth and tentacles facing downward. The medusa is usually free swimming. Jellyfish show the medusa body form. Although the two body forms look different, they possess the same basic structure—a hollow sac with a single opening, the mouth, surrounded by tentacles. Most adult coelenterates show radial symmetry.

32-6 Structure and Life Functions

The coelenterates show a tissue level of organization. There are two cell layers, the ectoderm and endoderm, which are separated by a jellylike material called the *mesoglea* (mez-uh-*glee*-uh). The mesoglea is composed of protein fibrils and sugars. In the medusa forms, the mesoglea makes up most of the body wall. The ectoderm cells contain contractile fibers. Movement is accomplished by contraction of these fibers. However, for the medusas, the free-swimming forms, the strength of these contractions is not great enough to overcome the movement of the water. Thus, medusas drift with currents in the water.

Specialized stinging cells called cnidoblasts are characteristic of coelenterates. They are used for defense and capturing food. Within the cnidoblast are nematocysts, which are small, fluid-filled capsules containing a coiled thread. When the cnidoblast on a tentacle is stimulated by pressure, the nematocyst is discharged. The thread uncoils and entangles the prey. Some nematocysts contain poison, which is injected into the prey and paralyzes it. Once the prey is captured, the tentacles stuff it into the mouth. The structure and function of cnidoblasts in the hydra is discussed on page 128.

The internal body cavity of coelenterates is called the gastrovascular cavity. Its single opening serves as both a mouth and an anus. Extracellular digestion takes place in the cavity. This is accomplished by enzymes secreted into the cavity by some of the cells of the endoderm. When the food is partially digested, it is engulfed by the endoderm cells, where digestion is completed within food vacuoles. Thus digestion is both extracellular and intracellular. No respiratory or excretory system is found in coelenterates. Oxygen is obtained and wastes are excreted by diffusion. The first true nerve cells are found in the coelenterates. The nerve cells form a nerve net that sends impulses in all directions. There is no brain in these animals, but the movement of the tentacles shows coordination.

Figure 32-7. Corals. Corals are small polyps that grow in colonies. Unlike hydras, they are surrounded by a hard skeleton.

32-7 Corals

Many of the structures and life functions of polyps have been described in the sections on the hydra in Unit 2 on animal maintenance. *Corals* (*kor*-ulz) are small polyps that grow in colonies (see Figure 32-7). Corals are surrounded by a hard, calcium-containing skeleton, which they secrete. In warm, shallow parts of the ocean, islands and large coral reefs are formed by massive colonies of corals.

32-8 Life Cycle of *Aurelia*

Aurelia (or-*eel*-yuh) is a common jellyfish. Its life cycle includes both medusa and polyp forms (see Figure 32-8). The jellylike body of the medusa is the form commonly seen on

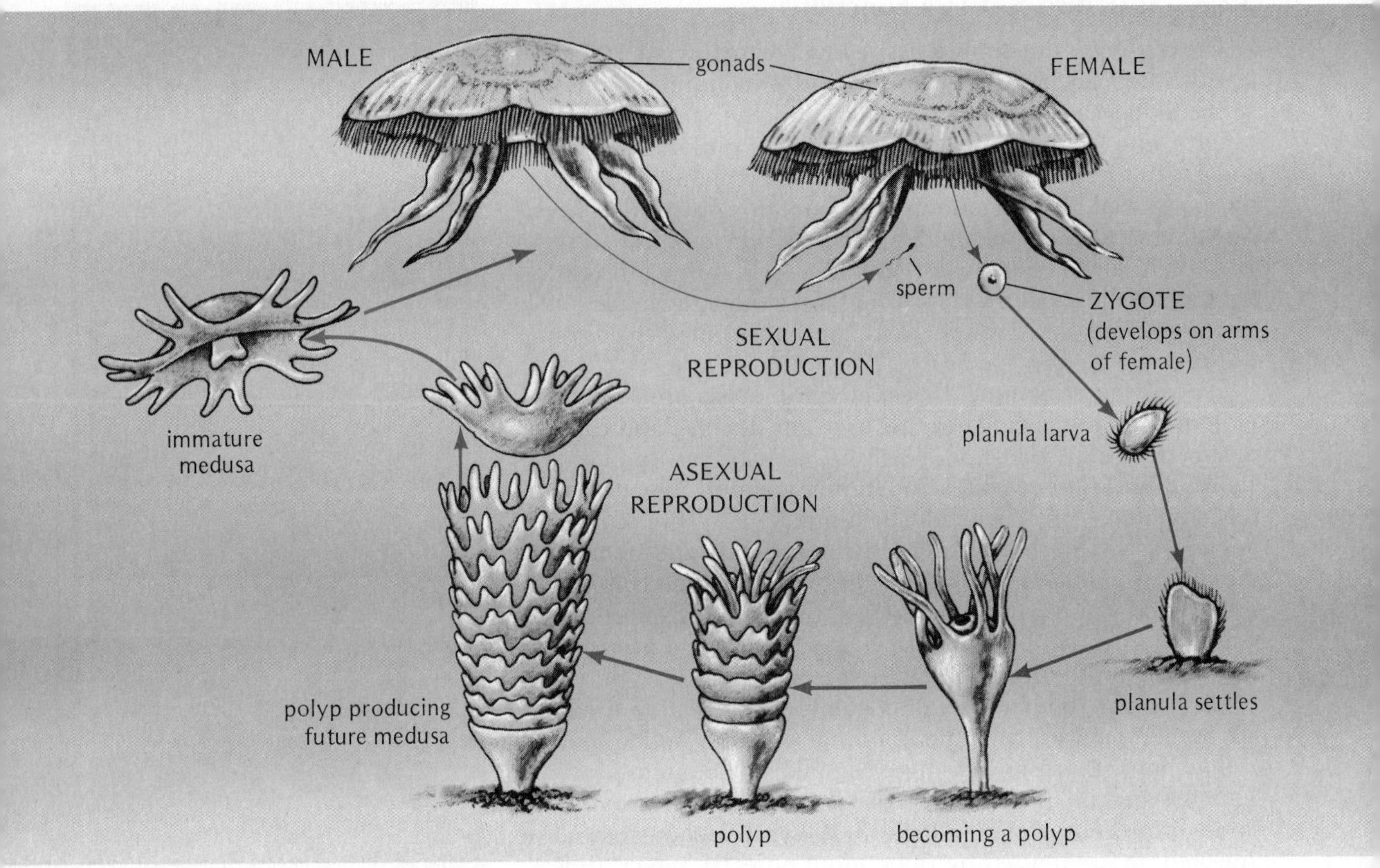

Figure 32-8. Life Cycle of *Aurelia*.

In jellyfish, the mesoglea is greatly enlarged, forming the major part of the animal's bulk.

beaches. Protective tentacles hang from the edge of the umbrellalike body. The sexes are separate in *Aurelia*, but the male and female look alike. Sperm from the male medusa are released into the surrounding water. Some sperm cells enter the gastrovascular cavity of a female medusa, where fertilization occurs. Early development occurs while the zygote is attached to the female. The zygote develops into a small, oval-shaped, ciliated larva called a **planula** (*plan*-yuh-luh). The planula is free swimming for some time. It then becomes attached by one end to a rock or some other structure on the ocean floor. The larva develops a mouth and tentacles at the unattached end and becomes a polyp. The polyp grows, eventually reproducing asexually to form medusas. This occurs in the fall and winter, when a series of horizontal divisions make the polyp look like a stack of saucers. One by one, the saucer-shaped structures break off from the top and grow into full-sized medusas.

The alternation of the medusa form with the polyp form is characteristic of some coelenterates. The medusa stage reproduces sexually by the production of eggs and sperm, and it gives rise to the polyp stage. The polyp stage reproduces asexually by budding and gives rise to the medusa stage.

PHYLUM PLATYHELMINTHES—THE FLATWORMS

After completing your study of this section, you should be able to:

1. Name the phylum to which flatworms belong, and name a representative animal from each of the three classes of flatworms.
2. Describe the type of symmetry and the level of organization found in flatworms.
3. Explain how nutrition, excretion, respiration, and reproduction are accomplished in planaria.
4. Describe the structure and life cycle of a blood fluke.
5. Describe the structure and life cycle of a tapeworm.

Figure 32-9. Planaria.

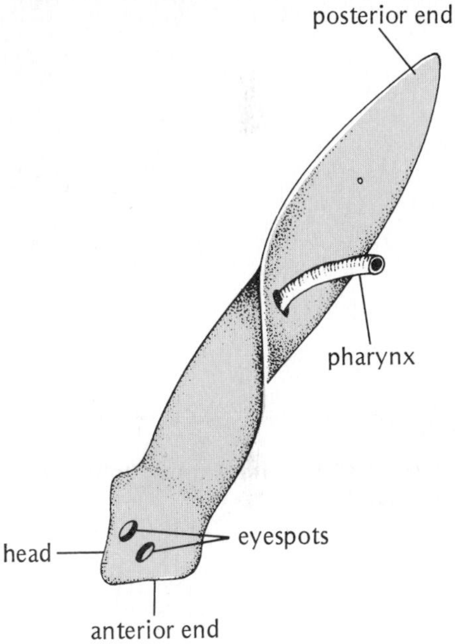

32-9 General Characteristics

The **flatworms,** phylum **Platyhelminthes** (plat-ee-hel-*min*-theez), are the simplest animals showing bilateral symmetry. In addition, the flatworms are the simplest invertebrate group showing definite head and tail regions. These animals are called flatworms because their bodies are flattened. There are three major groups of flatworms—free-living flatworms, such as planaria (pluh-*nehr*-ee-uh); parasitic flukes; and parasitic tapeworms. Free-living flatworms are usually aquatic, and are found in both fresh and salt water.

32-10 Structure and Life Functions

The body of the flatworm is composed of three distinct tissue layers—ectoderm, mesoderm, and endoderm. These tissues are organized into organs and organ systems. Thus, the flatworms are also the simplest animals showing organ and organ system levels of organization.

Planaria. We will use planaria, class Turbellaria (ter-buh-*lehr*-ee-uh), as an example of a typical flatworm.

Planaria are found in freshwater streams and ponds, where they cling to the bottom of leaves, rocks, and logs. These animals are gray or black in color and about 5 to 25 millimeters in length (see Figure 32-9). The triangular head contains a pair of *eyespots.* Although the eyes cannot actually form images, they are sensitive to light, which the animal avoids.

Planaria can move about freely, and a piece of liver placed in a stream will be covered with them in a few hours. Moving planaria appear to be gliding over a surface because the underside of the body is covered with microscopic cilia that propel the animal. Muscles enable them to change their shape or their direction of movement.

The planarian has a digestive system consisting of a mouth, pharynx, and a highly branched intestine (see Figure 32-10). The muscular pharynx is a tube that can be extended through the mouth opening for eating. The mouth is located at the

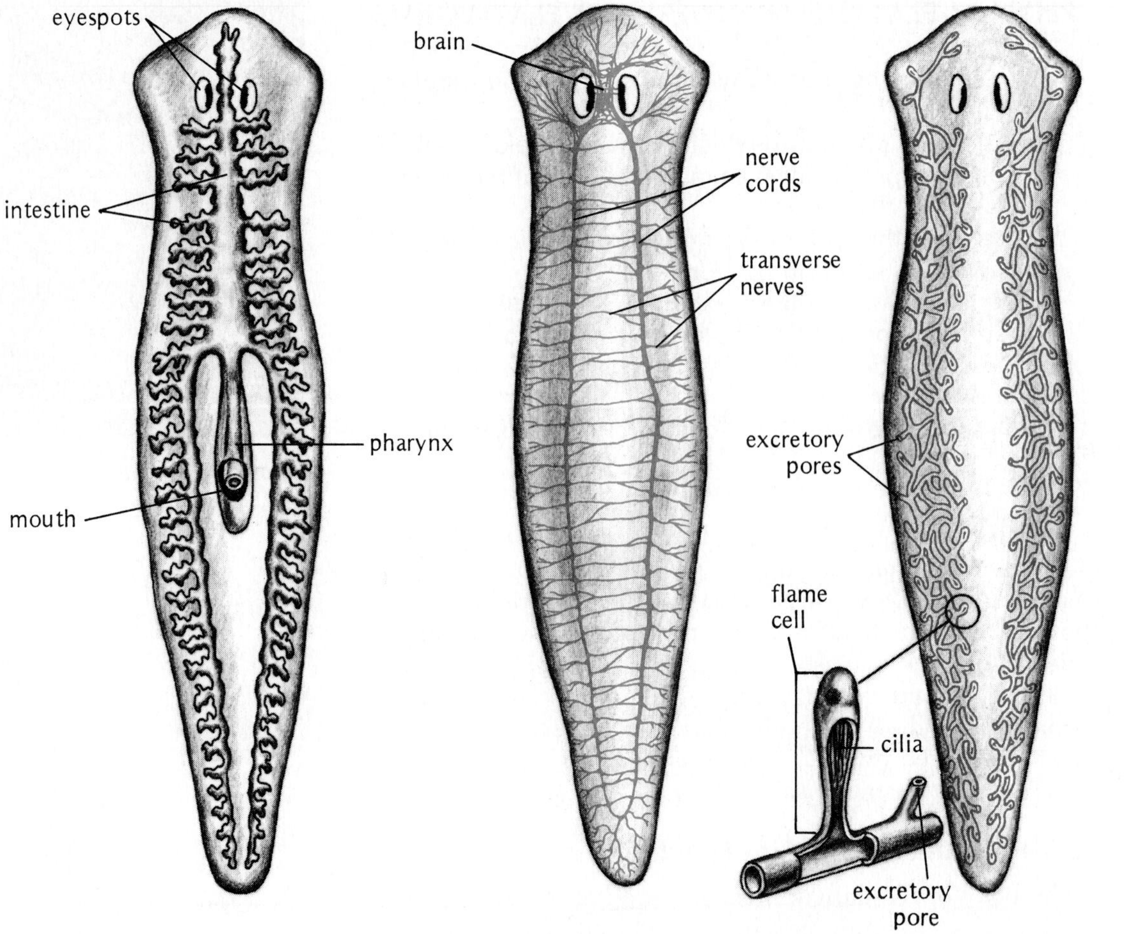

Figure 32-10. Internal Structure of a Planarian.

midline on the underside of the body. Planaria feed on living or dead small animals. The pharynx can suck small bits of food into the digestive cavity. The intestine is highly branched. Most digestion takes place within food vacuoles in the cells lining the intestine. Digested food diffuses to all cells of the body. Indigestible materials are expelled through the pharynx and mouth.

Planaria have no skeletal, circulatory, or respiratory system. Oxygen and carbon dioxide simply diffuse into and out of individual cells. However, they do have an excretory system consisting of a series of tubules that run the length of the body. Side branches of the tubules have cells called *flame cells* that remove excess water and liquid wastes from the body and pass them into ducts. The contents of the ducts pass out of the worm through small excretory pores on the dorsal surface.

The nervous system includes a small brain beneath the eyespots. From the brain, two nerve cords run the length of the body along either side. Connecting transverse nerves make the nervous system look like a ladder. This ladderlike nervous system enables the planarian to respond to stimuli in a coordinated manner.

Planaria have a well-developed reproductive system. Although they are hermaphroditic, self-fertilization does not occur. Instead, two planaria mate and exchange sperm. Fertilization is internal, and a short time later, the fertilized eggs are shed in capsules. In a few weeks, the eggs hatch into tiny worms, which grow into adults. The planarian can regenerate an entire animal from a fairly small segment. It can also reproduce asexually by fission, separating its tail end from its head end. Each half regenerates the missing structures.

Flukes. **Flukes** are parasitic flatworms of the class Trematoda (trem-uh-*tohd*-uh). The body of the fluke is covered by a thick cuticle that protects the parasite from the enzymes of its host. Flukes have suckers by which they attach themselves to the tissues of their host. They do not need a well-developed digestive system because the food obtained from the host has already been broken down.

The blood fluke is a typical fluke. In humans, this parasite causes a disease called *schistosomiasis* (shis-tuh-soh-*my*-uh-sis). The adult fluke is about 1 centimeter long and lives in the blood vessels of the human intestine and bladder (see Figure 32-11). Here it lays thousands of eggs that pass out of the body with digestive wastes. If the eggs land in water, they hatch into free-swimming larvae. They then enter the bodies of snails, where they undergo further development. They later leave the snails and infect streams, rice paddies and irrigation ditches. Upon contact with humans, the flukes bore through

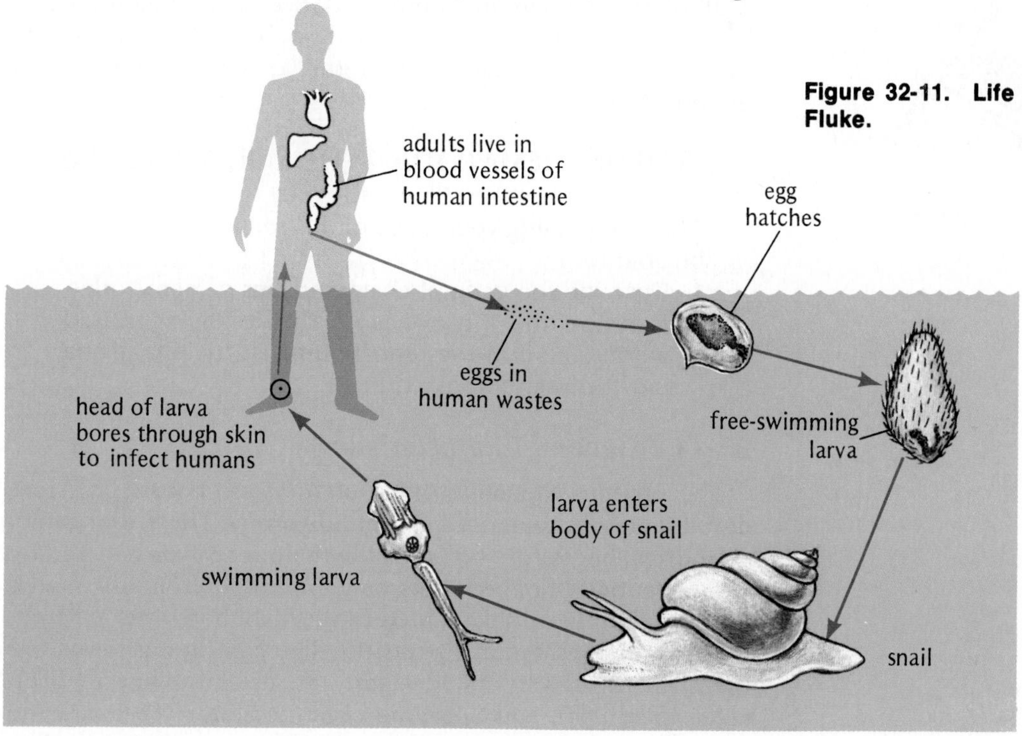
adults live in blood vessels of human intestine
egg hatches
eggs in human wastes
free-swimming larva
head of larva bores through skin to infect humans
larva enters body of snail
swimming larva
snail

Figure 32-11. Life Cycle of a Blood Fluke.

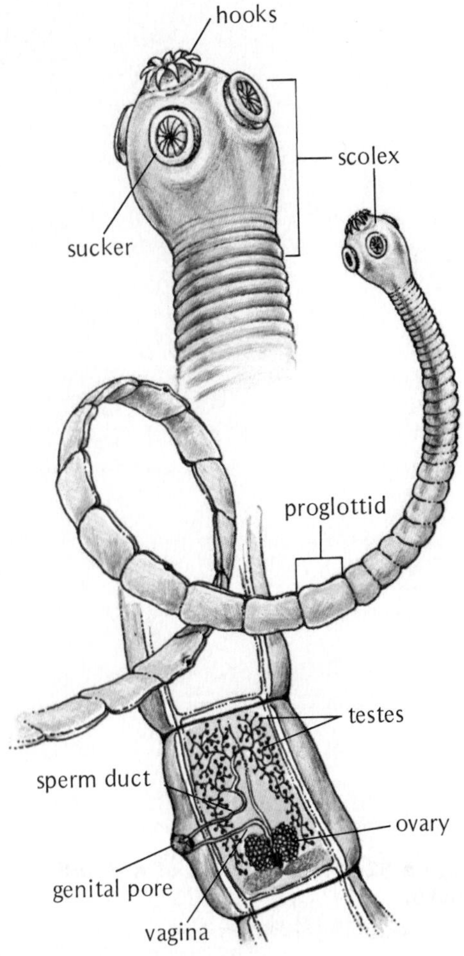

Figure 32-12. Structure of a Tapeworm.

the skin and start their reproductive cycle again. The blood fluke causes loss of blood, diarrhea, and much pain.

Tapeworms. **Tapeworms** are parasitic flatworms of the class Cestoda (ses-*tohd*-uh). The beef tapeworm, which can infect humans, is a long, ribbonlike flatworm (see Figure 32-12). Adults may be from 4 to 9 meters in length. These worms have excretory and nervous systems and a highly developed reproductive system. They lack a mouth and digestive system. Tapeworms live as parasites in the intestine, and absorb digested food through their skin. The suckers on the knoblike head, or *scolex* (*skoh*-leks), hold the tapeworm in place. Some tapeworms, such as the human pork tapeworm, have hooks as well as suckers.

Below the head and neck are square body segments called *proglottids* (proh-*glaht*-idz). These segments are produced continuously by budding from the neck region. Essentially, proglottids are reproductive structures, producing both sperm and eggs. Periodically, the end segments filled with over 100,000 fertilized eggs break off and pass out of the host in the feces. If cattle eat food contaminated with eggs, the eggs develop into larvae in the intestine. The larvae burrow into blood vessels and are carried to the muscle, where they form a dormant capsule.

Humans can become infected when they eat undercooked beef. The capsule surrounding the larva is digested, releasing the small tapeworm. The tapeworm then attaches itself to the wall of the human intestine, and the cycle begins again. Human tapeworms cause illness by absorbing needed nutrients, and may actually obstruct the passage of food through the intestine.

PHYLUM NEMATODA—THE ROUNDWORMS

After completing your study of this section, you should be able to:

1. Describe the general characteristics of nematodes.
2. Describe the life cycles of the following roundworms and how they affect humans: trichina, filaria, pinworm, and hookworm.

32-11 General Characteristics

The phylum **Nematoda** (nem-uh-*tohd*-uh) consists of slender, bilaterally symmetrical **roundworms.** Their elongated, cylindrical bodies are tapered at both ends and are covered by a tough cuticle. Roundworms range in length from less than 1 millimeter to more than a meter. Many roundworms are free living, while others are parasitic. The free-living forms are found in fresh water, salt water, and in soil. They feed on algae, plant sap, and decaying organic matter. The parasitic forms live on or in most kinds of plants and animals. The actual number of roundworms present in the environment is tremendous. It has been estimated that a million or more nematodes (*nem*-uh-tohdz) are present in one shovel load of garden soil.

32-12 Structure and Life Functions

Roundworms, unlike flatworms, have two openings to their tubular digestive system. Food is taken in through the mouth at the anterior end, and undigested material passes out through the anus at the posterior end. Roundworms are the simplest animals having a complete digestive system with two openings and a tube-within-a-tube body plan.

Nematodes have no circulatory or respiratory systems. They do have a simple excretory system as well as a nervous system. Well-developed muscles located in the body wall enable nematodes to move in a characteristic whiplike fashion.

Nematodes have well-developed reproductive systems. The sexes are separate, and fertilization occurs within the body of the female. In free-living forms the fertilized eggs, which are surrounded by a thick shell, are deposited in soil. The newly hatched young resemble the adults.

Ascaris is a large roundworm that sometimes reaches 30 cm in length. It is found in the intestines of horses, pigs, and occasionally, humans.

32-13 Parasitic Roundworms of Humans

Trichina, filaria, pinworm, and hookworm are parasitic roundworms that infect humans.

Trichina (trih-*ky*-nuh) is the nematode that causes *trichinosis* (trik-uh-*noh*-sis) in humans. Adult trichina worms live in the intestines of hogs (see Figure 32-13). When these worms reproduce, the resulting larvae invade the muscles of the hog. They grow to about 1 millimeter in length, and then curl up and become enclosed in hard cysts. When pork that

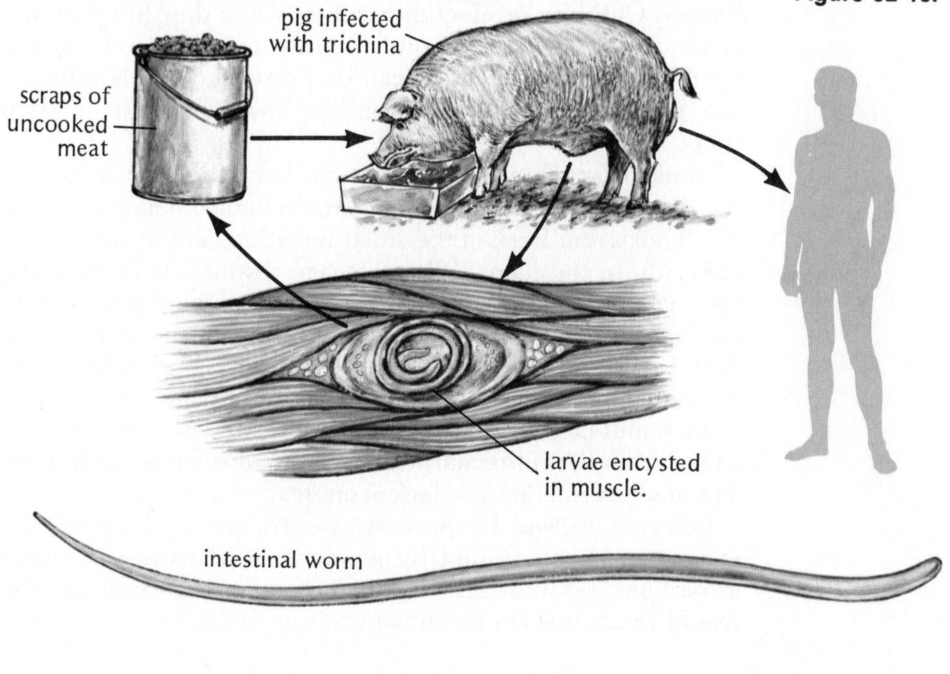

Figure 32-13. Life Cycle of *Trichina*.

has not been cooked well enough to kill the organisms is eaten by a human, digestive enzymes release the larvae from the cysts. The larvae develop into adults in the human intestines and reproduce sexually. The new larvae then move through the blood vessels and muscles just as the larvae did in hogs. The movement of the worms through muscle causes intense pain and can also cause permanent damage to the muscle. Trichinosis can be easily prevented by cooking pork thoroughly. Hogs become infected when they are fed infected scraps of uncooked meat. Because of better sanitary procedures used today for raising hogs, trichinosis is no longer very common.

Filaria (fuh-*lehr*-ee-uh) **worms** cause a disease known as *elephantiasis* (el-uh-fun-*ty*-uh-sis). These worms are carried by a species of mosquito found in tropical and subtropical regions. The worms are spread to humans by the bite of an infected mosquito. In the human body filaria worms invade the lymphatic system, blocking lymph vessels, and causing fluid to accumulate and tissues to swell. The affected area of the body often becomes abnormally enlarged, and the tissues involved become badly damaged. Within the lymph tissues, the worms reproduce sexually, producing larvae that enter the bloodstream. The mosquito becomes infected when it bites an infected person. The larvae mature within the mosquito, and the infection is spread by the bite of the infected mosquito.

Pinworms are one of the more common parasitic roundworms. They are tiny worms most often found in children. Adult pinworms live in the large intestine. The female worms deposit their eggs in the anal region. The presence of the eggs causes itching. When the child scratches, some eggs get on the fingers. Children reinfect themselves when they put their unclean fingers in their mouths. Pinworms live only a few weeks. Thus, if reinfection can be prevented by cleanliness, the pinworms disappear from the intestine with a short time.

Hookworm is a nematode that most commonly infects people in warm climates who walk barefoot on contaminated soil. The hookworm lives in the small intestine, and its eggs leave the body in the feces. When sewage disposal is inadequate, the eggs hatch into larvae on the ground, where people have contact with them. The larvae bore through the skin of bare feet. In the body, they are carried to the lungs by the circulatory system. They bore through the lungs, are coughed up, swallowed, and pass again to the small intestine, where they suck blood from the intestinal wall. Symptoms of hookworm infection include anemia and lack of energy.

Diseases caused by parasitic worms are widespread, but many can be controlled by good personal hygiene, proper sanitation, and thorough cooking of food. Some drugs are also useful in controlling these parasites.

PHYLUM ANNELIDA—THE SEGMENTED WORMS

After completing your study of this section, you should be able to:

1. Describe the general characteristics of members of the phylum Annelida.
2. Define the term *metamerism*.
3. Compare and contrast the structure of the marine worm *Nereis* with that of the earthworm.

32-14 General Characteristics

The most familiar of the worms are those of the phylum **Annelida** (uh-*nel*-uh-duh), the **segmented worms.** This phylum includes the earthworm, class Oligochaeta (ahl-ig-oh-*keet*-uh), and the leech, class Hirudinea (hir-yuh-*din*-ee-uh). The most striking characteristic of the *annelids* (*an*-uh-lidz) is the division of the body into separate sections, or segments. Segmented worms are found in both salt and fresh water and on land. Most of these worms are free living, but a few are parasites. Annelids range in length from less than 1 millimeter to more than 2 meters.

32-15 Structure and Life Functions

Annelids are bilaterally symmetrical. Their bodies are divided into segments, or *metameres* (*met*-uh-meerz), both externally and internally. This type of segmentation is called *metamerism* (muh-*tam*-uh-riz-um). Annelids are the simplest invertebrates having a closed circulatory system. In addition, like the more complex animals, they have a tube-within-a-tube body plan. The digestive tract, which is lined with endoderm, is the inner tube and is open at both ends—mouth and anus. The body wall makes up the outer tube and is covered with ectoderm. A fluid-filled body cavity is found between the two tubes. This cavity is called a **coelom** (*see*-lum) and is lined with mesoderm (see Figure 32-14).

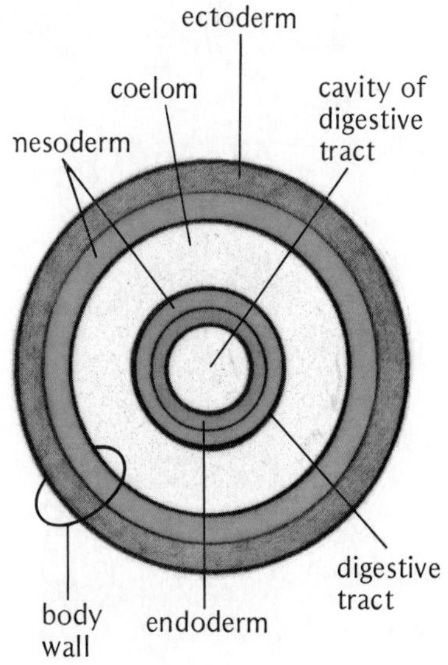

Figure 32-14. The Coelom. The coelom is a fluid-filled cavity found between the inner and outer body tubes of annelids and other animals.

Nereis. In most ways the structure and life functions of the marine sandworm *Nereis* (*nehr*-ee-is), class Polychaeta (pahl-ee-*keet*-uh), are very similar to those of the earthworm, which were described in Unit 2 on animal maintenance. However, there are a few important differences between these two animals.

Nereis lives at tide level (the intertidal zone) and emerges at night and crawls along the sand or swims in the shallow sea. During the day it stays in a temporary burrow in mud or sand with its head poking out. *Nereis* is green in color and is composed of about 200 similar segments (see Figure 32-15). The first two segments form a distinct head. The first segment, which is called the *prostomium* (proh-*stoh*-mee-um), has two short tentacles, two pairs of small eyes, and two other appendages called *palps*. The second segment, which is called the

Figure 32-15. Structure of the Marine Sandworm *Nereis*.

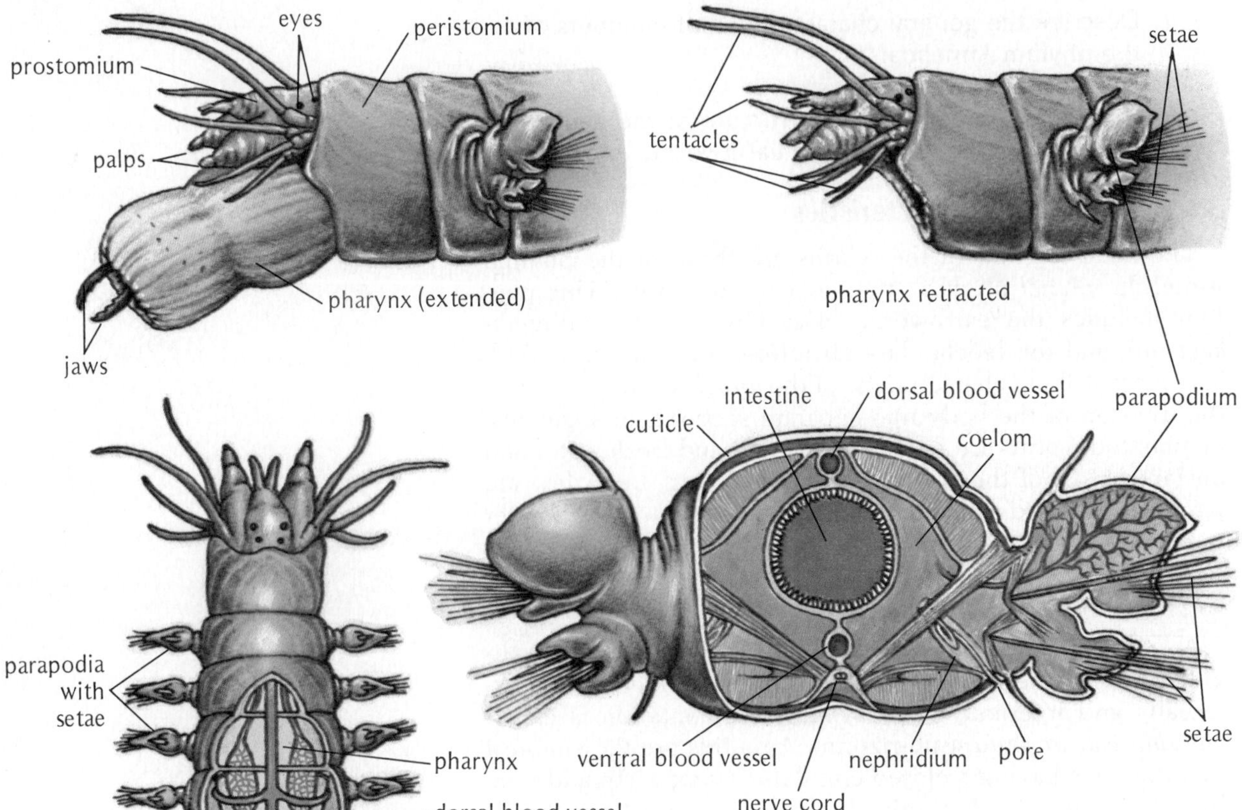

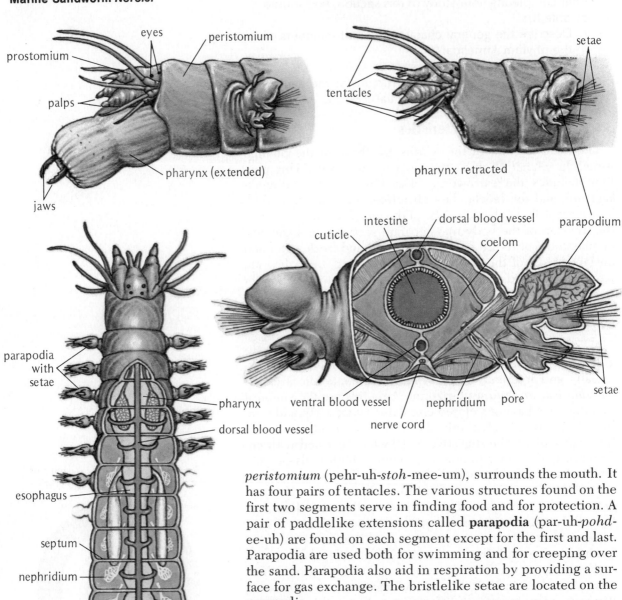

peristomium (pehr-uh-*stoh*-mee-um), surrounds the mouth. It has four pairs of tentacles. The various structures found on the first two segments serve in finding food and for protection. A pair of paddlelike extensions called **parapodia** (par-uh-*pohd*-ee-uh) are found on each segment except for the first and last. Parapodia are used both for swimming and for creeping over the sand. Parapodia also aid in respiration by providing a surface for gas exchange. The bristlelike setae are located on the parapodia .

Nereis eats small animals, which it captures by extending its pharynx out through its mouth. The pharynx has a pair of hard, pointed jaws that grasp the food. As the jaws are pulled back into the mouth, the food is swallowed. The food passes into the esophagus and then to the intestine, where it is digested. Undigested food is eliminated through the anus on the last segment.

Circulation, excretion, and respiration in *Nereis* are basically the same as in the earthworm. The nervous system is also similar.

In *Nereis,* sexes are separate. During the mating season, eggs and sperm develop in the body cavity, or coelom. Eventually they pass out through the nephridia or break through the body surface into the sea. Fertilization is external, and the zygote develops into a free-swimming, ciliated **trochophore** (*troh*-kuh-for) larva (see Figure 32-16). As the larva develops, the mouth and segments with parapodia appear. Eventually the young worm settles to the ocean bottom and begins the adult mode of life.

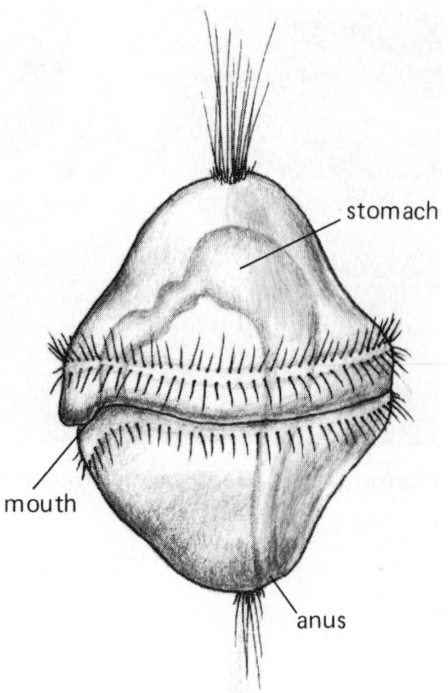

Figure 32-16. A Trochophore Larva.

Leeches. **Leeches** are mostly freshwater animals that are parasites of vertebrates. Some are found in moist soil. Most live on the blood of their prey (see Figure 32-17). The segmentation characteristic of annelids is not very prominent in leeches. Leeches have suckers at both their anterior and posterior ends. In feeding, the leech attaches itself to its host with its hind sucker. Then it attaches the anterior sucker, which surrounds the mouth and three small jaws. The jaws break through the host's skin. The saliva of the leech contains an enzyme that prevents the host's blood from clotting while it is being sucked up. The leech can ingest many times its own body weight of blood in one feeding. When the leech is full, it drops off the host and remains inactive for long periods, while the blood, which has been stored in the digestive tract, is gradually digested. Leeches are hermaphrodites, but cross fertilization takes place when two leeches exchange sperm. The fertilized eggs develop in water or soil.

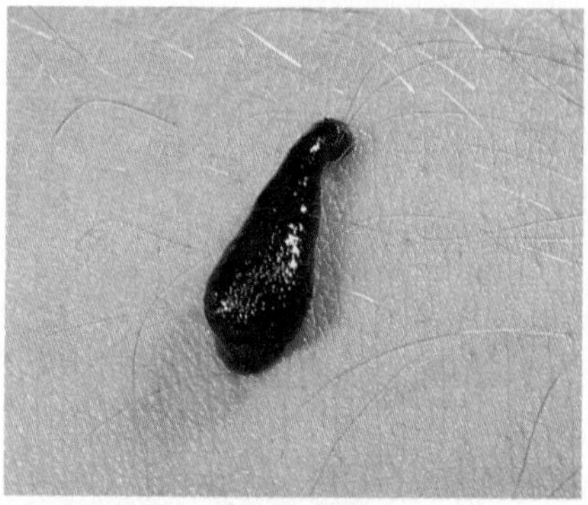
Figure 32-17. A Leech.

PHYLUM MOLLUSCA—THE MOLLUSKS

After completing your study of this section, you should be able to:

1. Name a representative animal from each class of mollusks.
2. Describe the general characteristics of mollusks.
3. Explain the functions of each of the following mollusk structures: the foot, mantle, and radula.
4. Describe nutrition, circulation, excretion, and reproduction in clams.
5. Describe some of the ways in which cephalopod mollusks, such as the squid, differ from mollusks of other classes.

32-16 General Characteristics

The phylum **Mollusca** (mahl-*us*-kuh) is a highly successful animal group. They are the second largest animal phylum, next to the arthropods. Oysters, clams, snails, squids, and octopuses are familiar mollusks. Mollusks are found in salt water, in fresh water, and on land. Members of this group vary greatly in size and shape (see Figure 32-18). They range from tiny snails 1 millimeter long to giant squids, which can reach

Figure 32-18. Nudibranch Mollusks.

16 meters in length and weigh 2 tons. The giant clam of the South Pacific Ocean can be 1.5 meters long and weigh 250 kilograms.

Many types of mollusks are used by humans for food. Among them are oysters, clams, scallops, mussels, snails, squid, and octopus. Pearls from oysters are used in jewelry, and mother-of-pearl is used in buttons and decorative objects. On the other hand, some snails and slugs feed on crops and are highly destructive.

There are three major classes of mollusks: the class Bivalvia (by-*valv*-ee-uh) includes mollusks with two-part shells, such as clams, oysters, and mussels; the class Gastropoda (ga-*strahp*-uh-duh) includes mollusks with a single shell, such as snails; and the class Cephalopoda (sef-uh-*lahp*-uh-duh) includes mollusks with little or no shell, such as squids and octopuses. Many marine mollusks have a trochophore larva similar to the trochophore larva of marine annelids. This is thought to indicate an evolutionary relationship between the two groups.

32-17 Structure and Life Functions

Although adult mollusks vary widely in appearance, they do share a number of common characteristics. They are bilaterally symmetrical and are composed of three tissue layers. They also have a true coelom. All mollusks have a soft body that houses all the organ systems—the digestive system, heart, nervous system, reproductive system, and so on. The foot, mantle, shell, and radula are structures found only in mollusks.

The large, ventral, muscular **foot** functions in locomotion. In clams, the foot is used to burrow or plow through wet sand or mud. The snail uses its foot to creep over rocks or plants. The foot of the squid and octopus is divided into tentacles and covered with suckers. The tentacles are used for seizing and holding prey.

The **mantle** is a fold of skin that surrounds the body organs. In the squid and octopus, the muscular mantle is used for locomotion. In mollusks with shells, the mantle is a glandular tissue that secretes part of the shell.

The **radula** (*rad*-joo-luh) is a rasping, tonguelike organ found in all mollusks except bivalves. The radula has many rows of teeth and can extend out of the mouth to scrape food from an object and bring it into the digestive system. Some snails use the radula to drill holes in the shells of other mollusks. They then suck out the soft body of the mollusk for food.

Figure 32-19. Oyster with Pearl.

The bivalves. **Bivalves** (*by*-valvz), such as clams, scallops, oysters, and mussels, have a shell made up of two parts. The smooth, shiny, innermost layer of the shell, which is just outside the mantle, is called *mother-of-pearl* (see Figure 32-19). In certain bivalves, pearls are produced when an irritating substance, such as a grain of sand, gets between the mantle

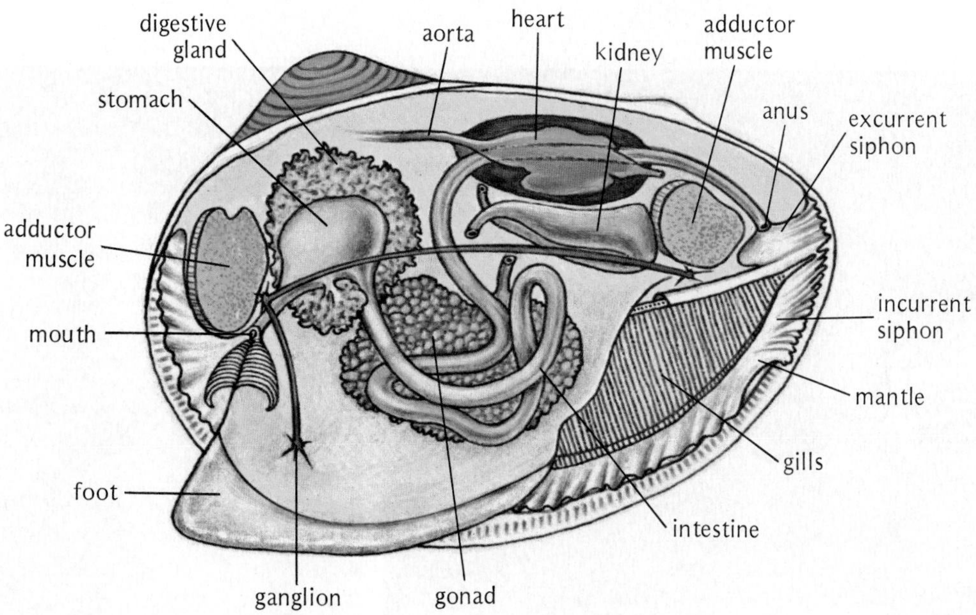

Figure 32-20. Structure of a Clam.

and the shell. The mantle walls off the irritant by secreting layers of mother-of-pearl around it. Eventually, a pearl is formed.

In terms of its life functions, the clam is a typical mollusk. Thus it will be discussed here as representative of the phylum.

The two halves of the clam's shell can be held firmly closed by two strong *adductor* muscles (see Figure 32-20). When the muscles relax, an elastic hinge keeps the shell open. Usually, the shells are partly open with two tubes extending into the water. One tube, the *incurrent siphon* (*sy*-fun), carries water containing food particles into the mantle cavity. The water is kept in motion by the beating of cilia on the gills. As the water moves over the gills, the exchange of respiratory gases occurs between the blood in the gills and the water. Oxygen diffuses through the gills and into the blood, and carbon dioxide diffuses from the blood into the water. Food particles in the water are trapped by mucus on the gills. The water then flows out of the mantle cavity through the *excurrent siphon*.

Food particles stuck in the mucus on the gills are transported by the cilia into the mouth and then into the rest of the digestive system. Animals that feed by filtering water through their bodies are called *filter feeders*. They feed on organic particles and dead and decaying microscopic organisms in the water.

The clam has an open circulatory system. It consists of a heart and vessels. When the blood reaches the body tissues, it flows out of the vessels and into the body spaces, or sinuses, where it bathes the body tissues. From the sinuses, the blood flows into vessels that carry it to the gills. After the exchange of respiratory gases, the blood flows back to the heart.

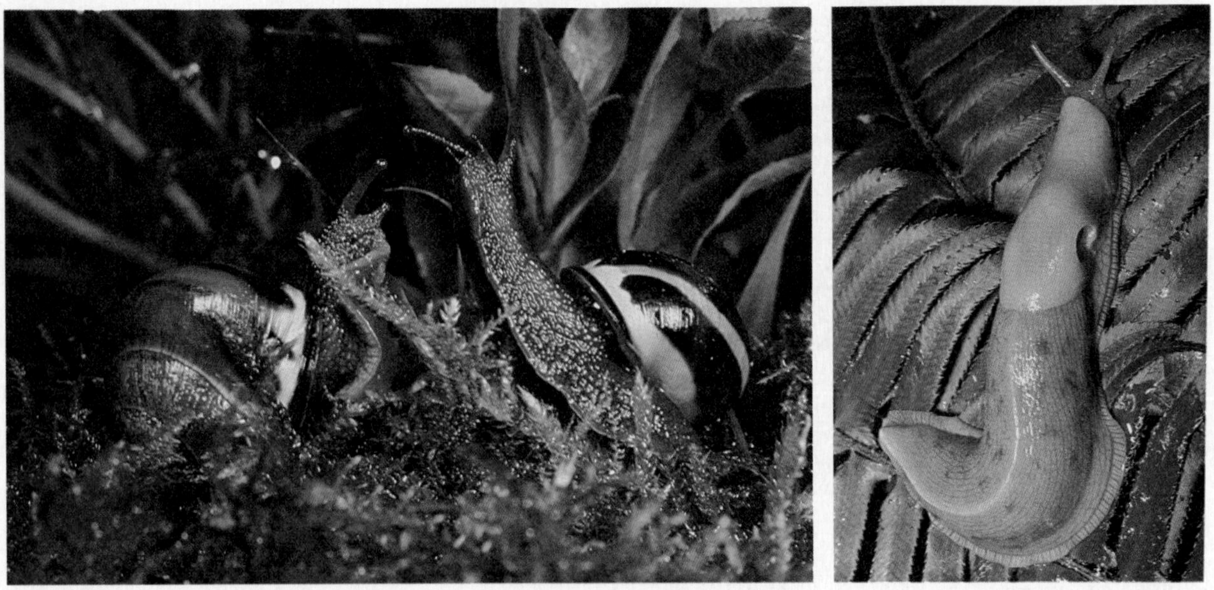

Figure 32-21. Gastropod Mollusks. The garden snails (left) have a single shell, while the slug (right) lacks a shell.

The clam has a pair of kidneys that remove organic wastes from the blood and empty them into the water leaving through the excurrent siphon. The nervous system consists of three pairs of ganglia connected by nerves to the foot and body organs. Sensory cells enable the clam to respond to chemical changes in the water, to touch, and to light.

In clams the sexes are separate. Sperm leave the male through the excurrent siphon. They then enter the female through her incurrent siphon. The eggs are held on the gills, where they are fertilized. The young bivalves pass through one or more distinct larval stages before reaching the adult form.

The gastropods. Snails, whelks, abalones (ab-uh-*loh*-neez), conches (*kahn*-chez), and slugs make up the largest group of mollusks, the **gastropods** (*gas*-truh-pahdz) (see Figure 32-21). Most gastropods have a single shell, which is often coiled. A few, such as the slug, lack a shell. Some are aquatic, some are terrestrial.

The common garden snail has a head with tentacles, eyes, and a mouth (see Figure 32-22). The head is connected to the foot. The shell is on top of the foot. For protection, all soft parts of the body can be drawn into the shell. Land snails have simple lungs rather than gills. Air is drawn into the mantle cavity and gas exchange occurs through the mantle.

Land snails usually travel at night when the air is moist. They slide along on a layer of mucus secreted by the foot. To keep from drying out during the day, the snail generally withdraws into its shell and seals the opening with mucus. The land snail feeds by rubbing its radula against plant material. As the pieces of plant are shredded, they are taken into the mouth.

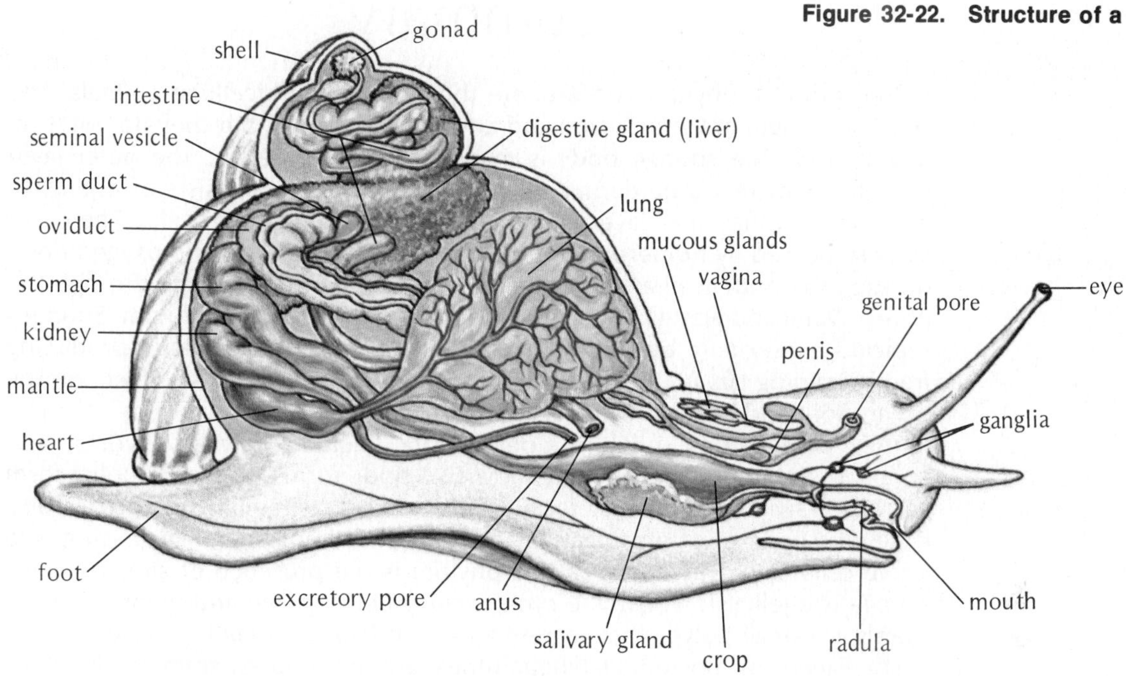

Figure 32-22. **Structure of a Snail.**

The cephalopods. Squids, octopuses, and cuttlefish are **cephalopods** (*sef*-uh-luh-pahdz). They are very different in appearance from other mollusks (see Figure 32-23). The most obvious difference is that most either have no shell (the octopus) or a small internal shell (the squid and cuttlefish). Only a few, such as the nautilus, are enclosed in a shell.

In cephalopods, the mouth is surrounded by tentacles. The tentacles are used to gather food and manipulate objects. The streamlined bodies of cephalopods are adapted for rapid swimming. They swim by expelling a jet of water from their mantle cavity. They have a well-developed nervous system with a large brain. The eye of the octopus is similar to the eye of vertebrates, and works in the same way. In times of danger, some cephalopods, such as squids and octopuses, discharge an inky fluid. This "smoke screen" distracts the enemy and enables the animal to escape.

Figure 32-23. An Octopus. The octopus has no shell.

summary

The sponges, phylum Porifera, are the simplest multicellular animals. The cells of sponges are specialized and are found in layers, but they do not form true tissues. The sponge body is made up of three layers. The outer layer consists of flattened epidermal cells, the middle layer consists of a jellylike material, and the inner layer is made up of flagellated collar cells. The outer layer is pierced by numerous pores. Water containing food and oxygen flows through the body wall and into the central cavity of the sponge through the pores. Water and wastes flow out of the sponge through the osculum. Sponges reproduce asexually by budding. They also reproduce sexually, producing free-swimming larvae that eventually become attached to an object on the ocean floor and grow into the sessile adult form.

The coelenterates, phylum Coelenterata, include jellyfish, hydras, and corals. Members of this phylum show two body forms—a sessile polyp form and a free-swimming medusa form. Coelenterates are radially symmetrical and have a tissue level of organization. They are the simplest animals having true nerve cells. A characteristic of this phylum is the presence of stinging cells. *Aurelia* is a jellyfish whose life cycle includes both polyp and medusa forms. Corals are small polyps that secrete a hard, calcium-containing skeleton.

The flatworms, phylum Platyhelminthes, are the simplest animals with bilateral symmetry and with definite head and tail regions. Flatworms show an organ system level of organization. Planaria are common, free-living flatworms. They have a digestive system that includes a mouth, pharynx, and intestine; an excretory system that runs the length of the body; and a fairly well-developed nervous system. Planaria reproduce both asexually and sexually. Flukes and tapeworms are parasitic flatworms. Some infect humans, causing disease. These worms have excretory and nervous systems and highly developed reproductive systems. However, they lack digestive systems.

Roundworms, phylum Nematoda, are extremely abundant. These animals are bilaterally symmetrical and are the simplest animals having a complete digestive system. Roundworms have an excretory and a nervous system, but lack a circulatory or respiratory system. They reproduce sexually. Some parasitic roundworms, including trichina, filaria, pinworms, and hookworms, can cause serious diseases in humans.

The segmented worms, phylum Annelida, include earthworms, marine sandworms, such as *Nereis,* and leeches, which are mainly parasitic. Annelids are bilaterally symmetrical and their bodies are divided into segments, or metameres. A true coelom is present. Annelids are the simplest animals that have a closed circulatory system. Reproduction is sexual.

The mollusks, phylum Mollusca, include clams, snails, and squids. Mollusks are bilaterally symmetrical. They have three tissue layers and a true coelom. The foot, mantle, shell, and radula are structures found only in mollusks. Bivalves, such as clams and oysters, have shells consisting of two parts. The gastropods, such as the snail, have one shell. Most cephalopods have no external shell.

vocabulary

Annelida
anterior
bilateral symmetry
bivalve
cephalopod
Coelenterata
coelenterate
coelom
collar cell
dorsal
filaria
flatworm
fluke
foot
gastropod
hookworm
larva
leech
mantle
medusa
Mollusca
Nematoda
osculum
parapodium
pinworm
planula
Platyhelminthes
polyp
pore
Porifera
posterior
radial symmetry
radula
roundworm
segmented worm
spherical symmetry
spicule
sponge
symmetry
tapeworm
trichina
trochophore
ventral
zoologist
zoology

test your learning

Section

32-1 **1.** Define the following terms: *zoology, invertebrate, vertebrate,* and *larva.*

32-2 **2.** Compare and contrast spherical, radial, and bilateral symmetry. Give an example of an animal showing each type of symmetry.

3. Define the following terms: *dorsal, ventral, anterior,* and *posterior.*

32-3 **4.** What types of animals belong to the phylum Porifera?

5. Where are adult sponges found?

32-4 **6.** Describe the three layers of the body wall of a sponge.

7. Describe the path of water flowing through a sponge.

8. Describe the following life processes in sponges: nutrition, respiration, and excretion.

9. Describe both asexual and sexual reproduction in sponges.

32-5 **10.** Name three members of the phylum Coelenterata.

11. Name the two body forms found among coelenterates. Give examples of animals showing each form.

32-6 **12.** What are the three layers of a coelenterate body?

13. What are cnidoblasts and nematocysts, and what are their functions?
14. Describe the following life functions in coelenterates: nutrition, respiration, and excretion.

32-7 15. What are corals?

32-8 16. Describe the life cycle of *Aurelia*.

32-9 17. Name the phylum to which flatworms belong.
18. What type of symmetry is found in flatworms?
19. Name the three major groups of flatworms.

32-10 20. What level of organization is found in flatworms?
21. Describe feeding and digestion in planaria.
22. Describe the excretory, nervous, and reproductive systems of a planarian.
23. What is a fluke? Describe the life cycle of the blood fluke.
24. Describe the structure and life cycle of the beef tapeworm.

32-11 25. Name the phylum to which roundworms belong.
26. Describe the general structure of roundworms, including symmetry.
27. In what types of environments are roundworms found?

32-12 28. Compare the digestive system of a roundworm with that of a planarian.

32-13 29. Name four parasitic roundworms that infect humans.
30. Name the roundworm that causes trichinosis in humans, and describe its life cycle.

32-14 31. To what phylum do segmented worms belong?

32-15 32. Describe the body plan of an annelid.
33. Define the terms *metamerism* and *coelom*.
34. What are parapodia, and what functions do they serve in *Nereis*?
35. Describe reproduction in *Nereis*.
36. How do most leeches obtain nourishment?

32-16 37. Name the three major classes of mollusks and a representative animal from each.
38. For each class of mollusk, state whether a shell is generally present or absent. If present, describe its most common form.

32-17 39. Describe the structure and function of the foot, mantle, and radula of mollusks.
40. Briefly describe the following life functions in the clam: nutrition, respiration, circulation, excretion, and reproduction.
41. Describe locomotion and feeding in land snails.
42. How do cephalopod mollusks differ from bivalves and gastropods?

test your understanding

1. Compare and contrast the levels of organization in sponges and flatworms.
2. State the type of symmetry found in members of each of the following phyla: Porifera, Coelenterata, Platyhelminthes, Nematoda, Annelida, and Mollusca.
3. What evidence is there of a possible evolutionary relationship between mollusks and annelids?
4. Describe three human diseases caused by parasitic worms—either flatworms or roundworms.

independent research

1. Prepare a report on one of the following topics:
   A. The giant squid.
   B. The Great Barrier Reef of Australia.
   C. Trichinosis, including means of infection, symptoms, and treatment.
2. Prepare a report on the importance of the earthworm in soil formation and soil aeration.

chapter 33

Invertebrates— Arthropods and Echinoderms

INTRODUCTION TO THE ARTHROPODS

After completing your study of this section, you should be able to describe the general characteristics of the arthropods.

33-1 Arthropods—The Most Numerous Animals

The phylum **Arthropoda** (ar-*thrahp*-uh-duh) includes such common animals as flies, bees, beetles, mosquitoes, butterflies, spiders, ants, crabs, lobsters, and shrimp. The **arthropods** are the most successful and abundant of all animal groups. There are more arthropod species than all other species of organisms put together. There are about 400,000 known species of plants and about 250,000 species of animals other than arthropods. But there are more than 1 million known species of arthropods.

The phylum Arthropoda is divided into five classes. These are Crustacea, Chilopoda, Diplopoda, Arachnida, and Insecta. Each class will be described separately later in the chapter.

33-2 General Characteristics of Arthropods

In many ways, arthropods are the most advanced invertebrates. They are bilaterally symmetrical and have a small coelom.

Figure 33-1. A Prawn Molting.

Although the phylum Arthropoda consists of a large number of dissimilar species, all arthropods share a number of common features.

1. Arthropods have jointed legs. The limbs of arthropods are composed of several pieces that are connected together at hinged joints. These joints are controlled by opposing sets of muscles, and they allow much freedom of movement. Different arrangements of these jointed limbs, or appendages, allow such varied functions as crawling, swimming, hopping, jumping, flying, grabbing, digging, and biting.

2. Arthropods have exoskeletons composed of chitin, a carbohydrate, and protein. The tough, lightweight exoskeleton protects the soft body parts within. The exoskeleton is also waterproof and prevents excessive water loss, enabling many arthropods to live successfully on land. Because the exoskeleton is nonelastic and cannot grow, young arthropods must periodically undergo a process called **molting** (see Figure 33-1). During molting, the exoskeleton is shed and replaced by a new, larger one. Growth takes place before the new exoskeleton hardens. Molting is a dangerous time for arthropods because before the new exoskeleton hardens, the animal cannot move or defend itself. Therefore, many arthropods hide until their new exoskeleton has hardened.

The presence of segmentation suggests that arthropods and annelids share a common ancestor.

3. Like annelids, all arthropods are segmented. However, the body segments are usually modified and fused to form specific body regions. In most arthropods, there is a head, **thorax** (*thor*-aks), and **abdomen** (*ab*-duh-men). The head is well developed and is always composed of six segments. It contains a mouth that is specialized for chewing or sucking. The thorax is the middle region of the arthropod, and the abdomen is the posterior region. While the head always con-

tains six segments, the number of segments in the thorax and abdomen varies greatly from one group of arthropods to another.

4. Arthropods have a well-developed nervous system. There is a distinct brain and a ventral nerve cord located beneath the digestive system. Arthropods have a variety of sense organs, including eyes, organs of hearing, sensory cells sensitive to touch, and antennae that are sensitive to touch and chemicals.

5. Arthropods have an open circulatory system. There is a dorsal tubular heart located above the digestive system. Arteries carry blood away from the heart to the body spaces, where it bathes the tissues directly. The blood eventually reenters the heart through openings in it sides.

CLASS CRUSTACEA—THE CRUSTACEANS

After completing your study of this section, you should be able to:

1. Describe the basic characteristics of the class Crustacea, and name four members of this group.
2. Describe the external structure of the crayfish.
3. Describe the following life processes in the crayfish: nutrition, excretion, circulation, and respiration.
4. Describe the nervous system and sense organs of the crayfish.
5. Describe reproduction in the crayfish.

33-3 Crustaceans and Their Habitats

The class **Crustacea** (krus-*tay*-shuh), the **crustaceans,** includes lobsters, crayfish, crabs, shrimp, water fleas, sow bugs, barnacles, and many others (see Figure 33-2). Most crusta-

Figure 33-2. Crustaceans. The hermit crab (left) lives in an empty shell. The purple anemone on the shell feeds on the crab's leftovers. (Right) Goose barnacles.

ceans are marine, but some live in fresh water. A few, such as the sow bug, live on land in moist places. Crustaceans vary in size from microscopic water fleas to huge crabs with leg spans of 3.5 meters. Microscopic crustaceans are the main source of food for many larger marine animals. Crustaceans are characterized by the presence of two pairs of antennae located on the head. The body is divided into a cephalothorax and abdomen, and there are five pairs of legs.

33-4 The Crayfish—External Structure

The crayfish, which is found in freshwater streams, lakes, and swamps, is a typical crustacean, showing many of the characteristics of its class. It is covered by an exoskeleton hardened with lime. At the joints, where bending occurs, the exoskeleton is softer and thinner, and also folded. The crayfish body has two main regions (see Figure 33-3). At the anterior end, the twelve segments of the head and thorax are fused to form the **cephalothorax** (sef-uh-luh-*thor*-aks). The part of the exoskeleton that protects and covers the dorsal and side surfaces of the cephalothorax is called the *carapace* (*kar*-uh-pays). The seven segments posterior to the cephalothorax form the jointed abdomen. The paddle-shaped last segment of the abdomen is called the *telson* (*tel*-sun).

The various paired appendages of the crayfish have specific functions. Starting at the anterior end, the first pair of appendages are the *antennules* (an-*ten*-yoolz), which function in touch, taste, and balance. Next come the *antennae* (an-*ten*-ee), which are also used for touching and tasting. The *mandibles* (*man*-duh-bulz), or jaws, crush food by moving from side to side. The two pairs of *maxillae* (mak-*sil*-ee) handle food. The three pairs of *maxillipeds* (mak-*sil*-uh-pedz) touch, taste, and also handle food. The large first legs are called *chelipeds* (*kihl*-uh-pedz). Their grasping claws are used to catch food and for defense. Behind the chelipeds are four pairs of *walk-*

Figure 33-3. External Structure of the Crayfish.

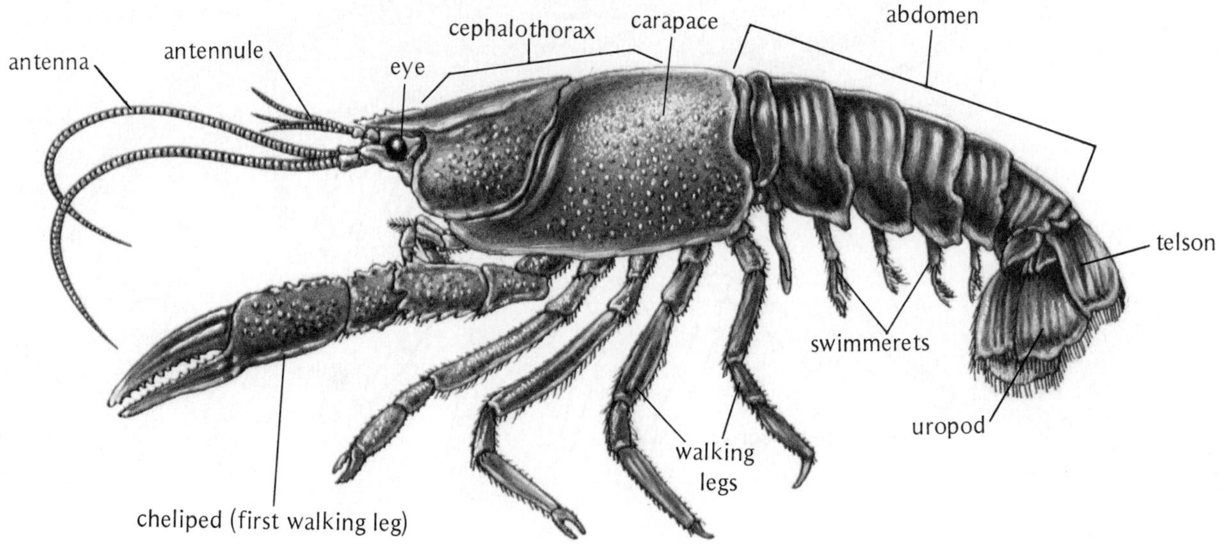

ing legs. On the abdomen are *swimmerets* (swim-uh-*rets*), which are used in swimming. In females they are used to carry the developing eggs. The last pair of appendages are the broad *uropods* (*yur*-uh-pahdz). The uropods, along with the telson, form a fan-shaped tail that is used for rapid backward movement. When the crayfish senses danger, the powerful abdominal muscles whip the tail forward under the abdomen, causing the crayfish to shoot backward.

33-5 The Crayfish—Internal Structure and Life Functions

Nutrition. The crayfish feeds on dead animals and catches living animals with its powerful chelipeds. The food is crushed by the mandibles and passed to the mouth by the maxillae and maxillipeds. The mouth leads into a short esophagus (see Figure 33-4). From the esophagus, food passes into the stomach, where it is chewed up by chitinous teeth in a structure called the *gastric mill.* The finely ground food particles are digested by enzymes, then passed into the digestive glands and absorbed into the blood. Undigested material passes through the intestine and out the anus.

Excretion. The excretory organs of the crayfish are called the *green glands.* They are located in the head region. The green glands remove wastes from the blood, and these wastes are excreted from the body through an opening near the base of the antennae.

Circulation and respiration. The open circulatory system consists of a dorsal heart surrounded by a cavity called the *pericardial* (pehr-uh-*kard*-ee-ul) *sinus.* Blood in the pericardial

Figure 33-4. Internal Structure of the Crayfish.

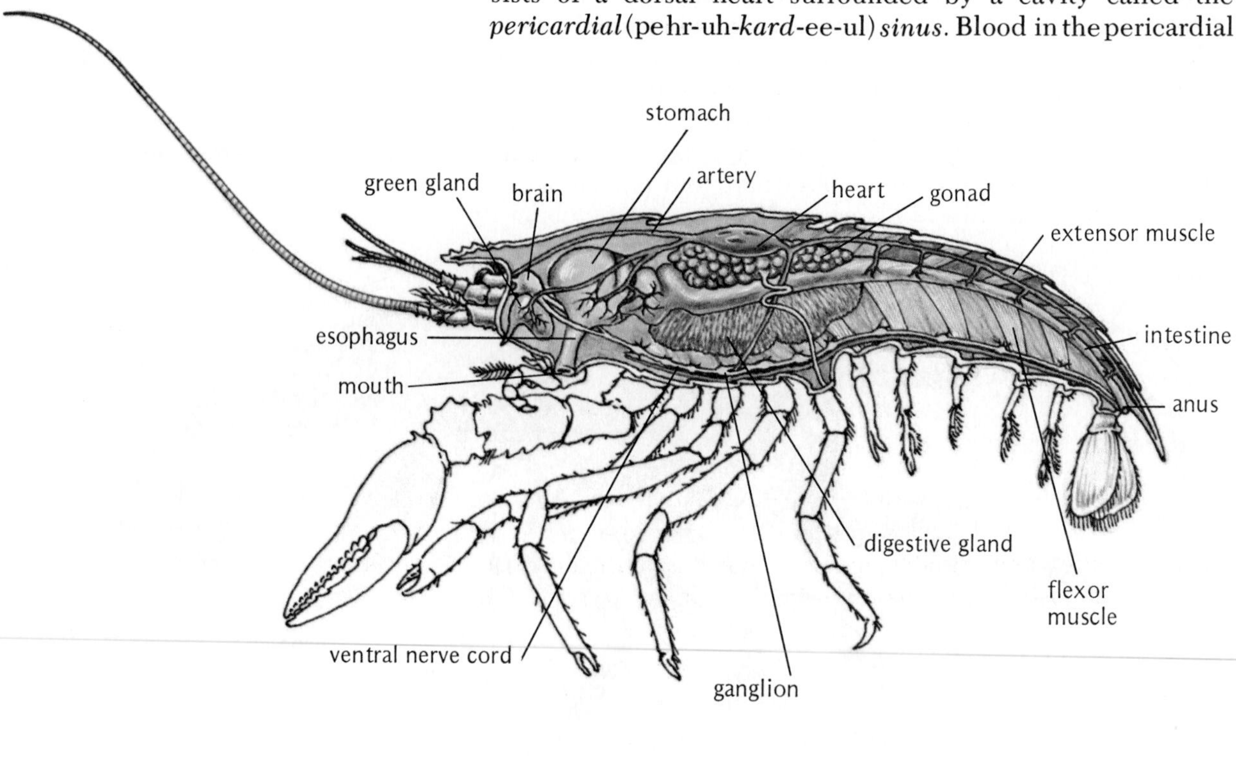

sinus enters the heart through three pairs of valves called *ostia* (*ahs*-tee-uh). When the heart contracts, the ostia close, and blood is pumped out through arteries to all parts of the body. There are no capillaries or veins. The arteries open into spaces, or sinuses, among the body tissues. There the blood bathes the cells directly. Oxygen and nutrients from the blood diffuse into the cells, and carbon dioxide and wastes from the cells diffuse into the blood. Eventually, the blood collects in the *sternal* (*stern*-ul) *sinus*. From there, it is channeled to the gills, where it picks up oxygen and gets rid of carbon dioxide. From the gills, the blood returns to the pericardial sinus. Dissolved in the plasma of the colorless blood is **hemocyanin** (hee-moh-*sy*-uh-nin), a copper-containing respiratory pigment that aids in the transport of oxygen.

The gills, where the exchange of respiratory gases occurs, are delicate, plumelike structures. They are located in *gill chambers* on each side of the thorax. The gill chambers are protected by the carapace. Water is kept flowing through the gill chambers by the movement of the second maxillae.

Nervous regulation. The nervous system of the crayfish resembles that of the annelids in form. The brain, which is in the head, is connected by nerves to the eyes, antennules, and antennae. Extending from the brain, two nerves circle the esophagus and join ventrally to form a double, ventral nerve cord. As the ventral nerve cord runs posteriorly, it enlarges into ganglia in each segment. From these ganglia, nerves branch to the appendages, muscles, and other organs.

The sensory organs of the crayfish are varied and well developed. They include a pair of *compound eyes* located at the ends of movable stalks. Each eye contains about 2,000 visual units. Each unit contains a lens system that, unlike the human eye, cannot focus at different distances. Such an eye is very sensitive to movement and offers a wide angle of vision. However, it produces only a crude image.

The crayfish has two kinds of small sensory hairs that are found on the appendages and other parts of the body. One type of hair is sensitive to touch. The other is sensitive to chemicals, providing information equivalent to the human senses of taste and smell.

The sense organs of equilibrium, or balance, are found in sacs called *statocysts* (*stat*-uh-sists), which are located at the bases of the antennules. Each statocyst contains sensory hairs and grains of sand. When the crayfish moves, the sand grains move, stimulating some of the sensory hairs. From the stimulated hairs, impulses pass to the brain. The brain interprets the information and initiates impulses that enable the crayfish to adjust its position and maintain its equilibrium. Each time the animal molts, the sand grains are shed along with the exoskeleton. New sand grains are picked up when the new exoskeleton forms.

Figure 33-5. Female Crayfish with Eggs and with Newly Hatched Young.

Reproduction. In crayfish, sexes are separate. Mating takes place in the fall. The male uses his first pair of swimmerets to transfer sperm from his body to the *seminal* (*sem*-in-ul) *receptacle* of the female. The sperm are kept in the receptacle until spring, when the female lays several hundred eggs that have been fertilized by the stored sperm. The eggs attach to the female's swimmerets (see Figure 33-5). The waving of the swimmerets back and forth keeps the embryos well supplied with oxygen. After 5 to 6 weeks, the eggs hatch, but the young remain attached to the mother for several more weeks. During this time, the young crayfish begins to molt. Crayfish live for 3 to 5 years.

Regeneration. If a crayfish injures an appendage, it can shed the injured limb at a joint. This process of self-amputation, which is called *autotomy* (aw-*taht*-uh-mee) prevents excessive loss of blood. Gradually, with each molt, the lost appendage grows back. Regeneration in crayfish is limited to the appendages and eyes.

CLASSES CHILOPODA AND DIPLOPODA— THE CENTIPEDES AND MILLIPEDES

After completing your study of this section, you should be able to:

1. Name the members of the classes Chilopoda and Diplopoda.
2. Describe the general characteristics of centipedes.
3. Describe the general characteristics of millipedes.

33-6 General Characteristics of the Chilopoda

Centipedes, or "hundred-leggers," belong to the class **Chilopoda** (ky-*lahp*-uh-duh). Actually, some centipedes have more than 150 pairs of legs, but 30 to 35 pairs is most common. A centipede has a distinct head made up of six segments. The

Figure 33-6. A Centipede.

head is followed by a long, wormlike, slightly flattened body made up of many similar segments (see Figure 33-6). Centipedes live on land and are commonly found in dark, damp places, such as under logs or stones.

In the centipedes, all body segments except the one behind the head and the last two have one pair of legs. The head has one pair of antennae and various mouthparts. Centipedes feed mainly on insects. The centipede bites its victim with *poison claws,* which are on the first body segment. Small centipedes are harmless to humans. The common house centipede is about 2.5 centimeters long. At night, it searches for food, eating cockroaches, bedbugs, and other insects.

33-7 General Characteristics of the Diplopoda

Millipedes, or "thousand-leggers," belong to the class **Diplopoda** (dih-*plahp*-uh-duh). They do not have a thousand legs, but they may have more than 300 pairs (see Figure 33-7). Like a centipede, a millipede has a distinct head and a long, wormlike body made up of many segments. Except for the last two segments, millipedes have two pairs of legs per segment. The head bears a pair of antennae and various mouthparts. Millipedes, unlike centipedes, do not have poison claws. Whereas centipedes can move rapidly, millipedes move much more slowly. They feed mainly on decaying plant material. When they are disturbed, millipedes usually roll themselves into a ball. Many have "stink" glands that give off an offensive odor.

Figure 33-7. A Millipede. The millipede is curled around a twig.

CLASS ARACHNIDA—THE ARACHNIDS

After completing your study of this section, you should be able to:

1. Name four members of the class Arachnida.
2. Describe the general characteristics of arachnids.

33-8 Introduction to the Arachnids

The **arachnids,** members of the class **Arachnida** (uh-*rak*-nih-duh), include spiders, scorpions, ticks, mites, and daddy

A

C

B

Figure 33-8. Arachnids. (A) Huntsman spider. (B) Scorpion. (C) Daddy longlegs.

longlegs (see Figure 33-8). Some arachnids are annoying and even dangerous to humans and other animals. Mites and ticks live as temporary parasites on the skin of many animals, including humans, dogs, chickens, and cattle. Mites often cause terrible itching. Ticks are carriers of several diseases, including Rocky Mountain spotted fever and Texas cattle fever. Scorpions sting with their tail. While the sting is very painful, it is usually not fatal to humans. Spiders are generally harmless. In fact, they are often helpful because they feed on insects. The poisonous spiders of the United States are the black widow and the brown recluse. Spiders rarely bite unless they are disturbed.

33-9 General Characteristics of Arachnids

Most arachnids live on land, and many resemble insects. The body of an arachnid consists of a cephalothorax and an abdomen. These animals do not have either antennae or chewing jaws. They have six pairs of jointed appendages, all on the cephalothorax (see Figure 33-9). The first pair of appendages are the fanglike chelicerae (kuh-*lis*-uh-ree), which are used to pierce the prey. The body fluids of the prey are then drawn into the spider's mouth by the action of the *sucking stomach.* Usually, poison glands associated with the chelicerae inject a poison that paralyzes the prey. The second pair of appendages, the *pedipalps* (*ped*-uh-palps), are sensitive both to chemicals and to touch. They also hold food and are used by the male in reproduction. The next appendages are the four pairs of walking legs.

The respiratory organs of the arachnids are called **book lungs.** Located in chambers on the underside of the abdomen, they consist of a series of leaflike plates containing blood vessels. Air drawn into the chambers through slits in the abdo-

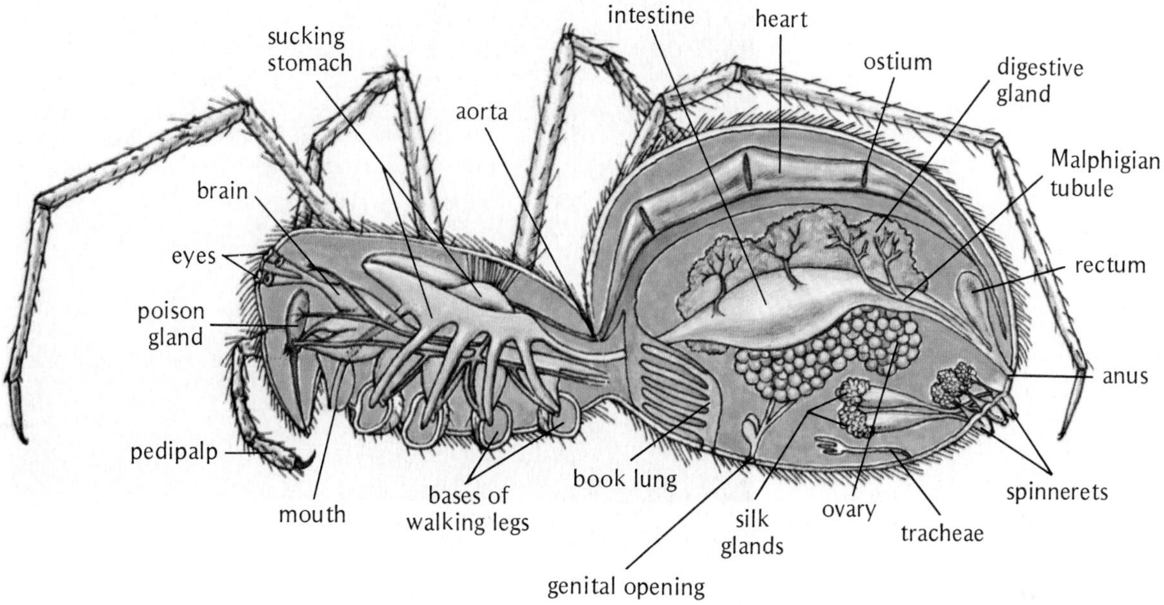

Figure 33-9. Structure of an Arachnid. The body of an arachnid is divided into a cephalothorax and an abdomen, and there are four pairs of legs.

men circulates between the plates. Gas exchange occurs between the blood in the plates and the air in the chamber. Oxygen and carbon dioxide are transported in the blood between the body cells and the book lungs. Although some insectlike tracheae, or air tubes, are present, they play only a minor role in respiration.

In spiders and some other arachnids, the pedipalps of the male are modified for sperm transfer. Following elaborate courtship behavior, the male uses the pedipalps to place the sperm in the seminal receptacle of the female. In spiders, as the female lays the eggs, they are fertilized by the stored sperm, and wrapped in a cocoon. In some species the female carries the cocoons until the young hatch (see Figure 33-10).

Female spiders are usually larger than the males, and they also differ in color.

Figure 33-10. Wolf Spider. Female wolf spider with egg case (left) and with newly hatched young (right).

Figure 33-11. Spider in Web.

In other spider species the eggs in their cocoons are deposited on the ground. In other types of arachnids, sperm are not transferred into the body of the female by the male. Instead, the sperm are enclosed in a case and deposited on the ground. The case is then taken up by the female into a special body opening called a *gonopore*.

In spiders and one other small group of arachnids, there are three pairs of *spinnerets* (spin-uh-*rets*) at the end of the abdomen. Spinnerets are used to spin silk produced by silk glands within the abdomen. As the fluid protein is squeezed out of the spinnerets, it hardens into a thread. Spiders use these threads for many purposes. Some use it to construct webs in which they capture prey (see Figure 33-11). It is also used to line nests and to make cocoons for the fertilized eggs. Spiders also use threads as a means of transportation. They can lower themselves from trees on a thread.

CLASS INSECTA—THE INSECTS

After completing your study of this section, you should be able to:

1. Give several reasons for the enormous success of insects as land animals.
2. Describe some of the structural variations in the mouthparts, legs, and body forms found among insects.
3. Describe the external structure of the head, thorax, and abdomen of the grasshopper.
4. Describe sexual reproduction in insects.
5. Compare and contrast complete and incomplete metamorphosis in insects.
6. Name two members of each of the six major insect orders.

7. Discuss some of the advantages and disadvantages of chemical and biological methods of insect control.

33-10 Introduction to the Insects

Biologically, the insects, class **Insecta** (in-*sek*-tuh), are the most successful group of animals. There are more than 900,000 known species. Nearly all insects are land animals, although a few live in fresh water and a few in salt water. Insects range in size from tiny beetles 0.25 millimeters long to some large tropical moths with a wingspan of 30 centimeters. Most insects, however, are less than 2.5 centimeters long.

There are several reasons for the remarkable success of insects.

1. Insects are the only invertebrates capable of flying. The ability to fly allows them to travel over great distances in search of food. It enables them to escape from their enemies and to spread into new environments.

2. Among the insects there is a tremendous variety of adaptations for feeding and reproduction. These adaptations allow insects to exist in all types of environments and to obtain nourishment from many sources.

3. Insects have a very high rate of reproduction. A single female can lay hundreds or even thousands of eggs at a time. These eggs develop rapidly and in turn may produce millions of offspring during a year.

4. Insects are generally small, which means that they do not need large areas in which to live.

33-11 Structural Variations Among Insects

All insects have three separate body regions—the head, thorax, and abdomen (see Figure 33-12). On the head is one

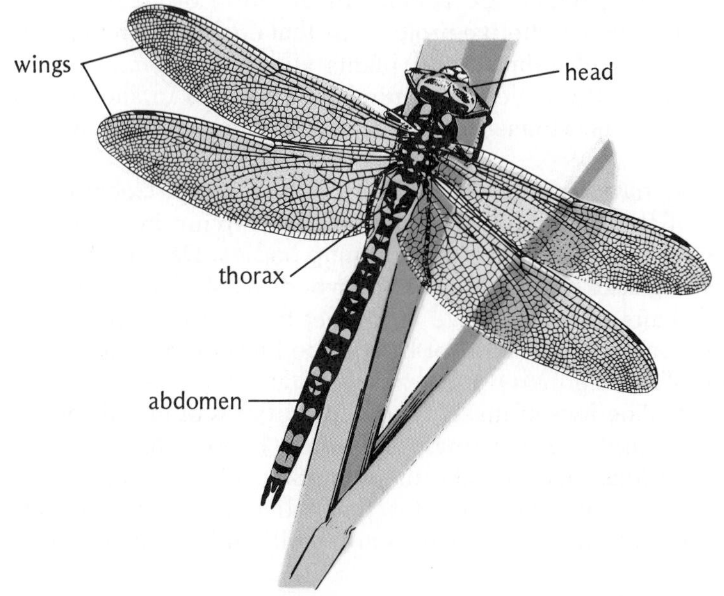

Figure 33-12. Structure of the Dragonfly. Like all insects, the body of the dragonfly is divided into a head, thorax, and abdomen.

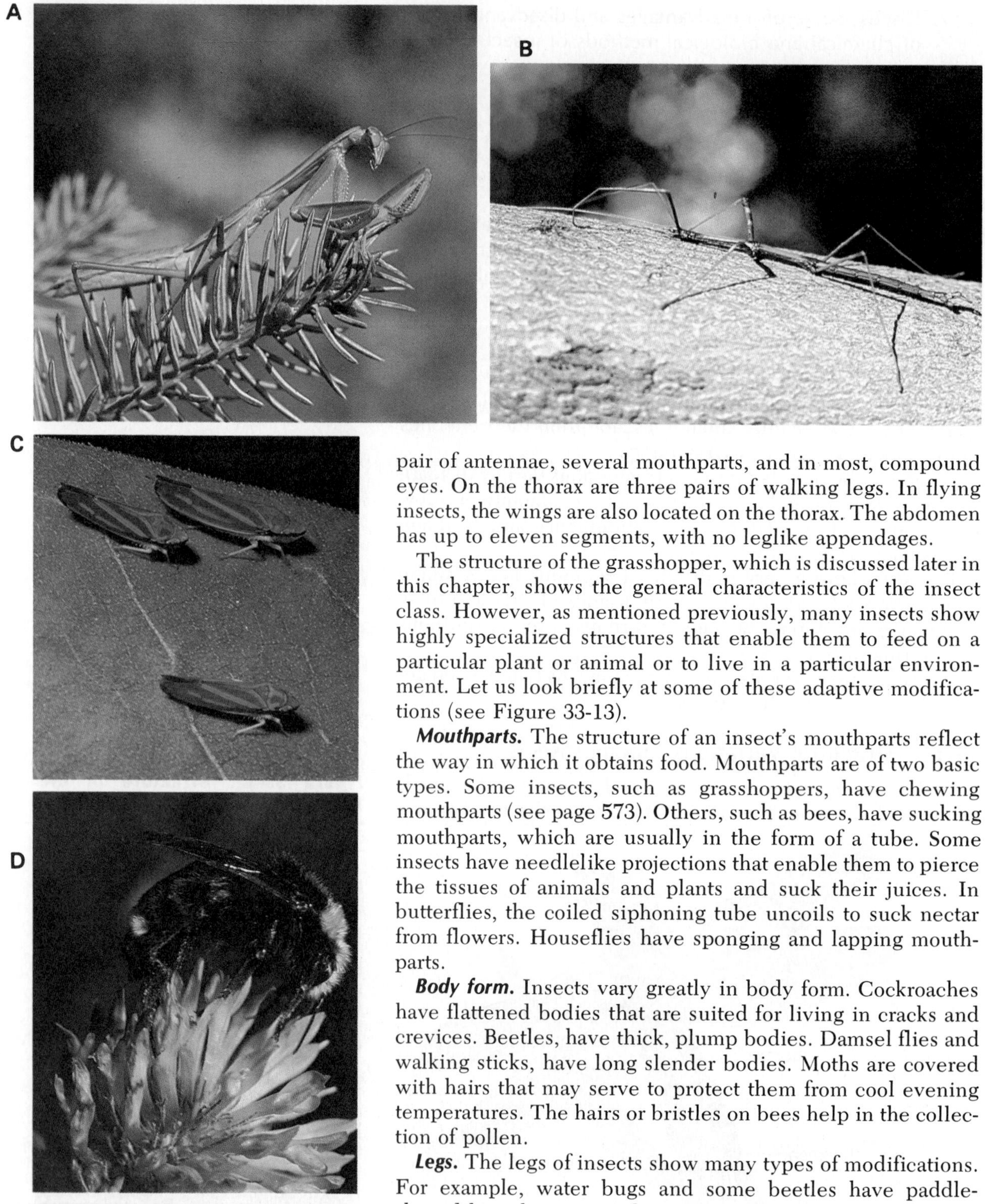

Figure 33-13. Insects. (A) Praying mantis. (B) Walking stick. (C) Leafhoppers. (D) Bee.

pair of antennae, several mouthparts, and in most, compound eyes. On the thorax are three pairs of walking legs. In flying insects, the wings are also located on the thorax. The abdomen has up to eleven segments, with no leglike appendages.

The structure of the grasshopper, which is discussed later in this chapter, shows the general characteristics of the insect class. However, as mentioned previously, many insects show highly specialized structures that enable them to feed on a particular plant or animal or to live in a particular environment. Let us look briefly at some of these adaptive modifications (see Figure 33-13).

Mouthparts. The structure of an insect's mouthparts reflect the way in which it obtains food. Mouthparts are of two basic types. Some insects, such as grasshoppers, have chewing mouthparts (see page 573). Others, such as bees, have sucking mouthparts, which are usually in the form of a tube. Some insects have needlelike projections that enable them to pierce the tissues of animals and plants and suck their juices. In butterflies, the coiled siphoning tube uncoils to suck nectar from flowers. Houseflies have sponging and lapping mouthparts.

Body form. Insects vary greatly in body form. Cockroaches have flattened bodies that are suited for living in cracks and crevices. Beetles, have thick, plump bodies. Damsel flies and walking sticks, have long slender bodies. Moths are covered with hairs that may serve to protect them from cool evening temperatures. The hairs or bristles on bees help in the collection of pollen.

Legs. The legs of insects show many types of modifications. For example, water bugs and some beetles have paddle-shaped legs that are used in swimming. The walking legs of honeybees are modified for the collection of pollen. The forelegs of the praying mantis are modified for grasping prey.

33-12 The Grasshopper—A Representative Insect

Like all insects, the body of the grasshopper is divided into three sections—the head, thorax, and abdomen. The head is made up of six fused segments. Two large compound eyes similar to those of the crayfish are located on the sides of the head (see Figure 33-14). In addition, the grasshopper also has three *simple eyes,* or *ocelli* (oh-*sel*-ee), located between the compound eyes. The simple eyes do not form images. They are only sensitive to light and dark. On the front of the head are a pair of jointed antennae. The antennae are sensitive to smell and touch.

The mouthparts used in chewing are located outside the mouth. These structures are adapted for eating leafy vegetation. The upper lip, or *labrum,* and the lower lip, or *labium,* function in holding the food (see Figure 33-15). The mandibles, or crushing jaws, are lined with rough-edged chitinous teeth. In biting off and chewing food, the mandibles move from side to side. Behind the mandibles are a second pair of jaws called the maxillae. These structures hold the food and pass it to the mandibles. Sensory palps on both the maxillae and labium feel and taste the food. Beneath the lower lip is a tonguelike organ.

The thorax is composed of three segments—the *prothorax,* the *mesothorax,* and the *metathorax* (see Figure 33-16). Each segment bears a pair of legs that are structurally similar. Each leg has five segments. The last segment is called the *tarsus,* or foot. The tarsus contains pads that enable the grasshopper to cling to smooth surfaces and claws that enable it to climb rough surfaces. The first two pairs of legs are for walking. The third pair of legs is larger than the first two and is modified for jumping.

Attached to the last two segments of the thorax are two pairs of wings. The outer pair, the fore wings, is hard and serves as a protective covering for the inner pair of wings, the hind wings.

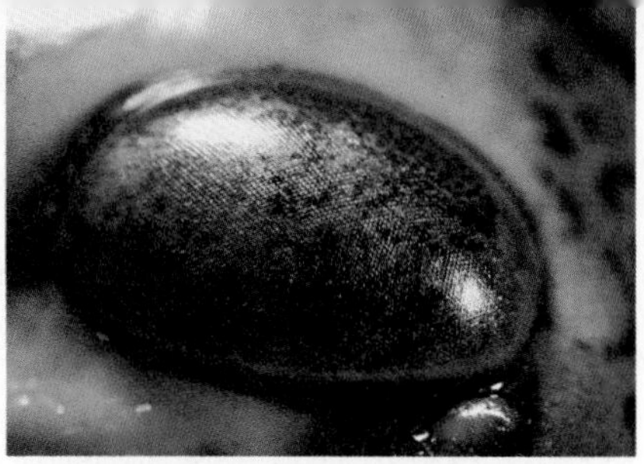

Figure 33-14. Compound Eye of the Grasshopper.

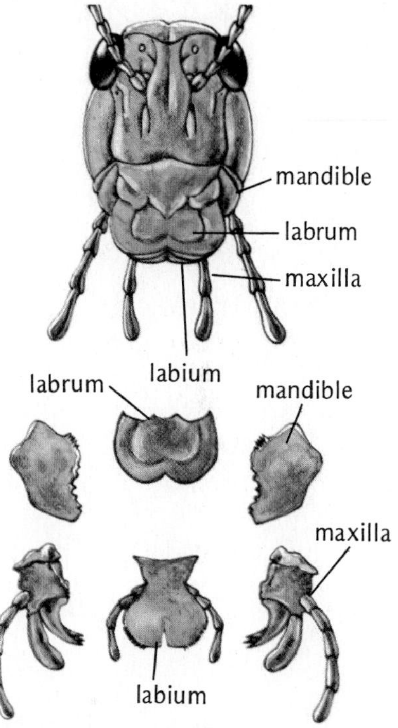

Figure 33-15. Mouthparts of the Grasshopper.

Figure 33-16. External Structure of the Grasshopper.

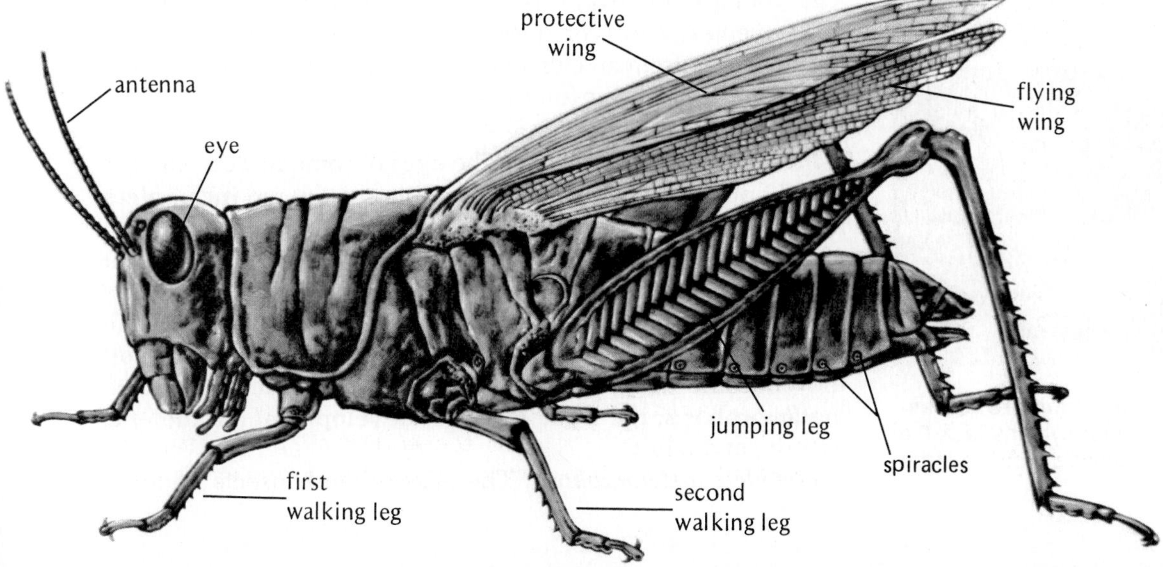

It is the flexible hind wings that are used in flight. When not in use, the hind wings are folded like fans. The thin membranes of the hind wings contain veins that serve to strengthen them.

The abdomen consists of ten segments. Along the lower sides of the abdomen and thorax are ten pairs of spiracles, which open into breathing tubes, or tracheae. Located on either side of the first abdominal segments are the *tympana* (*tim*-puh-nuh), the organs of hearing. Each tympanum consists of a circular, flat membrane that vibrates when hit by sound waves. The last segment of the abdomen is modified for reproduction.

The internal structure of the grasshopper and its life functions have been discussed in Unit 2. For a discussion of the digestive system, see page 130; for the circulatory system, see page 144; for the respiratory system, see page 179; for the excretory system, see page 195; for the musculoskeletal system, see page 211; for the nervous system, see page 236.

33-13 Reproduction in Insects

All insects reproduce sexually. Eggs are produced in the ovaries of the female, and sperm are produced in the testes of the male. When grasshoppers mate, the male transfers sperm into the body of the female. The sperm are stored in the seminal receptacle of the female. When the eggs leave the ovary of the female, they enter the oviduct, where fertilization occurs. They then pass out of the body of the female. On the end of the abdomen of the female is a hard, four-pointed organ called the **ovipositor** (*oh*-vee-pahz-it-er). It is used to dig holes in the ground in which the eggs are deposited. Although the eggs are laid in the fall, they do not hatch until spring.

33-14 Development in Insects

In a few insects, eggs hatch directly into miniature adults. The young molt several times, growing larger each time. In most species, however, insects undergo distinct changes as they develop from an egg to an adult. This series of changes is called **metamorphosis** (met-uh-*mor*-fuh-sis), and the process is under hormonal control.

Figure 33-17. An Immature Grasshopper. Grasshopper nymphs lack the wings and reproductive structures of the adult.

Incomplete metamorphosis. The eggs of some insects, such as grasshoppers, crickets, and cockroaches, undergo **incomplete metamorphosis.** In this type of development, the eggs hatch into **nymphs** (nimfs). The nymph resembles the adult, but lacks certain adult features. The grasshopper nymph looks like the adult, but it lacks wings and reproductive structures (see Figure 33-17). Nymphs molt several times. With each molt they become larger and more like the adult. In incomplete metamorphosis, the three stages of development are the egg, nymph, and adult.

Complete metamorphosis. The eggs of most insects undergo

complete metamorphosis. Among the insects exhibiting complete metamorphosis are moths, butterflies, beetles, bees, and flies. In this type of development, the eggs hatch into segmented, wormlike larvae. These larvae are commonly known as *caterpillars* (*kat*-er-pil-erz), *maggots* (*mag*-uts), or *grubs.* During this active stage, the larva eats and grows. After several molts, the larva passes into a resting stage called the **pupa** (*pyoo*-puh). The pupa is surrounded either by a cocoon or by a case made from its outer body covering. During the pupal stage, the tissues of the larva are reorganized into the adult form. When the changes are complete, the case or cocoon splits open, and the adult emerges. In complete metamorphosis, the four stages of development are the egg, larva, pupa, and adult.

The development of the cecropia (sih-*kroh*-pee-uh) moth is typical of insects that undergo complete metamorphosis. It includes the egg, larva, pupa, and adult stages (see Figure 33-18). The stages of metamorphosis are controlled by the interaction of three hormones—brain hormone, molting hormone, and juvenile hormone.

The egg hatches into the larva, in this case a caterpillar. As the caterpillar eats and grows, neurosecretory cells in the brain secrete a hormone called *brain hormone.* Brain hormone stimulates production of *molting hormone* by an endocrine gland in the thorax. Molting hormone stimulates periodic molting of the exoskeleton. The transformation of the larva into more mature forms is inhibited by a hormone called *juvenile hormone.* Juvenile hormone is produced by endocrine glands near the brain. As long as juvenile hormone is secreted, the larva can molt, but it will not change into the next stage, the pupa. At the end of the larval period, the secretion of juvenile hormone decreases. At the time of the next molt, the larva forms a pupa. During the pupal stage, the insect appears inactive, but great changes in body form are occurring. At the end of pupation, the adult moth emerges.

A recent approach to insect control involves the use of substances similar to juvenile hormone. These substances prevent the metamorphosis of larvae into adults, which prevents the insects from reproducing.

33-15 Classification of Insects

The branch of biology that deals with the study of insects is called **entomology** (ent-uh-*mahl*-uh-jee). The scientists who study insects are called **entomologists** (ent-uh-*mahl*-uh-jists). Entomologists divide the class Insecta into twenty-seven orders. Of these twenty-seven, only six are of major importance. The six major orders are the **Hymenoptera** (hy-muh-*nahp*-tuh-ruh), **Orthoptera** (or-*thahp*-tuh-ruh), **Coleoptera** (kohl-ee-*ahp*-tuh-ruh), **Lepidoptera** (lep-uh-*dahp*-tuh-ruh), **Diptera** (*dip*-tuh-ruh), and **Hemiptera** (heh-*mip*-tuh-ruh). Table 33-1 shows the basic characteristics of these and other insect orders.

A
B
C
D

Figure 33-18. Development of the Cecropia Moth. (A) Cocoon. (B) Larva. (C) Pupa. (D) Adult.

Table 33-1. Classification of Insects

Order	Examples	Mouthparts	Wings	Characteristics/Habitat
Anopleura	sucking lice	sucking	none	Parasites of mammals. Feed by sucking blood of their hosts, including humans. Their bites are irritating, and they spread disease.
Coleoptera	beetles (diving beetles, fireflies, bark beetles, ladybird beetles, Junebugs, carpet beetles, Japanese beetles)	chewing	usually 2 pairs	Largest insect order. Beetles are found in all habitats. Many feed on plants and are serious pests.
Collembola	springtails	chewing	none	Small insects found in leaf litter, rotting logs, on beaches, and on surface of pond water. Some species are jumpers.
Diptera	flies (houseflies, black flies, mosquitos, midges, gnats, horseflies)	sucking	1 pair	Flies are found in a wide variety of habitats. Some feed on plants, others are parasites, and still others feed on insects. Many types are pests. Some damage plants, some transmit animal diseases.
Ephemeroptera	mayflies	vestigial	2 pairs	Small or medium-sized, found in and around ponds and streams. Adults live only a day or so, and do not eat.
Hemiptera	bugs (water bugs, water striders, bedbugs, assassin bugs, stinkbugs)	sucking	none or 2 pairs	Very large group. Most terrestrial; some aquatic, few parasitic. Some feed on plants, others prey on insects.
Homoptera	cicadas, aphids, leafhoppers, spittlebugs, planthoppers, whiteflies, lac insects	sucking	none or 2 pairs	Members of this group feed on plants. Many cause serious damage, and some transmit diseases. Lac insects are the source of lac, from which shellac is made.
Hymenoptera	bees, wasps, ants, sawflies	bees: sucking wasps, ants, and sawflies: chewing	none or 2 pairs	Large order whose members live in a variety of habitats, mainly on vegetation, particularly flowers, and on the ground. Some are parasites of other insects. Ants and some wasps and bees are social insects. They live in colonies in which members are divided into several castes, each serving a particular function. Honeybees are very important in pollination of many types of plants.

Order	Examples	Mouthparts	Wings	Characteristics/Habitat
Isoptera	termites	chewing	none or 2 pairs	Small social insects that feed mainly on wood. Termites damage or destroy buildings and other objects made of wood.
Lepidoptera	butterflies and moths	sucking, with coiled sucking tube	usually 2 pairs	Found on vegetation. The larvae of this group are caterpillars, which feed on plants and often do serious damage. Adults commonly feed on plant nectar and may serve to pollinate the plants they visit. Salivary glands of larvae produce silk used to make cocoon. Silk is produced by silkworm moths.
Mallophaga	chewing lice	chewing	none	Parasites of birds and mammals (but not humans).
Odonata	dragonflies, damselflies	chewing	2 pairs	Found around water; feed on mosquitos and other small insects.
Orthoptera	cockroaches, crickets, grasshoppers, katydids, walking sticks, praying mantis	chewing	usually 2 pairs	Large insects found on ground or on low vegetation. Many make noise by rubbing body parts together. Many members of this group feed on plants and can do great damage. Cockroaches are pests in buildings.
Siphonaptera	fleas	sucking	none	Small parasites on birds and mammals. Fleas are pests, attacking domestic animals and humans. A few types of fleas transmit disease, including bubonic plague.
Thysanura	silverfish, bristletails	chewing	none	Small insects. Bristletails found in leaf litter, under logs, etc. Silverfish found in cool, damp places, often pests in buildings.

33-16 Economic Importance of Insects

Insects are so widespread and so numerous that they affect many aspects of daily life. Each year, insects cause billions of dollars of damage to crops. Insects spread many plant diseases, such as Dutch elm disease and corn smut. They also transmit animal diseases: mosquitoes carry malaria, yellow fever, and elephantiasis; houseflies carry dysentery and typhoid fever; tsetse (*seet*-see) flies carry African sleeping sickness; lice carry typhus; and fleas carry plague. Insects also destroy property: termites destroy wood; moths and carpet beetles damage clothing, fabrics, furs, and carpets; silverfish destroy paper; and weevils, cockroaches, and ants ruin food.

Insects also serve some valuable functions. Various insects are necessary for the pollination of important crop plants. For example, bees pollinate the flowers of apple and pear trees, clover, and berries. Products obtained from insects include honey from bees; lac, which is used to make shellac, from lac insects; and silk from silkworm moths.

Some insects destroy other insects that are harmful to humans and human property. Ladybird beetles eat scale insects, which injure orange and lemon crops. The praying mantis eats almost any insect it can catch. Wasps, by laying their eggs in caterpillars, eventually kill them. Aquatic bugs eat mosquito larvae. Insects also serve as a source of food for birds, frogs, and fish. Finally, some insects act as scavengers, eating dead plant and animal remains.

A major problem for scientists has been to find ways of controlling harmful insects without harming other insects or animals. Chemical insecticides poison the environment and kill both harmful and helpful insects. They are dangerous to other animals, including humans. In addition, in time, insect populations become resistant to chemical controls.

Many scientists believe that biological methods of insect control are safer than chemical insecticides. Biological controls include: sterilizing males and releasing them; developing resistant plants; introducing specific predators and parasites that destroy only harmful insects; and using insect sex attractants (pheromones) to lure insects into traps.

PHYLUM ECHINODERMATA—THE SPINY-SKINNED ANIMALS

After completing your study of this section, you should be able to:

1. Name three members of the phylum Echinodermata.
2. Describe the general characteristics of echinoderms.
3. Explain why echinoderms are considered to be more closely related to the vertebrates than other invertebrate phyla.

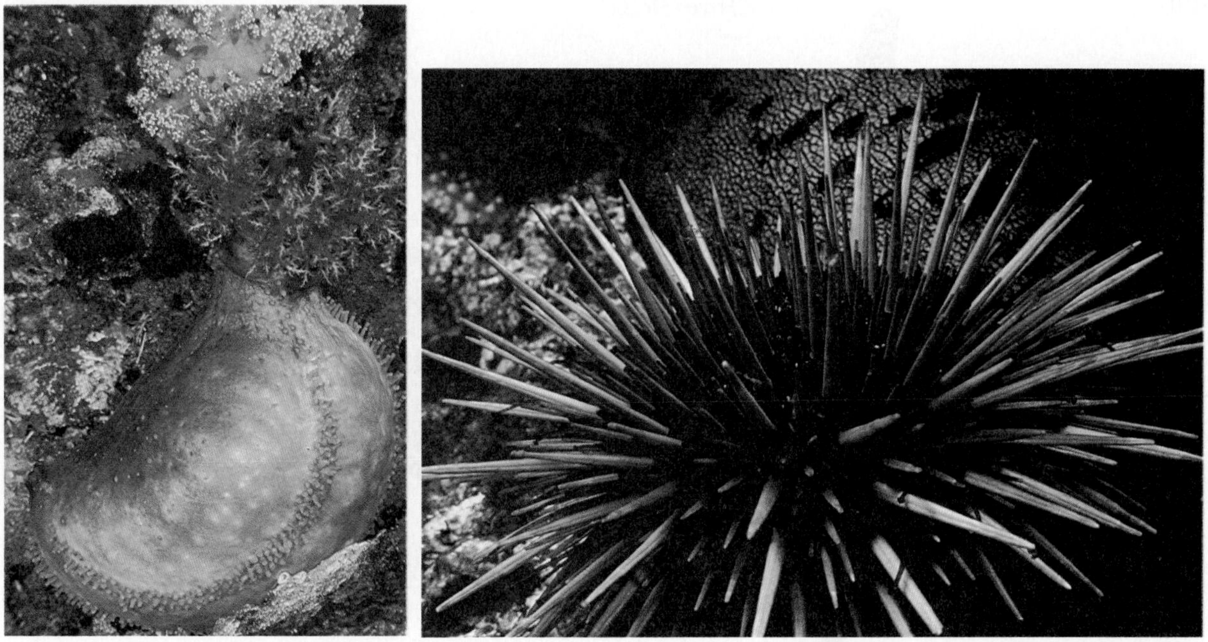

Figure 33-19. **Echinoderms.** Common echinoderms include the sea cucumber (left) and the sea urchin (right).

4. Describe the structure of the water-vascular system of the starfish and explain how it is used in locomotion and feeding.
5. Describe respiration, excretion, and reproduction in the starfish.

33-17 General Characteristics

The phylum **Echinodermata** (ih-ky-nuh-der-*mah*-tuh) includes starfish, sea urchins, sea cucumbers, and sand dollars (see Figure 33-19). These animals are all marine, and live mainly on the ocean floor. Some are sessile, but most are motile. The larvae are bilaterally symmetrical, but the adults are radially symmetrical. **Echinoderms** have a well-developed coelom.

Almost all echinoderms have an internal skeleton that serves both for support and protection. The skeleton consists of hard, calcified plates that are embedded in the body wall. Spiny projections on the plates stick out through the skin. These projections give echinoderms their spiny-skinned appearance.

In all the invertebrates that we have studied so far, the first opening of the digestive system formed in the embryo is the mouth, which is formed from the blastopore (see page 362). The opening for the anus breaks through later opposite the mouth. In the echinoderms the pattern is reversed. The blastopore becomes the anus, and the mouth forms later opposite the anus. This pattern of development is characteristic of vertebrates, and is thought to show a possible evolutionary relationship between echinoderms and more complex animals.

The starfish is representative of the phylum, so we will use it as an example to study the structure and life functions of echinoderms.

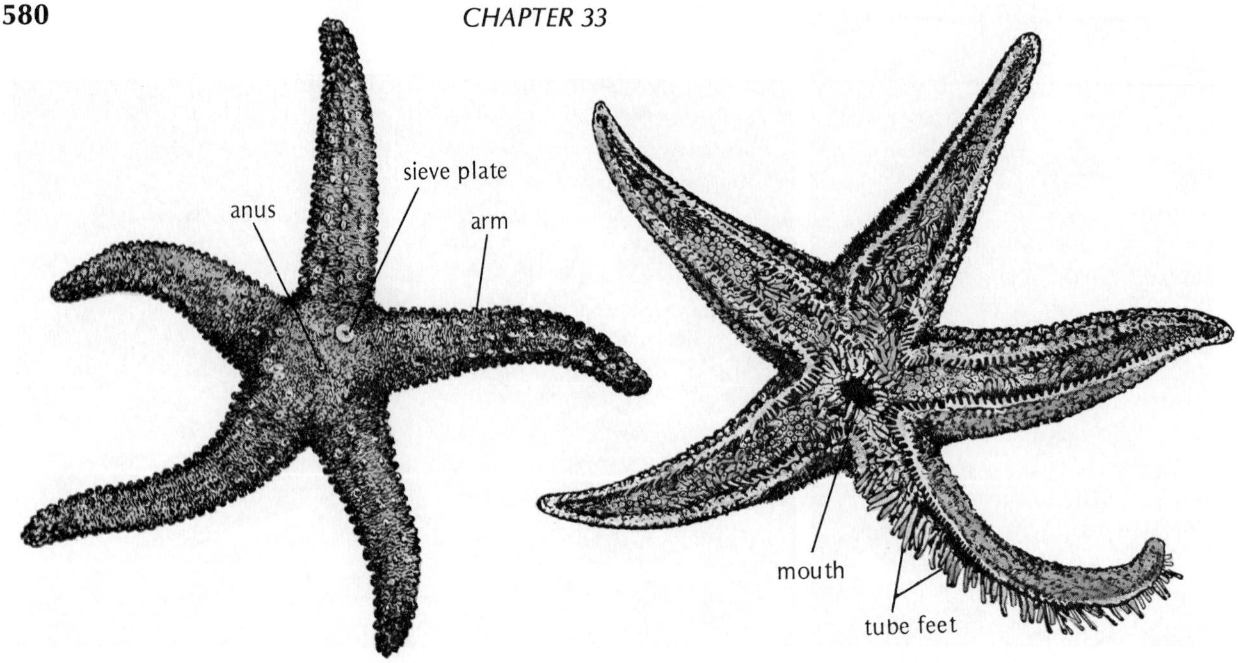

Figure 33-20. External Structure of the Starfish.

33-18 Structure and Life Functions of the Starfish

The body of the starfish consists of a *central disk* from which the arms, or rays, radiate (see Figure 33-20). Most starfish have five arms, but some have as many as twenty.

Locomotion and food-getting in starfish involve a system called the **water-vascular system,** which is found only in echinoderms (see Figure 33-21). On the dorsal surface of the starfish is an opening called the *sieve plate.* Sea water enters through the sieve plate and passes through the *stone canal* into the *ring canal.* A *radial canal* runs into each arm from the ring canal. Connected to each radial canal are many small, tubular structures called **tube feet.** Each tube foot has a bulblike structure at one end and a sucker at its tip. The bulbs are within the body of the starfish, but the tube feet extend out

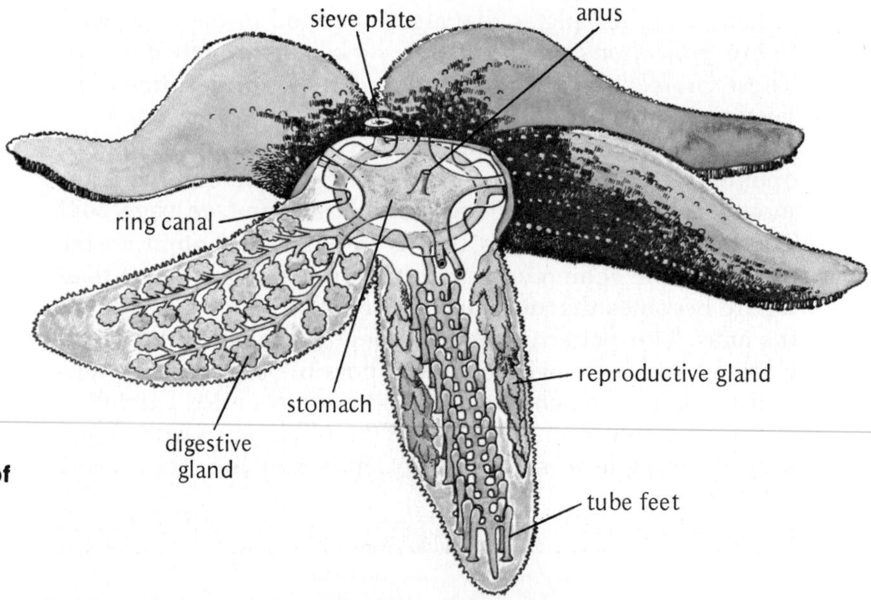

Figure 33-21. Internal Structure of the Starfish.

from the ventral, or bottom, surface of the arms (see Figure 33-22). When the bulb contracts, water is forced into the tube, causing it to elongate. When the tube foot touches a surface, its sucker holds fast. When the tube foot contracts, or shortens, water is forced back into the bulb, and the starfish is pulled forward. Movement of the animal requires the coordinated action of hundreds of tube feet.

Figure 33-22. Tube Feet of the Starfish.

Starfish feed on clams and oysters. They use their water-vascular system to pry open their prey. In feeding, the starfish wraps its arms around both sides of the mollusk, attaches tube feet to each shell, and pulls (see Figure 33-23). Eventually, the mollusk tires, and its shell opens slightly. The stomach of the starfish is then extended out through the mouth, and inserted into the small opening between the mollusk's shell. (The starfish can insert part of its stomach into an opening as small as 0.1 millimeter.) Enzymes secreted by the stomach partly digest the soft body of the mollusk. The food is then taken into the stomach, and the stomach is pulled back into the starfish. Food passes from the stomach into the digestive glands in the arms, where digestion is completed.

Respiration in the starfish occurs by diffusion of gases across the skin gills and tube feet. *Skin gills* are small, fingerlike structures that extend out from the body surface. They are filled with coelomic fluid. Many materials are distributed by the fluid in the coelom, which bathes the body organs and supplies them with nutrients and oxygen and removes wastes. Excretion takes place by diffusion through the body surface.

Sexes are separate in the starfish. Gametes are shed through openings in the central disk into the water, where fertilization occurs. The fertilized egg develops into a bilaterally symmetrical, free-swimming larva. After several weeks, the larva attaches to a solid surface and develops into a small starfish.

Starfish have an amazing ability to regenerate missing parts. An entire new body can grow from as little as a single arm and a tiny part of the central disk.

Figure 33-23. Starfish Feeding on an Oyster.

summary

The arthropods, phylum Arthropoda, are the most successful and abundant group of animals. Arthropods have flexible, jointed legs; a chitinous exoskeleton that is periodically molted; a segmented body arranged into head, thorax, and abdomen; a well-developed nervous system; and an open circulatory system with a dorsal, tubular heart.

The class Crustacea includes lobsters, crabs, barnacles, and crayfish. Most crustaceans live in salt water, but a few are found in fresh water. The crayfish is a typical crustacean. Its body has two main regions—the cephalothorax and the abdomen. Each pair of appendages has a specific function. The excretory glands, the green glands, are located in the head region. The open circulatory system directs blood to the gills, where the exchange of respiratory gases occurs. The well-developed nervous system of the crayfish is similar in form to that of the annelids. Sexes are separate.

The class Chilopoda consists of centipedes, which may have anywhere from 15 to 150 pairs of legs. The wormlike bodies have one pair of legs on most segments. Centipedes feed on insects, which they paralyze or kill with poison injected by their poison claws.

The class Diplopoda consists of millipedes. These arthropods have wormlike bodies similar to centipedes. Millipedes have two pairs of legs on most segments. Millipedes, which do not have poison claws, feed on decaying plant matter.

The class Arachnida includes spiders, scorpions, and ticks. Most arachnids live on land. The arachnid body consists of a cephalothorax and an abdomen, with four pairs of jointed appendages. The respiratory organs are book lungs, located on the underside of the abdomen. Sexes are separate and fertilization is internal. In spiders there are three pairs of spinnerets, which are used to spin silk. The silk is used to wrap the fertilized eggs in cocoons, to make webs and nests, and for transportation.

The insects, class Insecta, are the most successful animal group. All insects have distinct head, thorax, and abdomen body regions. Three pairs of legs are located on the thorax. In winged insects, the wings are also attached to the thorax. There are no leglike appendages on the abdomen. Fertilization is internal. Three different patterns of development are found in insects; a few hatch directly from the egg into miniature adults, while the rest undergo incomplete or complete metamorphosis. In incomplete metamorphosis, the egg develops first into a nymph, then into an adult. In complete metamorphosis, the egg develops into a larva and then into a pupa, before reaching the adult stage.

The phylum Echinodermata includes starfish, sea urchins, and sand dollars. Members of this phylum are thought to be more closely related to vertebrates than other invertebrates because in the embryo, the blastopore becomes the anus, not the mouth, a developmental pattern characteristic of the vertebrates. Echinoderms are radially symmetrical as adults, have a well-developed coelom, and a calcified internal skeleton. Locomotion and food-getting are accomplished by the water-vascular system. Respiration occurs by diffusion through the skin gills and tube feet. The sexes are separate, and fertilization is external.

vocabulary

abdomen
arachnid
Arachnida
arthropod
Arthropoda
book lung
cephalothorax
Chilopoda
Coleoptera
complete metamorphosis
Crustacea
crustacean
Diplopoda
Diptera
echinoderm
Echinodermata
entomologist
entomology
Hemiptera
hemocyanin
incomplete metamorphosis
Insecta
Lepidoptera
metamorphosis
molting
nymph
Orthoptera
ovipositor
pupa
thorax
tube foot
water-vascular system

test your learning

Section
33-1 **1.** Name the five major classes of the phylum Arthropoda.
33-2 **2.** Describe five characteristics shared by all arthropods.
3. What is molting?
33-3 **4.** Name four members of the class Crustacea.
33-4 **5.** Describe the external structure of the crayfish, naming the main body regions and the paired appendages.
6. State the functions of the appendages of the crayfish.
33-5 **7.** Describe the processes of feeding and digestion in the crayfish.
8. Describe the following life functions in the crayfish: circulation, respiration, and excretion.
9. Describe the nervous system and the sense organs of the crayfish.
10. How does reproduction occur in the crayfish?
33-6 **11.** Describe the structure and feeding habits of centipedes.
33-7 **12.** Describe the structure and feeding habits of millipedes.
33-8 **13.** Name three members of the class Arachnida.
33-9 **14.** Describe the body form of an arachnid and the functions of its appendages.
15. Describe respiration and reproduction in arachnids.
16. What is the function of spinnerets in spiders?

33-10 **17.** List four reasons for the biological success of insects.
33-11 **18.** Describe the body form of an insect.
19. What are some modifications in mouthparts, body form, and legs seen in insects?
33-12 **20.** Describe the head of the grasshopper, and state the functions of each of the mouthparts.
21. Describe the thorax of the grasshopper, and state the functions of its appendages.
22. Describe the functions of the spiracles and tympana in the grasshopper.
33-13 **23.** Describe reproduction in the grasshopper.
33-14 **24.** Describe the developmental stages in incomplete and complete metamorphosis in insects. Give examples of insects that undergo each type of development.
25. Describe the role of hormones in controlling metamorphosis.
33-15 **26.** List the six major orders of insects, and name two members of each.
33-16 **27.** In what ways are insects harmful? In what ways are insects helpful?
28. Describe several methods of insect control.
33-17 **29.** To what phylum do starfish, sea cucumbers, and sand dollars belong?
30. Describe the general characteristics of echinoderms.
31. Why are echinoderms thought to be more closely related to vertebrates than other invertebrates?
33-18 **32.** Describe the structure of the water-vascular system of the starfish.
33. Describe how the water-vascular system of the starfish functions in locomotion and nutrition.
34. Describe circulation, respiration, and reproduction in the starfish.

test your understanding

1. What are some of the advantages and disadvantages of the arthropod exoskeleton?
2. Compare and contrast the structure of a spider with that of an insect, for example, a beetle.
3. Why are insects considered to be the most successful animal group?
4. How do spiders catch and eat their prey?

independent research

1. Prepare a report on one of the following topics:
   A. Economic importance of crustaceans.
   B. Biological methods of insect control.
   C. Regeneration in arthropods and echinoderms.

2. Prepare a report on one of the following career opportunities:
   A. Entomologist.
   B. Marine biologist.
   C. Nature photographer.

If possible, interview an individual who works in the field. A tape recorder will be very helpful for the interview. Be sure to prepare your questions in advance.

chapter 34

Vertebrates—Fishes to Reptiles

PHYLUM CHORDATA—THE CHORDATES

After completing your study of this section, you should be able to:

1. List the three basic characteristics of chordates.
2. Name the three subphyla of the phylum Chordata.
3. Briefly describe the structure and life functions of tunicates and lancelets.
4. List the basic characteristics of vertebrates.
5. Define the terms *ectothermic* and *endothermic*.

The phylum **Chordata** (kor-*dahd*-uh) is divided into three subphyla. The largest of these is the subphylum **Vertebrata** (verd-uh-*brahd*-uh), which includes the vertebrates. The other two chordate subphyla are the **Urochordata** (*yur*-uh-kor-*dahd*-uh) and the **Cephalochordata** (*sef*-uh-loh-kor-*dahd*-uh). The members of these two subphyla do not have backbones and are considered to be more primitive than vertebrates.

34-1 Characteristics of Chordates

At some time in their life, all **chordates** show the three following characteristics, which distinguish them from all other animals.

1. Chordates have a dorsal, hollow nerve cord.

2. Chordates have a flexible, rodlike, internal supporting structure called a **notochord** (*noht*-uh-kord). The notochord, which is dorsal to the digestive tract, is found in the embryos of all chordates. In the urochordates and cephalochordates, it remains throughout life as the only supporting structure. In most vertebrates, it is replaced early in embryonic development by cartilage or bone. The cartilage or bone forms a supporting backbone, or vertebral column.

3. Chordates have paired **gill slits** in the throat region. In land-dwelling chordates, the gill slits are seen only during embryological development. In certain chordates, such as the fishes, the gill slits function in respiration throughout life.

Figure 34-1. A Tunicate and a Starfish.

34-2 Characteristics of Urochordates and Cephalochordates

The **urochordates** are soft-bodied, marine animals called *tunicates*. Adult tunicates are sessile animals that obtain food and oxygen from water that flows through their bodies (see Figure 34-1). Water enters the mouth, or incurrent siphon. It then passes into the pharynx and through the gill slits in the walls of the pharynx, where gas exchange occurs. The water then passes into a chamber called the atrium and out the excurrent siphon. The gill slits also trap food particles, which pass into the digestive system. Adult tunicates lack a dorsal, hollow nerve cord and notochord. Larval tunicates, unlike adults, show all three chordate characteristics. They are motile and resemble tadpoles. Eventually the larva settles to the ocean floor and develops into an adult.

The **cephalochordates** are small, marine animals called *lancelets*. The most common member of this group is *amphioxus* (am-fee-*ahk*-sus). Lancelets generally live buried in the sand with only their anterior end exposed. Adult lancelets show the three characteristic chordate structures (see Figure 34-2). As in the tunicates, water enters the body through the mouth and passes into the pharynx and through the gill slits, where gas exchange occurs. Food particles do not pass

Figure 34-2. Structure of a Lancelet. Adult lancelets show the characteristics of a chordate—they have a dorsal, hollow nerve cord, a notochord, and paired gill slits.

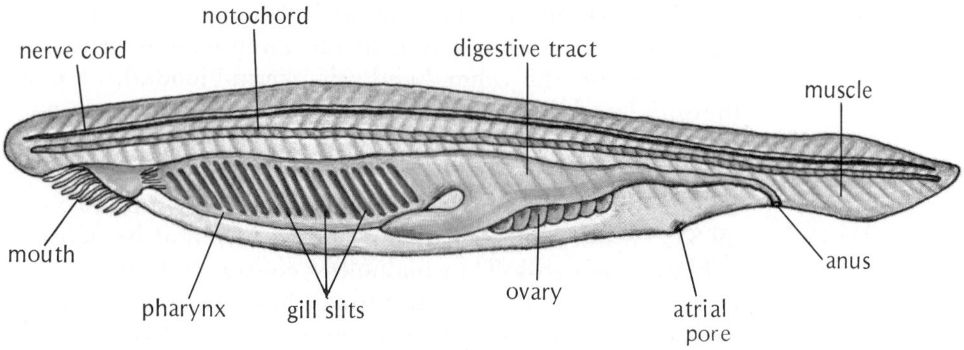

through the gill slits. Instead, they enter the digestive system directly. Water leaves the body through the atrial pore.

34-3 Characteristics of Vertebrates

The vertebrates are the most numerous and complex chordates. The basic characteristic distinguishing vertebrates from other chordates is the presence of a spinal column made up of vertebrae. This structure serves as the basis for an internal supporting skeleton and allows flexibility and movement. In adult vertebrates, the spinal column surrounds or replaces the notochord.

In addition to their backbone, vertebrates share a number of other characteristics.

1. The anterior part of the dorsal, hollow nerve cord is enlarged into a brain.
2. The body is generally divided into a head, neck, and trunk. The head contains the brain and various sense organs.
3. In most vertebrates, a tail is present at some stage of development.
4. There is a jointed, internal skeleton.
5. There are two pairs of appendages.
6. There is a heart with two to four chambers. The circulatory system is closed, and the red blood cells contain hemoglobin.
7. In aquatic vertebrates, gas exchange takes place in the gills, while in land vertebrates it occurs in the lungs.
8. There is a large body cavity, or coelom, containing the organs of digestion, excretion, and reproduction, as well as the heart and lungs.
9. The body covering, the skin, consists of at least two layers. The skin often forms accessory structures, such as glands, scales, feathers, hair, nails, claws, horns, and hoofs.

The subphylum Vertebrata is divided into seven classes. These are the jawless fishes, cartilaginous fishes, bony fishes, amphibians, reptiles, birds, and mammals.

34-4 Body Temperature in Vertebrates

Fishes, amphibians, and reptiles are **cold-blooded,** or **ectothermic** (ek-tuh-*ther*-mik), animals. Their body temperature varies with the temperature of the environment. Birds and mammals, on the other hand, are **warm-blooded,** or **endothermic** (en-duh-*ther*-mik). Their body temperature remains relatively constant regardless of the temperature of the environment. The normal body temperature of birds ranges between 40°C and 43°C. In mammals, it ranges from 36.5°C to 39.8°C. Warm-blooded animals can survive and be active in cold environments. They maintain a constant internal temperature by varying their metabolism rate to produce more heat, or less, as needed. Cold-blooded animals that live in areas with cold seasons become inactive or hibernate during the cold weather.

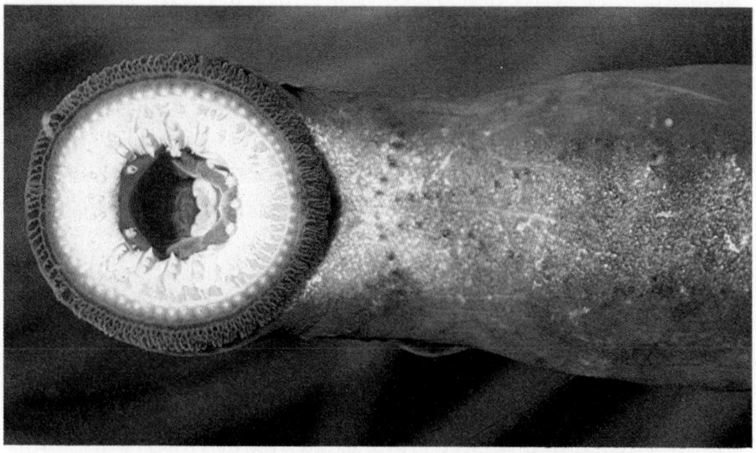

Figure 34-3. A Lamprey. Lampreys use their suckerlike mouth to attach themselves to other fish. They use their teeth to gnaw a hole in the body of their victim.

CLASS AGNATHA—THE JAWLESS FISHES

After completing your study of this section, you should be able to:

1. Name two members of the class Agnatha.
2. Describe the structure and life cycle of lampreys.

34-5 General Characteristics of Jawless Fishes

The class **Agnatha** (ag-*nath*-uh), the **jawless fishes,** includes only the *lampreys* and *hagfish.* These are the most primitive of all living vertebrates. They have long, snakelike bodies and smooth skin with no scales. They have two single fins and a tail fin. They lack the paired fins, true jaws, and scales of other fishes. The skeleton of jawless fishes is made up of cartilage, and the notochord persists throughout life. Sexes are separate, and fertilization is external.

34-6 Lampreys and Hagfish

Lampreys are found in both fresh and salt water. They are parasites, and obtain food by attaching themselves with their round, suckerlike mouth to the bodies of other fish (see Figure 34-3). Once attached, they use the teeth on their tongue to gnaw a hole in the body of their victim. The lamprey then sucks the blood and body fluids of the fish.

The completion of the St. Lawrence Seaway allowed the introduction of a species of lamprey into the Great Lakes, where they killed so many of the lake trout and whitefish that the commercial fishing industry was destroyed. The use of selective poisons on the larvae growing in the streams feeding the Great Lakes has brought the lampreys partially under control.

Lampreys shed their eggs, or spawn, in freshwater streams. The eggs are fertilized by the male, and they hatch into larvae about 1 centimeter long. The larvae live in the mud of the streams, maturing into adults in 3 to 7 years. The adult lives only a year or two. However, adult lampreys can do great damage to fish populations.

Hagfish are found only in salt water. They feed on dead fish, worms, or other small invertebrates that live on the ocean floor. Hagfish are also called "slime eels" because skin glands release large amounts of mucus if they are disturbed. Hagfish do not have a larval stage in their development.

CLASS CHONDRICHTHYES—THE CARTILAGINOUS FISHES

After completing your study of this section, you should be able to:

1. Name three members of the class Chondrichthyes.
2. Describe the general characteristics of the cartilaginous fishes.

34-7 General Characteristics of Cartilaginous Fishes

Ancestral forms of both jawless fishes and cartilaginous fishes had bony skeletons.

Class **Chondrichthyes** (kahn-*drik*-thee-eez), the **cartilaginous** (kard-ul-*aj*-uh-nus) **fishes,** includes sharks, rays, and skates. Almost all members of this group are found in salt water. They range in size from small sharks less than 1 meter in length to whale sharks 15 meters long. Manta rays may be 6 meters across and weigh over 1,200 kilograms. In members of this group, the skeleton is made up entirely of cartilage, and traces of the notochord are present in the adult. Unlike the jawless fishes, the cartilaginous fishes have movable upper and lower jaws equipped with several rows of sharp teeth. These biting jaws enable the cartilaginous fishes to eat a wide variety of food. Like all fishes, members of this class have a two-chambered heart.

34-8 Skates, Rays, and Sharks

The current produced by some electric rays is so strong that it can give an adult human a good jolt.

Skates and rays have flattened, winglike bodies with whiplike tails (see Figure 34-4). The rippling motion of their pectoral fins gracefully propels them through the water. They live on the ocean floor and feed on worms, mollusks, and crustaceans. Stingrays have poison stingers in their tails, which they use for defense. Electric rays produce a large electric charge, which they use to stun their prey.

Figure 34-4. A Reef Stingray.

Figure 34-5. Sharks. (Left) A bonnethead shark. (Below) Teeth of a shark.

Sharks are streamlined fish that swim by moving their trunk and powerful tail from side to side (see Figure 34-5). Swimming forces water through the mouth, over the gills, and out through five to seven pairs of gill slits. The shark obtains the oxygen it needs from this flow of water. If a shark is caught where it cannot move, in a net, for example, it will die from lack of oxygen. Fertilization is internal in the shark. In some species, the embryos develop within the body of the mother and are born live. In others, the eggs are covered with a leathery coat before they are released from the body of the female.

The sense organs of the shark are well developed, particularly those for odor and vibration. Water entering the two nostrils passes through the *olfactory sacs,* which are sensitive to various chemicals and can detect the presence of food. The **lateral line,** which extends along each side of the body, is an organ sensitive to vibration. Most sharks are meat eaters, and are active hunters. However, the two largest sharks, the basking shark and the whale shark, are filter feeders, and obtain food by straining microorganisms from the water.

Experiments have shown that sharks use their senses of smell and vibration to detect and locate their prey. They use their eyes only as they approach the prey.

The skin of the shark is covered with embedded, toothlike *placoid* (*plah*-koyd) *scales,* which make it so tough it can be used as sandpaper. Unlike the scales of bony fishes, these scales do not overlap one another.

CLASS OSTEICHTHYES—THE BONY FISHES

After completing your study of this section, you should be able to:

1. Name three members of the class Osteichthyes.
2. Describe the general characteristics of the bony fishes.
3. Describe the respiratory and circulatory systems of the bony fishes.
4. Describe the digestive and excretory systems of the bony fishes.
5. Explain how a bony fish adjusts the density of its body to maintain its level in the water.

Figure 34-6. **A Pufferfish.**

34-9 General Characteristics of Bony Fishes

The class **Osteichthyes** (ahs-tee-*ik*-thee-eez), the **bony fishes,** is the largest class of fishes. Members of this group have bony skeletons, paired fins, and protective overlapping scales. They are found in both fresh and salt water all over the earth. Bony fishes vary greatly in size, ranging from the Philippine goby, which is 10 millimeters long, to swordfish, which may be more than 4 meters long.

Many adaptations for protection are found among the bony fishes. The pufferfish, for example, is covered with sharp spines. In times of danger, it inflates itself with air or water so that its spines stand out (see Figure 34-6). Flying fish have a pair of winglike pectoral fins. To escape their enemies, they leap out of the water and glide through the air for distances of 100 meters or more. The large South American electric eel can stun or kill its enemies with a strong electric charge.

Bony fishes also show various types of protective coloration. Many are brightly colored so that they blend in with their surroundings. Some, such as flounders, can change color by varying the concentration of pigment in their pigment cells.

Some fish scales grow and form annual rings, like a tree trunk. By counting the annual rings, the age of the fish can be determined.

34-10 Structure and Life Functions of Bony Fishes

The bony fishes vary widely in structure, from the moray eel, which looks much like a snake, to the sea horse (see Figure 34-7). Most, however, are streamlined animals, like the perch. Their fins are made up of skin webbing, and are usually supported by bone or cartilage ribs. Most bony fishes swim by side-to-side movements of the body and tail. The fins aid in maintaining balance and in controlling the direction of movement.

Figure 34-7. **Bony Fishes.** Although most fish resemble the perch in form, sea horses and moray eels are also fishes.

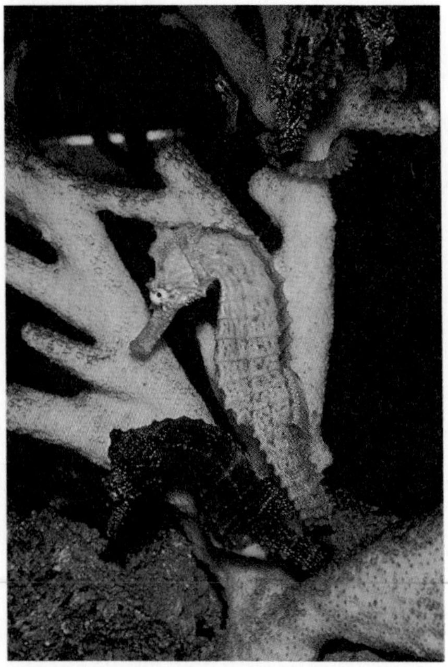

Figure 34-8. External Structure of a Perch.

Bony fishes usually have a pair of well-developed eyes, two nostrils, and lateral lines on each side of the body (see Figure 34-8). There are usually four pairs of gills, which lie on each side of the body under a protective bony flap called the **gill cover,** or **operculum** (oh-*perk*-yuh-lum). Water moves in through the mouth, passes over the gills, and then flows out of the body. The movement of muscles in the mouth and gill covers maintains the flow of water over the gills. Bony fishes have a two-chambered heart, consisting of an atrium and a ventricle. Blood travels from the heart to the gills, where oxygen is picked up and carbon dioxide is given off. The blood is then distributed through blood vessels to all parts of the body before it returns to the heart.

Like cartilaginous fishes, bony fishes have olfactory sacs and lateral lines.

Most of the body of the fish is muscle. Along the ventral side is a small space containing the digestive, excretory, and reproductive organs (see Figure 34-9). The digestive system consists of the mouth, pharynx, esophagus, stomach, intestine, liver, gallbladder, pancreas, and anus. The gills are located on the sides of the pharynx. Attached to the short intestine are three tubular structures called *pyloric caeca* (*see*-kuh). They aid in absorption of digested materials. Some nitrogenous

Figure 34-9. Internal Structure of a Perch.

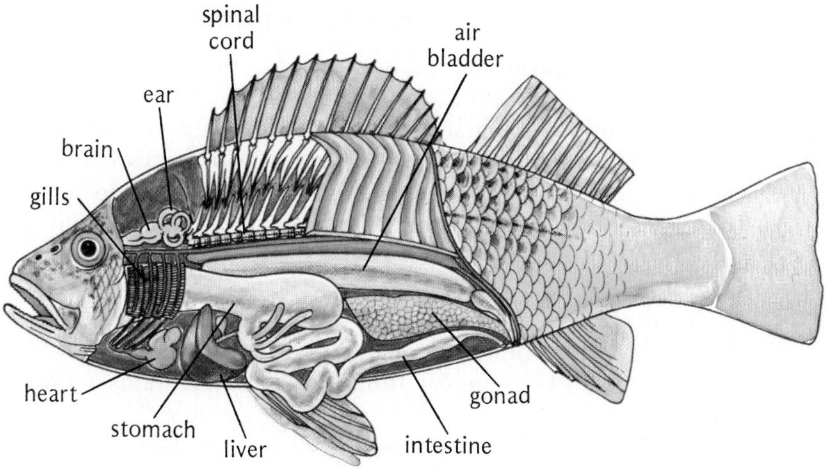

wastes are filtered from the blood by the two kidneys. These wastes, in the form of urea, pass through the ureters to the urinary opening. However, most of the nitrogenous wastes are excreted by the gills in the form of ammonia. Bony fishes have a complex nervous system. Ten pairs of cranial nerves extend from the brain, and spinal nerves radiate from the spinal cord.

All fish are slightly heavier than water. To keep from sinking, they must have some type of flotation device, or they must keep swimming to maintain their level in the water. Most bony fishes have a gas-filled sac called the **swim bladder,** or **air bladder,** in the upper part of their body cavity. This bladder acts as a float to regulate the buoyancy of the fish. By increasing or decreasing the amount of gas in the bladder, the fish can change the density of its body, enabling it to remain suspended in the water at any depth. In lungfish, which are air-breathing fish, the swim bladder serves as a lung.

Cartilaginous fishes, such as sharks, have no swim bladder. They begin to sink when they stop swimming.

As in vertebrates in general, the sexes are separate in bony fishes. The male has testes and the female has ovaries. Fertilization and development are most commonly external. The female deposits eggs in the water, and the male then discharges *milt,* a sperm-containing fluid, over the eggs.

CLASS AMPHIBIA—THE AMPHIBIANS

After completing your study of this section, you should be able to:

1. Name three members of the class Amphibia.
2. List the major characteristics of amphibians.
3. Describe the external structure of the frog.
4. Describe the circulatory and respiratory systems of the frog.
5. List the sense organs and the parts of the brain of the frog and describe their functions.
6. Describe metamorphosis in the frog.

34-11 General Characteristics of Amphibians

The class **Amphibia** (am-*fib*-ee-uh), the **amphibians,** includes frogs, toads, salamanders, and newts. Some amphibians live their entire adult lives on land. Others are found only in or around water. In any case, reproduction and development of most amphibians must take place in water or in a moist place. It is thought that amphibians evolved from air-breathing, lunged fishes, and were the first land-dwelling vertebrates.

In addition to their need of water for reproduction, amphibians share the following characteristics.

1. The skin is generally thin and contains mucus-secreting glands.

2. There are two pairs of limbs, which are used for walking, jumping, and/or swimming.

3. There is a pair of nostrils connected to the mouth cavity.

4. The heart has three chambers—two atria and one ventricle.

5. The young generally show a distinct larval form, and gradually develop adult characteristics.

There are two major groups of amphibians—the tailed amphibians, such as salamanders, and the tailless amphibians, such as frogs. A third group consists of small, tropical, wormlike animals that burrow in moist soil.

The tailed amphibians include salamanders and newts. (Newts are actually a type of salamander.) These animals have long bodies, long tails, and two pairs of short legs (see Figure 34-10). Most salamanders range from 8 to 20 centimeters in length. However, the Japanese giant salamander, which is the largest living amphibian, may reach lengths of 1.5 meters. Salamanders feed on fish, snails, insects, worms, and other salamanders. Some are entirely aquatic, while others live under rocks or logs or in other moist places. They are active only at night. The aquatic salamanders retain their gills, which are used for breathing. The mudpuppy is a well-known salamander that lives in the streams and lakes of the eastern United States. Both the mudpuppy and the *axolotl* (*ak*-suh-lahd-ul), which is a salamander found in the Rocky Mountains and Mexico, are actually larval forms that can reproduce sexually (see Figure 34-11).

The tailless amphibians include frogs and toads. As adults, they have a short, squat body and lack a tail. Their large, powerful hindlegs are modified for jumping.

Toads have a dry, rough, warty skin (see Figure 34-12). They can live on land far away from water. Toads burrow or take shelter during the day, and come out to feed at night, when it is cooler and more humid. Some toads live in the desert, but like most amphibians, they need water for reproduction. During the winter, toads hibernate by burrowing into the ground. During *hibernation*, life processes slow down, and the animal is inactive.

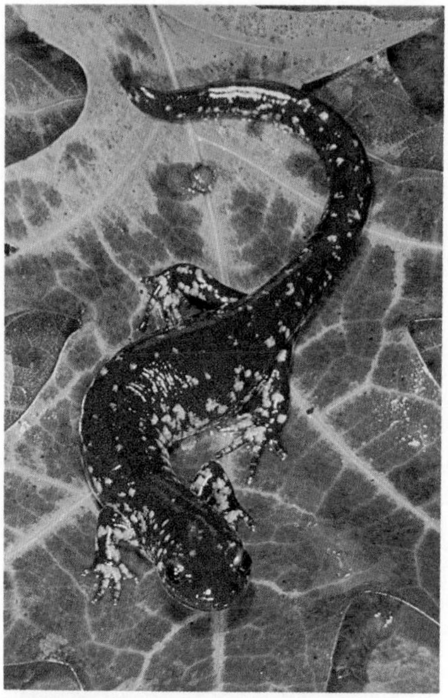

Figure 34-10. Blue-Spotted Salamander.

Figure 34-11. Axolotl. The gills of the axolotl remain throughout life.

Figure 34-12. A Toad. Unlike frogs, toads can live away from water.

Frogs have a thin, moist skin that is loosely attached to the body. They generally live near ponds, streams, swamps, or other bodies of water. During the winter, they hibernate in the mud at the bottom of pools and streams. Frogs and toads eat insects and worms. Tadpoles, on the other hand, eat aquatic plants.

Frogs and toads have many enemies, including snakes, birds, and turtles. Among their protective adaptations are their coloring, which provides good camouflage, and their ability to leap. They often dive underwater to escape their enemies. In addition, glands in their skin produce secretions that are unpleasant-tasting or poisonous to their enemies.

34-12 Structure of the Frog

The organ systems of the frog are similar to those of most other vertebrates, including humans. For this reason, they are often studied in detail in biology courses.

External features of the frog. The frog has a short, broad body with two short forelegs and two long, muscular hindlegs (see Figure 34-13). The front feet have four toes and are not webbed, while the hindlegs have five webbed toes and are adapted for jumping and swimming. The upper surface of the frog is yellow-green to green-brown in color, while the underside is whitish. This coloring allows the animal to blend into its surroundings. The skin can also change color to some extent to further camouflage the animal.

Two large, movable eyes protrude from the head. They permit vision in all directions. Each eye is protected by three

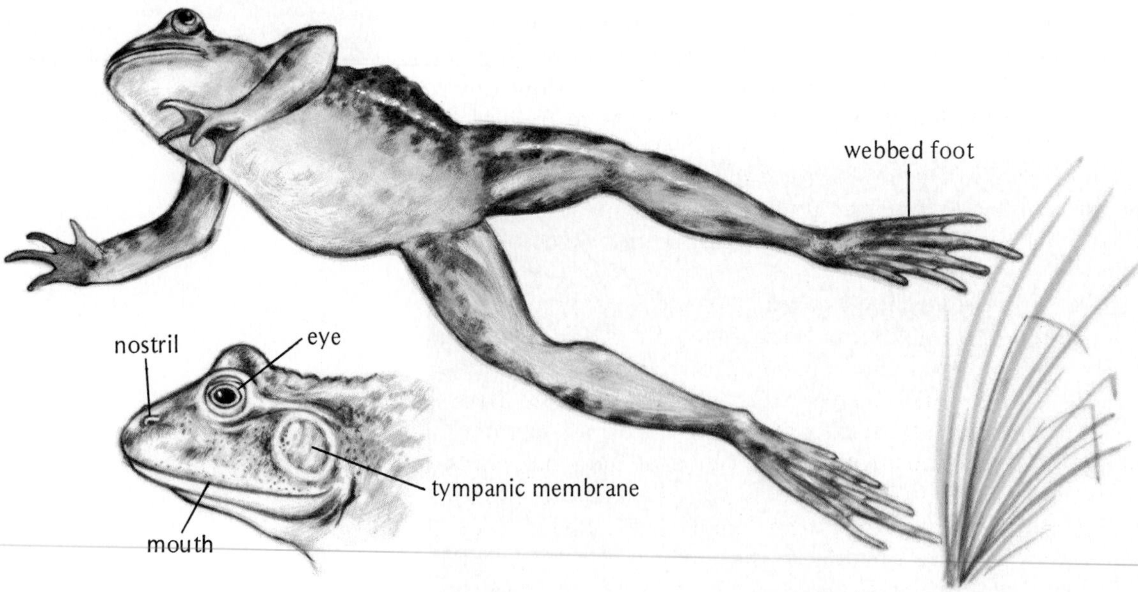

Figure 34-13. External Structure of the Frog.

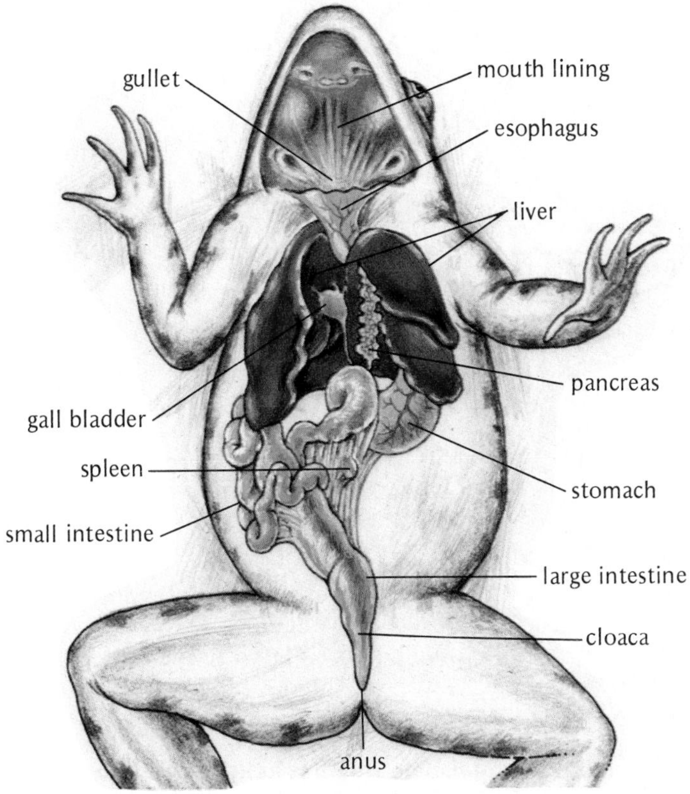

Figure 34-14. Digestive System of the Frog.

eyelids—the upper eyelid, the lower eyelid, and the **nictitating** (*nik*-tuh-tayt-ing) **membrane.** The transparent nictitating membrane permits the frog to see underwater. Behind each eye is a round eardrum called the **tympanic membrane,** which picks up sound waves from air or water. Two nostrils on the tip of the head enable the frog to breathe air while the rest of the body is floating underwater.

The mouth. The mouth of the frog is very large. The sticky tongue is attached at the front end of the lower jaw. The frog can rapidly flip out its tongue and catch insects in flight. The food sticks to the tongue, which is then pulled back into the mouth. Teeth along the edge of the upper jaw and on the roof of the mouth aid in gripping the food. From the mouth, the food is forced down the opening of the esophagus in the back of the throat. The glottis, the opening that leads to the lungs, is also in the back of the throat.

The digestive system. Food passes down the esophagus into the stomach, where digestion begins (see Figure 34-14). The partially digested food then passes through the pyloric valve into the small intestine. The pancreas and liver secrete digestive juices that pass through ducts into the small intestine. Most digestion and absorption take place in the small intestine. Undigested food passes from the small intestine into the large intestine and then into the **cloaca** (kloh-*ay*-kuh). The cloaca empties to the outside of the body through the anal opening. The cloaca also serves as a passageway for urine and for eggs and sperm.

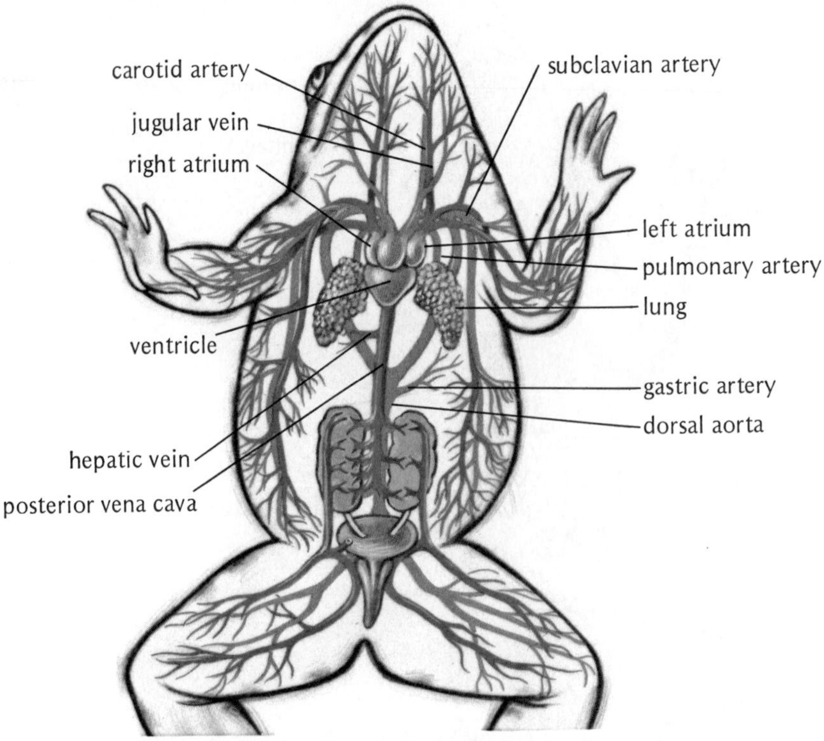

Figure 34-15. Circulatory System of the Frog.

The circulatory system. The frog has a three-chambered heart made up of two thin-walled atria and one muscular ventricle (see Figure 34-15). Blood leaving the ventricle enters a large blood vessel that branches immediately into two arteries. Each of these divides into many smaller arteries, and eventually into capillaries. Blood from the capillaries is returned to the heart through the veins. Blood from the lungs is carried to the left atrium by the right and left pulmonary veins. This blood is oxygenated only when the frog is breathing air with its lungs. Blood from all the other parts of the body is returned through three large veins into a thin-walled sac. Blood from the sac enters the right atrium. Both the right and left atria empty blood into the ventricle. Thus, blood pumped out by the ventricle is a mixture of oxygenated blood from the left atrium and deoxygenated blood from the right atrium.

The respiratory system. The respiratory system of the adult frog includes the lungs, the lining of the mouth, and the skin. All of these structures have thin, moist surfaces and are richly supplied with blood vessels.

The frog uses its lungs to meet most of its oxygen requirements. The two lungs are elastic sacs with thin walls. Air is forced into the lungs by the pumping action of muscles in the floor of the mouth. The floor of the mouth is lowered, and air is drawn into the closed mouth through the nostrils. Then the nostrils are closed, the floor of the mouth is raised, and air is forced through the glottis into the lungs. Exchange of oxygen and carbon dioxide occurs in the capillaries of the lungs. The thin roof of the mouth also serves as a respiratory surface. The thin, moist skin of the frog serves as a respiratory surface

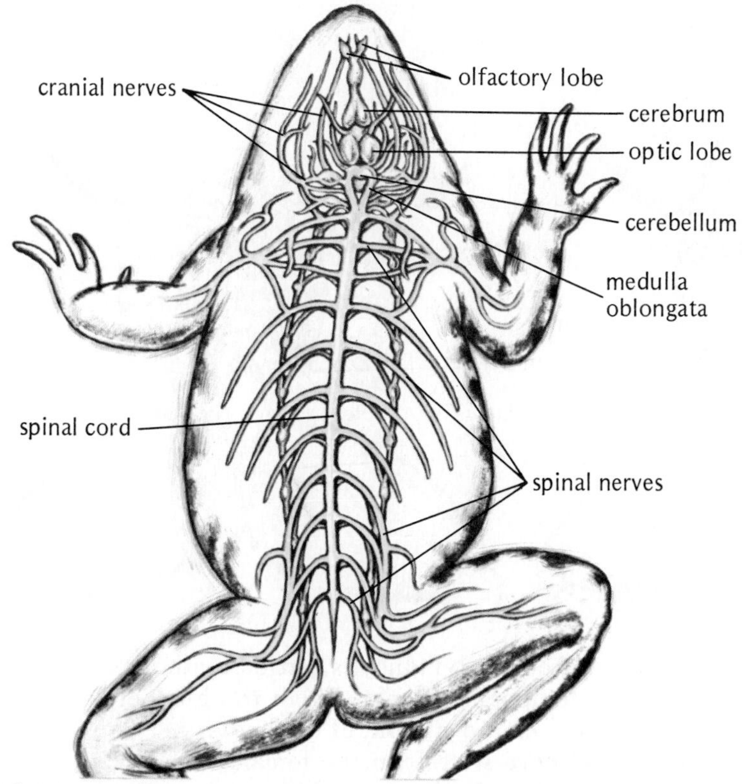

Figure 34-16. Nervous System of the Frog.

either in air or in water. This is especially important when the frog remains underwater for long periods of time. Also, when the frog is hibernating over the winter, the body metabolism is reduced so that skin respiration alone can provide all the oxygen needs of the animal.

The nervous system. Like humans, frogs have a central nervous system and a peripheral nervous system (see Figure 34-16). The central nervous system of the frog consists of the brain and spinal cord. The brain is connected to various parts of the head and abdomen by ten pairs of cranial nerves. The spinal cord, which is encased in bony vertebrae, is connected to various parts of the body by ten pairs of spinal nerves. The cranial nerves and the spinal nerves and their branches make up the peripheral nervous system.

The frog brain is divided into the following parts: the olfactory lobes, which function in smell; the cerebrum, which receives and interprets sensory information and controls voluntary muscles; the optic lobes, which function in vision; the cerebellum, which coordinates muscle action; and the medulla, which connects the brain to the spinal cord and controls many reflexes. The sense organs of the frog include the eyes, tympanic membranes for hearing, inner ears for balance, taste buds on the tongue, odor-sensitive nerve endings in the nasal passages, and sensory nerve endings in the skin.

The excretory system. Most of the carbon dioxide produced by the frog is excreted through the skin, but other metabolic wastes are excreted by the kidneys. The pair of kidneys are located in the back of the body cavity on either side of the spine (see Figure 34-17). Wastes filtered from the blood form

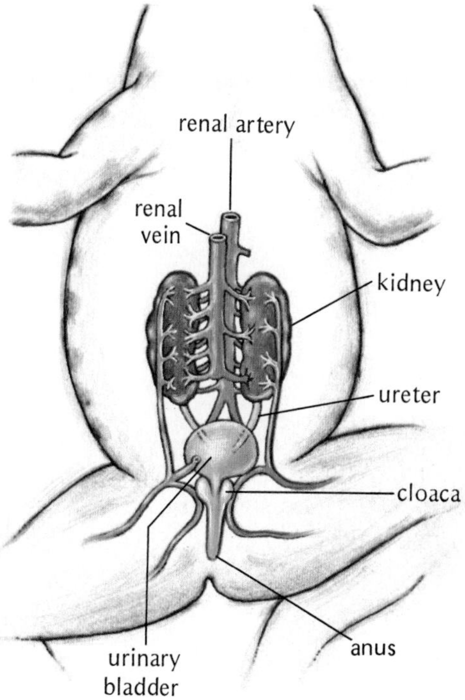

Figure 34-17. Excretory System of the Frog.

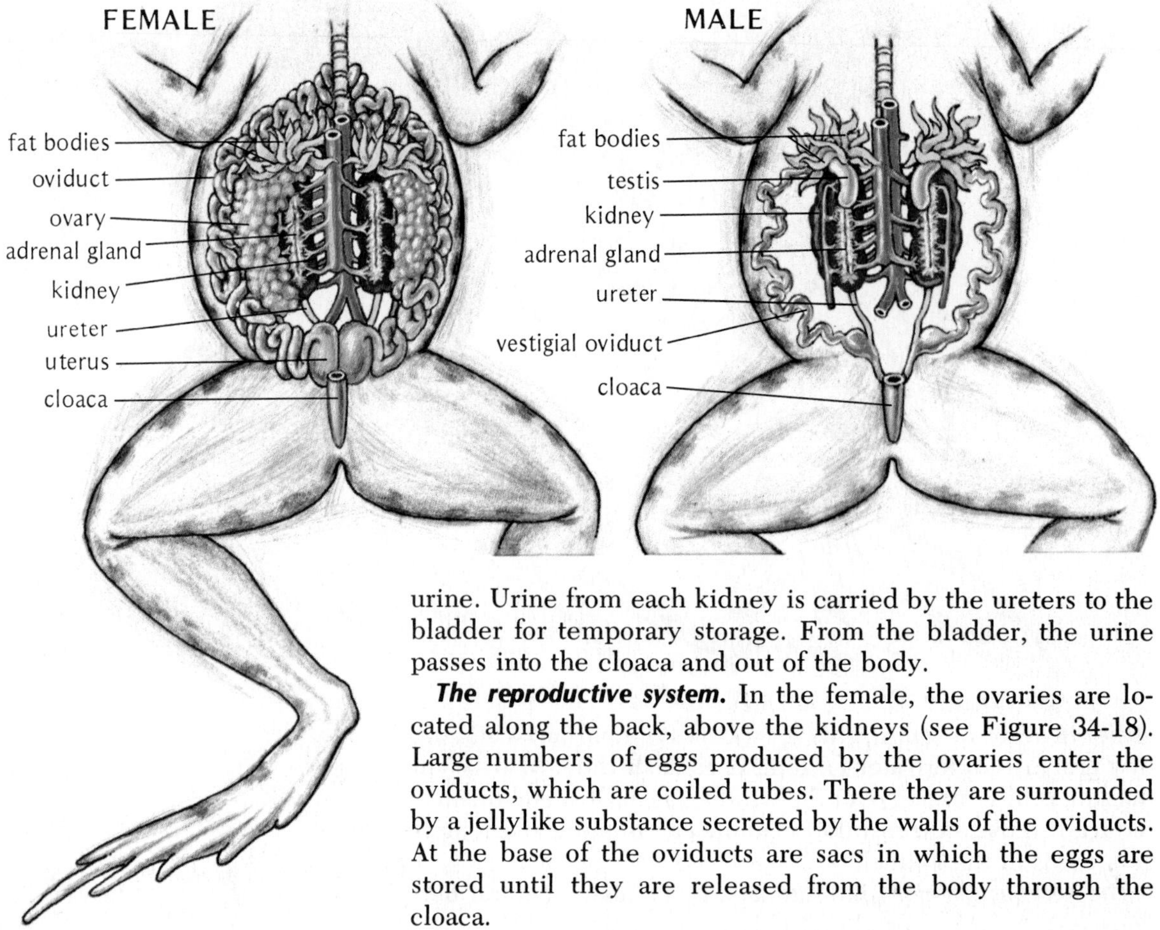

Figure 34-18. Reproductive System of the Frog.

urine. Urine from each kidney is carried by the ureters to the bladder for temporary storage. From the bladder, the urine passes into the cloaca and out of the body.

The reproductive system. In the female, the ovaries are located along the back, above the kidneys (see Figure 34-18). Large numbers of eggs produced by the ovaries enter the oviducts, which are coiled tubes. There they are surrounded by a jellylike substance secreted by the walls of the oviducts. At the base of the oviducts are sacs in which the eggs are stored until they are released from the body through the cloaca.

In the male, the testes are small, yellowish, bean-shaped organs located in the back just above the kidneys. Sperm produced in the testes pass to the kidneys through microscopic tubules. From the kidneys, the sperm are carried by the ureters to the cloaca. During mating, the sperm are discharged from the male through the cloaca.

34-13 Fertilization and Development in Frogs

Fertilization in frogs is external. During mating, the male clasps the female with his short front legs. This is known as *amplexus* (am-*plek*-sus)(see page 355). As the eggs leave the body of the female, the male releases sperm over them, so that many are fertilized.

After 6 to 9 days, the eggs hatch (see Figure 34-19). The young are called **tadpoles.** They are fishlike, with no legs, a long tail, and gills. The tadpole has a two-chambered heart. Metamorphosis of the tadpole into the adult frog involves the development of legs, the absorption of the tail, the disappearance of gills, and the development of lungs and a three-chambered heart, as well as still other changes. The leopard frog completes its metamorphosis in about 3 months, while bullfrogs take 2 or 3 years to complete the process.

A B C D

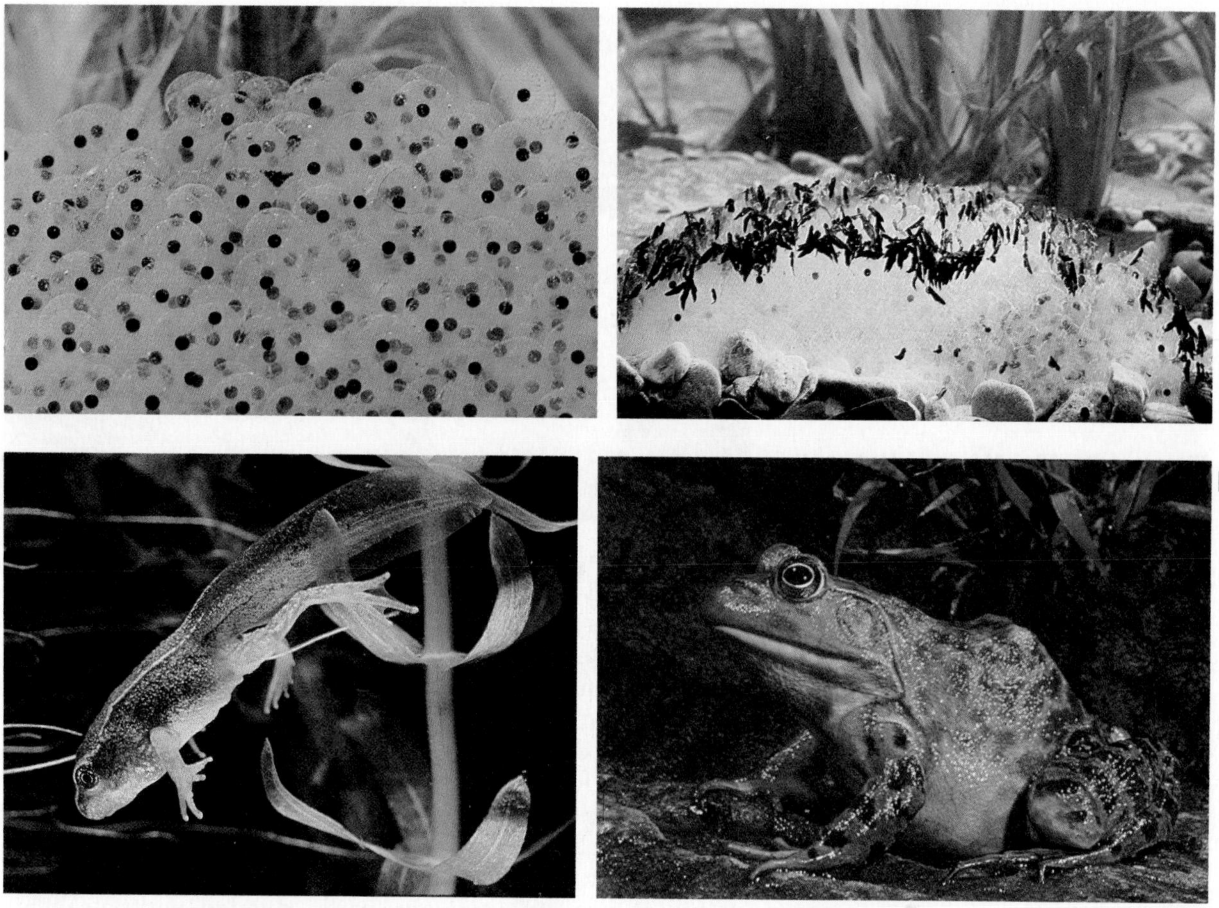

Figure 34-19. **Development of the Frog.** (A) A mass of eggs. (B) Newly hatched tadpoles. (C) Tadpole with tail. (D) Adult frog.

CLASS REPTILIA—THE REPTILES

After completing your study of this section, you should be able to:

1. Explain why reptiles are better adapted to life on land than amphibians.
2. List the general characteristics of reptiles.
3. Compare and contrast the external structures of crocodiles and turtles.
4. Describe the major characteristics of lizards and snakes.

34-14 General Characteristics of Reptiles

The **reptiles,** class **Reptilia** (rep-*til*-ee-uh), include crocodiles, alligators, turtles, tortoises, lizards, and snakes. Reptiles are very well adapted for life on land. Unlike amphibians, they do not require water for reproduction. Fertilization is internal. The fertilized egg is enclosed in a thick, leathery, waterproof shell that protects it from drying out (see page 366). Unlike amphibians, reptiles do not have gills at any stage in their life cycle, and they do not undergo metamorphosis.

Figure 34-20. Newly Hatched Crocodiles. The newly hatched young look like miniature adults.

When they hatch from eggs, they look like miniature adults (see Figure 34-20).

In addition to their shelled eggs, reptiles share a number of other characteristics.

1. The skin of reptiles is dry and covered with scales. This waterproof covering protects them from excessive water loss and from predators.

2. Except for snakes, reptiles have two pairs of legs. Most reptiles have five clawed toes on each leg. The legs are adapted for climbing, running, or paddling.

3. In most reptiles, there is a three-chambered heart consisting of two atria and one partly divided ventricle. This partial separation of the ventricle decreases the mixing of oxygenated and deoxygenated blood in the heart, thereby increasing the amount of oxygen carried to the body cells. Crocodiles and alligators have four-chambered hearts.

4. Reptiles have well-developed lungs that are protected by a rib cage.

5. Nitrogenous wastes are execreted mainly as uric acid, so that the urine of many reptiles is a semisolid paste. This is an excellent adaptation for conserving water.

From the fossil record, it appears that reptiles were once a highly successful group. Dinosaurs were reptiles. Prehistoric reptiles were a diverse group. There were swimming reptiles,

Figure 34-21. A Tuatara.

flying reptiles, reptiles that walked on four legs, and reptiles that walked on two legs. Today, however, there are only four orders of living reptiles. One of these orders has only one member, the *tuatara,* which is a lizardlike animal found only in New Zealand (see Figure 34-21). This primitive reptile has an extra eyelike structure on the top of its head.

34-15 Crocodiles and Alligators

Crocodiles and alligators are the largest living reptiles. They range in length from 2.5 meters to more than 7 meters. They are found in lakes, swamps, and rivers in tropical regions all over the world. Both alligators and crocodiles have long snouts, powerful jaws with large teeth, and long, muscular tails (see Figure 34-22). The tails are used in swimming. These two types of reptiles look very much alike, but the arrangement of their teeth is slightly different, and the American alligator has a much broader snout than the American crocodile. In both alligators and crocodiles there are nostrils at the tip of the snout. This allows the animals to lie submerged in water, with only the tip of the snout and the eyes projecting above the surface.

Alligators and crocodiles feed on animals that they capture with their massive, toothed jaws. Crocodiles are more vicious and aggressive than alligators. They will attack large animals, including humans, cattle, and deer. It is the less aggressive alligator that is most commonly found in the southern United States. Their hides are used for leather goods. Overkilling brought some species close to extinction, but protective laws have allowed the populations to increase again.

34-16 Turtles

Turtles are found on land and in both fresh and salt water. Land-dwelling turtles are sometimes called tortoises. The

Figure 34-22. An American Alligator.

Figure 34-23. Eastern Box Turtles.

body of a turtle is enclosed in protective shells (see Figure 34-23). The upper shell is called the *carapace*, and the lower shell is called the *plastron*. For defense, the legs, tails, and neck and head of some turtles can be pulled completely inside the shells. Turtles feed on plants and small animals. They have no teeth, but they grab and tear their food with the hard, sharp edges of their beak.

Land-dwelling turtles are slow moving. Their short legs have claws that are used in digging. In sea turtles, the legs are paddle-shaped and are used in swimming. All turtles, including ocean-dwelling turtles, lay their eggs on land in holes that they dig with their hind legs.

Some marine turtles reach lengths of 2 meters and weights of more than 500 kilograms. Some land turtles have reached weights of more than 180 kilograms. Turtles may live to be more than 100 years old.

34-17 Lizards and Snakes

Lizards and snakes belong to the same order, but there are many differences between them. Most lizards are four-legged, while snakes have no legs. Lizards have movable eyelids and external ear openings, while snakes have immovable eyelids and no external ear openings. In both lizards and snakes, the skin is covered with scales and is shed periodically. The scales of the lizard are almost uniform in size, while those of the snake vary in size. The scales on the back and sides of snakes are small. But on the belly there is a single row of large scales that act as cleats and give the snake traction as it moves.

Lizards. Lizards are an extremely diverse group. They are found in deserts, in forests, and in water. The smaller lizards feed on insects, worms, spiders, and snails. The larger ones may also eat eggs, small birds, other lizards, and small mammals. A few lizards feed on plants. Many lizards can shed their tail if seized by an enemy. The tail wiggles, distracting the other animal, and the lizard escapes. A new tail is regenerated in a short time.

A

B

C

Figure 34-24. Lizards. (A) The Komodo dragon is the largest of the lizards. (B) Anole. (C) Gecko.

The gecko is a small lizard that has sticky toe pads that allow it to walk on vertical surfaces and upside down (see Figure 34-24). It catches insects with a flick of its long, sticky tongue. The American chameleon, the anole, has a remarkable ability to change color and blend in with its surroundings. The Gila monster is a highly colored lizard found in the deserts of the southwestern United States. Its bite is poisonous, but rarely fatal to humans. The largest lizard is the Komodo dragon of Indonesia. It weighs over 100 kilograms and may be 3 meters long. The Malaysian flying lizard has skin extensions on its sides that enable it to glide from tree to tree.

Snakes. Although snakes in general have a bad reputation, only about 200 of the 2,500 known species are poisonous. Snakes are actually more helpful than harmful because they kill large numbers of rodents.

Snakes are widely distributed in nature. They are found on the ground, in trees, and in both fresh and salt water. They are most abundant in tropical areas. The body of a snake consists of the head, trunk, and tail (see Figure 34-25). The trunk contains the body cavity with the elongated internal organs. The digestive tract is essentially a straight tube running from the mouth to the anus. The tail is the portion of the body following the anus. The skeleton has a large number of vertebrae and ribs.

Figure 34-25. A Western Rattlesnake.

Snakes have special sense organs that are used in hunting food. The forked tongue of the snake picks up odor-bearing particles. These are identified by the *Jacobson's organs* in the roof of the mouth. Snakes are deaf to airborne sounds, but there are sense organs within the skull that respond to vibrations in the ground. Some snakes are *pit vipers.* They have heat-detecting pit organs on their head, between the nostrils and the eyes. With these organs they can accurately track and strike warm-blooded prey, even at night or in deep burrows.

Snakes feed on mice, rats, frogs, toads, insects, fish, and other small animals, depending on where they live. Some snakes eat only living animals, swallowing them alive, while others kill their prey before they swallow it. Large snakes,

Figure 34-26. Fangs of a Diamond-back Rattlesnake.

Snakes shed their outer layer of scales several times a year. Even the non-movable eyelids covering the eyes are shed. During the molting process, the snake frees its head first, then crawls out of its skin. In the rattlesnake, each molt leaves an additional rattle at the end of the tail.

such as pythons, boas, and king snakes, coil their body around their victim and crush or strangle it to death. Some snakes poison their victims.

Snakes can swallow animals that are much larger in diameter than they are. This is possible because the structure of the jaw allows the mouth to open very wide. Furthermore, the ribs are unattached at one end, allowing the body cavity to expand. Swallowing is a slow process. The teeth point backward so that the prey cannot pop out of the mouth, and the windpipe is projected forward so that breathing is not obstructed. After a large meal, a snake may go for weeks or months without eating.

Poisonous snakes have a pair of specialized teeth called *fangs* (see Figure 34-26). The fangs are connected to salivary glands, which produce a poison, or venom. Some venoms are *neurotoxins*, which attack nervous tissues. They cause paralysis of muscles and affect the action of the heart and lungs. Other venoms, called *hemotoxins*, break down red blood cells and blood vessels. When a snake bites, the venom is conducted into the victim by the fangs. Some snakes have hollow fangs that act like hypodermic needles, injecting the venom. In others, the fangs are grooved, and the venom passes into the victim by capillary action. The poisonous snakes of the United States include rattlesnakes, water moccasins, copperheads, and coral snakes. The best known and most common snake is the garter snake, which is harmless.

summary

The phylum Chordata includes the subphyla Urochordata, Cephalochordata, and Vertebrata. All chordates, at some stage in their life, have a dorsal, hollow nerve cord, a notochord, and paired gill slits. The urochordates and cephalochordates are small groups of soft-bodied, marine animals. The vertebrates are the most numerous and complex chordates. They have a spinal column made up of vertebrae. The vertebrates include the jawless fishes, cartilaginous fishes, bony fishes, amphibians, reptiles, birds, and mammals.

The jawless fishes include lampreys and hagfish, which are the most primitive vertebrates. The cartilaginous fishes include skates, rays, and sharks. Members of this class have skeletons made up of cartilage and movable upper and lower jaws. The bony fishes have skeletons of bone, paired fins, and overlapping scales. Amphibians generally live in and around water. All members of this class need water for reproduction and development. Development generally involves metamorphosis. The tailed amphibians include salamanders and newts. The tailless amphibians include frogs and toads. The reptiles include crocodiles, alligators, turtles, lizards, and snakes. Reptiles are well adapted for life on land. Fertilization is internal, and the egg is enclosed in a thick, leathery, waterproof shell. Reptiles do not undergo metamorphosis.

vocabulary

Agnatha
air bladder
Amphibia
amphibian
bony fish
cartilaginous fish
Cephalochordata
cephalochordate
Chondrichthyes
Chordata
chordate
cloaca
cold-blooded
ectothermic
endothermic
gill cover
gill slit
jawless fish
lateral line
nictitating membrane
notochord
operculum
Osteichthyes
reptile
Reptilia
swim bladder
tadpole
tympanic membrane
Urochordata
urochordate
Vertebrata
warm-blooded

test your learning

Section

34-1 1. List the three characteristics that distinguish chordates from other animals.

34-2 2. Describe the structure and general characteristics of larval and adult tunicates.

3. Describe the structure of lancelets.

34-3 4. What characteristic distinguishes vertebrates from other chordates?

5. List the general characteristics of vertebrates.

34-4 6. Define the terms *ectothermic* and *endothermic*, and name two animals of each type.

34-5 7. Describe the general characteristics of the jawless fishes.

34-6 8. Describe the feeding habits and life cycle of the lamprey.

34-7 9. Name three members of the class Chondrichthyes, and describe their general characteristics.

34-8 10. Describe the external structures of skates, rays, and sharks.

34-9 11. Describe the general characteristics of the bony fishes.

34-10 12. Describe the respiratory and circulatory systems of the bony fishes.

13. What is the function of the swim bladder in fish?

34-11 14. Describe the general characteristics of the amphibians.

15. What are the two main groups of amphibians? Name a member of each.

34-12 16. Describe the external structure of the frog.

17. How do frogs catch insects?

18. List the parts of the digestive system of the frog, and state the function of each.

19. Describe the path of the blood through the circulatory system of the frog.

20. Name the three respiratory surfaces of the frog, and explain the function of each.

21. Describe both the central and peripheral nervous systems of the frog.

22. Describe the reproductive system of the frog.

34-13 23. Describe the appearance of a young tadpole and the changes that occur during the metamorphosis of a tadpole to an adult frog.

34-14 24. Describe the general characteristics of reptiles.

34-15 25. Describe the external structure of a crocodile. List three structural features of the crocodile that are good adaptations for defense.

34-16 26. What are the two parts of the shell of the turtle called?

27. How do turtles obtain food?

34-17 28. How does the structure of a lizard differ from that of a snake?

29. Describe the special sense organs of a snake that are used in hunting food.

30. Describe the various feeding habits of snakes.

31. How do the two types of poisonous snake venoms affect the bite victim?

test your understanding

1. Compare and contrast the characteristics of the jawless, cartilaginous, and bony fishes.
2. In what ways are reptiles better adapted than amphibians for life on land?
3. How does the fact that reptiles are cold blooded limit their geographic distribution?
4. What characteristics have contributed to the biological success of the vertebrates as a group?

independent research

1. Prepare a report on one of the following topics:
   A. lampreys and hagfish
   B. sharks
   C. poisonous snakes
   D. endangered species of reptiles
2. Prepare a report on one of the following career opportunities:
   A. fishery biologist
   B. herpetologist
   C. museum curator
   D. vertebrate zoologist
3. If you raise fish as a hobby, prepare a report on the kinds of fish you have and how you care for them.

chapter 35

Vertebrates—Birds and Mammals

CLASS AVES—THE BIRDS

After completing your study of this section, you should be able to:

1. List the major characteristics of birds.
2. Describe the structure and functions of feathers.
3. Describe the respiratory system of birds.
4. Describe the circulatory, excretory, and nervous systems of the bird.

Stress the adaptations of birds for flight. Point out that flight requires reduction in weight and increase in power. For example, the wings have a large surface area, but are very light. A bird flies by applying power on the downstroke of the wings. This pushes the bird forward and provides lift. The upward stroke returns the wings for the next downstroke. In flight, the streamlined body cuts through the air with relatively little resistance.

The long bones of birds are hollow and may be filled with air. They are strengthened by internal struts. The muscles for flight are attached to the well-developed breastbone.

35-1 General Characteristics of Birds

The **birds,** class **Aves** (*ay*-veez), are a very successful animal group. Members of this class are found in almost all types of environments. The single characteristic that distinguishes birds from all other animals is the presence of feathers. Birds are thought to have evolved from reptiles, and the feathers are thought to be modified scales. Birds do have reptilelike scales on their legs and feet.

In addition to the presence of feathers, birds share a number of other common characteristics.

1. The body is usually spindle-shaped and divided into a head, neck, trunk, and tail.

2. There are two pairs of limbs. The forelimbs are wings, which in most birds are used for flying. The hindlimbs are legs that are adapted for perching, walking or swimming, or prey-catching.

A

B

3. The bones are strong and light, and many are filled with air spaces.
4. The circulatory system is well developed and includes a four-chambered heart.
5. The respiratory system is highly efficient and consists of lungs connected to air sacs.
6. The mouth is in the form of a horn-covered beak or bill. There are no teeth.
7. The excretory system does not include a urinary bladder.
8. Fertilization is internal. The large, shell-covered eggs are incubated by the parents, and at hatching, the young are cared for by the parents.
9. Birds are warm-blooded, and their body temperature is relatively high.

The bills and feet of birds show adaptations for different ways of life. The pelican uses its long, sharp bill for catching fish. The cardinal uses its strong bill to crack open seeds. The hooked bill of the hawk enables it to grasp its prey (see Figure 35-1). The woodpecker uses its bill to bore into trees and extract insects. A duck scoops and strains its food from mud with its bill. The ostrich and other ground-dwelling birds have sturdy feet and toes that enable them to run. Ducks and geese have webbed feet that are useful in swimming. The position of the toes and the presence of sharp claws enable woodpeckers to cling to the sides of trees. Grasping feet with sharp claws or talons are characteristic of falcons and hawks. The ability to grasp is also well developed in perching birds. The tendons of the feet are arranged so that when the bird lands on a branch, the weight of the body forces the toes to grasp the branch. These birds can sleep without falling off their perch.

C

Figure 35-1. Birds. (A) Ostriches. (B) Red-shouldered hawk. (C) Woodpecker.

Figure 35-2. Male and Female Peafowl. In many birds, including peafowl, the males are much more brightly colored than the females.

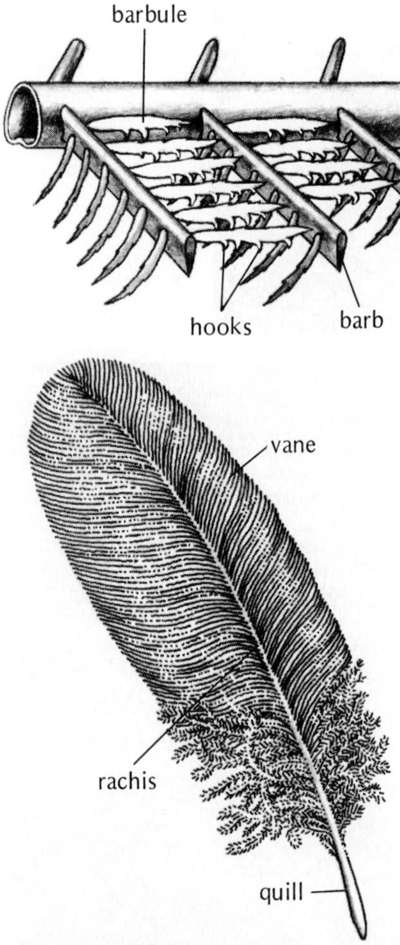

Figure 35-3. Structure of a Feather. The photo shows the barbs and barbules of a gull feather.

35-2 Feathers

Feathers are lightweight and flexible, yet incredibly tough. They provide a body covering that protects the skin from wear, supports the bird in flight, and provides insulation from the weather. Feathers grow from follicles in the skin. As the feather grows in the follicle, pigments are deposited in the epidermal cells making up the feather. The color pattern of the feathers is typical of the species. In many species, the male and female differ in coloring, with the male generally brighter (see Figure 35-2). The difference in coloring between sexes plays a role in the mating behavior of birds.

Figure 35-3 shows a typical feather. The flat area, the *vane,* is supported by a central shaft, or *rachis* (*ray*-kus). The hollow part of the shaft that is attached to the skin follicle is called the *quill.* Each vane consists of numerous, closely spaced *barbs.* The barbs spread out diagonally from the shaft. Each barb has numerous *barbules.* The barbules of one barb overlap the barbules of an adjacent barb, and they are held together by tiny hooks on the barbules themselves. When neighboring barbs become separated, the bird can zip them together with its beak.

Feathers grow only on certain parts of the skin known as *feather tracts.* When fully grown, feathers are not living structures. Usually in the late summer, molting occurs. The feathers are shed and replaced by new feathers. Molting is usually a gradual process so that no part of the body is ever completely without feathers.

There are several different types of feathers. The elongated *contour feathers* are the type shown in Figure 35-3. They cover, insulate, and protect the body. Contour feathers that extend beyond the body are called *flight feathers.* Those on the wings support the bird in flight, while those on the tail serve as a rudder for steering. *Down feathers* have a short

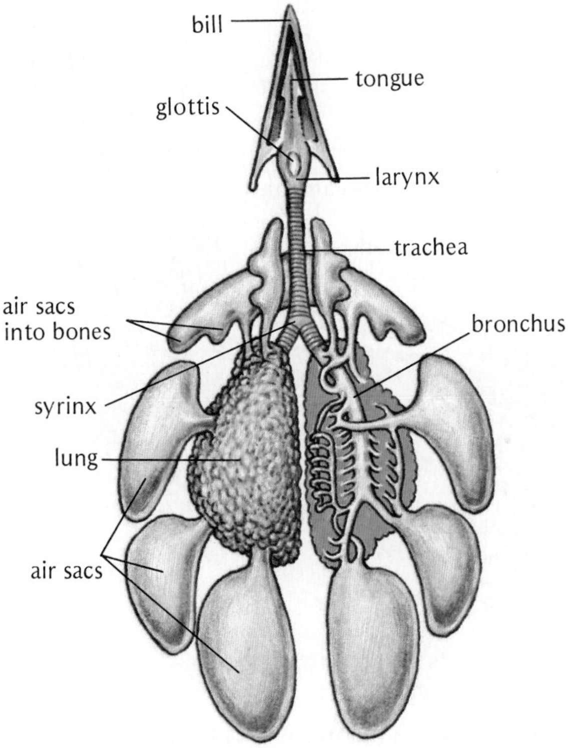

Figure 35-4. The Respiratory System of the Bird.

shaft with long barbs. They are soft because the barbules lack hooks. In ducks, geese, and other water birds, down feathers are present beneath the contour feathers.

Birds have oil glands near the base of their tail. They use their beaks to take oil from the gland and spread it over the feathers. The oil makes the feathers waterproof.

35-3 Internal Structure of Birds

Respiratory and circulatory systems. The unique and highly efficient respiratory system of birds provides the large amounts of oxygen needed for flight. Pouching out from the small lungs are *air sacs* (see Figure 35-4). These sacs occupy space between the internal organs and even run into the cavities of the larger bones. Air enters the respiratory system through the nostrils and passes down the trachea, which divides into two bronchi. One bronchus enters each lung. The bronchi pass through the lungs to the posterior air sacs. Thus, oxygen-rich air entering the respiratory system passes through the lungs to the air sacs without any exchange of respiratory gases. A system of small air tubes leads from the posterior air sacs into the lungs. The air tubes divide and subdivide many times and make close contact with blood capillaries in the lungs. Oxygen-rich air from the posterior sacs is forced through the fine air tubes in the lungs, and gas exchange occurs with the blood. The air, now oxygen-poor, enters the anterior air sacs. From these sacs, it passes back up the trachea

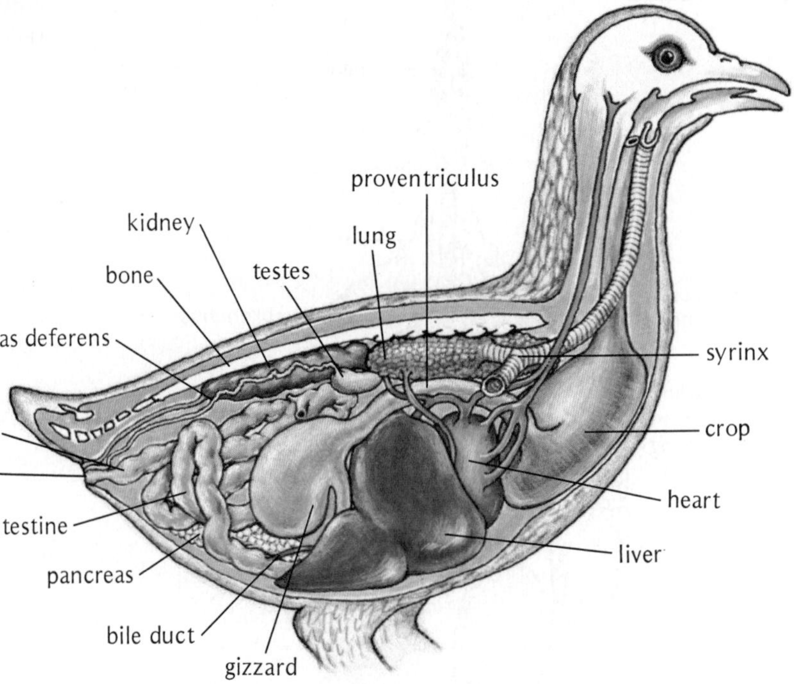

Figure 35-5. The Internal Structure of the Bird.

and out of the body. The one-way flow of air through the lungs for gas exchange increases the efficiency of the system.

The circulatory system of birds is similar to that of humans. There is a four-chambered heart with complete separation of oxygenated and deoxygenated blood.

Digestive system. Birds eat large amounts of food to provide energy for flight. They feed on seeds, fruit, insects, worms, and in some cases, small reptiles and mammals. Their compact digestive system functions very efficiently. For example, some small birds take in an amount of food equal to 30 percent of their body weight each day.

Food is taken into the mouth, mixed with saliva, and passed down the esophagus to the crop, where it is stored and softened (see Figure 35-5). From the crop, it passes into the first portion of the stomach, the *proventriculus* (proh-ven-*trik*-yuh-lus), where it is partially digested by gastric juice. It then passes to the gizzard, the second part of the stomach. The gizzard is a thick-walled, muscular organ that may contain small stones. Stones found in the gizzard have been swallowed by the bird. In the gizzard, the food is ground up and thoroughly mixed with the gastric juices. Next, the food moves into the intestine, where digestion is completed and nutrients are absorbed into the bloodstream. Undigested food enters the short rectum and leaves the body through the cloaca. The genital ducts and the ureters from the kidneys also open into the cloaca.

Point out that the lack of a bladder reduces body weight.

Excretory system. Nitrogenous wastes, in the form of uric acid, are removed from the blood by the kidneys. There is no urinary bladder, and these wastes pass through the ureters to the cloaca. They combine with the fecal matter in the cloaca to form a whitish, semisolid paste.

Nervous system. The brain of the bird is relatively large. The cerebellum, which is involved in muscle coordination, is well developed and enables birds to perform precise movements in flight. In most birds, the senses of smell and taste are poorly developed. However, the senses of sight, hearing, and balance are good.

Reproductive system. There are no external sex organs in birds. During mating, the sperm are transferred from male to female by contact of the cloacas. After fertilization in the female's reproductive tract, a protective shell is deposited around the egg. The female deposits her eggs in a nest, and they are incubated until hatching.

CLASS MAMMALIA—THE MAMMALS

After completing your study of this section, you should be able to:

1. List the major characteristics of mammals.
2. Name the three different kinds of mammals.
3. List the major orders of placental mammals, and name some members of each.

35-4 General Characteristics of Mammals

The **mammals,** class **Mammalia** (muh-*mayl*-ee-uh), include many familiar animals—cats, dogs, bats, monkeys, horses, cows, deer, whales, and also humans. Members of this group are found all over the earth, in both cold and warm climates. Most are land dwelling, but a few, such as the whale, porpoise, and seal, are found in the oceans. Mammals range in size from the tiny pygmy shrew, which is less than 5 centimeters long and weighs less than 5 grams, to the giant blue whale, which may be 30 meters long and weigh more than 100,000 kilograms.

Two characteristics distinguish mammals from all other vertebrates: (1) mammals nourish their young with milk produced by mammary glands; (2) the body covering of mammals is hair. The amount of hair varies from group to group. In whales and porpoises, just a few whiskers are found around the mouth. In many others, the hair is in the form of a thick coat of fur.

Mammals also share several other characteristics. Like birds, they are warm-blooded and have a four-chambered heart. An internal muscular wall, the diaphragm, separates the chest cavity from the abdominal cavity. The cerebrum of the brain is more highly developed than in any other group, and mammals are therefore the most intelligent animals.

Mammals have highly differentiated teeth. The structure and arrangement of the teeth vary from group to group, depending on feeding habits. The four types of teeth are **the**

sidelights

Some birds, particularly parrots and members of the starling family, have the ability to imitate human speech. The best-known talking member of the starling family is the myna bird, whose vocabulary can include as many as 50 words plus 15 or 20 sentences. Starlings themselves can be taught to speak and to whistle a number of clearly recognizable tunes.

In nature, each species has its own repertoire of songs and calls. These sounds are not genetically determined, but are learned at an early age from the parents or other members of the species. Most species do not respond to or imitate the sounds of other species. However, some birds, such as mockingbirds, sparrows, catbirds, and starlings, imitate sounds they hear made by other species of birds, and they use these sounds in nature. A few other types of birds learn to imitate sounds from the environment, such as car horns.

In birds, sounds are made by the syrinx, which is the equivalent of the human voice box, but is much simpler. Surprisingly, some of the bird species that are the best speakers have the simplest syrinxes.

Studies show that the ability to make sounds is controlled by an area in the front of the bird's brain. This area, called the forebrain, is generally larger in males than in females because in most species, the males, as part of their mating behavior, are the ones who do most of the singing and calling.

Scientists are currently investigating why some species of birds imitate other birds and sounds they hear, while other species are limited to their own distinct sounds.

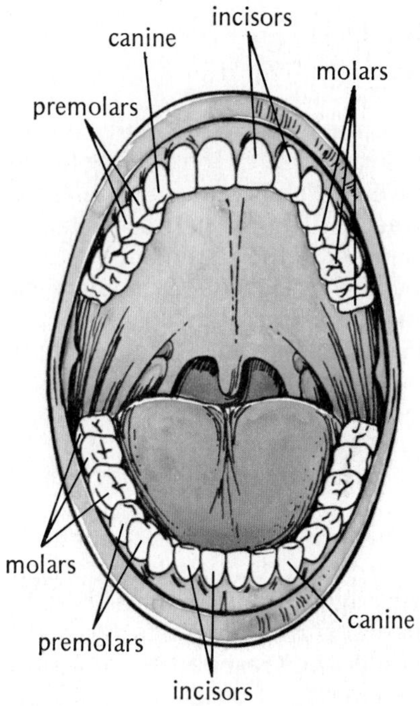

Figure 35-6. The Teeth of Mammals. Mammals have differentiated teeth, including incisors, canines, premolars, and molars.

incisors (in-*syz*-erz), which are for cutting; the **canines** (*kay*-nynz), which are for tearing; and the **premolars** (pree-*mohl*-erz) and **molars,** which are for grinding (see Figure 35-6).

Except for a few egg-laying mammals, all mammals give birth to living young. The number of offspring produced at each birth is fewer than in most other animals. However, because the young are protected and cared for by the parents, they have a better chance of survival.

There are three different kinds of mammals—the **monotremes,** the **marsupials,** and the **placental mammals.** The monotremes are the egg-laying mammals (see page 368). They are the most primitive and reptilelike of the mammals. The duckbill platypus and spiny anteater of Australia are the only living monotremes. The marsupials are the pouched mammals, such as the kangaroo, opossum, and koala. Marsupials are born at a very tiny, immature stage, and complete their development in their mother's pouch (see page 368). Marsupials were once much more numerous and widespread than they are today. Wherever placental mammals arose, the marsupials eventually died out. Only in Australia did marsupials become the dominant form of mammals. The largest and most successful group of mammals is the placentals. In the placental mammals the developing young are retained within the uterus of the female until embryonic development is completed. The young are born in a more advanced stage of development than the marsupials.

careers

Dental hygienists provide some of the services in a dental office. They clean teeth, note any abnormal conditions they observe for examination by the dentist, sterilize instruments, and develop X-ray photographs. Most dental hygienists work in private dental offices, where they may also make appointments, keep dental records, or handle the billing of patients. Some dental hygienists work for community agencies providing dental health education services, and some work for school systems.

Dental hygienists must be licensed by the state. To work for a private dentist a hygienist must complete a two-year course and be certified.

35-5 Kinds of Placental Mammals

There are about fifteen different orders of placental mammals. Members of these groups range from tiny bats to enormous whales. The major orders of placental mammals are discussed below.

Insect-eating mammals. Moles, hedgehogs, and shrews are insect-eating mammals, members of the order **Insectivora** (in-sek-*tiv*-uh-ruh) (see Figure 35-7). Insectivores are generally

Figure 35-7. The Hedgehog.

A

B

small, mouselike animals. Many live underground. They feed on ants, grubs, beetles, and other insects.

Rodents. Mice, rats, beavers, porcupines, squirrels, hamsters, and guinea pigs are all members of the order **Rodentia** (roh-*dench*-ee-uh), the largest order of placental mammals (see Figure 35-8). The sharp, chisel-like incisor teeth are used for gnawing. These teeth grow continuously to replace the ends that wear away. Rodents reproduce rapidly. Many are serious pests, destroying food and carrying disease.

Lagomorphs. Rabbits and hares are members of the order **Lagomorpha** (lag-uh-*mor*-fuh). Like rodents, they are gnawing animals that feed on plants. Both rabbits and hares have long ears and fluffy tails (see Figure 35-9). Newborn rabbits cannot see or move around, and they have no fur. Newborn hares, on the other hand, are covered with fur and become active within a few hours. Both rabbits and hares move by hopping, using their powerful hindlegs. They are among the fastest-moving mammals.

C

Figure 35-8. Rodents. (A) Porcupine.(B) Beaver.(C) Guinea pig.

The lagomorphs grind their food with a sideways motion of the lower jaw.

Figure 35-9. A Snowshoe Hare.

Figure 35-10. Bats. Bats are the only true flying mammals.

Flying mammals. Bats, members of the order **Chiroptera** (ky-*rahp*-tuh-ruh), are the only mammals capable of real flight. The wing of a bat consists of four long fingers covered by a membrane of skin. The first finger is used for grasping, as are the small hindlegs. At rest, bats hang upside down from a perch by their hindlegs (see Figure 35-10). Bats are generally active at night.

The most common bats feed on insects, while others feed on fruit, pollen, or small animals. The vampire bat, which is found in Central and South America, preys mainly on cattle. To obtain blood, the bat bites off a small piece of skin and then laps up the blood. The total amount of blood lost is very small, and the wound itself is generally not serious. However, the transmission of disease by bat bites can be a problem.

Bats use a sonarlike system of echo location to find their way around in the dark and to locate their prey. They produce high-frequency sound waves that bounce off any object they strike, producing an echo that the bat can hear. The distance to the object is determined by the time interval between the emission of the sound and the return of the echo.

Aquatic mammals. Whales, dolphins, and porpoises are aquatic mammals, members of the order **Cetacea** (see-*taysh*-ee-uh). These animals are well adapted to life in the ocean. Although they are air breathers, they can remain underwater for long periods of time by holding their breath. The forelimbs of cetaceans are modified as flippers (see Figure 35-11). There are no hindlimbs. Cetaceans swim by moving their powerful tails up and down through the water. Like other mammals, cetaceans give birth to live young, which are fed on milk from the mammary glands.

Figure 35-11. Bottle-Nosed Dolphin. Dolphins are intelligent animals and can be trained to do various kinds of tricks.

Figure 35-12. Mammals without Teeth. Both the anteater (left) and the armadillo (right) feed mainly on ants, termites, and other insects.

Porpoises, dolphins, and some whales have teeth and feed on fish. The largest whales feed on **plankton,** the small organisms that float in the oceans. Plankton is strained from the water by a series of horny plates called **whalebone.** Blue whales, which feed on plankton, are the largest animals that have ever lived.

Mammals without teeth. Anteaters, armadillos, and sloths belong to the order **Edentata** (ee-den-*tah*-duh). In these animals the teeth are either very small or completely lacking. Members of this order are found mainly in Central and South America. Anteaters and sloths are covered by long hair, while armadillos are covered by hard plates (see Figure 35-12). Sloths spend much of their time hanging on trees. They feed on leaves and young shoots. Anteaters and armadillos feed primarily on ants, termites, and other insects. They both have long claws and long tongues. They use their claws to break open anthills and termite mounds and their tongues to lick up the insects.

Mammals with trunks. The order **Proboscidea** (proh-buh-*sid*-ee-uh) includes only African and Asiatic elephants. The muscular trunk of the elephant is formed from a greatly elongated upper lip and nose. The trunk is used to bring food to the mouth. The huge ivory tusks of the elephant are actually greatly enlarged upper incisor teeth. Elephants feed on plants. They are the largest living land animals. To maintain their huge bodies, elephants must feed for up to 18 hours a day.

Elephants can weigh more than 6 metric tons.

Hoofed mammals. Mammals with feet in the form of hoofs are called **ungulates** (*ung*-yoo-lets). The ungulates are divided into two orders depending on whether the hoofs have an odd or even number of toes. Those with an even number belong to the order **Artiodactyla** (*art*-ee-uh-*dak*-tuh-luh). This order includes pigs, deer, antelopes, sheep, cattle, hippopotamuses,

The hoofs are actually modified toenails.

Figure 35-13. Hoofed Mammals. The hoofed mammals, or ungulates, include (A) camels, (B) giraffes, (C) rhinos, and (D) hippos.

giraffes, and camels (see Figure 35-13). Ungulates with an odd number of toes belong to the order **Perissodactyla** (puh-*ris*-uh-*dak*-tuh-luh). This order includes horses, rhinoceroses, and tapirs.

All ungulates are herbivores, or plant eaters, and tend to feed in herds. Their flattened teeth can readily crush and grind tough plant material. Some ungulates, such as cattle, sheep, camels, and deer, are **ruminants** (*roo*-muh-nents). Their stomachs have four chambers. When grazing, they store large amounts of food in a chamber of the stomach called the **rumen** (*roo*-men). Later, they bring the food back up into their mouths and chew it thoroughly before swallowing it for a second time.

Meat-eating mammals. The order **Carnivora** (kar-*niv*-uh-ruh) includes cats, dogs, bears, skunks, walruses, and other meat-eating mammals (see Figure 35-14). Some carnivores, such as the bear, eat plant material as well as meat. Most carnivores are strong and fast moving and have sharp claws. Their power-

ful jaws and large teeth are specialized for seizing, cutting, and tearing meat. They have a well-developed sense of smell. Carnivores are generally intelligent, and much of their hunting behavior is learned.

Walruses, sea lions, and seals are aquatic carnivores. They feed mainly on fish. Their limbs are modified as flippers, and their body shape is adapted for swimming.

Primates. Humans, apes, and monkeys are members of the order **Primates** (pry-*mayt*-eez). All **primates** (*pry*-mayts) have well-developed grasping hands that enable them to handle and manipulate objects (see Figure 35-15). Their fingers and toes have flat nails instead of claws. Except for humans, gorillas, and baboons, which live on the ground, most primates live in trees. Primates eat both plant material and meat. Primates are the most intelligent of the mammals. Their brains are large and complex, and their sense of sight is well developed.

Figure 35-14. Meat-Eating Mammals. The meat-eating mammals, or carnivores, include bears and walruses.

Figure 35-15. Primates. Primates include orangutans (left) and chimpanzees (right).

HUMAN ORIGINS

After completing your study of this section, you should be able to:

1. Describe the characteristics that distinguish humans from other primates.
2. Describe the humanlike characteristics of *Ramapithecus*.
3. Describe the characteristics of each of the species of *Australopithecus*.
4. Describe the characteristics of *Homo habilis* and *Homo erectus*.
5. Compare and contrast the major characteristics of Neanderthal man, Cro-Magnon man, and modern man.

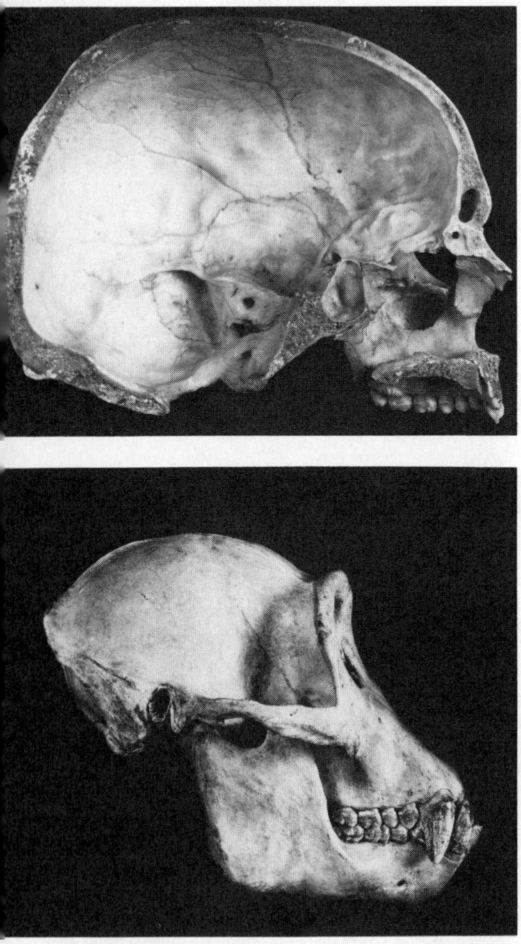

Figure 35-16. Comparison of Human and Ape Skulls. In the human skull (top), the brain case is higher and more rounded than in the ape skull (bottom). There is also a distinct difference in the eyebrow ridges and jaws of the two primates.

35-6 Identifying Human Fossils

The branch of science that attempts to trace the development of the human species is called **anthropology** (an-thruh-*pahl*-uh-jee). Few areas of scientific research have produced more confusion and disagreement than the interpretation of the human fossil record. This record is fragmentary. Often, it consists of a few teeth or scattered pieces of bone. Occasionally, a complete jawbone, skull, pelvis, or thigh bone is found. Putting these bone fragments together into a complete picture of an organism is like trying to do a jigsaw puzzle when all the pieces are the same color, many pieces are missing, and you don't know what the finished puzzle is supposed to look like. Dating the fossils is also difficult. Their age must be inferred from the age of the rocks in which they are found, and accurate measurements by absolute dating methods are not always possible .

Humans, apes, and monkeys are all primates. They are structurally similar in many ways. However, there are several characteristics that distinguish humans from other primates.

1. *The size and shape of the skull.* The human brain is much larger than that of other primates. To accommodate the brain, the human skull is generally larger than that of other primates and has a unique shape. The cranium, or brain case, is higher and more rounded than that of other primates (see Figure 35-16). In addition, humans have a relatively flat, vertical forehead, while other primates have a sloping forehead with heavy, bony eyebrow ridges.

2. *The jaws and teeth.* Primates other than humans generally have heavier jawbones that tend to be V-shaped in front, while the jawbones of humans are lighter and are typically U-shaped in front. Also, humans have distinct chins, while the other primates are chinless. Human teeth are generally smaller than those of other primates.

3. *The pelvis and foramen magnum.* Another unique characteristic of humans is their ability to walk on two legs in

an upright position. This is called **bipedal locomotion.** With the exception of birds and kangaroos, most other animals walk on four legs. There are several structural adaptations connected with bipedal locomotion. The pelvis is adapted for upright posture. The back of the pelvis is thick and strong and serves as a site of attachment for the long muscles of the legs. The bowl shape of the pelvis helps to support the internal organs. The S-shaped spinal column places the center of gravity over the pelvis and legs.

The **foramen magnum** (fuh-*ray*-men *mag*-num) is the opening in the skull where the spinal cord enters. In humans, this opening is under the skull. Its location allows the head to be balanced on top of the spinal column. In other primates, the foramen magnum is toward the back of the skull, which means that the skull is held forward and tends to face downward.

35-7 Fossil Evidence of Human Origins

Scientists believe that the first true primates appeared around 50 million years ago, and the first apes about 30 million years ago. The primates from which humans evolved are thought to have appeared about 20 million years ago.

Ramapithecus. In India in the 1930s, G. D. Lewis, an anthropologist from Yale University, discovered the upper jaw and teeth of a primate with some human characteristics. He called this fossil ***Ramapithecus*** (ram-uh-*pith*-uh-kus). Another fossilized upper jaw of *Ramapithecus* was later found in Africa. Both of these jaws were estimated to be 12 to 14 million years old.

The form of the jawbones indicates that the face of *Ramapithecus* was somewhat flatter and shorter than the face of a modern ape. The chin was intermediate between humans and apes. It is thought that *Ramapithecus* was relatively small, about the size of a chimpanzee. The type, number, and shape of the teeth were more human than apelike. The teeth were specialized for grinding food at the sides of the mouth, and the difference in the amount of wear shown by the teeth suggests that the teeth matured slowly. These are both human characteristics.

It is believed that members of this genus lived in East Africa, Asia, and Europe from 21 million years ago until 9 million years ago. Following *Ramapithecus*, there is a blank period in the fossil record of some 4 or 5 million years.

Australopithecus. In 1924, workers in a limestone quarry in South Africa found some skulls embedded in the rock. Most of the skulls were those of monkeys, but one skull displayed some human characteristics. It resembled the skull of a child about 5 years old. The brain size was greater than an ape's, but less than that of a modern human. The position of the foramen magnum indicated that the primate was bipedal. Finally, the teeth were more human than apelike. Raymond Dart, a famous anthropologist, named the new species *Australopithecus africanus* (aus-truh-luh-*pith*-uh-kus af-ruh-*kan*-us), which means "ape of southern Africa." He believed that ***Australopithecus*** was more human than apelike and represented an early type of human. In 1936, Dr. Robert Brown discovered

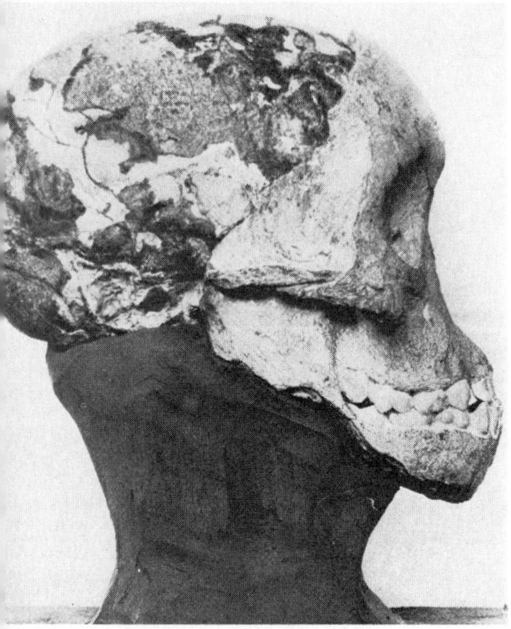

Figure 35-17. Skull of *Australopithecus.*

the remains of an adult *Australopithecus*, and since then hundreds of such fossils have been found.

It is believed that *A. africanus* lived more than 2 million years ago. Members of this group were about 1 meter tall and weighed about 25 kilograms (see Figure 35-17). They could stand and walk upright. Their brain was somewhat larger proportionately than a gorilla's.

In 1938, Robert Brown found a fossil of a species that was similar to *A. africanus*, but larger and more muscular. He named this related species *Australopithecus robustus* (roh-*bus*-tus). *A. robustus* was a little over 1.5 meters in height and weighed about 65 kilograms. The jaw of *A. robustus* was heavier than that of *A. africanus*, and the teeth were larger. Extensive pitting in the molars of *A. robustus* was thought to be caused by sand present in the vegetation that made up their diet. The teeth of *A. africanus* do not show this pitting, and it is therefore thought that they were meat eaters.

Homo habilis. Since 1959, fossils found in Tanzania indicate that other prehumans lived at the same time as *Australopithecus*. Compared to *Australopithecus*, these other fossils had more humanlike teeth and their brain was larger. Found with these other fossils were pebbles chipped to form sharp-edged tools. Because they were toolmakers, these fossils have been classified as *Homo*, the same genus as modern humans. They have been named *Homo habilis* (*hoh*-moh *hab*-uh-lus), which means "handy man."

The remains of *H. habilis* and many other primate fossils were found by the anthropologists Louis and Mary Leakey and their sons, Richard and Jonathan. The Leakeys and many other scientists believe that *H. habilis* and *Australopithecus* evolved separately from a common ancestor. Evidence for this theory has been provided by deposits containing fossils of *A. africanus*, *A. robustus*, and *H. habilis*. A widely accepted theory at this time is that the two genera, *Australopithecus* and *Homo*, both originated from *Ramapithecus* (see Figure 35-18).

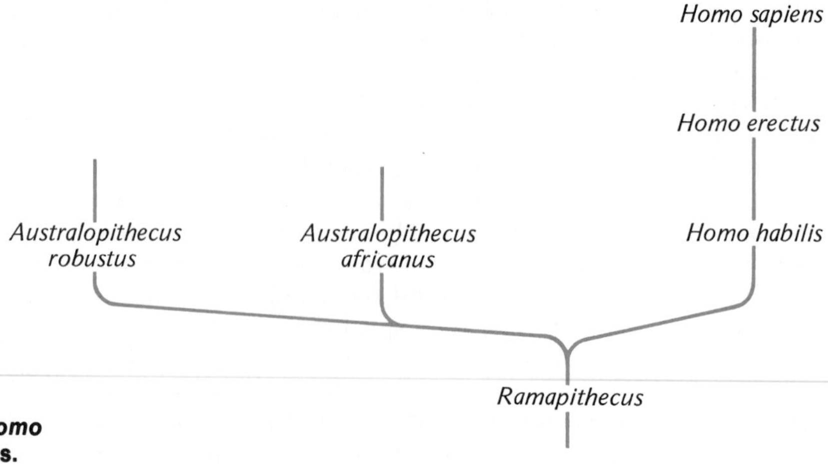

Figure 35-18. Evolution of *Homo sapiens* According to the Leakeys.

Australopithecus afarensis. The American anthropologist Donald Johanson disagrees with the Leakeys and other scientists on the origin of the genus *Homo*. Working at Hadar in Ethiopia, Johanson found what he considers to be still a third and earlier *Australopithecus* species. He and his colleagues have named this species *A. afarensis* (af-uh-*ren*-sis). The fossils of *A. afarensis* are between 3 and 4 million years old. Johanson believes that *Homo habilis*, as well as *A. africanus*, evolved from *A. afarenesis* (see Figure 35-19).

Homo erectus. The first remains showing truly human characteristics appear in the fossil record about 1.5 million years ago. These early humans, thought to be descendants of *Homo habilis*, are classified as *Homo erectus* (uh-*rek*-tus) (see Figure 35-20). Fossil bones, tools, and living sites of *H. erectus* have been found in Asia, Africa, and Europe. *H. erectus* was the first user of fire. Members of this species lived in groups. It is thought that *H. erectus* survived until between 250,000 and 350,000 years ago and that they gave rise to the earliest members of the species ***Homo sapiens*** (*say*-pee-inz), the species of modern humans.

Neanderthal man. **Neanderthal** (nee-*an*-der-thal) **man** was an early type of *Homo sapiens*, and is classified as *H. sapiens neanderthalensis*. The Neanderthals first appeared about 100,000 years ago. Their fossils have been found throughout Europe, Africa, and Southeast Asia. These humans were short—about 1.5 meters—but powerfully built (see Figure 35-21). Their faces had a heavy, bony eyebrow ridge. According to skull measurements, their brain was as large as or slightly larger than modern humans, but was shaped differently.

Neanderthals lived in family groups in caves or in simple shelters built of rocks. They used fire and produced a variety of stone tools. It appears that some of these tools were used to scrape hides, which were then used to make clothing. Tools were also used to kill large animals, such as mammoths and woolly rhinoceroses, which were trapped in pits lined with wooden spikes. The Neanderthals buried their dead in a ritualistic fashion, sometimes with weapons and food.

Cro-Magnon man. About 35,000 years ago, the Neanderthals disappeared from the fossil record and were replaced by **Cro-Magnon** (kroh *mag*-nun) **man.** The Cro-Magnons are considered to be the same as modern humans and are therefore classified as *Homo sapiens sapiens*. Scientists do not know what happened to the Neanderthals. They may have been killed off by the more advanced Cro-Magnons, or possibly the two groups interbred and the Neanderthals lost their distinct identity.

The skeleton of Cro-Magnons was like that of modern humans, and their brain was about the same size. They lived not only in caves, but also in dwellings built of rock, wood, and hides. They made finely chipped stone and bone tools, includ-

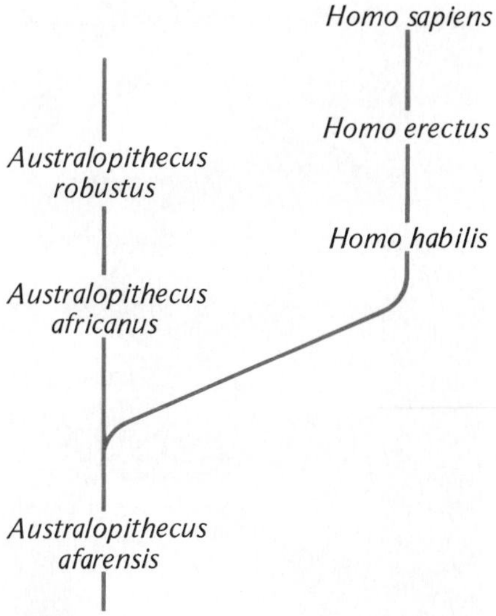

Figure 35-19. Evolution of *Homo sapiens* According to Johanson.

The fossils of *Homo erectus* have been given various names, including Java man and Peking man.

Figure 35-20. *Homo erectus.*

Figure 35-21. Neanderthal Man.

ing axes, knives, awls, chisels, and scrapers. They also made fishhooks, needles, and spear points. They wore clothing sewn from animal skins. On the walls of caves in France are paintings done by Cro-Magnons of the animals they hunted. These drawings may have had some magical significance. The Cro-Magnons buried their dead in a ritualistic manner. Often, the body was covered with dye and buried with food and personal articles.

Most of the evolutionary changes in the human species since the Cro-Magnons have been behavioral and cultural rather than physical. It is believed that the Cro-Magnons migrated to various parts of the world. The different groups, being geographically isolated, gave rise to the three primary human races—Negroid (black), Mongoloid (yellow), and Caucasoid (white).

summary

Birds have feathers and their forelimbs are wings. In most birds, the wings are used for flight. Fertilization is internal in birds, and the egg is enclosed in a shell. The young are cared for by the parents.

The mammals include monotremes, marsupials, and placental mammals. Members of this group nourish their young with milk produced by mammary glands. The body covering of mammals is hair. The most successful mammals are the placentals, whose young remain within the uterus of the female until embryonic development is complete. The largest order of placental mammals is the rodents—rats, mice, beavers, hamsters, and squirrels. The only mammals capable of true flight are the bats. Aquatic mammals include whales, dolphins, and porpoises. There are two orders of hoofed mammals, or ungulates. Those with an even number of toes include pigs, sheep, cattle, and camels. Those with an odd number of toes include horses and rhinoceroses. The ungulates are all herbivores. The carnivores include cats, dogs, bears, seals, and other meat-eating animals. The primates—monkeys, apes, and humans—are the most intelligent animals.

Human fossils are distinguished from other primate fossils by the size and shape of the skull, the structure of the jaws and teeth, the structure of the pelvis, and the location of the foramen magnum.

The earliest known fossil displaying some human characteristics is *Ramapithecus*. Another prehuman fossil primate group is *Australopithecus*. The first fossil group classified in the genus *Homo* is *Homo habilis*, the first toolmakers. The first fossil group showing true human characteristics is *H. erectus*, the first users of fire. *Homo sapiens*, the species of modern humans, is thought to have developed from *H. erectus*. An early variety of *H. sapiens* was Neanderthal man. Cro-Magnon man appeared about 35,000 years ago and was physically identical to modern man.

vocabulary

anthropology
Artiodactyla
Australopithecus
Aves
bipedal locomotion
bird
canine
Carnivora
Cetacea
Chiroptera
Cro-Magnon man
Edentata
foramen magnum
Homo sapiens
incisor
Insectivora
Lagomorpha
mammal
Mammalia
marsupial
molar
monotreme
Neanderthal man
Perissodactyla
placental mammal
plankton
premolar
primate
Primates
Proboscidea
Ramapithecus
Rodentia
rumen
ruminant
ungulate
whalebone

test your learning

Section

35-1 **1.** List the general characteristics of birds.

35-2 **2.** Describe the structure and functions of feathers.

35-3 **3.** Describe the respiratory and circulatory systems of birds.

4. Why do birds need large amounts of food?

5. Describe the digestive system of birds.

35-4 **6.** What two characteristics distinguish mammals from other vertebrates?

7. Name the four types of teeth found in mammals, and state the function of each.

8. Name the three different types of mammals.

35-5 **9.** List the major orders of placental mammals, and name two members of each.

35-6 **10.** How do scientists distinguish human and prehuman fossils from fossils of other primates?

35-7 **11.** List the major known prehuman fossil species.
12. Why is Neanderthal man classified as a variety of *Homo sapiens?*
13. Describe the characteristics of Cro-Magnon man.

test your understanding

1. Compare and contrast reproduction and embryonic development in monotremes, marsupials, and placental mammals.
2. What advantages do warm-blooded animals have over cold-blooded animals?
3. What structural adaptations enable birds to fly?
4. Name the order of placental mammals in which there are animals that:
A. are fishlike
B. use their teeth for gnawing
C. have hoofs with an odd number of toes
D. have no teeth
E. have grasping hands
F. eat insects
G. eat meat
H. move by hopping
I. have wings
5. Why have humans become the dominant animal species?
6. What evidence is there that early human species were intelligent?

independent research

1. Prepare a report on one of the following topics:
A. flightless birds
B. egg-laying mammals
C. prehistoric marsupials
D. prehistoric humans
2. Prepare a report on career opportunities in the field of anthropology or archeology.
3. If you have a pet bird or mammal (dog, cat, etc.), prepare a report on how you care for it and on its behavior, including its learning capabilities.

UNIT 8
ECOLOGY

chapter 36

Organization in the Biosphere

36-1 Chapter Introduction

All types of living organisms have adaptations that enable them to survive in a particular environment. They may show adaptations for food-getting and reproduction, as well as for surviving in a particular climate. Living organisms are affected by physical factors in their environment, such as the availability of water, the average temperature, and the amount of light. The physical environment is also affected by the organisms that live in it. For example, soil-forming organisms may change bare rock to soil, or the growth of plants may fill in a pond. Finally, organisms are affected by the other organisms living in the same area. The branch of biology that deals with the interactions between organisms and their environment is called **ecology** (ih-*kahl*-uh-jee).

In studying the interaction between organisms and their environment, both the living and nonliving factors must be considered. The **biotic** (by-*aht*-ik), or living, **factors** include all the living organisms in the environment and their effects, both direct and indirect, on other living things. The **abiotic** (ay-by-*aht*-ik), or nonliving, **factors** include water, oxygen, light, temperature, soil, and inorganic and organic nutrients.

ABIOTIC FACTORS IN THE ENVIRONMENT

After completing your study of this section, you should be able to:

1. List the most important abiotic factors in the environment.

2. Describe how light, temperature, and precipitation vary with position on the earth's surface.
3. Describe the process of soil formation.

The abiotic factors determine what types of organisms can survive in a particular environment. For example, in deserts there is very little available water, and the temperature can vary daily from very hot to cold. Only plants that are adapted to these conditions, such as sagebrush and cactus, can survive. Other types of plants, such as corn, oak trees, and orchids, cannot survive in deserts. They grow only in environments where the abiotic conditions suit them.

Abiotic factors can also limit population size. The factor present in the least amount will act as the limiting factor.

36-2 Light

The energy for almost all living things on earth comes directly or indirectly from sunlight. The amount of sunlight striking a given area of the earth's surface varies with latitude. **Latitude** is the distance north or south of the equator. Both the *intensity*, or strength, of sunlight and the *duration*, or length, of daylight vary with latitude. Areas around the equator receive sunlight of the strongest intensity, while areas around the North and South Poles receive light of the weakest intensity (see Figure 36-1). Areas at the equator receive about 12 hours of daylight throughout the year. At the North and South Poles, the sun never rises above the horizon during the six winter months of each year. During the summers, the sun never sets. In regions between the equator and the poles, the relative lengths of day and night vary with the season, with more hours of daylight in the summer and fewer in the winter. These variations in the amount of sunlight striking the earth are caused by the daily rotation of the earth, the movement of the earth around the sun, and the tilt of the earth's axis.

The intensity and duration of sunlight are basic factors affecting the growth and flowering of plants (see page 319). Some plants require high light intensity and long days, while

Figure 36-1. Intensity of Sunlight at Different Latitudes. In this diagram, each ray represents the same amount of light energy. Note that a given amount of surface is struck by many more rays near the equator than near the poles.

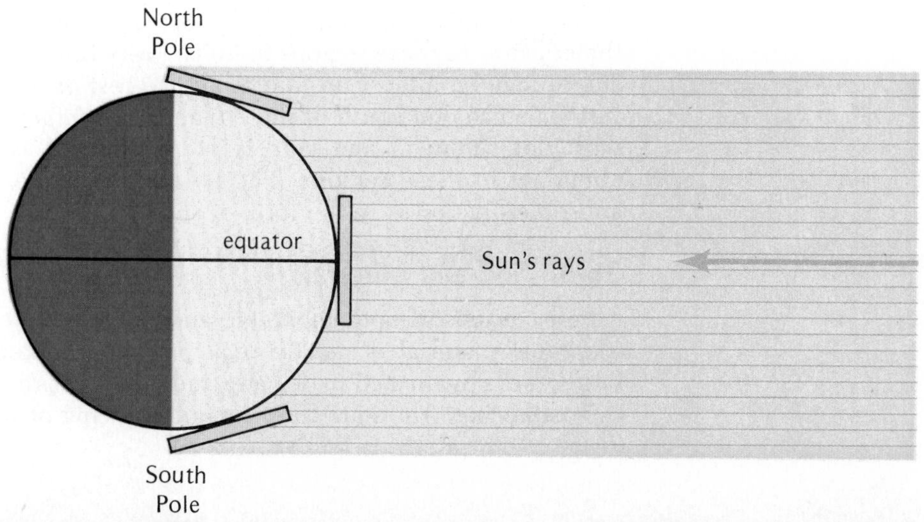

others grow where the light intensity is low and the days short. In many animals, migration, hibernation, and reproductive behavior are influenced by the relative lengths of day and night.

Light conditions also vary in aquatic environments. Light is absorbed as it passes through water. Thus the amount of light present decreases with increasing depth. The layer of water through which light penetrates is called the **photic** (*foh*-tik) **zone.** Approximately 80 percent of the earth's photosynthesis takes place in the photic zone. Below the photic zone is the **aphotic** (ay-*foh*-tik) **zone,** where there is no light. Except for a few chemotrophs, organisms that live in the aphotic zone are all heterotrophs.

36-3 Temperature

Temperature patterns on the earth's surface vary with latitude and with altitude. **Altitude** is the vertical distance below or above sea level. The temperature pattern of a region may also be affected by the presence of nearby major geographic features, such as a mountain or an ocean.

The warmest average temperatures on the earth's surface occur around the equator. Traveling north or south of the equator, the average temperatures drop. The North and South Poles are the coldest regions on earth. Temperatures also drop with increasing altitude. Thus, the tops of high mountains may be snow-covered even at the equator.

36-4 Water

Precipitation refers to the release of water from the atmosphere in such forms as rain, snow, dew, and fog. The annual amount of precipitation varies from one region to another on the earth's surface. Annual precipitation patterns are related both to latitude and to altitude, and are also influenced by local features, such as mountains and large bodies of water. Areas around the equator are generally hot and very humid, and there is relatively heavy rainfall throughout the year. Because of the pattern of airflow over the earth's surface, most deserts are found around latitudes 30° north and 30° south of the equator. In these regions there is a very brief rainy season. There may be almost no rain at all the rest of the year. Still further north and south of the equator are *temperate* regions with hot summers and cold winters. Rainfall is relatively abundant in these regions. The polar regions are very cold, and precipitation is in the form of snow.

36-5 Soil and Minerals

Soil consists of both inorganic and organic materials. The inorganic material is mostly rock particles broken off from larger rocks by the action of water and wind—a process known as **weathering.** Alternate freezing and thawing of water helps

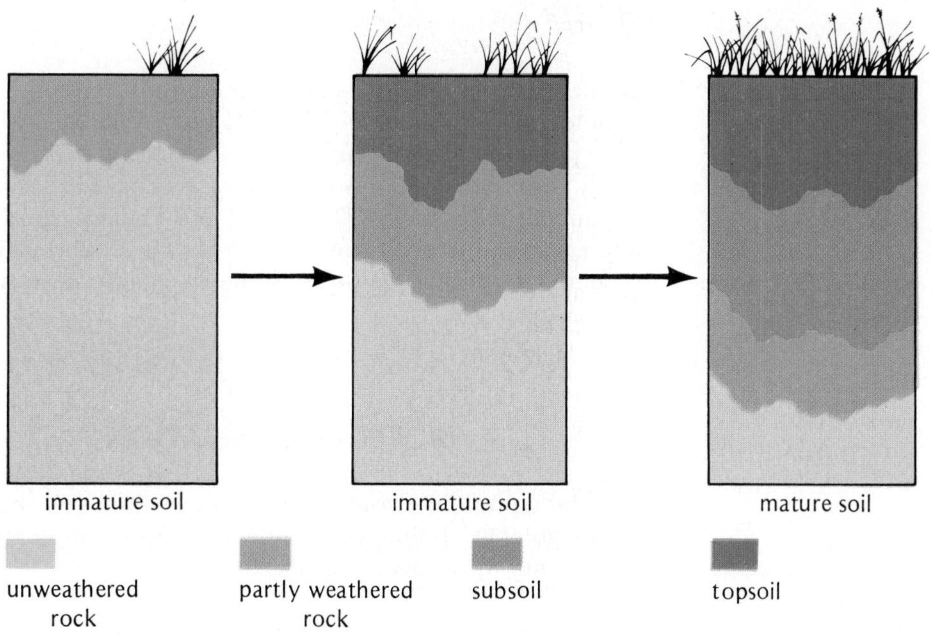

Figure 36-2. Three Stages in the Development of Soil. The forces of weathering and the action of certain small organisms gradually break down bedrock into fine particles. The products and remains of organisms add organic matter to the rock particles, forming soil.

to crack the rock and break off pieces. Soluble minerals in the rock dissolve in water, breaking down the rock still further. Bacteria, fungi, lichens, and other soil-forming organisms also act to break down rock. When these organisms die, their remains are intermingled with the rock particles, thus adding organic matter to the developing soil. Other plants may take root in the thin soil, and when they die, their remains add more organic matter.

The minerals present in soil depend partly on the type of rock from which the soil was formed and partly on the types of organisms living in the soil. The amount of precipitation determines which minerals will be retained in the soil and which will be washed, or leached, out.

As soil development proceeds, three distinct layers form (see Figure 36-2). The uppermost layer, called **topsoil,** includes organic matter and living organisms. Plant "litter," such as fallen leaves and twigs, overlies the topsoil and gradually blends into it. The dark, rich, organic matter in the topsoil is called **humus** (*hyoo*-mus). It is formed from the decay of dead plants and animals. The living organisms of the topsoil include plant roots, as well as earthworms, insects, and many other animals and protists. The organisms of decay—bacteria and fungi—are also found in this layer.

Beneath the topsoil is a layer of **subsoil.** The subsoil consists of rock particles mixed with inorganic compounds, including mineral nutrients. Water-soluble materials from the topsoil are constantly carried downward into the subsoil by the downward movement of water. The bottommost layer of the soil consists of bits of rock broken off from the parent bedrock below.

There are many types of soils. They are classified according to their organic content, mineral composition, pH, and size of the rock particles. Sandy soil has the largest particles, silt has particles of intermediate size, and clay is made up of very small particles. Water drains too quickly through sand and too slowly through clay. Thus the best soils consist of a mixture of clay and larger particles. Different types of plants grow best in different types of soil. Some plants thrive in more acid soils, some in more alkaline soils, some in sandy soils, some in clayey soils.

BIOTIC ORGANIZATION

After completing your study of this section, you should be able to define the following terms: *population, community, ecosystem,* and *biosphere.*

36-6 Populations, Communities, and Ecosystems

In studying organisms in nature, ecologists generally focus their attention on a particular group of organisms in a particular type of natural setting. The simplest grouping of organisms in nature is a **population,** which includes all individuals of a particular species within a certain area. All the black oak trees in a forest make up a population. All the bullfrogs in a pond make up a population. Populations can also be considered as parts of larger groups. All the different populations within a given area make up a **community.** For example, all the frogs, fish, algae, plants, and other living things in and around a pond make up a pond community.

An **ecosystem** includes a community and its physical environment. In an ecosystem, both the biotic and abiotic factors are included. There is an ongoing exchange of materials between the nonliving and living parts of an ecosystem. All the ecosystems of the earth are linked to one another. Organisms move from one ecosystem to another. Water and inorganic and organic substances pass from one ecosystem to another. Energy is also transferred between ecosystems.

36-7 The Biosphere

The portion of the earth in which living things exist is the **biosphere.** Compared to the diameter of the earth, the biosphere is a very thin zone. It is about 20 kilometers in thickness, extending from the ocean floor to the highest point in the atmosphere where life is found. The biosphere includes portions of the *lithosphere,* which is the solid part of the earth's surface; the *hydrosphere,* which includes the water on and under the earth's surface and the water vapor of the air; and the *atmosphere,* which is the mass of air surrounding the earth.

NUTRITIONAL AND ENERGY RELATIONSHIPS IN AN ECOSYSTEM

After completing your study of this section, you should be able to:

1. Define the following terms: *herbivore, carnivore, omnivore, predator, scavenger,* and *saprophyte.*
2. List the different types of symbiotic relationships and describe each of them.
3. Describe the roles of producers, consumers, and decomposers in an ecosystem.
4. Describe the feeding relationships in an ecosystem in terms of food chains and food webs.
5. Describe the flow of energy in an ecosystem in terms of a pyramid of energy and a pyramid of biomass.

An ecosystem includes all kinds of organisms—microorganisms, plants, and animals. These organisms interact on many levels, but their nutritional and energy relationships are among the most important.

36-8 Autotrophic and Heterotrophic Nutrition

Autotrophs are organisms that can synthesize all the organic nutrients they need from inorganic compounds. Most autotrophs carry on photosynthesis; however, a few carry on chemosynthesis. Directly or indirectly, autotrophs provide all the food of heterotrophs—those organisms, including animals, that cannot synthesize their own nutrients.

Heterotrophs are divided into several groups, depending on what they eat and how they obtain their food. Heterotrophs include herbivores, carnivores, omnivores, and saprophytes.

Herbivores (*her*-buh-vorz) are animals that feed only on plants. Rabbits, cattle, horses, sheep, and deer are herbivores. **Carnivores** (*kar*-nuh-vorz) are animals that feed on other animals. Among the carnivores, some are predators and some are scavengers. **Predators** (*pred*-uh-terz), such as lions, hawks, and wolves, attack and kill their prey and feed on their bodies. **Scavengers** (*skav*-en-jerz) feed on dead animals they find. Vultures and hyenas are scavengers. **Omnivores** (*ahm*-nih-vorz) are animals that feed on both plants and animals. Humans and bears are omnivores. **Saprophytes** are organisms that obtain nutrients by breaking down the remains of dead plants and animals. Bacteria and fungi are the most numerous saprophytes.

36-9 Symbiotic Relationships

Symbiotic relationships are those in which two different types of organisms live in a close association that benefits at least one of them. There are three types of symbiotic relationships: mutualism, commensalism, and parasitism.

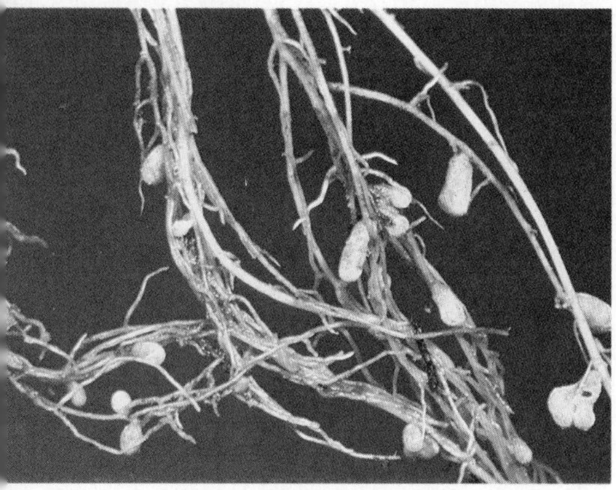

Figure 36-3. Root Nodules of Legume.

In **mutualism** (*myooch*-uh-wuh-liz-um), both organisms benefit from their association. For example, termites have cellulose-digesting microorganisms living in their digestive tracts. Without these microorganisms, termites could obtain no nutrients from the wood they eat. The termites, on the other hand, provide the microorganisms with food and a place to live. Cows have a similar association with microorganisms that live in their digestive tracts.

Lichens consist of both algal and fungal cells, and both types benefit from this association. It allows them to live in environments in which neither could survive alone. The algae produce food for themselves and the fungi by photosynthesis. The fungi provide moisture and the structural framework and attachment sites in which the algae grow.

Peas, clover, and alfalfa are *legumes*. Legumes have nodules on their roots in which certain bacteria grow (see Figure 36-3). The bacteria convert nitrogen gas from the air in the soil into forms usable by the plants. In this relationship, the plants are supplied with the nitrogen compounds they need, while the bacteria are given an environment in which they can grow and reproduce.

In **commensalism** (kuh-*men*-suh-liz-um), one organism benefits from a symbiotic relationship and the other is not affected. For example, the remora is a small fish that lives attached to a shark by a sucker. It detaches itself to eat the scraps left over from the shark's feeding. Thus the shark provides the remora with food. As far as is known, the remora neither helps nor hurts the shark. Barnacles may attach themselves to the large body surface of a whale. Barnacles are sessile and rely on water currents to bring them food. The movements of the whale provide them with a constantly changing environment and food supply. The whale is not affected by the presence of the barnacles.

Figure 36-4. Strangler Fig.

In **parasitism** (*par*-uh-suh-tiz-um), one organism benefits from a symbiotic relationship while the other one is harmed. The organism that benefits is called the *parasite*, while the organism that is harmed is the *host*. Some parasites cause only slight damage to their hosts, while others eventually kill the host. Tapeworms, for example, are parasites that live in the digestive tracts of various animals. There they are provided with nutrients and a suitable environment in which to grow and reproduce. However, the host is harmed by the presence of the tapeworms. The loss of nutrients and tissue damage caused by the worm can cause serious illness. There are parasitic plants that grow on other plants. Two examples of plant parasites are mistletoe and the stranger fig (see Figure 36-4).

Symbiotic relationships, particularly those involving mutualism or commensalism, are not always permanent. Also, it is not always possible to say definitely whether a particular organism is helped or harmed by such a relationship. For example, in many environments the algal cells of a lichen can survive perfectly well without the fungal cells. The fungal cells, on the other hand, may not be able to survive alone.

36-10 Producers, Consumers, and Decomposers

In all but a few small ecosystems, the autotrophs are plants and other photosynthetic organisms. They trap energy from sunlight and use it for the synthesis of sugars and starch. These substances can be converted to other organic compounds needed by the plant, or they can be broken down for energy. Heterotrophs cannot use any form of energy for their life processes except chemical energy stored in organic compounds. These organic nutrients must be obtained from the bodies of other organisms—either plants or animals. Since autotrophs are the only organisms in an ecosystem that can use light energy to produce organic compounds (food) from inorganic compounds, they are called **producers.** Since heterotrophs must obtain nutrients from other organisms, they are called **consumers.**

Saprophytes play an important role in an ecosystem. They function as *organisms of decay*, or **decomposers.** They break down the remains of dead plants and animals, releasing substances that can be reused by other members of the ecosystem. In this way many important substances are recycled in an ecosystem.

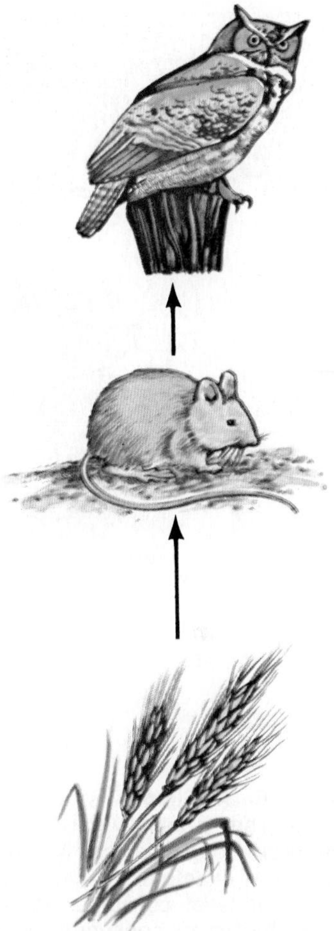

Figure 36-5. A Simple Food Chain. The grass is a producer; the field mouse is a first-level consumer; and the owl is a second-level consumer. The arrows show the flow of energy in the food chain.

36-11 Food Chains and Food Webs

Within an ecosystem, there is a pathway of energy flow that always begins with the producers. Energy stored in organic nutrients synthesized by the producers is transferred to consumers when the plants are eaten. Herbivores, which feed on plants, are the *primary*, or **first-level, consumers.** The carnivores that feed on the plant-eating animals are *secondary*, or **second-level, consumers.** For example, mice feed on plants and are first-level consumers. The snake that eats the mouse is a second-level consumer, while the hawk that eats the snake is a third-level consumer. Since many consumers have a varied diet, they may be second-, third-, or higher-level consumers, depending on their prey. Each of these feeding relationships forms a **food chain,** a series of organisms through which food energy is passed (see Figure 36-5).

Ecologists refer to feeding levels as *trophic* levels.

Feeding relationships in an ecosystem are never just simple food chains. There are many types of organisms at each feeding level, and there are always many food chains in an ecosystem. These food chains are interconnected at various points, forming a **food web** (see Figure 36-6).

At every level in an ecosystem there are decomposers. The decomposers make use of the wastes and remains of all organisms in the system. They use the energy in these materials for their own metabolism. At the same time, they break down

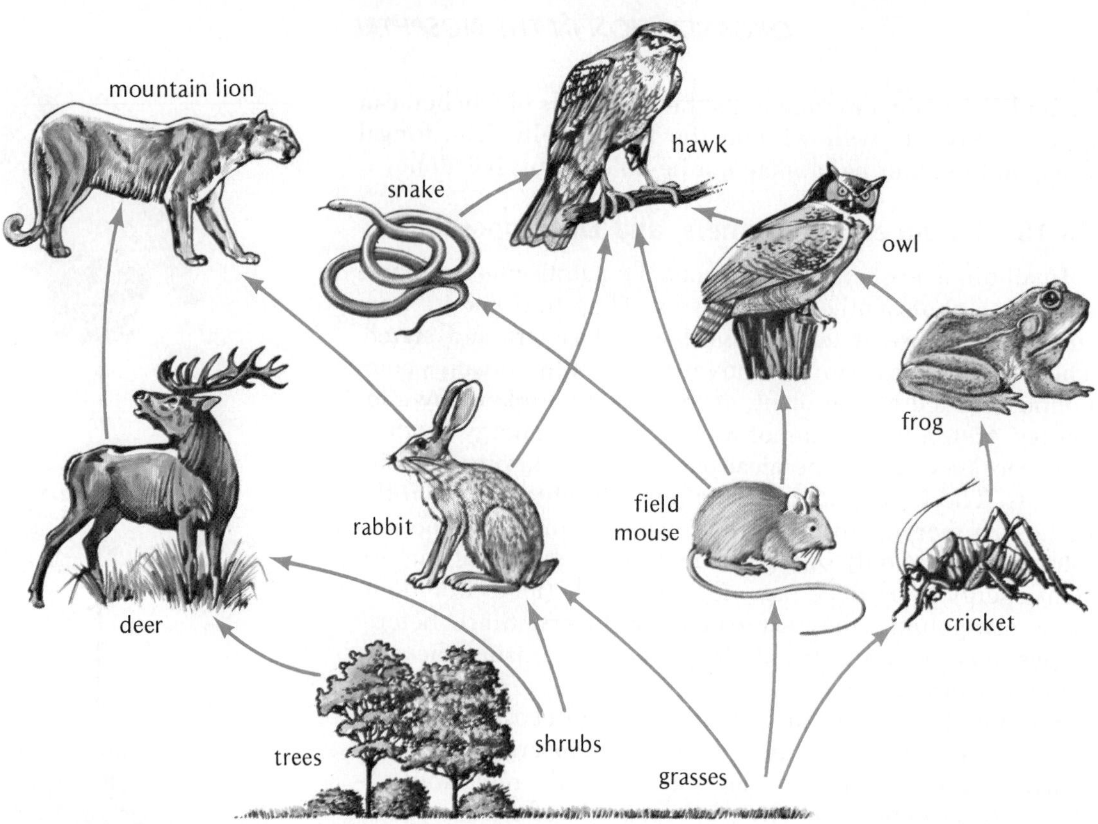

Figure 36-6. A Simple Food Web. Each organism is usually part of several different food chains. The same organism (for example, the hawk) can be a second-level consumer in one chain, a third-level consumer in another, and a fourth-level consumer in still another.

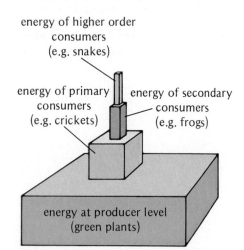

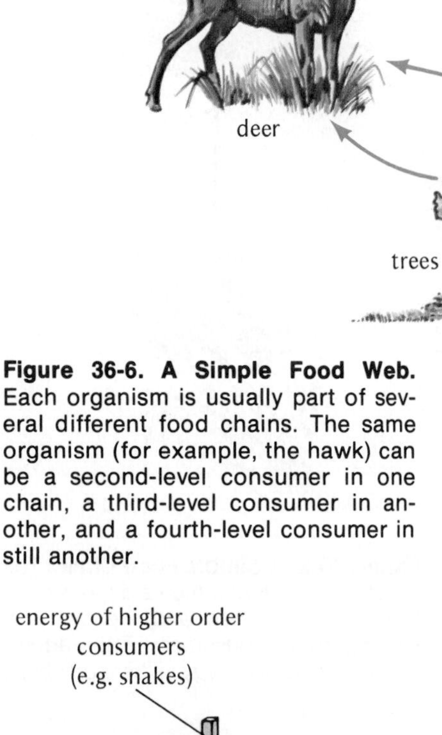

Figure 36-7. The Pyramid of Energy in an Ecosystem. At each level, the energy available is only about 10 percent of the energy at the level below it.

organic compounds into inorganic ones and make substances available for reuse in the system. The decomposers can be thought of as the final consumers in every food chain and food web.

36-12 Pyramids of Energy and Biomass

The amount of energy available in a food web decreases with each higher feeding level. The reason for this is that only a small fraction of the energy taken in as food becomes stored as new tissue. Much of the food ingested is not digested and absorbed. Furthermore, a large part of the energy in the food is used for respiration and maintenance. This energy is lost as heat. As a result, only about 10 percent of the energy taken in at any feeding level is passed upward to the next feeding level.

The amount of available energy in an ecosystem is commonly shown in the form of a pyramid—the **pyramid of energy** (see Figure 36-7). The greatest amount of energy is present in the producers—the base of the pyramid—and the least energy is present at the top of the pyramid—the highest-level consumers. Because the amount of available energy decreases so steeply, there are generally no more than four or five feeding levels in an ecosystem.

Because the total amount of energy available decreases with each higher feeding level, the total mass of living organisms that can be supported at each level decreases, too. This relationship can also be represented by a pyramid. This relationship, known as the **pyramid of biomass,** shows the relative mass of the organisms—the *biomass*—at each feeding level. The greatest amount of biomass is found in the lowest level, the producers. The least is found in the highest level of consumers.

CYCLES OF MATERIALS

After completing your study of this section, you should be able to describe each of the following biogeochemical cycles: the nitrogen cycle, the carbon and oxygen cycles, and the water cycle.

In all ecosystems there is a cycle of materials between living organisms and the environment. Living organisms incorporate certain substances obtained from the environment into their bodies. When these organisms die, their bodies are broken down by the decomposers, and the substances returned to the environment. If these substances were not returned to the environment, the supply would eventually become exhausted. The cycles of materials between living things and the physical environment are called *biogeochemical cycles.* Among the substances that are involved in such cycles are nitrogen, carbon, oxygen, and water.

36-13 The Nitrogen Cycle

Nitrogen is an important element in living things. It is a basic component of amino acids, which form proteins, and nucleotides, which form nucleic acids. Nitrogen gas makes up almost 80 percent of the earth's atmosphere. However, most organisms are unable to make use of nitrogen gas directly. Their supplies of nitrogen must be in the form of nitrogen compounds. Most plants can satisfy their nitrogen needs from *nitrates,* which are compounds containing the NO_3 group. Plants can synthesize amino acids and proteins from nitrates. Animals can obtain the nitrogen they need only from existing proteins. Animal foods must therefore include either plants or the bodies of other animals, both of which contain proteins.

A few types of bacteria and blue-green algae can produce nitrogen compounds from the gaseous nitrogen of the atmosphere. The process by which this is done is called **nitrogen fixation,** and the organisms that perform it are called **nitrogen-fixing organisms.** The products of nitrogen fixation are either *nitrites,* which are compounds containing the NO_2 group, or nitrates. Certain bacteria, called **nitrifying bacteria,** convert nitrites to nitrates. Through the action of the nitrogen-fixing and nitrifying organisms, nitrates enter the soil and water and become available to plants. Plants absorb the nitrates and incorporate the nitrogen into proteins. Plant proteins are ingested by animals and used to synthesize animal proteins.

Lightning produces some nitrogen oxide.

Nitrogen in the wastes and remains of organisms must be made available for reuse. This is accomplished by the decom-

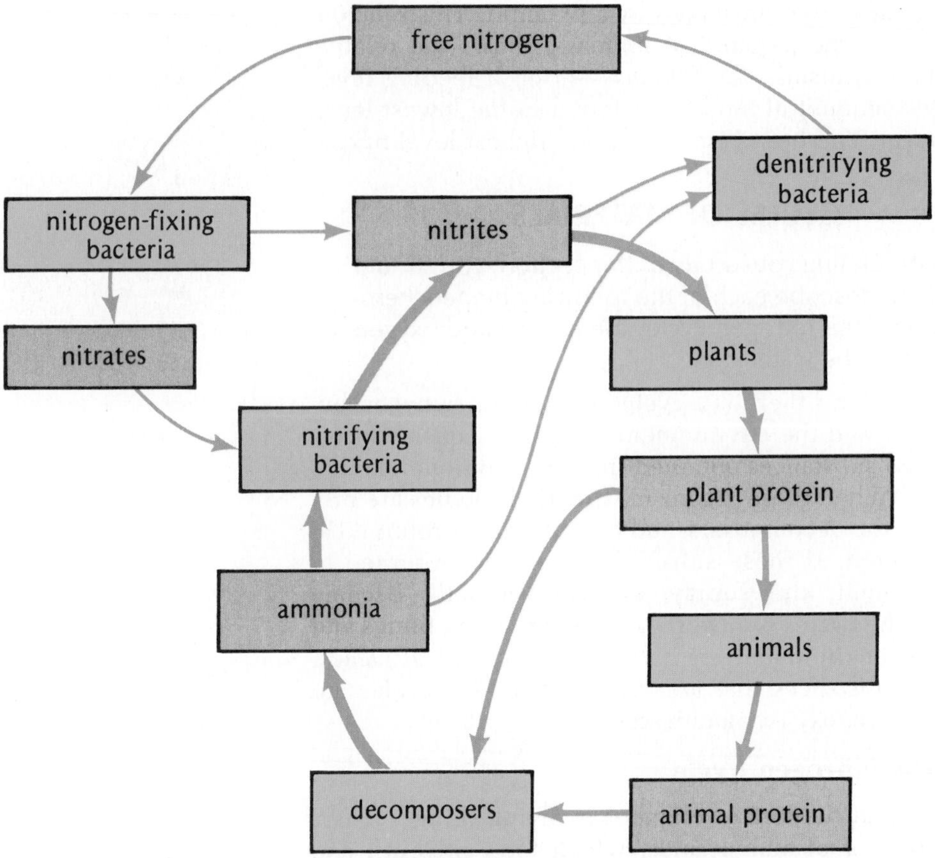

Figure 36-8. The Nitrogen Cycle. There are actually two interlocking nitrogen cycles. In the main cycle, nitrates are converted to plant and animal proteins, which are then broken down again to nitrates. The nitrogen remains in compound form throughout this cycle. In the secondary cycle, inorganic nitrogen compounds are broken down to free nitrogen by denitrifying bacteria and formed again by nitrogen-fixing and nitrifying bacteria.

Currently, gene-slicing techniques are being applied to nitrogen fixation. If the ability to produce nitrogen oxides can eventually be transferred to agricultural plants, the need for soil fertilizers will be reduced.

posers, which break down the complex compounds in plant and animal remains. One of the products of this breakdown is ammonia (NH_3). The nitrifying bacteria can convert ammonia to nitrates. Thus once nitrogen fixation has occurred, the nitrogen can be cycled repeatedly from plants and animals to the decomposers and nitrifying bacteria and back again to plants and animals. However, there is still another group of bacteria, called the **denitrifying bacteria,** which returns nitrogen to the atmosphere. These bacteria derive energy for their life processes by converting ammonia and nitrates to nitrogen gas. Only a small fraction of the nitrogen circulating between organisms is cycled through the atmosphere. Most of it remains combined in compounds.

Figure 36-8 shows the various pathways of the **nitrogen cycle.** The nitrogen cycle keeps the level of usable nitrogen in the soil fairly constant. The nitrogen cycle also occurs in lakes, streams, and oceans.

36-14 The Carbon and Oxygen Cycles

Carbon in the form of carbon dioxide makes up about 0.03 percent of the atmosphere. Carbon dioxide is also found dissolved in the waters of the earth. In the course of photosynthesis, carbon dioxide from the atmosphere is incorporated

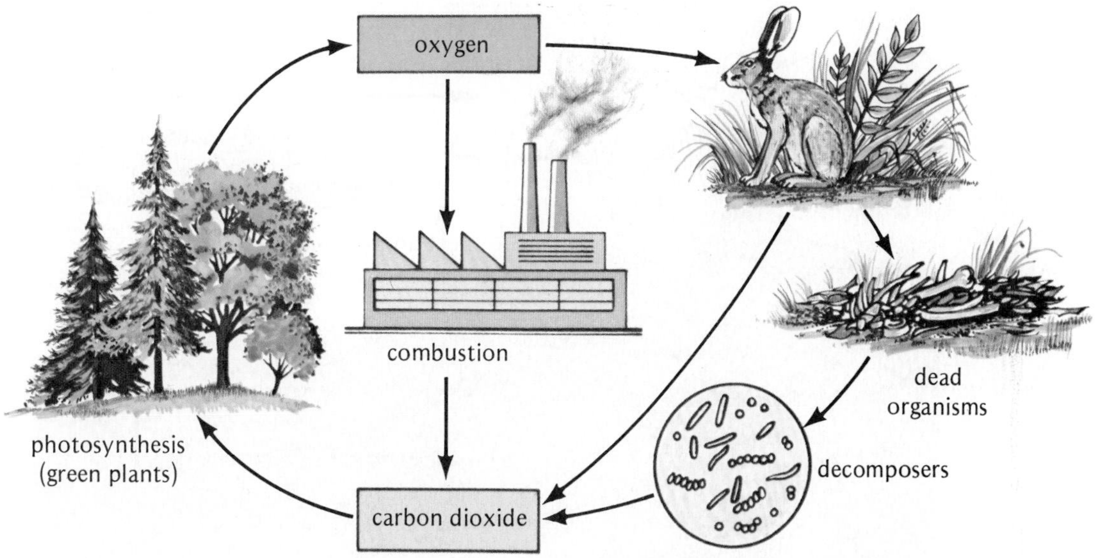

Figure 36-9. The Oxygen and Carbon Cycles. Carbon dioxide is removed from the air by photosynthesis and returned by cellular respiration and the burning of fossil fuels. Oxygen is removed from the air by cellular respiration and burning and returned by photosynthesis.

into organic compounds, a process known as *carbon fixation.* Some of these organic compounds are broken down during cellular respiration by the photosynthetic organisms, releasing carbon dioxide back into the atmosphere. If the plants or other photosynthetic organisms are eaten by animals, the carbon compounds pass through a food web. At each level, some are broken down by cellular respiration, releasing carbon dioxide into the atmosphere. Finally, the remains of dead plants and animals and animal wastes are broken down by decomposers, releasing carbon dioxide.

In the **carbon cycle,** carbon dioxide is removed from the atmosphere by photosynthesis, and it is returned to the atmosphere by cellular respiration (see Figure 36-9). These two processes are normally in balance, maintaining a relatively constant level of carbon dioxide in the atmosphere. However, the burning of fossil fuels (oil, coal, and natural gas) also releases carbon dioxide. Because of the increasing use of these fuels, there has been a gradual increase in the carbon dioxide content of the atmosphere since the mid-1800s. The long-term effects of this change are not known. However, some scientists think that it will result in an increase in temperature on the earth's surface. This would occur because the atmospheric carbon dioxide absorbs heat from the earth that would otherwise be radiated away into space.

Oxygen makes up about 20 percent of the earth's atmosphere. During photosynthesis, water molecules are split into hydrogen and oxygen. The hydrogen is used in the formation of carbohydrates, and the oxygen is released into the atmosphere. Animals, plants, and many protists use oxygen in cellular respiration and release carbon dioxide. Thus, in the **oxygen cycle,** oxygen is released into the atmosphere by the process of photosynthesis and removed from the atmosphere by cellular respiration.

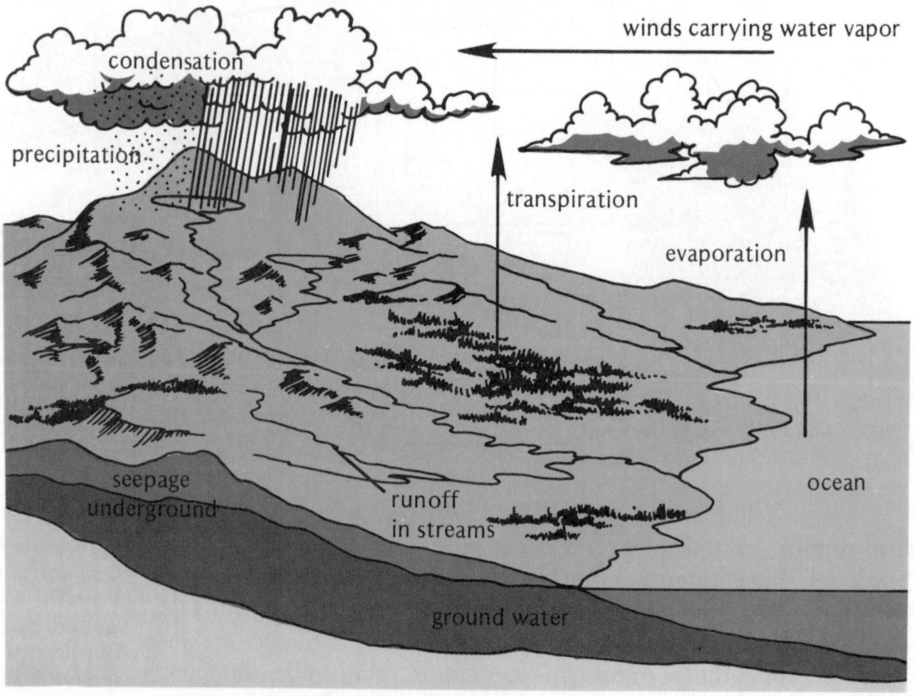

Figure 36-10. The Water Cycle. Water from the earth's surface enters the atmosphere in the form of water vapor through the processes of evaporation and transpiration. It returns to the surface by condensation and precipitation.

36-15 The Water Cycle

The cycling of water on the earth is almost entirely a physical process. Wherever water is exposed to the air, it continuously evaporates—escapes into the air in the form of water vapor. Plants also contribute to this loss of water to the air by the process of transpiration. However, there is a limit to the amount of water vapor the air can hold. Through various physical processes, excess water vapor condenses to form clouds and falls back to the earth's surface as precipitation.

This cycling of water between the surface of the earth and the atmosphere is called the **water cycle** (see Figure 36-10). Unlike the other cycles we have examined, no chemical changes are involved and no truly biological processes enter into it. It is true that some water is broken down chemically to hydrogen and oxygen during photosynthesis. This water is restored by cellular respiration. However, the amount of water involved in the photosynthesis-respiration cycle is only a small fraction of the total amount that passes through the water cycle.

COMPETITION IN ECOSYSTEMS

After completing your study of this section, you should be able to:

1. Define the terms *habitat* and *niche*.
2. Compare and contrast interspecific and intraspecific competition in an ecosystem.

36-16 Habitat and Niche

Each type of organism within an ecosystem has a particular part of the environment in which it lives. This is its **habitat.** For example, slime molds live on the damp floors of forests. This is their habitat. Because of the complex interactions that occur within an ecosystem, each species also plays a particular role. The role of a species in an ecosystem is its **niche.** An organism's habitat is part of its niche, but only part. Also included are how, when, and where it obtains nutrients, its reproductive behavior, and its direct and indirect effects both on the environment and on other species within the ecosystem.

36-17 Intraspecific and Interspecific Competition

In a balanced ecosystem, each species occupies its own niche. It occupies a particular territory (its habitat) and obtains nutrients in a particular way. Competition arises when the niches of two species overlap. The greater the overlap—the more requirements the two species have in common—the more intense the competition. Competition between two different species is called **interspecific competition.** As the resources being competed for become more scarce, the competition becomes more intense. Eventually one of the species is eliminated from the ecosystem, leaving the more successful species to occupy the niche.

Competition also occurs between members of the same species. This is called **intraspecific competition.** The intensity of the competition between members of the same species is affected by such things as population density and the availability of needed resources. If conditions become very harsh, those individuals with the most helpful adaptations will survive, while the less-well-adapted individuals will not.

MAINTENANCE AND CHANGE IN ECOSYSTEMS

After completing your study of this section, you should be able to:

1. Describe the conditions necessary for a stable, self-sustaining ecosystem.
2. Define the following terms: *ecological succession, dominant species, climax community, primary succession,* and *secondary succession.*
3. Describe primary succession on land leading to development of a forest community.
4. Describe succession in lakes and ponds leading to development of a forest community.

36-18 Maintenance in an Ecosystem

For an ecosystem to be stable and self-sustaining certain conditions must exist. (1) There must be a constant source of energy. For almost all ecosystems on earth the source of energy is light from the sun. Only a few ecosystems are based on chemosynthesis. In those ecosystems, the producers derive energy for the synthesis of organic compounds from chemical reactions involving various inorganic compounds. (2) There must be organisms within the ecosystem that can use incoming energy (light) for the synthesis of organic compounds. This role is filled by green plants and algae, which are the producers of the ecosystem. (3) There must be a cycle of materials between living organisms in the ecosystem and the environment. The producers incorporate inorganic compounds from the environment into organic compounds, which may then pass through a food chain or food web. Eventually, however, the decomposers break down the remains of dead organisms, releasing the inorganic substances back into the environment for reuse.

36-19 Ecological Succession

Although ecosystems appear stable, they do undergo change with time. Change occurs because the living organisms present in the ecosystem alter the environment. Some of the changes tend to make the environment more suitable for new types of organisms and less suitable for the existing organisms. Thus, the original organisms in an ecosystem are gradually replaced by other types. A new community replaces the original community in the ecosystem. Over time, this community is gradually replaced by still another community. The process by which an existing community is gradually replaced by another community is called **ecological succession.** In general, in land environments, ecological succession depends upon the types of plants that are present at any given time. Plants determine the type of community that develops because plants are the producers. The types of animals that can survive in the community depend, directly or indirectly, on the types of plants.

During each stage of ecological succession, a few species exert the greatest effect on the environment and on other members of the community. These species are called the **dominant species.** The conditions imposed on the environment by the dominant species determine the types of other species that can survive in each successive community.

Succession of one community by another continues until a mature, stable community develops. Such a community is called a **climax community.** In an ecosystem with a climax community, the conditions continue to be suitable for all the members of the community. The climax community remains until it is upset by a catastrophic event, such as a fire, flood, or volcanic eruption. After the destruction of a climax community, succession begins again and continues until a new climax community develops.

Succession that occurs in an area that has no existing life, for example, on bare rock, is called **primary succession.** Succes-

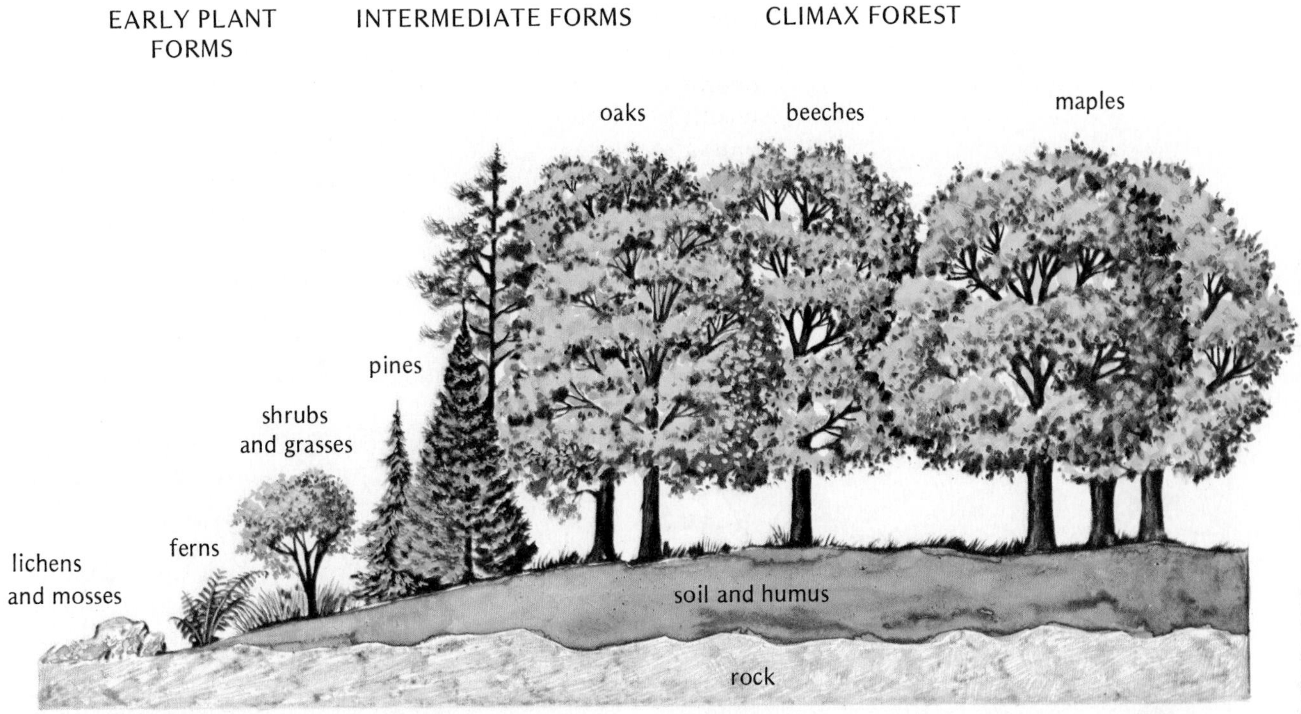

Figure 36-11. Stages of Primary Succession. The sequence of stages is represented from left to right. In an actual succession, only one stage is present at any given time.

sion that occurs in an area in which an existing community has been partially destroyed and its balance upset is called **secondary succession.**

Succession on land. Primary succession occurs on land in areas that are initially nearly lifeless (see Figure 36-11). Such conditions exist on rocky cliffs, sand dunes, newly formed volcanic islands, and newly exposed land areas. Primary succession is a very slow process because it must begin with the formation of soil.

Soil forms very slowly over thousands of years. By the process of weathering, large rocks are gradually broken into smaller and smaller pieces. Eventually, some of the rock is broken down into small particles. The first organisms to inhabit an area are called **pioneer organisms.** Such organisms generally include bacteria, fungi, and lichens. They break down the rock still further and add organic matter to the developing soil. Lichens are adapted to exposed conditions. They become attached to irregularities in the surface of the rock by rootlike rhizoids. They secrete acids that dissolve the rock. Some lichens die, and their remains are added to the soil. Mosses appear in areas where a little soil has accumulated. The mosses may shade the lichens, causing them to die and thus adding more organic material to the still primitive soil.

Eventually, grasses and annual plants grow in the areas where organic material has accumulated. When these plants die, the soil becomes richer. Small shrubs begin to grow, and their roots break rocks apart. The shrubs may shade the

Figure 36-12. Ecological Succession in a Pond. A pond may gradually change to dry land supporting a forest community.

grasses, killing them. Tree seedlings may take root. The trees eventually shade out the shrubs. The seedlings that grew among the shrubs probably required a fair amount of sunlight. Thus, when they become mature trees, there may not be enough sun on the forest floor for seedlings of the same type to survive. However, seedlings of other trees may grow well in the shade. In this way, one community of trees will be succeeded by another community with different types of trees. After many thousands of years, a climax community will develop. Climax communities are usually described in terms of their dominant plant forms.

The dominant plants of a climax community are determined by the physical factors of the environment. Where there is adequate rainfall and suitable soil, the climax community is likely to be a forest. However, if there is not enough water to support a forest, the climax community can consist of grasses or some other type of plant.

Animal life changes with the plant communities. For example, as a succession proceeds toward a forest community, animals that live among grasses and shrubs will eventually be replaced by animals that live on the forest floor and at varying levels in the trees.

Secondary succession occurs in areas in which the climax community has been destroyed. For example, a forest may be cut down in order to clear the land for farming. If, after being farmed for awhile, the land is left untended, a new succession will begin, ending eventually in another forest climax community. In secondary succession, the area already has existing soil. Since the sequence does not begin with soil formation, the process is much faster than primary succession. A climax community may become reestablished after a few hundreds of years, rather than the thousands originally needed for the primary succession.

Succession in lakes and ponds. Lakes and ponds may also pass through stages of ecological succession, eventually developing into a forest climax community (see Figure 36-12). The process begins when sediment, fallen leaves, and other debris gradually accumulate on the lake bottom, increasing its depth. Around the edges of the lake, many of the rooted plants, such as sphagnum moss, cattails, reeds, and rushes, grow out into the shallower water. They gradually extend the banks inward, decreasing the size of the lake. As the lake fills in, it becomes rich in nutrients that can support a large population of organisms. The increased number of plants and animals contribute organic material to the sediment, which hastens the filling-in process. As succession continues, the lake becomes a marsh. Still later, the marsh fills in, forming dry land. Land communities replace aquatic forms. Over a period of time, the filled area becomes part of the surrounding community.

summary

Ecology is the branch of biology that deals with the interactions between organisms and their environment. Abiotic factors of importance in the environment are light, temperature, water, soil, and nutrients. The biotic components of an ecosystem are grouped by ecologists into populations, communities, and ecosystems. The biosphere is the part of the earth in which living things are found.

Most autotrophs in an ecosystem are photosynthetic. Heterotrophs include herbivores, carnivores, omnivores, and saprophytes. Feeding relationships between organisms include symbiotic relationships. Mutualism, commensalism, and parasitism are the three major types of symbiotic relationships.

In an ecosystem, the autotrophs are the producers and the heterotrophs are the consumers. The saprophytes act as decomposers. The path of energy flow in an ecosystem begins with the producers. Energy, in the form of food, then passes to the first-level, second-level, and higher-level consumers. This transfer of food energy forms a food chain that ends with the decomposers. The food chains in an ecosystem are interconnected, forming a food web. The amount of energy in an ecosystem is greatest at the level of the producers and least at the level of highest-level consumers. This is represented as the pyramid of energy. Biomass also is greatest at the producer level and least at the highest level of consumers. This is represented as the pyramid of biomass.

In all ecosystems there are cycles of materials between the environment and the living organisms. The most important of these cycles are the nitrogen, carbon, oxygen, and water cycles.

In ecological succession, a new community gradually replaces an existing community. Succession continues until a climax community develops. Primary succession occurs where there has been no existing life. Secondary succession occurs where an existing community has been upset or destroyed.

vocabulary

abiotic factor
altitude
aphotic zone
biotic factor
biosphere
carbon cycle
carnivore
climax community
commensalism
community
consumer
decomposer
denitrifying bacteria
dominant species
ecological succession
ecology
ecosystem
first-level consumer
food chain
food web
habitat
herbivore
humus
interspecific competition
intraspecific competition
latitude
mutualism
niche
nitrifying bacteria
nitrogen cycle
nitrogen fixation
nitrogen-fixing bacteria
omnivore
oxygen cycle
parasitism
photic zone
pioneer organism
population
precipitation
predator
primary succession
producer
pyramid of biomass
pyramid of energy
saprophyte
scavenger
secondary succession
second-level consumer
subsoil
symbiotic relationship
topsoil
water cycle
weathering

test your learning

Section

36-1 **1.** What is ecology?

2. What are the biotic and abiotic factors in an ecosystem?

36-2 **3.** Discuss the importance of latitude in determining the intensity and duration of sunlight received at the earth's surface.

36-3 **4.** What factors affect the temperature patterns on the earth's surface?

5. Which areas on the earth's surface have the warmest average temperatures and which have the coldest?

36-4 **6.** What factors affect the average annual precipitation pattern on the earth's surface?

36-5 **7.** Describe soil formation, including the three layers found in mature soil.

36-6 **8.** Describe biotic organization in terms of populations, communities, and ecosystems.

36-7 **9.** Define the term *biosphere*, and describe the different parts of the biosphere.

36-8 **10.** What is a herbivore? Name three animals that are herbivores.

11. What is a carnivore? Name three animals that are carnivores.

12. What is the difference between a predator and a scavenger? Give examples of each.

13. Name three animals that are omnivores.

14. What are saprophytes? What types of organisms are saprophytes?

36-9 **15.** What is a symbiotic relationship?

16. Name and describe the three types of symbiotic relationships, and give an example of each.
36-10 **17.** Describe the relationship between producers, consumers, and decomposers in an ecosystem.
36-11 **18.** Describe the structures of a food chain and a food web.
36-12 **19.** How do the pyramids of energy and biomass represent the energy relationships in an ecosystem?
36-13 **20.** How is gaseous nitrogen from the atmosphere converted to forms that can be used by most plants?
21. How are nitrogen compounds present in the remains of dead organisms converted into forms that can be used by living plants?
22. How is nitrogen returned to the atmosphere?
36-14 **23.** What is carbon fixation, and when does it occur?
24. Describe the carbon cycle.
25. Why has the carbon dioxide content of the atmosphere increased in the last hundred years?
26. Describe the oxygen cycle.
36-15 **27.** Describe the water cycle.
36-16 **28.** Define the terms *habitat* and *niche*.
36-17 **29.** Under what circumstances does interspecific competition arise? What are the results of such competition?
30. What is intraspecific competition?
36-18 **31.** Under what circumstances is an ecosystem stable and self-sustaining?
36-19 **32.** What is ecological succession and why does it occur?
33. Define the terms *dominant species* and *climax community*.
34. Describe primary succession on land beginning with rock.
35. Name three types of pioneer organisms.
36. Describe succession in a pond leading to a forest community.

test your understanding

1. Why is the number of feeding levels in an ecosystem limited to relatively few?
2. Why are biogeochemical cycles important in an ecosystem?
3. Describe how the duration and intensity of sunlight and temperature and precipitation patterns vary with latitude and/or altitude.
4. Could there exist a climax community that contained no animals? Explain your answer.

independent research

1. Prepare a report on one of the following topics:
   A. The effects of length of daylight on plants and/or animals.
   B. The effects of nearby mountains and oceans on temperature and precipitation patterns.
   C. Soil formation.
   D. Symbiotic relationships.
2. Investigate a natural community near your home. The community could consist of a stand of trees, an empty lot with vegetation, a pond or stream, etc. Describe the various types of plant and animal life present, and discuss the food chains and food webs that could exist in this community.

chapter 37

Biomes of the Earth

37-1 Chapter Introduction

The type of climax community that can develop in a land area is determined by the climate and other physical conditions of that area. Areas that are similar in climate and other physical conditions develop similar types of climax communities. The term **biome** (*by*-ohm) refers to a large geographical region showing a particular type of climax community. In the case of a land, or terrestrial, biome, the climax community is defined by its dominant type of plant life. For example, one biome may consist of climax communities of grasses. Another may contain evergreen trees. The species may vary from one part of a biome to another, but the general type of plant life, or vegetation, is the same throughout. The major terrestrial biomes are the tundra, taiga, deciduous forest, grassland, desert, and tropical rain forest.

The term *biome* is also applied to communities that develop in aquatic environments. Ecologists refer to **freshwater biomes,** or communities of organisms inhabiting lakes and streams, and to saltwater, or **marine, biomes.**

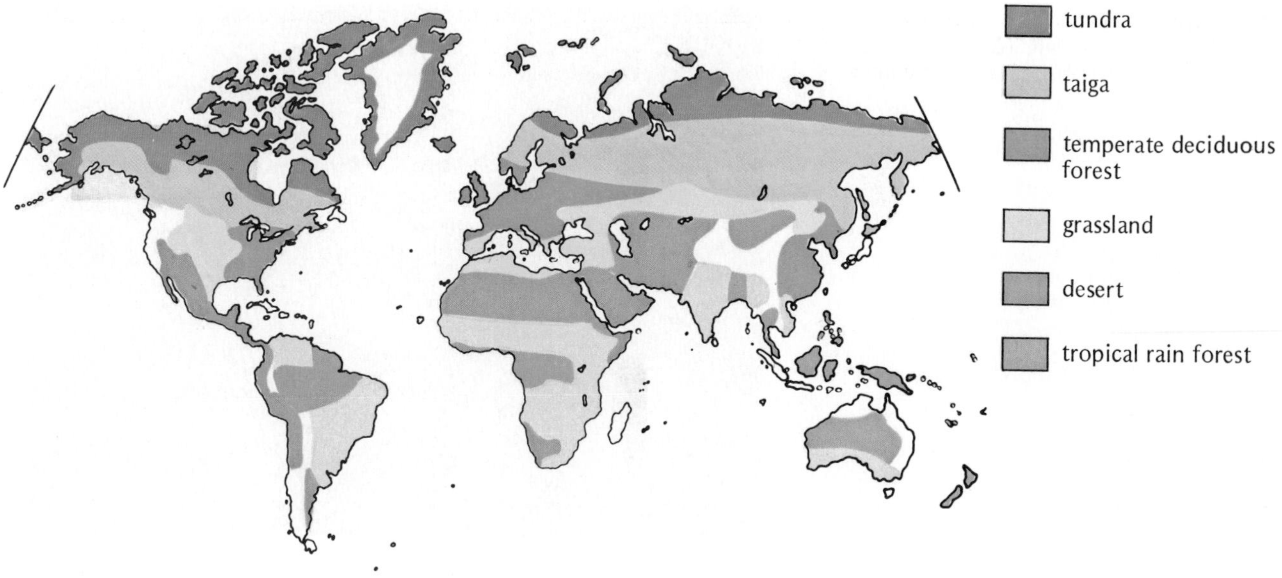

Figure 37-1. Biomes of the World.

TERRESTRIAL BIOMES

After completing your study of this section, you should be able to list the major terrestrial biomes of the earth, and name the dominant plant and animal species of each.

37-2 The Tundra

The **tundra** (*tun*-druh) is a region south of the ice caps of the Arctic and extending across North America, Europe, and Siberia (see Figure 37-1). (In the Southern Hemisphere, the latitudes that would be tundra are oceans.) The tundra is characterized by a low average temperature and a short growing season—about 60 days. During the long, cold winters, the ground is completely frozen. During the short summer, only the topmost layer of soil thaws. The layers beneath, which remain frozen, are called **permafrost** (*per*-muh-frost). The average precipitation in the tundra is only about 10 to 12 centimeters a year. However, because of the low rate of evaporation, the region is wet with bogs and ponds during the warm season.

Vegetation in the tundra is limited to lichens, mosses, grasses, sedges, and shrubs (see Figure 37-2). Because of the short growing season and the permafrost, there are almost no trees. Animals found in the tundra include reindeer, musk oxen, caribou, wolves, Arctic hares, Arctic foxes, lemmings, snowy owls, and ptarmigans, which are a type of bird. During the warm season there are great numbers of flies and mosquitos. Various types of birds, including sandpipers, ducks, and geese, migrate to the tundra during the warm season.

Figure 37-2. The Tundra. (Top) Tundra in the fall. (Bottom) A herd of reindeer on the tundra in the winter.

37-3 The Taiga

Moving south across the tundra, the vegetation gradually changes. Groups of stunted trees appear in sheltered places. Farther south, the trees become larger and closer together, eventually giving way to evergreen forests. This belt of evergreen forest, which extends across North America, Europe, and Asia, is the **taiga** (*ty*-guh). The taiga has cold winters in which the ground is covered by deep snow. However, the growing season is longer than that of the tundra—about 120 days. The summer days are warmer than in the tundra, and the ground thaws completely. As in the tundra, there are many ponds and bogs. Pines, firs, and spruce are the dominant vegetation (see Figure 37-3). However, some deciduous trees (those that shed their leaves) are also present. These include willows and birches. There are also shrubs and flowering plants.

Figure 37-3. The Taiga. In the taiga, pines, firs, and spruce are the dominant vegetation, and there are many ponds.

Animals of the taiga include moose, wolves, bears, lynx, deer, elks, wolverines, martens, snowshoe hares, porcupines, and various rodents, birds, and insects.

37-4 The Temperate Deciduous Forest

Regions south of the taiga show variations in rainfall, so that there is not a single type of biome that stretches in a belt across these latitudes. South of the taiga in eastern North America and in Europe are regions of **temperate deciduous forest** (see Figure 37-4). In this type of biome the summers are generally hot and humid, and the winters are cold. Rainfall averages 75 to 150 centimeters a year.

The species present in deciduous forests vary with the local rainfall. Common trees of deciduous forests include oak, maple, hickory, beech, chestnut, and birch. Smaller trees and shrubs are also present, as well as flowering plants, ferns, and mosses.

Figure 37-4. A Temperate Deciduous Forest in Summer. Common trees of the deciduous forest include oak, maple, hickory, beech, and birch.

Figure 37-5. Grasslands. In the past, pronghorn antelope were found in great numbers in the grasslands of North America.

Animals of the deciduous forest include wolves, gray foxes, bobcats, deer, raccoons, squirrels, and chipmunks, as well as a wide variety of birds and insects.

37-5 Grasslands

There are several different names for grasslands, including prairie, plain, and savannah. In Europe and Asia, grasslands are called steppes; in southern Africa, the veld; and in South America, the pampas.

Grasslands, or prairies, are found in North America, Asia, South America, and South Africa. They occur in both temperate and tropical climates. Grasslands usually cover large areas in the interior of a continent. They develop where rainfall ranges from 25 to 75 centimeters a year. This quantity of rainfall cannot support a deciduous forest, and grasses become the dominant form of vegetation (see Figure 37-5). The soil of the grasslands is often deep and rich, and such areas have become the most productive farmlands of the earth.

The natural vegetation of the grasslands includes many species of grasses and wildflowers. In wetter areas near rivers the vegetation may be quite dense and include various shrubs.

Animals of the North American grasslands include coyotes, badgers, rattlesnakes, prairie dogs, jackrabbits, and ground squirrels. In the past, great herds of bison and pronghorn antelope were common. Now, most have been replaced by domesticated cattle and sheep. In Africa, the grasslands are populated by zebras, giraffes, gazelles, and other large grazing animals. Predators, such as lions, that feed on the grazers are also present. There are fewer types of birds in the grasslands than in the deciduous forest. There are meadowlarks, ring-necked pheasant, prairie chickens, hawks, and owls. There are many insects, but the grasshopper populations in particular may be huge.

37-6 Deserts

Deserts occur in regions that are too dry to support grasses. Rainfall is usually less than 25 centimeters a year. In North

Figure 37-6. The Desert. (Left) The Painted Desert of Arizona. (Below) The fennec, a small desert fox of Africa.

America there is a desert extending from Mexico north to the eastern part of Washington. Huge areas of desert are also found in South America, Africa, Asia, and Australia. Temperatures in the desert vary widely in the course of a day. During the day, it is very hot. At night, however, the temperature may drop steeply, sometimes as much as 30°C. Some deserts have almost no vegetation at all, while others have a variety of plants (see Figure 37-6).

Plants found in the desert have special adaptations for the conservation of water and for the completion of their reproductive cycles. Most have widespread, shallow roots that enable them to absorb the maximum amount of water when it is available. Many desert plants, such as cacti, store water in their tissues. Many live only a short time. They sprout, flower, and produce seeds during the brief rainy periods, which may last only a few days. Plants characteristic of the deserts of North America are cactus, yucca, mesquite, sagebrush, and creosote bush.

Like desert plants, desert animals show a wide variety of adaptations for survival in the harsh environment. Most are active at night, spending the hot days in burrows in the ground or hidden in any available shade. Many desert rodents can survive with very little drinking water. They manage mostly on the water produced by cellular metabolism and water present in the plants they eat. The fennec, which is a small desert fox, spends its days in a burrow, coming out only at night to feed on birds and other small animals. Its long ears provide surface area for getting rid of excess body heat. Also found in the desert are snakes, lizards, spiders, and insects.

Figure 37-7. Tropical Rain Forest. The floor of the tropical rain forest is in constant shade from the dense tree cover above.

37-7 Tropical Rain Forests

Tropical rain forests are found in areas around the equator. In these regions the climate is uniform throughout the year. There is a constant supply of rainfall, which may total between 200 and 400 centimeters a year. Rain falls nearly every day, and the humidity is consistently high. Temperatures remain constant at about 25°C throughout the year. Tropical rain forests contain an enormous variety of plants and animals.

Within a tropical rain forest, the tree cover is so dense that little light reaches the ground (see Figure 37-7). The treetops form a canopy about 50 meters high. Below the canopy are shorter trees that can grow in the shade. The trees of the rain forest have shallow root systems that enable them to absorb nutrients from the thin layer of wet soil. Many have braces, or buttresses, that extend out from the trunks to the ground. Like prop roots, they help to keep the tree standing upright.

Organic materials decay very quickly in this warm, humid environment. Minerals released by decomposition are rapidly taken up again by the plants. Materials not absorbed by the plants are quickly washed away by the frequent rains. Therefore, in a tropical rain forest there is little organic matter stored in the soil. Most of the nutrients in this biome are found within the living organisms. Because of the basically poor soil, land cleared of a tropical rain forest cannot support crops for more than a year or two.

Figure 37-8. **Bromeliads and Orchids.** The bromeliads (left) and orchids (right) are both epiphytes.

Among the hundred or more different species of trees found in the rain forest, there are many with large, broad leaves. In addition to the trees there are thick vines, called *lianas,* that are attached to the tree trunks and grow up through the treetops. The roots of these vines are in the ground. There are also many *epiphytes* (*ep*-uh-fyts), which are plants that grow on other plants, but are not parasites. Various orchids, cacti, and ferns are epiphytes (see Figure 37-8). The roots of some epiphytes absorb moisture from the air. Others, such as the bromeliads, have leaves that form cups at their bases. Water-absorbing structures pick up moisture trapped in the leaves. On the floor of tropical rain forests are plants that are tolerant of almost complete shade.

Tropical rain forests have a wide variety of animal species, many of which show adaptations that enable them to live at a particular level in the trees (see Figure 37-9). Monkeys, bats, squirrels, and parrots and other birds feed on fruits and nuts in the treetops. Flying squirrels leap from one tree to another. Snakes and lizards live in the branches of the trees, as do opossums and porcupines. Rodents, tapirs, antelope, deer, and other large animals live on the forest floor. Spiders and insects are present at all levels. There are ants, termites, bees, butterflies, and moths.

Figure 37-9. **Animals of the Rain Forest.** Squirrel monkeys and parakeets are among the many animals that live in the trees of rain forests.

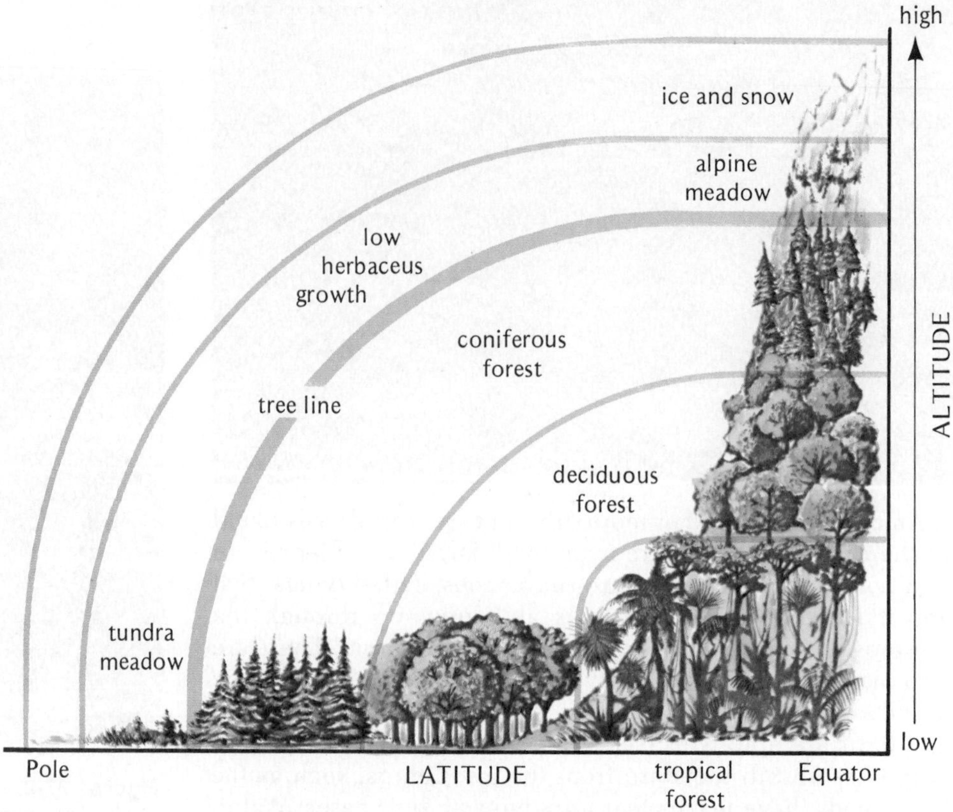

Figure 37-10. Effects of Altitude on Climax Vegetation.

37-8 Effects of Altitude on Climax Vegetation

With exceptions as noted, the terrestrial biomes of the earth are distributed in irregular belts, more or less in sequence according to latitude. However, mountainous regions are usually omitted from the biome classifications. The reason for this is that increasing altitude generally produces climatic effects similar to increasing latitude. Thus the sides of mountains may show a succession of plant communities that change with increasing altitude. These communities will have many characteristics in common with those of specific biomes. For example, the climatic conditions and types of plant life near the top of a mountain may resemble those of the tundra. Lower down the mountainside, evergreen forests that are characteristic of the taiga will appear. This relationship between higher altitude and higher latitude is shown in Figure 37-10.

AQUATIC BIOMES

After completing your study of this section, you should be able to describe the different types of aquatic biomes, and name some representative organisms of each.

37-9 Physical Factors in Aquatic Biomes

The problems of life in aquatic biomes are somewhat different from those in terrestrial biomes. For one thing, there is no problem about the availability of water. However, in fresh water, excess water must be excreted by organisms, while in salt water, excess salt must be excreted. Temperature variation in the course of a year is much less in aquatic environments than it is on land. Temperatures in the oceans show the least variation, while those in lakes and ponds show more of a change. Other physical factors that affect living things in aquatic biomes are the amounts of oxygen and carbon dioxide dissolved in the water, the availability of organic and inorganic nutrients, and light intensity.

37-10 The Marine Biome

Since all the oceans of the earth are interconnected, they are considered to form a single marine, or salt-water, biome. Conditions and life forms vary gradually from one region of the marine biome to another, but without the clearcut differences of the terrestrial biomes.

Characteristics of the marine biome. The marine biome is a continuous body of water that covers more than 70 percent of the earth's surface. Because of the heat capacity of water, the oceans can absorb solar heat energy during warm seasons and hold it during cold seasons. As a result, ocean temperatures remain relatively stable. The oceans also have a stabilizing effect on average temperatures of land areas. Temperatures on the earth would vary much more than they do if the oceans did not exist. The aquatic environment of the oceans is stable in other respects, too. In any given region, the supply of nutrients and the concentration of dissolved salts remain relatively constant.

Although environmental conditions tend to remain constant in any particular region of the marine biome, they do vary from region to region. In particular, the salt content varies from one place to another. It is lower where large rivers bring fresh water into the ocean and higher where high atmospheric temperature causes rapid evaporation. In general, salt concentrations in the ocean are very similar to those in living cells. Marine organisms therefore do not usually have the problem of water balance that freshwater organisms face.

Although temperatures remain fairly constant throughout the year in any given part of the marine biome, there is a variation with latitude. Ocean temperatures vary from near 0°C in the polar regions to 32°C near the equator.

Organisms of the oceans. The marine biome supports a very great variety of life forms. Some marine organisms are sessile and live attached to the ocean floor or to various other fixed surfaces. Sessile organisms include sponges, sea anemones, corals, and barnacles. Organisms that live on the ocean floor are called **benthos.** Starfish, clams, worms, snails, and crabs are benthic organisms. Small organisms that float near the surface and are carried by ocean currents are called **plankton.**

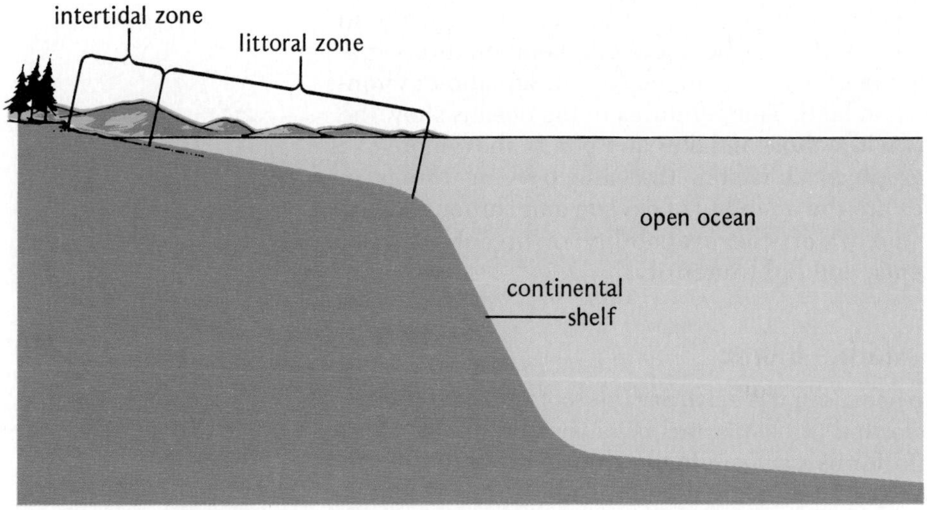

Figure 37-11. Zones of the Ocean.

Planktonic organisms include protists, algae, tiny crustaceans called copepods, the larvae of various animals, small jellyfish, and worms. Photosynthetic planktonic organisms, called **phytoplankton,** are the major producers of the oceans. Non-photosynthetic planktonic protists and planktonic animals are called **zooplankton.** Both phytoplankton and zooplankton make up the lowest level of the complex marine food web. Many types of animals, from small worms to whales, feed on plankton. Free-swimming organisms that live in the oceans are called **nekton.** Nektonic organisms include squid, fishes, turtles, seals, and whales.

Zones of the oceans. The oceans are divided into several zones based mainly on depth (see Figure 37-11). The **intertidal zone** is the area along the shoreline that is covered by water at high tide and uncovered at low tide. Various types of seaweeds—red and brown algae—are abundant in this zone. On sandy beaches, clams, crabs, sand fleas, and worms live in the sand. Many types of birds live along the shore, including gulls, terns, and sandpipers. On rocky coasts, algae, barnacles, mussels, and starfish cling to the rocks.

Beyond the intertidal zone is the **littoral zone,** which includes the relatively shallow waters above the continental shelf. The gently sloping continental shelf extends out from the edge of the continent for about 300 kilometers. This zone contains nutrients from the continents carried into the oceans by rivers and streams. Because the water is shallow, light reaches all the way to the ocean floor in the littoral zone. The littoral zone contains many different forms of life. In many places there are large populations of algae, as well as fish, oysters, mussels, crabs, barnacles, worms, and sea cucumbers.

The open ocean is also called the *neritic zone.* The deepest part of the ocean is the *abyssal zone.*

Beyond the continental shelf is the zone of the open ocean. Here the water is very deep, and light does not reach the ocean floor. The upper layer of the open ocean is occupied mainly by plankton. In this zone there are also large fish, including sharks, as well as porpoises, squids, and whales. Below the zone of photosynthesis, the organisms are all heterotrophs. They feed on organic matter that drifts downward from the photosynthetic zone above.

37-11 Freshwater Biomes

Freshwater biomes can be divided into two basic types—running water (streams) and standing water (lakes, ponds, swamps, and bogs). The volume of water in these biomes is very much smaller than that of the marine biome. As a result, the temperature variations in freshwater biomes are generally larger. Organisms living in fresh water must be able to adapt to greater seasonal variations than those living in the ocean. They also have the problem of maintaining water balance. In a freshwater environment, water enters living cells by osmosis (see page 82). Freshwater organisms usually need a mechanism for removing excess water by active transport. The contractile vacuoles of the ameba and paramecium are an example of such a mechanism.

Streams. In fast-moving streams, the bottom consists mainly of rocks and gravel. Most organisms are found in calmer, shallow areas near the banks of the stream . Here , algae grow on rocks and there are many insects and insect larvae. Fish and microscopic floating algae are found both in running water and in the calmer pools. Where streams are slow-moving, muddy sediment accumulates on the bottom. Many animals live in the bottom mud, including aquatic insects and their larvae, worms, snails, and crayfish. Raccoons, birds, and animals that live along the banks catch fish and other animals from the stream (see Figure 37-12).

Lakes and ponds. Lakes and ponds are bodies of standing water. Lakes are generally larger than ponds and are deep enough that light does not reach the bottom in all parts. Ponds are generally shallow enough so that light does reach the bottom throughout.

Around the shores of a lake is a zone of shallow water in which light reaches the bottom. In this zone, cattails, bulrushes, and other plants grow above the surface of the lake. These plants have roots in the lake bottom. In deeper water out from the shore there are floating plants, such as water lilies, which are also rooted in the bottom. Many types of animals are found in the bottom in the shallow water zone. There are insect larvae, crayfish, worms, hydra, clams, and snails. Free-swimming animals include diving beetles, mosquito larvae, giant water bugs, fish, frogs, salamanders, turtles, and snakes. On the surface there may be water striders, water boatmen, and whirligig beetles.

In the deep, open waters of the lake where light does not reach the bottom, the main producers are microscopic algae (phytoplankton) that float near the surface. Zooplankton is also

Figure 37-12. Raccoon Fishing in Stream.

frontiers of biology

Although it has long been known that various microorganisms obtain the energy they need for their metabolic processes by chemosynthesis, it was thought that energy for all communities of organisms was provided by photosynthesis. However, in 1977, marine biologists and oceanographers investigating the Galapagos Rift in the eastern part of the Pacific Ocean discovered a new type of community, one based on chemosynthesis.

The Galapagos Rift is an area in the ocean floor where molten material from the core of the earth comes up through cracks, or vents, in the earth's surface. On meeting the cold ocean waters, the molten material, called **magma,** solidifies to form a porous, black lava.

In most parts of the open ocean, the floor is dark and existing organisms are specialized heterotrophs that feed on organic matter drifting down from the water's surface. However, around the vent of the Galapagos Rift, about 2½ kilometers beneath the surface, are communities of mussels, clams, crabs, and worms, as well as other life forms not known to exist elsewhere.

Unlike the communities of the earth's surface, the energy source for organisms of the vent communities is **geothermal**—it is heat given off from the core of the earth. Near the vents, sea water percolates down through the porous lava and becomes saturated with minerals. Heat from the earth's core super-boils the water and spews it back into the ocean through cracks in the lava. These boiling plums can reach 350°C. The heat changes sulfate in the rock to hydrogen sulfide. Bacteria of the vent communities use the hydrogen sulfide in combination with oxygen and carbon dioxide to synthesize organic compounds. This chemosynthetic process serves the same functions for vent communities as photosynthesis does on the earth's surface. The chemosynthetic vent bacteria are the producers of this community and are the base of the food chain.

Among the animals of the vent communities are various mollusks and giant tube worms, some 1.5 meters long. Many of these animals have highly specialized symbiotic relationships with the chemosynthetic vent bacteria. The animals supply the bacteria with sulfides, carbon dioxide, and water. The bacteria supply the animals with carbohydrates. The mollusks have colonies of the bacteria growing on their gills. The structure of the tube worms appears to have developed around on the presence of the bacteria. There is no digestive tract. Instead, they have many tentacles through which they absorb nutrients from the water. Within their bodies is a specialized organ called a trophosome, which is made up of bacterial cells and small blood vessels. The exchange of materials between the worm and the bacteria occurs in the trophosome.

The environment of the vent communities is unlike any other on the modern earth. In fact, in some ways, the conditions are similar to those hyzothesized for the primitive earth at the time life arose. These is abundant energy in the form of heat, and the sea at the vents is tremendously rich in nutrients, both inorganic and organic. It is possible that this "hot, thin soup" will present biologists with an opportunity to learn something first hand about the origin of life.

present. These floating, microscopic, heterotrophic organisms are the primary consumers in a complex food web. The planktonic organisms are eaten by small fish, which are eaten by larger fish, and so on.

Life in ponds is much the same as that in the shallow waters of lakes.

Swamps and bogs. Swamps are low, wetland areas in which the vegetation includes shrubs and trees. Many types of plants and animals are found in wetlands. Wetlands are also important as nesting sites for water birds.

Bogs are shallow bodies of water that contain large growths of sphagnum moss. The moss and other factors create an acid environment in which the rate of decay is slowed. With decay slowed, the cycling of nitrogen through the ecosystem is reduced. Several plants common in bogs are insectivorous. These include pitcher plants and sundews.

summary

Biomes are large geographical areas showing a particular type of climax community. The type of vegetation found in a biome is determined by climate and other physical conditions. The major terrestrial biomes are the tundra, taiga, deciduous forest, grassland, desert, and tropical rain forest. The marine, or salt-water, biome includes all the oceans of the world. Freshwater biomes include streams, lakes and ponds, swamps, and bogs.

vocabulary

benthos
biome
desert
freshwater biome
grassland
intertidal zone
littoral zone
marine biome
phytoplankton
plankton
taiga
temperate deciduous forest
tropical rain forest
tundra
zooplankton

test your learning

Section		
37-1	**1.**	Define the term *biome*.
37-2	**2.**	What parts of the earth are tundra?
	3.	What are the physical characteristics of the tundra?
	4.	Describe the vegetation and animal life of the tundra.
37-3	**5.**	What parts of the earth are taiga?
	6.	What are the physical characteristics of the taiga?
	7.	Describe the vegetation and animal life of the taiga.
37-4	**8.**	Describe the location and physical characteristics of temperate deciduous forests.
	9.	Describe the vegetation and animal life of temperate deciduous forests.
37-5	**10.**	Describe the location and physical characteristics of grasslands.
	11.	Describe the vegetation and animal life of the grasslands.
37-6	**12.**	Describe the physical characteristics of deserts.
	13.	Describe the vegetation and animal life of deserts.
37-7	**14.**	Describe the location and physical characteristics of tropical rain forests.
	15.	Describe the vegetation and animal life of tropical rain forests.
37-8	**16.**	Discuss the effects of altitude on climax vegetation.
37-9	**17.**	How do the problems of life in aquatic biomes differ from those in terrestrial biomes?
37-10	**18.**	Give examples of sessile, free-floating, and free-swimming marine organisms.
	19.	Why are photosynthetic planktonic organisms of great importance in the marine biome?
	20.	Describe the zones of the oceans.
37-11	**21.**	Describe the physical characteristics, vegetation, and animal life of streams.
	22.	Describe the physical characteristics, vegetation, and animal life of lakes and ponds.
	23.	Describe the general characteristics of swamps and bogs.

test your understanding

1. Compare and contrast adaptations for dealing with water problems in desert plants and plants of the tropical rain forest.
2. Why is the soil in tropical rain forests generally poor in nutrients?
3. Discuss the problems faced by animals living in the tundra and in the desert.
4. Why don't most marine organisms have a problem with water balance?
5. Describe the organisms found in each of the various zones of the ocean.

independent research

1. Some of the animals that live in the deepest parts of the ocean produce their own light, a process known as bioluminescence. Prepare a report on bioluminescence in marine animals.
2. Prepare a report on the various types of plants found in a tropical rain forest.
3. Prepare a report on the animals of the desert, including the adaptations that enable them to survive.

chapter 38

Human Ecology

38-1 Chapter Introduction

In the past, there was relatively little concern about the effects of human activities on the environment. Forests were cut down, rivers were dammed, soil erosion was allowed to proceed unchecked, and wastes from mines and other industries were dumped on the land, into waterways, and into the air. Within the last 20 years or so, however, there has been increasing recognition of the fact that the environment cannot be used thoughtlessly any longer. It is evident that human activities have damaged the environment, and the damage may be dangerous and permanent. In response to this awareness, human activities in many areas are now devoted to restoring the environment. Rivers that had been so polluted that they contained no fish have now been cleaned up. In some cities where the air was dangerously polluted, it is now somewhat cleaner.

Human ecology deals with the relationship between humans and the environment. In this chapter we will discuss some of the most important aspects of this relationship.

CAUSES OF ENVIRONMENTAL DAMAGE

After completing your study of this section, you should be able to:

1. Discuss the importance of human population control in improving the quality of human life.
2. Define the terms *limiting factor* and *carrying capacity*.

3. Describe how urbanization and poor farming practices have damaged the environment.
4. List the major types of water pollutants and describe the ways in which they damage the environment and/or human health.
5. List the major types of air pollutants and describe the ways in which they damage the environment and/or human health.
6. Discuss the problem of land pollution.
7. Describe the problems that can arise from the use of chemical pesticides and from the importation of organisms into new environments.

38-2 Human Population Growth

Many of the most serious environmental problems of today are related to the tremendous increase in the human population in recent decades. In 1850, the population of the earth was estimated to be about 1 billion. Within 80 years, by about 1930, the population had doubled, reaching 2 billion. It doubled again, reaching 4 billion, by the mid-1970s. Note that the time required for the doubling of the population has been getting shorter. It is estimated that by the year 2,000, the human population will reach 7 billion.

The human population is increasing by about 200,000 people a day.

The human population cannot continue to grow indefinitely. As in other natural populations, it will eventually reach a point at which the environment cannot support any greater size. The unavailability of food, water, space, or some other necessity acts as a **limiting factor** for every population and halts any further growth. The size of a population that can be supported by the environment is called the **carrying capacity** of the environment. At some point in the future, human population growth must stop because the earth will reach its carrying capacity and will not be able to support any more humans.

A population remains the same size if the birth rate and death rate are equal and no changes result from migration. In this century, the death rate in the industrialized countries has declined sharply because of improvements in medical care, food production, and sanitation. In many of these countries there has also been a decline in the birth rate, resulting in a stable, but older, population. In a few, the birth rate has dropped below the death rate, resulting in a shrinking population. In the underdeveloped countries, the birth rate remains very high. The death rate in most of the underdeveloped countries has dropped because of improved conditions; thus the continued high birth rate is causing a rapid growth in the populations. However, many people in the underdeveloped nations are barely surviving. Food production is not increasing as fast as the population. Any failure in crop production in these countries could result in large numbers of deaths from starvation.

Directly or indirectly, the problem of human population growth affects everyone. If food is allowed to become the limiting factor in human population growth, then starvation will become the major means of population control in many parts of the world. One way to avoid this situation is to reduce the birth rate to the level that will maintain the population at its present size. This is the level of *reproductive replacement*, at which the number of births equals the number of deaths over a period of time.

The level of reproductive replacement is also referred to as "zero population growth."

Along with population control, steps could be taken to reduce the level of wasteful consumption by the industrialized nations. More resources would then be available for use by the underdeveloped countries. Strict application of conservation measures in farming, lumbering, mining, and water use could ensure the production of food and other needed materials at a constant level. Food production could also be increased. The use of fertilizers, pesticides, and irrigation, as well as the development of crops with higher yields, would increase the food supply. New sources of food could be developed—from the oceans, for example. Most ecologists feel, however, that no matter what steps are taken, the food supply will eventually become inadequate if the current rate of population growth continues.

38-3 Urbanization

Population increases coupled with technological advances have resulted in the careless destruction of many ecosystems. As the population has increased, patterns of land use have changed. There has been a shift from rural (farming) areas to the cities. Movement of the population to cities, or **urbanization,** has resulted in the destruction of productive farmland, as former farms were turned into housing developments and shopping centers. Such growth has also destroyed or endangered other ecosystems, such as wetlands, that had previously been untouched. These changes have destroyed the natural habitats of many species of plants and animals.

Discuss urban growth and unplanned urban sprawl, underscoring effects on the quality of life.

38-4 Poor Farming Practices

In a natural ecosystem, dead plants cover the ground. They decompose and form rich humus that is added to the soil. In farmland, the crops are harvested each year, and most of the plant parts are removed from the fields. Thus, nutrients from the soil taken up by the crop plants are removed from the field. If these nutrients are not returned, the soil becomes less fertile, and crop yield drops. In the past when this happened, the fields were abandoned, left only with a covering of poor soil. When fields are left without a cover of vegetation, heavy rains or winds can carry away the topsoil. In many areas, overgrazing by herds of cattle and sheep left former grasslands without a cover of vegetation (see Figure 38-1).

Figure 38-1. A Typical "Dust Bowl" Area. Without a protective covering of vegetation, the topsoil is washed away, and the land becomes useless for cultivation.

38-5 Pollution

Adding anything to the environment that makes it less fit for living things is called **pollution.** Pollution of the environment has increased with population growth and industrial development. Gaseous wastes from cars and trucks, the burning of fuels, and industrial gases have polluted the air. Sewage and industrial wastes dumped into streams and rivers have polluted the waterways. The land has been polluted by tremendous quantities of solid wastes generated by industry and by the population in general. Some of the industrial wastes are highly toxic.

38-6 Water Pollution

In the United States, enormous quantities of water are used each day, both by individuals and by industry. However, much of the available water is polluted (see Figure 38-2). The major sources of water pollution are discussed below.

1. Many *organic wastes* are materials of plant and animal origin. These materials are generally **biodegradable** (by-oh-duh-*grayd*-uh-bul)—that is, they can be broken down by bacteria and other decay organisms into simpler substances. Sewage and wastes from canning, brewing, meat packing, and paper mills are major sources of organic materials in waterways. If organic wastes are added in small quantities, bacteria and other decay organisms break them down, keeping the water clean. However, the breakdown of these materials uses oxygen from the water. If sewage and other organic materials are present in large quantities, the oxygen content of the water becomes seriously reduced. This kills off fish and other types of aquatic organisms.

Some organic wastes are plant nutrients. When these substances are present in large quantities, they stimulate the growth of algae and aquatic plants. In lakes, the presence of nutrients can hasten the process of succession. As the or-

Figure 38-2. An Example of Water Pollution. The wastes dumped into this stream have killed the fish.

ganisms die, material is added to the lake bottom and reduces its depth. Growth around the shores reduces the size of the lake. This accelerated aging process is called **eutrophication** (yoo-truh-fuh-*kay*-shun).

The nutrients occasionally cause an explosive growth of the algae populations. Only the topmost layer of algae receives adequate light and oxygen, and the lower layers die. When they decay, the oxygen content of the lake is reduced, killing off other forms of life.

Various synthetic organic chemicals, such as pesticides, fertilizers, and detergents, are poisonous to aquatic life. At the same time, fertilizers and detergents contain plant nutrients. The net effect is to upset the natural balance of an ecosystem and possibly to destroy it.

2. *Inorganic chemicals* are dumped into waterways by mining and other industrial processes. These substances add to the cost of purifying water for human use. Some wastes contain metals, particularly mercury and lead, that are toxic to humans and other animals.

When dumped into waterways, mercury, lead, and some pesticides are picked up first by small aquatic plants and algae. These are eaten by first-level consumers. Because the number of plants and algae eaten by these consumers is large, the toxic substances accumulate in their bodies. In the food web, larger second-level consumers eat many first-level consumers. The toxic substances then accumulate in higher concentrations in the bodies of the second-level consumers. As the food chain proceeds, each higher level of consumers accumulates larger quantities of toxic substances. This process is called **biological magnification.** At the end of the food chain where the concentrations are highest, the animals are most harmed by the pesticide or chemicals. In some cases this has been humans. People in Japan who rely heavily on fish in their diet have suffered mercury poisoning. The mercury had been dumped into the ocean. Through biological magnification, it accumulated in high concentrations in the bodies of large food fish.

3. *Disease-causing microorganisms* may enter the water from untreated sewage and wastes from farm animals. Contamination of water by sewage can be detected by testing for the presence of the bacterium *Escherichia coli.* These organisms, as well as other infectious bacteria and viruses, live in the intestines of warm-blooded animals and are found in their wastes.

4. Changes in the water temperature in streams and rivers can kill fish and other organisms living there. This type of pollution, called **thermal pollution,** occurs when water is taken from a stream and used for cooling various types of industrial equipment. The cold stream water is run through pipes next to pipes containing hot water from the plant. Heat is transferred from the hot water to the cold water, and the

Figure 38-3. Air Pollution.

stream water, now heated, is returned to the waterway. The warmed stream water, in addition to the direct effects it has on living organisms, holds less oxygen than the cold water. Nuclear power plants in particular require great amounts of water for cooling.

5. Other forms of water pollution involve oil spills and the presence of radioactive wastes. Oil is toxic to all forms of aquatic life, even killing many types of bacteria. Water birds die when they ingest the oil in trying to clean it off their feathers. Radioactive wastes are produced by nuclear reactors, mining, and the processing of radioactive materials. Exposure to relatively small amounts of radioactivity can be harmful.

38-7 Air Pollution

Air pollution is a problem in industrialized countries with large urban populations and many cars. In the United States alone, more than 200 million metric tons of pollutants are released into the atmosphere each year (see Figure 38-3).

Some pollutants are **aerosols.** They consist of tiny solid particles or liquid droplets suspended in air. Dust is an aerosol produced by grinding or crushing of solid materials. Smoke consists of carbon particles produced most commonly by burning of oil, coal, or wood. Mists form when gases condense into tiny droplets of liquid in the air.

Some pollutants are gases, which mix with the air. Sulfur dioxide (SO_2) is a pollutant produced by the burning of coal and oil that contain sulfur. In the atmosphere, sulfur dioxide may react chemically to form sulfuric acid, a harsh irritant to the respiratory system. Sulfuric acid dissolved in rainwater forms "acid rain," which can gradually destroy stone buildings and other structures. It can also change the pH of lakes and ponds, killing many of the organisms they contain.

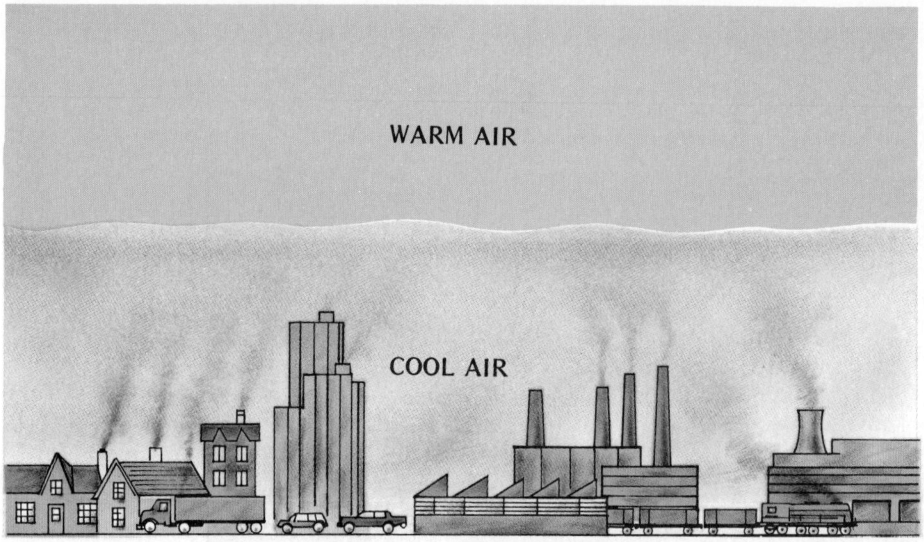

Figure 38-4. Temperature Inversion. In a temperature inversion, a layer of cool air becomes trapped beneath a layer of warm air.

Hydrogen sulfide (H_2S) is a pollutant produced by several industrial processes, including the refining of oil and the manufacture of paper pulp. This gas, which has an odor like rotten eggs, is mainly a nuisance at low concentrations, but can be toxic at high concentrations.

Carbon monoxide (CO) is produced by the burning of gasoline, coal, and oil. It combines readily with the hemoglobin of the red blood cells and reduces its capacity to carry oxygen. In low concentrations, carbon monoxide can cause drowsiness and slow reaction time. In high concentrations, it can cause death.

Nitrogen oxide (NO) and nitrogen dioxide (NO_2) are produced by the burning of gasoline, oil, and natural gas. When nitrogen dioxide is exposed to sunlight, it turns a dirty brownish color. Reactions in the atmosphere between nitrogen oxide, oxygen, and ultraviolet light produce ozone (O_3), which is also a pollutant.

Hydrocarbons, which are compounds of hydrogen and carbon, are produced by the burning of gasoline, coal, oil, natural gas, and wood. Several hydrocarbons, such as formaldehyde and acetaldehyde, irritate the eyes, nose, and throat, but most are not dangerous at existing levels. However, hydrocarbons react with nitrogen oxides in the presence of sunlight to form what is known as *photochemical smog*, the type of smog found in Los Angeles. This type of smog, which occurs in dry, warm climates, is highly irritating to the lungs and eyes. It also damages plants. The major component of photochemical smog is a compound known as PAN.

The air layer closest to the earth's surface is generally the warmest layer, and the air temperature drops with increasing altitude. Under these conditions, the less dense, warmer air rises, carrying pollutants away from the earth's surface. In a **temperature inversion**, a layer of cooler, denser air becomes trapped below a layer of warmer air (see Figure 38-4). The warm air acts as a lid, preventing the upward movement of air from the earth's surface. Pollutants accumulate in the cool layer, sometimes reaching very high concentrations. The condition lasts until the air masses move away.

38-8 Land Pollution

As cities have grown, land pollution has become an ever-increasing problem. Even small cities produce many tons of solid waste, or refuse, every day. Two acceptable ways of disposing of refuse are in sanitary landfills and by incineration (burning).

A *sanitary landfill* is a large area where the refuse is dumped into a trench. It is compacted (made as small as possible) and covered over with dirt. However, as cities have grown, it has become increasingly difficult to find land for this purpose.

Burning refuse in large furnaces, or incinerators, is another method of disposal. Incinerators must be equipped with pollution control devices, or they release large quantities of pollutants into the air. After burning, the ashes must still be disposed of in sanitary landfills. Some cities are conducting experiments in which they are using steam produced by the burning of refuse to generate electricity.

38-9 Pesticides

Pesticides, used indiscriminately, have contaminated the air and water in many places. They have also disrupted food chains, killing organisms that are not pests. Some widely used pesticides have been found after years of use to be dangerous. This is true of DDT, which was found to be highly toxic to many animals, including humans. DDT sprayed on plants was washed off by rainwater and carried into streams and rivers. Eventually it entered the oceans, where it was taken up by the plankton. Through biological magnification it became concentrated in the bodies of the higher-level consumers. The interconnected nature of the world's ecosystems can be illustrated by the fact that DDT has been found in the bodies of polar bears and in the ice of the Antarctic. DDT has been found to collect in the fatty tissues of humans, and it is thought to be a cancer-causing agent.

An additional problem with pesticides is that frequently populations of the organisms they were intended to kill become resistant to them. The resistance is an inherited trait, so that the pests are then even more difficult to get rid of.

38-10 Importation of Organisms

In a balanced ecosystem, the number of organisms at each level in a food chain is controlled by the number of organisms at the next higher feeding level. Thus, for example, the number of insects is controlled by the organisms that feed on them. When an organism is removed from its natural ecosystem and introduced into a new ecosystem, there may be no predator to control its numbers. This has happened in a number of cases where insects and other organisms have accidentally or intentionally been introduced into new environments in which they have no natural enemies. The Japanese beetle, the fungus that causes Dutch elm disease, and the gypsy moth were all imported into the United States. With few natural enemies, they have spread, doing great damage to plants (see Figure 38-5). Human diseases, such as influenza, are also carried by travelers from one part of the world to another.

Figure 38-5. Gypsy Moth Damage. Gypsy moth caterpillars feed on the leaves of many different types of trees, often stripping the tree completely bare.

RESTORING THE ENVIRONMENT

After completing your study of this section, you should be able to:

1. Describe some of the efforts that are being made to control pollution.
2. Explain how soil erosion occurs.
3. Describe how each of the following techniques is used in soil conservation: cover crops, strip cropping, terracing, contour farming, windbreaks, dams, crop rotation, and fertilizers.
4. Discuss methods of forest and wildlife conservation.
5. Describe several biological methods of pest control.

In many countries, programs have been introduced that would improve the lives of their citizens and halt the deterioration of the environment. There are programs aimed at family planning to slow the rate of population growth. Other programs deal with disease control and sanitation. In terms of the environment itself, there are national and international programs aimed at pollution control, conservation of natural resources, and preservation of existing species. Various methods of maintaining and restoring the environment are discussed in the following sections.

38-11 Pollution Control

Efforts are being made in many places to control pollution of the air, water, and land. In the United States, where much of the air pollution is caused by exhaust from automobiles, the introduction of emission controls and the use of unleaded gasoline have reduced pollution. Waste gases from industrial processes are being treated in various ways to remove the most serious pollutants before the gases are released into the atmosphere.

A major factor in the reduction of water pollution involves the use of sewage treatment plants, where the sewage is broken down by bacteria before being released into waterways. Where these plants have been built, the waterways are much cleaner. However, there is a great need for many additional plants. Although some of the most toxic industrial wastes are no longer being dumped into waterways, others are still pouring into lakes, streams, and rivers. The dumping of wastes into the oceans by coastal nations, along with wastes carried into the oceans by rivers, threaten the future productivity of these huge bodies of water.

Some efforts are being made to control the dumping of wastes on land. In many areas there are special sites for the disposal of toxic wastes. However, since the wastes remain toxic for long periods of time, there is always a problem with leakage and contamination of surrounding areas. A seemingly unsolvable problem exists with the disposal of radioactive wastes produced by nuclear reactors. There are no existing methods by which they can be made safe, and there is no place they can be safely stored for the thousands of years they will remain dangerous.

38-12 Conservation of Natural Resources

Natural resources are materials in the environment that are used by humans either for their life processes or for cultural needs. These resources can be divided into two types—renewable and nonrenewable. **Renewable natural resources** include air, water, soil, sunlight, and living things. Careless human activities can disrupt the natural events that replace renewable resources. **Nonrenewable natural resources** are those that can be used only once. Coal, oil, natural gas, metals, and minerals are nonrenewable natural resources. Some materials made from nonrenewable resources can be reprocessed and used again for their original purpose. This is called **recycling.** Paper, metals, and glass can be recycled.

38-13 Soil Conservation

Although soil is a renewable resource, the process of soil formation is very slow. It may take thousands of years to yield a few centimeters of topsoil. Therefore, it is important to prevent the loss of soil. The major cause of soil loss is **erosion**—the removal of soil by wind and water. Wind action blows the soil away, occasionally causing dust storms. After rainstorms, water running over the surface of the land carries soil into nearby streams. Soil conservation involves the prevention of erosion and the loss of nutrients from the soil. The following techniques are used in soil conservation (see Figure 38-6).

1. **Cover crops** are crops planted to cover a whole field and that have fibrous roots that form a dense mat in the soil. This mat prevents soil erosion. Commonly used cover crops include clover, alfalfa, oats, and wheat. Crops that are planted in rows, such as corn, beans, and cabbage, do not prevent erosion of the exposed soil between the rows of plants.

2. **Strip cropping** is a conservation practice in which cover crops are planted between strips of row crops. Thus no exposed soil is left open to erosion.

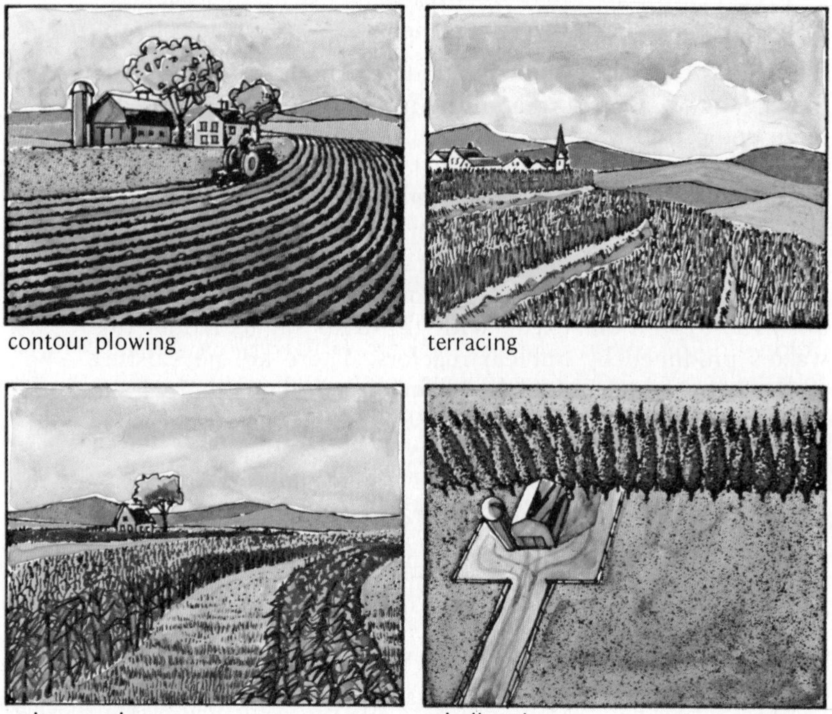

Figure 38-6. Some Soil Conservation Practices.

3. **Terracing** is used on the sides of hills. Flat areas, or terraces, are dug in the hillside, providing areas for planting. Each terrace has a boundary made up of an earth bank held in place by plants and rocks. Terracing prevents surface water from running directly down the hill, carrying the soil with it.

4. **Contour farming** is used on uneven landscapes. In contour farming, the rows are plowed across the slopes, following the contour of the land. The mounds of earth formed by the plow and the plants prevent water from running straight down the slopes.

5. **Windbreaks** are used to prevent wind erosion. Windbreaks usually consist of rows of trees. Poplar trees are commonly used for this purpose.

6. **Dams** are often built in eroded areas to slow down the running of water and reduce or prevent further erosion. Dams are also a major means of water conservation. Large amounts of water collect behind the dam. This water can be used for drinking water, irrigation, and recreation, as well as for the generation of electricity.

7. **Crop rotation** involves growing different crops in succeeding years. Since each plant has its own mineral requirements, planting different crops prevents the reduction of soil nutrients, which is known as *soil depletion*. Legumes, such as clover, are rotated along with other crops to restore nitrates to the soil.

8. **Fertilizers** are used to replace essential soil materials removed by crops. Both natural fertilizers, such as manure, and commercial chemical fertilizers are widely used by farmers.

38-14 Forest Conservation

Forests, which supply a wide variety of materials for human use, are a renewable natural resource. However, like soil, replacement of forests is a slow process, and poor tree-cutting practices can cause permanent damage to the forest ecosystem. In addition to furnishing wood, trees are also used for the production of paper, charcoal, turpentine, and rayon. Forest soils hold large quantities of water, and the trees and undergrowth of the forest prevent soil erosion.

As populations have grown, the need both for cleared land and for forest products has increased. As a result, in many parts of the world the amount of forest land is shrinking. In an attempt to raise productivity and ensure future supplies, the following conservation practices are being applied to remaining forests.

1. *Sustained-yield tree farming* involves cutting down trees in only certain areas of a forest, leaving surrounding areas untouched. In *block cutting,* square areas of forest are cut. Reseeding of the cut section takes place naturally by seeds coming from the surrounding forest. In *strip cutting,* strips of trees are cut between strips of untouched forest. In *selective harvesting,* certain trees are marked and cut, leaving the others undisturbed.

2. In *reforestation* programs, cut areas are planted with seeds or seedlings of a particular type. These are generally fast-growing, disease-resistant varieties that will produce good-quality lumber. In all forestry programs, undesirable, diseased, or dead trees are removed to allow space for growth of good timber.

38-15 Wildlife Conservation

The growth of cities and suburbs has led to the destruction of the natural habitats of many types of plants and animals. Indiscriminate hunting has brought about the extinction of a few species and the near-extinction of many others. The passenger pigeon was a bird that was found in large numbers in North America until the mid-1800s. A prime target of bird hunters, the huge flocks were killed off, and the last known passenger pigeon died in the early 1900s. Many other species of birds, as well as whales and other large mammals, are now in danger of becoming extinct. Several plant species have also become extinct, and others are endangered.

Concern over the possible extinction of various species of animals and plants has resulted in wildlife conservation practices that are being carried out in many areas. These include the following:

careers

A forester is a person involved in the management of forest lands. In addition to the wood they provide, forests are important in the water supplies of many areas, as homes for a wide variety of wildlife, and as recreation areas. Foresters are involved in all aspects of forest use. Working for government agencies or private companies, foresters plan both the harvesting and planting of trees so that lumber will be continuously available. They work to control plant diseases and pests that damage the trees. They fight forest fires and work to prevent soil erosion and flooding. Foresters are also involved in the management of forest wildlife, maintaining a balance between available food and water and animal populations, and of recreational areas.

For a career in forestry, a person should have a bachelor's degree with courses in forestry and biology and should enjoy outdoor work.

The International Union for Conservation of Nature and Natural Resources publishes the *Red Data Book* which lists the endangered animals. The list now exceeds 900 species, including the bighorn sheep, southern bald eagle, eastern timber wolf, and blue whale.

1. Hunting and fishing laws have been established that restrict the sex, size, and number of prey and limit the hunting season.

2. Game and bird preserves have been established where no hunting is allowed.

3. Game fish are being bred in fish hatcheries and used to restock heavily fished lakes and streams. This keeps the populations at a reasonable level, but also allows recreational fishing.

4. Restricted use of pesticides and herbicides limits the number of accidental deaths caused by these chemicals.

5. Legal protection for endangered species has made it possible for some species that were near extinction to begin to show a population increase. This is true of the bison, egret, and whooping crane. Other endangered species are still decreasing in numbers.

38-16 Biological Controls of Pests

Although chemical pesticides have been of great importance in controlling damage to agricultural crops, they have also created some serious ecological problems. Many chemical pesticides are not readily broken down in nature, so they accumulate in the environment. Plants and animals not intended as targets have been contaminated and harmed by them. Chemical pesticides have been developed that break down within a few days to harmless substances. Such pesticides will not accumulate. On the other hand, they have to be applied more frequently, which makes them more expensive and difficult to use.

As an alternative to chemical pesticides, various biological methods of pest control have been discovered. These methods are more specific than the chemical pesticides, and have much less of an effect on the environment in general.

1. In some areas, natural enemies have been imported to control certain pests. For example, ladybugs have been used to control aphids, and a wasp that preys on the alfalfa weevil has been used to control that insect pest. In introducing one organism to control the population of another organism, it is important to know in advance whether or not there is any way to control the population of the introduced organism.

2. Various insect larvae, including gypsy moth caterpillars and mosquito larvae, can be controlled by infection by a particular type of bacteria. Viruses have been used against worms that attack vegetable crops.

3. Another technique used in pest control is crop rotation. Planting different crops in succeeding years can remove the favored food source of a pest organism and thereby decrease the pest population.

4. **Pheromones** (*fehr*-uh-mohnz) are a type of animal secretion that serve as sex attractants between members of a species. Scientists have developed pheromones that are used to lure

insects into traps where they are exposed to contact poisons. In this way insecticides can be used without contaminating the environment.

5. Another method of insect control involves the release of sterile males into the population. The males, which have been sterilized by exposure to radiation, mate with the females, but no offspring result.

summary

Human activities are damaging the environment. The human population is growing at a rapid rate, putting a strain on environmental resources. Urbanization and poor farming practices have destroyed good farmland. Industrial and other wastes have been deposited on land and released into waterways and into the air. Pollutants have upset the natural balance of many ecosystems by killing off certain organisms and interrupting food chains or by changing the actual physical conditions in the ecosystem.

Currently, efforts are being made to halt the most severe forms of environmental pollution and to conserve natural resources, including soil, forests, and wildlife. Use of biological methods of pest control is reducing some of the ecological problems caused by chemical pesticides. In many countries, efforts are being made to reduce the birth rate and slow population growth.

vocabulary

aerosol
biodegradable
biological magnification
carrying capacity
contour farming
cover crop
crop rotation
dam
erosion
eutrophication
fertilizer
human ecology
limiting factor
nonrenewable natural resource
pheromone
pollution
recycling
renewable natural resource
strip cropping
temperature inversion
thermal pollution
urbanization
windbreak

test your learning

Section

38-1 **1.** What is human ecology?

38-2 **2.** Compare and contrast the current rates of population growth in industrialized and underdeveloped countries.

3. What could happen if human population growth continues at the present rate?

38-3 **4.** How has the shift of populations from rural to urban areas affected the environment?

38-4 **5.** How have poor farming practices ruined former farmlands?

38-5 **6.** Define the term *pollution*.

38-6 **7.** Describe the harmful effects of organic wastes as water pollutants. (Include eutrophication of lakes.)

8. Describe the process of biological magnification.

9. What is thermal pollution?

38-7 **10.** List the major air pollutants, and describe how each is harmful.

11. Describe what happens in a temperature inversion.

38-8 **12.** Describe two acceptable methods of getting rid of solid wastes.

38-9 **13.** Describe some of the problems that can arise from the use of chemical pesticides.

38-10 **14.** What are the dangers of importing an organism from one environment into a new environment?

38-11 **15.** Describe some of the current programs for reducing water, air, and land pollution.

38-12 **16.** List the major renewable and nonrenewable natural resources.

38-13 **17.** What is soil erosion and how does it occur?

18. Describe five farming techniques used to prevent soil erosion.

19. How do farmers prevent the loss of nutrients from the soil in their fields?

38-14 **20.** What techniques are being used in forest conservation to ensure future supplies of lumber?

38-15 **21.** List five wildlife conservation practices.

38-16 **22.** List five methods of biological pest control.

23. What are some of the advantages of biological pest control compared with chemical pesticides?

test your understanding

1. In almost all parts of the world, human population growth has resulted in damage to the environment. List as many of these damaging effects as you can think of.
2. What factors will eventually limit human population growth if it is not limited voluntarily?
3. Why has it become increasingly important to halt the pollution of the environment by human activities?
4. Why is it important to prevent the extinction of plant and animal species?

independent research

1. Prepare a report on one of the following topics:
   A. eutrophication
   B. DDT
   C. thermal pollution
   D. gypsy moths
2. Visit a recycling center. Prepare a report explaining the activities of the center, including what materials are collected and what use is made of them.
3. Visit a water treatment plant. Prepare a report explaining the techniques used in purifying water.

Classification of Organisms

KINGDOM MONERA

Monerans are the simplest organisms. Most are single-celled, although some form colonies or filaments of cells. Their cells are procaryotic—they lack nuclear membranes, mitochondria, chloroplasts, and other membranous organelles. Reproduction is mainly asexual by fission or budding.

PHYLUM CYANOPHYTA: The blue-green algae contain chlorophyll and other pigments and carry on photosynthesis. Most are aquatic. Some are unicellular, others form filaments made up of chains of cells, and still others are colonial. Examples: *Nostoc, Oscillatoria, Gleocapsa, Anabaena.*

PHYLUM SCHIZOMYCETES: Bacteria are tiny, mostly single-celled organisms. Some are found as pairs or chains of cells. Bacteria are classified according to shape: bacilli are rodlike; cocci are spherical; and spirilla are spiral. Most are saprophytic or parasitic. A few are photosynthetic or chemosynthetic. Examples: *Escherichia, Diplococcus, Streptococcus, Staphylococcus, Spirocheta, Treponema.*

KINGDOM PROTISTA

Protists are unicellular or very simple multicellular organisms. Their cells are eucaryotic, containing a membrane-bounded nucleus and a variety of cytoplasmic organelles. Some protists are plantlike, some are animal-like, and some are funguslike.

PHYLUM EUGLENOPHYTA: The euglenoids are unicellular, photosynthetic organisms with a light-sensitive eyespot. Found mainly in fresh water. Locomotion is by means of a single flagellum. Reproduction is asexual. Example: *Euglena.*

PHYLUM CHRYSOPHYTA: The yellow-green algae, golden-brown algae, and diatoms are mainly unicellular, photosynthetic organisms. Yellow-to-brown pigments mask the chlorophyll and give these organisms their characteristic colors. Food is stored as an oil or as a starchlike carbohydrate. Found in fresh and salt water. Examples: *Botrydium, Chrysamoeba, Pinnularia.*

PHYLUM PYRROPHYTA: The dinoflagellates are unicellular, photosynthetic algae with two flagella; most are marine. Their cell walls contain cellulose. Reproduction is asexual. Examples: *Gonyaulax, Gymnodinium.*

PROTOZOA: The protozoa are the animal-like protists. In these organisms locomotion is by pseudopods, cilia, or flagella. This group includes the phyla Sarcodina, Ciliata, Mastigophora, and Sporozoa.

PHYLUM SARCODINA: The sarcodines are unicellular freshwater or marine protozoans that use pseudopods for locomotion and/or food getting. Of the sarcodines, amebas are surrounded only by a cell membrane; foraminiferans are surrounded by a calcium-containing shell; and radiolarians by a silicon-containing shell. Examples: *Amoeba, Entamoeba, Globigerina, Pelomyxa.*

PHYLUM CILIATA: Ciliates are complex, unicellular protozoans that move by means of cilia. They are found in both fresh and salt water. The cells contain a micronucleus and a macronucleus. Reproduction is both asexual and sexual. Examples: *Paramecium, Stentor, Tetrahymena, Vorticella.*

PHYLUM MASTIGOPHORA: The zooflagellates are unicellular protozoans that move by means of flagella. Some are free living, but most are parasitic. Examples: *Trypanosoma, Trichonympha.*

PHYLUM SPOROZOA: The sporozoans are unicellular, spore-forming protozoans. They are nonmotile parasites with a life cycle that may include two hosts. Examples: *Plasmodium, Toxoplasma.*

PHYLUM MYXOMYCOTA: The true slime molds have a life cycle in which there is an ameboid, multinucleate plasmodium stage and a funguslike, spore-producing fruiting-body stage. Slime molds are found on damp soil, rotting logs, and in leaf litter. Example: *Physarum.*

PHYLUM ACRASIOMYCOTA: The cellular slime molds have a life cycle in which one stage consists of many separate ameboid cells and the other stage consists of a pseudoplasmodium, an aggregate of many individual cells. The pseudoplasmodium gives rise to spore-producing fruiting bodies. Example: *Dictyostelium.*

KINGDOM PLANTAE

Plants are nonmotile, multicellular, photosynthetic organisms. Their cells contain plastids and are surrounded by cell walls made of cellulose. Chlorophylls and carotenoids are generally present. Most plants have specialized tissues and organs. Reproduction may be asexual or sexual. Sexual reproduction shows an alternation of generations with diploid sporophyte and haploid gametophyte stages.

PHYLUM CHLOROPHYTA: The green algae are chiefly aquatic, and include unicellular, colonial, and multicellular forms. Some have flagella. Chloroplasts contain chlorophylls a and b; food is stored as starch in plastids. Multicellular forms show little structural differentiation. Examples: *Chlamydomonas, Chlorella, Protococcus, Volvox, Spirogyra, Ulva, Ulothrix.*

PHYLUM PHAEOPHYTA: The brown algae are multicellular marine seaweeds and kelps that contain the brownish pigment fucoxanthin as well as chlorophylls a and c. Food is stored as the carbohydrate laminarin. Some cells are motile, containing two flagella. Examples: *Sargassum, Macrocystis, Fucus, Laminaria.*

PHYLUM RHODOPHYTA: The red algae are mainly marine and include both unicellular organisms and multicellular seaweeds. In these algae, the chlorophyll is often masked by red pigments. Food is stored as a special form of starch. Life cycle is complex, but includes no motile cells. Examples: *Porphyra, Polysiphonia, Chondrus.*

PHYLUM BRYOPHYTA: The bryophytes are small multicellular land plants that look like higher plants. However, they lack xylem and phloem, and they do not have true leaves, stems, or roots. Bryophytes are found only in moist areas, and water is needed for fertilization. The gametophyte generation is dominant; the sporophyte generation is reduced in size and is dependent on the gametophyte. Reproduction is alternately sexual (gametes) and asexual (spores).

Class Musci: In mosses, the gametophyte generation consists of small, erect plants that have tiny leaflike structures arranged spirally around a stalk. Examples: *Sphagnum, Polytrichum.*

Class Hepaticae: In liverworts, the plants of the gametophyte generation are low with flattened and thallus-like or leaf-like structures. Examples: *Marchantia, Riccia.*

Class Antherocerotae: In hornworts, the gametophyte generation is thallus-like; the sporophyte generation is cylindrical. Example: *Anthoceros.*

PHYLUM TRACHEOPHYTA: The vascular plants contain xylem and phloem and have true leaves, stems, and roots. The sporophyte generation is dominant, and the gametophyte generation is greatly reduced. Chlorophylls a and b are present, and food is stored as starch in plastids. Tracheophytes are the dominant land plants.

SUBPHYLUM PSILOPSIDA: In whisk ferns, the highly branched vascular stems lack true leaves and roots. Whisk ferns are rare plants that are found mainly in warm regions. Example: *Psilotum.*

SUBPHYLUM LYCOPSIDA: Club mosses have small leaves arranged in a spiral. Spores are found at the tips of some branches in conelike strobili. Examples: *Lycopodium, Selaginella.*

SUBPHYLUM SPHENOPSIDA: Horsetails have small leaves arranged in whorls at specific points along the stems. Conelike strobili form at the ends of some stems. Example: *Equisetum.*

SUBPHYLUM PTEROPSIDA: This group includes the ferns, gymnosperms, and angiosperms. In these plants, the sporophyte generation is dominant, and the plants of this generation have true roots, stems, and leaves. The gametophyte generation is tiny.

Class Filicineae: Ferns have fronds that grow up from horizontal underground stems. Sori are found on the backs of the leaflets of some fronds. The sporophyte generation is dominant. The independent gametophyte generation consists of a small prothallus. The sperm are motile, and water is required for fertilization. Examples: *Polypodium, Dryopteri, Osmunda.*

Class Gymnospermae: Gymnosperms are the nonflowering, cone-bearing seed plants. The naked seeds are not enclosed in a fruit. The tiny gametophyte generation plant grows on the dominant sporophyte plant. Sperm are enclosed in a pollen tube, so water is not needed for fertilization.

Subclass Coniferophyta: Conifers, or evergreens, are cone-bearing trees with needlelike or scalelike leaves. Examples: pines *(Pinus)*, spruce *(Picea)*, hemlocks *(Tsuga)*, firs *(Abies)*, redwoods *(Sequoia).*

Subclass Cycadophyta: Cycads are tropical, palmlike gymnosperms. Examples: *Cycas, Zamia.*

Subclass Ginkgophyta: Ginkgo, or maidenhair, trees, have fan-shaped leaves. The only surviving species is *Ginkgo biloba.*

Class Angiospermae: Angiosperms are flowering plants whose seeds are enclosed in an ovary that ripens into a fruit. The tiny gametophyte grows on the dominant sporophyte plant. Sperm are enclosed in a pollen tube so that water is not needed for fertilization.

Subclass Monocotyledonae: Monocots have an embryo with a single cotyledon; leaves with parallel veins; flower parts in threes or sixes; and vascular bundles scattered throughout the stem tissue. Primarily herbaceous plants. Examples: grasses, including rye *(Secale)*, corn *(Zea)*, and wheat *(Triticum)*; lilies *(Lilium)*; tulips *(Tulipa)*; orchids *(Orchis).*

Subclass Dicotyledonae: Dicots have an embryo with two cotyledons; veins of leaves in form of network; flower parts in fours or fives; vascular tissue organized in concentric rings. Includes both herbaceous and woody plants. Examples: oaks *(Quercus, Lithocarpus)*, maples *(Acer)*, magnolias *(Magnolia)*, cucumbers *(Cucumis)*, carrots *(Daucus)*, roses *(Rosa).*

KINGDOM FUNGI

Fungi are eucaryotic, heterotrophic organisms that absorb nutrients from dead or living organisms. A few are unicellular, but most are multicellular and are made up of masses of threadlike hyphae. In most, the cell walls are composed of chitin. Reproduction can be either asexual or sexual.

PHYLUM ZYGOMYCOTA: Conjugation fungi are terrestrial; their cell walls are made of chitin. They reproduce sexually by conjugation and asexually by spore formation. Examples: *Rhizopus, Phycomyces.*

PHYLUM OOMYCOTA: Water molds are mainly aquatic and have flagellated spores. Their cell walls contain cellulose. Example: *Saprolegnia.*

PHYLUM ASCOMYCOTA: The sac fungi include both aquatic and terrestrial forms. Their cell walls are made of chitin. Sexual reproduction results in the formation of ascospores; asexual reproduction results in the formation of spores called conidia. This group includes cup fungi, yeasts, powdery mildews, truffles, morels, and blue and green molds. Examples: *Saccharomyces, Aspergillus, Penicillium, Neurospora.*

PHYLUM BASIDIOMYCOTA: The club fungi are terrestrial. Their cell walls are made of chitin. Sexual reproduction involves the formation of spores on club-shaped structures. This group includes mushrooms, bracket fungi, puffballs, rusts, and smuts. Examples: *Amanita, Lycoperdon, Phragmidium.*

FUNGI IMPERFECTI: In the Fungi Imperfecti, the pattern of sexual reproduction is unknown. Most members of this group show the other characteristics of the Ascomycota. Example: *Trichophyton* (athlete's foot fungus).

KINGDOM ANIMALIA

Animals are multicellular, heterotrophic organisms with specialized tissues. Most are motile. Their cells are eucaryotic and lack cell walls. Reproduction is mainly sexual.

PHYLUM PORIFERA: Sponges are sessile, aquatic animals; most are marine. Their asymmetrical bodies have two cell layers and are pierced by pores; they are stiffened by skeletal elements called spicules. Reproduction is both asexual and sexual. Examples: *Grantia, Scypha, Euplectella.*

PHYLUM COELENTERATA: In coelenterates, the radially symmetrical body is saclike and is made up of two cell layers. The digestive cavity has a single opening surrounded by tentacles containing stinging cells. Coelenterates are all aquatic, most are marine. There are two body forms—the polyp and the medusa. Some coelenterates, such as corals, are colonial. Reproduction is both asexual and sexual, and some show an alternation of generations. Examples: hydra *(Hydra)*; jellyfish *(Obelia, Physalia)*; corals *(Gorgonia)*; and sea anemones *(Actinia)*.

PHYLUM PLATYHELMINTHES: The flatworms have flattened, bilaterally symmetrical bodies made up of three tissue layers. Digestive system has only one opening.

Class Turbellaria: Free-living flatworms with eyespots. examples: *Planaria, Dugesia.*

Class Trematoda: Parasitic flatworms, usually with suckers. Flukes. Examples: *Schistosoma, Fasciola.*

Class Cestoda: Parasitic flatworms without digestive systems. Tapeworms. Example: *Taenia.*

PHYLUM NEMATODA: Roundworms have long, cylindrical bodies; there is a digestive system with both a mouth and an anus. Most are parasitic. Examples: *Ascaris, Necatur, Trichinella.*

PHYLUM ANNELIDA: Segmented worms have a body made up of many similar segments. They have a well-developed coelom, a complete digestive tract, a closed circulatory system, and a ventral nervous system.

Class Polychaeta: Mostly marine worms. They have a well-developed head. Example: *Nereis.*

Class Oligochaeta: Includes terrestrial and aquatic worms. Members of this group, including earthworms, have poorly developed heads. Examples: *Lumbricus, Tubifex.*

Class Hirudinea: Parasitic annelids with suckers at one or both ends of the body. Leeches. Example: *Hirudo.*

PHYLUM MOLLUSCA: Mollusks have a soft, unsegmented body, often with a muscular foot, mantle, and radula. The digestive, circulatory, and nervous systems are well developed.

Class Bivalvia: Bivalves include clams, oysters, mussels, and scallops. These mollusks have a two-part, hinged shell and no head or radula. Examples: *Mytilus, Pecten, Teredo.*

Class Gastropoda: Gastropods include snails, slugs, and whelks. These mollusks have a head with tentacles; most have a spiral shell. Examples: *Limax, Helix, Busycon.*

Class Cephalopoda: Cephalopod mollusks have a large head surrounded by arms, or tentacles. The octopus has no shell, the squid has an internal shell, and the nautilus has an external shell. The nervous system, is particularly well developed. Examples: octopus *(Octopus)*, squid *(Loligo)*, and nautilus *(Nautilus)*.

PHYLUM ARTHROPODA: Arthropods have a segmented body with paired, jointed appendages and an exoskeleton composed of chitin.

Class Crustacea: Crustaceans have two pairs of antennae. Most are aquatic and respiration is by gills. Examples: lobsters (*Homarus*), crabs (*Cancer*), crayfish (*Cambarus*), water fleas (*Cyclops, Daphnia*).

Class Chilopoda: Centipedes have one pair of antennae, many body segments, and one pair of legs on most body segments. Example: *Scolopendra.*

Class Diplopoda: Millipedes have one pair of antennae, many body segments, and two pairs of legs on most body segments. Example: *Glomeris.*

Class Arachnida: Arachnida have no antennae, two body regions, four pairs of legs, and book lungs. Examples: spiders (*Argiope*), scorpions (*Chelifer*).

Class Insecta: Insects have one pair of antennae, three body regions, three pairs of legs, and tracheal respiration; many have two pairs of wings. Group includes flies, ants, beetles, fleas, lice, bees, and roaches. (See pages 576-577 for a table of insect classification.)

PHYLUM ECHINODERMATA: Echinoderms have a water-vascular system, an internal skeleton, and a spiny skin. Adults are radially symmetrical. All are marine. Examples: starfish *(Asterias)*, sea urchins *(Arbacia)*, sea cucumbers *(Cucumaria)*, sand dollars *(Echinarachnius)*.

PHYLUM CHORDATA: At some stage of development, all chordates have a notochord, paired gill slits, and a dorsal, hollow nerve cord.

SUBPHYLUM UROCHORDATA: Adult tunicates are soft, saclike, sessile, marine animals. Larvae are free swimming. Examples: *Ciona, Appendicularia.*

SUBPHYLUM CEPHALOCHORDATA: Lancelets are small, fishlike, marine animals. Notochord present in adults. Prominent gill slits. Example: *Branchiostoma.*

SUBPHYLUM VERTEBRATA: Vertebrates have a spinal column made up of vertebrae that enclose the dorsal nerve cord. Enlarged brain.

Class Agnatha: The jawless fishes, lampreys and hagfish, have a cartilaginous skeleton, a snakelike body, and smooth skin without scales. They lack true jaws. Examples: *Petromyzon, Myxine.*

Class Chondrichthyes: The cartilaginous fishes have a skeleton composed of cartilage, movable jaws, scales, and fins. Examples: sharks *(Squalus)*, skates *(Raja).*

Class Osteichthyes: The bony fishes have a skeleton made of bone, movable jaws, overlapping scales, paired fins, and an air bladder. Examples: salmons and trouts *(Salmo)*, carps *(Cyprinus)*, perches *(Perca)*, codfish *(Gadus).*

Class Amphibia: Most amphibians have moist, smooth, scaleless skin and four limbs. Water is needed for reproduction. Aquatic larvae have gills and undergo metamorphosis. Adults are usually terrestrial and have lungs and a three-chambered heart. Cold-blooded. Examples: frogs *(Rana)*, toads *(Bufo)*, salamanders *(Necturus, Triturus).*

Class Reptilia: The reptiles have dry skin and a scale-covered body with four limbs (absent in snakes). Fertilization is internal. Their eggs have a leathery shell and protective membranes. Most reptiles live and reproduce on land. They have lungs and a three-chambered heart with a partially divided ventricle. Cold-blooded. Examples: turtles *(Chelydra, Terrapene)*, crocodiles *(Crocodylus)*, alligators *(Alligator)*, snakes *(Crotalus).*

Class Aves: Birds have feathers and their front limbs are wings. Their eggs have a hard shell. They have a four-chambered heart and are warm-blooded. Examples: robins and thrushes *(Turdus)*, chickens *(Gallus)*, ducks *(Anas)*, sparrows *(Passer, Melospiza)*, starlings *(Sturnus).*

Class Mammalia: Mammals nourish their young with milk. Their body covering is hair or fur. They have a four-chambered heart and are warm-blooded.

Subclass Prototheria: Monotremes are egg-laying mammals. Examples: duckbill platypus *(Ornithorhynchus)*, spiny anteater *(Tachyglossus).*

Subclass Metatheria: Marsupials are pouched mammals, found mainly in Australia. Examples: kangaroos *(Macropus)*, opossums *(Didelphis)*, koalas *(Phascolarctos).*

Subclass Eutheria: The placental mammals include most living mammals.

Order Insectivora: moles *(Scalopus)*, shrews *(Sorex)*

Order Rodentia: rats *(Rattus)*, mice *(Mus)*, squirrels *(Sciurus)*

Order Lagomorpha: rabbits *(Sylvilagus)*, hares *(Lepus)*

Order Chiroptera: bats *(Myotis)*

Order Cetacea: whales *(Balaena)*, dolphins *(Delphinus)*, porpoises *(Phocaena)*

Order Edentata: anteaters *(Myrmecophaga)*, armadillos *(Dasypus)*

Order Proboscidea: elephants *(Elephas, Loxodonta)*

Order Artiodactyla: camels *(Camelus)*, sheep *(Ovis)*, pigs *(Sus)*, cattle *(Bos)*

Order Perissodactyla: horses *(Equus)*, rhinoceroses *(Rhinoceros)*

Order Carnivora: cats *(Felis)*, dogs *(Canis)*, bears *(Ursus)*, raccoons *(Procyon)*

Order Primates: humans *(Homo)*, chimpanzees *(Pan)*, orangutans *(Pongo)*, monkeys *(Macacus)*

Further Reading

Chapter 1

Bates, Marston, *The Forest and the Sea.* Random House, New York, 1960.

Carson, Rachel, *The Sea Around Us.* Oxford University Press, New York, 1970.

Schrodinger, Erwin, *What Is Life?* Cambridge University Press, New York, 1967.

Chapter 2

Beck, William, *Modern Science and the Nature of Life.* Doubleday, New York, 1960.

Berger, Melvin, *Tools of Modern Biology.* Thomas Y. Crowell Co., New York, 1970.

Beveridge, W. I., *The Art of Scientific Investigation.* Random House, New York, 1957.

Gould, Stephen J., "On Heroes and Fools in Science," *Natural History,* Aug.-Sept., 1974.

Shippen, Kathrine, *Men, Microscopes, and Living Things.* Viking Press, New York, 1976.

Chapter 3

Freeden, E., "The Chemical Elements of Life," *Scientific American,* July, 1972.

Gamow, George, *Mr. Thompkins Explores the Atom.* Cambridge University Press, New York, 1967

White, E. H., *Chemical Background for the Biological Sciences.* Prentice-Hall, Englewood Cliffs, N.J., 1970.

Chapter 4

Asimov, Isaac, *The Chemicals of Life.* New American Library, New York, 1962.

Asimov, Isaac, *The World of Carbon.* New American Library, New York, 1966.

Baker, Jeffrey W., and Allen, Garland E., *Matter, Energy, and Life.* Addison-Wesley, Reading, Mass., 1970.

Chapter 5

Brachet, J., "The Living Cell," *Scientific American,* Sept., 1961.

Lewis, R.W., "The Structure of the Cell Theory," *The American Biology Teacher,* April, 1972.

McElroy, W.D., and Swanson, C.P., *Modern Cell Biology,* 2nd ed. Prentice-Hall, Englewood Cliffs, N.J., 1975.

Swanson, C.P., *The Cell,* 3rd ed. Prentice-Hall, Englewood Cliffs, N.J., 1969.

Chapter 6

Gould, S.J., "The Five Kingdoms," *Natural History*, June-July, 1976.

Palmer, E.L., and Fowler, H.S., *Fieldbook of Natural History*. McGraw-Hill, New York, 1975.

Savory, T., *Animal Taxonomy*. Heinemann Educational, London, 1970.

Savory, T., *Naming the Living World*. Wiley, New York, 1962.

Whittaker, R.H., "New Concepts of Kingdoms of Organisms," *Science, 163*:150, 1969.

Chapter 7

Asimov, Isaac, *Life and Energy*. Avon, New York, 1972.

Chappell, J.B., "ATP," *Oxford Biology Reader*, Carolina Biological Supply Co., Burlington, N.C., 1977.

Harrison, Kenneth, *A Guidebook to Biochemistry*, 2nd ed. Cambridge University Press, New York, 1975.

Lehninger, Albert L., "Energy Transformation in the Cell," *Scientific American*, May, 1960.

Chapter 8

Beaumont, W., *Experiments and Observations on the Gastric Juice and the Physiology of Digestion*. Dover, New York, 1959.

Davenport, H.W., "Why the Stomach Does Not Digest Itself," *Scientific American*, Jan., 1972.

McMinn, R.M.H., "The Human Gut," *Carolina Biology Reader*, Carolina Biological Supply Co., Burlington, N.C., 1977.

Scrimshaw, N.S., and Young, V.R., "The Requirements of Human Nutrition," *Scientific American*, Sept., 1976.

Chapter 9

Adolph, E.F., "The Heart's Pacemaker," *Scientific American*, March, 1967.

Chapman, C.B., and Mitchell, J.H., "The Physiology of Exercise," *Scientific American*, May, 1965.

Kilgour, F.G., "William Harvey," *Scientific American*, June, 1952.

Mayerson, H.S., "The Lymphatic System," *Scientific American*, June, 1963.

Neil, E., "The Human Circulation," *Carolina Biology Reader*, Carolina Biological Supply Co., Burlington, N.C., 1979.

Vassalle, M., "The Human Heart," *Carolina Biology Reader*, Carolina Biological Supply Co., Burlington, N.C., 1979.

Chapter 10

Arehart-Treichel, J., *Immunity: How Our Bodies Resist Disease*. Holiday House, New York, 1976.

Bardell, D., "Edward Jenner and the First Vaccination," *The American Biology Teacher*, Oct., 1977.

Gowans, J.L., "Cellular Immunity," *Carolina Biology Reader*, Carolina Biological Supply Co., Burlington, N.C., 1977.

Jerne, N.K., "The Immune System," *Scientific American*, July, 1973.

Lewin, R., *In Defense of the Body*. Anchor Books, New York, 1974.

Nossal, G.J., *Antibodies and Immunity*. Basic Books, New York, 1978.

Porter, R.R., "The Chemical Aspects of Immunity," *Carolina Biology Reader*, Carolina Biological Supply Co., Burlington, N.C., 1976.

Chapter 11

Comroe, J.H., Jr., "The Lung," *Scientific American*, Feb., 1966.

Hammond, E.D., "The Effects of Smoking," *Scientific American*, July, 1962.

Hughes, G.M., "The Vertebrate Lung," *Carolina Biology Reader*, Carolina Biological Supply Co., Burlington, N.C., 1979.

Johansen, K., "Air-Breathing Fishes," *Scientific American*, Oct., 1968.

Wigglesworth, V.B., "Insect Respiration," *Oxford Biology Reader*, Carolina Biological Supply Co., Burlington, N.C., 1972.

Chapter 12

Heller, H., *et al.*, "The Thermostat of Vertebrate Animals," *Scientific American*, Aug., 1978.

Moffat, D.B, "The Control of Water Balance by the Kidney," *Carolina Biology Reader*, Carolina Biological Supply Co., Burlington, N.C., 1978.

Montagna, W., "The Skin," *Scientific American*, Feb., 1965.

Sherlock, S., "The Human Liver," *Carolina Biology Reader*, Carolina Biological Supply Co., Burlington, N.C., 1978.

Smith, H.W., "The Kidney," *Scientific American*, Jan., 1953.

Subak-Sharpe, G., "What Your Blood and Urine Tell About You," *Reader's Digest*, Oct., 1975.

Chapter 13

Allen, R.D., "Amoeboid Movement," *Scientific American*, Feb., 1962.

Hildebrand, M., "How Animals Move," *Scientific American*, May, 1960.

Merton, P.A., "How We Control the Contraction of Our Muscles," *Scientific American*, May, 1972.

McLean, F.D., "Bone," *Scientific American*, Feb. 1955.

Pritchard, J.J., "Bones," *Carolina Biology Reader*, Carolina Biological Supply Co., Burlington, N.C., 1979.

Chapter 14

Adrian, R.H., "The Nerve Impulse," *Carolina Biology Reader*, Carolina Biological Supply Co., Burlington, N.C., 1980.

Eccles, J., "The Synapse," *Scientific American*, Jan., 1965.

Gray, E.G., "The Synapse," *Carolina Biology Reader*, Carolina Biological Supply Co., Burlington, N.C., 1977.

Chapter 15

Dowling, J.E., "Night Blindness," *Scientific American*, Oct, 1966.

Friedmann, I., "The Human Ear," *Carolina Biology Reader*, Carolina Biological Supply Co., Burlington, N.C., 1979.

Gazzaniga, M.S., "The Split Brain in Man," *Scientific American*, Aug., 1967.

Geschwind, N., "Language and the Brain," *Scientific American*, April, 1972.

Gregory R.L., "Visual Perception," *Oxford Biology Reader*, Carolina Biological Supply Co., Burlington, N.C., 1973.

Hodgson, E.S., "Taste Receptors," *Scientific American*, May, 1961.

Llinas, R., "The Cortex of the Cerebellum," *Scientific American*, Jan., 1975.

Luria, A.R., "The Functional Organization of the Brain," *Scientific American*, March, 1970.

Scientific American, Sept., 1979. The entire issue is devoted to neurons and the nervous system.

Weale, R.A., "The Vertebrate Eye," *Carolina Biology Reader*, Carolina Biological Supply Co., Burlington, N.C., 1978.

Young, J.Z., "The Evolution of Memory," *Carolina Biology Reader*, Carolina Biological Supply Co., Burlington, N.C., 1976.

Chapter 16

Guillemin, R., and Burgus, R., "The Hormones of the Hypothalamus," *Scientific American*, Nov., 1972.

McEwen, B.W., "Interactions Between Hormones and Nerve Tissue," *Scientific American*, July, 1976.

Nathanson, J.A., and Greenguard, P., "Second Messengers in the Brain," *Scientific American*, Aug., 1977.

Randle, P.J., and Denton, R.M., "Hormones and Cell Metabolism," *Oxford Biology Reader*, Carolina Biological Supply Co., Burlington, N.C., 1974.

Turner, C.D., and Bagnara, J.T., *General Endocrinology*. Saunders, Philadelphia, 1976.

Chapter 17

Asimov, Isaac, *Photosynthesis*. Basic Books, New York, 1969.

Basshan, J.A., "The Path of Carbon in Photosynthesis," *Scientific American*, June, 1962.

Galston, A.W., *The Life of the Green Plant*. Prentice-Hall, Englewood Cliffs, N.J., 1970.

Levine, R.P., "The Mechanism of Photosynthesis, "*Scientific American*, Dec., 1969.

Chapter 18

Bold, Harold C., *The Plant Kingdom*. Prentice-Hall, Englewood Cliffs, N.J. 1976.

Epstein, Emanuel, "Roots," *Scientific American*, May, 1973.

Raven, Peter H., *Biology of Plants*. Worth, New York, 1970.

Ray, Peter M., *The Living Plant*. Holt, Rinehart & Winston, New York, 1972.

Chapter 19

Heath, O.V.S., "Stomata," *Oxford Biology Reader*, Carolina Biological Supply Co., Burlington, N.C., 1975.

Noggle, G., and Fritz, George J., *Introductory Plant Physiology*. Prentice-Hall, Englewood Cliffs, N.J., 1976.

Peel, A.J., *Transport of Nutrients in Plants*. Wiley, New York, 1974.

Wilson, C.L., Loomis, W. E., and Steeves, T.A., *Botany*, 5th ed. Holt, Rinehart & Winston, New York, 1971.

Zimmerman, Martin H., "How Sap Moves in Trees," *Scientific American*, March, 1963.

Chapter 20

Lewis, B.J., and Lewis, K.R., "Somatic Cell Division," *Carolina Biology Reader*, Carolina Biological Supply Co., Burlington, N.C., 1980.

Mazia, D., "The Cell Cycle," *Scientific American*, Jan., 1974.

Old, L.J., "Cancer Immunology," *Scientific American*, May, 1977.

Prescott, David M., "The Reproduction of Eukaryotic Cells," *Carolina Biology Reader*, Carolina Biological Supply Co., Burlington, N.C., 1978.

Chapter 21

Lewis, B.J., and Lewis, K.R., "The Meiotic Mechanism," *Oxford Biology Reader*, Carolina Biological Supply Co., Burlington, N.C., 1975.

Tinbergen, N., "The Courtship of Animals," *Scientific American*, Nov., 1954.

Wendt, H., *The Sex Life of the Animals*. Simon and Schuster, New York, 1965.

Chapter 22

Balinsky, B.I., *An Introduction to Embryology*, 4th ed. Saunders, Philadelphia, 1975.

Etkin, W., "How a Tadpole Becomes a Frog," *Scientific American*, May, 1966.

Gurdon, J.B., "Transplanted Nuclei and Cell Differentiation," *Scientific American*, Dec., 1968.

Gurdon, J.B., "Gene Expression During Cell Differentiation," *Carolina Biology Reader*, Carolina Biological Supply Co., Burlington, N.C., 1978.

Taylor, T.E., "How an Eggshell is Made," *Scientific American*, March, 1970.

Wolpert, L., "The Development of Pattern and Form in Animals," *Carolina Biology Reader*, Carolina Biological Supply Co., Burlington, N.C., 1977.

Chapter 23

Epel, D., "The Program of Fertilization," *Scientific American*, Nov., 1977.

Friedmann, T., "Prenatal Diagnosis of Genetic Disease," *Scientific American*, Nov., 1971.

Hart, G., "Human Sexual Behavior," *Carolina Biology Reader*, Carolina Biological Supply Co., Burlington, N.C., 1977.

Segal, S.J., "The Physiology of Human Reproduction," *Scientific American*, Sept. 1974.

Chapter 24

Bantes, H., *Evolution and Plants of the Past.* Wadsworth, Belmont, Calif., 1970.

Cronquist, A., *Introductory Botany*, 2nd ed. Harper & Row, New York, 1971.

Wendt, Frits, *et al.*, *The Plants.* Time, Inc., New York, 1963.

Chapter 25

Jenkins, J.B., *Genetics*, Houghton Mifflin, Boston, 1979.

Kemp, R., *Cell Division and Heredity.* University Park Press, Baltimore, 1976.

Klein, Aaron, *Threads of Life.* Natural History Press, New York, 1970.

Lewis, K.R., and Lewis, B.J., *The Matter of Mendelian Heredity.* Wiley, New York, 1972.

Peters, James A., *Classic Papers in Genetics.* Prentice-Hall, Englewood Cliffs, N.J., 1959.

Chapter 26

Boyer, Samuel H., (ed.) *Papers on Human Genetics.* Prentice-Hall, Englewood Cliffs, N.J., 1963.

Crow, J.F., "Genes that Violate Mendel's Rules," *Scientific American*, Feb., 1979.

Scheinfeld, Amram, *Heredity in Humans.* Lippincott, Philadelphia, 1972.

Chapter 27

Baer, A.S., *The Genetic Perspective.* Saunders, Philadelphia, 1977.

Beadle, George, and Beadle, Muriel, *The Language of Life.* Doubleday, New York, 1966.

Lessing, Lawrence, *DNA, at the Core of Life Itself.* Macmillan, New York, 1967.

Miller, O.L., Jr., "The Visualization of Genes in Action," *Scientific American*, March, 1973.

Provjan, Carl, "Genes Made to Order," *Science World*, Nov. 17, 1977.

Stein, G.S., Stein, J.S., and Kleinsmith, L.J.,"Chromosomal Proteins and Gene Regulation," *Scientific American*, Feb, 1975.

Watson, J.D., *The Double Helix.* New American Library, New York, 1969.

Chapter 28

Brues, C.T., "Insects in Amber," *Scientific American*, Nov., 1951.

DeBeer, G., "Homology, An Unsolved Problem," *Oxford Biology Reader*, Carolina Biological Supply Co., Burlington, N.C., 1971.

Dobzhansky, T., *et al.*, *Evolution.* Freeman, San Francisco, 1977.
Stebbins, G.L., *Processes of Organic Evolution.* Prentice-Hall, Englewood Cliffs, N.J., 1977.
Zuckerkandl, E., "The Evolution of Hemoglobin," *Scientific American,* May, 1965.

Chapter 29
Bernal, J.D., and Synge, A., "The Origin of Life," *Oxford Biology Reader,* Carolina Biological Supply Co., Burlington, N.C., 1972.
Bishop, J.A., and Cook, L.M., "Moths, Melanism, and Clean Air," *Scientific American,* Jan., 1975.
Clarke, B., "The Causes of Biological Diversity," *Scientific American,* Aug., 1975.
Darlington, C.D., "The Origins of Darwinism," *Scientific American,* May, 1959.
Darwin, Charles, *On the Origin of Species.* Cambridge University Press, New York, 1975.
DeBeer, G., "Adaptation," *Carolina Biology Reader,* Carolina Biological Supply Co., Burlington, N.C., 1978.
Dodson, E.O., and Dodson, P., *Evolution.* Van Nostrand Reinhold, New York, 1976.
Eisley, L.C., "Charles Darwin," *Scientific American,* Feb., 1956.
Ford, E.B., "Evolution Studies by Observation and Experiment," *Oxford Biology Reader,* Carolina Biological Supply Co., Burlington, N.C., 1973.
Fox, S.W., and Dose, K., *Molecular Evolution and the Origin of Life.* Freeman, San Francisco, 1972.
Grant, V., *Organic Evolution.* Freeman, San Francisco, 1977.
Kettlewell, H.B.D., "Darwin's Missing Evidence," *Scientific American,* March, 1959.
Miller, S.L., and Urey, H.C., "Organic Compound Synthesis on the Primitive Earth," *Science,* July 31, 1959.
Oparin, A., *The Origin of Life.* Dover, New York, 1953.
Scientific American, Sept., 1978. The entire issue is devoted to evolution.

Chapter 30
Anderson, Dean A., *Introduction to Microbiology.* C.V. Mosby Co., St. Louis, Mo., 1973.
Aylesworth, Thomas, *The World of Microbes.* Franklin Watts, New York, 1975.
Dixon, Bernard, *Magnificent Microbes.* Atheneum, New York, 1976.
Dubos, Rene, *The Unseen World.* Oxford University Press, New York, 1962.
Sanders, F. Kingsley, "The Growth of Viruses," *Carolina Biology Reader,* Carolina Biological Supply Co., Burlington, N.C., 1975.

Chapter 31
Christensen, Clyde M., *Molds, Mushrooms, and Mycotoxins.* University of Minnesota Press, Minneapolis, Minn., 1975.
Laetsch, Watson M., *Plants: Basic Concepts in Botany.* Little, Brown, Boston, 1979.
Northen, Henry, and Northen, Rebecca, *Ingenious Kingdom.* Prentice-Hall, Englewood Cliffs, N.J, 1970.
Tribe, Ian, *The Plant Kingdom.* Grosset & Dunlap, New York, 1970.

Chapters 32 and 33

Barnes, R.D., *Invertebrate Zoology.* Saunders, Philadelphia, 1980.

Borror, D.J., and Delong, D.M., *An Introduction to the Study of Insects.* Holt, Rinehart & Winston, New York, 1976.

Buchsbaum, Ralph, *Animals Without Backbones.* University of Chicago Press, Chicago, 1972.

Buchsbaum, Ralph, and Milne, Lorus J., *The Lower Animals: Living Invertebrates of the World.* Doubleday, New York, 1960.

Nichols, D., "The Uniqueness of the Echinoderms," *Oxford Biology Reader,* Carolina Biological Supply Co., Burlington, N.C., 1975.

Pringle, J.W.S., "Insect Flight," *Oxford Biology Reader,* Carolina Biological Supply Co., Burlington, N.C., 1975.

Wigglesworth, V.B., "Insect Hormones," *Oxford Biology Reader,* Carolina Biological Supply Co., Burlington, N.C., 1974.

Chapter 34

Alexander, R.M., *The Chordates.* Cambridge University Press, New York, 1975.

Bellairs, A., and Carrington, R., *The Life of Reptiles.* Universe Books, New York, 1970.

Bone, Q., "The Origin of Chordates," *Carolina Biology Reader,* Carolina Biological Supply Co., Burlington, N.C., 1979.

Cochran, D.M., *Living Amphibians of the World.* Doubleday, New York, 1961.

Herald, E.S., *Living Fishes of the World.* Doubleday, New York, 1961.

McFarland, W.N., *et al., Vertebrate Life.* Macmillan, New York, 1979.

Romer, A.S., *The Vertebrate Body.* Saunders, Philadelphia, 1977.

Chapter 35

Day, M.H., "The Fossil History of Man," *Carolina Biology Reader,* Carolina Biological Supply Co., Burlington, N.C., 1977.

Harrison, R.H., and Montagna, W., *Man.* Appleton-Century-Crofts, New York, 1973.

Leakey, R.E., and Lewin, R., *Origins.* E.P. Dutton, New York, 1977.

Napier, J.R., "Primates and Their Adaptations," *Carolina Biology Reader,* Carolina Biological Supply Co., Burlington, N.C., 1977.

Sanderson, I.T., *Living Mammals of the World.* Doubleday, New York, 1955.

Schmidt-Neilsen, K., "How Birds Breathe," *Scientific American,* Dec., 1971.

Tullar, R.M., *The Human Species: Its Nature, Evolution, and Ecology.* McGraw-Hill, New York, 1977.

Washburn, S.L., "The Evolution of Man," *Scientific American,* Sept., 1978

Welty, J.C., *The Life of Birds.* Saunders, Philadelphia, 1975.

Chapter 36

Emmel, Thomas, *An Introduction to Ecology and Population Biology.* W.W. Norton, New York, 1973.

Kormondy, E.J., *Concepts of Ecology,* 2nd ed. Prentice-Hall, Englewood Cliffs, N.J., 1976.

Odom, Eugene P., *Fundamentals of Ecology,* 3rd ed. Saunders, Philadelphia, 1971.

Smith, R.L., *Elements of Ecology and Field Biology.* Harper & Row, New York, 1977.

Storer, John H., *The Web of Life.* New American Library, New York, 1972.

Whittaker, R.H., *Communities and Ecosystems,* 2nd ed. Macmillan, New York, 1975.

Chapter 37

Abbey, Edward, *Cactus Country*. Times Books, New York, 1973.

Allen, Durwood, *The Life of Prairies and Plains*. McGraw-Hill, New York, 1967.

Cousteau, Jacques-Yves, *Life and Death in a Coral Sea*. Doubleday, New York, 1971.

Friendly, Natalie, *Miraculous Web, the Balance of Life*. Prentice-Hall, Englewood Cliffs, N.J., 1968.

Raskin, Edith, *The Pyramid of Living Things*. McGraw-Hill, New York, 1967.

Chapter 38

Archer, Sellers G., *Soil Conservation*. University of Oklahoma Press, Norman, Okla., 1969.

Blake, Peter, *God's Own Junkyard. The Planned Deterioration of America's Landscape*. Holt, Rinehart & Winston, New York, 1964.

Carson, Rachel, *Silent Spring*. Houghton Mifflin, Boston, 1962.

Ehrenfeld, David W., *Biological Conservation*. Holt, Rinehart & Winston, New York, 1970.

Ehrlich, Paul, *The Population Bomb*. Ballantine, New York, 1971.

Leen, Nina, *And Then There Were None: America's Vanishing Wildlife*. Holt, Rinehart & Winston, New York, 1973.

Wagner, R.H., *Environment and Man*, 3rd ed. W.W. Norton, New York, 1978.

Glossary

a

abiogenesis: See **spontaneous generation.**

abiotic factor: A physical factor of the environment, such as water, air, light, or temperature.

abscisic acid: An organic compound that influences the shedding of leaves and the seasonal slowing down of plant activities.

abscission layer: A separation layer that forms at the point of attachment of leaves, flowers, or fruits to the stem, causing them to drop off the plant.

absolute dating: A dating method based on the rate of disintegration of radioactive isotopes; used to determine the age in years of rocks and fossils.

absorption: The passage of materials across a cell membrane into the cell; the process by which usable materials are taken into an organism.

absorption spectrum: The wavelengths of light absorbed by a test solution.

accessory organ: The corolla or calyx of a flower.

acetylcholine: A neurotransmitter.

acid: A compound that produces an excess of hydrogen ions in a water solution.

acquired behavior: Learned behavior; behavior that is not inborn.

acquired immunity: Immunity that develops after birth.

acrosome: Part of the head of a sperm containing enzymes that help in penetration of an egg.

ACTH (adrenocorticotropic hormone): A hormone secreted by the anterior pituitary that stimulates the secretion of hormones by the adrenal cortex.

actin: A protein found in microfilaments and skeletal muscle.

activation energy: The energy that must be supplied to substances to start a chemical reaction.

active immunity: An acquired immunity in which the body produces its own antibodies and/or sensitized lymphocytes to destroy a particular antigen.

active site: The region on an enzyme where the reaction it catalyzes takes place.

active transport: A process in which the movement of materials across a cell membrane requires the expenditure of cellular energy.

adaptation: An inherited trait or modification that improves the chance of survival and reproduction of an organism in a given environment.

adaptive radiation: The process by which an ancestral species evolves into a number of different species, each occupying a different habitat or ecological niche.

addition: The breaking-off of a segment of a chromosome and its attachment to the homologous chromosome.

adenine: A nitrogenous base found in DNA and RNA.

adenoid: Lymphoid tissue found in the throat.

adenosine diphosphate: See **ADP.**

adenosine triphosphate: See **ATP.**

adhesion: The attractive force between unlike molecules.

adipose tissue: Fat tissue found beneath the dermis of the skin.

ADP (adenosine diphosphate): The lower-energy compound remaining after one phosphate group is removed from ATP.

adrenal gland: An endocrine gland that secretes hormones that help the body deal with stress.

adrenaline: See **epinephrine.**

adrenocorticotropic hormone: See **ACTH.**

adventitious root: A root that grows from an unusual part of a stem.

aerial root: An adventitious root that absorbs moisture from the air.

aerobic respiration: Respiration carried on in the presence of free oxygen, in which glucose is completely oxidized to carbon dioxide and water.

aerosol: Tiny solid particles or liquid droplets suspended in air.

afterbirth: The placenta and the amnion, which are expelled from the uterus after birth of the baby.

agglutination: A process in which red blood cells clump together.

agglutinin: An antibody that reacts with an agglutinogen to produce agglutination.

agglutinogen: A substance that stimulates the production of an agglutinin.

air bladder: See **swim bladder.**

air sac: The structure at the end of a bronchiole where gas exchange takes place.

albumin: A plasma protein that affects the diffusion of plasma out of the capillaries into the intercellular spaces.

aldosterone: A corticosteroid hormone secreted by the adrenal cortex that maintains the normal mineral balance in the blood.

alimentary canal: The digestive tube; the passageway through which food moves from mouth to anus.

allantois: In bird and reptile eggs, a saclike extraembryonic membrane that grows out of the digestive system of the embryo and controls gas exchange and collects metabolic wastes; in placental mammals, an extraembryonic membrane that forms part of the umbilical cord.

allele: One of the two or more forms of the gene for a specific trait.

allergy: A disorder caused by the release of histamine by the body cells following an antigen-antibody reaction.

alternation of generations: A life cycle that has both sexual and asexual stages.

altitude: The vertical distance above or below sea level.

alveolus: A cavity in an air sac that is the respiratory surface in the lung.

amber: A transparent yellow material formed by the hardening of tree resin; may contain fossils of insects that have been trapped and preserved.

ameboid movement: Locomotion by means of pseudopods.

amino acid: The structural unit of proteins; contains a carboxyl group ($-COOH$), an amino group ($-NH_2$), and a side chain.

amniocentesis: A technique in which amniotic fluid, which contains fetal cells, is withdrawn from the amniotic sac of a pregnant woman and the cells examined for the presence of genetic abnormalities.

amnion: In both shelled eggs and mammals, a fluid-filled extraembryonic sac that surrounds the embryo; provides a watery environment and protects the embryo.

amniotic fluid: The fluid that fills the amnion.

amphetamine: A drug that acts as a stimulant and increases the release of norepinephrine.

anabolism: The synthesis of materials needed for life processes in an organism.

anaerobic respiration: Respiration in the absence of free oxygen, in which glucose is partially oxidized.

anal pore: The opening through which indigestible wastes are ejected from a paramecium.

analogous structures: Structures found in different types of organisms that are similar in function or outward appearance, but are dissimilar in basic structure or embryonic development.

anaphase: The stage of mitosis during which the daughter chromosomes move to opposite poles.

androgen: A male sex hormone.

anemia: A disorder in which the blood contains too few red blood cells or insufficient hemoglobin.

angiosperm: A flowering plant.

annual ring: The xylem formed each year in a woody dicot stem.

anterior: Pertaining to the front, or head, end of a bilaterally symmetrical animal.

anther: The saclike structure of a stamen in which pollen grains are produced.

antheridium: The male reproductive organ in plants.

anthropology: The branch of science that attempts to trace the development of the human species.

antibody: A protein produced by leukocytes, which reacts with a specific foreign substance, or antigen, and inactivates it.

anticoagulant: A substance that prevents blood clotting.

anticodon: A sequence of three bases on tRNA that is complementary to a mRNA codon and specifies the amino acid that the tRNA carries.

antidiuretic hormone (ADH): See **vasopressin.**

antigen: Any substance that can cause a response of the immune system.

antihistamine: A drug used to counteract the effects of histamine.

anus: The opening of the digestive tube through which undigested materials are eliminated from the body.

anvil: The small bone in the middle ear that connects the hammer to the stirrup.

aorta: The major artery carrying oxygenated blood away from the heart.

aortic arch: A heartlike blood vessel in the earthworm.

aphotic zone: In a body of water, the lower layer of water that receives no light; the zone below the photic zone.

appendicular skeleton: The division of the human skeleton that includes the arms, legs, pectoral girdle, and pelvic girdle.

appendix: A small pouch found where the small intestine joins the large intestine.

aqueous humor: The transparent, watery fluid that fills the cavity between the cornea and the lens of the eye.

archegonium: The female reproductive organ in plants.

archenteron: The cavity in the developing embryo that later becomes the cavity of the digestive system.

arteriole: The smallest type of artery.

artery: A blood vessel that carries blood away from the heart to the organs and tissues of the body.

asexual reproduction: A type of reproduction in which there is only one parent; all offspring are genetically identical to the parent.

assimilation: The incorporation of materials into the body of an organism.

associative neuron: See **interneuron.**

aster: A star-shaped structure formed during mitosis by fibers extending from the centrioles.

asthma: An allergic reaction in which narrowing of the bronchioles makes breathing difficult.

atom: The smallest particle of an element that has the properties of that element; the unit of which elements are made.

atomic mass: See **mass number.**

atomic number: The number of protons in the nucleus of an atom; the number that identifies an element.

ATP (adenosine triphosphate): The compound in which energy released by cellular respiration is stored.

atrioventricular valve (A-V valve): A heart valve that controls the flow of blood from the atrium into the ventricle.

atrium: One of the upper, thin-walled chambers of the heart; auricle.

auditory canal: The passage leading from the outer ear to the middle ear.

auricle: See **atrium.**

Australopithecus: A fossil about 2 million years old that is believed to represent an early form of human.

autoimmune disease: A disease in which the tolerance of the immune system breaks down, and antibodies and sensitized lymphocytes develop in response to the body's own antigens.

autonomic nervous system: A division of the peripheral nervous system consisting of motor fibers from the brain and spinal cord that serve the internal organs of the body; not under voluntary control.

autosome: A chromosome other than a sex chromosome.

autotomy: The process of self-amputation, in which an injured appendage is separated from the body.

autotroph: An organism capable of synthesizing its needed organic nutrients from inorganic substances.

autotrophic nutrition: A type of nutrition in which the organism does not require preformed organic substances from its environment.

auxin: A hormone that affects the growth of all types of plant tissues.

A-V valve: See **atrioventricular valve.**

axial skeleton: The division of the human skeleton that includes the skull, vertebrae, ribs, and breastbone.

axillary bud: See **lateral bud.**

axon: A long, thin fiber that carries nerve impulses away from the cell body of a neuron.

b

bacillus: A rod-shaped bacterium.

backbone: See **spinal column.**

bacteriochlorophyll: The form of chlorophyll found in bacteria.

bacteriophage: A virus that infects bacteria.

ball-and-socket joint: A joint that permits movement in all directions.

barbiturate: A drug that produces a depressant effect by blocking the formation of norepinephrine.

bark: The protective, outermost layer of a woody stem.

basal body: The structure from which a cilium or flagellum arises.

base: A compound that produces an excess of hydroxyl ions when dissolved in water.

bicuspid valve: The atrioventricular valve on the left side of the heart; the mitral valve.

bilateral symmetry: A type of symmetry in which there is only one longitudinal section that will divide the organism into two parts that are mirror images of each other.

bile: A fluid secretion of liver cells that aids in the breakdown of fats.

bile duct: The duct that carries bile from the gallbladder to the small intestine.

binary fission: The simplest form of asexual reproduction, in which the parent organism divides into two approximately equal parts.

binocular microscope: See **stereomicroscope.**

binomial nomenclature: The two-word system that identifies each kind of organism by use of its genus and species names.

biodegradable: Able to be broken down by bacteria and other decay organisms into simpler substances.

biogenesis: The idea that all living things arise only by reproduction of other living things.

biological magnification: The process in which toxic substances accumulate in larger and larger quantities in the bodies of organisms at each higher level of a food chain.

biome: A large geographical region showing a particular type of climax vegetation.

biosphere: The portion of the earth in which living things exist.

biotic factor: An organism in an environment and its effects on other living things.

bipedal locomotion: The ability to walk on two legs in an upright position.

birth canal: See **vagina.**

bladder: The organ that temporarily stores urine after it has left the kidneys.

blastocoel: The fluid-filled cavity in a blastula.

blastopore: The opening in a gastrula created by the gastrulation process; becomes an opening to the digestive system in the adult organism.

blastula: A stage of development in which the embryo consists of a single layer of cells surrounding a fluid-filled cavity.

blending inheritance: See **incomplete dominance.**

blood: The fluid in the circulatory system of an animal.

bolus: A soft mass of chewed food.

bone: A type of connective tissue consisting of bone cells surrounded by a hard matrix of mineral matter that they secrete.

Bowman's capsule: A double-walled, cup-shaped structure surrounding the glomerulus in the kidney.

brain: A group of specialized nerve cells that control and coordinate the activities of a nervous system.

brain hormone: A hormone that stimulates the production of molting hormone in insect development.

breastbone: See **sternum.**

breathing: The movement of air into and out of the lungs.

bronchial tube: One of the branches of a bronchus.

bronchioles: The finest branches of the bronchial tubes.

bronchitis: An inflammation of the lining of the bronchial tubes.

bronchus: A cartilage-ringed tube that branches from the trachea and enters a lung.

brush border: The microvilli that line the epithelial cells of the small intestine.

bud: An outgrowth of the parent organism; in plants, the bud gives rise to a new shoot; in protists and animals, the bud gives rise to a new, smaller individual organism.

budding: A type of asexual reproduction in which the parent organism divides into two unequal parts.

bud scale: A protective covering for the terminal bud of a woody dicot.

bud scale scar: The mark left on a woody dicot twig where the bud scales drop off; it indicates the point at which the season's growth began.

bulb: A short underground stem with leaves and stored food that can give rise to new plants by vegetative reproduction.

bundle scar: A small dot within a leaf scar that marks the point at which vascular bundles passed from the stem into the leaf.

C

calcitonin: A hormone secreted by the thyroid that regulates the blood calcium level.

calorie: The amount of heat that will raise the temperature of 1 g of water 1°C. (The large calorie, used to measure the energy contents of foods, is equal to 1,000 calories.)

calorimeter: An instrument used to measure the energy content of food.

calyx: The complete circle of sepals in a flower.

cambium: A meristematic tissue that increases the diameter of stems and roots.

camouflage: A protective adaptation that enables an organism to blend into the environment.

canine: A type of tooth specialized for tearing food.

capillary: A microscopic blood vessel that connects the smallest arteries to the smallest veins.

capillary action: The upward movement of a liquid in a tube of narrow diameter.

capsule: A slimy covering around a bacterial cell wall that provides protection for the cell.

carapace: The part of the exoskeleton that protects and covers the dorsal and side surfaces of the cephalothorax of a crustacean; the upper shell of a turtle.

carbohydrate: A compound of carbon, hydrogen, and oxygen in which the ratio of hydrogen to oxygen is 2:1.

carbon cycle: The pathways by which carbon is circulated through the biosphere.

carbon fixation: The process in which carbon dioxide from the atmosphere is incorporated into organic compounds by the process of photosynthesis.

carboxyl group: –COOH; part of the structure of organic acids.

cardiac muscle: A type of involuntary muscle tissue found in the heart.

cardiac sphincter: The sphincter that controls the passage of food between the esophagus and the stomach.

cardioaccelerator nerve: A nerve that speeds up the pacemaker of the heart.

carnivore: An animal that feeds on other animals.

carotene: An orange pigment found in the leaves of many plants.

carrier: An individual who is heterozygous for a defective recessive gene and therefore does not show the trait, but can transmit it to offspring.

carrying capacity: The size of a population that can be supported by an environment.

cartilage: A type of flexible connective tissue.

cast: A type of fossil formed when a mold becomes filled with minerals and hardens, producing a copy of the external features of an organism.

catabolism: All the processes that result in the breakdown of complex substances in the body.

catalyst: A substance that increases the rate of a particular chemical reaction without being changed itself.

cell: The basic unit of structure and function in living things; the smallest unit in living things that shows the characteristics of life.

cell body: The part of a nerve cell that contains the nucleus and is the site of the metabolic activities of the cell; cyton.

cell membrane: The structure that separates the interior of a cell from the surrounding environment and controls the passage of materials into and out of the cell; plasma membrane.

cell plate: A structure formed during telophase in a plant cell that divides the cell in half and becomes part of the new cell walls of the daughter cells.

cell theory: The theory that states that all living things are made of cells and that cells arise only from other cells.

cell wall: The rigid structure, often composed of cellulose, that encloses the cells of plants and various microorganisms.

cellular respiration: The process by which energy stored in food is released by cells.

cellulose: The polysaccharide that makes up the cell walls of plants.

central cylinder: See **vascular cylinder.**

central nervous system: The division of the nervous system that includes the brain and spinal cord .

centrifuge: A device in which materials of different

densities can be separated from one another by whirling them at high speed in a tubular cylinder.

centriole: A cylindrical organelle found near the nucleus in animal cells that is involved in cell division.

centromere: The region of attachment of two sister chromatids.

cephalothorax: The anterior portion of some arthropods, made up of the fused segments of the head and thorax.

cerebellum: A part of the brain located below the rear part of the cerebrum; coordinates voluntary movements.

cerebral cortex: The outer layer of the cerebrum; the gray matter.

cerebral hemisphere: One of the two halves of the cerebrum, which are partially separated from each other by a deep groove.

cerebrospinal fluid: A liquid that cushions the brain and spinal cord.

cerebrum: The largest part of the human brain.

cervix: The narrow neck of the uterus.

chemical bond: A force of attraction between atoms that holds them together in compounds.

chemical equation: A written representation of a chemical reaction.

chemical formula: A representation of a compound in which the symbols of elements show the composition of the compound.

chemical reaction: The process in which chemical bonds of substances are broken and the atoms form new bonds, producing different substances.

chemical transmitter: See **neurotransmitter.**

chemosynthesis: A form of autotrophic nutrition in which the organism obtains energy for synthesizing organic compounds from inorganic compounds rather than from light.

chemotroph: An autotroph that carries on chemosynthesis.

chest cavity: The area enclosed by the sternum, ribs, backbone, and diaphragm.

chitin: The polysaccharide that makes up the exoskeleton of arthropods.

chlorophyll: The major photosynthetic pigment of plants and algae.

chloroplast: A plastid that contains chlorophyll and is a site of photosynthesis.

cholecystokinin: A hormone secreted by cells in the intestinal lining, which stimulates the release of bile from the gallbladder.

cholesterol: A steroid found in most animal tissues; plays a role in the buildup of fatty deposits in arteries.

chorion: The membrane that surrounds the embryo and the other extraembryonic membranes in mammals, birds, and reptiles.

chorionic villi: Small fingerlike projections on the outer surface of the chorion, which, with the uterine lining, form the placenta.

choroid coat: The darkly pigmented middle layer of the eye.

chromatid: One of the two strands of a doubled chromosome.

chromatin: In nondividing cells, the material of the chromosomes in the form of long, thin threads.

chromatography: A process used to separate and analyze mixtures of chemical substances.

chromoplast: A plastid that contains colored pigments.

chromosomal mutation: A change in chromosome structure, resulting in new gene combinations.

chromosome: During cell division, a rodlike structure in the nucleus on which the genes are located.

chyme: The thin, soupy liquid produced from food by the stomach.

chymotrypsin: An enzyme that breaks down proteins in the small intestine.

ciliary muscle: A muscle of the eye that holds the lens in place.

cilium: **A short, hairlike organelle at the surface of a cell, with the capacity for movement.**

circulation: The movement of materials within a cell or between parts of an organism.

class: A group of related orders.

cleavage: In a fertilized egg, the first series of cell divisions that occur without growth and continue until the cells of the embryo are reduced to the size of the cells of the adult organism.

climax community: A mature, stable community that is the final stage of ecological succession.

climbing root: An adventitious root that grows from a stem and attaches the plant to a solid support.

clone: A group of individual organisms that have identical genetic makeups.

closed circulatory system: A circulatory system in which blood is always confined in vessels.

cnidoblast: A stinging cell found in coelenterates, which is used for defense and capturing food.

coacervate: According to the heterotroph hypothesis, an aggregate of large proteinlike molecules; thought to have developed into the first forms of life on the primitive earth.

coccus: A spherical bacterium.

cochlea: The organ of hearing, found in the inner ear, consisting of coiled, liquid-filled tubes.

codon: A group of three bases in a mRNA sequence that specifies a particular amino acid.

coelom: The fluid-filled body cavity between the body wall and the digestive tube.

coenzyme: A nonprotein, organic substance necessary to the functioning of a particular enzyme.

cohesion: The attractive force between like molecules.

cold-blooded: Having a body temperature that varies

with the temperature of the environment; ectothermic.

collagen: A fibrous connective tissue.

collar cell: A type of flagellated cell found in the inner layer of a sponge.

collenchyma: A fundamental plant tissue that strengthens and supports stems, leaves, and other parts of a plant.

colloidal dispersion: A mixture in which the solute particles are larger than molecules or ions, but are too small to settle out; colloid.

color blindness: A sex-linked trait in which an individual cannot perceive certain colors.

commensalism: A type of symbiotic relationship in which one organism benefits from the association and the other is not affected.

community: All the different populations within a given area.

companion cell: In vascular plants, the type of cell thought to control the transport activities of the sieve cells of the phloem.

compound: A substance made of two or more kinds of atoms combined in definite proportions.

compound eye: In arthropods, an eye made up of many units, each with its own lens and light-sensitive cells.

compound microscope: A microscope with two lenses or lens systems—an ocular and an objective.

concentration gradient: The difference in concentration between a region of greater concentration and a region of lesser concentration.

conditioned response: The simplest type of learned behavior.

conducting tissue: The xylem and phloem of a plant; vascular tissue.

cone: A structure in the retina of the eye responsible for color vision. In gymnosperms, the seed-bearing structure.

conifer: A cone-bearing plant with leaves in the form of needles.

conjugation: A form of sexual reproduction found in protists; the individual organisms appear to be identical, but are of different mating types.

conjugation tube: A passageway that forms between two cells of different mating types during conjugation.

consumer: A heterotroph; an organism that obtains nutrients from other organisms.

contour farming: A method of farming in which rows are plowed horizontally across slopes, following the contour of the land, and acting to reduce the flow of water down the slopes.

contractile vacuole: In protists, a specialized cytoplasmic structure that collects excess water from the cell and then expels it into the environment by active transport.

controlled experiment: An experiment set up in duplicate, with a single factor changed in one of the setups.

convergent evolution: The evolution of outward similarities in organisms that are not closely related because they have to meet similar problems in their habitats.

convolution: A ridge in the cerebral cortex.

cork: A protective plant tissue that covers the surface of woody stems and roots.

cork cambium: The meristematic tissue that produces cork.

corm: A short underground stem containing stored food; it can give rise to new plants by vegetative reproduction.

cornea: The transparent part of the sclera in the front of the eye through which light enters.

corolla: The complete circle of petals in a flower.

coronary circulation: The subdivision of the systemic circulation that supplies blood to the muscle of the heart.

corpus luteum: A progesterone-secreting yellow body in the ovary, formed when LH causes a ruptured follicle to fill with cells.

cortex: In plants, a cell layer beneath the epidermis of the root. In the brain, the outermost layer of the cerebrum.

corticosteroid: A type of hormone produced by the adrenal cortex, synthesized from cholesterol.

cortisol: A hormone secreted by the adrenal cortex that affects the metabolism of carbohydrates, proteins, and fats.

cotyledon: A modified leaf of the plant embryo, which often provides nourishment for the developing seedling.

covalent bond: A chemical bond formed by the sharing of electrons.

cover crop: A crop planted over a whole field instead of in rows; used to prevent soil erosion.

Cowper's gland: In the male, a gland that secretes a fluid that forms part of semen.

cranial nerve: A nerve connected directly to the brain.

cranium: The upper part of the skull, which houses and protects the brain.

cristae: The highly folded inner membranes of a mitochondrion, on which many of the reactions of cellular respiration occur.

Cro-Magnon man: A type of prehistoric human, considered to be the same as modern humans; replaced the Neanderthals about 35,000 years ago.

crop: In birds and many invertebrates, a thin-walled organ that temporarily stores food from the esophagus.

crop rotation: A method of farming in which different crops are grown on a field in successive years to prevent the reduction of soil nutrients.

crossing-over: The process in which pieces of homologous chromosomes are exchanged during synapsis in the first meiotic division.

cross-pollination: The transfer of pollen from an anther on one plant to a stigma on another plant.

curare: A drug that blocks the functioning of acetylcholine at neuromuscular junctions.

cuticle: The layer of cutin that covers plant epidermis.

cutin: A waxy substance found in the cell walls of the epidermis of aboveground parts of a plant.

cutting: Any vegetative part of a plant used to produce a new plant by artificial vegetative reproduction.

cycads: A small group of nonflowering seed plants.

cyclosis: A streaming motion of the cytoplasm that circulates materials within a cell.

cytokinin: A plant hormone that stimulates cell division and growth.

cyton: See **cell body.**

cytoplasm: The watery material between the nucleus and the cell membrane of a cell.

cytoplasmic division: In cell division, the separation of the cytoplasm that follows division of the nucleus.

cytosine: A nitrogenous base found in DNA and RNA.

d

dark reactions: The series of reactions in photosynthesis in which carbon fixation occurs and which do not require light.

day-neutral plant: A plant that is either unaffected or only slightly influenced by the relative lengths of day and night.

deamination: The removal of an amino group ($-NH_2$) from a chemical compound.

decomposer: An organism of decay.

deficiency disease: A disease or disorder resulting from the lack of a necessary nutrient in the diet.

dehydration synthesis: A type of reaction in which two molecules are bonded together by the removal of a water molecule.

deletion: A type of chromosomal alteration in which a portion of a chromosome and the genes it contains is lost.

denaturation: A breakdown in protein structure caused by high temperature or other factors, and destroying the ability of the protein to function.

dendrite: A short, branched part of a neuron specialized for receiving nerve impulses and transmitting them to the cell body.

denitrifying bacteria: Bacteria that convert nitrates and ammonia to nitrogen gas, which is released into the atmosphere.

deoxyribose: A 5-carbon sugar found in DNA.

depressant: A drug that slows down body activities.

dermis: The layer of skin beneath the epidermis, consisting of elastic connective tissue.

desert: A biome in which there is too little rainfall to support trees or grasses; may show great variation in temperature between day and night.

diabetes mellitus: A condition caused by an insufficient concentration of insulin in the blood.

diaphragm: The muscle that forms the floor of the chest cavity.

diastole: The period of relaxation during the heartbeat cycle.

diatomic molecule: A molecule formed when two atoms of the same element form a covalent bond, such as O_2.

dicot: A plant whose seeds have two cotyledons.

differential reproduction: The idea that individuals with favorable variations survive longer and produce more offspring than those without the variations, thus causing certain gene frequencies to gradually increase or decline within a population.

differentiation: The series of changes that transforms unspecialized embryonic cells into the specialized cells, tissues, and organs that make up an organism.

diffusion: The movement of molecules or particles from an area of greater concentration to an area of lesser concentration.

digestion: The breakdown of complex food materials into simpler forms that can be used by the organism.

dihybrid cross: A genetic cross in which two pairs of contrasting traits are studied.

dipeptide: A type of molecule formed when two amino acids are joined by a peptide bond.

diploid chromosome number: The full number of chromosomes characteristic of a species; the $2n$ chromosome number.

disaccharide: A double sugar formed by joining two monosaccharides by dehydration synthesis.

disjunction: The separation of homologous pairs of doubled chromosomes during meiosis.

dissociation: The process in which an ionic substance dissolves in a solution and breaks up into ions.

DNA (deoxyribonucleic acid): The nucleic acid that contains the hereditary information.

dominance: The principle of genetics stating that when organisms pure for contrasting traits are crossed, all their offspring will show the dominant trait.

dominant gene: A gene whose phenotype is always expressed.

dominant trait: The trait that appears in the offspring of a cross between two pure individuals showing contrasting forms of the trait.

dominant generation: The more obvious generation in a life cycle with an alternation of generations.

dominant species: The species that exert the greatest effects on the environment and on other members of the community.

dormancy: A resting period that many seeds undergo, during which they will not sprout.

dorsal: Pertaining to the upper side or the back of a bilaterally symmetrical animal.

dorsal root: The back part of the spinal cord where sensory fibers enter.

dorsal vessel: A major blood vessel of the earthworm

that runs along the top of the digestive tract.

double fertilization: In flowering plants, the fertilization of the egg and of the two polar nuclei.

double helix: The structure of the DNA molecule, formed by the coiling of the two parallel strands.

Down's syndrome: A genetic disorder caused by the nondisjunction of chromosome 21, and resulting in the presence of an extra chromosome; mongolism.

ductless gland: A gland of the endocrine system.

e

eardrum: A delicate membrane stretched across the inner end of the auditory canal of the ear; tympanic membrane.

ecdysone: A hormone that influences molting in insects.

ECG: See **electrocardiogram.**

ecological succession: The process by which an existing community in an ecosystem is gradually replaced by another community.

ecology: The branch of biology that deals with all the interactions between organisms and their environment.

ecosystem: The interaction of a community with its physical environment.

ectoderm: The outer layer of cells in a simple animal or embryo. One of the germ layers of the embryo.

ectothermic: See **cold-blooded.**

edema: Swelling caused by the accumulation of fluid in the tissues.

effector: A muscle or gland.

egestion: The elimination of undigested material from the digestive tract.

egg cell: The female gamete.

ejaculation: The release of semen from the urethra.

electrocardiogram (ECG or EKG): A recording of the electrical current produced by the heartbeat cycle.

electron: A negatively charged particle found in the space outside the nucleus of an atom.

electron microscope: A microscope that uses an electron beam and electromagnetic lenses to produce very great magnifications.

electron transport chain: A series of oxidation-reduction reactions in which most of the energy produced from the breakdown of glucose is transferred to ATP.

electrophoresis: A technique used to separate and analyze mixtures of chemical substances whose particles have an electrical charge.

element: A substance made entirely of one kind of atom.

elongation zone: In plants, a region behind the meristematic zone of the root, in which the cells produced in the meristematic zone grow longer.

embolus: A blood clot that travels through the bloodstream.

embryo: An organism in the early stages of development.

embryology: The study of embryonic development of animals.

embryonic induction: The process by which one group of cells (the organizer) induces another group of cells to differentiate.

embryo sac: A seven-celled structure in the ovule of a flower that is the female gametophyte.

emphysema: A disease of the lungs in which the tissues lose their elasticity and the walls of the alveoli break down.

empirical formula: A formula that shows the atoms in a compound in their simplest proportions.

emulsification: The process of breaking fats and oils into tiny droplets.

endocrine gland: A gland of the endocrine system; a ductless gland.

endocrine system: A system of glands that secrete hormones directly into the blood.

endoderm: The inner layer of cells in a simple animal or embryo. One of the germ layers of the embryo.

endodermis: In plants, the innermost layer of the cortex of the root.

endometrium: The lining of the uterus.

endoplasmic reticulum: A system of membrane-enclosed, fluid-filled canals that form a network through the cytoplasm of a cell.

endoskeleton: A skeleton composed of bone and cartilage located within the body walls.

endosperm: The tissue that develops from the endosperm nucleus, often serving as a food supply for the plant embryo.

endosperm nucleus: In plants, a triploid ($3n$) nucleus formed by the fusion of a sperm nucleus with the two polar nuclei in an ovule.

endothermic: See **warm-blooded.**

entomology: The branch of biology that deals with the study of insects.

enzyme: A protein that acts as a catalyst, increasing the rate of a specific chemical reaction.

enzyme-substrate complex: The temporary union of an enzyme and its substrate.

epicotyl: The part of a plant embryo above the point of attachment of the cotyledons; gives rise to the terminal bud, leaves, and upper part of the stem.

epidermis: In plants, a protective tissue that forms the outer layer of leaves, green stems, and roots; in animals, the outer layer of skin consisting of layers of tightly packed epithelial cells.

epididymis: A storage area for sperm on the upper, rear part of the testis.

epiglottis: A flap of tissue that covers the trachea during swallowing, so that food passes only into the esophagus.

epinephrine: A hormone produced by the adrenal medulla; a neurotransmitter produced by some nerve cells; adrenaline.

equatorial plane: In mitosis, the region midway between the poles of the cell.

erosion: The removal of soil by the action of wind and/or water.

erythrocyte: See **red blood cell.**

esophagus: The tube that is the passageway for food from the mouth to the stomach.

essential amino acid: An amino acid that the body cannot synthesize and that must be obtained from proteins in food.

essential organ: The stamen or pistil of a flower.

estrogen: A hormone secreted by the ovaries that promotes development of female secondary sex characteristics and regulates the reproductive cycle.

ethylene: An organic compound that stimulates flowering in some plants and hastens the ripening of fruit.

eucaryote: A cell containing a membrane-bounded nucleus.

Eustachian tube: The tube extending between the middle ear and the throat that equalizes the pressure between the middle ear and the environment.

eutrophication: An accelerated aging process in a lake or pond, in which the body of water fills in and is reduced in size.

evolution: The theory that life arose by natural processes at an early stage of the earth's history and that complex organisms developed from simple organisms by a process of gradual change.

excretion: The process by which the wastes of cellular metabolism are removed from an organism.

exhalation: The phase of breathing in which air is expelled from the lungs.

exocrine gland: A gland that discharges its secretions into a duct.

exoskeleton: A skeleton found on the outside of the body, enclosing the soft parts.

extensor: A muscle that extends a joint.

external fertilization: The process in which eggs are fertilized outside the body of the female.

external respiration: The exchange of oxygen and carbon dioxide between the air and the blood in the lungs.

extracellular digestion: Digestion occurring outside the cell under the action of enzymes secreted by the cell.

f

facilitated diffusion: A process by which certain molecules are moved very quickly across a cell membrane.

FAD (flavin adenine dinucleotide): A coenzyme that acts as a hydrogen acceptor in cellular respiration.

Fallopian tubes: The oviducts of placental mammals.

family: A group of related genera.

fatty acid: A type of organic molecule a carbon chain with at least one carboxyl group at tached to it; one of the end products of the digestion of fats.

feces: Undigested and undigestible food material that is solidified in the large intestine and then eliminated from the body.

fermentation: Following glycolysis, the conversion of pyruvic acid to an end product with no further release of energy.

fertilization: The union of an egg cell nucleus and a sperm cell nucleus to form a zygote.

fertilization membrane: A membrane formed around an egg after fertilization to prevent additional sperm from penetrating it.

fertilizer: A material used to provide or replace soil nutrients.

fertilizin: A chemical secreted by an egg that stimulates sperm to move faster and aids in their attachment to the surface of the egg.

fetus: The developing baby after about the second month of pregnancy.

fibrillation: A disorder in which the heart beats irregularly and without force.

fibrin: An insoluble protein that forms a meshwork of strands in the blood-clotting process.

fibrinogen: A soluble plasma protein that is converted into insoluble fibrin strands during the blood-clotting process.

fibrous root system: A root system in which the branching secondary roots are as large as or larger than the primary root.

filament: The stalklike structure that supports the anther in a stamen.

filter feeder: An animal that feeds by passing water through its body and filtering out food particles.

filtrate: The fluid in the Bowman's capsules of the kidney.

filtration: The process in which substances pass from the blood into the nephron of the kidney.

first-level consumer: See **primary consumer.**

flagellum: A long, hairlike organelle at the surface of a cell, with the capacity for movement.

flame cell: A cell that removes excess water and liquid wastes from the body of a flatworm and passes them into ducts to be excreted.

flavin adenine dinucleotide: See **FAD.**

flexor: A muscle that bends a joint.

follicle: A structure in the ovary in which the mature egg develops.

follicle-stimulating hormone: See **FSH.**

food chain: A series of organisms through which food energy is passed in an ecosystem.

food vacuole: A vacuole in which food is digested in microorganisms and simple animals.

food web: Interconnected food chains in an ecosystem.

foot: A large ventral, muscular structure that functions in locomotion in mollusks.

foramen magnum: The opening in the skull where the spinal cord enters.

fossil: The remains or traces of an extinct organism.

fraternal twins: Two individuals formed when two eggs are fertilized at the same time; twins that are genetically different.

freshwater biome: A community of organisms inhabiting a lake or stream.

frond: The large leaf of a fern, usually having many leaflets.

fruit: A structure that develops from the ovary and other associated flower parts after fertilization and that contains the seeds.

FSH (follicle-stimulating hormone): A hormone secreted by the anterior pituitary that stimulates the development of eggs in the ovaries.

fundamental tissue: A tissue involved in the production and storage of food and in the support of the plant; parenchyma, collenchyma, and sclerenchyma.

g

gallbladder: The organ that stores bile produced by the liver.

gamete: A monoploid sex cell; a sperm cell or egg cell.

gametogenesis: The process by which gametes develop in the gonads.

gametophyte generation: The gamete-producing generation in a plant showing an alternation of generations.

ganglion: A group of cell bodies and associative neurons that switch, relay, and coordinate nerve impulses.

gastric gland: A gland in the lining of the stomach that secretes gastric juice.

gastric juice: The digestive secretion of glands in the stomach, containing hydrochloric acid and pepsin.

gastrin: A hormone secreted by cells in the lining of the stomach that stimulates the flow of gastric juice.

gastrovascular cavity: The internal body cavity of a coelenterate.

gastrula: In animals, an early stage of embryonic development during which the second germ layer is formed.

gastrulation: The process in which the cells on one side of a blastula push in to form the two-layered gastrula.

gene: A distinct unit of hereditary material found in chromosomes; a sequence of nucleotides in DNA that codes for a particular polypeptide.

gene frequency: The percentage of individuals in a population carrying a certain gene.

gene linkage: See **linked genes.**

gene mutation: A change in the sequence of the bases in a gene, which changes the structure of the polypeptide that the gene codes for.

gene pool: The total of all the genes in a population.

generative nucleus: The nucleus in the pollen grain that divides to form two sperm nuclei.

gene splicing: See **genetic engineering.**

genetic engineering: The process of producing altered DNA, usually by breaking a DNA molecule and inserting new genes.

genetics: The branch of biology concerned with the ways in which hereditary information is transmitted from parents to offspring.

genotype: The genetic makeup of an individual.

genus: A group of closely related species.

geographic isolation: The first stage of speciation, in which a population of organisms is prevented from interbreeding with other populations of that species by a natural barrier.

geotropism: The growth response of a plant to the force of gravity.

germ theory of disease: The idea that bacteria and other microorganisms can cause disease.

gestation period: The length of a pregnancy.

GH: See **growth hormone.**

gibberellin: A hormone that affects plant growth as well as the development of fruits and seeds.

gill: In aquatic animals, a thin filament of skin richly supplied with blood vessels that is the respiratory organ. In some fungi, a reproductive structure that consists of many hyphae pressed closely together.

gill cover: See **operculum.**

gill slit: A structure found in pairs in the throat region of all chordates during some part of their lives.

gizzard: In birds and many invertebrates, a thick-walled grinding organ that crushes food released from the crop.

gland: An organ that produces certain substances that are released into ducts or into the blood.

gliding joint: A joint that permits limited flexibility in all directions.

glomerulus: A cluster of capillaries in the nephron of a kidney.

glucagon: The hormone secreted by the pancreas that increases the blood glucose level.

glucose: A monosaccharide that is the main source of energy for cellular respiration in most organisms.

glycerol: An alcohol that reacts with fatty acids to form fats; one of the end products of the digestion of fats.

glycogen: A polysaccharide that is the main food storage compound in animals.

glycolysis: The series of reactions in which a glucose molecule is converted into two molecules of pyruvic acid with a net gain of 2 ATP.

goiter: An enlargement of the thyroid gland, sometimes due to a deficiency of iodine.

Golgi body: An organelle consisting of stacks of membranes forming flattened sacs in the cytoplasm, which serves as a storage center for proteins synthesized by a cell.

gonad: In animals, a specialized organ in which gametes develop.

grafting: A type of artificial vegetative propagation accomplished by permanently joining a part of one plant to another plant.

grana: Stacks of lamellae in a chloroplast that contain the pigments for photosynthesis.

grassland: A biome in which there is not enough rainfall to support trees and the dominant form of vegetation is grasses: prairie.

gray matter: See **cerebral cortex.**

growth: The process by which living organisms increase in size.

growth hormone (GH): A hormone secreted by the anterior pituitary that controls the growth of the body.

grub: The larva stage of some insects.

guanine: A nitrogenous base found in DNA and RNA.

guard cell: In leaves, a specialized epidermal cell that regulates the opening and closing of the stomates.

gullet: The part of the paramecium where food particles enter the cell.

gymnosperm: A cone-bearing seed plant.

h

habit: Learned behavior that becomes automatic.

habitat: The particular part of the environment in which an organism lives.

hammer: The small bone in the middle ear attached to the eardrum.

haploid chromosome number: See **monoploid chromosome number.**

Hardy-Weinberg law: The principle that sexual reproduction by itself does not change gene frequencies in a population.

Haversian canal: A cavity in bone that contains the blood vessels and nerves that serve the osteocytes.

heart: The organ that pumps blood through a circulatory system.

heartwood: In older woody dicot stems, the inner region of xylem that does not conduct water.

hemocyanin: A copper-containing respiratory pigment.

hemoglobin: A red, iron-containing respiratory pigment that increases the oxygen-carrying capacity of the blood.

hemophilia: A hereditary disease in which one or more of the clotting factors are missing from the blood.

heparin: A naturally occurring anticoagulant.

hepatic-portal circulation: A subdivision of the systemic circulation that transports blood from the digestive tract to the liver.

herbaceous stem: A stem that is soft, green, and juicy.

herbivore: A heterotroph that feeds only on plants.

hermaphrodite: An individual organism that possesses both testes and ovaries.

heterotroph: An organism that cannot synthesize its own nutrients and must obtain them ready-made.

heterotroph hypothesis: The hypothesis that the first organic compounds were formed by natural chemical processes on the primitive earth and that the first lifelike structures developed from coacervates and were heterotrophs.

heterotrophic nutrition: A type of nutrition in which the organism requires preformed organic substances in its food.

heterozygous: Having two different alleles for a trait.

high blood pressure: See **hypertension.**

high-energy bond: A chemical bond that releases a relatively large amount of energy when broken.

hilum: A scar on the outside of a seed that marks the attachment of the ovule to the ovary.

hinge joint: A joint that permits back-and-forth motion.

histamine: A substance released by body cells during an allergic reaction.

homeostasis: The maintenance of a stable internal environment in an organism.

homologous chromosomes: A pair of chromosomes having the same size and shape and carrying alleles for the same traits.

homologous structures: Structures found in different kinds of organisms that have the same basic arrangement of parts and a similar pattern of embryonic development.

Homo sapiens: The species of modern humans.

homozygous: Having two identical alleles for a trait.

hormone: A substance that is secreted by a gland directly into the bloodstream and that produces a specific effect on a particular tissue.

host: In parasitism, the organism in which the parasite lives and from which it obtains nutrients.

human ecology: The study of the relationship between humans and the environment.

humus: The dark, rich organic matter in topsoil formed from the decay of dead plants and animals.

hybrid: An individual that is heterozygous for a particular trait; an individual produced by a cross between members of two closely related species.

hybrid vigor: Superior characteristics that are often found in hybrids produced by a cross of two closely related species; heterosis.

hydrogen acceptor: A molecule that accepts hydrogen atoms in a biochemical pathway.

hydrogenation: The addition of hydrogen atoms to an unsaturated fat.

hydrolysis: The process by which molecules are broken apart by the addition of water molecules.

hydroxyl ion (OH^-): A negatively charged ion consisting of an oxygen atom, a hydrogen atom, and an extra electron.

hypertension: A condition in which the blood pressure remains much above normal throughout the heartbeat cycle; high blood pressure.

hyphae: Threadlike filaments that make up the bodies of most fungi.

hypocotyl: The part of a plant embryo below the attachment of the cotyledons, which gives rise to the lower portion of the stem and the roots.

hypothalamus: The part of the human brain located below the thalamus; controls body temperature, blood pressure, and emotions.

hypothesis: A possible explanation of an observed set of facts.

I

identical twins: Two individuals formed when one fertilized egg divides in half at an early stage of development, producing two organisms with the same genetic makeup.

immovable joint: A joint in which the bones are fitted tightly together and cannot move.

immune response: The reaction of the immune system to the presence of foreign cells or molecules.

immunity: The ability of the body to resist a particular disease.

implantation: The attachment of the embryo to the uterine lining.

imprint: A type of fossil formed when an impression made in mud by a living thing is preserved when the mud is transformed into rock.

impulse: A region of electrical and chemical change that passes along the nerve cell membrane.

inborn immunity: Immunity that is present at birth.

inbreeding: A breeding method in which closely related individuals are mated to retain or strengthen certain desirable traits.

incisor: A type of tooth specialized for cutting food.

incomplete dominance: A type of inheritance in which neither of a pair of contrasting alleles is dominant over the other, and the heterozygous individual is intermediate in phenotype; blending inheritance.

independent assortment: The principle of genetics stating that genes for different traits are inherited independently of one another.

index fossil: The fossil of an organism that was common in many areas, but which existed for only a short period of time; used in relative dating.

indicator: A substance that changes color when the pH goes above or below a certain value.

industrial melanism: The development of dark-colored organisms in a population exposed to industrial air pollution.

inferior vena cava: A large vein that collects blood from the lower half of the body and returns it to the right atrium of the heart.

ingestion: The taking in of food from the environment.

inhalation: The phase of breathing in which air is drawn into the lungs.

innate behavior: Behavior determined by heredity.

inner ear: The innermost part of the ear, consisting of the cochlea and semicircular canals.

inorganic compound: A compound that does not contain carbon and hydrogen.

insectivorous plant: A plant that relies partly on trapped insects as a source of proteins and other nutrients.

instinct: A complex, inborn behavior pattern.

insulin: A hormone secreted by the pancreas that lowers blood glucose levels.

intercellular fluid: The colorless, watery fluid that bathes all the cells of the body; interstitial fluid.

internal fertilization: The process in which eggs are fertilized within the body of the female.

internal respiration: The exchange of oxygen and carbon dioxide between the blood and the body cells.

interneuron: A neuron that relays impulses from one neuron to another; associative neuron.

internode: The space between two nodes on a woody stem.

interphase: The stage of the cell reproductive cycle lasting from the end of one cell division to the beginning of the next.

interspecific competition: Competition between two different species in an ecosystem.

interstitial fluid: See **intercellular fluid.**

intestinal juice: A secretion of the walls of the small intestine containing digestive enzymes.

intestine: The organ in which digestion and absorption of food occurs.

intracellular digestion: Digestion that occurs in vacuoles within the cytoplasm of a cell.

intraspecific competition: Competition between members of the same species in an ecosystem.

inversion: A type of chromosomal alteration in which a portion of a chromosome is rotated, resulting in the reversal of the order of the genes in that segment.

involuntary muscle: Muscle that is not under conscious control; smooth muscle.

ion: An atom or group of atoms with an electrical charge.

ionic bond: The force of attraction between two ions in a chemical compound.

iris: The round, colored part of the eye formed from the choroid layer.

irritability: The capacity of a cell or organism to respond to stimuli.

islets of Langerhans: The endocrine portion of the pancreas, consisting of clusters of hormone-secreting cells.

isolation: Anything that prevents two groups within a species from interbreeding.

isotope: An atom that differs from other atoms of the

same element by the number of neutrons in its nucleus.

j

joint: A point in the skeleton where bones meet.

juvenile hormone: A hormone that prevents the transformation of larvae into more mature forms in insect development.

k

karyotyping: A technique for examining the chromosome makeup of an individual.

keratin: A tough, waterproof protein found in epidermis cells.

kidney: An excretory organ .

kilocalorie: The amount of heat needed to raise the temperature of 1 kg of water 1°C; 1,000 calories or 1 Calorie.

kingdom: A group of related phyla; the largest category in classification systems.

Krebs cycle: The biochemical pathway in which pyruvic acid is broken down, releasing carbon dioxide, hydrogen, and energy.

kwashiorkor: A deficiency disease caused by a lack of protein in the diet.

l

labor: The slow, rhythmic contractions of the uterine muscles during childbirth.

lacteal: A small lymph vessel found in the center of a villus.

lamellae: The system of double membranes inside a chloroplast.

larva: An early developmental stage of some animals; must undergo metamorphosis to reach the adult form.

larynx: The voice box; connects the pharynx with the trachea.

lateral bud: A bud found above a leaf scar on a woody dicot stem; axillary bud.

lateral line: An organ found in fishes that is sensitive to vibration.

latitude: Distance north or south of the equator.

layering: A type of artificial vegetative propagation, accomplished by covering part of a growing plant with soil.

leaf cutting: A leaf used to produce a new plant in a type of artificial vegetative propagation.

leaf scar: A mark on a woody dicot stem that indicates the point of attachment of leaves from previous growing seasons.

lens: In the eye, the structure behind the iris that focuses light on the retina.

lenticel: An opening in the surface of a green stem that allows the exchange of respiratory gases between the atmosphere and the plant tissues.

leucoplast: A colorless plastid in which glucose is converted to starch, and in which nutrients are stored.

leukemia: A form of blood cancer in which there is an uncontrolled increase in the number of white blood cells.

leukocyte: See **white blood cell.**

ligament: A tough, fibrous band of connective tissue that holds the bones together at a movable joint.

light microscope: A microscope that uses light rays and glass lenses to produce an enlarged image; optical microscope.

light reactions: In photosynthesis, a series of reactions requiring light in which water is split and ATP and $NADPH_2$ are produced.

limiting factor: A condition of the environment that limits the growth of a population, such as limited availability of food, water, space, or some other necessity.

linked genes: Genes located on the same chromosome; they are not independently assorted, but instead are generally distributed together during meiosis.

lipase: An enzyme that breaks down lipids.

lipid: An organic compound other than a carbohydrate, consisting of carbon, hydrogen, and oxygen; a fat, oil, or wax.

litmus: A pH indicator that turns red in acid solutions and blue in basic solutions.

liver: An organ that secretes bile and removes toxic substances from the blood.

locomotion: Self-generated movement from one place to another.

long-day plant: A plant that produces flowers in summer when there are 12 to 14 hours of daylight.

long-term memory: Memory lasting weeks or years.

loop of Henle: In a nephron, the long, untwisted part of the tubule between Bowman's capsule and the collecting duct.

lung: In vertebrates, an organ specialized for the exchange of gases between the blood and the atmosphere.

luteinizing hormone (LH): A hormone secreted by the anterior pituitary that stimulates production of a corpus luteum.

lymph: The fluid inside the lymph vessels.

lymphatic system: A system of vessels that returns excess fluid and proteins from the intercellular spaces to the blood.

lymph node: A lymphatic gland that plays an important role in the body's defense against disease.

lymphocyte: A white blood cell that recognizes and destroys antigens present in the body tissues.

lysosome: A small, saclike organelle that contains hydrolytic enzymes.

m

macronucleus: In ciliates, the larger nucleus that controls metabolism.

macrophage: A large phagocytic cell.

maggot: The larval stage of some insects.

magnification: The amount of enlargement of an image that a lens or a microscope produces.

Malpighian tubule: The excretory organ of grasshoppers and other insects.

mammary gland: An exocrine gland in female mammals that secretes milk for the nourishment of young after they are born.

mantle: A fold of skin that surrounds the body organs in mollusks.

marine biome: A community of organisms inhabiting salt water.

marrow: The soft tissue that fills the hollow spaces in bone.

marsupial: Nonplacental mammal in which the fetus is born at a very immature stage and completes its development in a pouch on the mother's body.

mass number: The total number of protons and neutrons in the nucleus of an atom.

mass spectrometer: An instrument used to detect the presence of different atoms by separating them according to their masses.

maternal immunity: A form of passive immunity in which the baby receives antibodies from the mother.

mating types: In protists, different strains that will reproduce sexually with each other; usually called plus or minus.

maturation zone: The region behind the elongation zone of the root in which cells differentiate.

medulla: The part of the brain beneath the cerebellum and continuous with the spinal cord; controls involuntary activities.

medusa: The body form of free-swimming coelenterates.

meiosis: Cell division that occurs only in sex cells and that produces monoploid cells; reduction division.

melanin: A dark pigment of the skin.

melanocyte: A pigment-containing cell in the skin.

melanocyte-stimulating hormone (MSH): A hormone produced by the anterior pituitary that stimulates the melanocytes in the skin.

melatonin: A hormone produced by the pineal gland.

memory cell: A cell, produced by B lymphocytes, that remains in the lymphoid tissue and provides immunity to the disease that caused its production.

meninges: A tough membrane that covers and protects the brain and spinal cord.

meningitis: An infection or inflammation of the meninges.

menopause: The cessation of the menstrual cycle.

menstrual cycle: The hormone-controlled cycle in the human female in which an egg matures and is released from the ovary and the uterus prepares to receive it.

menstruation: The shedding of some of the uterine lining, the unfertilized egg, and a small amount of blood through the vagina, which occurs about once a month in the human female.

meristematic tissue: The only tissue of a mature plant capable of cell division; meristem.

meristematic zone: A region of actively dividing cells just behind the root cap.

mescaline: A hallucinatory drug that interferes with the effect of serotonin.

mesoderm: The germ layer between the endoderm and ectoderm.

mesophyll: A layer of photosynthetic tissue found between the upper and lower layers of the epidermis of a leaf.

messenger RNA (mRNA): The type of RNA strand that carries the code for a polypeptide from DNA in the nucleus to the cytoplasm, where it is translated by ribosomes together with transfer RNA.

metabolism: All the chemical reactions of the life processes of an organism.

metamerism: The type of segmentation found in annelids in which each body segment contains the same internal organs.

metamorphosis: The series of changes that certain types of organisms undergo as they develop from an egg to an adult.

metaphase: The stage of mitosis during which the chromosomes are lined up at the equatorial plane and the chromatids separate.

microdissection: Operations done under a microscope on living cells, using very small instruments.

microfilament: A solid, threadlike organelle that can function as a supporting structure or aid in cell movement.

micrometer: One-millionth of a meter; one micron.

micron: See **micrometer.**

micronucleus: In ciliates, the smaller nucleus that controls reproduction.

micropyle: A small opening in the ovule through which the pollen tube grows.

microtome: An instrument used to slice thin sections of a specimen for viewing with a microscope.

microtubule: A long, cylindrical organelle found in cilia and flagella.

microvillus: A tiny projection on the surface of an

epithelial cell in the small intestine.

middle ear: An air-filled chamber between the eardrum and the oval window, which contains the hammer, anvil, and stirrup, and from which the Eustachian tube extends.

migration: The movement of animals from one region or community to another.

mimicry: A protective adaptation in which one species is protected from its enemies by its resemblance to another species.

mineral: An inorganic substance found naturally in the earth's crust.

mitochondrion: An oval membrane-enclosed organelle in which most of the reactions of cellular respiration occur.

mitosis: The process by which the nucleus of a cell divides.

mitotic cell division: Cell division in which the nucleus divides by mitosis and the cell cytoplasm also divides.

mitral valve: See **bicuspid valve.**

mixed nerve: A nerve composed of both sensory and motor fibers.

mixture: A combination of substances in which the substances are physically mingled but are not chemically bonded to each other.

molar: A type of tooth specialized for grinding food.

mold: A type of fossil formed when sediment in which an organism is embedded hardens, preserving the shape of the organism after its remains decompose. A kind of fungus.

molecular formula: A formula that shows the composition of a molecule of a compound.

molecule: An uncharged group of atoms held together by covalent bonds.

molting: The process in which an exoskeleton or other outer covering is shed and replaced by a new one.

molting hormone: A hormone that stimulates the periodic molting of the exoskeleton.

momentary memory: Memory retained for only a few moments.

Monera: The kingdom that includes the simplest one-celled organisms—the bacteria and blue-green algae.

mongolism: See **Down's syndrome.**

monocot: A plant whose seeds have one cotyledon.

monohybrid cross: A genetic cross in which only one pair of contrasting traits is studied.

monoploid chromosome number: Half the diploid number of chromosomes; the haploid, or n , chromosome number.

monosaccharide: The simplest type of carbohydrate, with the empirical formula CH_2O; a simple sugar.

morula: An early stage of development in which the embryo consists of a solid ball of cells; formed by cleavage of the fertilized egg.

motile: Capable of locomotion.

motor end plate: The structure at the end of a motor neuron.

motor nerve: A nerve that contains only motor neurons.

motor neuron: A neuron that carries impulses from the spinal cord and brain toward an effector.

mRNA: See **messenger RNA.**

MSH: See **melanocyte-stimulating hormone.**

mucus: A lubricant secreted by cells in the linings of the respiratory and digestive systems.

multiple alleles: Three or more different forms of a gene, each producing a different phenotype.

multiple birth: The birth of more than one child from the same pregnancy.

multiple-gene inheritance: The type of inheritance in which two or more pairs of genes affect the same characteristic; polygenic inheritance.

muscle: A tissue consisting of cells that have the capacity to contract and exert a pull.

muscle tone: The state of partial contraction in which all muscles are kept.

mutagenic agent: A material or environmental factor that causes mutations.

mutant: A variation resulting from a mutation.

mutation: The appearance of a new allele on a chromosome.

mutualism: A symbiotic relationship in which both organisms benefit from their association.

mycelium: A tangled mass of hyphae.

myelin: A white, fatty substance produced by Schwann cells on some axons.

myosin: A protein found in skeletal muscle.

n

NAD (nicotinamide adenine dinucleotide): A coenzyme that acts as a hydrogen acceptor in cellular respiration.

natural selection: The idea that organisms with favorable variations are better able to survive and reproduce than less well-adapted organisms.

Neanderthal man: An early type of *Homo sapiens* that first appeared about 100,000 years ago.

nematocyst: The capsule within a cnidoblast containing a coiled, hollow thread that is discharged when the cnidoblast is stimulated.

nephridiopore: An opening to the outside of the body for the bladder of the earthworm.

nephridium: The organ of excretion in the earthworm and other annelids.

nephron: The functional unit of the kidney.

nerve: A bundle of axons, or fibers, that are bound together by connective tissue.

nerve cell: A neuron.

neurohumor: See **neurotransmitter.**

neuromuscular junction: The junction between motor neurons and muscle fibers.

neuron: A cell specialized for the transmission of impulses; a nerve cell.

neurotransmitter: A substance released from the synaptic knob into the synaptic cleft that initiates impulses in adjacent neurons.

neutral: Neither acidic or basic; a neutral solution has a pH of 7.

neutralization: The reaction of an acid and a base to produce a neutral solution.

neutron: An electrically neutral particle found in the nuclei of atoms.

niche: The particular way in which a species functions in an ecosystem.

nictitating membrane: A transparent eyelid which allows a frog to see underwater.

night blindness: An inability to see in dim light, resulting from a deficiency of vitamin A.

nitrifying bacteria: Bacteria that can convert nitrites to nitrates.

nitrogen cycle: The pathways by which nitrogen is circulated through the biosphere.

nitrogen fixation: The process by which nitrogen-fixing organisms produce nitrogen compounds from the gaseous nitrogen of the atmosphere.

nitrogen-fixing bacteria: Bacteria that can produce nitrogen compounds from the gaseous nitrogen of the atmosphere.

node: A point along the stem of a woody dicot where leaves and lateral buds form.

node of Ranvier: A gap in the myelin between adjacent Schwann cells along an axon.

nondisjunction: The failure of homologous chromosomes to separate normally during meiosis, producing offspring with one more or one less chromosome than normal.

nonplacental mammal: A mammal in which no placenta forms during development of the embryo; a marsupial or egg-laying mammal.

nonrenewable natural resource: A resource that can be used only once, such as coal, oil, and minerals, and cannot be replaced.

norepinephrine: An excitatory neurotransmitter; noradrenaline.

nostril: An opening in the nose through which air enters the respiratory system.

notochord: A flexible, rodlike, internal supporting structure found in all chordates during some part of their lives.

nucleic acid: An organic compound with a very large molecule made up of repeating units called nucleotides, which form the genetic code for transmitting hereditary information; DNA or RNA.

nucleolar organizer: The area on a chromosome where nucleoli are formed.

nucleolus: A dense, granular body that is found in the nucleus of cells and that is a site of RNA production.

nucleotide: The basic unit of nucleic acids, containing a sugar, a phosphate group, and one of four nitrogenous bases.

nucleus: In a cell, a large, dense, membrane-enclosed body that controls the cell's metabolism and reproduction. In an atom, the central core of the atom, containing protons and neutrons.

nutrient: A substance that can be used in metabolism for energy, for growth and repair, or for regulation.

nutrition: The process by which materials from the environment are taken into an organism and changed into usable forms.

O

objective: The lens of a compound microscope that is close to the specimen and forms an image that is further enlarged by the ocular.

ocellus: The simple eye of a grasshopper.

ocular: The lens of a compound microscope that is placed close to the eye and through which the image of the specimen is observed.

olfactory cell: A receptor for smell located in the mucous membrane lining the upper nasal cavity.

omnivore: A heterotroph that feeds on both plants and animals.

one gene—one polypeptide hypothesis: The hypothesis that every gene directs the synthesis of a particular polypeptide chain; originally called the one gene—one enzyme hypothesis.

oocyte: An immature egg cell that undergoes meiotic division.

oogenesis: The formation of eggs in the ovaries.

oogonium: An immature egg cell in the ovary.

ootid: The large, monoploid daughter cell produced by the meiotic division of the secondary oocyte.

open circulatory system: A circulatory system in which blood is not always enclosed in blood vessels, but flows into open spaces to bathe the tissues.

operculum: A protective, bony flap that covers the gills of bony fishes; gill cover.

optical microscope: See **light microscope.**

optic nerve: The nerve that carries impulses from the receptors in the retina of the eye to the brain.

oral groove: The opening in the paramecium through which food is ingested.

order: A group of related families.

organelle: A specialized structure in the cytoplasm of a cell that carries out a specific function.

organic acid: An organic compound that releases hydrogen ions in solution, usually containing a $-COOH$ group.

organic compound: A compound that contains carbon

along with hydrogen; found in nature only in the bodies and products of living organisms.

organism: An individual living thing.

osculum: An opening at the unattached end of a sponge that serves as the excurrent opening.

osmosis: The diffusion of water across a semipermeable membrane from a region of high concentration of water to a region of low concentration of water.

osmotic pressure: The increase in pressure resulting from the flow of water in osmosis.

ossification: The process by which cartilage is replaced by bone in the skeletons of most vertebrates.

osteoblast: A bone cell that secretes collagen and polysaccharides.

osteocyte: An osteoblast entrapped in a small cavity within the bone substance.

outbreeding: A breeding method in which individuals not closely related are mated to introduce new beneficial genes into the population.

outer ear: The visible part of the ear, and extending to the eardrum.

oval window: The membrane between the middle and inner ear, connected to the eardrum by three small bones.

ovary: In animals, the female gonad, which produces egg cells; in flowering plants, the structure at the base of the pistil in which fertilization occurs and which develops into a fruit.

oviduct: A tube that carries the egg away from the ovary.

ovulation: The release of an egg from an ovary.

ovule: In seed plants, a structure within the ovary that contains the egg-cell nucleus and that develops into the seed after fertilization.

ovum: Egg cell.

oxidation: A type of chemical reaction in which an atom or molecule loses electrons or hydrogen atoms.

oxidation-reduction reaction: A reaction in which one substance is oxidized and another substance is reduced.

oxygen cycle: The pathways of oxygen in the biosphere.

oxygen debt: The amount of oxygen needed to dispose of the lactic acid accumulated in muscle cells after exercise.

oxyhemoglobin: Hemoglobin combined with oxygen; HbO_2.

oxytocin: A hormone secreted by the posterior pituitary that stimulates labor contractions during childbirth.

p

pacemaker: A specialized group of cells in the wall of the right atrium that initiates contraction of the heart by electrical impulses.

paleontology: The study of fossils.

palisade cells: The tall, tightly packed cells filled with chloroplasts that make up the upper layer of the mesophyll of the leaf.

pancreas: An organ that is both an exocrine gland and endocrine gland and that secretes digestive juice and the hormones insulin and glucagon.

pancreatic juice: The digestive secretion of the pancreas containing sodium bicarbonate, amylase, proteases, and lipases.

parapodia: Paired, paddlelike extensions found on each segment of some annelids; used for swimming and creeping.

parasite: A heterotroph that obtains nutrients from the organism in or on which it lives.

parasitism: A symbiotic relationship in which one organism benefits from the association and the other is harmed.

parasympathetic nervous system: The division of the autonomic nervous system that slows down the functioning of various body systems.

parathormone: A hormone secreted by the parathyroid glands that regulates calcium and phosphate metabolism.

parathyroid glands: Four small glands embedded in back of the thyroid that secrete parathormone.

parenchyma: A fundamental plant tissue made up of unspecialized cells and used for food storage.

parthenogenesis: The development of an unfertilized egg into an adult animal.

passive immunity: An acquired immunity in which a person receives antibodies from the blood of another person or an animal.

passive transport: A process by which materials move across cell membranes without the expenditure of cellular energy.

pectoral girdle: The shoulder blades and the collar bones, which connect the arms to the spine.

pedicel: The structure that connects a flower to the stem of a plant.

pellicle: A grooved, flexible protein structure found inside the cell membrane of some protists.

pelvic girdle: The hipbones, which connect the legs to the spine.

penis: In mammals, the male organ through which the urethra passes to the outside of the body and through which urine and sperm pass out of the body.

pepsin: A digestive enzyme in gastric juice.

peptide bond: The bond formed between two amino acids by dehydration synthesis.

pericardium: The tough, protective membrane surrounding the outside of the heart.

pericycle: A ring of parenchyma cells surrounding the vascular cylinder of the root from which all secondary roots originate.

periosteum: A tough membrane covering the outside of bones, except at joints.

peripheral nervous system: The division of the nervous system that includes all the neurons and nerve fibers outside the brain and spinal cord.

peristalsis: The alternate waves of contraction and relaxation in the walls of the alimentary canal.

permafrost: The lower layers of the soil in the tundra that remain frozen throughout the year.

petals: The flower structures found within the sepals, surrounding the reproductive organs.

petiole: The structure that attaches the leaf to the stem of a plant.

petrifaction: The process by which the body of a dead organism is slowly replaced by dissolved minerals.

pH: A unit that indicates the concentration of hydrogen ions in a solution; a measure of the acidity of a solution.

phagocyte: A leukocyte that engulfs foreign matter in the same way an ameba engulfs food.

phagocytosis: The process in which large particles or small organisms are ingested into a cell when they are engulfed by pseudopods.

pharynx: The throat.

phenolphthalein: An indicator that changes from colorless to red in basic solutions.

phenotype: The physical traits that appear in an individual as a result of its genetic makeup.

phenylketonuria: A genetic disease in which an enzyme necessary for the normal breakdown of the amino acid phenylalanine is missing, causing brain damage and mental retardation; PKU.

pheromone: A type of animal secretion that serves as a means of communication between members of the same species.

phloem: The tissue that conducts food and other dissolved materials throughout the plant.

phosphorylation: The transfer of a phosphate group to a compound, usually accompanied by a transfer of energy.

photic zone: In a body of water, the layer of water through which light penetrates.

photon: A particle of light.

photoperiodism: The response of a plant to the changing duration of light and darkness during the year.

photosynthesis: The process by which organic nutrients are synthesized from inorganic compounds in the presence of light in most autotrophic organisms.

phototropism: The growth of a plant toward a light source.

phylum: The largest or most inclusive group within a kingdom.

phytoplankton: Photosynthetic planktonic organisms, the major producers of the oceans.

pigment: A substance that absorbs light of particular wavelengths.

pineal gland: A pea-sized gland attached to the base of the brain that produces melatonin.

pinocytosis: The process in which liquids or very small particles from the surrounding medium are taken into a cell by an inpocketing of the cell membrane.

pioneer organism: One of the first organisms to inhabit an area.

pistil: The female reproductive organ of flowering plants.

pistillate flower: A flower that contains pistils but no stamens.

pith: The center of a herbaceous dicot stem, made up of parenchyma cells.

pituitary gland: The endocrine gland attached to the hypothalamus that controls the activities of many other endocrine glands in the body.

pivot joint: A joint that permits rotation from side to side as well as up-and-down movement.

PKU: See **phenylketonuria.**

placenta: In mammals, a temporary organ through which the fetus receives food and oxygen from the mother's body and gets rid of wastes.

placental mammal: A mammal in which a placenta forms during development of the embryo.

plankton: Organisms that float near the surface of the ocean and are carried by the ocean's currents.

planula: The small, ciliated larva of many coelenterates.

plasma: The liquid portion of blood, consisting mostly of water and dissolved proteins.

plasma cell: An antibody-forming cell produced by B lymphocytes.

plasma membrane: See **cell membrane.**

plasmid: A small, ring-shaped segment of DNA that is found in bacteria and that stays separate from the bacterial chromosome; used in genetic engineering.

plasmolysis: The shrinking of cytoplasm resulting from loss of water by osmosis in a cell placed in a hypertonic solution.

plastid: A membrane-enclosed organelle found in the cells of some protists and almost all plants; chloroplasts are the most important type of plastid.

plastron: The lower shell of a turtle.

platelet: A small, round or oval blood cell fragment that triggers the blood-clotting process.

pleura: A two-layered membrane that encloses the human lung.

plexus: A large cluster of ganglia.

pneumonia: A condition in which the alveoli become filled with fluid, preventing the exchange of gases in the lungs.

polar body: The small daughter cell produced by the meiotic divisions of the primary and secondary oocytes.

polar nuclei: In flowering plants, the two nuclei found in the embryo sac that fuse with a sperm nucleus to form the endosperm nucleus.

pole: In cell division, the two regions from which the spindle fibers radiate and toward which the chromosomes move during anaphase.

pollen cone: The male cone of a gymnosperm.

pollen grain: A small capsule containing the male monoploid gamete produced by the anther in flowering plants.

pollen tube: The structure through which sperm nuclei pass from the pollen grain to the ovule of a flower.

pollination: The transfer of pollen from an anther to a stigma of a flower.

pollution: The addition of anything to the environment that makes it less fit for living things.

polygenic inheritance: See **multiple-gene inheritance.**

polymer: A large molecule consisting of chains of repeating units.

polyp: The sessile body form of a coelenterate.

polypeptide: A chain of amino acids joined by peptide bonds.

polyploidy: A condition in which the cells have some multiple of the normal chromosome number.

polysaccharide: A long chain of repeating sugar units formed by joining simple sugars by dehydration synthesis.

population: A group of organisms of the same species living together in a given region and capable of interbreeding.

population genetics: The study of the changes in the genetic makeup of populations.

posterior: Pertaining to the rear or tail end of a bilaterally symmetrical animal.

precapillary sphincter: A ring of muscle at the capillary end of an arteriole that controls blood flow through the capillary.

precipitation: The release of water from the atmosphere in such forms as rain, snow, dew, and fog.

predator: A carnivore that attacks and kills its prey and feeds on their bodies.

premolar: A type of tooth specialized for grinding food.

primary consumer: An animal that feeds on plants; a herbivore, or first-level consumer.

primary root: The first structure to emerge from a sprouting seed.

primary succession: Succession that occurs in an area that had no previously existing life.

procaryote: A cell that lacks a distinct, membrane-bounded nucleus; a moneran.

producer: An organism that produces organic compounds from inorganic compounds; an autotroph.

progesterone: A hormone secreted by the ovaries that helps to regulate the menstrual cycle and maintains the uterus during pregnancy.

prophase: The stage of mitosis in which the chromatids and spindle appear, and the nuclear membrane disappears.

prop root: An adventitious root that grows from the aboveground portion of the stem down into the soil and helps to brace the plant.

prostaglandin: A local hormone that produces its effects on the cells in which it is synthesized, without entering the bloodstream.

prostate gland: A gland that secretes fluid into the urethra to form semen.

protease: An enzyme that breaks down proteins into shorter polypeptides or into separate amino acids.

protein: A compound consisting of one or more chains of amino acids.

prothallus: The small, heart-shaped structure that is the monoploid gametophyte plant of the fern.

prothrombin: A plasma protein converted to thrombin in the blood-clotting process.

Protista: A kingdom that includes simple, mostly unicellular organisms that contain a membrane-bounded nucleus.

proton: A positively charged particle found in the nucleus of all atoms.

pseudopod: A temporary projection of the cell surface in amebas and similar cells.

ptyalin: See **salivary amylase.**

puberty: The stage of human development in which the individual begins to produce gametes and becomes capable of reproduction; the onset of sexual maturity.

pulmonary circulation: The pathways in which blood flows between the heart and the lungs.

pulse: The alternate expansion and contraction that can be felt in an artery each time the left ventricle contracts.

pupa: The resting stage of metamorphosis in which the tissues of an insect are organized into the adult form.

pupil: The opening in the center of the iris of the eye, which allows light to enter the inside of the eye.

pure: Homozygous for a trait.

purine: A type of nitrogenous base found in DNA and RNA; adenine and guanine.

pyloric gland: A gland in the lining of the stomach that secretes mucus.

pyloric sphincter: The sphincter muscle that controls the passage of food from the stomach to the small intestine.

pyramid of biomass: The relative mass of organisms at each feeding level in an ecosystem.

pyramid of energy: The relative amount of available energy at each feeding level in an ecosystem.

pyrimidine: A type of nitrogenous base found in DNA and RNA; thymine, cytosine, and uracil.

pyruvic acid: A 3-carbon compound formed by glycolysis.

r

radial symmetry: A type of symmetry in which any cross section through the central axis of the organism divides it into similar halves.

radicle: The lowermost part of the hypocotyl, which usually gives rise to the roots of the plant.

radioactivity: The process in which an atom changes

to another isotope or element by giving off charged particles and/or radiation.

radioisotope: A radioactive isotope.

radula: A rasping, tonguelike organ in mollusks.

Ramapithecus: A fossil estimated to be 12 to 14 million years old that is intermediate in form between apes and humans.

range: The particular region of the earth where a species is found.

reabsorption: The process in which needed substances pass out of the nephron and are returned to the blood.

receptacle: The expanded end of the pedicel of a flower, to which the other flower parts are attached.

receptor: In a nervous system, a specialized structure sensitive to a certain type of stimulus; a sense organ.

recessive gene: A gene whose phenotype is not expressed if the dominant allele is also present.

recombinant DNA: DNA that has been altered by genetic engineering.

rectum: A structure in which undigested food (feces) is stored prior to elimination from the body.

recycling: The process of reusing materials rather than discarding them as waste.

red blood cell: A hemoglobin-containing cell in blood that carries oxygen to the body tissues and carbon dioxide to the lungs; an erythrocyte.

reduction: A type of chemical reaction in which an atom or molecule gains electrons or hydrogen atoms.

reduction division: See **meiosis.**

reflex: An involuntary, automatic response to a given stimulus not involving the brain.

reflex arc: The pathway over which the nerve impulses travel in a reflex.

refractory period: The brief recovery period during which a nerve-cell membrane cannot be stimulated to carry impulses.

regeneration: The regrowth of lost body parts by an animal.

regulation: The processes by which an organism maintains a stable internal environment in a constantly changing external environment.

relative dating: A technique in which the relative ages of layers of sedimentary rocks are determined, allowing the relative ages of the fossils in the layers to be determined.

releasing factor: A hormone that is produced by the hypothalamus and that controls the release of a hormone from the anterior pituitary.

renal circulation: A subdivision of the systemic circulation that carries blood to and from the kidneys.

renewable natural resource: A natural resource, such as air, water, soil, sunlight, and living organisms, that can be replaced by natural processes.

replication: Duplication, especially of DNA.

reproduction: The process by which living things produce new organisms of their own kind.

reproductive isolation: The loss of ability to interbreed successfully by two groups of a population that have been separated geographically for a long time.

resolution: The ability of a microscope to show two points that are close together as separate images; resolving power.

respiration: The process by which organisms obtain the energy they need by releasing chemical energy stored in nutrients.

respiratory surface: A moist surface through which the exchange of respiratory gases takes place.

response: Any change in or action by an organism resulting from a stimulus.

retina: The innermost layer of the eye, on which an image is produced.

retinal: A light-sensitive pigment synthesized from vitamin A involved in both color and black-and-white vision.

Rh factor: One of a group of antigens found on the surface of red blood cells.

rhizoid: An underground structure that functions as a root in many bryophytes, anchoring the plant and absorbing water and minerals.

rhizome: A thick, horizontal stem containing stored food, which forms new plants by vegetative reproduction.

ribonucleic acid: See **RNA.**

ribosomal RNA (rRNA): A type of RNA formed by DNA in the nucleolus and found in the ribosomes.

ribosome: An organelle that is the site of protein synthesis in a cell.

right lymph duct: The large lymphatic vessel that drains lymph from the upper right half of the body into a large vein on the right side of the neck.

RNA (ribonucleic acid): The nucleic acid that carries out instructions coded in DNA.

rod: A structure in the retina of the eye responsible for black-and-white vision.

root: A structure adapted for anchoring a plant and absorbing water and dissolved substances.

root cap: A thimble-shaped group of cells that form a protective covering for the root tip.

root hair: A hairlike extension of a root epidermal cell that increases the surface area for absorption.

root pressure: The osmotic pressure in the root cells.

roughage: Bulky, indigestible material in food.

rRNA: See **ribosomal RNA.**

rumen: In ruminants, the chamber of the stomach in which food is stored.

ruminant: An ungulate that stores food in its four-chambered stomach the first time it is swallowed and then brings it up to chew again before swallowing it a second time.

runner: A horizontal stem with buds that forms independent plants by vegetative production; a stolon.

S

saliva: The secretion of the salivary glands.

salivary amylase: The enzyme in saliva that hydrolyzes starch into maltose; ptyalin.

salivary gland: A gland that secretes saliva into the mouth.

salt: A compound produced by a neutralization reaction between an acid and a base.

saltatory conduction: Conduction of a nerve impulse in a myelinated nerve where the impulse jumps from one node of Ranvier to the next.

saprophyte: An organism that obtains nutrients by breaking down the remains of dead plants and animals.

sapwood: The functional xylem next to the cambium in woody dicot stems.

saturated fat: A fat formed from fatty acids in which all carbon-to-carbon bonds are single bonds.

scale: The modified leaf of a pine cone, on which the spore-producing structures are found.

scanning electron microscope: A microscope that passes an electron beam over the surface of a specimen to produce an image of great depth.

scavenger: A carnivore that feeds on dead animals that it finds.

Schwann cell: A type of cell that surrounds axons and forms the myelin sheath.

scion: The detached, or unrooted, piece of a plant used in grafting.

sclera: The tough, fibrous, white,outer layer of the eye.

sclerenchyma: A fundamental plant tissue made up of thick-walled cells that function in support.

scrotum: A sac of skin outside the body wall in which the testes of the male are located.

sebaceous gland: A gland in the skin that produces oily secretions.

secondary consumer: In a food chain, a carnivore that feeds on primary consumers, or herbivores; a second-level consumer.

secondary root: A branch of a primary root.

secondary sex characteristic: A characteristic, such as body hair, muscle development, broadened pelvis, or voice depth, controlled by the male and female sex hormones, but not essential to the reproductive process.

secondary succession: Succession that occurs in an area in which an existing community has been partially destroyed and its balance upset.

second-level consumer: See **secondary consumer.**

secretin: A hormone secreted by cells in the lining of the small intestine; stimulates secretion of pancreatic juice.

sedimentary rock: A type of rock formed from layers of particles that settled to the bottom of a body of water, often containing fossils.

seed: In seed plants, the structure formed from the ovule following fertilization; contains the plant embryo and nutrients.

seed coat: A tough, protective covering around a seed that develops from the wall of the ovule.

seed cone: The female cone of a gymnosperm.

seed plant: A plant that reproduces by means of seeds; gymnosperms and angiosperms.

segregation: In genetics, the separation of alleles during meiosis; the presence of only one allele for a particular trait in each gamete.

selection: A technique in which only those animals and plants with the most desirable traits are chosen for breeding.

self-pollination: Pollination in which pollen grains are transferred from an anther to a stigma on the same plant.

semen: The mixture of sperm and fluids released during ejaculation.

semicircular canals: A system of loop-shaped tubes in the inner ear that enable the body to maintain balance.

semilunar valve: The valve that allows blood to flow from a ventricle into an artery.

seminal vesicle: A gland that secretes fluid into the urethra to form semen.

seminiferous tubules: Small, coiled tubes in which immature sperm are produced.

semipermeable membrane: A membrane that allows the passage of some materials but not others.

sense organ: See **receptor.**

sensory nerve: A nerve that contains only sensory neurons.

sensory neuron: A neuron that carries impulses from a receptor toward the spinal cord and brain.

sepal: A leaflike structure at the base of a flower outside the petals.

septum: A partition; the partition that separates the right and left sides of the heart.

serotonin: An inhibitory neurotransmitter.

serum: The blood plasma minus the clotting factors.

sessile: Living attached to some object.

setae: Tiny bristles on the body segments of annelids, used in locomotion.

sex chromosomes: The two unmatched chromosomes that determine the sex of an individual; represented as X and Y.

sex gland: A gland in which gametes are produced; ovary or testis.

sex-linked trait: A trait that is controlled by a gene found on one of the sex chromosomes.

sexual reproduction: A form of reproduction in which a new individual is produced by the union of the nuclei of two specialized sex cells, usually from two separate parent organisms.

short-day plant: A plant that flowers in the early spring, late summer, or fall, when the nights are longer than 10-12 hours.

short-term memory: Memory that can be recalled for up to several hours.

sickle-cell anemia: A genetic disease in which the red blood cells have an abnormal hemoglobin molecule and an abnormal shape.

sieve tube cell: The type of cell that makes up the conducting tubes of the phloem.

simple eye: A type of eye that does not form images, but is sensitive only to light and dark.

simple microscope: A magnifying glass.

simple sugar: A monosaccharide.

sinoatrial node: The structure in the heart that acts as the pacemaker.

sinus: A body space.

skeletal muscle: Muscle that is attached to bone and is involved in locomotion and voluntary movement; striated muscle.

skull: The bony framework of the head that encloses the brain.

slime sheath: A protective, jellylike layer that surrounds the outside of the cell walls of blue-green algae.

smooth muscle: Muscle tissue made up of individual cells, not marked by striations, and not under voluntary control.

sodium-potassium pump: An active transport mechanism that pumps sodium ions out of and potassium ions into a nerve cell; sodium pump.

solute: A substance dissolved in a solvent.

solution: A mixture, usually liquid, in which one substance, in the form of molecules or ions, is uniformly distributed through another substance.

solvent: The liquid substance that makes up the bulk of a solution.

somatic cell: A body cell, as distinguished from a sex cell.

somatic nervous system: The division of the peripheral nervous system that contains sensory and motor neurons that connect the central nervous system to skeletal muscles, skin, and sense organs.

sori: Small, dotlike structures on the underside of some fern fronds; produce monoploid spores by meiosis.

speciation: The formation of new species.

species: All organisms of one kind that can interbreed in nature.

spectrophotometer: An instrument that measures the wavelengths of light absorbed by a solution.

spectrum: The arrangement of the different colors of visible light in order of wavelength.

spermatogenesis: The formation of sperm in the testes.

spermatid: The monoploid cell that develops into a mature sperm.

spermatogonium: An immature sex cell in the testis.

sperm cell: The male gamete.

sperm receptacle: The organ in which sperm are deposited during mating between hermaphrodites.

spherical symmetry: A type of symmetry in which any cut passing through the center of the organism divides it into matching halves.

sphincter: A ring of muscle that acts as a valve.

sphygmomanometer: An instrument used to measure arterial blood pressure.

spicule: A small skeletal structure embedded in the middle layer of sponges that provides support and gives shape to the sponge.

spinal canal: The canal that is in the center of the spinal cord and is filled with cerebrospinal fluid.

spinal column: In vertebrates, the series of vertebrae connected by cartilage discs that surrounds and protects the spinal cord; the backbone.

spinal cord: The cord of nervous tissue that extends down from the brain, running through the vertebrae of the spinal column.

spinal nerve: A nerve connected to the spinal cord.

spindle: A cone-shaped structure formed by fibers during mitosis.

spiracle: The opening through which air enters and leaves the body of a grasshopper.

spirillum: A spiral or coiled bacterium.

spongy mesophyll: The lower portion of mesophyll in a leaf, consisting of irregularly shaped cells separated by large air spaces.

spontaneous generation: The idea that living things regularly arise from nonliving matter; abiogenesis.

sporangium: A structure that produces spores.

spore: A small reproductive cell that can give rise to a new organism under favorable conditions.

sporophyte generation: The spore-producing generation in a plant showing an alteration of generations.

sporulation: Spore formation.

stamen: The male reproductive organ of a flower.

staminate flower: A flower that contains stamens but no pistils.

starch: A polysaccharide that is the main food storage compound in plants.

stem: The supporting structure of a plant, through which materials are transported between the roots and leaves.

stereomicroscope: A microscope with an ocular and an objective for each eye, which provides a three-dimensional image of the specimen being viewed; binocular microscope.

sternum: The bone to which the ribs are attached ventrally; the breastbone.

steroids: A group of organic compounds containing carbon rings and alcohol groups; includes cholesterol, the sex hormones, and other hormones.

stigma: In a pistil, the enlarged, sticky knob on top of a style that receives the pollen. In protists, an eyespot.

stimulus: Any factor that causes a receptor to trigger impulses in a nerve pathway.

stipe: Stalk.

stirrup: The small bone in the middle ear connected to the oval window.

stock: In grafting, the rooted plant onto which the scion is attached.

stolon: In fungi, a hypha that grows in a network over the surface of food; a runner.

stomach: The organ in which food is temporarily stored and partially digested.

stomate: An opening in the epidermis of leaves that allows the exchange of respiratory gases between the internal tissues of the leaf and the atmosphere.

striated muscle: See **skeletal muscle**

strip cropping: A conservation practice in which cover crops are planted between strips of row crops, leaving no soil open to erosion.

stroma: The protein-containing material that surrounds the lamellae in a chloroplast.

structural formula: A molecular formula that shows how the atoms in a molecule are bonded to one another.

style: In flowers, the part of the pistil that supports the stigma.

subsoil: The layer of soil beneath the topsoil, composed of rock particles mixed with inorganic compounds.

substrate: The substance upon which an enzyme acts.

superior vena cava: The large vein that collects blood from the upper half of the body and returns it to the right atrium of the heart.

suspension: A mixture that separates on standing.

sweat gland: A gland composed of a tiny coiled tube that opens to the surface of the skin and secretes perspiration.

swim bladder: In bony fishes, a gas-filled sac that acts as a float to regulate the buoyancy of the fish; air bladder.

symbiotic relationship: A relationship in which two different types of organisms live in a close association that benefits at least one of them.

symmetry: A property of an organism or structure that allows it to be cut into two halves that have matching shapes.

sympathetic nervous system: The division of the autonomic nervous system that generally accelerates body activities.

synapse: The region where nerve impulses pass from one neuron to another.

synapsis: In meiosis, the process in which the four strands of the two doubled homologous chromosomes come together to form a tetrad.

synaptic cleft: The space between the synaptic knob of one neuron and the cell membrane of an adjacent neuron.

synaptic knob: A bulblike structure at the end of the terminal branch of an axon.

synaptic vesicle: A sac within a synaptic knob containing a neurotransmitter.

synovial fluid: The fluid secreted into movable joints to reduce friction.

synthesis: A process in which simple substances are combined chemically to form more complex substances.

systemic circulation: The circulatory pathways that carry blood from the heart to all parts of the body except the lungs.

systole: The period of contraction during the heartbeat cycle.

t

tadpole: The immature body form of a frog.

taiga: A biome in which the climax vegetation is evergreen forest, characterized by cold winters and warmer, moist summers.

tap root system: A root system in which the primary root grows most rapidly and remains the largest.

target tissue: The tissue regulated by a given hormone.

taste bud: A taste receptor on the tongue.

taxonomy: The branch of biology that deals with the classification and naming of living things.

Tay-Sachs disease: A genetic disease in which an enzyme necessary for the breakdown of lipids in the brain is missing.

telophase: The stage of mitosis during which the chromatin reappears, the spindle and asters disappear, and the nuclear membrane reforms.

temperate deciduous forest: A biome in which the climax vegetation is deciduous trees; characterized by hot, humid summers and cold winters.

temperature inversion: A situation in which a layer of cooler, denser air becomes trapped below a layer of warmer air.

tendon: A strong band of connective tissue that attaches skeletal muscle to bone.

terminal bud: The bud at the tip of a plant shoot.

terracing: A method of planting in flat areas cut into the sides of a hill to reduce soil erosion from water running over the surface.

test cross: A genetic cross in which a test organism showing the dominant trait is crossed with one showing the recessive trait; used to determine whether the test organism is homozygous dominant or heterozygous.

testis: The male gonad, which produces sperm and

secretes male sex hormones.

testosterone: A male sex hormone secreted by the testes; stimulates development of the male reproductive system and promotes male secondary sex characteristics.

tetany: A violent contraction of the skeletal muscles caused by a deficiency of calcium ions in the blood.

tetrad: A pair of double-stranded, homologous chromosomes joined at their centromeres during meiosis.

thalamus: A part of the brain that serves as a relay center.

theory: An explanation that applies to a broad range of phenomena.

thermal pollution: A type of pollution in which warmed water, which has been used to cool industrial equipment, is returned to a stream or river; the change in water temperature kills fish and other organisms.

thoracic duct: The largest lymphatic vessel in the body.

thrombin: An enzyme that converts the soluble plasma protein fibrinogen into insoluble fibrin strands in blood clotting.

thromboplastin: An enzyme that functions in blood clotting.

thrombus: A blood clot attached to the wall of a blood vessel.

thymine: A nitrogenous base found in DNA.

thymosin: The hormone secreted by the thymus that stimulates the development of T lymphocytes.

thymus gland: A gland located in the upper chest cavity that is involved in immunity.

thyroid: The endocrine gland that is located in front of the trachea and that secretes thyroxine and calcitonin.

thyroid-stimulating hormone (TSH): A hormone secreted by the anterior pituitary that stimulates the production of thyroxin by the thyroid gland.

thyroxine: An iodine-containing hormone that is secreted by the thyroid and that regulates the rate of metabolism in the body.

tissue culture: A technique for maintaining living cells or tissues in a culture medium outside the body.

tolerance: A property of the immune system in which the cells of the immune system do not react with or destroy the other cells of the body.

tonsil: Lymphoid tissue found in the throat.

topsoil: The uppermost layer of soil, which includes organic matter and living organisms.

toxin: A poisonous substance produced by bacteria.

trachea: The tube through which air passes from the pharynx to the lungs

tracheid: A conducting cell in the xylem.

transcription: The copying of a genetic message from a strand of DNA into a molecule of mRNA.

transduction: The process in which pieces of DNA are transferred from one bacterial cell to another by viruses.

transfer RNA (tRNA): The type of RNA that carries a particular amino acid to mRNA at the ribosome in protein synthesis.

transformation: The process in which living bacteria take in DNA from dead bacteria and develop the traits of the dead bacteria.

translocation: The movement of dissolved materials through a plant. In genetics, the transfer of a chromosome segment to a nonhomologous chromosome.

transpiration: The loss of water vapor from a plant through the stomates of the leaves.

transpiration pull: The chief process by which water rises through the xylem of a plant.

transport: All the processes by which substances pass into or out of cells and circulate within the organism.

tricuspid valve: The atrioventricular valve on the right side of the heart.

trochophore: A type of free-swimming, ciliated larva.

tropical rain forest: A biome found around the equator in which there is a constant supply of rainfall and the temperature remains constant at about 25°C throughout the year.

tropism: A growth response in a plant caused by an environmental stimulus that comes primarily from one direction.

trypsin: An enzyme that breaks down large protein molecules in the small intestine.

TSH: See **thyroid-stimulating hormone.**

tuber: An enlarged portion of an underground stem that can grow into a new plant by vegetative reproduction.

tubulin: The protein that makes up microtubules.

tundra: A biome characterized by a low average temperature, permafrost, and a very short growing season.

turgor pressure: The pressure against a plant cell wall resulting from the osmotic flow of water into the cell.

tympanic membrane: See **eardrum.**

U

ultracentrifuge: A high-speed centrifuge that can be used to separate the various parts of a cell from one another.

umbilical cord: In placental mammals, the structure that connects the fetus and the placenta.

ungulate: A hoofed mammal.

universal donor: A person with type O blood.

universal recipient: A person with type AB blood.

unsaturated fat: A fat formed from a fatty acid in which there is one or more double or triple bonds.

uracil: A nitrogenous base that is found in RNA in place of thymine.

urea: A nitrogenous waste formed from ammonia and carbon dioxide.

ureter: A tube that carries urine from the kidney to the bladder.

urethra: The tube that carries urine from the bladder to the outside of the body.

uric acid: A dry, nitrogenous waste product excreted by birds, reptiles, and insects.

urinary system: The system involved in the production and excretion of urine, including the kidneys, bladder, and associated tubes.

urine: A liquid nitrogenous waste composed of water, urea, and salts.

uterus: The thick, muscular, pear-shaped organ in the female mammal in which the embryo develops.

V

vaccine: An injection of dead or weakened bacteria or viruses or modified bacterial toxins that produces an active immunity.

vacuole: A membrane-enclosed organelle that contains fluid or some other material to be kept separate from the rest of the cell contents.

vagina: The structure leading from the uterus to the outside of the body in females; the birth canal.

vagus nerve: A cranial nerve that can slow down the pacemaker of the heart.

variation: A characteristic in an individual that differs from the typical characteristic of other individuals of the same species.

varicose vein: A vein in which blood accumulates because the walls have stretched.

vascular bundle: A plant structure containing the xylem and phloem vessels; may also contain cambium. bium.

vascular cylinder: The central core of the root, which contains xylem and phloem; central cylinder.

vascular tissue: See **conducting tissue.**

vas deferens: The tubes that carry sperm from each testis to the urethra.

vasopressin: A hormone secreted by the posterior pituitary that controls reabsorption of water by the nephrons of the kidney; antidiuretic hormone, or ADH.

vegetative reproduction: The process in which undifferentiated plant cells divide mitotically and then differentiate to form an independent plant; vegetative propagation.

vein: In leaves, a structure that contains the vascular tissues. In animals, a blood vessel that carries blood from the body tissues to the heart.

ventral: Pertaining to the lower or belly side of a bilaterally symmetrical animal.

ventral root: The front of the spinal cord from which motor fibers leave.

ventricle: One of the lower, thick-walled chambers of the heart. A space within the brain that is filled with cerebrospinal fluid.

venule: The smallest type of vein.

vertebra: One of the bones of the spinal column that surrounds and protects the spinal cord.

vestigial structure: A nonfunctional structure in a modern organism that is a remnant of a structure that was functional in some ancestral form.

villus: A small, fingerlike projection of the lining of the small intestine.

virus: An extremely small particle of DNA or RNA surrounded by a protein coat and capable of reproducing itself inside a living cell.

vitamin: An organic nutrient needed in very small amounts for certain body functions.

vitreous humor: The colorless, jellylike liquid that fills the cavity behind the lens of the eye.

voice box: See **larynx.**

voluntary muscle: See **skeletal muscle.**

W

warm-blooded: Having a body temperature that remains relatively constant regardless of the temperature of the environment; endothermic.

warning coloration: A protective adaptation in which the bright colors of an organism make it easy to recognize.

water cycle: The cycling of water between the surface of the earth and the atmosphere.

water of metabolism: Water produced by cell respiration.

water-vascular system: The locomotion and food-getting system in echinoderms.

wavelength: The distance between the crest of one wave and the crest of the next wave of light and other forms of electromagnetic radiation.

weathering: The processes by which rocks are broken down into smaller pieces by the action of natural forces.

white blood cell: A nucleated blood cell that serves as part of the body's defense against disease; leukocyte.

white matter: The inner part of the cerebrum, made up of myelinated nerve fibers.

windbreak: A row of trees used to prevent wind erosion.

woody stem: A stem containing wood.

X

xanthophyll: A yellow pigment found in the leaves of many plants.

xylem: The tissue that conducts water and minerals from the roots upward through the plant, and helps to support the plant.

Y

yolk: Stored food in an animal egg.

yolk sac: In shelled eggs, the extraembryonic membrane that surrounds the yolk, containing blood vessels that transport food to the embryo; in mammals, an extraembryonic membrane that forms part of the umbilical cord.

Z

zygospore: A zygote covered by a thick, protective wall.

zygote: The diploid cell resulting from fertilization.

Index

a

f

g

h

V

W

X

Y

Z

Photo Credits

Cover: butterfly fish (Carl Roessler)
page 1: hummingbird (Bob & Clara Calhoun/Bruce Coleman, Inc.)
page 2: black bear and cubs (ANIMALS ANIMALS/Z. Leszczynski)
page 10: scientist in laboratory (Renee Purse/Photo Researchers, Inc.)
page 22: CAT scan showing presence of only one kidney (Sherban G. Pavlovici, M.D.)
page 26: fireworks display (D. Sparks/The Image Bank)
page 48: molecular model of amino acid glycine (George Bakacs)
page 66: cork cells as drawn by Robert Hooke (The Bettmann Archive)
page 90: several species of ducks and geese (George Bakacs)
page 105: puffins (Soames Summerhays/Photo Researchers, Inc.)
page 106: hurdler (Stan Pantovic/Photo Researchers, Inc.)
page 122: giant panda eating bamboo (ANIMALS ANIMALS/Mary Stouffer Productions)
page 142: scanning electron micrograph of cardiac muscle (From H.D. Sybers & M. Ashraf, "Preparation of cardiac muscle for SEM," in O. Johari and I. Corvin (eds.), *Scanning Electron Microscopy/1973.* ITT Research Institute, pp. 345-346.
page 160: frog's blood (Eric V. Grave/Photo Researchers, Inc.)
page 176: diver (Focus on Sports)
page 192: kidney tubules (Gennaro/Photo Researchers, Inc.)
page 206: striated muscle (Manfred Kage/Peter Arnold, Inc.)
page 222: paramecium, showing system of fibers that control the cilia (Walker/Photo Researchers, Inc.)
page 240: surfing (Turner/The Image Bank)
page 264: section of adrenal gland (Manfred Kage/Peter Arnold, Inc.)
page 279: sundew plant on log (Roy Whitehead/Photo Researchers, Inc.)
page 280: moss cells with chloroplasts (Manfred Kage/Peter Arnold, Inc.)
page 294: peach flowers (George Bakacs)
page 310: leaf of peach tree (Jerome Wexler/Photo Researchers, Inc.)
page 323: Pacific kittiwakes (Henry C. Kyllingstad/Photo Researchers, Inc.)
page 324: mitosis in whitefish blastula (Michael Abbey/Photo Researchers, Inc.)
page 342: sea urchin egg (Michael Abbey/Photo Researchers, Inc.)
page 360: larva of black swallowtail butterfly (D.J. Hochreich)
page 372: human embryo (Sasaki/Photo Researchers, Inc.)
page 384: cotton anther with pollen (B. Beasley, Biology Media/Photo Researchers, Inc.)
page 401: portion of lampbrush chromosome from newt oocyte (Dr. Joseph Gall/Photo Researchers, Inc.)
page 402: glory peas (Philippa Scott/Photo Researchers, Inc.)
page 418: fruit flies (Ken Miyata/Photo Researchers, Inc.)
page 434: replicating DNA (Dr. Kakefuda/Photo Researchers, Inc.)
page 455: "bird robber" (*Ornitholestes*) chasing pterodactyl (Jane Burton/Bruce Coleman, Inc.)
page 456: fossil fish (Simon/Photo Researchers, Inc.)
page 476: clownfish in tentacles of anemones (Jeff Rotman/Peter Arnold, Inc.)
page 501: mandarin fish (Jane Burton/Bruce Coleman, Inc.)
page 502: bacteria *Spirillum volutans* (M. Abbey/Photo Researchers, Inc.)
page 520: angel's wing fungus (Manual Rodriguez)
page 536: reef in Fiji (ANIMALS ANIMALS/Carl Roessler)
page 560: butterfly (ANIMALS ANIMALS/Raymond A. Mendez)
page 586: long-nosed butterfly fish (ANIMALS ANIMALS/Z. Leszczynski)
page 610: pelicans (Tom McHugh/Photo Researchers, Inc.)
page 629: elephant (William & Marcia Levy/Photo Researchers, Inc.)
page 630: herd of Burchell's zebras (C. Haagner/Bruce Coleman, Inc.)
page 650: African grasslands (Grant Heilman Photography)
page 662: giant tube worms of Galapagos Rift (Jack Donnelly/WHOI)
page 666: crowd of people (Carl Frank/Photo Researchers, Inc.)

Chapter 1
1-1 George Bakacs; 1-2 George Bakacs; 1-3 ANIMALS ANIMALS/Breck P. Kent
Chapter 2
2-1 George Bakacs; 2-3 George Bakacs; 2-4 George Bakacs; 2-7 Walker/Photo Researchers, Inc.; 2-8 Instrument Division, Nikon, Inc.; 2-10 Hitachi/The Grey Consulting Group, Inc.; 2-11 David Scharf/Peter Arnold, Inc.; 2-12 Brinkmann Instruments, Inc./Sybron Corp.
Chapter 3
3-1 (top) Ken Karp (bottom) George Bakacs; 3-5 Louis Appel, M.D.; 3-13 Ken Karp; 3-15 Ken Karp; 3-17 Edward M. Steele
Chapter 5
5-1 The Bettmann Archive; 5-6 Richard G. Kessel; 5-7 Myron C. Ledbetter; 5-8 K.R. Porter; 5-9 Myron C. Ledbetter; 5-10 K.R. Porter; 5-11 Richard G. Kessel; 5-12 K.R. Porter; 5-14 Myron C. Ledbetter; 5-18 George Bakacs; 5-19 William H. Amos/Bruce Coleman, Inc.
Chapter 6
6-1 George Bakacs; 6-3 (left) Hans Reinhard/Bruce Coleman, Inc. (center) Jane Burton/Bruce Coleman, Inc. (right) ANIMALS ANIMALS/Michael & Barbara Reed; 6-4 (A) Hans Reinhard/Bruce Cole man, Inc. (B) Kenneth W. Fink/Bruce Coleman, Inc. (C) Bob & Clara Calhoun/Bruce Coleman, Inc. (D) Bruce Coleman, Inc.; 6-7 (left) EARTH SCENES/Breck P. Kent; 6-8 Walker/Photo Researchers, Inc.; 6-9 Kim Taylor/Bruce Coleman, Inc.; 6-10 Manuel Rodriguez; 6-11 D.J. Hochreich
Chapter 7
7-5 (left) George Bakacs (right) United States Brewers Association, Inc.; 7-8 Robert Goldstein/Photo Researchers, Inc.
Chapter 8
8-2 Eric Grave/Photo Researchers, Inc.; 8-3 Michael Abbey/Photo Researchers, Inc.; 8-5 Kim Taylor/Bruce Coleman, Inc.
Chapter 9
9-5 From *Tissues and Organs: A Text-Atlas of Scanning Electron Microscopy*, by Richard G. Kessel and Randy H. Kardon, W.H. Freeman and Company. Copyright © 1979; 9-10 Martin M. Rotker/Taurus Photos
Chapter 10
10-1 Martin M. Rotker/Taurus Photos; 10-2, 10-4, and 10-5 From *Tissues and Organs: A Text-Atlas of Scanning Electron Microscopy*, by Richard G. Kessel and Randy H. Kardon, W.H. Freeman and Company. Copyright © 1979; 10-3 Photo Courtesy Pfizer Inc.; 10-8 Runk/Schoenberger, Grant Heilman Photography
Chapter 11
11-3 Leonard Lee Rue III/Photo Researchers, Inc.; 11-5 William E. Ferguson; 11-7 and 11-8 From *Tissues and Organs: A Text-Atlas of Scanning Electron Microscopy*, by Richard G. Kessel and Randy H. Kardon, W.H. Freeman and Company. Copyright © 1979.
Chapter 12
12-1 Walker/Photo Researchers, Inc.
Chapter 13
13-1 ANIMALS ANIMALS/Z. Leszczynski; 13-2 Tom McHugh/Photo Researchers, Inc.: 13-7 ANIMALS ANIMALS; 13-8 H. Vible/Photo Researchers, Inc.; 13-9 and 13-10 From *Tissues and Organs: A Text-Atlas of Scanning Electron Microscopy*, by Richard G. Kessel and Randy H. Kardon, W.H. Freeman and Company. Copyright © 1979.
Chapter 14
14-1 George Bakacs; 14-5 From *Tissues and Organs: A Text-Atlas of Scanning Electron Microscopy*, by Richard G. Kessel and Randy H. Kardon, W.H. Freeman and Company. Copyright © 1979.
Chapter 15
15-11 E.R. Lewis, Y.Y. Zeevi, and F.S. Werblin; 15-15 From *Tissues and Organs: A Text Atlas of Scanning Electron Microscopy*, by Richard G. Kessel and Randy H. Kardon, W.H. Freeman and Company. Copyright © 1979.
Chapter 17
17-2 Runk/Schoenberger, Grant Heilman Photography; 17-4 Grant Heilman Photography; 17-10 Runk/Schoenberger, Grant Heilman Photography; 17-11 Runk/Schoenberger, Grant Heilman Photography
Chapter 18
18-3 EARTH SCENES/L.L.T. Rhodes; 18-6 William E. Ferguson; 18-7 (left and center) Runk/Shoenberger, Grant Heilman Photography (right) Grant Heilman Photography; 18-8 (left) Runk/Schoenberger, Grant Heilman Photography (right) George Bakacs; 18-11 Runk/Schoenberger, Grant Heilman Photography; 18-13 William E. Ferguson; 18-14 Runk/Schoenberger, Grant Heilman Photography; 18-15 Runk/Schoenberger, Grant Heilman Photography

Chapter 19
19-1 Myron C. Ledbetter; 19-5 George Bakacs; 19-6 George Bakacs
Chapter 20
20-14 ANIMALS ANIMALS/Oxford Scientific Films; 20-16 Jane Burton/ Bruce Coleman, Inc.; 20-18 (A, B, C, and E) Manuel Rodriguez (D) Grant Heilman Photography; 20-19 (A) George Bakacs (B) Jerome Wexler/Photo Researchers, Inc. (C) Grant Heilman Photography
Chapter 21
21-6 Runk/Schoenberger, Grant Heilman Photography; 21-10 Landrum B. Shettles, M.D.; 21-11 S. Rannels/Grant Heilman Photography
Chapter 22
22-10 (top) D.J. Hochreich (bottom) Grant Heilman Photography; 22-12 (A, B, and D) Kim Taylor/Bruce Coleman, Inc. (C) Runk/Schoenberger, Grant Heilman Photography; 22-13 ANIMALS ANIMALS/Doug Baglin
Chapter 23
23-6 Russ Kinne/Photo Researchers, Inc.
Chapter 24
24-3 George Bakacs; 24-4 George Bakacs; 24-5 George Bakacs; 24-10 George Bakacs; 24-11 George Bakacs; 24-14 George Bakacs
Chapter 25
25-1The Bettmann Archive
Chapter 27
27-10 Phillip A. Harrington/Peter Arnold, Inc.; 27-11 Myron C. Ledbetter
Chapter 28
28-2 Richard Frear/National Park Service; 28-3 Richard Frear/National Park Service; 28-4 Courtesy of the AMERICAN MUSEUM OF NATURAL HISTORY; 28-6 G.K. Gilbert/U.S.G.S.; 28-12 The Bettmann Archive
Chapter 29
29-1 Ken Brate/Photo Researchers, Inc.; 29-3 Jen & Des Bartlett/Bruce Coleman, Inc.; 29-4 (left) Sefton/DPI (right) ANIMALS ANIMALS/ Stouffer Productions; 29-5 (left) William E. Ferguson (right) Danny Brass/Photo Researchers, Inc.; 29-6 (left) Manuel Rodriguez (below) William E. Ferguson; 29-7 Willis Peterson; 29-8 G.R. Roberts/ Documentary Photographs; 29-9 Michael Tweedie/Photo Researchers, Inc.
Chapter 30
30-1 (B) R. Knauft/Photo Researchers, Inc.; (C) Phil Degginger/Bruce Coleman, Inc.; 30-5 ANIMALS ANIMALS/Oxford Scientific Films; 30-6 Eric Grave/Photo Researchers, Inc.; 30-7 Manfred Kage/Peter Arnold, Inc.; 30-8 Manfred Kage/Peter Arnold, Inc.; 30-9 Eric Grave/Photo Researchers, Inc.; 30-12 Richard E. Ferguson/William E. Ferguson
Chapter 31
31-2 (A) Chesher/Photo Researchers, Inc. (B) Tom McHugh/Photo Researchers, Inc. (C) Nancy Sefton/Photo Researchers, Inc.; 31-3 (left) Bob Evans/Peter Arnold, Inc. (right) W.H. Hodge/Peter Arnold, Inc.; 31-4 (top) Bob Evans/Peter Arnold, Inc. (bottom) William H. Amos/Bruce Coleman, Inc.; 31-5 J.M. Conrader/Photo Researchers, Inc.; 31-6 EARTH SCENES/Ronald Orenstein; 31-7 Manuel Rodriguez; 31-8 Manuel Rodriguez; 31-9 Manuel Rodriguez; 31-10 Dr. Georg Gerster/ Photo Researchers, Inc.; 31-11 EARTH SCENES/George K. Bryce; 31-13 Manuel Rodriguez; 31-14 Shirley Hawn/Taurus Photos; 31-15 Manuel Rodriguez; 31-17 (left and center) Manuel Rodriguez (right) George Bakacs
Chapter 32
32-1 Manfred Kage/Peter Arnold, Inc.; 32-2 ANIMALS ANIMALS/Carl Roessler; 32-4 (top) ANIMALS ANIMALS/Mike Schick (bottom) ANIMALS ANIMALS/Z. Leszczynski; 32-6 William H. Amos/Bruce Coleman, Inc.; 32-7 (top) ANIMALS ANIMALS/Steve Earley (center) ANIMALS ANIMALS/Tim Rock (bottom) ANIMALS ANIMALS/Carl Roessler; 32-9 Runk Schoenberger, Grant Heilman Photography; 32-17 ANIMALS ANIMALS/Oxford Scientific Films; 32-18 ANIMALS ANIMALS/Z. Leszczynski; 32-19 Jack Fields/Photo Researchers, Inc.; 32-21 (left) ANIMALS ANIMALS/Oxford Scientific Films (right) Manuel Rodriguez; 32-23 ANIMALS ANIMALS/Z. Leszczynski
Chapter 33
33-1 Tom McHugh/Photo Researchers, Inc.; 33-2 (left) ANIMALS ANIMALS/Z. Leszczynski (right) ANIMALS ANIMALS/Oxford Scientific Films; 33-5 ANIMALS ANIMALS/Breck P. Kent; 33-6 William E. Ferguson; 33-7 ANIMALS ANIMALS/Z. Leszczynski; 33-8 (A) Manuel Rodriguez (B) ANIMALS ANIMALS/Z. Leszczynski (C) William E. Ferguson; 33-10 Manuel Rodriguez; 33-11 George Bakacs; 33-12 ANIMALS ANIMALS/Bruce Macdonald; 33-13 (A) George Bakacs (B) George Bakacs (C) D.J. Hochreich (D) Manuel Rodriguez; 33-14 ANIMALS ANIMALS/Raymond A. Mendez; 33-17 William E. Ferguson; 33-18(A) Marjorie Dezell /Photo Researchers, Inc.(B) Dr. A.C. Twomey/ Photo Researchers, Inc. (C) Paul Metzger/Photo Researchers, Inc. (D) Frank E. Toman/Taurus Photos; 33-19 (left) ANIMALS ANIMALS/Z. Leszczynski (right) Jeff Rotman; 33-22 Jeff Rotman; 33-23 Jeff Rotman
Chapter 34
34-1 Jeff Rotman; 34-3 Tom McHugh/Photo Researchers, Inc.; 34-4 Jeff Rotman/Peter Arnold; 34-6 R.C. Hermes/Photo Researchers, Inc.; 34-7 (left) Russ Kinne/Photo Researchers, Inc. (right) ANIMALS ANIMALS/ Z. Leszczynski; 34-8 Tom McHugh/Photo Researchers, Inc.; 34-10 John M. Burnley/Photo Researchers, Inc.; 34-11 Russ Kinne/Photo Researchers, Inc.; 34-12 Manuel Rodriguez; 34-19 (A, B, and C) ANIMALS ANIMALS/Oxford Scientific Films (D) R.J. Erwin/Photo Researchers, Inc.; 34-20 Des Bartlett/Bruce Coleman Inc.; 34-21 Tom McHugh/ Photo Researchers, Inc.; 34-22 Manuel Rodriguez; 34-23 (left) Joseph T. Collins/Photo Researchers, Inc. (right) Charles R. Belinsky/Photo Researchers, Inc.; 34-24 (A) Tom McHugh/Photo Researchers, Inc. (B) Robert J. Ashworth/Photo Researchers, Inc. (C) Tom McHugh/Photo Researchers, Inc.; 34-25 William E. Ferguson; 34-26 Tom McHugh/ Photo Researchers, Inc.
Chapter 35
35-1 (A) Tom McHugh/Photo Researchers, Inc. (B) Manuel Rodriguez (C) Ron Willocks/Photo Researchers, Inc.; 35-2 Tom McHugh/Photo Researchers, Inc.; 35-3 Pat Lynch/Photo Researchers, Inc.; 35-7 Leonard Lee Rue III/DPI; 35-8 (A) Stephen J. Krasemann/Peter Arnold, Inc. (B) Phil Dotson/DPI (C) Jane Burton/Bruce Coleman, Inc.; 35-9 Manuel Rodriguez; 35-10 Gilbert Grant/Photo Researchers, Inc.; 35-11 Lowell Georgia/Photo Researchers, Inc.; 35-12 (left) ANIMALS ANIMALS/Breck P. Kent (right) Phil Dotson/DPI; 35-13 (A) ANIMALS ANIMALS/J.C. Stevenson (B) ANIMALS ANIMALS (C) ANIMALS ANIMALS/Bradley Smith (D) ANIMALS ANIMALS; 35-14 (left) ANIMALS ANIMALS/David C. Fritts (right) ANIMALS ANIMALS/ Leonard Lee Rue III; 35-15 (left) ANIMALS ANIMALS/Zig Leszczynski (right) ANIMALS ANIMALS/Miriam Austerman; 35-16 Courtesy of the AMERICAN MUSEUM OF NATURAL HISTORY: 35-17 Courtesy of the AMERICAN MUSEUM OF NATURAL HISTORY; 35-20 Courtesy of the AMERICAN MUSEUM OF NATURAL HISTORY; 35-21 Courtesy of the AMERICAN MUSEUM OF NATURAL HISTORY
Chapter 36
36-3 EARTH SCENES/Breck P. Kent; 36-4 Kit & Max Hunn, National Audubon Society Collection/Photo Researchers, Inc.; 36-12 George Bakacs
Chapter 37
37-2 (top) Manuel Rodriguez (bottom) Steve Wilson/DPI; 37-3 Charlie Ott/DPI; 37-4 George Bakacs; 37-5 (left) ANIMALS ANIMALS/Brian Milne (right) ANIMALS ANIMALS/Harry Engels; 37-6 (left) Manuel Rodriguez (right) Joseph van Wormer/Bruce Coleman, Inc.; 37-7 C.B. & D.W. Frith/Bruce Coleman, Inc.; 37-8 (left) M.P.L. Fogler/Bruce Coleman, Inc. (right) Jacques Janjoux/Peter Arnold, Inc.; 37-9 (left) Loren A. McIntire (right) John Markham/Bruce Coleman, Inc.; 37-12 William W. Bacon III/Photo Researchers, Inc.
Chapter 38
38-1 The Bettmann Archive; 38-2 Paul Stephanus/DPI; 38-3 J. Alex Langley/DPI; 38-5 George Bakacs